INSTRUCTOR'S SOLUTIONS MANUAL

KEVIN BODDEN   RANDY GALLAHER

LEWIS AND CLARK COMMUNITY COLLEGE

VOLUME I

Algebra & Trigonometry[8]

MICHAEL SULLIVAN

PEARSON

Prentice
Hall

Upper Saddle River, NJ 07458

Vice President and Editorial Director, Mathematics: Christine Hoag
Senior Editor: Adam Jaworski
Editorial Assistant/Print Supplements Editor: Christine Whitlock
Senior Managing Editor: Linda Behrens
Assistant Managing Editor: Lynn Savino Wendel
Production Editor: Ashley M. Booth
Supplement Cover Manager: Paul Gourhan
Supplement Cover Designer: Victoria Colotta
Manufacturing Buyer: Ilene Kahn
Associate Director of Operations: Alexis Heydt-Long

© 2008 Pearson Education, Inc.
Pearson Prentice Hall
Pearson Education, Inc.
Upper Saddle River, NJ 07458

Printed in the United States of America

10 9 8 7 6 5 4 3 2 1

ISBN 13:   978-0-13-239359-1

ISBN 10   0-13-239359-X

Pearson Education Ltd., *London*
Pearson Education Australia Pty. Ltd., *Sydney*
Pearson Education Singapore, Pte. Ltd.
Pearson Education North Asia Ltd., *Hong Kong*
Pearson Education Canada, Inc., *Toronto*
Pearson Educación de Mexico, S.A. de C.V.
Pearson Education—Japan, *Tokyo*
Pearson Education Malaysia, Pte. Ltd.

Table of Contents

Preface

Chapter R   Review
R.1   Real Numbers 1
R.2   Algebra Essentials 5
R.3   Geometry Essentials 11
R.4   Polynomials 16
R.5   Factoring Polynomials 23
R.6   Synthetic Division 27
R.7   Rational expressions 29
R.8 nth Roots; Rational Exponents 38
Chapter Review 46
Chapter Test 54

Chapter 1   Equations and Inequalities
1.1   Linear Equations 57
1.2   Quadratic Equations 74
1.3   Complex Numbers; Quadratic Equations in the Complex Number System 91
1.4   Radical Equations; Equations Quadratic in Form; Factorable Equations 97
1.5   Solving Inequalities 115
1.6   Equations and Inequalities Involving Absolute Value 125
1.7   Problem Solving: Interest, Mixture, Uniform Motion, and Constant Rate Job Applications ... 134
Chapter Review 141
Chapter Test 155
Chapter Projects 157

Chapter 2   Graphs
2.1   The Distance and Midpoint Formulas 159
2.2   Graphs of Equations in Two Variables; Intercepts; Symmetry 169
2.3   Lines 181
2.4   Circles 197
2.5   Variation 208
Chapter Review 212
Chapter Test 223
Cumulative Review 225
Chapter Projects 227

Chapter 3   Functions and Their Graphs
3.1   Functions 229
3.2   The Graph of a Function 242
3.3   Properties of Functions 250
3.4   Library of Functions; Piecewise-defined Functions 264
3.5   Graphing Techniques: Transformations 275
3.6   Mathematical Models: Building Functions 291
Chapter Review 296
Chapter Test 310
Cumulative Review 313
Chapter Projects 317

Chapter 4   Linear and Quadratic Functions

4.1   Linear Functions and Their Properties 321
4.2   Building Linear Functions from Data.. 330
4.3   Linear and Quadratic Functions... 335
4.4   Properties of Quadratic Functions 355
4.5   Inequalities Involving Quadratic Functions... 362
Chapter Review.. 381
Chapter Test... 393
Cumulative Review... 395
Chapter Projects 397

Chapter 5   Polynomial and Rational Functions

5.1   Polynomial Functions and Models... 401
5.2   Properties of Rational Functions 420
5.3   The Graph of a Rational Function 428
5.4   Polynomial and Rational Inequalities.. 473
5.5   The Real Zeros of a Polynomial Function 486
5.6   Complex Zeros; Fundamental Theorem of Algebra 520
Chapter Review.. 527
Chapter Test... 557
Cumulative Review... 561
Chapter Projects 566

Chapter 6   Exponential and Logarithmic Functions

6.1   Composite Functions... 568
6.2   One-to-One Functions; Inverse Functions.. 584
6.3   Exponential Functions 603
6.4   Logarithmic Functions.. 620
6.5   Properties of Logarithms 639
6.6   Logarithmic and Exponential Equations.. 646
6.7   Compound Interest 663
6.8   Exponential Growth and Decay Models; Newton's Law; Logistic Growth
        and Decay Models 670
6.9   Building Exponential, Logarithmic, and Logistic Models from Data 678
Chapter Review.. 683
Chapter Test... 702
Cumulative Review... 706
Chapter Projects 709

Preface

This solution manual accompanies *Algebra & Trigonometry, 8e* by Michael Sullivan. The Instructor Solutions Manual (ISM) contains detailed solutions to all exercises in the text and the chapter projects (both in the text and those posted on the internet). The Student Solutions Manual (SSM) contains detailed solutions to all odd exercises in the text and all solutions to chapter tests. In both manuals, some TI-84 Plus graphing calculator screenshots have been included to demonstrate how technology can be used to solve problems and check solutions. A concerted effort has been made to make this manual as user-friendly and error free as possible. Please feel free to send us any suggestions or corrections.

We would like to extend our thanks to Dawn Murrin, Christine Whitlock and Bob Walters from Prentice Hall for all their help with manuscript pages and logistics. Thanks for everything!

We would also like to thank our wives (Angie and Karen) and our children (Annie, Ben, Ethan, Logan, Payton, and Shawn) for their patient support and for enduring many late evenings.

Kevin Bodden and Randy Gallaher
Department of Mathematics
Lewis and Clark Community College
5800 Godfrey Road
Godfrey, IL 62035
kbodden@lc.edu   rgallahe@lc.edu

Chapter R
Review

Section R.1

1. rational

2. $4 + 5 \cdot 6 - 3 = 4 + 30 - 3 = 31$

3. Distributive

4. $5(x+3) = 6$

5. True

6. False; The Zero-Product Property states that if a product equals 0, then at least one of the factors must equal 0.

7. False; 6 is the Greatest Common Factor of 12 and 18. The Least Common Multiple is the smallest value that both numbers will divide evenly. The LCM for 12 and 18 is 36.

8. True

9. $A \cup B = \{1, 3, 4, 5, 9\} \cup \{2, 4, 6, 7, 8\}$
   $ = \{1, 2, 3, 4, 5, 6, 7, 8, 9\}$

10. $A \cup C = \{1, 3, 4, 5, 9\} \cup \{1, 3, 4, 6\}$
    $ = \{1, 3, 4, 5, 6, 9\}$

11. $A \cap B = \{1, 3, 4, 5, 9\} \cap \{2, 4, 6, 7, 8\} = \{4\}$

12. $A \cap C = \{1, 3, 4, 5, 9\} \cap \{1, 3, 4, 6\} = \{1, 3, 4\}$

13. $(A \cup B) \cap C$
    $= (\{1, 3, 4, 5, 9\} \cup \{2, 4, 6, 7, 8\}) \cap \{1, 3, 4, 6\}$
    $= \{1, 2, 3, 4, 5, 6, 7, 8, 9\} \cap \{1, 3, 4, 6\}$
    $= \{1, 3, 4, 6\}$

14. $(A \cap B) \cup C$
    $= (\{1, 3, 4, 5, 9\} \cap \{2, 4, 6, 7, 8\}) \cup \{1, 3, 4, 6\}$
    $= \{4\} \cup \{1, 3, 4, 6\}$
    $= \{1, 3, 4, 6\}$

15. $\overline{A} = \{0, 2, 6, 7, 8\}$

16. $\overline{C} = \{0, 2, 5, 7, 8, 9\}$

17. $\overline{A \cap B} = \overline{\{1, 3, 4, 5, 9\} \cap \{2, 4, 6, 7, 8\}}$
    $\phantom{\overline{A \cap B}} = \overline{\{4\}} = \{0, 1, 2, 3, 5, 6, 7, 8, 9\}$

18. $\overline{B \cup C} = \overline{\{2, 4, 6, 7, 8\} \cup \{1, 3, 4, 6\}}$
    $\phantom{\overline{B \cup C}} = \overline{\{1, 2, 3, 4, 6, 7, 8\}} = \{0, 5, 9\}$

19. $\overline{A} \cup \overline{B} = \{0, 2, 6, 7, 8\} \cup \{0, 1, 3, 5, 9\}$
    $\phantom{\overline{A} \cup \overline{B}} = \{0, 1, 2, 3, 5, 6, 7, 8, 9\}$

20. $\overline{B} \cap \overline{C} = \{0, 1, 3, 5, 9\} \cap \{0, 2, 5, 7, 8, 9\}$
    $\phantom{\overline{B} \cap \overline{C}} = \{0, 5, 9\}$

21. a. $\{2, 5\}$

    b. $\{-6, 2, 5\}$

    c. $\left\{-6, \dfrac{1}{2}, -1.333... = -1.\overline{3}, 2, 5\right\}$

    d. $\{\pi\}$

    e. $\left\{-6, \dfrac{1}{2}, -1.333... = -1.\overline{3}, \pi, 2, 5\right\}$

22. a. $\{1\}$

    b. $\{0, 1\}$

    c. $\left\{-\dfrac{5}{3}, 2.060606... = 2.\overline{06}, 1.25, 0, 1\right\}$

    d. $\left\{\sqrt{5}\right\}$

    e. $\left\{-\dfrac{5}{3}, 2.060606... = 2.\overline{06}, 1.25, 0, 1, \sqrt{5}\right\}$

23. a. $\{1\}$

    b. $\{0, 1\}$

    c. $\left\{0, 1, \dfrac{1}{2}, \dfrac{1}{3}, \dfrac{1}{4}\right\}$

1

d. None

e. $\left\{0,1,\dfrac{1}{2},\dfrac{1}{3},\dfrac{1}{4}\right\}$

24. a. None

   b. $\{-1\}$

   c. $\{-1.3,-1.2,-1.1,-1\}$

   d. None

   e. $\{-1.3,-1.2,-1.1,-1\}$

25. a. None

   b. None

   c. None

   d. $\left\{\sqrt{2},\pi,\sqrt{2}+1,\pi+\dfrac{1}{2}\right\}$

   e. $\left\{\sqrt{2},\pi,\sqrt{2}+1,\pi+\dfrac{1}{2}\right\}$

26. a. None

   b. None

   c. $\left\{\dfrac{1}{2}+10.3\right\}$

   d. $\left\{-\sqrt{2},\pi+\sqrt{2}\right\}$

   e. $\left\{-\sqrt{2},\pi+\sqrt{2},\dfrac{1}{2}+10.3\right\}$

27. a. 18.953   **b.** 18.952

28. a. 25.861   **b.** 25.861

29. a. 28.653   **b.** 28.653

30. a. 99.052   **b.** 99.052

31. a. 0.063   **b.** 0.062

32. a. 0.054   **b.** 0.053

33. a. 9.999   **b.** 9.998

34. a. 1.001   **b.** 1.000

35. a. 0.429   **b.** 0.428

36. a. 0.556   **b.** 0.555

37. a. 34.733   **b.** 34.733

38. a. 16.200   **b.** 16.200

39. $3+2=5$

40. $5\cdot 2=10$

41. $x+2=3\cdot 4$

42. $3+y=2+2$

43. $3y=1+2$

44. $2x=4\cdot 6$

45. $x-2=6$

46. $2-y=6$

47. $\dfrac{x}{2}=6$

48. $\dfrac{2}{x}=6$

49. $9-4+2=5+2=7$

50. $6-4+3=2+3=5$

51. $-6+4\cdot 3=-6+12=6$

52. $8-4\cdot 2=8-8=0$

53. $4+5-8=9-8=1$

54. $8-3-4=5-4=1$

55. $4+\dfrac{1}{3}=\dfrac{12+1}{3}=\dfrac{13}{3}$

56. $2-\dfrac{1}{2}=\dfrac{4-1}{2}=\dfrac{3}{2}$

57. $6-\left[3\cdot 5+2\cdot(3-2)\right]=6-\left[15+2\cdot(1)\right]$
$$=6-17$$
$$=-11$$

58. $2 \cdot \left[8 - 3 \cdot (4+2) \right] - 3 = 2 \cdot \left[8 - 3 \cdot (6) \right] - 3$
$$= 2 \cdot [8 - 18] - 3$$
$$= 2 \cdot [-10] - 3$$
$$= -20 - 3$$
$$= -23$$

59. $2 \cdot (3-5) + 8 \cdot 2 - 1 = 2 \cdot (-2) + 16 - 1$
$$= -4 + 16 - 1$$
$$= 12 - 1$$
$$= 11$$

60. $1 - (4 \cdot 3 - 2 + 2) = 1 - (12 - 2 + 2)$
$$= 1 - 12$$
$$= -11$$

61. $10 - \left[6 - 2 \cdot 2 + (8-3) \right] \cdot 2 = 10 - [6 - 4 + 5] \cdot 2$
$$= 10 - [2 + 5] \cdot 2$$
$$= 10 - [7] \cdot 2$$
$$= 10 - 14$$
$$= -4$$

62. $2 - 5 \cdot 4 - \left[6 \cdot (3-4) \right] = 2 - 20 - \left[6 \cdot (-1) \right]$
$$= -18 - [-6]$$
$$= -18 + 6$$
$$= -12$$

63. $(5-3)\dfrac{1}{2} = (2)\dfrac{1}{2} = 1$

64. $(5+4)\dfrac{1}{3} = (9)\dfrac{1}{3} = 3$

65. $\dfrac{4+8}{5-3} = \dfrac{12}{2} = 6$

66. $\dfrac{2-4}{5-3} = \dfrac{-2}{2} = -1$

67. $\dfrac{3}{5} \cdot \dfrac{10}{21} = \dfrac{3 \cdot 2 \cdot 5}{5 \cdot 3 \cdot 7} = \dfrac{\cancel{3} \cdot 2 \cdot \cancel{5}}{\cancel{5} \cdot \cancel{3} \cdot 7} = \dfrac{2}{7}$

68. $\dfrac{5}{9} \cdot \dfrac{3}{10} = \dfrac{5 \cdot 3}{3 \cdot 3 \cdot 5 \cdot 2} = \dfrac{\cancel{5} \cdot \cancel{3}}{\cancel{3} \cdot 3 \cdot \cancel{5} \cdot 2} = \dfrac{1}{6}$

69. $\dfrac{6}{25} \cdot \dfrac{10}{27} = \dfrac{2 \cdot 3 \cdot 5 \cdot 2}{5 \cdot 5 \cdot 3 \cdot 9} = \dfrac{2 \cdot \cancel{3} \cdot \cancel{5} \cdot 2}{\cancel{5} \cdot 5 \cdot \cancel{3} \cdot 9} = \dfrac{4}{45}$

70. $\dfrac{21}{25} \cdot \dfrac{100}{3} = \dfrac{3 \cdot 7 \cdot 4 \cdot 25}{25 \cdot 3} = \dfrac{\cancel{3} \cdot 7 \cdot 4 \cdot \cancel{25}}{\cancel{25} \cdot \cancel{3}} = 28$

71. $\dfrac{3}{4} + \dfrac{2}{5} = \dfrac{15 + 8}{20} = \dfrac{23}{20}$

72. $\dfrac{4}{3} + \dfrac{1}{2} = \dfrac{8 + 3}{6} = \dfrac{11}{6}$

73. $\dfrac{5}{6} + \dfrac{9}{5} = \dfrac{25 + 54}{30} = \dfrac{79}{30}$

74. $\dfrac{8}{9} + \dfrac{15}{2} = \dfrac{16 + 135}{18} = \dfrac{151}{18}$

75. $\dfrac{5}{18} + \dfrac{1}{12} = \dfrac{10 + 3}{36} = \dfrac{13}{36}$

76. $\dfrac{2}{15} + \dfrac{8}{9} = \dfrac{6 + 40}{45} = \dfrac{46}{45}$

77. $\dfrac{1}{30} - \dfrac{7}{18} = \dfrac{3 - 35}{90} = -\dfrac{32}{90} = -\dfrac{16}{45}$

78. $\dfrac{3}{14} - \dfrac{2}{21} = \dfrac{9 - 4}{42} = \dfrac{5}{42}$

79. $\dfrac{3}{20} - \dfrac{2}{15} = \dfrac{9 - 8}{60} = \dfrac{1}{60}$

80. $\dfrac{6}{35} - \dfrac{3}{14} = \dfrac{12 - 15}{70} = -\dfrac{3}{70}$

81. $\dfrac{\left(\dfrac{5}{18}\right)}{\left(\dfrac{11}{27}\right)} = \dfrac{5}{18} \cdot \dfrac{27}{11} = \dfrac{5 \cdot 9 \cdot 3}{9 \cdot 2 \cdot 11} = \dfrac{5 \cdot \cancel{9} \cdot 3}{\cancel{9} \cdot 2 \cdot 11} = \dfrac{15}{22}$

82. $\dfrac{\left(\dfrac{5}{21}\right)}{\left(\dfrac{2}{35}\right)} = \dfrac{5}{21} \cdot \dfrac{35}{2} = \dfrac{5 \cdot 7 \cdot 5}{7 \cdot 3 \cdot 2} = \dfrac{5 \cdot \cancel{7} \cdot 5}{\cancel{7} \cdot 3 \cdot 2} = \dfrac{25}{6}$

83. $\dfrac{1}{2} \cdot \dfrac{3}{5} + \dfrac{7}{10} = \dfrac{3}{10} + \dfrac{7}{10} = \dfrac{3 + 7}{10} = \dfrac{10}{10} = 1$

3

84. $\dfrac{2}{3}+\dfrac{4}{5}\cdot\dfrac{1}{6}=\dfrac{2}{3}+\dfrac{2\cdot2}{5\cdot3\cdot2}=\dfrac{2}{3}+\dfrac{2\cdot\cancel{2}}{5\cdot3\cdot\cancel{2}}=\dfrac{2}{3}+\dfrac{2}{15}$

$\qquad=\dfrac{2}{3}\cdot\dfrac{5}{5}+\dfrac{2}{15}=\dfrac{10}{15}+\dfrac{2}{15}=\dfrac{10+2}{15}=\dfrac{12}{15}$

$\qquad=\dfrac{4\cdot3}{5\cdot3}=\dfrac{4\cdot\cancel{3}}{5\cdot\cancel{3}}=\dfrac{4}{5}$

85. $2\cdot\dfrac{3}{4}+\dfrac{3}{8}=\dfrac{2}{1}\cdot\dfrac{3}{4}+\dfrac{3}{8}=\dfrac{6}{4}+\dfrac{3}{8}=\dfrac{6}{4}\cdot\dfrac{2}{2}+\dfrac{3}{8}$

$\qquad=\dfrac{12}{8}+\dfrac{3}{8}=\dfrac{12+3}{8}=\dfrac{15}{8}$

86. $3\cdot\dfrac{5}{6}-\dfrac{1}{2}=\dfrac{3}{1}\cdot\dfrac{5}{6}-\dfrac{1}{2}=\dfrac{3\cdot5}{3\cdot2}-\dfrac{1}{2}=\dfrac{\cancel{3}\cdot5}{\cancel{3}\cdot2}-\dfrac{1}{2}$

$\qquad=\dfrac{5}{2}-\dfrac{1}{2}=\dfrac{5-1}{2}=\dfrac{4}{2}=2$

87. $6(x+4)=6x+24$

88. $4(2x-1)=8x-4$

89. $x(x-4)=x^2-4x$

90. $4x(x+3)=4x^2+12x$

91. $2\left(\dfrac{3}{4}x-\dfrac{1}{2}\right)=2\cdot\dfrac{3}{4}x-2\cdot\dfrac{1}{2}=\dfrac{2\cdot3x}{2\cdot2}-\dfrac{2}{2}$

$\qquad=\dfrac{\cancel{2}\cdot3x}{\cancel{2}\cdot2}-\dfrac{2}{2}=\dfrac{3}{2}x-1$

92. $3\left(\dfrac{2}{3}x+\dfrac{1}{6}\right)=3\cdot\dfrac{2}{3}x+3\cdot\dfrac{1}{6}=\dfrac{3\cdot2x}{3}+\dfrac{3}{3\cdot2}$

$\qquad=\dfrac{\cancel{3}\cdot2x}{\cancel{3}}+\dfrac{\cancel{3}}{\cancel{3}\cdot2}=2x+\dfrac{1}{2}$

93. $(x+2)(x+4)=x^2+4x+2x+8$

$\qquad=x^2+6x+8$

94. $(x+5)(x+1)=x^2+x+5x+5$

$\qquad=x^2+6x+5$

95. $(x-2)(x+1)=x^2+x-2x-2$

$\qquad=x^2-x-2$

96. $(x-4)(x+1)=x^2+x-4x-4$

$\qquad=x^2-3x-4$

97. $(x-8)(x-2)=x^2-2x-8x+16$

$\qquad=x^2-10x+16$

98. $(x-4)(x-2)=x^2-2x-4x+8$

$\qquad=x^2-6x+8$

99. $2x+3x=2\cdot x+3\cdot x$

$\qquad=(2+3)\cdot x$

$\qquad=(5)\cdot x$

$\qquad=5x$

100. $2+3\cdot4=2+12=14$

since multiplication comes before addition in the order of operations for real numbers.

$(2+3)\cdot4=5\cdot4=20$

since operations inside parentheses come before multiplication in the order of operations for real numbers.

101. $2(3\cdot4)=2(12)=24$

$(2\cdot3)\cdot(2\cdot4)=(6)(8)=48$

102. $\dfrac{4+3}{2+5}=\dfrac{7}{7}=1$, but

$\dfrac{4}{2}+\dfrac{3}{5}=\dfrac{4\cdot5+3\cdot2}{10}=\dfrac{20+6}{10}=\dfrac{26}{10}=\dfrac{13}{5}=2.6$

103. Subtraction is not commutative; for example: $2-3=-1\neq1=3-2$.

104. Subtraction is not associative; for example: $(5-2)-1=2\neq4=5-(2-1)$.

105. Division is not commutative; for example: $\dfrac{2}{3}\neq\dfrac{3}{2}$.

106. Division is not associative; for example: $(12\div2)\div2=6\div2=3$, but $12\div(2\div2)=12\div1=12$.

107. The Symmetric Property implies that if $2=x$, then $x=2$.

108. From the *principle of substitution,* if $x = 5$, then
$$(x)(x) = (5)(5)$$
$$\Rightarrow x^2 = 25$$
$$\Rightarrow x^2 + x = 25 + 5$$
$$\Rightarrow x^2 + x = 30$$

109. There are no real numbers that are both rational and irrational, since an irrational number, by definition, is a number that cannot be expressed as the ratio of two integers; that is, not a rational number

Every real number is either a rational number or an irrational number, since the decimal form of a real number either involves an infinitely repeating pattern of digits or an infinite, non-repeating string of digits.

110. The sum of an irrational number and a rational number must be irrational. Otherwise, the irrational number would then be the difference of two rational numbers, and therefore would have to be rational.

111. Answers will vary.

112. Since 1 day = 24 hours, we compute
$$\frac{12997}{24} = 541.541\overline{6}.$$
Now we only need to consider the decimal part of the answer in terms of a 24 hour day. That is,
$(0.541\overline{6})(24) \approx 13$ hours. So it must be 13 hours later than 12 noon, which makes the time 1 AM CST.

113. Answers will vary.

Section R.2

1. variable

2. origin

3. strict

4. base; exponent (or power)

5. 1.2345678×10^3

6. True.

7. True

8. False; the absolute value of a real number is nonnegative. $|0| = 0$ which is not a positive number.

9. False; a number in scientific notation is expressed as the product of a number, x, $1 \le x < 10$ or $-10 < x \le -1$, and a power of 10.

10. False; to multiply two expressions with the same base, retain the base and *add* the exponents.

11.
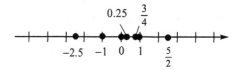

12.
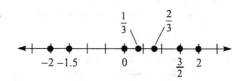

13. $\frac{1}{2} > 0$

14. $5 < 6$

15. $-1 > -2$

16. $-3 < -\frac{5}{2}$

17. $\pi > 3.14$

18. $\sqrt{2} > 1.41$

19. $\frac{1}{2} = 0.5$

20. $\frac{1}{3} > 0.33$

21. $\frac{2}{3} < 0.67$

22. $\frac{1}{4} = 0.25$

23. $x > 0$

5

24. $z < 0$

25. $x < 2$

26. $y > -5$

27. $x \le 1$

28. $x \ge 2$

29. Graph on the number line: $x \ge -2$

30. Graph on the number line: $x < 4$

31. Graph on the number line: $x > -1$

32. Graph on the number line: $x \le 7$

33. $d(C,D) = d(0,1) = |1-0| = |1| = 1$

34. $d(C,A) = d(0,-3) = |-3-0| = |-3| = 3$

35. $d(D,E) = d(1,3) = |3-1| = |2| = 2$

36. $d(C,E) = d(0,3) = |3-0| = |3| = 3$

37. $d(A,E) = d(-3,3) = |3-(-3)| = |6| = 6$

38. $d(D,B) = d(1,-1) = |-1-1| = |-2| = 2$

39. $x + 2y = -2 + 2 \cdot 3 = -2 + 6 = 4$

40. $3x + y = 3(-2) + 3 = -6 + 3 = -3$

41. $5xy + 2 = 5(-2)(3) + 2 = -30 + 2 = -28$

42. $-2x + xy = -2(-2) + (-2)(3) = 4 - 6 = -2$

43. $\dfrac{2x}{x-y} = \dfrac{2(-2)}{-2-3} = \dfrac{-4}{-5} = \dfrac{4}{5}$

44. $\dfrac{x+y}{x-y} = \dfrac{-2+3}{-2-3} = \dfrac{1}{-5} = -\dfrac{1}{5}$

45. $\dfrac{3x+2y}{2+y} = \dfrac{3(-2)+2(3)}{2+3} = \dfrac{-6+6}{5} = \dfrac{0}{5} = 0$

46. $\dfrac{2x-3}{y} = \dfrac{2(-2)-3}{3} = \dfrac{-4-3}{3} = -\dfrac{7}{3}$

47. $|x+y| = |3+(-2)| = |1| = 1$

48. $|x-y| = |3-(-2)| = |5| = 5$

49. $|x|+|y| = |3|+|-2| = 3+2 = 5$

50. $|x|-|y| = |3|-|-2| = 3-2 = 1$

51. $\dfrac{|x|}{x} = \dfrac{|3|}{3} = \dfrac{3}{3} = 1$

52. $\dfrac{|y|}{y} = \dfrac{|-2|}{-2} = \dfrac{2}{-2} = -1$

53. $|4x-5y| = |4(3)-5(-2)|$
$\qquad = |12+10|$
$\qquad = |22|$
$\qquad = 22$

54. $|3x+2y| = |3(3)+2(-2)| = |9-4| = |5| = 5$

55. $||4x|-|5y|| = ||4(3)|-|5(-2)||$
$\qquad = ||12|-|-10||$
$\qquad = |12-10|$
$\qquad = |2|$
$\qquad = 2$

56. $3|x|+2|y| = 3|3|+2|-2|$
$\qquad = 3 \cdot 3 + 2 \cdot 2$
$\qquad = 9 + 4$
$\qquad = 13$

57. $\dfrac{x^2-1}{x}$

Part (c) must be excluded. The value $x = 0$ must be excluded from the domain because it causes division by 0.

58. $\dfrac{x^2+1}{x}$

Part (c) must be excluded. The value $x = 0$ must be excluded from the domain because it causes division by 0.

59. $\dfrac{x}{x^2-9} = \dfrac{x}{(x-3)(x+3)}$

Part (a) must be excluded. The values $x = -3$ and $x = 3$ must be excluded from the domain because they cause division by 0.

60. $\dfrac{x}{x^2+9}$

None of the given values are excluded. The domain is all real numbers.

61. $\dfrac{x^2}{x^2+1}$

None of the given values are excluded. The domain is all real numbers.

62. $\dfrac{x^3}{x^2-1} = \dfrac{x^3}{(x-1)(x+1)}$

Parts (b) and (d) must be excluded. The values $x = 1$, and $x = -1$ must be excluded from the domain because they cause division by 0.

63. $\dfrac{x^2+5x-10}{x^3-x} = \dfrac{x^2+5x-10}{x(x-1)(x+1)}$

Parts (b), (c), and (d) must be excluded. The values $x = 0$, $x = 1$, and $x = -1$ must be excluded from the domain because they cause division by 0.

64. $\dfrac{-9x^2-x+1}{x^3+x} = \dfrac{-9x^2-x+1}{x(x^2+1)}$

Part (c) must be excluded. The value $x = 0$ must be excluded from the domain because it causes division by 0.

65. $\dfrac{4}{x-5}$

$x = 5$ must be exluded because it makes the denominator equal 0.
Domain $= \{x \mid x \neq 5\}$

66. $\dfrac{-6}{x+4}$

$x = -4$ must be excluded sine it makes the denominator equal 0.
Domain $= \{x \mid x \neq -4\}$

67. $\dfrac{x}{x+4}$

$x = -4$ must be excluded sine it makes the denominator equal 0.
Domain $= \{x \mid x \neq -4\}$

68. $\dfrac{x-2}{x-6}$

$x = 6$ must be excluded sine it makes the denominator equal 0.
Domain $= \{x \mid x \neq 6\}$

69. $C = \dfrac{5}{9}(F-32) = \dfrac{5}{9}(32-32) = \dfrac{5}{9}(0) = 0°C$

70. $C = \dfrac{5}{9}(F-32) = \dfrac{5}{9}(212-32) = \dfrac{5}{9}(180) = 100°C$

71. $C = \dfrac{5}{9}(F-32) = \dfrac{5}{9}(77-32) = \dfrac{5}{9}(45) = 25°C$

72. $C = \dfrac{5}{9}(F-32) = \dfrac{5}{9}(-4-32)$

$\quad\quad = \dfrac{5}{9}(-36)$

$\quad\quad = -20°C$

73. $(-4)^2 = (-4)(-4) = 16$

74. $-4^2 = -(4)^2 = -16$

75. $4^{-2} = \dfrac{1}{4^2} = \dfrac{1}{16}$

76. $-4^{-2} = -\dfrac{1}{4^2} = -\dfrac{1}{16}$

77. $3^{-6} \cdot 3^4 = 3^{-6+4} = 3^{-2} = \dfrac{1}{3^2} = \dfrac{1}{9}$

78. $4^{-2} \cdot 4^3 = 4^{-2+3} = 4^1 = 4$

79. $\left(3^{-2}\right)^{-1} = 3^{(-2)(-1)} = 3^2 = 9$

7

80. $\left(2^{-1}\right)^{-3} = 2^{(-1)(-3)} = 2^3 = 8$

81. $\sqrt{25} = \sqrt{5^2} = 5$

82. $\sqrt{36} = \sqrt{6^2} = 6$

83. $\sqrt{(-4)^2} = |-4| = 4$

84. $\sqrt{(-3)^2} = |-3| = 3$

85. $\left(8x^3\right)^2 = 8^2\left(x^3\right)^2 = 64x^6$

86. $\left(-4x^2\right)^{-1} = \dfrac{1}{-4x^2} = -\dfrac{1}{4x^2}$

87. $\left(x^2 y^{-1}\right)^2 = \left(x^2\right)^2 \cdot \left(y^{-1}\right)^2 = x^4 y^{-2} = \dfrac{x^4}{y^2}$

88. $\left(x^{-1} y\right)^3 = \left(x^{-1}\right)^3 \cdot y^3 = x^{-3} y^3 = \dfrac{y^3}{x^3}$

89. $\dfrac{x^2 y^3}{x y^4} = x^{2-1} y^{3-4} = x^1 y^{-1} = \dfrac{x}{y}$

90. $\dfrac{x^{-2} y}{x y^2} = x^{-2-1} y^{1-2} = x^{-3} y^{-1} = \dfrac{1}{x^3 y}$

91. $\dfrac{(-2)^3 x^4 (yz)^2}{3^2 x y^3 z} = \dfrac{-8 x^4 y^2 z^2}{9 x y^3 z}$

$= \dfrac{-8}{9} x^{4-1} y^{2-3} z^{2-1}$

$= \dfrac{-8}{9} x^3 y^{-1} z^1$

$= -\dfrac{8x^3 z}{9y}$

92. $\dfrac{4 x^{-2} (yz)^{-1}}{2^3 x^4 y} = \dfrac{4 x^{-2} y^{-1} z^{-1}}{8 x^4 y}$

$= \dfrac{4}{8} x^{-2-4} y^{-1-1} z^{-1}$

$= \dfrac{1}{2} x^{-6} y^{-2} z^{-1}$

$= \dfrac{1}{2 x^6 y^2 z}$

93. $\left(\dfrac{3x^{-1}}{4y^{-1}}\right)^{-2} = \left(\dfrac{3y}{4x}\right)^{-2} = \left(\dfrac{4x}{3y}\right)^2 = \dfrac{4^2 x^2}{3^2 y^2} = \dfrac{16x^2}{9y^2}$

94. $\left(\dfrac{5x^{-2}}{6y^{-2}}\right)^{-3} = \left(\dfrac{5y^2}{6x^2}\right)^{-3} = \left(\dfrac{6x^2}{5y^2}\right)^3$

$= \dfrac{6^3 \left(x^2\right)^3}{5^3 \left(y^2\right)^3} = \dfrac{216 x^6}{125 y^6}$

95. $2xy^{-1} = \dfrac{2x}{y} = \dfrac{2(2)}{(-1)} = -4$

96. $-3x^{-1} y = \dfrac{-3y}{x} = \dfrac{-3(-1)}{(2)} = \dfrac{3}{2}$

97. $x^2 + y^2 = (2)^2 + (-1)^2 = 4 + 1 = 5$

98. $x^2 y^2 = (2)^2 (-1)^2 = 4 \cdot 1 = 4$

99. $(xy)^2 = (2 \cdot (-1))^2 = (-2)^2 = 4$

100. $(x + y)^2 = (2 + (-1))^2 = (1)^2 = 1$

101. $\sqrt{x^2} = |x| = |2| = 2$

102. $\left(\sqrt{x}\right)^2 = x = 2$

103. $\sqrt{x^2 + y^2} = \sqrt{(2)^2 + (-1)^2} = \sqrt{4 + 1} = \sqrt{5}$

104. $\sqrt{x^2} + \sqrt{y^2} = |x| + |y| = |2| + |-1| = 2 + 1 = 3$

105. $x^y = 2^{-1} = \dfrac{1}{2}$

106. $y^x = (-1)^2 = 1$

107. If $x = 2$,

$$2x^3 - 3x^2 + 5x - 4 = 2 \cdot 2^3 - 3 \cdot 2^2 + 5 \cdot 2 - 4$$
$$= 16 - 12 + 10 - 4$$
$$= 10$$

If $x = 1$,

$$2x^3 - 3x^2 + 5x - 4 = 2 \cdot 1^3 - 3 \cdot 1^2 + 5 \cdot 1 - 4$$
$$= 2 - 3 + 5 - 4$$
$$= 0$$

108. If $x = 1$,

$$4x^3 + 3x^2 - x + 2 = 4 \cdot 1^3 + 3 \cdot 1^2 - 1 + 2$$
$$= 4 + 3 - 1 + 2$$
$$= 8$$

If $x = 2$,

$$4x^3 + 3x^2 - x + 2 = 4 \cdot 2^3 + 3 \cdot 2^2 - 2 + 2$$
$$= 32 + 12 - 2 + 2$$
$$= 44$$

109. $\dfrac{(666)^4}{(222)^4} = \left(\dfrac{666}{222}\right)^4 = 3^4 = 81$

110. $(0.1)^3 (20)^3 = \left(\dfrac{1}{10}\right)^3 \cdot (2 \cdot 10)^3$

$$= \dfrac{1}{10^3} \cdot 2^3 \cdot 10^3$$
$$= 2^3 = 8$$

111. $(8.2)^6 \approx 304,006.671$

112. $(3.7)^5 \approx 693.440$

113. $(6.1)^{-3} \approx 0.004$

114. $(2.2)^{-5} \approx 0.019$

115. $(-2.8)^6 \approx 481.890$

116. $-(2.8)^6 \approx -481.890$

117. $(-8.11)^{-4} \approx 0.000$

118. $-(8.11)^{-4} \approx -0.000$

119. $454.2 = 4.542 \times 10^2$

120. $32.14 = 3.214 \times 10^1$

121. $0.013 = 1.3 \times 10^{-2}$

122. $0.00421 = 4.21 \times 10^{-3}$

123. $32,155 = 3.2155 \times 10^4$

124. $21,210 = 2.121 \times 10^4$

125. $0.000423 = 4.23 \times 10^{-4}$

126. $0.0514 = 5.14 \times 10^{-2}$

127. $6.15 \times 10^4 = 61,500$

128. $9.7 \times 10^3 = 9700$

129. $1.214 \times 10^{-3} = 0.001214$

130. $9.88 \times 10^{-4} = 0.000988$

131. $1.1 \times 10^8 = 110,000,000$

132. $4.112 \times 10^2 = 411.2$

133. $8.1 \times 10^{-2} = 0.081$

134. $6.453 \times 10^{-1} = 0.6453$

135. $A = lw$

136. $P = 2(l + w)$

137. $C = \pi d$

138. $A = \dfrac{1}{2} bh$

139. $A = \dfrac{\sqrt{3}}{4} x^2$

140. $P = 3x$

141. $V = \dfrac{4}{3} \pi r^3$

142. $S = 4\pi r^2$

9

143. $V = x^3$

144. $S = 6x^2$

145. a. If $x = 1000$,

$C = 4000 + 2x$

$= 4000 + 2(1000)$

$= 4000 + 2000$

$= \$6000$

The cost of producing 1000 watches is $6000.

b. If $x = 2000$,

$C = 4000 + 2x$

$= 4000 + 2(2000)$

$= 4000 + 4000$

$= \$8000$

The cost of producing 2000 watches is $8000.

146. $210 + 80 - 120 + 25 - 60 - 32 - 5 = \$98$

His balance at the end of the month was $98.

147. We want the difference between x and 4 to be at least 6 units. Since we don't care whether the value for x is larger or smaller than 4, we take the absolute value of the difference. We want the inequality to be non-strict since we are dealing with an 'at least' situation. Thus, we have

$|x - 4| \ge 6$

148. We want the difference between x and 2 to be more than 5 units. Since we don't care whether the value for x is larger or smaller than 2, we take the absolute value of the difference. We want the inequality to be strict since we are dealing with a 'more than' situation. Thus, we have

$|x - 2| > 5$

149. a. $|x - 110| = |108 - 110| = |-2| = 2 \le 5$

108 volts is acceptable.

b. $|x - 110| = |104 - 110| = |-6| = 6 > 5$

104 volts is *not* acceptable.

150. a. $|x - 220| = |214 - 220| = |-6| = 6 \le 8$

214 volts is acceptable.

b. $|x - 220| = |209 - 220| = |-11| = 11 > 8$

209 volts is *not* acceptable.

151. a. $|x - 3| = |2.999 - 3|$

$= |-0.001|$

$= 0.001 \le 0.01$

A radius of 2.999 centimeters is acceptable.

b. $|x - 3| = |2.89 - 3|$

$= |-0.11|$

$= 0.11 \not\le 0.01$

A radius of 2.89 centimeters is *not* acceptable.

152. a. $|x - 98.6| = |97 - 98.6|$

$= |-1.6|$

$= 1.6 \ge 1.5$

97°F is unhealthy.

b. $|x - 98.6| = |100 - 98.6|$

$= |1.4|$

$= 1.4 < 1.5$

100°F is *not* unhealthy.

153. The distance from Earth to the Moon is about $4 \times 10^8 = 400,000,000$ meters.

154. The height of Mt. Everest is about $8872 = 8.872 \times 10^3$ meters.

155. The wavelength of visible light is about $5 \times 10^{-7} = 0.0000005$ meters.

156. The diameter of an atom is about $1 \times 10^{-10} = 0.0000000001$ meters.

157. The smallest commercial copper wire has a diameter of about $0.0005 = 5 \times 10^{-4}$ inches.

158. The smallest motor ever made is less than $0.05 = 5 \times 10^{-2}$ centimeters wide.

10

159. $186,000 \cdot 60 \cdot 60 \cdot 24 \cdot 365$

$= \left(1.86 \times 10^5\right)\left(6 \times 10^1\right)^2 \left(2.4 \times 10^1\right)\left(3.65 \times 10^2\right)$

$= 586.5696 \times 10^{10} = 5.865696 \times 10^{12}$

There are about 5.9×10^{12} miles in one light-year.

160. $\dfrac{93,000,000}{186,000} = \dfrac{9.3 \times 10^7}{1.86 \times 10^5} = 5 \times 10^2$

$= 500 \text{ seconds} \approx 8 \text{ min. } 20 \text{ sec.}$

It takes about 8 minutes 20 seconds for a beam of light to reach Earth from the Sun.

161. $\dfrac{1}{3} = 0.333333\ldots > 0.333$

$\dfrac{1}{3}$ is larger by approximately $0.0003333\ldots$

162. $\dfrac{2}{3} = 0.666666\ldots > 0.666$

$\dfrac{2}{3}$ is larger by approximately $0.0006666\ldots$

163. No. For any positive number a, the value $\dfrac{a}{2}$ is smaller and therefore closer to 0.

164. We are given that $1 < x^2 < 10$. This implies that $1 < x < \sqrt{10}$. Since $x < \sqrt{10} \approx 3.162$ and $x > \pi \approx 3.142$, the number could be 3.15 or 3.16 (which are between 1 and 10 as required). The number could also be 3.14 since numbers such as 3.146 which lie between π and $\sqrt{10}$ would equal 3.14 when truncated to two decimal places.

165. Answers will vary.

166. Answers will vary.
$5 < 8$ is a true statement because 5 is further to the left than 8 on a real number line.

Section R.3

1. right; hypotenuse

2. $A = \dfrac{1}{2}bh$

3. $C = 2\pi r$

4. similar

5. True.

6. True. $6^2 + 8^2 = 36 + 64 = 100 = 10^2$

7. False; the volume of a sphere of radius r is given by $V = \dfrac{4}{3}\pi r^3$.

8. True. The lengths of the corresponding sides are equal.

9. True. Two corresponding angles are equal.

10. False. The sides are not proportional.

11. $a = 5, \ b = 12,$
$c^2 = a^2 + b^2$
$= 5^2 + 12^2$
$= 25 + 144$
$= 169 \implies c = 13$

12. $a = 6, \ b = 8,$
$c^2 = a^2 + b^2$
$= 6^2 + 8^2$
$= 36 + 64$
$= 100 \implies c = 10$

13. $a = 10, \ b = 24,$
$c^2 = a^2 + b^2$
$= 10^2 + 24^2$
$= 100 + 576$
$= 676 \implies c = 26$

14. $a = 4, \ b = 3,$
$c^2 = a^2 + b^2$
$= 4^2 + 3^2$
$= 16 + 9$
$= 25 \implies c = 5$

15. $a = 7, \ b = 24,$
$c^2 = a^2 + b^2$
$= 7^2 + 24^2$
$= 49 + 576$
$= 625 \implies c = 25$

16. $a = 14, \ b = 48,$

$$c^2 = a^2 + b^2$$
$$= 14^2 + 48^2$$
$$= 196 + 2304$$
$$= 2500 \ \Rightarrow \ c = 50$$

17. $5^2 = 3^2 + 4^2$

$25 = 9 + 16$

$25 = 25$

The given triangle is a right triangle. The hypotenuse is 5.

18. $10^2 = 6^2 + 8^2$

$100 = 36 + 64$

$100 = 100$

The given triangle is a right triangle. The hypotenuse is 10.

19. $6^2 = 4^2 + 5^2$

$36 = 16 + 25$

$36 = 41$ false

The given triangle is not a right triangle.

20. $3^2 = 2^2 + 2^2$

$9 = 4 + 4$

$9 = 8$ false

The given triangle is not a right triangle.

21. $25^2 = 7^2 + 24^2$

$625 = 49 + 576$

$625 = 625$

The given triangle is a right triangle. The hypotenuse is 25.

22. $26^2 = 10^2 + 24^2$

$676 = 100 + 576$

$676 = 676$

The given triangle is a right triangle. The hypotenuse is 26.

23. $6^2 = 3^2 + 4^2$

$36 = 9 + 16$

$36 = 25$ false

The given triangle is not a right triangle.

24. $7^2 = 5^2 + 4^2$

$49 = 25 + 16$

$49 = 41$ false

The given triangle is not a right triangle.

25. $A = l \cdot w = 4 \cdot 2 = 8 \text{ in}^2$

26. $A = l \cdot w = 9 \cdot 4 = 36 \text{ cm}^2$

27. $A = \dfrac{1}{2} b \cdot h = \dfrac{1}{2}(2)(4) = 4 \text{ in}^2$

28. $A = \dfrac{1}{2} b \cdot h = \dfrac{1}{2}(4)(9) = 18 \text{ cm}^2$

29. $A = \pi r^2 = \pi (5)^2 = 25\pi \text{ m}^2$

$C = 2\pi r = 2\pi(5) = 10\pi \text{ m}$

30. $A = \pi r^2 = \pi (2)^2 = 4\pi \text{ ft}^2$

$C = 2\pi r = 2\pi(2) = 4\pi \text{ ft}$

31. $V = l\,w\,h = 8 \cdot 4 \cdot 7 = 224 \text{ ft}^3$

$S = 2lw + 2lh + 2wh$

$$= 2(8)(4) + 2(8)(7) + 2(4)(7)$$
$$= 64 + 112 + 56$$
$$= 232 \text{ ft}^2$$

32. $V = l\,w\,h = 9 \cdot 4 \cdot 8 = 288 \text{ in}^3$

$S = 2lw + 2lh + 2wh$

$$= 2(9)(4) + 2(9)(8) + 2(4)(8)$$
$$= 72 + 144 + 64$$
$$= 280 \text{ in}^2$$

33. $V = \dfrac{4}{3}\pi r^3 = \dfrac{4}{3}\pi \cdot 4^3 = \dfrac{256}{3}\pi \text{ cm}^3$

$S = 4\pi r^2 = 4\pi \cdot 4^2 = 64\pi \text{ cm}^2$

34. $V = \dfrac{4}{3}\pi r^3 = \dfrac{4}{3}\pi \cdot 3^3 = 36\pi \text{ ft}^3$

$S = 4\pi r^2 = 4\pi \cdot 3^2 = 36\pi \text{ ft}^2$

35. $V = \pi r^2 h = \pi(9)^2(8) = 648\pi$ in^3

$S = 2\pi r^2 + 2\pi rh$

$\quad = 2\pi(9)^2 + 2\pi(9)(8)$

$\quad = 162\pi + 144\pi$

$\quad = 306\pi$ in^2

36. $V = \pi r^2 h = \pi(8)^2(9) = 576\pi$ in^3

$S = 2\pi r^2 + 2\pi rh$

$\quad = 2\pi(8)^2 + 2\pi(8)(9)$

$\quad = 128\pi + 144\pi$

$\quad = 272\pi$ in^2

37. The diameter of the circle is 2, so its radius is 1.
$A = \pi r^2 = \pi(1)^2 = \pi$ square units

38. The diameter of the circle is 2, so its radius is 1.
$A = 2^2 - \pi(1)^2 = 4 - \pi$ square units

39. The diameter of the circle is the length of the diagonal of the square.

$d^2 = 2^2 + 2^2$

$\quad = 4 + 4$

$\quad = 8$

$d = \sqrt{8} = 2\sqrt{2}$

$r = \dfrac{d}{2} = \dfrac{2\sqrt{2}}{2} = \sqrt{2}$

The area of the circle is:

$A = \pi r^2 = \pi\left(\sqrt{2}\right)^2 = 2\pi$ square units

40. The diameter of the circle is the length of the diagonal of the square.

$d^2 = 2^2 + 2^2$

$\quad = 4 + 4$

$\quad = 8$

$d = \sqrt{8} = 2\sqrt{2}$

$r = \dfrac{d}{2} = \dfrac{2\sqrt{2}}{2} = \sqrt{2}$

The area is:

$A = \pi\left(\sqrt{2}\right)^2 - 2^2 = 2\pi - 4$ square units

41. Since the triangles are similar, the lengths of corresponding sides are proportional. Therefore, we get

$\dfrac{8}{4} = \dfrac{x}{2}$

$\dfrac{8\cdot 2}{4} = x$

$4 = x$

In addition, corresponding angles must have the same angle measure. Therefore, we have $A = 90°$, $B = 60°$, and $C = 30°$.

42. Since the triangles are similar, the lengths of corresponding sides are proportional. Therefore, we get

$\dfrac{6}{12} = \dfrac{x}{16}$

$\dfrac{6\cdot 16}{12} = x$

$8 = x$

In addition, corresponding angles must have the same angle measure. Therefore, we have $A = 30°$, $B = 75°$, and $C = 75°$.

43. Since the triangles are similar, the lengths of corresponding sides are proportional. Therefore, we get

$\dfrac{30}{20} = \dfrac{x}{45}$

$\dfrac{30\cdot 45}{20} = x$

$\dfrac{135}{2} = x$ or $x = 67.5$

In addition, corresponding angles must have the same angle measure. Therefore, we have $A = 60°$, $B = 95°$, and $C = 25°$.

44. Since the triangles are similar, the lengths of corresponding sides are proportional. Therefore, we get

$\dfrac{8}{10} = \dfrac{x}{50}$

$\dfrac{8\cdot 50}{10} = x$

$40 = x$

In addition, corresponding angles must have the same angle measure. Therefore, we have $A = 50°$, $B = 125°$, and $C = 5°$.

45. The total distance traveled is 4 times the circumference of the wheel.

$$\text{Total Distance} = 4C = 4(\pi d) = 4\pi \cdot 16$$
$$= 64\pi \approx 201.1 \text{ inches} \approx 16.8 \text{ feet}$$

46. The distance traveled in one revolution is the circumference of the disk 4π.

The number of revolutions =

$$\frac{\text{dist. traveled}}{\text{circumference}} = \frac{20}{4\pi} = \frac{5}{\pi} \approx 1.6 \text{ revolutions}$$

47. Area of the border = area of EFGH – area of

$$\text{ABCD} = 10^2 - 6^2 = 100 - 36 = 64 \text{ ft}^2$$

48. FG = 4 feet; BG = 4 feet and BC = 10 feet, so CG= 6 feet. The area of the triangle CGF is:

$$A = \frac{1}{2} \cdot (4)(6) = 12 \text{ ft}^2$$

49. Area of the window = area of the rectangle + area of the semicircle.

$$A = (6)(4) + \frac{1}{2} \cdot \pi \cdot 2^2 = 24 + 2\pi \approx 30.28 \text{ ft}^2$$

Perimeter of the window = 2 heights + width + one-half the circumference.

$$P = 2(6) + 4 + \frac{1}{2} \cdot \pi(4) = 12 + 4 + 2\pi$$
$$= 16 + 2\pi \approx 22.28 \text{ feet}$$

50. Area of the deck = area of the pool and deck – area of the pool.

$$A = \pi(13)^2 - \pi(10)^2 = 169\pi - 100\pi$$
$$= 69\pi \text{ ft}^2 \approx 216.77 \text{ ft}^2$$

The amount of fence is the circumference of the circle with radius 13 feet.

$$C = 2\pi(13) = 26\pi \text{ ft} \approx 81.68 \text{ ft}$$

51. We can form similar triangles using the Great Pyramid's height/shadow and Thales' height/shadow:

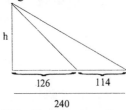

This allows us to write

$$\frac{h}{240} = \frac{2}{3}$$
$$h = \frac{2 \cdot 240}{3} = 160$$

The height of the Great Pyramid is 160 paces.

52. Let x = the approximate distance from San Juan to Hamilton and y = the approximate distance from Hamilton to Fort Lauderdale. Using similar triangles, we get

$$\frac{1046}{58} = \frac{x}{53.5} \qquad \frac{1046}{58} = \frac{y}{57}$$
$$\frac{1046 \cdot 53.5}{58} = x \qquad \frac{1046 \cdot 57}{58} = y$$
$$964.8 \approx x \qquad 1028.0 \approx y$$

The approximate distance between San Juan and Hamilton is 965 miles and the approximate distance between Hamilton and Fort Lauderdale is 1028 miles.

53. Convert 20 feet to miles, and solve the Pythagorean Theorem to find the distance:

$$20 \text{ feet } = 20 \text{ feet } \cdot \frac{1 \text{ mile}}{5280 \text{ feet}} = 0.003788 \text{ miles}$$
$$d^2 = (3960 + 0.003788)^2 - 3960^2 = 30 \text{ sq. miles}$$
$$d \approx 5.477 \text{ miles}$$

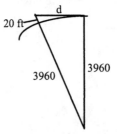

54. Convert 6 feet to miles, and solve the Pythagorean Theorem to find the distance:

$$6 \text{ feet } = 6 \text{ feet } \cdot \frac{1 \text{ mile}}{5280 \text{ feet}} = 0.001136 \text{ miles}$$
$$d^2 = (3960 + 0.001136)^2 - 3960^2 = 9 \text{ sq. miles}$$
$$d \approx 3 \text{ miles}$$

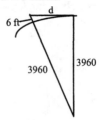

55. Convert 100 feet to miles, and solve the Pythagorean Theorem to find the distance:

$$100 \text{ feet } = 100 \text{ feet } \cdot \frac{1 \text{ mile}}{5280 \text{ feet}} = 0.018939 \text{ miles}$$

$$d^2 = (3960 + 0.018939)^2 - 3960^2 \approx 150 \text{ sq. miles}$$

$$d \approx 12.2 \text{ miles}$$

Convert 150 feet to miles, and solve the Pythagorean Theorem to find the distance:

$$150 \text{ feet } = 150 \text{ feet } \cdot \frac{1 \text{ mile}}{5280 \text{ feet}} = 0.028409 \text{ miles}$$

$$d^2 = (3960 + 0.028409)^2 - 3960^2 \approx 225 \text{ sq. miles}$$

$$d \approx 15.0 \text{ miles}$$

56. Given $m > 0$, $n > 0$ and $m > n$,

if $a = m^2 - n^2, b = 2mn$ and $c = m^2 + n^2$, then

$$a^2 + b^2 = \left(m^2 - n^2\right)^2 + \left(2mn\right)^2$$

$$= m^4 - 2m^2n^2 + n^4 + 4m^2n^2$$

$$= m^4 + 2m^2n^2 + n^4$$

and $c^2 = \left(m^2 + n^2\right)^2 = m^4 + 2m^2n^2 + n^4$

$\therefore a^2 + b^2 = c^2 \rightarrow a, b$ and c represent the sides of a right triangle.

57. Let $l =$ length of the rectangle and $w =$ width of the rectangle. Notice that

$$(l + w)^2 - (l - w)^2$$

$$= [(l + w) + (l - w)][(l + w) - (l - w)]$$

$$= (2l)(2w) = 4lw = 4A$$

So $A = \frac{1}{4}[(l + w)^2 - (l - w)^2]$

Since $(l - w)^2 \geq 0$, the largest area will occur when $l - w = 0$ or $l = w$; that is, when the rectangle is a square. But

$$1000 = 2l + 2w = 2(l + w)$$

$$500 = l + w = 2l$$

$$250 = l = w$$

The largest possible area is $250^2 = 62500$ sq ft. A circular pool with circumference $= 1000$ feet

yields the equation: $2\pi r = 1000 \Rightarrow r = \frac{500}{\pi}$

The area enclosed by the circular pool is:

$$A = \pi r^2 = \pi \left(\frac{500}{\pi}\right)^2 = \frac{500^2}{\pi} \approx 79577.47 \text{ ft}^2$$

Thus, a circular pool will enclose the most area.

58. Consider the diagram showing the lighthouse at point L, relative to the center of Earth, using the radius of Earth as 3960 miles. Let P refer to the furthest point on the horizon from which the light is visible. Note also that

$$362 \text{ feet } = \frac{362}{5280} \text{ miles.}$$

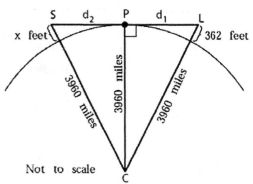

Not to scale

Apply the Pythagorean Theorem to $\triangle CPL$:

$$(3960)^2 + \left(d_1\right)^2 = \left(3960 + \frac{362}{5280}\right)^2$$

$$\left(d_1\right)^2 = \left(3960 + \frac{362}{5280}\right)^2 - \left(3960\right)^2$$

$$d_1 = \sqrt{\left(3960 + \frac{362}{5280}\right)^2 - \left(3960\right)^2} \approx 23.30 \text{ mi.}$$

Therefore, the light from the lighthouse can be seen at point P on the horizon, where point P is approximately 23.30 miles away from the lighthouse. Brochure information is slightly overstated.

Verify the ship information:

Let S refer to the ship's location, and let x equal the height, in feet, of the ship.

We need $d_1 + d_2 \geq 40$.

Since $d_1 \approx 23.30$ miles we need

$$d_2 \geq 40 - 23.30 = 16.70 \text{ miles.}$$

Apply the Pythagorean Theorem to $\triangle CPS$:

$$\left(3960\right)^2 + \left(16.7\right)^2 = \left(3960 + x\right)^2$$

$$\sqrt{\left(3960\right)^2 + \left(16.7\right)^2} = 3960 + x$$

$$\sqrt{\left(3960\right)^2 + \left(16.7\right)^2} - 3960 = x$$

$$x \approx 0.035 \text{ miles}$$

$$x \approx 185.93 \text{ feet.}$$

The ship would have to be at least 186 feet tall to see the lighthouse from 40 miles away.

Verify the airplane information:

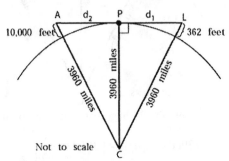

Not to scale

Let A refer to the airplane's location. The distance from the plane to point P is d_2.

We want to show that $d_1 + d_2 \geq 120$.

Assume the altitude of the airplane is

$$10{,}000 \text{ feet} = \frac{10000}{5280} \text{ miles.}$$

Apply the Pythagorean Theorem to $\triangle CPA$:

$$\left(3960\right)^2 + \left(d_2\right)^2 = \left(3960 + \frac{10000}{5280}\right)^2$$

$$\left(d_2\right)^2 = \left(3960 + \frac{10000}{5280}\right)^2 - \left(3960\right)^2$$

$$d_2 = \sqrt{\left(3960 + \frac{10000}{5280}\right)^2 - \left(3960\right)^2}$$

$$\approx 122.49 \text{ miles.}$$

Therefore,

$$d_1 + d_2 \approx 23.30 + 122.49 = 145.79 \geq 120.$$

The brochure information is slightly understated. Note that a plane at an altitude of 6233 feet could see the lighthouse from 120 miles away.

Section R.4

1. 4; 3

2. $x^4 - 16$

3. $x^3 - 8$

4. False; monomials cannot have negative degrees.

5. True

6. False; $x^3 + a^3 = \left(x + a\right)\left(x^2 - ax + a^2\right)$

7. $2x^3$ Monomial; Variable: x; Coefficient: 2; Degree: 3

8. $-4x^2$ Monomial; Variable: x; Coefficient: -4; Degree: 2

9. $\dfrac{8}{x} = 8x^{-1}$ Not a monomial; when written in the form ax^k, the variable has a negative exponent.

10. $-2x^{-3}$ Not a monomial; when written in the form ax^k, the variable has a negative exponent.

11. $-2xy^2$ Monomial; Variable: x, y; Coefficient: -2; Degree: 3

12. $5x^2y^3$ Monomial; Variable: x, y; Coefficient: 5; Degree: 5

13. $\dfrac{8x}{y} = 8xy^{-1}$ Not a monomial; when written in the form $ax^n y^m$, the exponent on the variable y is negative.

14. $-\dfrac{2x^2}{y^3} = -2x^2 y^{-3}$ Not a monomial; when written in the form $ax^n y^m$, the exponent on the variable y is negative.

15. $x^2 + y^2$ Not a monomial; the expression contains more than one term. This expression is a binomial.

16. $3x^2 + 4$ Not a monomial; the expression contains more than one term. This expression is a binomial.

17. $3x^2 - 5$ Polynomial; Degree: 2

18. $1 - 4x$ Polynomial; Degree: 1

19. 5 Polynomial; Degree: 0

20. $-\pi$ Polynomial; Degree: 0

21. $3x^2 - \dfrac{5}{x}$ Not a polynomial; the variable in the denominator results in an exponent that is not a nonnegative integer.

22. $\dfrac{3}{x} + 2$ Not a polynomial; the variable in the denominator results in an exponent that is not a nonnegative integer.

23. $2y^3 - \sqrt{2}$ Polynomial; Degree: 3

24. $10z^2 + z$ Polynomial; Degree: 2

25. $\dfrac{x^2 + 5}{x^3 - 1}$ Not a polynomial; the polynomial in the denominator has a degree greater than 0.

26. $\dfrac{3x^3 + 2x - 1}{x^2 + x + 1}$ Not a polynomial; the polynomial in the denominator has a degree greater than 0.

27. $(x^2 + 4x + 5) + (3x - 3)$
$= x^2 + (4x + 3x) + (5 - 3)$
$= x^2 + 7x + 2$

28. $(x^3 + 3x^2 + 2) + (x^2 - 4x + 4)$
$= x^3 + (3x^2 + x^2) + (-4x) + (2 + 4)$
$= x^3 + 4x^2 - 4x + 6$

29. $(x^3 - 2x^2 + 5x + 10) - (2x^2 - 4x + 3)$
$= x^3 - 2x^2 + 5x + 10 - 2x^2 + 4x - 3$
$= x^3 + (-2x^2 - 2x^2) + (5x + 4x) + (10 - 3)$
$= x^3 - 4x^2 + 9x + 7$

30. $(x^2 - 3x - 4) - (x^3 - 3x^2 + x + 5)$
$= x^2 - 3x - 4 - x^3 + 3x^2 - x - 5$
$= -x^3 + (x^2 + 3x^2) + (-3x - x) + (-4 - 5)$
$= -x^3 + 4x^2 - 4x - 9$

31. $\left(6x^5 + x^3 + x\right) + \left(5x^4 - x^3 + 3x^2\right)$
$= 6x^5 + 5x^4 + 3x^2 + x$

32. $\left(10x^5 - 8x^2\right) + \left(3x^3 - 2x^2 + 6\right)$
$= 10x^5 + 3x^3 - 10x^2 + 6$

33. $(x^2 - 3x + 1) + 2(3x^2 + x - 4)$
$= x^2 - 3x + 1 + 6x^2 + 2x - 8$
$= 7x^2 - x - 7$

34. $-2(x^2 + x + 1) + (-5x^2 - x + 2)$
$= -2x^2 - 2x - 2 - 5x^2 - x + 2$
$= -7x^2 - 3x$

35. $6(x^3 + x^2 - 3) - 4(2x^3 - 3x^2)$
$= 6x^3 + 6x^2 - 18 - 8x^3 + 12x^2$
$= -2x^3 + 18x^2 - 18$

36. $8(4x^3 - 3x^2 - 1) - 6(4x^3 + 8x - 2)$
$= 32x^3 - 24x^2 - 8 - 24x^3 - 48x + 12$
$= 8x^3 - 24x^2 - 48x + 4$

37. $\left(x^2 - x + 2\right) + \left(2x^2 - 3x + 5\right) - \left(x^2 + 1\right)$
$= x^2 - x + 2 + 2x^2 - 3x + 5 - x^2 - 1$
$= 2x^2 - 4x + 6$

38. $\left(x^2 + 1\right) - \left(4x^2 + 5\right) + \left(x^2 + x - 2\right)$
$= x^2 + 1 - 4x^2 - 5 + x^2 + x - 2$
$= -2x^2 + x - 6$

39. $9\left(y^2 - 3y + 4\right) - 6\left(1 - y^2\right)$
$= 9y^2 - 27y + 36 - 6 + 6y^2$
$= 15y^2 - 27y + 30$

40. $8\left(1 - y^3\right) + 4\left(1 + y + y^2 + y^3\right)$
$= 8 - 8y^3 + 4 + 4y + 4y^2 + 4y^3$
$= -4y^3 + 4y^2 + 4y + 12$

41. $x(x^2 + x - 4) = x^3 + x^2 - 4x$

42. $4x^2(x^3 - x + 2) = 4x^5 - 4x^3 + 8x^2$

43. $-2x^2(4x^3 + 5) = -8x^5 - 10x^2$

44. $5x^3(3x - 4) = 15x^4 - 20x^3$

45. $(x + 1)(x^2 + 2x - 4)$
$= x(x^2 + 2x - 4) + 1(x^2 + 2x - 4)$
$= x^3 + 2x^2 - 4x + x^2 + 2x - 4$
$= x^3 + 3x^2 - 2x - 4$

46. $(2x - 3)(x^2 + x + 1)$
$= 2x(x^2 + x + 1) - 3(x^2 + x + 1)$
$= 2x^3 + 2x^2 + 2x - 3x^2 - 3x - 3$
$= 2x^3 - x^2 - x - 3$

47. $(x + 2)(x + 4) = x^2 + 4x + 2x + 8$
$= x^2 + 6x + 8$

48. $(x + 3)(x + 5) = x^2 + 5x + 3x + 15$
$= x^2 + 8x + 15$

49. $(2x + 5)(x + 2) = 2x^2 + 4x + 5x + 10$
$= 2x^2 + 9x + 10$

50. $(3x + 1)(2x + 1) = 6x^2 + 3x + 2x + 1$
$= 6x^2 + 5x + 1$

51. $(x - 4)(x + 2) = x^2 + 2x - 4x - 8$
$= x^2 - 2x - 8$

52. $(x + 4)(x - 2) = x^2 - 2x + 4x - 8$
$= x^2 + 2x - 8$

53. $(x - 3)(x - 2) = x^2 - 2x - 3x + 6$
$= x^2 - 5x + 6$

54. $(x - 5)(x - 1) = x^2 - x - 5x + 5$
$= x^2 - 6x + 5$

55. $(2x + 3)(x - 2) = 2x^2 - 4x + 3x - 6$
$= 2x^2 - x - 6$

56. $(2x - 4)(3x + 1) = 6x^2 + 2x - 12x - 4$
$= 6x^2 - 10x - 4$

57. $(-2x + 3)(x - 4) = -2x^2 + 8x + 3x - 12$
$= -2x^2 + 11x - 12$

58. $(-3x - 1)(x + 1) = -3x^2 - 3x - x - 1$
$= -3x^2 - 4x - 1$

59. $(-x - 2)(-2x - 4) = 2x^2 + 4x + 4x + 8$
$= 2x^2 + 8x + 8$

60. $(-2x - 3)(3 - x) = -6x + 2x^2 - 9 + 3x$
$= 2x^2 - 3x - 9$

61. $(x - 2y)(x + y) = x^2 + xy - 2xy - 2y^2$
$= x^2 - xy - 2y^2$

62. $(2x + 3y)(x - y) = 2x^2 - 2xy + 3xy - 3y^2$
$= 2x^2 + xy - 3y^2$

63. $(-2x - 3y)(3x + 2y) = -6x^2 - 4xy - 9xy - 6y^2$
$= -6x^2 - 13xy - 6y^2$

64. $(x - 3y)(-2x + y) = -2x^2 + xy + 6xy - 3y^2$
$= -2x^2 + 7xy - 3y^2$

65. $(x - 7)(x + 7) = x^2 - 7^2 = x^2 - 49$

66. $(x - 1)(x + 1) = x^2 - 1^2 = x^2 - 1$

67. $(2x + 3)(2x - 3) = (2x)^2 - 3^2 = 4x^2 - 9$

68. $(3x + 2)(3x - 2) = (3x)^2 - 2^2 = 9x^2 - 4$

69. $(x + 4)^2 = x^2 + 2 \cdot x \cdot 4 + 4^2 = x^2 + 8x + 16$

70. $(x + 5)^2 = x^2 + 2 \cdot x \cdot 5 + 5^2 = x^2 + 10x + 25$

71. $(x - 4)^2 = x^2 - 2 \cdot x \cdot 4 + 4^2 = x^2 - 8x + 16$

72. $(x - 5)^2 = x^2 - 2 \cdot x \cdot 5 + 5^2 = x^2 - 10x + 25$

73. $(3x + 4)(3x - 4) = (3x)^2 - 4^2 = 9x^2 - 16$

74. $(5x - 3)(5x + 3) = (5x)^2 - 3^2 = 25x^2 - 9$

75. $(2x-3)^2 = (2x)^2 - 2(2x)(3) + 3^2$
$= 4x^2 - 12x + 9$

76. $(3x-4)^2 = (3x)^2 - 2(3x)(4) + 4^2$
$= 9x^2 - 24x + 16$

77. $(x+y)(x-y) = (x)^2 - (y)^2 = x^2 - y^2$

78. $(x+3y)(x-3y) = (x)^2 - (3y)^2 = x^2 - 9y^2$

79. $(3x+y)(3x-y) = (3x)^2 - (y)^2 = 9x^2 - y^2$

80. $(3x+4y)(3x-4y) = (3x)^2 - (4y)^2 = 9x^2 - 16y^2$

81. $(x+y)^2 = x^2 + 2xy + y^2$

82. $(x-y)^2 = x^2 - 2xy + y^2$

83. $(x-2y)^2 = x^2 + 2(x \cdot (-2y)) + (2y)^2$
$= x^2 - 4xy + 4y^2$

84. $(2x+3y)^2 = (2x)^2 + 2(2x \cdot 3y) + (3y)^2$
$= 4x^2 + 12xy + 9y^2$

85. $(x-2)^3 = x^3 - 3 \cdot x^2 \cdot 2 + 3 \cdot x \cdot 2^2 - 2^3$
$= x^3 - 6x^2 + 12x - 8$

86. $(x+1)^3 = x^3 + 3 \cdot x^2 \cdot 1 + 3 \cdot x \cdot 1^2 + 1^3$
$= x^3 + 3x^2 + 3x + 1$

87. $(2x+1)^3 = (2x)^3 + 3(2x)^2(1) + 3(2x) \cdot 1^2 + 1^3$
$= 8x^3 + 12x^2 + 6x + 1$

88. $(3x-2)^3 = (3x)^3 - 3(3x)^2(2) + 3(3x) \cdot 2^2 - 2^3$
$= 27x^3 - 54x^2 + 36x - 8$

89.
$$\begin{array}{r} 4x^2 - 11x + 23 \\ x+2\overline{)4x^3 - 3x^2 + x + 1} \\ \underline{4x^3 + 8x^2} \\ -11x^2 + x \\ \underline{-11x^2 - 22x} \\ 23x + 1 \\ \underline{23x + 46} \\ -45 \end{array}$$

Check:
$(x+2)(4x^2 - 11x + 23) + (-45)$
$= 4x^3 - 11x^2 + 23x + 8x^2 - 22x + 46 - 45$
$= 4x^3 - 3x^2 + x + 1$
The quotient is $4x^2 - 11x + 23$; the remainder is –45.

90.
$$\begin{array}{r} 3x^2 - 7x + 15 \\ x+2\overline{)3x^3 - x^2 + x - 2} \\ \underline{3x^3 + 6x^2} \\ -7x^2 + x \\ \underline{-7x^2 - 14x} \\ 15x - 2 \\ \underline{15x + 30} \\ -32 \end{array}$$

Check:
$(x+2)(3x^2 - 7x + 15) + (-32)$
$= 3x^3 - 7x^2 + 15x + 6x^2 - 14x + 30 - 32$
$= 3x^3 - x^2 + x - 2$
The quotient is $3x^2 - 7x + 15$; the remainder is –32.

91.
$$\begin{array}{r} 4x - 3 \\ x^2\overline{)4x^3 - 3x^2 + x + 1} \\ \underline{4x^3} \\ -3x^2 + x + 1 \\ \underline{-3x^2} \\ x + 1 \end{array}$$

Check:
$(x^2)(4x-3) + (x+1) = 4x^3 - 3x^2 + x + 1$
The quotient is $4x - 3$; the remainder is $x + 1$.

92.

$$\begin{array}{r} 3x - 1 \\ x^2 \overline{)3x^3 - x^2 + x - 2} \\ \underline{3x^3} \\ -x^2 + x - 2 \\ \underline{-x^2} \\ x - 2 \end{array}$$

Check:

$(x^2)(3x-1)+(x-2) = 3x^3 - x^2 + x - 2$

The quotient is $3x-1$; the remainder is $x-2$.

93.

$$\begin{array}{r} 5x^2 - 13 \\ x^2 + 2 \overline{)5x^4 + 0x^3 - 3x^2 + x + 1} \\ \underline{5x^4 \qquad +10x^2} \\ -13x^2 + x + 1 \\ \underline{-13x^2 \qquad -26} \\ x + 27 \end{array}$$

Check:

$\left(x^2 + 2\right)\left(5x^2 - 13\right) + (x + 27)$

$= 5x^4 + 10x^2 - 13x^2 - 26 + x + 27$

$= 5x^4 - 3x^2 + x + 1$

The quotient is $5x^2 - 13$; the remainder is $x + 27$.

94.

$$\begin{array}{r} 5x^2 - 11 \\ x^2 + 2 \overline{)5x^4 + 0x^3 - x^2 + x - 2} \\ \underline{5x^4 \qquad +10x^2} \\ -11x^2 + x - 2 \\ \underline{-11x^2 \qquad -22} \\ x + 20 \end{array}$$

Check:

$\left(x^2 + 2\right)\left(5x^2 - 11\right) + (x + 20)$

$= 5x^4 + 10x^2 - 11x^2 - 22 + x + 20$

$= 5x^4 - x^2 + x - 2$

The quotient is $5x^2 - 11$; the remainder is $x + 20$.

95.

$$\begin{array}{r} 2x^2 \\ 2x^3 - 1 \overline{)4x^5 + 0x^4 + 0x^3 - 3x^2 + x + 1} \\ \underline{4x^5 \qquad\qquad -2x^2} \\ -x^2 + x + 1 \end{array}$$

Check:

$\left(2x^3 - 1\right)\left(2x^2\right) + \left(-x^2 + x + 1\right)$

$= 4x^5 - 2x^2 - x^2 + x + 1 = 4x^5 - 3x^2 + x + 1$

The quotient is $2x^2$; the remainder is $-x^2 + x + 1$.

96.

$$\begin{array}{r} x^2 \\ 3x^3 - 1 \overline{)3x^5 + 0x^4 + 0x^3 - x^2 + x - 2} \\ \underline{3x^5 \qquad\qquad -x^2} \\ x - 2 \end{array}$$

Check:

$\left(3x^3 - 1\right)\left(x^2\right) + (x - 2) = 3x^5 - x^2 + x - 2$

The quotient is x^2; the remainder is $x - 2$.

97.

$$\begin{array}{r} x^2 - 2x + \frac{1}{2} \\ 2x^2 + x + 1 \overline{)2x^4 - 3x^3 + 0x^2 + x + 1} \\ \underline{2x^4 + x^3 + x^2} \\ -4x^3 - x^2 + x \\ \underline{-4x^3 - 2x^2 - 2x} \\ x^2 + 3x + 1 \\ \underline{x^2 + \frac{1}{2}x + \frac{1}{2}} \\ \frac{5}{2}x + \frac{1}{2} \end{array}$$

Check:

$\left(2x^2 + x + 1\right)\left(x^2 - 2x + \frac{1}{2}\right) + \frac{5}{2}x + \frac{1}{2}$

$= 2x^4 - 4x^3 + x^2 + x^3 - 2x^2 + \frac{1}{2}x$

$\quad + x^2 - 2x + \frac{1}{2} + \frac{5}{2}x + \frac{1}{2}$

$= 2x^4 - 3x^3 + x + 1$

The quotient is $x^2 - 2x + \frac{1}{2}$; the remainder is

$\frac{5}{2}x + \frac{1}{2}$.

98.

$$3x^2 + x + 1 \overline{\smash{\big)}\,3x^4 - x^3 + 0x^2 + x - 2} \quad \overset{\displaystyle x^2 - \tfrac{2}{3}x - \tfrac{1}{9}}{}$$

$$\underline{3x^4 + x^3 + x^2}$$
$$-2x^3 - x^2 + x$$
$$\underline{-2x^3 - \tfrac{2}{3}x^2 - \tfrac{2}{3}x}$$
$$-\tfrac{1}{3}x^2 + \tfrac{5}{3}x - 2$$
$$\underline{-\tfrac{1}{3}x^2 - \tfrac{1}{9}x - \tfrac{1}{9}}$$
$$\tfrac{16}{9}x - \tfrac{17}{9}$$

Check:

$$\left(3x^2 + x + 1\right)\left(x^2 - \tfrac{2}{3}x - \tfrac{1}{9}\right) + \left(\tfrac{16}{9}x - \tfrac{17}{9}\right)$$
$$= 3x^4 + x^3 + x^2 - 2x^3 - \tfrac{2}{3}x^2 - \tfrac{2}{3}x$$
$$\quad -\tfrac{1}{3}x^2 - \tfrac{1}{9}x - \tfrac{1}{9} + \tfrac{16}{9}x - \tfrac{17}{9}$$
$$= 3x^4 - x^3 + x - 2$$

The quotient is $x^2 - \tfrac{2}{3}x - \tfrac{1}{9}$; the remainder is

$$\tfrac{16}{9}x - \tfrac{17}{9}.$$

99.

$$x - 1 \overline{\smash{\big)}\,-4x^3 + x^2 + 0x - 4} \quad \overset{\displaystyle -4x^2 - 3x - 3}{}$$

$$\underline{-4x^3 + 4x^2}$$
$$-3x^2$$
$$\underline{-3x^2 + 3x}$$
$$-3x - 4$$
$$\underline{-3x + 3}$$
$$-7$$

Check:

$$(x-1)(-4x^2 - 3x - 3) + (-7)$$
$$= -4x^3 - 3x^2 - 3x + 4x^2 + 3x + 3 - 7$$
$$= -4x^3 + x^2 - 4$$

The quotient is $-4x^2 - 3x - 3$; the remainder is
-7.

100.

$$x - 1 \overline{\smash{\big)}\,-3x^4 + 0x^3 + 0x^2 - 2x - 1} \quad \overset{\displaystyle -3x^3 - 3x^2 - 3x - 5}{}$$

$$\underline{-3x^4 + 3x^3}$$
$$-3x^3$$
$$\underline{-3x^3 + 3x^2}$$
$$-3x^2 - 2x$$
$$\underline{-3x^2 + 3x}$$
$$-5x - 1$$
$$\underline{-5x + 5}$$
$$-6$$

Check:

$$(x-1)(-3x^3 - 3x^2 - 3x - 5) + (-6)$$
$$= -3x^4 - 3x^3 - 3x^2 - 5x + 3x^3 + 3x^2$$
$$\quad + 3x + 5 - 6$$
$$= -3x^4 - 2x - 1$$

The quotient is $-3x^3 - 3x^2 - 3x - 5$; the
remainder is -6.

101.

$$x^2 + x + 1 \overline{\smash{\big)}\,x^4 + 0x^3 - x^2 + 0x + 1} \quad \overset{\displaystyle x^2 - x - 1}{}$$

$$\underline{x^4 + x^3 + x^2}$$
$$-x^3 - 2x^2$$
$$\underline{-x^3 - x^2 - x}$$
$$-x^2 + x + 1$$
$$\underline{-x^2 - x - 1}$$
$$2x + 2$$

Check:

$$(x^2 + x + 1)(x^2 - x - 1) + 2x + 2$$
$$= x^4 + x^3 + x^2 - x^3 - x^2 - x - x^2 - x$$
$$\quad -1 + 2x + 2$$
$$= x^4 - x^2 + 1$$

The quotient is $x^2 - x - 1$; the remainder is
$2x + 2$.

102.

$$x^2 - x + 1 \overline{)x^4 + 0x^3 - x^2 + 0x + 1}$$

quotient: $x^2 + x - 1$

$$\underline{x^4 - x^3 + x^2}$$
$$x^3 - 2x^2$$
$$\underline{x^3 - x^2 + x}$$
$$-x^2 - x + 1$$
$$\underline{-x^2 + x - 1}$$
$$-2x + 2$$

Check:

$(x^2 - x + 1)(x^2 + x - 1) + (-2x + 2)$

$= x^4 + x^3 - x^2 - x^3 - x^2 + x + x^2 + x$

$\quad -1 - 2x + 2$

$= x^4 - x^2 + 1$

The quotient is $x^2 + x - 1$; the remainder is $-2x + 2$.

103.

$$x - a \overline{)x^3 + 0x^2 + 0x - a^3}$$

quotient: $x^2 + ax + a^2$

$$\underline{x^3 - ax^2}$$
$$ax^2$$
$$\underline{ax^2 - a^2x}$$
$$a^2x - a^3$$
$$\underline{a^2x - a^3}$$
$$0$$

Check:

$(x - a)(x^2 + ax + a^2) + 0$

$= x^3 + ax^2 + a^2x - ax^2 - a^2x - a^3$

$= x^3 - a^3$

The quotient is $x^2 + ax + a^2$; the remainder is 0.

104.

$$x - a \overline{)x^5 + 0x^4 + 0x^3 + 0x^2 + 0x - a^5}$$

quotient: $x^4 + ax^3 + a^2x^2 + a^3x + a^4$

$$\underline{x^5 - ax^4}$$
$$ax^4$$
$$\underline{ax^4 - a^2x^3}$$
$$a^2x^3$$
$$\underline{a^2x^3 - a^3x^2}$$
$$a^3x^2$$
$$\underline{a^3x^2 - a^4x}$$
$$a^4x - a^5$$
$$\underline{a^4x - a^5}$$
$$0$$

Check:

$(x - a)(x^4 + ax^3 + a^2x^2 + a^3x + a^4) + 0$

$= x^5 + ax^4 + a^2x^3 + a^3x^2 + a^4x - ax^4$

$\quad - a^2x^3 - a^3x^2 - a^4x - a^5$

$= x^5 - a^5$

The quotient is $x^4 + ax^3 + a^2x^2 + a^3x + a^4$; the remainder is 0.

105. When we multiply polynomials $p_1(x)$ and $p_2(x)$, each term of $p_1(x)$ will be multiplied by each term of $p_2(x)$. So when the highest-powered term of $p_1(x)$ multiplies by the highest powered term of $p_2(x)$, the exponents on the variables in those terms will add according to the basic rules of exponents. Therefore, the highest powered term of the product polynomial will have degree equal to the sum of the degrees of $p_1(x)$ and $p_2(x)$.

106. When we add two polynomials $p_1(x)$ and $p_2(x)$, where the degree of $p_1(x) \neq$ the degree of $p_2(x)$, each term of $p_1(x)$ will be added to each term of $p_2(x)$. Since only the terms with equal degrees will combine via addition, the degree of the sum polynomial will be the degree of the highest powered term overall, that is, the degree of the polynomial that had the higher degree.

107. When we add two polynomials $p_1(x)$ and $p_2(x)$, where the degree of $p_1(x)$ = the degree of $p_2(x)$, the new polynomial will have degree $\leq$ the degree of $p_1(x)$ and $p_2(x)$.

108. Answers will vary.

109. Answers will vary.

Section R.5

1. $3x(x-2)(x+2)$

2. prime

3. True; x^2+4 is prime over the set of real numbers.

4. False; $3x^3-2x^2-6x+4=(3x-2)(x^2-2)$

5. $3x+6=3(x+2)$

6. $7x-14=7(x-2)$

7. $ax^2+a=a(x^2+1)$

8. $ax-a=a(x-1)$

9. $x^3+x^2+x=x(x^2+x+1)$

10. $x^3-x^2+x=x(x^2-x+1)$

11. $2x^2-2x=2x(x-1)$

12. $3x^2-3x=3x(x-1)$

13. $3x^2y-6xy^2+12xy=3xy(x-2y+4)$

14. $60x^2y-48xy^2+72x^3y=12xy(5x-4y+6x^2)$

15. $x^2-1=x^2-1^2=(x-1)(x+1)$

16. $x^2-4=x^2-2^2=(x-2)(x+2)$

17. $4x^2-1=(2x)^2-1^2=(2x-1)(2x+1)$

18. $9x^2-1=(3x)^2-1^2=(3x-1)(3x+1)$

19. $x^2-16=x^2-4^2=(x-4)(x+4)$

20. $x^2-25=x^2-5^2=(x-5)(x+5)$

21. $25x^2-4=(5x-2)(5x+2)$

22. $36x^2-9=9(4x^2-1)=9(2x-1)(2x+1)$

23. $x^2+2x+1=(x+1)^2$

24. $x^2-4x+4=(x-2)^2$

25. $x^2+4x+4=(x+2)^2$

26. $x^2-2x+1=(x-1)^2$

27. $x^2-10x+25=(x-5)^2$

28. $x^2+10x+25=(x+5)^2$

29. $4x^2+4x+1=(2x+1)^2$

30. $9x^2+6x+1=(3x+1)^2$

31. $16x^2+8x+1=(4x+1)^2$

32. $25x^2+10x+1=(5x+1)^2$

33. $x^3-27=x^3-3^3=(x-3)(x^2+3x+9)$

34. $x^3+125=x^3+5^3=(x+5)(x^2-5x+25)$

35. $x^3+27=x^3+3^3=(x+3)(x^2-3x+9)$

36. $27-8x^3=3^3-(2x)^3$
$$=(3-2x)(9+6x+4x^2)$$
$$=-(2x-3)(4x^2+6x+9)$$

37. $8x^3+27=(2x)^3+3^3$
$$=(2x+3)(4x^2-6x+9)$$

23

38. $64 - 27x^3 = 4^3 - (3x)^3$
$$= (4 - 3x)(16 + 12x + 9x^2)$$
$$= -(3x - 4)\left(9x^2 + 12x + 16\right)$$

39. $x^2 + 5x + 6 = (x + 2)(x + 3)$

40. $x^2 + 6x + 8 = (x + 2)(x + 4)$

41. $x^2 + 7x + 6 = (x + 6)(x + 1)$

42. $x^2 + 9x + 8 = (x + 8)(x + 1)$

43. $x^2 + 7x + 10 = (x + 2)(x + 5)$

44. $x^2 + 11x + 10 = (x + 10)(x + 1)$

45. $x^2 - 10x + 16 = (x - 2)(x - 8)$

46. $x^2 - 17x + 16 = (x - 16)(x - 1)$

47. $x^2 - 7x - 8 = (x + 1)(x - 8)$

48. $x^2 - 2x - 8 = (x + 2)(x - 4)$

49. $x^2 + 7x - 8 = (x + 8)(x - 1)$

50. $x^2 + 2x - 8 = (x + 4)(x - 2)$

51. $2x^2 + 4x + 3x + 6 = 2x(x + 2) + 3(x + 2)$
$$= (x + 2)(2x + 3)$$

52. $3x^2 - 3x + 2x - 2 = 3x(x - 1) + 2(x - 1)$
$$= (x - 1)(3x + 2)$$

53. $2x^2 - 4x + x - 2 = 2x(x - 2) + 1(x - 2)$
$$= (x - 2)(2x + 1)$$

54. $3x^2 + 6x - x - 2 = 3x(x + 2) - 1(x + 2)$
$$= (x + 2)(3x - 1)$$

55. $6x^2 + 9x + 4x + 6 = 3x(2x + 3) + 2(2x + 3)$
$$= (2x + 3)(3x + 2)$$

56. $9x^2 - 6x + 3x - 2 = 3x(3x - 2) + 1(3x - 2)$
$$= (3x - 2)(3x + 1)$$

57. $3x^2 + 4x + 1 = (3x + 1)(x + 1)$

58. $2x^2 + 3x + 1 = (2x + 1)(x + 1)$

59. $2z^2 + 5z + 3 = (2z + 3)(z + 1)$

60. $6z^2 + 5z + 1 = (3z + 1)(2z + 1)$

61. $3x^2 + 2x - 8 = (3x - 4)(x + 2)$

62. $3x^2 + 10x + 8 = (3x + 4)(x + 2)$

63. $3x^2 - 2x - 8 = (3x + 4)(x - 2)$

64. $3x^2 - 10x + 8 = (3x - 4)(x - 2)$

65. $3x^2 + 14x + 8 = (3x + 2)(x + 4)$

66. $3x^2 - 14x + 8 = (3x - 2)(x - 4)$

67. $3x^2 + 10x - 8 = (3x - 2)(x + 4)$

68. $3x^2 - 10x - 8 = (3x + 2)(x - 4)$

69. $x^2 - 36 = (x - 6)(x + 6)$

70. $x^2 - 9 = (x - 3)(x + 3)$

71. $2 - 8x^2 = 2(1 - 4x^2) = 2(1 - 2x)(1 + 2x)$

72. $3 - 27x^2 = 3(1 - 9x^2) = 3(1 - 3x)(1 + 3x)$

73. $x^2 + 11x + 10 = (x + 1)(x + 10)$

74. $x^2 + 5x + 4 = (x + 4)(x + 1)$

75. $x^2 - 10x + 21 = (x - 7)(x - 3)$

76. $x^2 - 6x + 8 = (x - 2)(x - 4)$

77. $4x^2 - 8x + 32 = 4\left(x^2 - 2x + 8\right)$

78. $3x^2 - 12x + 15 = 3(x^2 - 4x + 5)$

79. $x^2 + 4x + 16$ is prime over the reals because there are no factors of 16 whose sum is 4.

80. $x^2 + 12x + 36 = (x + 6)^2$

81. $15 + 2x - x^2 = -(x^2 - 2x - 15) = -(x - 5)(x + 3)$

82. $14 + 6x - x^2 = -(x^2 - 6x - 14)$ is prime over the integers because there are no factors of -14 whose sum is -6.

83. $3x^2 - 12x - 36 = 3(x^2 - 4x - 12)$
$\qquad\qquad\qquad = 3(x - 6)(x + 2)$

84. $x^3 + 8x^2 - 20x = x(x^2 + 8x - 20)$
$\qquad\qquad\qquad = x(x + 10)(x - 2)$

85. $y^4 + 11y^3 + 30y^2 = y^2(y^2 + 11y + 30)$
$\qquad\qquad\qquad\quad = y^2(y + 5)(y + 6)$

86. $3y^3 - 18y^2 - 48y = 3y(y^2 - 6y - 16)$
$\qquad\qquad\qquad = 3y(y + 2)(y - 8)$

87. $4x^2 + 12x + 9 = (2x + 3)^2$

88. $9x^2 - 12x + 4 = (3x - 2)^2$

89. $6x^2 + 8x + 2 = 2(3x^2 + 4x + 1)$
$\qquad\qquad\qquad = 2(3x + 1)(x + 1)$

90. $8x^2 + 6x - 2 = 2(4x^2 + 3x - 1)$
$\qquad\qquad\qquad = 2(4x - 1)(x + 1)$

91. $x^4 - 81 = (x^2)^2 - 9^2 = (x^2 - 9)(x^2 + 9)$
$\qquad\qquad = (x - 3)(x + 3)(x^2 + 9)$

92. $x^4 - 1 = (x^2)^2 - 1^2 = (x^2 - 1)(x^2 + 1)$
$\qquad\qquad = (x - 1)(x + 1)(x^2 + 1)$

93. $x^6 - 2x^3 + 1 = (x^3 - 1)^2$
$\qquad\qquad\qquad = \left[(x - 1)(x^2 + x + 1) \right]^2$
$\qquad\qquad\qquad = (x - 1)^2 (x^2 + x + 1)^2$

94. $x^6 + 2x^3 + 1 = (x^3 + 1)^2$
$\qquad\qquad\qquad = \left[(x + 1)(x^2 - x + 1) \right]^2$
$\qquad\qquad\qquad = (x + 1)^2 (x^2 - x + 1)^2$

95. $x^7 - x^5 = x^5(x^2 - 1) = x^5(x - 1)(x + 1)$

96. $x^8 - x^5 = x^5(x^3 - 1) = x^5(x - 1)(x^2 + x + 1)$

97. $16x^2 + 24x + 9 = (4x + 3)^2$

98. $9x^2 - 24x + 16 = (3x - 4)^2$

99. $5 + 16x - 16x^2 = -(16x^2 - 16x - 5)$
$\qquad\qquad\qquad = -(4x - 5)(4x + 1)$

100. $5 + 11x - 16x^2 = -(16x^2 - 11x - 5)$
$\qquad\qquad\qquad = -(16x + 5)(x - 1)$

101. $4y^2 - 16y + 15 = (2y - 5)(2y - 3)$

102. $9y^2 + 9y - 4 = (3y + 4)(3y - 1)$

103. $1 - 8x^2 - 9x^4 = -(9x^4 + 8x^2 - 1)$
$\qquad\qquad\qquad = -(9x^2 - 1)(x^2 + 1)$
$\qquad\qquad\qquad = -(3x - 1)(3x + 1)(x^2 + 1)$

104. $4 - 14x^2 - 8x^4 = -2(4x^4 + 7x^2 - 2)$
$\qquad\qquad\qquad = -2(4x^2 - 1)(x^2 + 2)$
$\qquad\qquad\qquad = -2(2x - 1)(2x + 1)(x^2 + 2)$

105. $x(x + 3) - 6(x + 3) = (x + 3)(x - 6)$

106. $5(3x - 7) + x(3x - 7) = (3x - 7)(x + 5)$

107. $(x + 2)^2 - 5(x + 2) = (x + 2)\left[(x + 2) - 5 \right]$
$\qquad\qquad\qquad = (x + 2)(x - 3)$

108. $(x-1)^2 - 2(x-1) = (x-1)[(x-1)-2]$
$= (x-1)(x-3)$

109. $(3x-2)^3 - 27$
$= (3x-2)^3 - 3^3$
$= [(3x-2)-3][(3x-2)^2 + 3(3x-2)+9]$
$= (3x-5)(9x^2 - 12x + 4 + 9x - 6 + 9)$
$= (3x-5)(9x^2 - 3x + 7)$

110. $(5x+1)^3 - 1$
$= (5x+1)^3 - 1^3$
$= [(5x+1)-1][(5x+1)^2 + (1)(5x+1)+1]$
$= 5x(25x^2 + 10x + 1 + 5x + 1 + 1)$
$= 5x(25x^2 + 15x + 3)$

111. $3(x^2 + 10x + 25) - 4(x+5)$
$= 3(x+5)^2 - 4(x+5)$
$= (x+5)[3(x+5)-4]$
$= (x+5)(3x+15-4)$
$= (x+5)(3x+11)$

112. $7(x^2 - 6x + 9) + 5(x-3)$
$= 7(x-3)^2 + 5(x-3)$
$= (x-3)[7(x-3)+5]$
$= (x-3)(7x - 21 + 5)$
$= (x-3)(7x - 16)$

113. $x^3 + 2x^2 - x - 2 = x^2(x+2) - 1(x+2)$
$= (x+2)(x^2 - 1)$
$= (x+2)(x-1)(x+1)$

114. $x^3 - 3x^2 - x + 3 = x^2(x-3) - 1(x-3)$
$= (x-3)(x^2 - 1)$
$= (x-3)(x-1)(x+1)$

115. $x^4 - x^3 + x - 1 = x^3(x-1) + 1(x-1)$
$= (x-1)(x^3 + 1)$
$= (x-1)(x+1)(x^2 - x + 1)$

116. $x^4 + x^3 + x + 1 = x^3(x+1) + 1(x+1)$
$= (x+1)(x^3 + 1)$
$= (x+1)(x+1)(x^2 - x + 1)$
$= (x+1)^2(x^2 - x + 1)$

117. $2(3x+4)^2 + (2x+3) \cdot 2(3x+4) \cdot 3$
$= 2(3x+4)((3x+4)+(2x+3) \cdot 3)$
$= 2(3x+4)(3x+4+6x+9)$
$= 2(3x+4)(9x+13)$

118. $5(2x+1)^2 + (5x-6) \cdot 2(2x+1) \cdot 2$
$= (2x+1)(5(2x+1)+(5x-6) \cdot 4)$
$= (2x+1)(10x+5+20x-24)$
$= (2x+1)(30x-19)$

119. $2x(2x+5) + x^2 \cdot 2 = 2x((2x+5)+x)$
$= 2x(2x+5+x)$
$= 2x(3x+5)$

120. $3x^2(8x-3) + x^3 \cdot 8 = x^2(3(8x-3)+8x)$
$= x^2(24x-9+8x)$
$= x^2(32x-9)$

121. $2(x+3)(x-2)^3 + (x+3)^2 \cdot 3(x-2)^2$
$= (x+3)(x-2)^2(2(x-2)+(x+3) \cdot 3)$
$= (x+3)(x-2)^2(2x-4+3x+9)$
$= (x+3)(x-2)^2(5x+5)$
$= 5(x+3)(x-2)^2(x+1)$

122. $4(x+5)^3(x-1)^2 + (x+5)^4 \cdot 2(x-1)$
$= 2(x+5)^3(x-1)(2(x-1)+(x+5))$
$= 2(x+5)^3(x-1)(2x-2+x+5)$
$= 2(x+5)^3(x-1)(3x+3)$
$= 2 \cdot 3(x+5)^3(x-1)(x+1)$
$= 6(x+5)^3(x-1)(x+1)$

123. $(4x-3)^2 + x \cdot 2(4x-3) \cdot 4$

$= (4x-3)((4x-3)+8x)$

$= (4x-3)(4x-3+8x)$

$= (4x-3)(12x-3)$

$= 3(4x-3)(4x-1)$

124. $3x^2(3x+4)^2 + x^3 \cdot 2(3x+4) \cdot 3$

$= 3x^2(3x+4)((3x+4)+2x)$

$= 3x^2(3x+4)(3x+4+2x)$

$= 3x^2(3x+4)(5x+4)$

125. $2(3x-5) \cdot 3(2x+1)^3 + (3x-5)^2 \cdot 3(2x+1)^2 \cdot 2$

$= 6(3x-5)(2x+1)^2((2x+1)+(3x-5))$

$= 6(3x-5)(2x+1)^2(2x+1+3x-5)$

$= 6(3x-5)(2x+1)^2(5x-4)$

126. $3(4x+5)^2 \cdot 4(5x+1)^2 + (4x+5)^3 \cdot 2(5x+1) \cdot 5$

$= 2(4x+5)^2(5x+1)(6(5x+1)+5(4x+5))$

$= 2(4x+5)^2(5x+1)(30x+6+20x+25)$

$= 2(4x+5)^2(5x+1)(50x+31)$

127. Factors of 4: 1, 4   2, 2   −1, −4   −2, −2
Sum: 5   4   −5   −4

None of the sums of the factors is 0, so

x^2+4 is prime.

Alternatively, the possibilities are

$(x\pm1)(x\pm4) = x^2 \pm 5x + 4$ or

$(x\pm2)(x\pm2) = x^2 \pm 4x + 4$, none of which

equals x^2+4.

128. Factors of 1: 1, 1   −1, −1
Sum: 2   −2

None of the sums of the factors is 1, so

x^2+x+1 is prime.

Alternatively, the possibilities are

$(x\pm1)^2 = x^2 \pm 2x + 1$, neither of which equals

x^2+x+1.

129. Answers will vary.

130. Answers will vary.

Section R.6

1. quotient; divisor; remainder

2. $-3\overline{)2 \quad 0 \quad -5 \quad 1}$

3. True

4. True

5.
```
2)1  -1   2   4
      2   2   8
   ─────────────
   1   1   4  12
```
Quotient: $x^2 + x + 4$
Remainder: 12

6.
```
-1)1   2  -3   1
     -1  -1   4
   ──────────────
   1   1  -4   5
```
Quotient: $x^2 + x - 4$
Remainder: 5

7.
```
3)3   2   -1    3
     9   33   96
   ───────────────
   3  11   32   99
```
Quotient: $3x^2 + 11x + 32$
Remainder: 99

8.
```
-2)-4   2   -1    1
        8  -20   42
   ─────────────────
   -4  10  -21   43
```
Quotient: $-4x^2 + 10x - 21$
Remainder: 43

9.
```
-3)1   0   -4    0    1     0
      -3    9  -15   45  -138
   ───────────────────────────
   1  -3    5  -15   46  -138
```
Quotient: $x^4 - 3x^3 + 5x^2 - 15x + 46$
Remainder: −138

10.
```
2)1   0   1    0    2
     2   4   10   20
   ──────────────────
   1   2   5   10   22
```
Quotient: $x^3 + 2x^2 + 5x + 10$
Remainder: 22

27

11.
$$\begin{array}{r} 1\overline{)4 \quad 0 \quad -3 \quad 0 \quad 1 \quad 0 \quad 5} \\ 4 \quad 4 \quad 1 \quad 1 \quad 2 \quad 2 \\ \hline 4 \quad 4 \quad 1 \quad 1 \quad 2 \quad 2 \quad 7 \end{array}$$
Quotient: $4x^5 + 4x^4 + x^3 + x^2 + 2x + 2$
Remainder: 7

12.
$$\begin{array}{r} -1\overline{)1 \quad 0 \quad 5 \quad 0 \quad 0 \quad -10} \\ -1 \quad 1 \quad -6 \quad 6 \quad -6 \\ \hline 1 \quad -1 \quad 6 \quad -6 \quad 6 \quad -16 \end{array}$$
Quotient: $x^4 - x^3 + 6x^2 - 6x + 6$
Remainder: -16

13.
$$\begin{array}{r} -1.1\overline{)0.1 \quad 0 \quad 0.2 \quad 0} \\ -0.11 \quad 0.121 \quad -0.3531 \\ \hline 0.1 \quad -0.11 \quad 0.321 \quad -0.3531 \end{array}$$
Quotient: $0.1x^2 - 0.11x + 0.321$
Remainder: -0.3531

14.
$$\begin{array}{r} -2.1\overline{)0.1 \quad 0 \quad -0.2} \\ -0.21 \quad 0.441 \\ \hline 0.1 \quad -0.21 \quad 0.241 \end{array}$$
Quotient: $0.1x - 0.21$
Remainder: 0.241

15.
$$\begin{array}{r} 1\overline{)1 \quad 0 \quad 0 \quad 0 \quad 0 \quad -1} \\ 1 \quad 1 \quad 1 \quad 1 \quad 1 \\ \hline 1 \quad 1 \quad 1 \quad 1 \quad 1 \quad 0 \end{array}$$
Quotient: $x^4 + x^3 + x^2 + x + 1$
Remainder: 0

16.
$$\begin{array}{r} -1\overline{)1 \quad 0 \quad 0 \quad 0 \quad 0 \quad 1} \\ -1 \quad 1 \quad -1 \quad 1 \quad -1 \\ \hline 1 \quad -1 \quad 1 \quad -1 \quad 1 \quad 0 \end{array}$$
Quotient: $x^4 - x^3 + x^2 - x + 1$
Remainder: 0

17.
$$\begin{array}{r} 2\overline{)4 \quad -3 \quad -8 \quad 4} \\ 8 \quad 10 \quad 4 \\ \hline 4 \quad 5 \quad 2 \quad 8 \end{array}$$
Remainder $= 8 \neq 0$. Therefore, $x - 2$ is not a factor of $4x^3 - 3x^2 - 8x + 4$.

18.
$$\begin{array}{r} -3\overline{)-4 \quad 5 \quad 0 \quad 8} \\ 12 \quad -51 \quad 153 \\ \hline -4 \quad 17 \quad -51 \quad 161 \end{array}$$
Remainder $= 161 \neq 0$. Therefore, $x + 3$ is not a factor of $-4x^3 + 5x^2 + 8$.

19.
$$\begin{array}{r} 2\overline{)3 \quad -6 \quad 0 \quad -5 \quad 10} \\ 6 \quad 0 \quad 0 \quad -10 \\ \hline 3 \quad 0 \quad 0 \quad -5 \quad 0 \end{array}$$
Remainder $= 0$. Therefore, $x - 2$ is a factor of $3x^4 - 6x^3 - 5x + 10$.

20.
$$\begin{array}{r} 2\overline{)4 \quad 0 \quad -15 \quad 0 \quad -4} \\ 8 \quad 16 \quad 2 \quad 4 \\ \hline 4 \quad 8 \quad 1 \quad 2 \quad 0 \end{array}$$
Remainder $= 0$. Therefore, $x - 2$ is a factor of $4x^4 - 15x^2 - 4$.

21.
$$\begin{array}{r} -3\overline{)3 \quad 0 \quad 0 \quad 82 \quad 0 \quad 0 \quad 27} \\ -9 \quad 27 \quad -81 \quad -3 \quad 9 \quad -27 \\ \hline 3 \quad -9 \quad 27 \quad 1 \quad -3 \quad 9 \quad 0 \end{array}$$
Remainder $= 0$. Therefore, $x + 3$ is a factor of $3x^6 + 82x^3 + 27$.

22.
$$\begin{array}{r} -3\overline{)2 \quad 0 \quad -18 \quad 0 \quad 1 \quad 0 \quad -9} \\ -6 \quad 18 \quad 0 \quad 0 \quad -3 \quad 9 \\ \hline 2 \quad -6 \quad 0 \quad 0 \quad 1 \quad -3 \quad 0 \end{array}$$
Remainder $= 0$. Therefore, $x + 3$ is a factor of $2x^6 - 18x^4 + x^2 - 9$.

23.
$$\begin{array}{r} -4\overline{)4 \quad 0 \quad -64 \quad 0 \quad 1 \quad 0 \quad -15} \\ -16 \quad 64 \quad 0 \quad 0 \quad -4 \quad 16 \\ \hline 4 \quad -16 \quad 0 \quad 0 \quad 1 \quad -4 \quad 1 \end{array}$$
Remainder $= 1 \neq 0$. Therefore, $x + 3$ is not a factor of $4x^6 - 64x^4 + x^2 - 15$.

24.
$$\begin{array}{r} -4\overline{)1 \quad 0 \quad -16 \quad 0 \quad 1 \quad 0 \quad -16} \\ -4 \quad 16 \quad 0 \quad 0 \quad -4 \quad 16 \\ \hline 1 \quad -4 \quad 0 \quad 0 \quad 1 \quad -4 \quad 0 \end{array}$$
Remainder $= 0$. Therefore, $x + 4$ is a factor $x^6 - 16x^4 + x^2 - 16$.

25. $\frac{1}{2}\overline{)2 \quad -1 \quad 0 \quad 2 \quad -1}$
$\underline{\qquad 1 \quad 0 \quad 0 \quad 1}$
$\quad\, 2 \quad 0 \quad 0 \quad 2 \quad 0$

Remainder = 0; therefore $x-\frac{1}{2}$ is a factor of

$2x^4 - x^3 + 2x - 1$.

26. $-\frac{1}{3}\overline{)3 \quad 1 \quad 0 \quad -3 \quad 1}$
$\underline{\qquad -1 \quad 0 \quad 0 \quad 1}$
$\quad\, 3 \quad 0 \quad 0 \quad -3 \quad 2$

Remainder = $2 \neq 0$; therefore $x+\frac{1}{3}$ is not a

factor of $3x^4 + x^3 - 3x + 1$.

27. $-2\overline{)1 \quad -2 \quad 3 \quad 5}$
$\underline{\qquad -2 \quad 8 \quad -22}$
$\quad\, 1 \quad -4 \quad 11 \quad -17$

$\dfrac{x^3 - 2x^2 + 3x + 5}{x+2} = x^2 - 4x + 11 + \dfrac{-17}{x+2}$

$a + b + c + d = 1 - 4 + 11 - 17 = -9$

28. Answers will vary.

Section R.7

1. lowest terms

2. Least Common Multiple

3. True; $\dfrac{2x^3 - 4x}{x-2} = \dfrac{2x\left(x^2 - 2\right)}{x-2}$

4. False;
$2x^3 + 6x^2 = 2x^2\left(x+3\right)$
$6x^4 + 4x^3 = 2x^3\left(3x+2\right)$
$LCM = 2x^3\left(x+3\right)\left(3x+2\right)$

5. $\dfrac{3x+9}{x^2-9} = \dfrac{3(x+3)}{(x-3)(x+3)} = \dfrac{3}{x-3}$

6. $\dfrac{4x^2+8x}{12x+24} = \dfrac{4x(x+2)}{12(x+2)} = \dfrac{x}{3}$

7. $\dfrac{x^2-2x}{3x-6} = \dfrac{x(x-2)}{3(x-2)} = \dfrac{x}{3}$

8. $\dfrac{15x^2+24x}{3x^2} = \dfrac{3x(5x+8)}{3x^2} = \dfrac{5x+8}{x}$

9. $\dfrac{24x^2}{12x^2-6x} = \dfrac{24x^2}{6x(2x-1)} = \dfrac{4x}{2x-1}$

10. $\dfrac{x^2+4x+4}{x^2-4} = \dfrac{(x+2)(x+2)}{(x-2)(x+2)} = \dfrac{x+2}{x-2}$

11. $\dfrac{y^2-25}{2y^2-8y-10} = \dfrac{(y+5)(y-5)}{2\left(y^2-4y-5\right)}$

$= \dfrac{(y+5)(y-5)}{2(y-5)(y+1)}$

$= \dfrac{y+5}{2(y+1)}$

12. $\dfrac{3y^2-y-2}{3y^2+5y+2} = \dfrac{(3y+2)(y-1)}{(3y+2)(y+1)} = \dfrac{y-1}{y+1}$

13. $\dfrac{x^2+4x-5}{x^2-2x+1} = \dfrac{(x+5)(x-1)}{(x-1)(x-1)} = \dfrac{x+5}{x-1}$

14. $\dfrac{x-x^2}{x^2+x-2} = \dfrac{-x(x-1)}{(x+2)(x-1)} = \dfrac{-x}{x+2} = -\dfrac{x}{x+2}$

15. $\dfrac{x^2+5x-14}{2-x} = \dfrac{(x+7)(x-2)}{2-x}$

$= \dfrac{(x+7)(x-2)}{-1(x-2)}$

$= -(x+7)$

$= -x-7$

16. $\dfrac{2x^2+5x-3}{1-2x} = \dfrac{(2x-1)(x+3)}{-1(2x-1)} = -(x+3) = -x-3$

17. $\dfrac{3x+6}{5x^2} \cdot \dfrac{x}{x^2-4} = \dfrac{3(x+2)}{5x^2} \cdot \dfrac{x}{(x-2)(x+2)}$

$= \dfrac{3}{5x(x-2)}$

18. $\dfrac{3}{2x} \cdot \dfrac{x^2}{6x+10} = \dfrac{3}{2} \cdot \dfrac{x}{2(3x+5)} = \dfrac{3x}{4(3x+5)}$

19. $\dfrac{4x^2}{x^2-16}\cdot\dfrac{x^3-64}{2x}$

$=\dfrac{4x^2}{(x-4)(x+4)}\cdot\dfrac{(x-4)\left(x^2+4x+16\right)}{2x}$

$=\dfrac{2x\cdot 2x(x-4)\left(x^2+4x+16\right)}{2x(x-4)(x+4)}$

$=\dfrac{2x\left(x^2+4x+16\right)}{x+4}$

20. $\dfrac{12}{x^2+x}\cdot\dfrac{x^3+1}{4x-2}=\dfrac{12}{x(x+1)}\cdot\dfrac{(x+1)(x^2-x+1)}{2(2x-1)}$

$=\dfrac{2\cdot 6(x+1)\left(x^2-x+1\right)}{2x(x+1)(2x-1)}$

$=\dfrac{6\left(x^2-x+1\right)}{x(2x-1)}$

21. $\dfrac{4x-8}{-3x}\cdot\dfrac{12}{12-6x}=\dfrac{4(x-2)}{-3x}\cdot\dfrac{12}{6(2-x)}$

$=\dfrac{4(x-2)}{-3x}\cdot\dfrac{2}{(-1)(x-2)}$

$=\dfrac{8}{3x}$

22. $\dfrac{6x-27}{5x}\cdot\dfrac{2}{4x-18}=\dfrac{3(2x-9)}{5x}\cdot\dfrac{2}{2(2x-9)}=\dfrac{3}{5x}$

23. $\dfrac{x^2-3x-10}{x^2+2x-35}\cdot\dfrac{x^2+4x-21}{x^2+9x+14}$

$=\dfrac{(x-5)(x+2)}{(x+7)(x-5)}\cdot\dfrac{(x+7)(x-3)}{(x+7)(x+2)}$

$=\dfrac{x-3}{x+7}$

24. $\dfrac{x^2+x-6}{x^2+4x-5}\cdot\dfrac{x^2-25}{x^2+2x-15}$

$=\dfrac{(x-2)(x+3)}{(x+5)(x-1)}\cdot\dfrac{(x+5)(x-5)}{(x+5)(x-3)}$

$=\dfrac{(x-2)(x+3)(x-5)}{(x+5)(x-1)(x-3)}$

25. $\dfrac{\dfrac{6x}{x^2-4}}{\dfrac{3x-9}{2x+4}}=\dfrac{6x}{x^2-4}\cdot\dfrac{2x+4}{3x-9}$

$=\dfrac{6x}{(x-2)(x+2)}\cdot\dfrac{2(x+2)}{3(x-3)}$

$=\dfrac{4x}{(x-2)(x-3)}$

26. $\dfrac{\dfrac{12x}{5x+20}}{\dfrac{4x^2}{x^2-16}}=\dfrac{12x}{5x+20}\cdot\dfrac{x^2-16}{4x^2}$

$=\dfrac{12x}{5(x+4)}\cdot\dfrac{(x+4)(x-4)}{4x^2}$

$=\dfrac{3(x-4)}{5x}$

27. $\dfrac{\dfrac{8x}{x^2-1}}{\dfrac{10x}{x+1}}=\dfrac{8x}{x^2-1}\cdot\dfrac{x+1}{10x}$

$=\dfrac{8x}{(x-1)(x+1)}\cdot\dfrac{x+1}{10x}$

$=\dfrac{4}{5(x-1)}$

28. $\dfrac{\dfrac{x-2}{4x}}{\dfrac{x^2-4x+4}{12x}}=\dfrac{x-2}{4x}\cdot\dfrac{12x}{x^2-4x+4}$

$=\dfrac{x-2}{4x}\cdot\dfrac{12x}{(x-2)(x-2)}$

$=\dfrac{3}{x-2}$

29. $\dfrac{\dfrac{4-x}{4+x}}{\dfrac{4x}{x^2-16}}=\dfrac{4-x}{4+x}\cdot\dfrac{x^2-16}{4x}$

$=\dfrac{4-x}{4+x}\cdot\dfrac{(x+4)(x-4)}{4x}$

$=\dfrac{(4-x)(x-4)}{4x}$

$=-\dfrac{(x-4)^2}{4x}$

30. $\dfrac{\frac{3+x}{3-x}}{\frac{x^2-9}{9x^3}} = \dfrac{3+x}{3-x} \cdot \dfrac{9x^3}{x^2-9}$

$\qquad = \dfrac{3+x}{3-x} \cdot \dfrac{9x^3}{(x+3)(x-3)}$

$\qquad = \dfrac{9x^3}{(3-x)(x-3)}$

$\qquad = \dfrac{9x^3}{-(x-3)^2}$

$\qquad = -\dfrac{9x^3}{(x-3)^2}$

31. $\dfrac{\frac{x^2+7x+12}{x^2-7x+12}}{\frac{x^2+x-12}{x^2-x-12}} = \dfrac{x^2+7x+12}{x^2-7x+12} \cdot \dfrac{x^2-x-12}{x^2+x-12}$

$\qquad = \dfrac{(x+3)(x+4)}{(x-3)(x-4)} \cdot \dfrac{(x-4)(x+3)}{(x+4)(x-3)}$

$\qquad = \dfrac{(x+3)^2}{(x-3)^2}$

32. $\dfrac{\frac{x^2+7x+6}{x^2+x-6}}{\frac{x^2+5x-6}{x^2+5x+6}} = \dfrac{x^2+7x+6}{x^2+x-6} \cdot \dfrac{x^2+5x+6}{x^2+5x-6}$

$\qquad = \dfrac{(x+6)(x+1)}{(x+3)(x-2)} \cdot \dfrac{(x+2)(x+3)}{(x+6)(x-1)}$

$\qquad = \dfrac{(x+1)(x+2)}{(x-2)(x-1)}$

33. $\dfrac{\frac{2x^2-x-28}{3x^2-x-2}}{\frac{4x^2+16x+7}{3x^2+11x+6}} = \dfrac{2x^2-x-28}{3x^2-x-2} \cdot \dfrac{3x^2+11x+6}{4x^2+16x+7}$

$\qquad = \dfrac{(2x+7)(x-4)}{(3x+2)(x-1)} \cdot \dfrac{(3x+2)(x+3)}{(2x+7)(2x+1)}$

$\qquad = \dfrac{(x-4)(x+3)}{(x-1)(2x+1)}$

34. $\dfrac{\frac{9x^2+3x-2}{12x^2+5x-2}}{\frac{9x^2-6x+1}{8x^2-10x-3}} = \dfrac{9x^2+3x-2}{12x^2+5x-2} \cdot \dfrac{8x^2-10x-3}{9x^2-6x+1}$

$\qquad = \dfrac{(3x+2)(3x-1)}{(3x+2)(4x-1)} \cdot \dfrac{(4x+1)(2x-3)}{(3x-1)(3x-1)}$

$\qquad = \dfrac{(4x+1)(2x-3)}{(4x-1)(3x-1)}$

35. $\dfrac{x}{2} + \dfrac{5}{2} = \dfrac{x+5}{2}$

36. $\dfrac{3}{x} - \dfrac{6}{x} = \dfrac{3-6}{x} = \dfrac{-3}{x} = -\dfrac{3}{x}$

37. $\dfrac{x^2}{2x-3} - \dfrac{4}{2x-3} = \dfrac{x^2-4}{2x-3} = \dfrac{(x+2)(x-2)}{2x-3}$

38. $\dfrac{3x^2}{2x-1} - \dfrac{9}{2x-1} = \dfrac{3x^2-9}{2x-1} = \dfrac{3(x^2-3)}{2x-1}$

39. $\dfrac{x+1}{x-3} + \dfrac{2x-3}{x-3} = \dfrac{x+1+2x-3}{x-3} = \dfrac{3x-2}{x-3}$

40. $\dfrac{2x-5}{3x+2} + \dfrac{x+4}{3x+2} = \dfrac{2x-5+x+4}{3x+2} = \dfrac{3x-1}{3x+2}$

41. $\dfrac{3x+5}{2x-1} - \dfrac{2x-4}{2x-1} = \dfrac{(3x+5)-(2x-4)}{2x-1}$

$\qquad = \dfrac{3x+5-2x+4}{2x-1}$

$\qquad = \dfrac{x+9}{2x-1}$

42. $\dfrac{5x-4}{3x+4} - \dfrac{x+1}{3x+4} = \dfrac{(5x-4)-(x+1)}{3x+4}$

$\qquad = \dfrac{5x-4-x-1}{3x+4}$

$\qquad = \dfrac{4x-5}{3x+4}$

43. $\dfrac{4}{x-2} + \dfrac{x}{2-x} = \dfrac{4}{x-2} - \dfrac{x}{x-2} = \dfrac{4-x}{x-2}$

44. $\dfrac{6}{x-1} - \dfrac{x}{1-x} = \dfrac{6}{x-1} + \dfrac{x}{x-1} = \dfrac{x+6}{x-1}$

31

45. $\dfrac{4}{x-1} - \dfrac{2}{x+2} = \dfrac{4(x+2)}{(x-1)(x+2)} - \dfrac{2(x-1)}{(x+2)(x-1)}$

$\qquad = \dfrac{4x+8-2x+2}{(x+2)(x-1)}$

$\qquad = \dfrac{2x+10}{(x+2)(x-1)}$

$\qquad = \dfrac{2(x+5)}{(x+2)(x-1)}$

46. $\dfrac{2}{x+5} - \dfrac{5}{x-5} = \dfrac{2(x-5)}{(x+5)(x-5)} - \dfrac{5(x+5)}{(x+5)(x-5)}$

$\qquad = \dfrac{2x-10-5x-25}{(x+5)(x-5)}$

$\qquad = \dfrac{-3x-35}{(x+5)(x-5)}$

$\qquad = -\dfrac{3x+35}{(x+5)(x-5)}$

47. $\dfrac{x}{x+1} + \dfrac{2x-3}{x-1} = \dfrac{x(x-1)}{(x+1)(x-1)} + \dfrac{(2x-3)(x+1)}{(x-1)(x+1)}$

$\qquad = \dfrac{x^2-x+2x^2-x-3}{(x-1)(x+1)}$

$\qquad = \dfrac{3x^2-2x-3}{(x-1)(x+1)}$

48. $\dfrac{3x}{x-4} + \dfrac{2x}{x+3} = \dfrac{3x(x+3)}{(x-4)(x+3)} + \dfrac{2x(x-4)}{(x-4)(x+3)}$

$\qquad = \dfrac{3x^2+9x+2x^2-8x}{(x-4)(x+3)}$

$\qquad = \dfrac{5x^2+x}{(x-4)(x+3)}$

$\qquad = \dfrac{x(5x+1)}{(x-4)(x+3)}$

49. $\dfrac{x-3}{x+2} - \dfrac{x+4}{x-2} = \dfrac{(x-3)(x-2)}{(x+2)(x-2)} - \dfrac{(x+4)(x+2)}{(x-2)(x+2)}$

$\qquad = \dfrac{x^2-5x+6-(x^2+6x+8)}{(x+2)(x-2)}$

$\qquad = \dfrac{x^2-5x+6-x^2-6x-8}{(x+2)(x-2)}$

$\qquad = \dfrac{-11x-2}{(x+2)(x-2)} \quad \text{or} \quad \dfrac{-(11x+2)}{(x+2)(x-2)}$

50. $\dfrac{2x-3}{x-1} - \dfrac{2x+1}{x+1} = \dfrac{(2x-3)(x+1)}{(x-1)(x+1)} - \dfrac{(2x+1)(x-1)}{(x+1)(x-1)}$

$\qquad = \dfrac{2x^2-x-3-(2x^2-x-1)}{(x+1)(x-1)}$

$\qquad = \dfrac{2x^2-x-3-2x^2+x+1}{(x+1)(x-1)}$

$\qquad = \dfrac{-2}{(x+1)(x-1)}$

$\qquad = -\dfrac{2}{(x+1)(x-1)}$

51. $\dfrac{x}{x^2-4} + \dfrac{1}{x} = \dfrac{x^2+x^2-4}{x\left(x^2-4\right)}$

$\qquad = \dfrac{2x^2-4}{x\left(x^2-4\right)}$

$\qquad = \dfrac{2\left(x^2-2\right)}{x(x-2)(x+2)}$

52. $\dfrac{x-1}{x^3} + \dfrac{x}{x^2+1} = \dfrac{(x-1)\left(x^2+1\right)+x^4}{x^3\left(x^2+1\right)}$

$\qquad = \dfrac{x^3-x^2+x-1+x^4}{x^3\left(x^2+1\right)}$

$\qquad = \dfrac{x^4+x^3-x^2+x-1}{x^3\left(x^2+1\right)}$

53. $x^2-4 = (x+2)(x-2)$

$\quad x^2-x-2 = (x+1)(x-2)$

Therefore, $\text{LCM} = (x+2)(x-2)(x+1)$.

54. $x^2-x-12 = (x+3)(x-4)$

$\quad x^2-8x+16 = (x-4)(x-4)$

Therefore, $\text{LCM} = (x+3)(x-4)^2$.

55. $x^3-x = x\left(x^2-1\right) = x(x+1)(x-1)$

$\quad x^2-x = x(x-1)$

Therefore, $\text{LCM} = x(x+1)(x-1)$.

56. $3x^2-27 = 3\left(x^2-9\right) = 3(x+3)(x-3)$

$\quad 2x^2-x-15 = (2x+5)(x-3)$

Therefore, $\text{LCM} = 3(2x+5)(x-3)(x+3)$.

57. $4x^3 - 4x^2 + x = x\left(4x^2 - 4x + 1\right)$
$$= x(2x-1)(2x-1)$$
$2x^3 - x^2 = x^2(2x-1)$
x^3
Therefore, LCM $= x^3(2x-1)^2$.

58. $x - 3$
$x^2 + 3x = x(x+3)$
$x^3 - 9x = x\left(x^2 - 9\right) = x(x+3)(x-3)$
Therefore, LCM $= x(x+3)(x-3)$.

59. $x^3 - x = x\left(x^2 - 1\right) = x(x+1)(x-1)$
$x^3 - 2x^2 + x = x\left(x^2 - 2x + 1\right) = x(x-1)^2$
$x^3 - 1 = (x-1)\left(x^2 + x + 1\right)$
Therefore, LCM $= x(x+1)(x-1)^2\left(x^2 + x + 1\right)$.

60. $x^2 + 4x + 4 = (x+2)^2$
$x^3 + 2x^2 = x^2(x+2)$
$(x+2)^3$
Therefore, LCM $= x^2(x+2)^3$.

61. $\dfrac{x}{x^2 - 7x + 6} - \dfrac{x}{x^2 - 2x - 24}$
$$= \dfrac{x}{(x-6)(x-1)} - \dfrac{x}{(x-6)(x+4)}$$
$$= \dfrac{x(x+4)}{(x-6)(x-1)(x+4)} - \dfrac{x(x-1)}{(x-6)(x+4)(x-1)}$$
$$= \dfrac{x^2 + 4x - x^2 + x}{(x-6)(x+4)(x-1)} = \dfrac{5x}{(x-6)(x+4)(x-1)}$$

62. $\dfrac{x}{x-3} - \dfrac{x+1}{x^2 + 5x - 24}$
$$= \dfrac{x}{(x-3)} - \dfrac{x+1}{(x-3)(x+8)}$$
$$= \dfrac{x(x+8)}{(x-3)(x+8)} - \dfrac{x+1}{(x-3)(x+8)}$$
$$= \dfrac{x^2 + 8x - x - 1}{(x-3)(x+8)} = \dfrac{x^2 + 7x - 1}{(x-3)(x+8)}$$

63. $\dfrac{4x}{x^2 - 4} - \dfrac{2}{x^2 + x - 6}$
$$= \dfrac{4x}{(x-2)(x+2)} - \dfrac{2}{(x+3)(x-2)}$$
$$= \dfrac{4x(x+3)}{(x-2)(x+2)(x+3)} - \dfrac{2(x+2)}{(x+3)(x-2)(x+2)}$$
$$= \dfrac{4x^2 + 12x - 2x - 4}{(x-2)(x+2)(x+3)}$$
$$= \dfrac{4x^2 + 10x - 4}{(x-2)(x+2)(x+3)}$$
$$= \dfrac{2(2x^2 + 5x - 2)}{(x-2)(x+2)(x+3)}$$

64. $\dfrac{3x}{x-1} - \dfrac{x-4}{x^2 - 2x + 1} = \dfrac{3x}{(x-1)} - \dfrac{x-4}{(x-1)^2}$
$$= \dfrac{3x(x-1)}{(x-1)(x-1)} - \dfrac{x-4}{(x-1)^2}$$
$$= \dfrac{3x^2 - 3x - x + 4}{(x-1)^2}$$
$$= \dfrac{3x^2 - 4x + 4}{(x-1)^2}$$

65. $\dfrac{3}{(x-1)^2(x+1)} + \dfrac{2}{(x-1)(x+1)^2}$
$$= \dfrac{3(x+1) + 2(x-1)}{(x-1)^2(x+1)^2}$$
$$= \dfrac{3x + 3 + 2x - 2}{(x-1)^2(x+1)^2}$$
$$= \dfrac{5x + 1}{(x-1)^2(x+1)^2}$$

66. $\dfrac{2}{(x+2)^2(x-1)} - \dfrac{6}{(x+2)(x-1)^2}$
$$= \dfrac{2(x-1) - 6(x+2)}{(x+2)^2(x-1)^2}$$
$$= \dfrac{2x - 2 - 6x - 12}{(x+2)^2(x-1)^2}$$
$$= \dfrac{-4x - 14}{(x+2)^2(x-1)^2}$$
$$= \dfrac{-2(2x + 7)}{(x+2)^2(x-1)^2}$$

33

67. $\dfrac{x+4}{x^2-x-2} - \dfrac{2x+3}{x^2+2x-8}$

$= \dfrac{x+4}{(x-2)(x+1)} - \dfrac{2x+3}{(x+4)(x-2)}$

$= \dfrac{(x+4)(x+4)}{(x-2)(x+1)(x+4)} - \dfrac{(2x+3)(x+1)}{(x+4)(x-2)(x+1)}$

$= \dfrac{x^2+8x+16-(2x^2+5x+3)}{(x-2)(x+1)(x+4)}$

$= \dfrac{-x^2+3x+13}{(x-2)(x+1)(x+4)}$

68. $\dfrac{2x-3}{x^2+8x+7} - \dfrac{x-2}{(x+1)^2}$

$= \dfrac{2x-3}{(x+1)(x+7)} - \dfrac{x-2}{(x+1)^2}$

$= \dfrac{(2x-3)(x+1)}{(x+1)(x+7)(x+1)} - \dfrac{(x-2)(x+7)}{(x+1)^2(x+7)}$

$= \dfrac{2x^2-x-3-(x^2+5x-14)}{(x+1)^2(x+7)}$

$= \dfrac{x^2-6x+11}{(x+1)^2(x+7)}$

69. $\dfrac{1}{x} - \dfrac{2}{x^2+x} + \dfrac{3}{x^3-x^2}$

$= \dfrac{1}{x} - \dfrac{2}{x(x+1)} + \dfrac{3}{x^2(x-1)}$

$= \dfrac{x(x+1)(x-1)-2x(x-1)+3(x+1)}{x^2(x+1)(x-1)}$

$= \dfrac{x(x^2-1)-2x^2+2x+3x+3}{x^2(x+1)(x-1)}$

$= \dfrac{x^3-x-2x^2+5x+3}{x^2(x+1)(x-1)}$

$= \dfrac{x^3-2x^2+4x+3}{x^2(x+1)(x-1)}$

70. $\dfrac{x}{(x-1)^2} + \dfrac{2}{x} - \dfrac{x+1}{x^3-x^2}$

$= \dfrac{x}{(x-1)^2} + \dfrac{2}{x} - \dfrac{x+1}{x^2(x-1)}$

$= \dfrac{x^3+2x(x-1)^2-(x+1)(x-1)}{x^2(x-1)^2}$

$= \dfrac{x^3+2x(x^2-2x+1)-(x^2-1)}{x^2(x-1)^2}$

$= \dfrac{x^3+2x^3-4x^2+2x-x^2+1}{x^2(x-1)^2}$

$= \dfrac{3x^3-5x^2+2x+1}{x^2(x-1)^2}$

71. $\dfrac{1}{h}\left(\dfrac{1}{x+h} - \dfrac{1}{x}\right) = \dfrac{1}{h}\left(\dfrac{1\cdot x}{(x+h)x} - \dfrac{1(x+h)}{x(x+h)}\right)$

$= \dfrac{1}{h}\left(\dfrac{x-x-h}{x(x+h)}\right)$

$= \dfrac{-h}{hx(x+h)}$

$= \dfrac{-1}{x(x+h)}$

72. $\dfrac{1}{h}\left(\dfrac{1}{(x+h)^2} - \dfrac{1}{x^2}\right)$

$= \dfrac{1}{h}\left(\dfrac{1\cdot x^2}{(x+h)^2 x^2} - \dfrac{1(x+h)^2}{x^2(x+h)^2}\right)$

$= \dfrac{1}{h}\left(\dfrac{x^2-(x^2+2xh+h^2)}{x^2(x+h)^2}\right)$

$= \dfrac{-2xh-h^2}{hx^2(x+h)^2}$

$= \dfrac{h(-2x-h)}{hx^2(x+h)^2}$

$= \dfrac{-2x-h}{x^2(x+h)^2}$

$= -\dfrac{2x+h}{x^2(x+h)^2}$

73. $\dfrac{1+\dfrac{1}{x}}{1-\dfrac{1}{x}} = \dfrac{\left(\dfrac{x}{x}+\dfrac{1}{x}\right)}{\left(\dfrac{x}{x}-\dfrac{1}{x}\right)} = \dfrac{\left(\dfrac{x+1}{x}\right)}{\left(\dfrac{x-1}{x}\right)} = \dfrac{x+1}{x}\cdot\dfrac{x}{x-1} = \dfrac{x+1}{x-1}$

74. $\dfrac{4+\dfrac{1}{x^2}}{3-\dfrac{1}{x^2}} = \dfrac{\left(\dfrac{4x^2}{x^2}+\dfrac{1}{x^2}\right)}{\left(\dfrac{3x^2}{x^2}-\dfrac{1}{x^2}\right)} = \dfrac{\left(\dfrac{4x^2+1}{x^2}\right)}{\left(\dfrac{3x^2-1}{x^2}\right)}$

$= \dfrac{4x^2+1}{x^2}\cdot\dfrac{x^2}{3x^2-1}$

$= \dfrac{4x^2+1}{3x^2-1}$

75. $\dfrac{2-\dfrac{x+1}{x}}{3+\dfrac{x-1}{x+1}} = \dfrac{\dfrac{2x}{x}-\dfrac{x+1}{x}}{\dfrac{3(x+1)}{x+1}+\dfrac{x-1}{x+1}} = \dfrac{\dfrac{2x-x-1}{x}}{\dfrac{3x+3+x-1}{x+1}}$

$= \dfrac{\dfrac{x-1}{x}}{\dfrac{4x+2}{x+1}} = \dfrac{x-1}{x}\cdot\dfrac{x+1}{2(2x+1)}$

$= \dfrac{(x-1)(x+1)}{2x(2x+1)}$

76. $\dfrac{1-\dfrac{x}{x+1}}{2-\dfrac{x-1}{x}} = \dfrac{\left(\dfrac{x+1}{x+1}-\dfrac{x}{x+1}\right)}{\left(\dfrac{2x}{x}-\dfrac{x-1}{x}\right)} = \dfrac{\left(\dfrac{1}{x+1}\right)}{\left(\dfrac{x+1}{x}\right)}$

$= \dfrac{1}{x+1}\cdot\dfrac{x}{x+1}$

$= \dfrac{x}{(x+1)^2}$

77. $\dfrac{\dfrac{x+4}{x-2}-\dfrac{x-3}{x+1}}{x+1}$

$= \dfrac{\left(\dfrac{(x+4)(x+1)}{(x-2)(x+1)}-\dfrac{(x-3)(x-2)}{(x+1)(x-2)}\right)}{x+1}$

$= \dfrac{\left(\dfrac{x^2+5x+4-(x^2-5x+6)}{(x-2)(x+1)}\right)}{x+1}$

$= \dfrac{10x-2}{(x-2)(x+1)}\cdot\dfrac{1}{x+1}$

$= \dfrac{2(5x-1)}{(x-2)(x+1)^2}$

78. $\dfrac{\dfrac{x-2}{x+1}-\dfrac{x}{x-2}}{x+3}$

$= \dfrac{\left(\dfrac{(x-2)(x-2)}{(x+1)(x-2)}-\dfrac{x(x+1)}{(x-2)(x+1)}\right)}{x+3}$

$= \dfrac{\left(\dfrac{x^2-4x+4-(x^2+x)}{(x-2)(x+1)}\right)}{x+3}$

$= \dfrac{-5x+4}{(x-2)(x+1)}\cdot\dfrac{1}{x+3}$

$= \dfrac{-5x+4}{(x-2)(x+1)(x+3)}$

$= \dfrac{-(5x-4)}{(x-2)(x+1)(x+3)}$

79. $\dfrac{\dfrac{x-2}{x+2}+\dfrac{x-1}{x+1}}{\dfrac{x}{x+1}-\dfrac{2x-3}{x}}$

$= \dfrac{\left(\dfrac{(x-2)(x+1)}{(x+2)(x+1)}+\dfrac{(x-1)(x+2)}{(x+1)(x+2)}\right)}{\left(\dfrac{x^2}{(x+1)(x)}-\dfrac{(2x-3)(x+1)}{x(x+1)}\right)}$

$= \dfrac{\left(\dfrac{x^2-x-2+x^2+x-2}{(x+2)(x+1)}\right)}{\left(\dfrac{x^2-(2x^2-x-3)}{x(x+1)}\right)}$

$= \dfrac{\left(\dfrac{2x^2-4}{(x+2)(x+1)}\right)}{\left(\dfrac{-x^2+x+3}{x(x+1)}\right)}$

$= \dfrac{2(x^2-2)}{(x+2)(x+1)}\cdot\dfrac{x(x+1)}{-(x^2-x-3)}$

$= \dfrac{2x(x^2-2)}{-(x+2)(x^2-x-3)}$

$= \dfrac{-2x(x^2-2)}{(x+2)(x^2-x-3)}$

80. $\dfrac{\dfrac{2x+5}{x}-\dfrac{x}{x-3}}{\dfrac{x^2}{x-3}-\dfrac{(x+1)^2}{x+3}}$

$=\dfrac{\left(\dfrac{(2x+5)(x-3)}{x(x-3)}-\dfrac{x(x)}{x(x-3)}\right)}{\left(\dfrac{x^2(x+3)}{(x-3)(x+3)}-\dfrac{(x-3)(x+1)^2}{(x-3)(x+3)}\right)}$

$=\dfrac{\left(\dfrac{2x^2-x-15-x^2}{x(x-3)}\right)}{\left(\dfrac{x^3+3x^2-(x^3-x^2-5x-3)}{(x-3)(x+3)}\right)}$

$=\dfrac{\left(\dfrac{x^2-x-15}{x(x-3)}\right)}{\left(\dfrac{4x^2+5x+3}{(x-3)(x+3)}\right)}$

$=\dfrac{x^2-x-15}{x(x-3)}\cdot\dfrac{(x-3)(x+3)}{4x^2+5x+3}$

$=\dfrac{(x^2-x-15)(x+3)}{x(4x^2+5x+3)}$

81. $1-\dfrac{1}{1-\dfrac{1}{x}}=1-\dfrac{1}{\dfrac{x-1}{x}}$

$=1-\dfrac{x}{x-1}$

$=\dfrac{x-1-x}{x-1}$

$=\dfrac{-1}{x-1}$

82. $1-\dfrac{1}{1-\dfrac{1}{1-x}}=1-\dfrac{1}{\dfrac{1-x-1}{1-x}}=1-\dfrac{1}{\dfrac{-x}{1-x}}$

$=1-\dfrac{1-x}{-x}=1+\dfrac{1-x}{x}$

$=\dfrac{x+1-x}{x}$

$=\dfrac{1}{x}$

83. $\dfrac{2(x-1)^{-1}+3}{3(x-1)^{-1}+2}=\dfrac{\dfrac{2}{x-1}+3}{\dfrac{3}{x-1}+2}=\dfrac{\dfrac{2}{x-1}+\dfrac{3(x-1)}{x-1}}{\dfrac{3}{x-1}+\dfrac{2(x-1)}{x-1}}$

$=\dfrac{\dfrac{2+3(x-1)}{x-1}}{\dfrac{3+2(x-1)}{x-1}}$

$=\dfrac{2+3(x-1)}{x-1}\cdot\dfrac{x-1}{3+2(x-1)}$

$=\dfrac{2+3(x-1)}{3+2(x-1)}=\dfrac{2+3x-3}{3+2x-2}$

$=\dfrac{3x-1}{2x+1}$

84. $\dfrac{4(x+2)^{-1}-3}{3(x+2)^{-1}-1}=\dfrac{\dfrac{4}{x+2}-3}{\dfrac{3}{x+2}-1}=\dfrac{\dfrac{4}{x+2}-\dfrac{3(x+2)}{x+2}}{\dfrac{3}{x+2}-\dfrac{1(x+2)}{x+2}}$

$=\dfrac{\dfrac{4-3(x+2)}{x+2}}{\dfrac{3-(x+2)}{x+2}}$

$=\dfrac{4-3(x+2)}{x+2}\cdot\dfrac{x+2}{3-(x+2)}$

$=\dfrac{4-3(x+2)}{3-(x+2)}=\dfrac{4-3x-6}{3-x-2}$

$=\dfrac{-3x-2}{-x+1}=\dfrac{3x+2}{x-1}$

85. $\dfrac{(2x+3)\cdot3-(3x-5)\cdot2}{(3x-5)^2}=\dfrac{6x+9-6x+10}{(3x-5)^2}$

$=\dfrac{19}{(3x-5)^2}$

86. $\dfrac{(4x+1)\cdot5-(5x-2)\cdot4}{(5x-2)^2}=\dfrac{20x+5-20x+8}{(5x-2)^2}$

$=\dfrac{13}{(5x-2)^2}$

87. $\dfrac{x\cdot 2x-\left(x^2+1\right)\cdot 1}{\left(x^2+1\right)^2}=\dfrac{2x^2-x^2-1}{\left(x^2+1\right)^2}$

$\qquad\qquad\qquad =\dfrac{x^2-1}{\left(x^2+1\right)^2}$

$\qquad\qquad\qquad =\dfrac{(x-1)(x+1)}{\left(x^2+1\right)^2}$

88. $\dfrac{x\cdot 2x-\left(x^2-4\right)\cdot 1}{\left(x^2-4\right)^2}=\dfrac{2x^2-x^2+4}{\left(x^2-4\right)^2}=\dfrac{x^2+4}{\left(x^2-4\right)^2}$

$\qquad\qquad\qquad =\dfrac{x^2+4}{\left(x+2\right)^2\left(x-2\right)^2}$

89. $\dfrac{(3x+1)\cdot 2x-x^2\cdot 3}{(3x+1)^2}=\dfrac{6x^2+2x-3x^2}{(3x+1)^2}$

$\qquad\qquad\qquad =\dfrac{3x^2+2x}{(3x+1)^2}$

$\qquad\qquad\qquad =\dfrac{x(3x+2)}{(3x+1)^2}$

90. $\dfrac{(2x-5)\cdot 3x^2-x^3\cdot 2}{(2x-5)^2}=\dfrac{6x^3-15x^2-2x^3}{(2x-5)^2}$

$\qquad\qquad\qquad =\dfrac{4x^3-15x^2}{(2x-5)^2}$

$\qquad\qquad\qquad =\dfrac{x^2(4x-15)}{(2x-5)^2}$

91. $\dfrac{\left(x^2+1\right)\cdot 3-(3x+4)\cdot 2x}{\left(x^2+1\right)^2}=\dfrac{3x^2+3-6x^2-8x}{\left(x^2+1\right)^2}$

$\qquad\qquad\qquad =\dfrac{-3x^2-8x+3}{\left(x^2+1\right)^2}$

$\qquad\qquad\qquad =\dfrac{-\left(3x^2+8x-3\right)}{\left(x^2+1\right)^2}$

$\qquad\qquad\qquad =-\dfrac{(3x-1)(x+3)}{\left(x^2+1\right)^2}$

92. $\dfrac{\left(x^2+9\right)\cdot 2-(2x-5)\cdot 2x}{\left(x^2+9\right)^2}=\dfrac{2x^2+18-4x^2+10x}{\left(x^2+9\right)^2}$

$\qquad\qquad\qquad =\dfrac{-2x^2+10x+18}{\left(x^2+9\right)^2}$

$\qquad\qquad\qquad =\dfrac{-2\left(x^2-5x-9\right)}{\left(x^2+9\right)^2}$

93. $\dfrac{1}{f}=(n-1)\left(\dfrac{1}{R_1}+\dfrac{1}{R_2}\right)$

$\qquad \dfrac{1}{f}=(n-1)\left(\dfrac{R_2+R_1}{R_1\cdot R_2}\right)$

$\qquad \dfrac{R_1\cdot R_2}{f}=(n-1)\left(R_2+R_1\right)$

$\qquad \dfrac{f}{R_1\cdot R_2}=\dfrac{1}{(n-1)\left(R_2+R_1\right)}$

$\qquad f=\dfrac{R_1\cdot R_2}{(n-1)\left(R_2+R_1\right)}$

$\qquad f=\dfrac{0.1(0.2)}{(1.5-1)(0.2+0.1)}$

$\qquad\quad =\dfrac{0.02}{0.5(0.3)}=\dfrac{0.02}{0.15}=\dfrac{2}{15}$ meters

94. $\dfrac{1}{R}=\dfrac{1}{R_1}+\dfrac{1}{R_2}+\dfrac{1}{R_3}=\dfrac{R_2R_3+R_1R_3+R_1R_2}{R_1R_2R_3}$

$\qquad R=\dfrac{R_1R_2R_3}{R_2R_3+R_1R_3+R_1R_2}$

$\qquad\quad =\dfrac{5\cdot 4\cdot 10}{4\cdot 10+5\cdot 10+5\cdot 4}$

$\qquad\quad =\dfrac{200}{110}=\dfrac{20}{11}$ ohms

95. $1+\dfrac{1}{x}=\dfrac{x+1}{x}\Rightarrow a=1,b=1,c=0$

$1+\dfrac{1}{1+\dfrac{1}{x}}=1+\dfrac{1}{\left(\dfrac{x+1}{x}\right)}=1+\dfrac{x}{x+1}$

$=\dfrac{x+1+x}{x+1}=\dfrac{2x+1}{x+1}$

$\Rightarrow a=2,b=1,c=1$

$1+\dfrac{1}{1+\dfrac{1}{1+\dfrac{1}{x}}}=1+\dfrac{1}{\left(\dfrac{2x+1}{x+1}\right)}=1+\dfrac{x+1}{2x+1}$

$=\dfrac{2x+1+x+1}{2x+1}=\dfrac{3x+2}{2x+1}$

$\Rightarrow a=3,b=2,c=1$

$1+\dfrac{1}{1+\dfrac{1}{1+\dfrac{1}{1+\dfrac{1}{x}}}}=1+\dfrac{1}{\left(\dfrac{3x+2}{2x+1}\right)}=1+\dfrac{2x+1}{3x+2}$

$=\dfrac{3x+2+2x+1}{3x+2}=\dfrac{5x+3}{3x+2}$

$\Rightarrow a=5,b=3,c=2$

If we continue this process, the values of a, b and c produce the following sequences:

$a:1,2,3,5,8,13,21,....$

$b:1,1,2,3,5,8,13,21,.....$

$c:0,1,1,2,3,5,8,13,21,.....$

In each case we have a *Fibonacci Sequence*, where the next value in the list is obtained from the sum of the previous 2 values in the list.

96. Answers will vary.

97. Answers will vary.

Section R.8

1. 9; –9

2. 4; $|-4|=4$

3. index

4. True

5. cube root

6. False; $\sqrt[4]{(-3)^4}=|-3|=3$

7. $\sqrt[3]{27}=\sqrt[3]{3^3}=3$

8. $\sqrt[4]{16}=\sqrt[4]{2^4}=2$

9. $\sqrt[3]{-8}=\sqrt[3]{(-2)^3}=-2$

10. $\sqrt[3]{-1}=\sqrt[3]{(-1)^3}=-1$

11. $\sqrt{8}=\sqrt{4\cdot2}=2\sqrt{2}$

12. $\sqrt[3]{54}=\sqrt[3]{27\cdot2}=3\sqrt[3]{2}$

13. $\sqrt[3]{-8x^4}=\sqrt[3]{-8x^3\cdot x}=-2x\sqrt[3]{x}$

14. $\sqrt[4]{48x^5}=\sqrt[4]{16x^4\cdot3x}=2x\sqrt[4]{3x}$

15. $\sqrt[4]{x^{12}y^8}=\sqrt[4]{\left(x^3\right)^4\left(y^2\right)^4}=x^3y^2$

16. $\sqrt[5]{x^{10}y^5}=\sqrt[5]{\left(x^2\right)^5 y^5}=x^2y$

17. $\sqrt[4]{\dfrac{x^9y^7}{xy^3}}=\sqrt[4]{x^8y^4}=x^2y$

18. $\sqrt[3]{\dfrac{3xy^2}{81x^4y^2}}=\sqrt[3]{\dfrac{1}{27x^3}}=\dfrac{\sqrt[3]{1}}{\sqrt[3]{27x^3}}=\dfrac{1}{3x}$

19. $\sqrt{36x}=6\sqrt{x}$

20. $\sqrt{9x^5}=3\sqrt{x^4\cdot x}=3x^2\sqrt{x}$

21. $\sqrt{3x^2}\sqrt{12x}=\sqrt{36x^2\cdot x}=6x\sqrt{x}$

22. $\sqrt{5x}\sqrt{20x^3}=\sqrt{100x^4}=10x^2$

23. $\left(\sqrt{5}\sqrt[3]{9}\right)^2=\left(\sqrt{5}\right)^2\left(\sqrt[3]{9}\right)^2$

$=5\cdot\sqrt[3]{9^2}=5\sqrt[3]{81}=5\cdot3\sqrt[3]{3}=15\sqrt[3]{3}$

24. $\left(\sqrt[3]{3}\sqrt{10}\right)^4=\left(\sqrt[3]{3}\right)^4\left(\sqrt{10}\right)^4$

$=\sqrt[3]{3^4}\cdot10^2=3\sqrt[3]{3}\cdot100=300\sqrt[3]{3}$

25. $\left(3\sqrt{6}\right)\left(2\sqrt{2}\right) = 6\sqrt{12} = 6\sqrt{4 \cdot 3} = 12\sqrt{3}$

26. $\left(5\sqrt{8}\right)\left(-3\sqrt{3}\right) = -15\sqrt{24} = -30\sqrt{6}$

27. $3\sqrt{2} + 4\sqrt{2} = (3+4)\sqrt{2} = 7\sqrt{2}$

28. $6\sqrt{5} - 4\sqrt{5} = (6-4)\sqrt{5} = 2\sqrt{5}$

29. $-\sqrt{18} + 2\sqrt{8} = -\sqrt{9 \cdot 2} + 2\sqrt{4 \cdot 2}$
$\phantom{-\sqrt{18} + 2\sqrt{8}} = -3\sqrt{2} + 4\sqrt{2}$
$\phantom{-\sqrt{18} + 2\sqrt{8}} = (-3+4)\sqrt{2}$
$\phantom{-\sqrt{18} + 2\sqrt{8}} = \sqrt{2}$

30. $2\sqrt{12} - 3\sqrt{27} = 2\sqrt{4 \cdot 3} - 3\sqrt{9 \cdot 3}$
$\phantom{2\sqrt{12} - 3\sqrt{27}} = 4\sqrt{3} - 9\sqrt{3}$
$\phantom{2\sqrt{12} - 3\sqrt{27}} = (4-9)\sqrt{3}$
$\phantom{2\sqrt{12} - 3\sqrt{27}} = -5\sqrt{3}$

31. $\left(\sqrt{3}+3\right)\left(\sqrt{3}-1\right) = \left(\sqrt{3}\right)^2 + 3\sqrt{3} - \sqrt{3} - 3$
$\phantom{\left(\sqrt{3}+3\right)\left(\sqrt{3}-1\right)} = 3 + 2\sqrt{3} - 3$
$\phantom{\left(\sqrt{3}+3\right)\left(\sqrt{3}-1\right)} = 2\sqrt{3}$

32. $\left(\sqrt{5}-2\right)\left(\sqrt{5}+3\right) = \left(\sqrt{5}\right)^2 - 2\sqrt{5} + 3\sqrt{5} - 6$
$\phantom{\left(\sqrt{5}-2\right)\left(\sqrt{5}+3\right)} = 5 + \sqrt{5} - 6$
$\phantom{\left(\sqrt{5}-2\right)\left(\sqrt{5}+3\right)} = \sqrt{5} - 1$

33. $5\sqrt[3]{2} - 2\sqrt[3]{54} = 5\sqrt[3]{2} - 2 \cdot 3\sqrt[3]{2}$
$\phantom{5\sqrt[3]{2} - 2\sqrt[3]{54}} = 5\sqrt[3]{2} - 6\sqrt[3]{2}$
$\phantom{5\sqrt[3]{2} - 2\sqrt[3]{54}} = (5-6)\sqrt[3]{2}$
$\phantom{5\sqrt[3]{2} - 2\sqrt[3]{54}} = -\sqrt[3]{2}$

34. $9\sqrt[3]{24} - \sqrt[3]{81} = 9 \cdot 2\sqrt[3]{3} - 3\sqrt[3]{3}$
$\phantom{9\sqrt[3]{24} - \sqrt[3]{81}} = 18\sqrt[3]{3} - 3\sqrt[3]{3}$
$\phantom{9\sqrt[3]{24} - \sqrt[3]{81}} = (18-3)\sqrt[3]{3}$
$\phantom{9\sqrt[3]{24} - \sqrt[3]{81}} = 15\sqrt[3]{3}$

35. $\left(\sqrt{x}-1\right)^2 = \left(\sqrt{x}\right)^2 - 2\sqrt{x} + 1$
$\phantom{\left(\sqrt{x}-1\right)^2} = x - 2\sqrt{x} + 1$

36. $\left(\sqrt{x}+\sqrt{5}\right)^2 = \left(\sqrt{x}\right)^2 + 2\left(\sqrt{x}\right)\left(\sqrt{5}\right) + \left(\sqrt{5}\right)^2$
$\phantom{\left(\sqrt{x}+\sqrt{5}\right)^2} = x + 2\sqrt{5x} + 5$

37. $\sqrt[3]{16x^4} - \sqrt[3]{2x} = \sqrt[3]{8x^3 \cdot 2x} - \sqrt[3]{2x}$
$\phantom{\sqrt[3]{16x^4} - \sqrt[3]{2x}} = 2x\sqrt[3]{2x} - \sqrt[3]{2x}$
$\phantom{\sqrt[3]{16x^4} - \sqrt[3]{2x}} = (2x-1)\sqrt[3]{2x}$

38. $\sqrt[4]{32x} + \sqrt[4]{2x^5} = \sqrt[4]{16 \cdot 2x} + \sqrt[4]{x^4 \cdot 2x}$
$\phantom{\sqrt[4]{32x} + \sqrt[4]{2x^5}} = 2\sqrt[4]{2x} + x\sqrt[4]{2x}$
$\phantom{\sqrt[4]{32x} + \sqrt[4]{2x^5}} = (2+x)\sqrt[4]{2x} \;\; \text{or} \;\; (x+2)\sqrt[4]{2x}$

39. $\sqrt{8x^3} - 3\sqrt{50x} = \sqrt{4x^2 \cdot 2x} - 3\sqrt{25 \cdot 2x}$
$\phantom{\sqrt{8x^3} - 3\sqrt{50x}} = 2x\sqrt{2x} - 15\sqrt{2x}$
$\phantom{\sqrt{8x^3} - 3\sqrt{50x}} = (2x-15)\sqrt{2x}$

40. $3x\sqrt{9y} + 4\sqrt{25y} = 9x\sqrt{y} + 20\sqrt{y}$
$\phantom{3x\sqrt{9y} + 4\sqrt{25y}} = (9x+20)\sqrt{y}$

41. $\sqrt[3]{16x^4 y} - 3x\sqrt[3]{2xy} + 5\sqrt[3]{-2xy^4}$
$= \sqrt[3]{8x^3 \cdot 2xy} - 3x\sqrt[3]{2xy} + 5\sqrt[3]{-y^3 \cdot 2xy}$
$= 2x\sqrt[3]{2xy} - 3x\sqrt[3]{2xy} - 5y\sqrt[3]{2xy}$
$= (2x-3x-5y)\sqrt[3]{2xy}$
$= (-x-5y)\sqrt[3]{2xy} \;\; \text{or} \;\; -(x+5y)\sqrt[3]{2xy}$

42. $8xy - \sqrt{25x^2 y^2} + \sqrt[3]{8x^3 y^3} = 8xy - 5xy + 2xy$
$\phantom{8xy - \sqrt{25x^2 y^2} + \sqrt[3]{8x^3 y^3}} = (8-5+2)xy$
$\phantom{8xy - \sqrt{25x^2 y^2} + \sqrt[3]{8x^3 y^3}} = 5xy$

43. $\dfrac{1}{\sqrt{2}} = \dfrac{1}{\sqrt{2}} \cdot \dfrac{\sqrt{2}}{\sqrt{2}} = \dfrac{\sqrt{2}}{2}$

44. $\dfrac{2}{\sqrt{3}} = \dfrac{2}{\sqrt{3}} \cdot \dfrac{\sqrt{3}}{\sqrt{3}} = \dfrac{2\sqrt{3}}{3}$

45. $\dfrac{-\sqrt{3}}{\sqrt{5}} = \dfrac{-\sqrt{3}}{\sqrt{5}} \cdot \dfrac{\sqrt{5}}{\sqrt{5}} = \dfrac{-\sqrt{15}}{5}$

46. $\dfrac{-\sqrt{3}}{\sqrt{8}} = \dfrac{-\sqrt{3}}{2\sqrt{2}} = \dfrac{-\sqrt{3}}{2\sqrt{2}} \cdot \dfrac{\sqrt{2}}{\sqrt{2}} = \dfrac{-\sqrt{6}}{2 \cdot 2} = \dfrac{-\sqrt{6}}{4}$

47. $\dfrac{\sqrt{3}}{5-\sqrt{2}} = \dfrac{\sqrt{3}}{5-\sqrt{2}} \cdot \dfrac{5+\sqrt{2}}{5+\sqrt{2}}$

$\qquad = \dfrac{\sqrt{3}\left(5+\sqrt{2}\right)}{25-2}$

$\qquad = \dfrac{\sqrt{3}\left(5+\sqrt{2}\right)}{23}$ or $\dfrac{5\sqrt{3}+\sqrt{6}}{23}$

48. $\dfrac{\sqrt{2}}{\sqrt{7}+2} = \dfrac{\sqrt{2}}{\sqrt{7}+2} \cdot \dfrac{\sqrt{7}-2}{\sqrt{7}-2}$

$\qquad = \dfrac{\sqrt{2}\left(\sqrt{7}-2\right)}{7-4}$

$\qquad = \dfrac{\sqrt{2}\left(\sqrt{7}-2\right)}{3}$ or $\dfrac{\sqrt{14}-2\sqrt{2}}{3}$

49. $\dfrac{2-\sqrt{5}}{2+3\sqrt{5}} = \dfrac{2-\sqrt{5}}{2+3\sqrt{5}} \cdot \dfrac{2-3\sqrt{5}}{2-3\sqrt{5}}$

$\qquad = \dfrac{4-2\sqrt{5}-6\sqrt{5}+15}{4-45}$

$\qquad = \dfrac{19-8\sqrt{5}}{-41} = \dfrac{8\sqrt{5}-19}{41}$

50. $\dfrac{\sqrt{3}-1}{2\sqrt{3}+3} = \dfrac{\sqrt{3}-1}{2\sqrt{3}+3} \cdot \dfrac{2\sqrt{3}-3}{2\sqrt{3}-3}$

$\qquad = \dfrac{6-2\sqrt{3}-3\sqrt{3}+3}{12-9} = \dfrac{9-5\sqrt{3}}{3}$

51. $\dfrac{5}{\sqrt[3]{2}} = \dfrac{5}{\sqrt[3]{2}} \cdot \dfrac{\sqrt[3]{4}}{\sqrt[3]{4}} = \dfrac{5\sqrt[3]{4}}{2}$

52. $\dfrac{-2}{\sqrt[3]{9}} = \dfrac{-2}{\sqrt[3]{9}} \cdot \dfrac{\sqrt[3]{3}}{\sqrt[3]{3}} = \dfrac{-2\sqrt[3]{3}}{3}$

53. $\dfrac{\sqrt{x+h}-\sqrt{x}}{\sqrt{x+h}+\sqrt{x}} = \dfrac{\sqrt{x+h}-\sqrt{x}}{\sqrt{x+h}+\sqrt{x}} \cdot \dfrac{\sqrt{x+h}-\sqrt{x}}{\sqrt{x+h}-\sqrt{x}}$

$\qquad = \dfrac{(x+h)-2\sqrt{x(x+h)}+x}{(x+h)-x}$

$\qquad = \dfrac{x+h-2\sqrt{x^2+xh}+x}{x+h-x}$

$\qquad = \dfrac{2x+h-2\sqrt{x^2+xh}}{h}$

54. $\dfrac{\sqrt{x+h}+\sqrt{x-h}}{\sqrt{x+h}-\sqrt{x-h}}$

$\qquad = \dfrac{\sqrt{x+h}+\sqrt{x-h}}{\sqrt{x+h}-\sqrt{x-h}} \cdot \dfrac{\sqrt{x+h}+\sqrt{x-h}}{\sqrt{x+h}+\sqrt{x-h}}$

$\qquad = \dfrac{(x+h)+2\sqrt{(x-h)(x+h)}+(x-h)}{(x+h)-(x-h)}$

$\qquad = \dfrac{x+h+2\sqrt{x^2-h^2}+x-h}{x+h-x+h}$

$\qquad = \dfrac{2x+2\sqrt{x^2-h^2}}{2h}$

$\qquad = \dfrac{x+\sqrt{x^2-h^2}}{h}$

55. $8^{2/3} = \left(\sqrt[3]{8}\right)^2 = 2^2 = 4$

56. $4^{3/2} = \left(\sqrt{4}\right)^3 = 2^3 = 8$

57. $(-27)^{1/3} = \sqrt[3]{-27} = -3$

58. $16^{3/4} = \left(\sqrt[4]{16}\right)^3 = 2^3 = 8$

59. $16^{3/2} = \left(\sqrt{16}\right)^3 = 4^3 = 64$

60. $25^{3/2} = \left(\sqrt{25}\right)^3 = 5^3 = 125$

61. $9^{-3/2} = \dfrac{1}{9^{3/2}} = \dfrac{1}{\left(\sqrt{9}\right)^3} = \dfrac{1}{3^3} = \dfrac{1}{27}$

62. $16^{-3/2} = \dfrac{1}{16^{3/2}} = \dfrac{1}{\left(\sqrt{16}\right)^3} = \dfrac{1}{4^3} = \dfrac{1}{64}$

63. $\left(\dfrac{9}{8}\right)^{3/2} = \left(\sqrt{\dfrac{9}{8}}\right)^3 = \left(\dfrac{3}{2\sqrt{2}}\right)^3 = \dfrac{3^3}{2^3\left(\sqrt{2}\right)^3}$

$\qquad = \dfrac{27}{8\cdot 2\sqrt{2}} = \dfrac{27}{16\sqrt{2}} = \dfrac{27}{16\sqrt{2}} \cdot \dfrac{\sqrt{2}}{\sqrt{2}}$

$\qquad = \dfrac{27\sqrt{2}}{32}$

64. $\left(\dfrac{27}{8}\right)^{2/3} = \left(\sqrt[3]{\dfrac{27}{8}}\right)^2 = \left(\dfrac{3}{2}\right)^2 = \dfrac{9}{4}$

65. $\left(\dfrac{8}{9}\right)^{-3/2} = \left(\dfrac{9}{8}\right)^{3/2} = \left(\sqrt{\dfrac{9}{8}}\right)^3 = \left(\dfrac{3}{2\sqrt{2}}\right)^3$

$\qquad = \dfrac{3^3}{2^3\left(\sqrt{2}\right)^3} = \dfrac{27}{8\cdot2\sqrt{2}} = \dfrac{27}{16\sqrt{2}}$

$\qquad = \dfrac{27}{16\sqrt{2}}\cdot\dfrac{\sqrt{2}}{\sqrt{2}} = \dfrac{27\sqrt{2}}{32}$

66. $\left(\dfrac{8}{27}\right)^{-2/3} = \left(\dfrac{27}{8}\right)^{2/3} = \left(\sqrt[3]{\dfrac{27}{8}}\right)^2 = \left(\dfrac{3}{2}\right)^2 = \dfrac{9}{4}$

67. $x^{3/4}x^{1/3}x^{-1/2} = x^{3/4+1/3-1/2} = x^{7/12}$

68. $x^{2/3}x^{1/2}x^{-1/4} = x^{2/3+1/2-1/4} = x^{11/12}$

69. $\left(x^3y^6\right)^{1/3} = \left(x^3\right)^{1/3}\left(y^6\right)^{1/3} = xy^2$

70. $\left(x^4y^8\right)^{3/4} = \left(x^4\right)^{3/4}\left(y^8\right)^{3/4} = x^3y^6$

71. $\dfrac{\left(x^2y\right)^{1/3}\left(xy^2\right)^{2/3}}{x^{2/3}y^{2/3}} = \dfrac{\left(x^2\right)^{1/3}(y)^{1/3}(x)^{2/3}\left(y^2\right)^{2/3}}{x^{2/3}y^{2/3}}$

$\qquad = \dfrac{x^{2/3}y^{1/3}x^{2/3}y^{4/3}}{x^{2/3}y^{2/3}}$

$\qquad = x^{2/3+2/3-2/3}y^{1/3+4/3-2/3}$

$\qquad = x^{2/3}y^1 = x^{2/3}y$

72. $\dfrac{(xy)^{1/4}\left(x^2y^2\right)^{1/2}}{\left(x^2y\right)^{3/4}} = \dfrac{x^{1/4}y^{1/4}\left(x^2\right)^{1/2}\left(y^2\right)^{1/2}}{\left(x^2\right)^{3/4}y^{3/4}}$

$\qquad = \dfrac{x^{1/4}y^{1/4}xy}{x^{3/2}y^{3/4}}$

$\qquad = x^{1/4+1-3/2}y^{1/4+1-3/4}$

$\qquad = x^{-1/4}y^{1/2} = \dfrac{y^{1/2}}{x^{1/4}}$

73. $\dfrac{\left(16x^2y^{-1/3}\right)^{3/4}}{\left(xy^2\right)^{1/4}} = \dfrac{16^{3/4}\left(x^2\right)^{3/4}\left(y^{-1/3}\right)^{3/4}}{x^{1/4}\left(y^2\right)^{1/4}}$

$\qquad = \dfrac{\left(\sqrt[4]{16}\right)^3 x^{3/2}y^{-1/4}}{x^{1/4}y^{1/2}}$

$\qquad = 2^3 x^{3/2-1/4}y^{-1/4-1/2}$

$\qquad = 8x^{5/4}y^{-3/4}$

$\qquad = \dfrac{8x^{5/4}}{y^{3/4}}$

74. $\dfrac{\left(4x^{-1}y^{1/3}\right)^{3/2}}{(xy)^{3/2}} = \dfrac{4^{3/2}\left(x^{-1}\right)^{3/2}\left(y^{1/3}\right)^{3/2}}{x^{3/2}y^{3/2}}$

$\qquad = \dfrac{\left(\sqrt{4}\right)^3 x^{-3/2}y^{1/2}}{x^{3/2}y^{3/2}}$

$\qquad = 2^3 x^{-3/2-3/2}y^{1/2-3/2}$

$\qquad = 8x^{-3}y^{-1}$

$\qquad = \dfrac{8}{x^3y}$

75. $\dfrac{x}{(1+x)^{1/2}} + 2(1+x)^{1/2} = \dfrac{x+2(1+x)^{1/2}(1+x)^{1/2}}{(1+x)^{1/2}}$

$\qquad = \dfrac{x+2(1+x)}{(1+x)^{1/2}}$

$\qquad = \dfrac{x+2+2x}{(1+x)^{1/2}}$

$\qquad = \dfrac{3x+2}{(1+x)^{1/2}}$

76. $\dfrac{1+x}{2x^{1/2}} + x^{1/2} = \dfrac{1+x+x^{1/2}\cdot2x^{1/2}}{2x^{1/2}}$

$\qquad = \dfrac{1+x+2x}{2x^{1/2}} = \dfrac{3x+1}{2x^{1/2}}$

77. $2x\left(x^2+1\right)^{1/2}+x^2\cdot\dfrac{1}{2}\left(x^2+1\right)^{-1/2}\cdot 2x$

$=2x\left(x^2+1\right)^{1/2}+\dfrac{x^3}{\left(x^2+1\right)^{1/2}}$

$=\dfrac{2x\left(x^2+1\right)^{1/2}\cdot\left(x^2+1\right)^{1/2}+x^3}{\left(x^2+1\right)^{1/2}}$

$=\dfrac{2x\left(x^2+1\right)^{1/2+1/2}+x^3}{\left(x^2+1\right)^{1/2}}=\dfrac{2x\left(x^2+1\right)^{1}+x^3}{\left(x^2+1\right)^{1/2}}$

$=\dfrac{2x^3+2x+x^3}{\left(x^2+1\right)^{1/2}}=\dfrac{3x^3+2x}{\left(x^2+1\right)^{1/2}}$

$=\dfrac{x\left(3x^2+2\right)}{\left(x^2+1\right)^{1/2}}$

78. $(x+1)^{1/3}+x\cdot\dfrac{1}{3}(x+1)^{-2/3},\ x\neq-1$

$=(x+1)^{1/3}+\dfrac{x}{3(x+1)^{2/3}}$

$=\dfrac{3(x+1)^{2/3}(x+1)^{1/3}+x}{3(x+1)^{2/3}}$

$=\dfrac{3(x+1)^{2/3+1/3}+x}{3(x+1)^{2/3}}=\dfrac{3(x+1)^{1}+x}{3(x+1)^{2/3}}$

$=\dfrac{3x+3+x}{3(x+1)^{2/3}}=\dfrac{4x+3}{3(x+1)^{2/3}}$

79. $\sqrt{4x+3}\cdot\dfrac{1}{2\sqrt{x-5}}+\sqrt{x-5}\cdot\dfrac{1}{5\sqrt{4x+3}},\ x>5$

$=\dfrac{\sqrt{4x+3}}{2\sqrt{x-5}}+\dfrac{\sqrt{x-5}}{5\sqrt{4x+3}}$

$=\dfrac{\sqrt{4x+3}\cdot5\cdot\sqrt{4x+3}+\sqrt{x-5}\cdot2\cdot\sqrt{x-5}}{10\sqrt{x-5}\sqrt{4x+3}}$

$=\dfrac{5(4x+3)+2(x-5)}{10\sqrt{(x-5)(4x+3)}}$

$=\dfrac{20x+15+2x-10}{10\sqrt{(x-5)(4x+3)}}$

$=\dfrac{22x+5}{10\sqrt{(x-5)(4x+3)}}$

80. $\dfrac{\sqrt[3]{8x+1}}{3\sqrt[3]{(x-2)^2}}+\dfrac{\sqrt[3]{x-2}}{24\sqrt[3]{(8x+1)^2}},\ x\neq2,\ x\neq-\dfrac{1}{8}$

$=\dfrac{8\sqrt[3]{8x+1}\cdot\sqrt[3]{(8x+1)^2}+\sqrt[3]{x-2}\cdot\sqrt[3]{(x-2)^2}}{24\sqrt[3]{(x-2)^2}\cdot\sqrt[3]{(8x+1)^2}}$

$=\dfrac{8\sqrt[3]{(8x+1)^3}+\sqrt[3]{(x-2)^3}}{24\sqrt[3]{(x-2)^2}\cdot\sqrt[3]{(8x+1)^2}}$

$=\dfrac{8\,(8x+1)+x-2}{24\sqrt[3]{(x-2)^2(8x+1)^2}}$

$=\dfrac{64x+8+x-2}{24\sqrt[3]{(x-2)^2(8x+1)^2}}$

$=\dfrac{65x+6}{24\sqrt[3]{(x-2)^2(8x+1)^2}}$

81. $\dfrac{\left(\sqrt{1+x}-x\cdot\dfrac{1}{2\sqrt{1+x}}\right)}{1+x}=\dfrac{\left(\sqrt{1+x}-\dfrac{x}{2\sqrt{1+x}}\right)}{1+x}$

$=\dfrac{\left(\dfrac{2\sqrt{1+x}\sqrt{1+x}-x}{2\sqrt{1+x}}\right)}{1+x}$

$=\dfrac{2(1+x)-x}{2(1+x)^{1/2}}\cdot\dfrac{1}{1+x}$

$=\dfrac{2+x}{2(1+x)^{3/2}}$

82. $\dfrac{\left(\sqrt{x^2+1}-x\cdot\dfrac{2x}{2\sqrt{x^2+1}}\right)}{x^2+1}$

$=\dfrac{\left(\sqrt{x^2+1}-\dfrac{x^2}{\sqrt{x^2+1}}\right)}{x^2+1}$

$=\dfrac{\left(\sqrt{x^2+1}\cdot\dfrac{\sqrt{x^2+1}}{\sqrt{x^2+1}}-\dfrac{x^2}{\sqrt{x^2+1}}\right)}{x^2+1}$

$=\dfrac{\left(\dfrac{x^2+1-x^2}{\sqrt{x^2+1}}\right)}{x^2+1}=\dfrac{1}{\sqrt{x^2+1}}\cdot\dfrac{1}{x^2+1}$

$=\dfrac{1}{\left(x^2+1\right)^{3/2}}$

83. $\dfrac{(x+4)^{1/2} - 2x(x+4)^{-1/2}}{x+4}$

$= \dfrac{\left((x+4)^{1/2} - \dfrac{2x}{(x+4)^{1/2}}\right)}{x+4}$

$= \dfrac{\left((x+4)^{1/2} \cdot \dfrac{(x+4)^{1/2}}{(x+4)^{1/2}} - \dfrac{2x}{(x+4)^{1/2}}\right)}{x+4}$

$= \dfrac{\left(\dfrac{x+4-2x}{(x+4)^{1/2}}\right)}{x+4}$

$= \dfrac{-x+4}{(x+4)^{1/2}} \cdot \dfrac{1}{x+4}$

$= \dfrac{-x+4}{(x+4)^{3/2}}$

$= \dfrac{4-x}{(x+4)^{3/2}}$

84. $\dfrac{(9-x^2)^{1/2} + x^2(9-x^2)^{-1/2}}{9-x^2}, -3 < x < 3$

$= \dfrac{\left((9-x^2)^{1/2} + \dfrac{x^2}{(9-x^2)^{1/2}}\right)}{9-x^2}$

$= \dfrac{\left(\dfrac{(9-x^2)^{1/2} \cdot (9-x^2)^{1/2} + x^2}{(9-x^2)^{1/2}}\right)}{9-x^2}$

$= \dfrac{(9-x^2)^{1/2} \cdot (9-x^2)^{1/2} + x^2}{(9-x^2)^{1/2}} \cdot \dfrac{1}{9-x^2}$

$= \dfrac{9-x^2+x^2}{(9-x^2)^{1/2}} \cdot \dfrac{1}{9-x^2}$

$= \dfrac{9}{(9-x^2)^{3/2}}$

85. $\dfrac{\dfrac{x^2}{(x^2-1)^{1/2}} - (x^2-1)^{1/2}}{x^2}, x < -1 \text{ or } x > 1$

$= \dfrac{\left(\dfrac{x^2 - (x^2-1)^{1/2} \cdot (x^2-1)^{1/2}}{(x^2-1)^{1/2}}\right)}{x^2}$

$= \dfrac{x^2 - (x^2-1)^{1/2} \cdot (x^2-1)^{1/2}}{(x^2-1)^{1/2}} \cdot \dfrac{1}{x^2}$

$= \dfrac{x^2 - (x^2-1)}{(x^2-1)^{1/2}} \cdot \dfrac{1}{x^2}$

$= \dfrac{x^2 - x^2 + 1}{(x^2-1)^{1/2}} \cdot \dfrac{1}{x^2}$

$= \dfrac{1}{x^2(x^2-1)^{1/2}}$

86. $\dfrac{(x^2+4)^{1/2} - x^2(x^2+4)^{-1/2}}{x^2+4}$

$= \dfrac{\left((x^2+4)^{1/2} - \dfrac{x^2}{(x^2+4)^{1/2}}\right)}{x^2+4}$

$= \dfrac{\left(\dfrac{(x^2+4)^{1/2} \cdot (x^2+4)^{1/2} - x^2}{(x^2+4)^{1/2}}\right)}{x^2+4}$

$= \dfrac{(x^2+4)^{1/2} \cdot (x^2+4)^{1/2} - x^2}{(x^2+4)^{1/2}} \cdot \dfrac{1}{x^2+4}$

$= \dfrac{x^2+4-x^2}{(x^2+4)^{1/2}} \cdot \dfrac{1}{x^2+4} = \dfrac{4}{(x^2+4)^{3/2}}$

87. $\dfrac{\dfrac{1+x^2}{2\sqrt{x}}-2x\sqrt{x}}{\left(1+x^2\right)^2}, x>0$

$=\dfrac{\left(\dfrac{1+x^2-\left(2\sqrt{x}\right)\left(2x\sqrt{x}\right)}{2\sqrt{x}}\right)}{\left(1+x^2\right)^2}$

$=\dfrac{1+x^2-\left(2\sqrt{x}\right)\left(2x\sqrt{x}\right)}{2\sqrt{x}}\cdot\dfrac{1}{\left(1+x^2\right)^2}$

$=\dfrac{1+x^2-4x^2}{2\sqrt{x}}\cdot\dfrac{1}{\left(1+x^2\right)^2}=\dfrac{1-3x^2}{2\sqrt{x}\left(1+x^2\right)^2}$

88. $\dfrac{2x\left(1-x^2\right)^{1/3}+\dfrac{2}{3}x^3\left(1-x^2\right)^{-2/3}}{\left(1-x^2\right)^{2/3}}, x\neq -1, x\neq 1$

$=\dfrac{\left(2x\left(1-x^2\right)^{1/3}+\dfrac{2x^3}{3\left(1-x^2\right)^{2/3}}\right)}{\left(1-x^2\right)^{2/3}}$

$=\dfrac{\left(\dfrac{2x\left(1-x^2\right)^{1/3}3\left(1-x^2\right)^{2/3}+2x^3}{3\left(1-x^2\right)^{2/3}}\right)}{\left(1-x^2\right)^{2/3}}$

$=\dfrac{6x\left(1-x^2\right)^{1/3+2/3}+2x^3}{3\left(1-x^2\right)^{2/3}}\cdot\dfrac{1}{\left(1-x^2\right)^{2/3}}$

$=\dfrac{6x\left(1-x^2\right)+2x^3}{3\left(1-x^2\right)^{2/3+2/3}}=\dfrac{6x-6x^3+2x^3}{3\left(1-x^2\right)^{4/3}}$

$=\dfrac{6x-4x^3}{3\left(1-x^2\right)^{4/3}}=\dfrac{2x\left(3-2x^2\right)}{3\left(1-x^2\right)^{4/3}}$

89. $(x+1)^{3/2}+x\cdot\dfrac{3}{2}(x+1)^{1/2}$

$=(x+1)^{1/2}\left(x+1+\dfrac{3}{2}x\right)$

$=(x+1)^{1/2}\left(\dfrac{5}{2}x+1\right)$

$=\dfrac{1}{2}(x+1)^{1/2}(5x+2)$

90. $(x^2+4)^{4/3}+x\cdot\dfrac{4}{3}(x^2+4)^{1/3}\cdot 2x$

$=(x^2+4)^{1/3}\left(x^2+4+\dfrac{8}{3}x^2\right)$

$=(x^2+4)^{1/3}\left(\dfrac{11}{3}x^2+4\right)$

$=\dfrac{1}{3}\left(x^2+4\right)^{1/3}\left(11x^2+12\right)$

91. $6x^{1/2}\left(x^2+x\right)-8x^{3/2}-8x^{1/2}$

$=2x^{1/2}\left(3(x^2+x)-4x-4\right)$

$=2x^{1/2}\left(3x^2-x-4\right)$

$=2x^{1/2}(3x-4)(x+1)$

92. $6x^{1/2}\left(2x+3\right)+x^{3/2}\cdot 8$

$=2x^{1/2}\left(3(2x+3)+4x\right)$

$=2x^{1/2}\left(10x+9\right)$

93. $3\left(x^2+4\right)^{4/3}+x\cdot 4\left(x^2+4\right)^{1/3}\cdot 2x$

$=\left(x^2+4\right)^{1/3}\left[3\left(x^2+4\right)+8x^2\right]$

$=\left(x^2+4\right)^{1/3}\left[3x^2+12+8x^2\right]$

$=\left(x^2+4\right)^{1/3}\left(11x^2+12\right)$

94. $2x\left(3x+4\right)^{4/3}+x^2\cdot 4\left(3x+4\right)^{1/3}$

$=2x\left(3x+4\right)^{1/3}\left[(3x+4)+2x\right]$

$=2x\left(3x+4\right)^{1/3}\left(5x+4\right)$

95. $4\left(3x+5\right)^{1/3}\left(2x+3\right)^{3/2}+3\left(3x+5\right)^{4/3}\left(2x+3\right)^{1/2}$

$=\left(3x+5\right)^{1/3}\left(2x+3\right)^{1/2}\left[4(2x+3)+3(3x+5)\right]$

$=\left(3x+5\right)^{1/3}\left(2x+3\right)^{1/2}\left(8x+12+9x+15\right)$

$=\left(3x+5\right)^{1/3}\left(2x+3\right)^{1/2}\left(17x+27\right)$

where $x\geq -\dfrac{3}{2}$.

44

96. $6(6x+1)^{1/3}(4x-3)^{3/2} + 6(6x+1)^{4/3}(4x-3)^{1/2}$

$= 6(6x+1)^{1/3}(4x-3)^{1/2}\left[(4x-3)+(6x+1)\right]$

$= 6(6x+1)^{1/3}(4x-3)^{1/2}(10x-2)$

$= 6(6x+1)^{1/3}(4x-3)^{1/2}(2)(5x-1)$

$= 12(6x+1)^{1/3}(4x-3)^{1/2}(5x-1)$

where $x \geq \dfrac{3}{4}$.

97. $3x^{-1/2} + \dfrac{3}{2}x^{1/2}, x > 0$

$= \dfrac{3}{x^{1/2}} + \dfrac{3}{2}x^{1/2}$

$= \dfrac{3 \cdot 2 + 3x^{1/2} \cdot x^{1/2}}{2x^{1/2}} = \dfrac{6+3x}{2x^{1/2}} = \dfrac{3(x+2)}{2x^{1/2}}$

98. $8x^{1/3} - 4x^{-2/3}, x \neq 0$

$= 8x^{1/3} - \dfrac{4}{x^{2/3}}$

$= \dfrac{8x^{1/3} \cdot x^{2/3} - 4}{x^{2/3}} = \dfrac{8x-4}{x^{2/3}} = \dfrac{4(2x-1)}{x^{2/3}}$

99. $\sqrt{2} \approx 1.41$

```
√(2)
         1.414213562
```

100. $\sqrt{7} \approx 2.65$

```
√(7)
         2.645751311
```

101. $\sqrt[3]{4} \approx 1.59$

```
³√(4)
         1.587401052
```

102. $\sqrt[3]{-5} \approx -1.71$

```
³√(-5)
         -1.709975947
```

103. $\dfrac{2+\sqrt{3}}{3-\sqrt{5}} \approx 4.89$

```
(2+√(3))/(3-√(5)
)
         4.885317931
```

104. $\dfrac{\sqrt{5}-2}{\sqrt{2}+4} \approx 0.04$

```
(√(5)-2)/(√(2)+4
)
         .0436015268
```

105. $\dfrac{3\sqrt[3]{5}-\sqrt{2}}{\sqrt{3}} \approx 2.15$

```
(3*³√(5)-√(2))/√
(3)
         2.145268638
```

106. $\dfrac{2\sqrt{3}-\sqrt[3]{4}}{\sqrt{2}} \approx 1.33$

```
(2√(3)-³√(4))/√(
2)
         1.327027694
```

107. a. $V = 40(12)^2 \sqrt{\dfrac{96}{12} - 0.608}$

$\approx 15,660.4$ gallons

b. $V = 40(1)^2 \sqrt{\dfrac{96}{1} - 0.608} \approx 390.7$ gallons

108. a. $v = \sqrt{64 \cdot 4 + 0^2} = \sqrt{256}$

$= 16$ feet per second

b. $v = \sqrt{64 \cdot 16 + 0^2} = \sqrt{1024}$

$= 32$ feet per second

c. $v = \sqrt{64 \cdot 2 + 4^2} = \sqrt{144}$

$= 12$ feet per second

45

109. $T = 2\pi\sqrt{\dfrac{64}{32}} = 2\pi\sqrt{2} \approx 8.89$ seconds

110. $T = 2\pi\sqrt{\dfrac{16}{32}} = 2\pi\sqrt{\dfrac{1}{2}} = \dfrac{2\pi}{\sqrt{2}}$

$= \pi\sqrt{2} \approx 4.44$ seconds

111. 8 inches = 8/12 = 2/3 feet

$T = 2\pi\sqrt{\dfrac{\left(\dfrac{2}{3}\right)}{32}} = 2\pi\sqrt{\dfrac{1}{48}} = 2\pi\left(\dfrac{1}{4\sqrt{3}}\right)$

$= \dfrac{\pi}{2\sqrt{3}} = \dfrac{\pi\sqrt{3}}{6} \approx 0.91$ seconds

112. 4 inches = 4/12 = 1/3 feet

$T = 2\pi\sqrt{\dfrac{\left(\dfrac{1}{3}\right)}{32}} = 2\pi\sqrt{\dfrac{1}{96}} = 2\pi\left(\dfrac{1}{4\sqrt{6}}\right)$

$= \dfrac{\pi}{2\sqrt{6}} = \dfrac{\pi\sqrt{6}}{12} \approx 0.64$ seconds

113. Answers may vary. One possibility follows: If
$a = -5$, then $\sqrt{a^2} = \sqrt{(-5)^2} = \sqrt{25} = 5 \neq a$.

Since we use the principal square root, which is always non-negative,

$\sqrt{a^2} = \begin{cases} a & \text{if } a \geq 0 \\ -a & \text{if } a < 0 \end{cases}$

which is the definition of $|a|$, so $\sqrt{a^2} = |a|$.

Chapter R Review Exercises

1. $A \cup B = \{1,3,5,7\} \cup \{3,5,6,7,8\}$
$= \{1,3,5,6,7,8\}$

2. $B \cup C = \{3,5,6,7,8\} \cup \{2,3,7,8,9\}$
$= \{2,3,5,6,7,8,9\}$

3. $A \cap C = \{1,3,5,7\} \cap \{2,3,7,8,9\}$
$= \{3,7\}$

4. $A \cap B = \{1,3,5,7\} \cap \{3,5,6,7,8\}$
$= \{3,5,7\}$

5. $\overline{A} = \{2,4,6,8,9\}$

6. $\overline{B} = \{1,2,4,9\}$

7. $B \cap C = \{3,7,8\}$
$\overline{B \cap C} = \{1,2,4,5,6,9\}$

8. $\overline{A \cup B} = \{2,4,9\}$

9. (a) none

(b) $\{-10\}$

(c) $\left\{-10, 0.65, 1.343434..., \dfrac{1}{9}\right\}$

(d) $\{\sqrt{7}\}$

(e) $\left\{-10, 0.65, 1.343434..., \sqrt{7}, \dfrac{1}{9}\right\}$

10. (a) none

(b) $\{0, -5\}$

(c) $\left\{0, -5, \dfrac{1}{3}, 0.59, 1.333...\right\}$

(d) $\left\{2\sqrt{2}, \dfrac{\pi}{2}\right\}$

(e) $\left\{0, -5, \dfrac{1}{3}, 0.59, 1.333..., 2\sqrt{2}, \dfrac{\pi}{2}\right\}$

11. $-6 + 4 \cdot (8 - 3) = -6 + 4(5) = -6 + 20 = 14$

12. $\dfrac{5}{18} + \dfrac{1}{12} = \dfrac{5 \cdot 2 + 1 \cdot 3}{36} = \dfrac{10 + 3}{36} = \dfrac{13}{36}$

13. $\dfrac{4}{3} \cdot \dfrac{9}{16} = \dfrac{4 \cdot 3 \cdot 3}{3 \cdot 4 \cdot 4} = \dfrac{3}{4}$

14. $\dfrac{\dfrac{5}{18}}{\dfrac{11}{27}} = \left(\dfrac{5}{18}\right)\left(\dfrac{27}{11}\right) = \dfrac{5 \cdot 3 \cdot 9}{2 \cdot 9 \cdot 11} = \dfrac{15}{22}$

15. $\sqrt{(-3)^2} = |-3| = 3$

16. $(-3)^5 = -243$

17. $4(x-3) = 4x - 12$

18. $(x-2)(3x+1) = 3x^2 + x - 6x - 2$
$$= 3x^2 - 5x - 2$$

19. $x > 3$

20. $x \le 5$

21. $d(P,Q) = d(-2,3) = |3 - (-2)|$
$$= |3 + 2| = |5| = 5$$

22. $d(Q,R) = d(3,9) = |9 - 3| = |6| = 6$

23. $x = -5, y = 7 \Rightarrow \dfrac{4x}{x+y} = \dfrac{4(-5)}{-5+7} = \dfrac{-20}{2} = -10$

24. $x = -5, y = 7 \Rightarrow |2x - 3y| = |2(-5) - 3(7)|$
$$= |-10 - 21| = |-31| = 31$$

25. $x = -5, y = 7 \Rightarrow 5x^{-1}y^2 = 5(-5)^{-1}(7)^2$
$$= \dfrac{5 \cdot 49}{-5} = -49$$

26. $x = -5, y = 7 \Rightarrow 2x^2 y^{-2} = 2(-5)^2(7)^{-2}$
$$= \dfrac{2 \cdot 25}{49} = \dfrac{50}{49}$$

27. $x = -5 \Rightarrow \sqrt{x^2} = \sqrt{(-5)^2} = |-5| = 5$

28. $x = -5 \Rightarrow \sqrt[3]{x^3} = \sqrt[3]{(-5)^3} = -5$

29. $\dfrac{3}{x-6}$ Domain $= \{x | x \ne 6\}$

30. $\dfrac{x+1}{x+5}$ Domain $= \{x | x \ne -5\}$

31. Since the triangles are similar, corresponding sides have the same ratio and corresponding angles have the same measure. Thus, $A = 90°$, $B = 45°$, $C = 45°$
$$\dfrac{3}{1} = \dfrac{x}{\sqrt{2}}$$
$$1 \cdot x = 3 \cdot \sqrt{2}$$
$$x = 3\sqrt{2}$$

32. Since the triangles are similar, corresponding sides have the same ratio and corresponding angles have the same measure. Thus, $A = 50°$, $B = 70°$, and $C = 60°$.
$$\dfrac{2}{1} = \dfrac{1.5}{x}$$
$$2 \cdot x = 1 \cdot 1.5$$
$$2x = 1.5$$
$$x = \dfrac{1.5}{2} = 0.75$$

33. $(1.5)^4 = 5.0625$

34. $-5x^3$, the coefficient is -5 and the degree is 3

35. $3x^5 + 4x^4 - 2x^3 + 5x - 12$ The coefficients are 3, 4, -2, 0, 5, and -12, and the degree is 5.

36. $3.275 \times 10^5 = 327,500$

37. $(2x^4 - 8x^3 + 5x - 1) + (6x^3 + x^2 + 4)$
$$= 2x^4 - 2x^3 + x^2 + 5x + 3$$

38. $(x^3 + 8x^2 - 3x + 4) - (4x^3 - 7x^2 - 2x + 3)$
$$= x^3 + 8x^2 - 3x + 4 - 4x^3 + 7x^2 + 2x - 3$$
$$= -3x^3 + 15x^2 - x + 1$$

39. $(2x+y)(3x-5y) = 6x^2 - 10xy + 3xy - 5y^2$
$$= 6x^2 - 7xy - 5y^2$$

40. $(2x-5y)(3x+2y) = 6x^2 + 4xy - 15xy - 10y^2$
$$= 6x^2 - 11xy - 10y^2$$

41. $(4x+1)(4x-1) = (4x)^2 + 1^2 = 16x^2 - 1$

42. $(5x+2)^2 = (5x)^2 + 2(5x)(2) + 2^2$
$= 25x^2 + 20x + 4$

43. $(x+1)(x+2)(x-3) = (x^2 + 2x + x + 2)(x-3)$
$= (x^2 + 3x + 2)(x-3)$
$= x^3 - 3x^2 + 3x - 9x + 2x - 6$
$= x^3 - 7x - 6$

44. $(x+1)(x+3)(x-5) = (x^2 + 3x + x + 3)(x-5)$
$= (x^2 + 4x + 3)(x-5)$
$= x^3 - 5x^2 + 4x^2 - 20x + 3x - 15$
$= x^3 - x^2 - 17x - 15$

45.
$$\require{enclose}
\begin{array}{r}
3x^2 + 8x + 25 \\
x-3 \enclose{longdiv}{3x^3 - x^2 + x + 4} \\
\underline{3x^3 - 9x^2} \\
8x^2 + x \\
\underline{8x^2 - 24x} \\
25x + 4 \\
\underline{25x - 75} \\
79
\end{array}$$

Check:
$(x-3)(3x^2 + 8x + 25) + (79)$
$= 3x^3 + 8x^2 + 25x - 9x^2 - 24x - 75 + 79$
$= 3x^3 - x^2 + x + 4$
The quotient is $3x^2 + 8x + 25$; the remainder is 79.

46.
$$\require{enclose}
\begin{array}{r}
2x^2 + x + 3 \\
x-2 \enclose{longdiv}{2x^3 - 3x^2 + x + 1} \\
\underline{2x^3 - 4x^2} \\
x^2 + x \\
\underline{x^2 - 2x} \\
3x + 1 \\
\underline{3x - 6} \\
7
\end{array}$$

Check:
$(x-2)(2x^2 + x + 3) + (7)$
$= 2x^3 + x^2 + 3x - 4x^2 - 2x - 6 + 7$
$= 2x^3 - 3x^2 + x + 1$
The quotient is $2x^2 + x + 3$; the remainder is 7.

47.
$$\require{enclose}
\begin{array}{r}
-3x^2 + 4 \\
x^2 + 1 \enclose{longdiv}{-3x^4 \quad\; + x^2 \quad\quad\; + 2} \\
\underline{-3x^4 \quad\; - 3x^2} \\
4x^2 + 2 \\
\underline{4x^2 + 4} \\
-2
\end{array}$$

Check:
$(x^2 + 1)(-3x^2 + 4) + (-2)$
$= -3x^4 + 4x^2 - 3x^2 + 4 - 2$
$= -3x^4 + x^2 + 2$
The quotient is $-3x^2 + 4$; the remainder is –2.

48.
$$\require{enclose}
\begin{array}{r}
-4x + 1 \\
x^2 - 1 \enclose{longdiv}{-4x^3 + x^2 \quad\quad - 2} \\
\underline{-4x^3 \quad\; + 4x} \\
x^2 - 4x - 2 \\
\underline{x^2 \quad\quad - 1} \\
-4x - 1
\end{array}$$

Check:
$(x^2 - 1)(-4x + 1) + (-4x - 1)$
$= -4x^3 + x^2 + 4x - 1 - 4x - 1$
$= -4x^3 + x^2 - 2$
The quotient is $-4x + 1$; the remainder is $-4x - 1$.

49.

$$
\begin{array}{r}
x^4 - x^3 + x^2 - x + 1 \\
x+1{\overline{\smash{\big)}\,x^5 \qquad\qquad\quad +1}} \\
\underline{x^5 + x^4 } \\
-x^4 \\
\underline{-x^4 - x^3 } \\
x^3 \\
\underline{x^3 + x^2 } \\
-x^2 \\
\underline{-x^2 - x } \\
x + 1 \\
\underline{x + 1} \\
0
\end{array}
$$

Check:

$(x+1)(x^4 - x^3 + x^2 - x + 1) + (0)$

$= x^5 - x^4 + x^3 - x^2 + x + x^4 - x^3 + x^2 - x + 1$

$= x^5 + 1$

The quotient is $x^4 - x^3 + x^2 - x + 1$; the remainder is 0.

50.

$$
\begin{array}{r}
x^4 + x^3 + x^2 + x + 1 \\
x-1{\overline{\smash{\big)}\,x^5 \qquad\qquad\quad -1}} \\
\underline{x^5 - x^4 } \\
x^4 \\
\underline{x^4 - x^3 } \\
x^3 \\
\underline{x^3 - x^2 } \\
x^2 \\
\underline{x^2 - x } \\
x - 1 \\
\underline{x - 1} \\
0
\end{array}
$$

Check:

$(x-1)(x^4 + x^3 + x^2 + x + 1) + (0)$

$= x^5 + x^4 + x^3 + x^2 + x - x^4 - x^3 - x^2 - x - 1$

$= x^5 - 1$

The quotient is $x^4 + x^3 + x^2 + x + 1$; the remainder is 0.

51. $x^2 + 5x - 14 = (x+7)(x-2)$

52. $x^2 - 9x + 14 = (x-7)(x-2)$

53. $6x^2 - 5x - 6 = (3x+2)(2x-3)$

54. $6x^2 + x - 2 = (3x+2)(2x-1)$

55. $3x^2 - 15x - 42 = (3x+6)(x-7)$
$\qquad\qquad\qquad\quad = 3(x+2)(x-7)$

56. $2x^3 + 18x^2 + 28x = 2x(x^2 + 9x + 14)$
$\qquad\qquad\qquad\qquad = 2x(x+7)(x+2)$

57. $8x^3 + 1 = (2x)^3 + 1^3$
$\qquad\qquad = (2x+1)\left((2x)^2 - (2x)(1) + 1^2\right)$
$\qquad\qquad = (2x+1)(4x^2 - 2x + 1)$

58. $27x^3 - 8 = (3x)^3 - 2^3$
$\qquad\qquad = (3x-2)\left((3x)^2 + (3x)(2) + (2)^2\right)$
$\qquad\qquad = (3x-2)(9x^2 + 6x + 4)$

59. $2x^3 + 3x^2 - 2x - 3 = x^2(2x+3) - (2x+3)$
$\qquad\qquad\qquad\qquad\quad = (2x+3)(x^2 - 1)$
$\qquad\qquad\qquad\qquad\quad = (2x+3)(x-1)(x+1)$

60. $2x^3 + 3x^2 + 2x + 3 = x^2(2x+3) + (2x+3)$
$\qquad\qquad\qquad\qquad\quad = (2x+3)(x^2 + 1)$

61. $25x^2 - 4 = (5x)^2 - 2^2 = (5x+2)(5x-2)$

62. $16x^2 - 1 = (4x)^2 - 1^2 = (4x+1)(4x-1)$

63. $9x^2 + 1$; a sum of perfect squares is always prime over the set of real numbers

64. $x^2 - x + 1$; prime since the factors of 1 will not add to produce -1.

65. $x^2 + 8x + 16 = (x+4)(x+4) = (x+4)^2$

49

66. $4x^2 + 12x + 9 = (2x+3)(2x+3) = (2x+3)^2$

67. $\dfrac{2x^2 + 11x + 14}{x^2 - 4} = \dfrac{(2x+7)(x+2)}{(x+2)(x-2)} = \dfrac{2x+7}{x-2}$

68. $\dfrac{x^2 - 5x - 14}{4 - x^2} = \dfrac{(x-7)(x+2)}{(2+x)(2-x)} = \dfrac{x-7}{2-x} = -\dfrac{x-7}{x-2}$

69. $\dfrac{9x^2 - 1}{x^2 - 9} \cdot \dfrac{3x - 9}{9x^2 + 6x + 1}$

$= \dfrac{(3x+1)(3x-1)}{(x+3)(x-3)} \cdot \dfrac{3(x-3)}{(3x+1)^2}$

$= \dfrac{3(3x-1)}{(x+3)(3x+1)}$

70. $\dfrac{x^2 - 25}{x^3 - 4x^2 - 5x} \cdot \dfrac{x^2 + x}{1 - x^2}$

$= \dfrac{(x+5)(x-5)}{x(x^2 - 4x - 5)} \cdot \dfrac{x(x+1)}{(1+x)(1-x)}$

$= \dfrac{(x+5)(x-5)}{x(x-5)(x+1)} \cdot \dfrac{x(x+1)}{(1+x)(1-x)}$

$= \dfrac{(x+5)}{(x+1)(1-x)}$

$= -\dfrac{(x+5)}{(x+1)(x-1)}$

71. $\dfrac{x+1}{x-1} - \dfrac{x-1}{x+1} = \dfrac{(x+1)(x+1) - (x-1)(x-1)}{(x-1)(x+1)}$

$= \dfrac{(x^2 + 2x + 1) - (x^2 - 2x + 1)}{(x-1)(x+1)}$

$= \dfrac{x^2 + 2x + 1 - x^2 + 2x - 1}{(x-1)(x+1)} = \dfrac{4x}{(x-1)(x+1)}$

72. $\dfrac{x}{x+1} - \dfrac{2x}{x+2} = \dfrac{x(x+2) - 2x(x+1)}{(x+1)(x+2)}$

$= \dfrac{x^2 + 2x - 2x^2 - 2x}{(x+1)(x+2)}$

$= \dfrac{-x^2}{(x+1)(x+2)} = -\dfrac{x^2}{(x+1)(x+2)}$

73. $\dfrac{3x+4}{x^2 - 4} - \dfrac{2x-3}{x^2 + 4x + 4}$

$= \dfrac{3x+4}{(x+2)(x-2)} - \dfrac{2x-3}{(x+2)^2}$

$= \dfrac{(3x+4)(x+2) - (2x-3)(x-2)}{(x+2)^2(x-2)}$

$= \dfrac{3x^2 + 6x + 4x + 8 - (2x^2 - 4x - 3x + 6)}{(x+2)^2(x-2)}$

$= \dfrac{3x^2 + 10x + 8 - (2x^2 - 7x + 6)}{(x+2)^2(x-2)}$

$= \dfrac{3x^2 + 10x + 8 - 2x^2 + 7x - 6}{(x+2)^2(x-2)}$

$= \dfrac{x^2 + 17x + 2}{(x+2)^2(x-2)}$

74. $\dfrac{x^2}{2x^2 + 5x - 3} + \dfrac{x^2}{2x^2 - 5x + 2}$

$= \dfrac{x^2}{(2x-1)(x+3)} + \dfrac{x^2}{(2x-1)(x-2)}$

$= \dfrac{x^2(x-2) + x^2(x+3)}{(2x-1)(x+3)(x-2)}$

$= \dfrac{x^3 - 2x^2 + x^3 + 3x^2}{(2x-1)(x+3)(x-2)}$

$= \dfrac{2x^3 + x^2}{(2x-1)(x+3)(x-2)}$

$= \dfrac{x^2(2x+1)}{(2x-1)(x+3)(x-2)}$

75. $\dfrac{\dfrac{x^2 - 1}{x^2 - 5x + 6}}{\dfrac{x+1}{x-2}} = \left(\dfrac{x^2 - 1}{x^2 - 5x + 6}\right)\left(\dfrac{x-2}{x+1}\right)$

$= \left(\dfrac{(x+1)(x-1)}{(x-3)(x-2)}\right)\left(\dfrac{x-2}{x+1}\right) = \dfrac{x-1}{x-3}$

76. $\dfrac{\dfrac{x+4}{3}}{\dfrac{1}{4} + \dfrac{2}{x}} = \dfrac{\dfrac{x+4}{3}}{\dfrac{x+8}{4x}} = \left(\dfrac{x+4}{3}\right)\left(\dfrac{4x}{x+8}\right) = \dfrac{4x(x+4)}{3(x+8)}$

77. $\sqrt{32} = \sqrt{16 \cdot 2} = 4\sqrt{2}$

78. $\sqrt{75} = \sqrt{25 \cdot 3} = 5\sqrt{3}$

79. $\sqrt[3]{-16} = \sqrt[3]{-8 \cdot 2} = -2 \cdot \sqrt[3]{2}$

80. $\sqrt[5]{64} = \sqrt[5]{32 \cdot 2} = 2 \cdot \sqrt[5]{2}$

81. $5\sqrt{8} - 2\sqrt{32} = 5\sqrt{4 \cdot 2} - 2\sqrt{16 \cdot 2}$
$$= 10\sqrt{2} - 8\sqrt{2} = 2\sqrt{2}$$

82. $4\sqrt{12} + 5\sqrt{27} = 4\sqrt{4 \cdot 3} + 5\sqrt{9 \cdot 3}$
$$= 8\sqrt{3} + 15\sqrt{3} = 23\sqrt{3}$$

83. $\dfrac{\left(x^2 y\right)^{-4}}{\left(xy\right)^{-3}} = \dfrac{x^{-8} y^{-4}}{x^{-3} y^{-3}} = \dfrac{x^3 y^3}{x^8 y^4}$
$$= x^{3-8} y^{3-4} = x^{-5} y^{-1} = \dfrac{1}{x^5 y}$$

84. $\left(\dfrac{x^2 y^2}{x^{-1}}\right)^2 = \left(x^{2-(-1)} y^2\right)^2 = \left(x^3 y^2\right)^2$
$$= x^{3 \cdot 2} y^{2 \cdot 2} = x^6 y^4$$

85. $\left(25 x^{-4/3} y^{-2/3}\right)^{3/2}$
$$= \left(5^2 x^{-4/3} y^{-2/3}\right)^{3/2}$$
$$= \left(5^2\right)^{3/2} \left(x^{-4/3}\right)^{3/2} \left(y^{-2/3}\right)^{3/2}$$
$$= 5^3 x^{-2} y^{-1} = \dfrac{125}{x^2 y}$$

86. $\left(27 x^{-3/2} y^{5/2}\right)^{2/3} = \left(3^3 x^{-3/2} y^{5/2}\right)^{2/3}$
$$= 3^{3 \cdot 2/3} x^{(-3/2)(2/3)} y^{(5/2)(2/3)}$$
$$= 3^2 x^{-1} y^{5/3} = \dfrac{9 y^{5/3}}{x}$$

87. $\sqrt{\dfrac{9x^2}{25y^4}} = \dfrac{\sqrt{9x^2}}{\sqrt{25y^4}} = \dfrac{3x}{5y^2}$

88. $\dfrac{\sqrt{2x}\sqrt{5xy^3}}{\sqrt{10y}} = \dfrac{\sqrt{(2x)5xy^3}}{\sqrt{10y}}$
$$= \dfrac{\sqrt{10x^2 y^3}}{\sqrt{10y}} = \sqrt{\dfrac{10x^2 y^3}{10y}}$$
$$= \sqrt{\dfrac{x^2 y^2}{1}} = xy$$

89. $\sqrt[3]{27 x^4 y^{12}} = \sqrt[3]{3^3 x^3 \cdot x \left(y^4\right)^3} = 3xy^4 \sqrt[3]{x}$

90. $\dfrac{\sqrt[4]{243 x^5 y}}{\sqrt[4]{3 x y^9}} = \sqrt[4]{\dfrac{243 x^5 y}{3 x y^9}} = \sqrt[4]{\dfrac{81 x^4}{y^8}}$
$$= \dfrac{\sqrt[4]{81 x^4}}{\sqrt[4]{y^8}} = \dfrac{3x}{y^2}$$

91. $\dfrac{4}{\sqrt{5}} = \dfrac{4}{\sqrt{5}} \cdot \dfrac{\sqrt{5}}{\sqrt{5}} = \dfrac{4\sqrt{5}}{5}$

92. $\dfrac{-2}{\sqrt{3}} = \dfrac{-2}{\sqrt{3}} \cdot \dfrac{\sqrt{3}}{\sqrt{3}} = \dfrac{-2\sqrt{3}}{3} = -\dfrac{2\sqrt{3}}{3}$

93. $\dfrac{2}{1-\sqrt{2}} = \dfrac{2}{1-\sqrt{2}} \cdot \dfrac{1+\sqrt{2}}{1+\sqrt{2}} = \dfrac{2\left(1+\sqrt{2}\right)}{1-\left(\sqrt{2}\right)^2}$
$$= \dfrac{2\left(1+\sqrt{2}\right)}{1-2} = \dfrac{2\left(1+\sqrt{2}\right)}{-1}$$
$$= -2\left(1+\sqrt{2}\right)$$

94. $\dfrac{-4}{1+\sqrt{3}} = \dfrac{-4}{1+\sqrt{3}} \cdot \dfrac{1-\sqrt{3}}{1-\sqrt{3}} = \dfrac{-4\left(1-\sqrt{3}\right)}{1-\left(\sqrt{3}\right)^2}$
$$= \dfrac{-4\left(1-\sqrt{3}\right)}{1-3} = \dfrac{-4\left(1-\sqrt{3}\right)}{-2}$$
$$= 2\left(1-\sqrt{3}\right)$$

95. $\dfrac{1+\sqrt{5}}{1-\sqrt{5}} = \dfrac{1+\sqrt{5}}{1-\sqrt{5}} \cdot \dfrac{1+\sqrt{5}}{1+\sqrt{5}}$

$\qquad = \dfrac{1+2\sqrt{5}+\left(\sqrt{5}\right)^2}{1-\left(\sqrt{5}\right)^2} = \dfrac{1+2\sqrt{5}+5}{1-5}$

$\qquad = \dfrac{6+2\sqrt{5}}{-4} = \dfrac{-3-\sqrt{5}}{2}$

$\qquad = -\dfrac{3+\sqrt{5}}{2}$

96. $\dfrac{4\sqrt{3}+2}{2\sqrt{3}+1} = \dfrac{4\sqrt{3}+2}{2\sqrt{3}+1} \cdot \dfrac{2\sqrt{3}-1}{2\sqrt{3}-1}$

$\qquad = \dfrac{8\left(\sqrt{3}\right)^2 - 4\sqrt{3}+4\sqrt{3}-2}{\left(2\sqrt{3}\right)^2-(1)^2} = \dfrac{8\cdot 3 - 2}{4\cdot 3 - 1}$

$\qquad = \dfrac{24-2}{12-1} = \dfrac{22}{11} = 2$

97. $\left(2+x^2\right)^{1/2} + x\cdot\dfrac{1}{2}\left(2+x^2\right)^{-1/2}\cdot 2x$

$\qquad = \left(2+x^2\right)^{1/2} + \dfrac{2x^2}{2\left(2+x^2\right)^{1/2}}$

$\qquad = \left(2+x^2\right)^{1/2} + \dfrac{x^2}{\left(2+x^2\right)^{1/2}}$

$\qquad = \dfrac{\left(2+x^2\right)^{1/2}\left(2+x^2\right)^{1/2} + x^2}{\left(2+x^2\right)^{1/2}}$

$\qquad = \dfrac{2+x^2+x^2}{\left(2+x^2\right)^{1/2}} = \dfrac{2+2x^2}{\left(2+x^2\right)^{1/2}}$

$\qquad = \dfrac{2\left(1+x^2\right)}{\left(2+x^2\right)^{1/2}}$

98. $\left(x^2+4\right)^{2/3} + x\cdot\dfrac{2}{3}\left(x^2+4\right)^{-1/3}\cdot 2x$

$\qquad = \left(x^2+4\right)^{2/3} + \dfrac{4x^2}{3\left(x^2+4\right)^{1/3}}$

$\qquad = \dfrac{3\left(x^2+4\right)^{1/3}\left(x^2+4\right)^{2/3} + 4x^2}{3\left(x^2+4\right)^{1/3}}$

$\qquad = \dfrac{3\left(x^2+4\right)+4x^2}{3\left(x^2+4\right)^{1/3}} = \dfrac{3x^2+12+4x^2}{3\left(x^2+4\right)^{1/3}}$

$\qquad = \dfrac{7x^2+12}{3\left(x^2+4\right)^{1/3}}$

99. $\dfrac{\left(x+4\right)^{1/2}\cdot 2x - x^2\cdot\dfrac{1}{2}\left(x+4\right)^{-1/2}}{x+4}$

$\qquad = \dfrac{\left(x+4\right)^{1/2}\cdot 2x - \dfrac{x^2}{2\left(x+4\right)^{1/2}}}{x+4}$

$\qquad = \dfrac{\dfrac{2\left(x+4\right)^{1/2}\left(x+4\right)^{1/2}\cdot 2x - x^2}{2\left(x+4\right)^{1/2}}}{x+4}$

$\qquad = \dfrac{\dfrac{2\left(x+4\right)\cdot 2x - x^2}{2\left(x+4\right)^{1/2}}}{x+4} = \dfrac{\dfrac{4x^2+16x-x^2}{2\left(x+4\right)^{1/2}}}{x+4}$

$\qquad = \left(\dfrac{3x^2+16x}{2\left(x+4\right)^{1/2}}\right)\left(\dfrac{1}{x+4}\right) = \dfrac{3x^2+16x}{2\left(x+4\right)^{3/2}}$

$\qquad = \dfrac{x\left(3x+16\right)}{2\left(x+4\right)^{3/2}}$

100.
$$\frac{\left(x^2+4\right)^{1/2}\cdot 2x - x^2\cdot\dfrac{1}{2}\left(x^2+4\right)^{-1/2}\cdot 2x}{x^2+4}$$

$$=\frac{\left(x^2+4\right)^{1/2}\cdot 2x - \dfrac{x^3}{\left(x^2+4\right)^{1/2}}}{x^2+4}$$

$$=\frac{\dfrac{\left(x^2+4\right)^{1/2}\left(x^2+4\right)^{1/2}\cdot 2x - x^3}{\left(x^2+4\right)^{1/2}}}{x^2+4}$$

$$=\frac{\dfrac{\left(x^2+4\right)\cdot 2x - x^3}{2\left(x^2+4\right)^{1/2}}}{x^2+4}=\frac{\dfrac{2x^3+8x-x^3}{\left(x^2+4\right)^{1/2}}}{x^2+4}$$

$$=\left(\frac{2x^3+8x}{\left(x^2+4\right)^{1/2}}\right)\left(\frac{1}{x^2+4}\right)$$

$$=\frac{x\left(x^2+8\right)}{\left(x^2+4\right)^{3/2}}$$

101.
$$\frac{\left(\dfrac{x^2}{\sqrt{x^2-1}}-\sqrt{x^2-1}\right)}{x^2}=\frac{\dfrac{x^2-\sqrt{x^2-1}\cdot\sqrt{x^2-1}}{\sqrt{x^2-1}}}{x^2}$$

$$=\frac{\dfrac{x^2-\left(x^2-1\right)}{\sqrt{x^2-1}}}{x^2}=\left(\frac{x^2-x^2+1}{\sqrt{x^2-1}}\right)\left(\frac{1}{x^2}\right)$$

$$=\left(\frac{1}{\sqrt{x^2-1}}\right)\left(\frac{1}{x^2}\right)=\frac{1}{x^2\cdot\sqrt{x^2-1}}$$

102.
$$\frac{\left(\dfrac{4+x^2}{2\sqrt{x}}-2x\sqrt{x}\right)}{\left(4+x^2\right)^2}=\frac{\left(\dfrac{4+x^2-2\sqrt{x}\cdot 2x\sqrt{x}}{2\sqrt{x}}\right)}{\left(4+x^2\right)^2}$$

$$=\frac{\left(\dfrac{4+x^2-4x^2}{2\sqrt{x}}\right)}{\left(4+x^2\right)^2}=\left(\frac{4-3x^2}{2\sqrt{x}}\right)\left(\frac{1}{\left(4+x^2\right)^2}\right)$$

$$=\frac{4-3x^2}{2\sqrt{x}\left(4+x^2\right)^2}$$

103. $3\left(x^2+4\right)^{4/3}+x\cdot 4\left(x^2+4\right)^{1/3}\cdot 2x$

$$=\left(x^2+4\right)^{1/3}\left[3\left(x^2+4\right)+8x^2\right]$$

$$=\left(x^2+4\right)^{1/3}\left[3x^2+12+8x^2\right]$$

$$=\left(x^2+4\right)^{1/3}\left(11x^2+12\right)$$

104. $2x\left(3x+5\right)^{4/3}+x^2\cdot 4\left(3x+5\right)^{1/3}$

$$=2x\left(3x+5\right)^{1/3}\left[\left(3x+5\right)+2x\right]$$

$$=2x\left(3x+5\right)^{1/3}\left(5x+5\right)$$

$$=2x\left(3x+5\right)^{1/3}\cdot 5\left(x+1\right)$$

$$=10x\left(3x+5\right)^{1/3}\left(x+1\right)$$

105. $281,421,906 = 2.81421906\times 10^8$

106. $5^2+8^2=\left(\text{hypotenuse}\right)^2$

$$\sqrt{5^2+8^2}=\text{hypotenuse}$$

$$\sqrt{25+64}=\text{hypotenuse}$$

$$\sqrt{89}=\text{hypotenuse}$$

107. $12^2+16^2=144+256=400=20^2$, therefore we have a right triangle by the converse of the Pythagorean Theorem.

108. $C(x)=3000+6x-\dfrac{x^2}{1000}$

a. $C(1000)=3000+6(1000)-\dfrac{(1000)^2}{1000}$

$$=3000+6000-1000$$

$$=\$8000$$

b. $C(3000)=3000+6(3000)-\dfrac{(3000)^2}{1000}$

$$=3000+18,000-9000$$

$$=\$12,000$$

109. Total annual earnings per share
= (1st quarter earnings) + (2nd quarter earnings) + (3rd quarter earnings) + (4th quarter earnings)
= 1.2 − 0.75 − 0.30 + 0.20 = \$0.35 per share.

110. The total area enclosed by the window is given by

Total Area = area of the triangle + area of the rectangle

$$\text{Total Area} = \frac{1}{2}(\text{base})(\text{height}) + (\text{length})(\text{width})$$

By the Pythagorean Theorem we have

$$(2.5)^2 + h^2 = (4)^2$$

$$h^2 = (4)^2 - (2.5)^2$$

$$= 16 - 6.25$$

$$h = \sqrt{9.75}$$

$$\text{Total Area} = \frac{1}{2}(5)\left(\sqrt{9.75}\right) + (6)(5) \approx 37.81 \text{ square}$$

feet.

The perimeter of the window $= 4 + 4 + 6 + 5 + 6 = 25$. So the window requires 25 feet of wood frame.

111. Pond Area = area of outer circle − area of inner circle

$$= \pi(5)^2 - \pi(3)^2 = 25\pi - 9\pi$$

$$= 16\pi \approx 50.27 \text{ square feet}$$

Outer Perimeter $= 2\pi(\text{outer radius})$

$$= 2\pi(5) = 10\pi \approx 31.42 \text{ feet}$$

112. Recall that 1 mile = 5280 feet. Consider the diagram (not drawn to scale) showing the bridge at point B, relative to the center of Earth, using the radius of Earth as 3960 miles. Let P refer to the furthest point on the horizon from which the bridge is visible. Note also that

$$35,000 \text{ feet} = \frac{35,000}{5280} \text{ miles.}$$

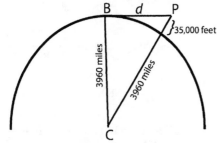

Apply the Pythagorean Theorem to the right triangle, $\triangle CBP$,

$$(3960)^2 + (d)^2 = \left(3960 + \frac{35,000}{5280}\right)^2$$

$$(d)^2 = \left(3960 + \frac{35,000}{5280}\right)^2 - (3960)^2$$

$$\Rightarrow d = \sqrt{\left(3960 + \frac{35,000}{5280}\right)^2 - (3960)^2}$$

$$\approx 229.22 \text{ miles.}$$

Therefore, the bridge can be seen at point P on the horizon, whenever point P is less than or equal to 229.22 miles away from the bridge. So the pilot could see the bridge when the plane was 139 miles from San Francisco. Moreover, he could see a maximum distance of 229.22 miles.

113. Answers will vary.

Chapter R Test

1. (a) Recall that the *Natural Numbers* are also called the *Counting Numbers*. These are the numbers 1, 2, 3, 4, …
   For the given set, the only natural number is 7. $\{7\}$

   (b) Recall that the set of *Integers* is the set of positive and negative whole numbers and 0. $\{\ldots, -3, -2, -1, 0, 1, 2, 3, \ldots\}$
   For the given set, the only integers are 0 and 7. Notice that this includes our result from part (a) because the set of natural numbers is a subset of the set of integers. $\{0, 7\}$

   (c) Recall that a rational number can be written as a ratio of two integers. In decimal form, this set contains terminating decimals and repeating decimals.
   For the given set, the only rational numbers are 0, 1.2, 7, and $\frac{1}{2}$. Notice that this includes our result from part (b) because the set of integers is a subset of the set of rational numbers. $\left\{0, 1.2, 7, \frac{1}{2}\right\}$

(d) Recall that an irrational number is a real number that cannot be written as the ratio of two integers. In decimal form, this set contains decimals that do not terminate and do not repeat.

For the given set, the only irrational numbers are $\sqrt{2}$ and π.

$$\left\{\sqrt{2}, \pi\right\}$$

(e) Recall that the set of real numbers is the union of the set of irrational numbers and the set of rational numbers. In parts (c) and (d), we listed each entry from our set as either rational or irrational, therefore all the numbers in the given set are real numbers.

$$\left\{0, 1.2, \sqrt{2}, 7, \frac{1}{2}, \pi\right\}$$

2. a. $3x^{-1}y^2$

$$3(-3)^{-1}(4)^2 = 3 \cdot \frac{1}{-3} \cdot 16 = -1 \cdot 16 = -16$$

b. $\left|2x - 3y\right| = \left|2(-3) - 3(4)\right|$

$$= \left|-6 - 12\right| = \left|-18\right|$$
$$= 18$$

c. $\sqrt{x^2 + y^2} = \sqrt{(-3)^2 + (4)^2}$

$$= \sqrt{9 + 16} = \sqrt{25}$$
$$= 5$$

d. $5x^3 - 3x^2 + 2x - 6$

$$= 5(-3)^3 - 3(-3)^2 + 2(-3) - 6$$
$$= 5(-27) - 3(9) + 2(-3) - 6$$
$$= -135 - 27 - 6 - 6$$
$$= -174$$

3. Since the two triangles are similar, their corresponding angle measures are the same. Therefore, we have

$A = 40°$, $B = 95°$, and $C = 45°$

For similar triangles, the ratio of the lengths of corresponding sides is the same.

$$\frac{1}{2} = \frac{x}{3} \text{ or } x = \frac{3}{2} \text{ units}$$

4. a. Remember to distribute the minus sign across the second polynomial.

$$\left(-2x^3 + 4x^2 - 6x + 10\right) - \left(6x^3 - 7x^2 + 8x - 1\right)$$
$$= -2x^3 + 4x^2 - 6x + 10 - 6x^3 + 7x^2 - 8x + 1$$
$$= -2x^3 - 6x^3 + 4x^2 + 7x^2 - 6x - 8x + 10 + 1$$
$$= -8x^3 + 11x^2 - 14x + 11$$

b. Since we are multiplying two binomials, we multiply by first distributing each term from the first binomial.

$$(2x - 3)(-5x + 2) = 2x(-5x + 2) - 3(-5x + 2)$$
$$= 2x \cdot -5x + 2x \cdot 2 - 3 \cdot (-5x) - 3 \cdot 2$$
$$= -10x^2 + 4x + 15x - 6$$
$$= -10x^2 + 19x - 6$$

5. a. $x^2 - 6x + 8$

Since the leading coefficient is 1, we are looking for two factors of 8 whose sum is -6. Since the product is positive and the sum is negative, the two factors must be negative. The factors we are looking for are -2 and -6. Thus, we can factor the expression as $x^2 - 6x + 8 = (x - 2)(x - 4)$.

b. $4x^2 - 25$

We notice that this is really the difference of two squares. That is, we can rewrite this as $(2x)^2 - (5)^2$. To factor this expression we use the special form $a^2 - b^2 = (a - b)(a + b)$. This gives us

$$4x^2 - 25 = (2x - 5)(2x + 5)$$

c. $6x^2 - 19x - 7$

Here we have the form $Ax^2 + Bx + C$ with $A = 6$, $B = -19$, and $C = -7$. We find that $AC = (6)(-7) = -42$. Therefore, we are looking for two factors of -42 whose sum is -19. Since the product is negative, the two factors have opposite signs. Since the sum is also negative, the factor with the larger absolute value must be negative.

$1, -42 \quad 2, -21 \quad 3, -14 \quad 6, -7$

The factors 2 and -21 sum to -19.

$$6x^2 + 2x - 21x - 7$$
$$2x(3x + 1) - 7(3x + 1)$$
$$(3x + 1)(2x - 7)$$

6. Since we are dividing the polynomial by $x - c$ where $c = 2$, we can use synthetic division.

$$2\overline{)1 \quad -3 \quad 8 \quad -10}$$
$$\underline{ \quad 2 \quad -2 \quad 12}$$
$$1 \quad -1 \quad 6 \quad 2$$

Therefore, the quotient is $x^2 - x + 6$ and the remainder is 2. That is,

$$\frac{x^3 - 3x^2 + 8x - 10}{x - 2} = x^2 - x + 6 + \frac{2}{x - 2}$$

7. a. $\sqrt{27} = \sqrt{9 \cdot 3} = \sqrt{9} \cdot \sqrt{3} = 3\sqrt{3}$

b. $\sqrt[3]{-8} = \sqrt[3]{(-2)^3} = -2$

c. $\dfrac{\left(xy^2\right)^{-3}}{\left(x^2 y\right)^{-2}} = \dfrac{x^{-3} \cdot y^{2(-3)}}{x^{2(-2)} \cdot y^{-2}} = \dfrac{x^{-3} \cdot y^{-6}}{x^{-4} \cdot y^{-2}}$

$$= x^{-3 - (-4)} \cdot y^{-6 - (-2)}$$

$$= x^1 \cdot y^{-4} = \frac{x}{y^4}$$

d. $\left(16 x^{4/3} y^{-2/3}\right)^{3/2}$

$$= (16)^{3/2} \cdot \left(x^{4/3}\right)^{3/2} \cdot \left(y^{-2/3}\right)^{3/2}$$

$$= \left(\sqrt{16}\right)^3 \cdot x^{\frac{4}{3}\frac{3}{2}} \cdot y^{-\frac{2}{3}\frac{3}{2}}$$

$$= 4^3 x^2 y^{-1} = \frac{64 x^2}{y}$$

8. To rationalize the denominator, we need to multiply the numerator and denominator by $5 - \sqrt{3}$ to eliminate the radical in the denominator.

$$\frac{3}{5 + \sqrt{3}} \cdot \frac{5 - \sqrt{3}}{5 - \sqrt{3}} = \frac{3 \cdot 5 - 3 \cdot \sqrt{3}}{5^2 - \left(\sqrt{3}\right)^2}$$

$$= \frac{15 - 3\sqrt{3}}{25 - 3}$$

$$= \frac{15 - 3\sqrt{3}}{22}$$

9. We want to graph the set of values for x such that they are greater than 3. On a number line we plot 3 with a parenthesis and then draw an arrow to the right. We use a parenthesis because the inequality is strict.

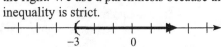

10. If $a \cdot b = 0$ then either $a = 0$ or $b = 0$ or both.

11. Looking at the diagram, we can see a rectangle, the pool, inside another rectangle. To find the area of the deck, we can subtract the area of the pool from the area of the larger rectangle (pool and deck).
The width of the larger rectangle is $10 + 3 + 3 = 16$ feet and the length is $20 + 3 + 3 = 26$ feet. Note that we add 3 twice because the deck is on each side of the pool.
The area of the deck is then
$16 \cdot 26 - 10 \cdot 20 = 416 - 200 = 216$ square feet.
The fencing will go along the outside of the larger rectangle so we simply need to determine the perimeter of the larger rectangle to find the required amount of fencing.
$16 + 16 + 26 + 26 = 32 + 52 = 84$ feet of fencing is needed.

Chapter 1
Equations and Inequalities

Section 1.1

1. Distributive

2. Zero-Product

3. $\{x \mid x \neq 4\}$

4. False. Multiplying both sides of an equation by zero will not result in an equivalent equation.

5. identity

6. linear; first-degree

7. False. The solution is $\dfrac{8}{3}$.

8. True

9. $7x = 21$

$\dfrac{7x}{7} = \dfrac{21}{7}$

$x = 3$

The solution set is $\{3\}$.

10. $6x = -24$

$\dfrac{6x}{6} = \dfrac{-24}{6}$

$x = -4$

The solution set is $\{-4\}$.

11. $\quad 3x + 15 = 0$

$3x + 15 - 15 = 0 - 15$

$3x = -15$

$\dfrac{3x}{3} = \dfrac{-15}{3}$

$x = -5$

The solution set is $\{-5\}$.

12. $\quad 6x + 18 = 0$

$6x + 18 - 18 = 0 - 18$

$6x = -18$

$\dfrac{6x}{6} = \dfrac{-18}{6}$

$x = -3$

The solution set is $\{-3\}$.

13. $\quad 2x - 3 = 0$

$2x - 3 + 3 = 0 + 3$

$2x = 3$

$\dfrac{2x}{2} = \dfrac{3}{2}$

$x = \dfrac{3}{2}$

The solution set is $\left\{\dfrac{3}{2}\right\}$.

14. $\quad 3x + 4 = 0$

$3x + 4 - 4 = 0 - 4$

$3x = -4$

$\dfrac{3x}{3} = \dfrac{-4}{3}$

$x = -\dfrac{4}{3}$

The solution set is $\left\{-\dfrac{4}{3}\right\}$.

15. $\quad \dfrac{1}{3}x = \dfrac{5}{12}$

$3\left(\dfrac{1}{3}x\right) = 3\left(\dfrac{5}{12}\right)$

$x = \dfrac{5}{4}$

The solution set is $\left\{\dfrac{5}{4}\right\}$.

16.
$$\frac{2}{3}x = \frac{9}{2}$$
$$6\left(\frac{2}{3}x\right) = 6\left(\frac{9}{2}\right)$$
$$4x = 27$$
$$\frac{4x}{4} = \frac{27}{4}$$
$$x = \frac{27}{4}$$

The solution set is $\left\{\frac{27}{4}\right\}$.

17.
$$3x + 4 = x$$
$$3x + 4 - 4 = x - 4$$
$$3x = x - 4$$
$$3x - x = x - 4 - x$$
$$2x = -4$$
$$\frac{2x}{2} = \frac{-4}{2}$$
$$x = -2$$

The solution set is $\{-2\}$.

18.
$$2x + 9 = 5x$$
$$2x + 9 - 9 = 5x - 9$$
$$2x = 5x - 9$$
$$2x - 5x = 5x - 9 - 5x$$
$$-3x = -9$$
$$\frac{-3x}{-3} = \frac{-9}{-3}$$
$$x = 3$$

The solution set is $\{3\}$.

19.
$$2t - 6 = 3 - t$$
$$2t - 6 + 6 = 3 - t + 6$$
$$2t = 9 - t$$
$$2t + t = 9 - t + t$$
$$3t = 9$$
$$\frac{3t}{3} = \frac{9}{3}$$
$$t = 3$$

The solution set is $\{3\}$.

20.
$$5y + 6 = -18 - y$$
$$5y + 6 - 6 = -18 - y - 6$$
$$5y = -y - 24$$
$$5y + y = -y - 24 + y$$
$$6y = -24$$
$$\frac{6y}{6} = \frac{-24}{6}$$
$$y = -4$$

The solution set is $\{-4\}$.

21.
$$6 - x = 2x + 9$$
$$6 - x - 6 = 2x + 9 - 6$$
$$-x = 2x + 3$$
$$-x - 2x = 2x + 3 - 2x$$
$$-3x = 3$$
$$\frac{-3x}{-3} = \frac{3}{-3}$$
$$x = -1$$

The solution set is $\{-1\}$.

22.
$$3 - 2x = 2 - x$$
$$3 - 2x - 3 = 2 - x - 3$$
$$-2x = -x - 1$$
$$-2x + x = -x - 1 + x$$
$$-x = -1$$
$$\frac{-x}{-1} = \frac{-1}{-1}$$
$$x = 1$$

The solution set is $\{1\}$.

23.
$$3 + 2n = 4n + 7$$
$$3 + 2n - 3 = 4n + 7 - 3$$
$$2n = 4n + 4$$
$$2n - 4n = 4n + 4 - 4n$$
$$-2n = 4$$
$$\frac{-2n}{-2} = \frac{4}{-2}$$
$$n = -2$$

The solution set is $\{-2\}$.

24.
$$6 - 2m = 3m + 1$$
$$6 - 2m - 6 = 3m + 1 - 6$$
$$-2m = 3m - 5$$
$$-2m - 3m = 3m - 5 - 3m$$
$$-5m = -5$$
$$\frac{-5m}{-5} = \frac{-5}{-5}$$
$$m = 1$$
The solution set is $\{1\}$.

25.
$$2(3 + 2x) = 3(x - 4)$$
$$6 + 4x = 3x - 12$$
$$6 + 4x - 6 = 3x - 12 - 6$$
$$4x = 3x - 18$$
$$4x - 3x = 3x - 18 - 3x$$
$$x = -18$$
The solution set is $\{-18\}$.

26.
$$3(2 - x) = 2x - 1$$
$$6 - 3x = 2x - 1$$
$$6 - 3x - 6 = 2x - 1 - 6$$
$$-3x = 2x - 7$$
$$-3x - 2x = 2x - 7 - 2x$$
$$-5x = -7$$
$$\frac{-5x}{-5} = \frac{-7}{-5}$$
$$x = \frac{7}{5}$$
The solution set is $\left\{\frac{7}{5}\right\}$.

27.
$$8x - (3x + 2) = 3x - 10$$
$$8x - 3x - 2 = 3x - 10$$
$$5x - 2 = 3x - 10$$
$$5x - 2 + 2 = 3x - 10 + 2$$
$$5x = 3x - 8$$
$$5x - 3x = 3x - 8 - 3x$$
$$2x = -8$$
$$\frac{2x}{2} = \frac{-8}{2}$$
$$x = -4$$
The solution set is $\{-4\}$.

28.
$$7 - (2x - 1) = 10$$
$$7 - 2x + 1 = 10$$
$$8 - 2x = 10$$
$$8 - 2x - 8 = 10 - 8$$
$$-2x = 2$$
$$\frac{-2x}{-2} = \frac{2}{-2}$$
$$x = -1$$
The solution set is $\{-1\}$.

29.
$$\frac{3}{2}x + 2 = \frac{1}{2} - \frac{1}{2}x$$
$$2\left(\frac{3}{2}x + 2\right) = 2\left(\frac{1}{2} - \frac{1}{2}x\right)$$
$$3x + 4 = 1 - x$$
$$3x + 4 - 4 = 1 - x - 4$$
$$3x = -3 - x$$
$$3x + x = -3 - x + x$$
$$4x = -3$$
$$\frac{4x}{4} = \frac{-3}{4}$$
$$x = -\frac{3}{4}$$
The solution set is $\left\{-\frac{3}{4}\right\}$.

30.
$$\frac{1}{3}x = 2 - \frac{2}{3}x$$
$$3\left(\frac{1}{3}x\right) = 3\left(2 - \frac{2}{3}x\right)$$
$$x = 6 - 2x$$
$$x + 2x = 6 - 2x + 2x$$
$$3x = 6$$
$$\frac{3x}{3} = \frac{6}{3}$$
$$x = 2$$
The solution set is $\{2\}$.

31.
$$\frac{1}{2}x - 5 = \frac{3}{4}x$$
$$4\left(\frac{1}{2}x - 5\right) = 4\left(\frac{3}{4}x\right)$$
$$2x - 20 = 3x$$
$$2x - 20 - 2x = 3x - 2x$$
$$-20 = x$$
$$x = -20$$
The solution set is $\{-20\}$.

32.
$$1 - \frac{1}{2}x = 6$$
$$2\left(1 - \frac{1}{2}x\right) = 2(6)$$
$$2 - x = 12$$
$$2 - x - 2 = 12 - 2$$
$$-x = 10$$
$$\frac{-x}{-1} = \frac{10}{-1}$$
$$x = -10$$
The solution set is $\{-10\}$.

33.
$$\frac{2}{3}p = \frac{1}{2}p + \frac{1}{3}$$
$$6\left(\frac{2}{3}p\right) = 6\left(\frac{1}{2}p + \frac{1}{3}\right)$$
$$4p = 3p + 2$$
$$4p - 3p = 3p + 2 - 3p$$
$$p = 2$$
The solution set is $\{2\}$.

34.
$$\frac{1}{2} - \frac{1}{3}p = \frac{4}{3}$$
$$6\left(\frac{1}{2} - \frac{1}{3}p\right) = 6\left(\frac{4}{3}\right)$$
$$3 - 2p = 8$$
$$3 - 2p - 3 = 8 - 3$$
$$-2p = 5$$
$$\frac{-2p}{-2} = \frac{5}{-2}$$
$$p = -\frac{5}{2}$$
The solution set is $\left\{-\frac{5}{2}\right\}$.

35.
$$0.9t = 0.4 + 0.1t$$
$$0.9t - 0.1t = 0.4 + 0.1t - 0.1t$$
$$0.8t = 0.4$$
$$\frac{0.8t}{0.8} = \frac{0.4}{0.8}$$
$$t = 0.5$$
The solution set is $\{0.5\}$.

36.
$$0.9t = 1 + t$$
$$0.9t - t = 1 + t - t$$
$$-0.1t = 1$$
$$\frac{-0.1t}{-0.1} = \frac{1}{-0.1}$$
$$t = -10$$
The solution set is $\{-10\}$.

37.
$$\frac{x+1}{3} + \frac{x+2}{7} = 2$$
$$21\left(\frac{x+1}{3} + \frac{x+2}{7}\right) = 21(2)$$
$$7(x+1) + (3)(x+2) = 42$$
$$7x + 7 + 3x + 6 = 42$$
$$10x + 13 = 42$$
$$10x + 13 - 13 = 42 - 13$$
$$10x = 29$$
$$\frac{10x}{10} = \frac{29}{10}$$
$$x = \frac{29}{10}$$
The solution set is $\left\{\frac{29}{10}\right\}$.

38.
$$\frac{2x+1}{3} + 16 = 3x$$
$$3\left(\frac{2x+1}{3} + 16\right) = 3(3x)$$
$$2x + 1 + 48 = 9x$$
$$2x + 49 = 9x$$
$$2x + 49 - 2x = 9x - 2x$$
$$49 = 7x$$
$$\frac{49}{7} = \frac{7x}{7}$$
$$x = 7$$
The solution set is $\{7\}$.

39.
$$\frac{2}{y}+\frac{4}{y}=3$$

$$y\left(\frac{2}{y}+\frac{4}{y}\right)=y(3)$$

$$2+4=3y$$

$$6=3y$$

$$\frac{6}{3}=\frac{3y}{3}$$

$$2=y$$

Since $y = 2$ does not cause a denominator to equal zero, the solution set is $\{2\}$.

40.
$$\frac{4}{y}-5=\frac{5}{2y}$$

$$2y\left(\frac{4}{y}-5\right)=2y\left(\frac{5}{2y}\right)$$

$$8-10y=5$$

$$8-10y-8=5-8$$

$$-10y=-3$$

$$\frac{-10y}{-10}=\frac{-3}{-10}$$

$$y=\frac{3}{10}$$

Since $y=\frac{3}{10}$ does not cause a denominator to equal zero, the solution set is $\left\{\frac{3}{10}\right\}$.

41.
$$\frac{1}{2}+\frac{2}{x}=\frac{3}{4}$$

$$4x\left(\frac{1}{2}+\frac{2}{x}\right)=4x\left(\frac{3}{4}\right)$$

$$2x+8=3x$$

$$2x+8-2x=3x-2x$$

$$8=x$$

Since $x = 8$ does not cause any denominator to equal zero, the solution set is $\{8\}$.

42.
$$\frac{3}{x}-\frac{1}{3}=\frac{1}{6}$$

$$6x\left(\frac{3}{x}-\frac{1}{3}\right)=6x\left(\frac{1}{6}\right)$$

$$18-2x=x$$

$$18-2x+2x=x+2x$$

$$18=3x$$

$$\frac{18}{3}=\frac{3x}{3}$$

$$6=x$$

Since $x = 6$ does not cause a denominator to equal zero, the solution set is $\{6\}$.

43.
$$(x+7)(x-1)=(x+1)^2$$

$$x^2+6x-7=x^2+2x+1$$

$$x^2+6x-7-x^2=x^2+2x+1-x^2$$

$$6x-7=2x+1$$

$$6x-7+7=2x+1+7$$

$$6x=2x+8$$

$$6x-2x=2x+8-2x$$

$$4x=8$$

$$\frac{4x}{4}=\frac{8}{4}$$

$$x=2$$

The solution set is $\{2\}$.

44.
$$(x+2)(x-3)=(x+3)^2$$

$$x^2-x-6=x^2+6x+9$$

$$x^2-x-6-x^2=x^2+6x+9-x^2$$

$$-x-6=6x+9$$

$$-x-6+6=6x+9+6$$

$$-x=6x+15$$

$$-x-6x=6x+15-6x$$

$$-7x=15$$

$$\frac{-7x}{-7}=\frac{15}{-7}$$

$$x=-\frac{15}{7}$$

The solution set is $\left\{-\frac{15}{7}\right\}$.

45.
$$x(2x-3) = (2x+1)(x-4)$$
$$2x^2 - 3x = 2x^2 - 7x - 4$$
$$2x^2 - 3x - 2x^2 = 2x^2 - 7x - 4 - 2x^2$$
$$-3x = -7x - 4$$
$$-3x + 7x = -7x - 4 + 7x$$
$$4x = -4$$
$$\frac{4x}{4} = \frac{-4}{4}$$
$$x = -1$$
The solution set is $\{-1\}$.

46.
$$x(1+2x) = (2x-1)(x-2)$$
$$x + 2x^2 = 2x^2 - 5x + 2$$
$$x + 2x^2 - 2x^2 = 2x^2 - 5x + 2 - 2x^2$$
$$x = -5x + 2$$
$$x + 5x = -5x + 2 + 5x$$
$$6x = 2$$
$$\frac{6x}{6} = \frac{2}{6}$$
$$x = \frac{1}{3}$$
The solution set is $\left\{\dfrac{1}{3}\right\}$.

47.
$$z(z^2 + 1) = 3 + z^3$$
$$z^3 + z = 3 + z^3$$
$$z^3 + z - z^3 = 3 + z^3 - z^3$$
$$z = 3$$
The solution set is $\{3\}$.

48.
$$w(4 - w^2) = 8 - w^3$$
$$4w - w^3 = 8 - w^3$$
$$4w - w^3 + w^3 = 8 - w^3 + w^3$$
$$4w = 8$$
$$\frac{4w}{4} = \frac{8}{4}$$
$$w = 2$$
The solution set is $\{2\}$.

49.
$$\frac{x}{x-2} + 3 = \frac{2}{x-2}$$
$$\left(\frac{x}{x-2} + 3\right)(x-2) = \left(\frac{2}{x-2}\right)(x-2)$$
$$x + 3(x-2) = 2$$
$$x + 3x - 6 = 2$$
$$4x - 6 = 2$$
$$4x - 6 + 6 = 2 + 6$$
$$4x = 8$$
$$\frac{4x}{4} = \frac{8}{4}$$
$$x = 2$$
Since $x = 2$ causes a denominator to equal zero, we must discard it. Therefore the original equation has no solution.

50.
$$\frac{2x}{x+3} = \frac{-6}{x+3} - 2$$
$$\left(\frac{2x}{x+3}\right)(x+3) = \left(\frac{-6}{x+3} - 2\right)(x+3)$$
$$2x = -6 - (2)(x+3)$$
$$2x = -6 - 2x - 6$$
$$2x = -12 - 2x$$
$$2x + 2x = -12 - 2x + 2x$$
$$4x = -12$$
$$\frac{4x}{4} = \frac{-12}{4}$$
$$x = -3$$
Since $x = -3$ causes a denominator to equal zero, we must discard it. Therefore the original equation has no solution.

51.

$$\frac{2x}{x^2-4}=\frac{4}{x^2-4}-\frac{3}{x+2}$$

$$\frac{2x}{(x+2)(x-2)}=\frac{4}{(x+2)(x-2)}-\frac{3}{x+2}$$

$$\left(\frac{2x}{(x+2)(x-2)}\right)(x+2)(x-2)=\left(\frac{4}{(x+2)(x-2)}-\frac{3}{x+2}\right)(x+2)(x-2)$$

$$2x=4-3(x-2)$$

$$2x=4-3x+6$$

$$2x=10-3x$$

$$2x+3x=10-3x+3x$$

$$5x=10$$

$$\frac{5x}{5}=\frac{10}{5}$$

$$x=2$$

Since $x=2$ causes a denominator to equal zero, we must discard it. Therefore the original equation has no solution.

52.

$$\frac{x}{x^2-9}+\frac{4}{x+3}=\frac{3}{x^2-9}$$

$$\frac{x}{(x+3)(x-3)}+\frac{4}{x+3}=\frac{3}{(x+3)(x-3)}$$

$$\left(\frac{x}{(x+3)(x-3)}+\frac{4}{x+3}\right)(x+3)(x-3)=\left(\frac{3}{(x+3)(x-3)}\right)(x+3)(x-3)$$

$$x+4(x-3)=3$$

$$x+4x-12=3$$

$$5x-12=3$$

$$5x-12+12=3+12$$

$$5x=15$$

$$\frac{5x}{5}=\frac{15}{5}$$

$$x=3$$

Since $x=3$ causes a denominator to equal zero, we must discard it. Therefore the original equation has no solution.

53.

$$\frac{x}{x+2}=\frac{3}{2}$$

$$2(x+2)\left(\frac{x}{x+2}\right)=2(x+2)\left(\frac{3}{2}\right)$$

$$2x=3(x+2)$$

$$2x=3x+6$$

$$2x-3x=3x+6-3x$$

$$-x=6$$

$$\frac{-x}{-1}=\frac{6}{-1}$$

$$x=-6$$

Since $x=-6$ does not cause any denominator to equal zero, the solution set is $\{-6\}$.

54.

$$\frac{3x}{x-1}=2$$

$$\left(\frac{3x}{x-1}\right)(x-1)=2(x-1)$$

$$3x=2x-2$$

$$3x-2x=2x-2-2x$$

$$x=-2$$

Since $x=-2$ does not cause any denominator to equal zero, the solution set is $\{-2\}$.

55.

$$\frac{5}{2x-3} = \frac{3}{x+5}$$

$$\left(\frac{5}{2x-3}\right)(2x-3)(x+5) = \left(\frac{3}{x+5}\right)(2x-3)(x+5)$$

$$5(x+5) = 3(2x-3)$$

$$5x+25 = 6x-9$$

$$5x+25-6x = 6x-9-6x$$

$$25-x = -9$$

$$25-x-25 = -9-25$$

$$-x = -34$$

$$\frac{-x}{-1} = \frac{-34}{-1}$$

$$x = 34$$

Since $x = 34$ does not cause any denominator to equal zero, the solution is $\{34\}$.

56.

$$\frac{-4}{x+4} = \frac{-3}{x+6}$$

$$\left(\frac{-4}{x+4}\right)(x+6)(x+4) = \left(\frac{-3}{x+6}\right)(x+6)(x+4)$$

$$-4(x+6) = -3(x+4)$$

$$-4x-24 = -3x-12$$

$$-4x-24+4x = -3x-12+4x$$

$$-24 = -12+x$$

$$-24+12 = -12+x+12$$

$$-12 = x$$

Since $x = -12$ does not cause any denominator to equal zero, the solution set is $\{-12\}$.

57.

$$\frac{6t+7}{4t-1} = \frac{3t+8}{2t-4}$$

$$\left(\frac{6t+7}{4t-1}\right)(4t-1)(2t-4) = \left(\frac{3t+8}{2t-4}\right)(4t-1)(2t-4)$$

$$(6t+7)(2t-4) = (3t+8)(4t-1)$$

$$12t^2 -24t+14t-28 = 12t^2 -3t+32t-8$$

$$12t^2 -10t-28 = 12t^2 +29t-8$$

$$12t^2 -10t-28-12t^2 = 12t^2 +29t-8-12t^2$$

$$-10t-28 = 29t-8$$

$$-10t-28-29t = 29t-8-29t$$

$$-28-39t = -8$$

$$-28-39t+28 = -8+28$$

$$-39t = 20$$

$$\frac{-39t}{-39} = \frac{20}{-39}$$

$$t = -\frac{20}{39}$$

Since $t = -\frac{20}{39}$ does not cause any denominator to equal zero, the solution set is $\left\{-\frac{20}{39}\right\}$.

58.

$$\frac{8w+5}{10w-7} = \frac{4w-3}{5w+7}$$

$$\left(\frac{8w+5}{10w-7}\right)(10w-7)(5w+7) = \left(\frac{4w-3}{5w+7}\right)(10w-7)(5w+7)$$

$$(8w+5)(5w+7) = (4w-3)(10w-7)$$

$$40w^2 + 56w + 25w + 35 = 40w^2 - 28w - 30w + 21$$

$$40w^2 + 81w + 35 = 40w^2 - 58w + 21$$

$$40w^2 + 81w + 35 - 40w^2 = 40w^2 - 58w + 21 - 40w^2$$

$$81w + 35 = -58w + 21$$

$$81w + 35 + 58w = -58w + 21 + 58w$$

$$139w + 35 = 21$$

$$139w + 35 - 35 = 21 - 35$$

$$139w = -14$$

$$\frac{139w}{139} = \frac{-14}{139}$$

$$w = -\frac{14}{139}$$

Since $w = -\dfrac{14}{139}$ does not cause any denominator to equal zero, the solution set is $\left\{-\dfrac{14}{139}\right\}$.

59.

$$\frac{4}{x-2} = \frac{-3}{x+5} + \frac{7}{(x+5)(x-2)}$$

$$\left(\frac{4}{x-2}\right)(x+5)(x-2) = \left(\frac{-3}{x+5} + \frac{7}{(x+5)(x-2)}\right)(x+5)(x-2)$$

$$4(x+5) = -3(x-2) + 7$$

$$4x + 20 = -3x + 6 + 7$$

$$4x + 20 = -3x + 13$$

$$4x + 20 + 3x = -3x + 13 + 3x$$

$$7x + 20 = 13$$

$$7x + 20 - 20 = 13 - 20$$

$$7x = -7$$

$$\frac{7x}{7} = \frac{-7}{7}$$

$$x = -1$$

Since $x = -1$ does not cause any denominator to equal zero, the solution set is $\{-1\}$.

60.

$$\frac{-4}{2x+3}+\frac{1}{x-1}=\frac{1}{(2x+3)(x-1)}$$

$$\left(\frac{-4}{2x+3}+\frac{1}{x-1}\right)(2x+3)(x-1)=\left(\frac{1}{(2x+3)(x-1)}\right)(2x+3)(x-1)$$

$$-4(x-1)+1(2x+3)=1$$

$$-4x+4+2x+3=1$$

$$-2x+7=1$$

$$-2x+7-7=1-7$$

$$-2x=-6$$

$$\frac{-2x}{-2}=\frac{-6}{-2}$$

$$x=3$$

Since $x=3$ does not cause any denominator to equal zero, the solution set is $\{3\}$.

61.

$$\frac{2}{y+3}+\frac{3}{y-4}=\frac{5}{y+6}$$

$$\left(\frac{2}{y+3}+\frac{3}{y-4}\right)(y+3)(y-4)(y+6)=\left(\frac{5}{y+6}\right)(y+3)(y-4)(y+6)$$

$$2(y-4)(y+6)+3(y+3)(y+6)=5(y+3)(y-4)$$

$$2(y^2+6y-4y-24)+3(y^2+6y+3y+18)=5(y^2-4y+3y-12)$$

$$2(y^2+2y-24)+3(y^2+9y+18)=5(y^2-y-12)$$

$$2y^2+4y-48+3y^2+27y+54=5y^2-5y-60$$

$$5y^2+31y+6=5y^2-5y-60$$

$$5y^2+31y+6-5y^2=5y^2-5y-60-5y^2$$

$$31y+6=-5y-60$$

$$31y+6+5y=-5y-60+5y$$

$$36y+6=-60$$

$$36y+6-6=-60-6$$

$$36y=-66$$

$$\frac{36y}{36}=\frac{-66}{36}$$

$$y=-\frac{11}{6}$$

Since $y=-\dfrac{11}{6}$ does not cause any denominator to equal zero, the solution set is $\left\{-\dfrac{11}{6}\right\}$.

62.

$$\frac{5}{5z-11}+\frac{4}{2z-3}=\frac{-3}{5-z}$$

$$\left(\frac{5}{5z-11}+\frac{4}{2z-3}\right)(5z-11)(2z-3)(5-z)=\left(\frac{-3}{5-z}\right)(5z-11)(2z-3)(5-z)$$

$$5(2z-3)(5-z)+4(5z-11)(5-z)=-3(5z-11)(2z-3)$$

$$5\left(10z-2z^2-15+3z\right)+4\left(25z-5z^2-55+11z\right)=-3\left(10z^2-15z-22z+33\right)$$

$$5\left(-2z^2+13z-15\right)+4\left(-5z^2+36z-55\right)=-3\left(10z^2-37z+33\right)$$

$$-10z^2+65z-75-20z^2+144z-220=-30z^2+111z-99$$

$$-30z^2+209z-295=-30z^2+111z-99$$

$$-30z^2+209z-295+30z^2=-30z^2+111z-99+30z^2$$

$$209z-295=111z-99$$

$$209z-295-209z=111z-99-209z$$

$$-295=-98z-99$$

$$-295+99=-98z-99+99$$

$$-196=-98z$$

$$\frac{-196}{-98}=\frac{-118z}{-98}$$

$$2=z$$

Since $z=2$ does not cause any denominator to equal zero, the solution set is $\{2\}$.

63.

$$\frac{x}{x^2-1}-\frac{x+3}{x^2-x}=\frac{-3}{x^2+x}$$

$$\frac{x}{(x+1)(x-1)}-\frac{x+3}{x(x-1)}=\frac{-3}{x(x+1)}$$

$$\left(\frac{x}{(x+1)(x-1)}-\frac{x+3}{x(x-1)}\right)x(x+1)(x-1)=\left(\frac{-3}{x(x+1)}\right)x(x+1)(x-1)$$

$$(x)(x)-(x+3)(x+1)=-3(x-1)$$

$$x^2-\left(x^2+x+3x+3\right)=-3x+3$$

$$x^2-\left(x^2+4x+3\right)=-3x+3$$

$$x^2-x^2-4x-3=-3x+3$$

$$-4x-3=-3x+3$$

$$-4x-3+4x=-3x+3+4x$$

$$-3=3+x$$

$$-3-3=3+x-3$$

$$-6=x$$

Since $x=-6$ does not cause any denominator to equal zero, the solution set is $\{-6\}$.

64.

$$\frac{x+1}{x^2+2x} - \frac{x+4}{x^2+x} = \frac{-3}{x^2+3x+2}$$

$$\frac{x+1}{x(x+2)} - \frac{x+4}{x(x+1)} = \frac{-3}{(x+2)(x+1)}$$

$$\left(\frac{x+1}{x(x+2)} - \frac{x+4}{x(x+1)}\right)x(x+2)(x+1) = \left(\frac{-3}{(x+2)(x+1)}\right)x(x+2)(x+1)$$

$$(x+1)(x+1) - (x+4)(x+2) = -3x$$

$$\left(x^2+x+x+1\right) - \left(x^2+2x+4x+8\right) = -3x$$

$$x^2+2x+1 - \left(x^2+6x+8\right) = -3x$$

$$x^2+2x+1 - x^2-6x-8 = -3x$$

$$2x+1-6x-8 = -3x$$

$$-4x-7 = -3x$$

$$-4x-7+4x = -3x+4x$$

$$-7 = x$$

Since $x = -7$ does not cause any denominator to equal zero, the solution set is $\{-7\}$.

65.

$$3.2x + \frac{21.3}{65.871} = 19.23$$

$$3.2x + \frac{21.3}{65.871} - \frac{21.3}{65.871} = 19.23 - \frac{21.3}{65.871}$$

$$3.2x = 19.23 - \frac{21.3}{65.871}$$

$$\left(\frac{1}{3.2}\right)(3.2x) = \left(19.23 - \frac{21.3}{65.871}\right)\left(\frac{1}{3.2}\right)$$

$$x = \left(19.23 - \frac{21.3}{65.871}\right)\left(\frac{1}{3.2}\right) \approx 5.91$$

The solution set is approximately $\{5.91\}$.

66.

$$6.2x - \frac{19.1}{83.72} = 0.195$$

$$6.2x - \frac{19.1}{83.72} + \frac{19.1}{83.72} = 0.195 + \frac{19.1}{83.72}$$

$$6.2x = 0.195 + \frac{19.1}{83.72}$$

$$\left(\frac{1}{6.2}\right)(6.2x) = \left(0.195 + \frac{19.1}{83.72}\right)\left(\frac{1}{6.2}\right)$$

$$x = \left(0.195 + \frac{19.1}{83.72}\right)\left(\frac{1}{6.2}\right) \approx 0.07$$

The solution set is approximately $\{0.07\}$.

67.
$$14.72 - 21.58x = \frac{18}{2.11}x + 2.4$$

$$14.72 - 21.58x - \frac{18}{2.11}x = \frac{18}{2.11}x + 2.4 - \frac{18}{2.11}x$$

$$14.72 - 21.58x - \frac{18}{2.11}x = 2.4$$

$$14.72 - 21.58x - \frac{18}{2.11}x - 14.72 = 2.4 - 14.72$$

$$-21.58x - \frac{18}{2.11}x = -12.32$$

$$\left(-21.58 - \frac{18}{2.11}\right)x = -12.32$$

$$\left(\frac{1}{-21.58 - \frac{18}{2.11}}\right)\left(-21.58 - \frac{18}{2.11}\right)x = -12.32\left(\frac{1}{-21.58 - \frac{18}{2.11}}\right)$$

$$x = -12.32\left(\frac{1}{-21.58 - \frac{18}{2.11}}\right) \approx 0.41$$

The solution set is approximately $\{0.41\}$.

68.
$$18.63x - \frac{21.2}{2.6} = \frac{14}{2.32}x - 20$$

$$18.63x - \frac{21.2}{2.6} - \frac{14}{2.32}x = \frac{14}{2.32}x - 20 - \frac{14}{2.32}x$$

$$18.63x - \frac{21.2}{2.6} - \frac{14}{2.32}x = -20$$

$$18.63x - \frac{21.2}{2.6} - \frac{14}{2.32}x + \frac{21.2}{2.6} = -20 + \frac{21.2}{2.6}$$

$$18.63x - \frac{14}{2.32}x = -20 + \frac{21.2}{2.6}$$

$$\left(18.63 - \frac{14}{2.32}\right)x = -20 + \frac{21.2}{2.6}$$

$$\left(\frac{1}{18.63 - \frac{14}{2.32}}\right)\left(18.63 - \frac{14}{2.32}\right)x = \left(-20 + \frac{21.2}{2.6}\right)\left(\frac{1}{18.63 - \frac{14}{2.32}}\right)$$

$$x = \left(-20 + \frac{21.2}{2.6}\right)\left(\frac{1}{18.63 - \frac{14}{2.32}}\right) \approx -0.94$$

The solution set is approximately $\{-0.94\}$.

69.

$$ax - b = c, \quad a \neq 0$$
$$ax - b + b = c + b$$
$$ax = b + c$$
$$\frac{ax}{a} = \frac{b+c}{a}$$
$$x = \frac{b+c}{a}$$

70.

$$1 - ax = b, \quad a \neq 0$$
$$1 - ax - 1 = b - 1$$
$$-ax = b - 1$$
$$\frac{-ax}{-a} = \frac{b-1}{-a}$$
$$x = \frac{b-1}{-a} = \frac{1-b}{a}$$

71.

$$\frac{x}{a} + \frac{x}{b} = c, \quad a \neq 0, b \neq 0, a \neq -b$$
$$ab\left(\frac{x}{a} + \frac{x}{b}\right) = ab \cdot c$$
$$bx + ax = abc$$
$$(a+b)x = abc$$
$$\frac{(a+b)x}{a+b} = \frac{abc}{a+b}$$
$$x = \frac{abc}{a+b}$$

72.

$$\frac{a}{x} + \frac{b}{x} = c, \quad c \neq 0$$
$$x\left(\frac{a}{x} + \frac{b}{x}\right) = x \cdot c$$
$$a + b = cx$$
$$\frac{a+b}{c} = \frac{cx}{c}$$
$$x = \frac{a+b}{c}$$

73.

$$\frac{1}{x-a} + \frac{1}{x+a} = \frac{2}{x-1}$$
$$\left(\frac{1}{x-a} + \frac{1}{x+a}\right)(x-a)(x+a)(x-1) = \left(\frac{2}{x-1}\right)(x-a)(x+a)(x-1)$$
$$(x+a)(x-1) + (x-a)(x-1) = 2(x-a)(x+a)$$
$$x^2 - x + ax - a + x^2 - x - ax + a = 2(x^2 + ax - ax - a^2)$$
$$2x^2 - 2x = 2(x^2 - a^2)$$
$$2x^2 - 2x = 2x^2 - 2a^2$$
$$-2x = -2a^2$$
$$\frac{-2x}{-2} = \frac{-2a^2}{-2}$$
$$x = a^2$$

such that $x \neq \pm a, x \neq 1$

74.
$$\frac{b+c}{x+a} = \frac{b-c}{x-a}, c \neq 0, a \neq 0$$

$$\left(\frac{b+c}{x+a}\right)(x+a)(x-a) = \left(\frac{b-c}{x-a}\right)(x+a)(x-a)$$

$$(b+c)(x-a) = (b-c)(x+a)$$

$$bx - ba + cx - ca = bx + ba - cx - ca$$

$$-ba + cx - ca = ba - cx - ca$$

$$-ba + cx = ba - cx$$

$$-ba + cx + ba = ba - cx + ba$$

$$2cx = 2ba$$

$$\frac{2cx}{2c} = \frac{2ba}{2c}$$

$$x = \frac{ba}{c}$$

such that $x \neq \pm a$

75. $x + 2a = 16 + ax - 6a$, if $x = 4$

$$4 + 2a = 16 + a(4) - 6a$$

$$4 + 2a = 16 + 4a - 6a$$

$$4 + 2a = 16 - 2a$$

$$4a = 12$$

$$\frac{4a}{4} = \frac{12}{4}$$

$$a = 3$$

76. $x + 2b = x - 4 + 2bx$, for $x = 2$

$$2 + 2b = 2 - 4 + 2b(2)$$

$$2 + 2b = 2 - 4 + 4b$$

$$2 + 2b = -2 + 4b$$

$$4 = 2b$$

$$\frac{4}{2} = b$$

$$b = 2$$

77.
$$\frac{1}{R} = \frac{1}{R_1} + \frac{1}{R_2}$$

$$RR_1R_2\left(\frac{1}{R}\right) = RR_1R_2\left(\frac{1}{R_1} + \frac{1}{R_2}\right)$$

$$R_1R_2 = RR_2 + RR_1$$

$$R_1R_2 = R(R_2 + R_1)$$

$$\frac{R_1R_2}{R_2 + R_1} = \frac{R(R_2 + R_1)}{R_2 + R_1}$$

$$\frac{R_1R_2}{R_2 + R_1} = R$$

78.
$$A = P(1 + rt)$$

$$A = P + Prt$$

$$A - P = Prt$$

$$\frac{A - P}{Pt} = \frac{Prt}{Pt}$$

$$\frac{A - P}{Pt} = r$$

79.
$$F = \frac{mv^2}{R}$$

$$RF = R\left(\frac{mv^2}{R}\right)$$

$$RF = mv^2$$

$$\frac{RF}{F} = \frac{mv^2}{F}$$

$$R = \frac{mv^2}{F}$$

80. $PV = nRT$

$$\frac{PV}{nR} = \frac{nRT}{nR}$$

$$\frac{PV}{nR} = T$$

81.
$$S = \frac{a}{1-r}$$

$$S(1-r) = \left(\frac{a}{1-r}\right)(1-r)$$

$$S - Sr = a$$

$$S - Sr - S = a - S$$

$$-Sr = a - S$$

$$\frac{-Sr}{-S} = \frac{a - S}{-S}$$

$$r = \frac{S - a}{S}$$

82.
$$v = -gt + v_0$$

$$v - v_0 = -gt$$

$$\frac{v - v_0}{-g} = \frac{-gt}{-g}$$

$$t = \frac{v - v_0}{-g} = \frac{v_0 - v}{g}$$

71

83.

Amount in bonds	Amount in CDs	Total
x	$x - 3000$	$20,000$

$$x + (x - 3000) = 20,000$$
$$2x - 3000 = 20,000$$
$$2x = 23,000$$
$$x = 11,500$$

$11,500 will be invested in bonds and $8500 will be invested in CD's.

84.

Sean's Amount	George's Amount	Total
x	$x - 3000$	$10,000$

$$x + (x - 3000) = 10,000$$
$$2x - 3000 = 10,000$$
$$2x = 13,000$$
$$x = 6500$$

Sean will receive $6500 and George will receive $3500.

85.

Yahoo! searches	Google searches	Total
x	$x + 0.53$	3.57

$$x + (x + 0.53) = 3.57$$
$$2x + 0.53 = 3.57$$
$$2x = 3.04$$
$$x = 1.52$$

Yahoo! was used for 1.52 billion searches and Google was used for 2.05 billion searches.

86.

Judy's Amount	Tom's Amount	Total
x	$\dfrac{2}{3}x$	18

$$x + \frac{2}{3}x = 18$$
$$\frac{5}{3}x = 18$$
$$x = \frac{3}{5}(18)$$
$$x = 10.80$$

Judy pays $10.80 and Tom pays $7.20.

87.

	Dollars per hour	Hours worked	Money earned
Regular wage	x	40	$40x$
Overtime wage	$1.5x$	8	$8(1.5x)$

$$40x + 8(1.5x) = 442$$
$$40x + 12x = 442$$
$$52x = 442$$
$$x = \frac{442}{52} = 8.50$$

Sandra's regular hourly wage is $8.50.

88.

	Dollars per hour	Hours worked	Money earned
Regular wage	x	40	$40x$
Overtime wage	$1.5x$	6	$6(1.5x)$
Sunday wage	$2x$	4	$4(2x)$

$$40x + 6(1.5x) + 4(2x) = 342$$
$$40x + 9x + 8x = 342$$
$$57x = 342$$
$$x = \frac{342}{57} = 6$$

Leigh's regular hourly wage is $6.00.

89. Let x represent the score on the final exam.

$$\frac{80 + 83 + 71 + 61 + 95 + x + x}{7} = 80$$
$$\frac{390 + 2x}{7} = 80$$
$$390 + 2x = 560$$
$$2x = 170$$
$$x = 85$$

Brooke needs a score of 85 on the final exam.

90. Let x represent the score on the final exam.
Note: since the final exam counts for two-thirds of the overall grade, the average of the four test scores count for one-third of the overall grade. For a B, the average score must be 80.

$$\frac{1}{3}\left(\frac{86+80+84+90}{4}\right)+\frac{2}{3}x=80$$

$$\frac{1}{3}\left(\frac{340}{4}\right)+\frac{2}{3}x=80$$

$$\frac{85}{3}+\frac{2}{3}x=80$$

$$3\left(\frac{85}{3}+\frac{2}{3}x\right)=3(80)$$

$$85+2x=240$$

$$2x=155$$

$$x=77.5$$

Mike needs a score of 78 to earn a B.

For an A, the average score must be 90.

$$\frac{1}{3}\left(\frac{86+80+84+90}{4}\right)+\frac{2}{3}x=90$$

$$\frac{1}{3}\left(\frac{340}{4}\right)+\frac{2}{3}x=90$$

$$\frac{85}{3}+\frac{2}{3}x=90$$

$$3\left(\frac{85}{3}+\frac{2}{3}x\right)=3(90)$$

$$85+2x=270$$

$$2x=185$$

$$x=92.5$$

Mike needs a score of 93 to earn an A.

91. Let x represent the original price of the house.
Then $0.15x$ represents the reduction in the price of the house.
The new price of the home is $425,000.
original price – reduction = new price

$$x-0.15x=425,000$$

$$0.85x=425,000$$

$$x=500,000$$

The original price of the house was $500,000.
The amount of the reduction (i.e., the savings) is $0.15(\$500,000)=\$75,000$.

92. Let x represent the original price of the car.
Then $0.15x$ represents the reduction in the price of the car.
The new price of the car is $8000.
list price – reduction = new price

$$x-0.15x=8000$$

$$0.85x=8000$$

$$x\approx9411.76$$

The list price of the car was $9411.76.
The amount of the reduction (i.e., the savings) is $0.15(\$9411.76)\approx\$1411.76$.

93. Let x represent the price the bookstore pays for the book.
Then $0.35x$ represents the markup on the book.
The selling price of the book is $92.00.
publisher price + markup = selling price

$$x+0.35x=92.00$$

$$1.35x=92.00$$

$$x\approx68.15$$

The bookstore paid $68.15 for the book.

94. Let x represent selling price for the new car.
The dealer's cost is $0.85(\$18,000)=\$15,300$.
The markup is $100.
selling price = dealer's cost + markup
$x=15,300+100=\$15,400$
At $100 over the dealer's cost, the price of the care is $15,400.

95.

	Tickets sold	Price per ticket	Money earned
Adults	x	7.50	7.50x
Children	$5200-x$	4.50	$4.50(5200-x)$

$$7.50x+4.50(5200-x)=29,961$$

$$7.50x+23,400-4.50x=29,961$$

$$3.00x+23,400=29,961$$

$$3.00x=6561$$

$$x=2187$$

There were 2187 adult patrons.

96. Let p represent the original price for the suit.
Then, $0.30p$ represents the discounted amount.
original price – discount = clearance price

$$p-0.30p=399$$

$$0.70p=399$$

$$p=570$$

The suit originally cost $570.

73

97. Let w represent the width of the rectangle.
Then $w+8$ is the length.
Perimeter is given by the formula $P = 2l + 2w$.

$$2(w+8) + 2w = 60$$
$$2w + 16 + 2w = 60$$
$$4w + 16 = 60$$
$$4w = 44$$
$$w = 11$$

Now, $11 + 8 = 19$.
The width of the rectangle is 11 feet and the length is 19 feet.

98. Let w represent the width of the rectangle.
Then $2w$ is the length.
Perimeter is given by the formula $P = 2l + 2w$.

$$2(2w) + 2w = 42$$
$$4w + 2w = 42$$
$$6w = 42$$
$$w = 7$$

Now, $2(7) = 14$.
The width of the rectangle is 7 meters and the length is 14 meters.

99. Let x represent the number of worldwide Internet users in March 2006.
Then $0.219x$ represents the number U.S. Internet users, which equals 152 million

$$0.219x = 152$$
$$x \approx 694.06$$

In March 2006, there were about 694.06 million Internet users worldwide.

100. To move from step (6) to step (7), we divided both sides of the equation by the expression $x - 2$. From step (1), however, we know $x = 2$, so this means we divided both sides of the equation by zero.

101 – 102. Answers will vary.

Section 1.2

1. $x^2 - 5x - 6 = (x-6)(x+1)$

2. $2x^2 - x - 3 = (2x-3)(x+1)$

3. $\left\{-\dfrac{5}{3}, 3\right\}$

4. True

5. add; $\left(\dfrac{5}{2}\right)^2 = \dfrac{25}{4}$

6. discriminant; negative

7. False; a quadratic equation may have no real solutions.

8. False; if the discriminant is positive, the equation has two distinct real solutions.

9. $x^2 - 9x = 0$
$x(x-9) = 0$
$x = 0$ or $x - 9 = 0$
$x = 0$ or $\quad x = 9$
The solution set is $\{0, 9\}$.

10. $x^2 + 4x = 0$
$x(x+4) = 0$
$x = 0$ or $x + 4 = 0$
$x = 0$ or $\quad x = -4$
The solution set is $\{-4, 0\}$.

11. $x^2 - 25 = 0$
$(x+5)(x-5) = 0$
$x + 5 = 0 \quad$ or $\quad x - 5 = 0$
$x = -5$ or $\quad\quad x = 5$
The solution set is $\{-5, 5\}$.

12. $x^2 - 9 = 0$
$(x+3)(x-3) = 0$
$x + 3 = 0 \quad$ or $\quad x - 3 = 0$
$x = -3$ or $\quad\quad x = 3$
The solution set is $\{-3, 3\}$.

13. $z^2 + z - 6 = 0$
$(z+3)(z-2) = 0$
$z + 3 = 0 \quad$ or $\quad z - 2 = 0$
$z = -3$ or $\quad\quad z = 2$
The solution set is $\{-3, 2\}$.

14. $v^2 + 7v + 6 = 0$
$(v+6)(v+1) = 0$
$v + 6 = 0 \quad$ or $\quad v + 1 = 0$
$v = -6$ or $\quad\quad v = -1$
The solution set is $\{-6, -1\}$

15. $2x^2 - 5x - 3 = 0$

$(2x+1)(x-3) = 0$

$2x+1 = 0$ or $x - 3 = 0$

$x = -\dfrac{1}{2}$ or $x = 3$

The solution set is $\left\{ -\dfrac{1}{2}, 3 \right\}$

16. $3x^2 + 5x + 2 = 0$

$(3x+2)(x+1) = 0$

$3x+2 = 0$ or $x + 1 = 0$

$x = -\dfrac{2}{3}$ or $x = -1$

The solution set is $\left\{ -1, -\dfrac{2}{3} \right\}$.

17. $3t^2 - 48 = 0$

$3(t^2 - 16) = 0$

$3(t+4)(t-4) = 0$

$t+4 = 0$ or $t - 4 = 0$

$t = -4$ or $t = 4$

The solution set is $\{-4, 4\}$.

18. $2y^2 - 50 = 0$

$2(y^2 - 25) = 0$

$2(y+5)(y-5) = 0$

$y+5 = 0$ or $y - 5 = 0$

$y = -5$ or $y = 5$

The solution set is $\{-5, 5\}$.

19. $x(x-8) + 12 = 0$

$x^2 - 8x + 12 = 0$

$(x-6)(x-2) = 0$

$x-6 = 0$ or $x - 2 = 0$

$x = 6$ or $x = 2$

The solution set is $\{2, 6\}$.

20. $x(x+4) = 12$

$x^2 + 4x - 12 = 0$

$(x+6)(x-2) = 0$

$x+6 = 0$ or $x - 2 = 0$

$x = -6$ or $x = 2$

The solution set is $\{-6, 2\}$.

21. $4x^2 + 9 = 12x$

$4x^2 - 12x + 9 = 0$

$(2x-3)^2 = 0$

$2x - 3 = 0$

$x = \dfrac{3}{2}$

The solution set is $\left\{ \dfrac{3}{2} \right\}$.

22. $25x^2 + 16 = 40x$

$25x^2 - 40x + 16 = 0$

$(5x-4)^2 = 0$

$5x - 4 = 0$

$x = \dfrac{4}{5}$

The solution set is $\left\{ \dfrac{4}{5} \right\}$.

23. $6(p^2 - 1) = 5p$

$6p^2 - 6 = 5p$

$6p^2 - 5p - 6 = 0$

$(3p+2)(2p-3) = 0$

$3p+2 = 0$ or $2p - 3 = 0$

$p = -\dfrac{2}{3}$ or $p = \dfrac{3}{2}$

The solution set is $\left\{ -\dfrac{2}{3}, \dfrac{3}{2} \right\}$.

24. $2(2u^2 - 4u) + 3 = 0$

$4u^2 - 8u + 3 = 0$

$(2u-1)(2u-3) = 0$

$2u-1 = 0$ or $2u - 3 = 0$

$u = \dfrac{1}{2}$ or $u = \dfrac{3}{2}$

The solution set is $\left\{ \dfrac{1}{2}, \dfrac{3}{2} \right\}$.

25.
$$6x - 5 = \frac{6}{x}$$
$$(6x - 5)x = \left(\frac{6}{x}\right)x$$
$$6x^2 - 5x = 6$$
$$6x^2 - 5x - 6 = 0$$
$$(3x + 2)(2x - 3) = 0$$
$$3x + 2 = 0 \quad \text{or} \quad 2x - 3 = 0$$
$$x = -\frac{2}{3} \quad \text{or} \quad x = \frac{3}{2}$$
Neither of these values causes a denominator to equal zero, so the solution set is $\left\{-\frac{2}{3}, \frac{3}{2}\right\}$.

26.
$$x + \frac{12}{x} = 7$$
$$\left(x + \frac{12}{x}\right)x = 7x$$
$$x^2 + 12 = 7x$$
$$x^2 - 7x + 12 = 0$$
$$(x - 3)(x - 4) = 0$$
$$x - 3 = 0 \quad \text{or} \quad x - 4 = 0$$
$$x = 3 \quad \text{or} \quad x = 4$$
Neither of these values causes a denominator to equal zero, so the solution set is $\{3, 4\}$.

27.
$$\frac{4(x - 2)}{x - 3} + \frac{3}{x} = \frac{-3}{x(x - 3)}$$
$$\left(\frac{4(x - 2)}{x - 3} + \frac{3}{x}\right)x(x - 3) = \left(\frac{-3}{x(x - 3)}\right)x(x - 3)$$
$$4x(x - 2) + 3(x - 3) = -3$$
$$4x^2 - 8x + 3x - 9 = -3$$
$$4x^2 - 5x - 6 = 0$$
$$(4x + 3)(x - 2) = 0$$
$$4x + 3 = 0 \quad \text{or} \quad x - 2 = 0$$
$$x = -\frac{3}{4} \quad \text{or} \quad x = 2$$
Neither of these values causes a denominator to equal zero, so the solution set is $\left\{-\frac{3}{4}, 2\right\}$.

28.
$$\frac{5}{x + 4} = 4 + \frac{3}{x - 2}$$
$$\left(\frac{5}{x + 4}\right)(x + 4)(x - 2) = \left(4 + \frac{3}{x - 2}\right)(x + 4)(x - 2)$$
$$5(x - 2) = 4(x + 4)(x - 2) + 3(x + 4)$$
$$5x - 10 = 4\left(x^2 + 2x - 8\right) + 3x + 12$$
$$5x - 10 = 4x^2 + 8x - 32 + 3x + 12$$
$$0 = 4x^2 + 6x - 10$$
$$0 = 2\left(2x^2 + 3x - 5\right)$$
$$0 = 2(2x + 5)(x - 1)$$
$$2x + 5 = 0 \quad \text{or} \quad x - 1 = 0$$
$$x = -\frac{5}{2} \quad \text{or} \quad x = 1$$
Neither of these values causes a denominator to equal zero, so the solution set is $\left\{-\frac{5}{2}, 1\right\}$.

29.
$$x^2 = 25$$
$$x = \pm\sqrt{25}$$
$$x = \pm 5$$
The solution set is $\{-5, 5\}$.

30.
$$x^2 = 36$$
$$x = \pm\sqrt{36}$$
$$x = \pm 6$$
The solution set is $\{-6, 6\}$.

31.
$$(x - 1)^2 = 4$$
$$x - 1 = \pm\sqrt{4}$$
$$x - 1 = \pm 2$$
$$x - 1 = 2 \quad \text{or} \quad x - 1 = -2$$
$$x = 3 \quad \text{or} \quad x = -1$$
The solution set is $\{-1, 3\}$.

32.
$$(x + 2)^2 = 1$$
$$x + 2 = \pm\sqrt{1}$$
$$x + 2 = \pm 1$$
$$x + 2 = 1 \quad \text{or} \quad x + 2 = -1$$
$$x = -1 \quad \text{or} \quad x = -3$$
The solution set is $\{-3, -1\}$.

33. $(2x+3)^2 = 9$

$$2x+3 = \pm\sqrt{9}$$
$$2x+3 = \pm 3$$
$$2x+3 = 3 \text{ or } 2x+3 = -3$$
$$2x = 0 \text{ or } \quad 2x = -6$$
$$x = 0 \text{ or } \quad x = -3$$

The solution set is $\{-3, 0\}$.

34. $(3x-2)^2 = 4$

$$3x-2 = \pm\sqrt{4}$$
$$3x-2 = \pm 2$$
$$3x-2 = 2 \text{ or } 3x-2 = -2$$
$$3x = 4 \text{ or } \quad 3x = 0$$
$$x = \frac{4}{3} \text{ or } \quad x = 0$$

The solution set is $\left\{0, \frac{4}{3}\right\}$.

35. $\left(\frac{1}{2} \cdot (-8)\right)^2 = (-4)^2 = 16$

36. $\left(\frac{1}{2} \cdot (-4)\right)^2 = (-2)^2 = 4$

37. $\left(\frac{1}{2} \cdot \frac{1}{2}\right)^2 = \left(\frac{1}{4}\right)^2 = \frac{1}{16}$

38. $\left(\frac{1}{2} \cdot \left(-\frac{1}{3}\right)\right)^2 = \left(-\frac{1}{6}\right)^2 = \frac{1}{36}$

39. $\left(\frac{1}{2} \cdot \left(-\frac{2}{3}\right)\right)^2 = \left(-\frac{1}{3}\right)^2 = \frac{1}{9}$

40. $\left(\frac{1}{2} \cdot \left(-\frac{2}{5}\right)\right)^2 = \left(-\frac{1}{5}\right)^2 = \frac{1}{25}$

41. $x^2 + 4x = 21$

$$x^2 + 4x + 4 = 21 + 4$$
$$(x+2)^2 = 25$$
$$x+2 = \pm\sqrt{25}$$
$$x+2 = \pm 5$$
$$x = -2 \pm 5$$
$$x = 3 \text{ or } x = -7$$

The solution set is $\{-7, 3\}$.

42. $x^2 - 6x = 13$

$$x^2 - 6x + 9 = 13 + 9$$
$$(x-3)^2 = 22$$
$$x-3 = \pm\sqrt{22}$$
$$x = 3 \pm\sqrt{22}$$

The solution set is $\left\{3-\sqrt{22}, 3+\sqrt{22}\right\}$.

43. $x^2 - \frac{1}{2}x - \frac{3}{16} = 0$

$$x^2 - \frac{1}{2}x = \frac{3}{16}$$
$$x^2 - \frac{1}{2}x + \frac{1}{16} = \frac{3}{16} + \frac{1}{16}$$
$$\left(x - \frac{1}{4}\right)^2 = \frac{1}{4}$$
$$x - \frac{1}{4} = \pm\sqrt{\frac{1}{4}} = \pm\frac{1}{2}$$
$$x = \frac{1}{4} \pm \frac{1}{2}$$
$$x = \frac{3}{4} \text{ or } x = -\frac{1}{4}$$

The solution set is $\left\{-\frac{1}{4}, \frac{3}{4}\right\}$.

44. $x^2 + \frac{2}{3}x - \frac{1}{3} = 0$

$$x^2 + \frac{2}{3}x = \frac{1}{3}$$
$$x^2 + \frac{2}{3}x + \frac{1}{9} = \frac{1}{3} + \frac{1}{9}$$
$$\left(x + \frac{1}{3}\right)^2 = \frac{4}{9}$$
$$x + \frac{1}{3} = \pm\sqrt{\frac{4}{9}} = \pm\frac{2}{3}$$
$$x = -\frac{1}{3} \pm \frac{2}{3}$$
$$x = \frac{1}{3} \text{ or } x = -1$$

The solution set is $\left\{-1, \frac{1}{3}\right\}$.

45. $3x^2 + x - \dfrac{1}{2} = 0$

$$x^2 + \dfrac{1}{3}x - \dfrac{1}{6} = 0$$

$$x^2 + \dfrac{1}{3}x = \dfrac{1}{6}$$

$$x^2 + \dfrac{1}{3}x + \dfrac{1}{36} = \dfrac{1}{6} + \dfrac{1}{36}$$

$$\left(x + \dfrac{1}{6}\right)^2 = \dfrac{7}{36}$$

$$x + \dfrac{1}{6} = \pm\sqrt{\dfrac{7}{36}}$$

$$x + \dfrac{1}{6} = \pm\dfrac{\sqrt{7}}{6}$$

$$x = \dfrac{-1 \pm \sqrt{7}}{6}$$

The solution set is $\left\{\dfrac{-1-\sqrt{7}}{6}, \dfrac{-1+\sqrt{7}}{6}\right\}$.

46. $2x^2 - 3x - 1 = 0$

$$x^2 - \dfrac{3}{2}x - \dfrac{1}{2} = 0$$

$$x^2 - \dfrac{3}{2}x = \dfrac{1}{2}$$

$$x^2 - \dfrac{3}{2}x + \dfrac{9}{16} = \dfrac{1}{2} + \dfrac{9}{16}$$

$$\left(x - \dfrac{3}{4}\right)^2 = \dfrac{17}{16}$$

$$x - \dfrac{3}{4} = \pm\sqrt{\dfrac{17}{16}}$$

$$x - \dfrac{3}{4} = \pm\dfrac{\sqrt{17}}{4}$$

$$x = \dfrac{3 \pm \sqrt{17}}{4}$$

The solution set is $\left\{\dfrac{3-\sqrt{17}}{4}, \dfrac{3+\sqrt{17}}{4}\right\}$.

47. $x^2 - 4x + 2 = 0$

$a = 1, \quad b = -4, \quad c = 2$

$$x = \dfrac{-(-4) \pm \sqrt{(-4)^2 - 4(1)(2)}}{2(1)} = \dfrac{4 \pm \sqrt{16-8}}{2}$$

$$= \dfrac{4 \pm \sqrt{8}}{2} = \dfrac{4 \pm 2\sqrt{2}}{2} = 2 \pm \sqrt{2}$$

The solution set is $\left\{2 - \sqrt{2}, \, 2 + \sqrt{2}\right\}$.

48. $x^2 + 4x + 2 = 0$

$a = 1, \quad b = 4, \quad c = 2$

$$x = \dfrac{-4 \pm \sqrt{4^2 - 4(1)(2)}}{2(1)} = \dfrac{-4 \pm \sqrt{16-8}}{2}$$

$$= \dfrac{-4 \pm \sqrt{8}}{2} = \dfrac{-4 \pm 2\sqrt{2}}{2} = -2 \pm \sqrt{2}$$

The solution set is $\left\{-2 - \sqrt{2}, \, -2 + \sqrt{2}\right\}$.

49. $x^2 - 4x - 1 = 0$

$a = 1, \quad b = -4, \quad c = -1$

$$x = \dfrac{-(-4) \pm \sqrt{(-4)^2 - 4(1)(-1)}}{2(1)} = \dfrac{4 \pm \sqrt{16+4}}{2}$$

$$= \dfrac{4 \pm \sqrt{20}}{2} = \dfrac{4 \pm 2\sqrt{5}}{2} = 2 \pm \sqrt{5}$$

The solution set is $\left\{2 - \sqrt{5}, \, 2 + \sqrt{5}\right\}$.

50. $x^2 + 6x + 1 = 0$

$a = 1, \quad b = 6, \quad c = 1$

$$x = \dfrac{-6 \pm \sqrt{6^2 - 4(1)(1)}}{2(1)} = \dfrac{-6 \pm \sqrt{36-4}}{2}$$

$$= \dfrac{-6 \pm \sqrt{32}}{2} = \dfrac{-6 \pm 4\sqrt{2}}{2} = -3 \pm 2\sqrt{2}$$

The solution set is $\left\{-3 - 2\sqrt{2}, -3 + 2\sqrt{2}\right\}$.

51. $2x^2 - 5x + 3 = 0$

$a = 2, \quad b = -5, \quad c = 3$

$$x = \dfrac{-(-5) \pm \sqrt{(-5)^2 - 4(2)(3)}}{2(2)}$$

$$= \dfrac{5 \pm \sqrt{25-24}}{4} = \dfrac{5 \pm \sqrt{1}}{4} = \dfrac{5 \pm 1}{4}$$

$$x = \dfrac{5+1}{4} \quad \text{or} \quad x = \dfrac{5-1}{4}$$

$$x = \dfrac{6}{4} \quad \text{or} \quad x = \dfrac{4}{4}$$

$$x = \dfrac{3}{2} \quad \text{or} \quad x = 1$$

The solution set is $\left\{1, \dfrac{3}{2}\right\}$.

52. $2x^2 + 5x + 3 = 0$

$a = 2, \quad b = 5, \quad c = 3$

$$x = \frac{-5 \pm \sqrt{5^2 - 4(2)(3)}}{2(2)}$$

$$= \frac{-5 \pm \sqrt{25 - 24}}{4} = \frac{-5 \pm \sqrt{1}}{4} = \frac{-5 \pm 1}{4}$$

$x = \frac{-5 + 1}{4} \quad \text{or} \quad x = \frac{-5 - 1}{4}$

$x = \frac{-4}{4} \quad \text{or} \quad x = \frac{-6}{4}$

$x = -1 \quad \text{or} \quad x = -\frac{3}{2}$

The solution set is $\left\{ -\frac{3}{2}, -1 \right\}$.

53. $4y^2 - y + 2 = 0$

$a = 4, \quad b = -1, \quad c = 2$

$$y = \frac{-(-1) \pm \sqrt{(-1)^2 - 4(4)(2)}}{2(4)}$$

$$= \frac{1 \pm \sqrt{1 - 32}}{8} = \frac{1 \pm \sqrt{-31}}{8}$$

No real solution.

54. $4t^2 + t + 1 = 0$

$a = 4, \quad b = 1, \quad c = 1$

$$t = \frac{-1 \pm \sqrt{1^2 - 4(4)(1)}}{2(4)}$$

$$= \frac{-1 \pm \sqrt{1 - 16}}{8} = \frac{-1 \pm \sqrt{-15}}{8}$$

No real solution.

55. $\qquad 4x^2 = 1 - 2x$

$4x^2 + 2x - 1 = 0$

$a = 4, \quad b = 2, \quad c = -1$

$$x = \frac{-2 \pm \sqrt{2^2 - 4(4)(-1)}}{2(4)}$$

$$= \frac{-2 \pm \sqrt{4 + 16}}{8} = \frac{-2 \pm \sqrt{20}}{8}$$

$$= \frac{-2 \pm 2\sqrt{5}}{8} = \frac{-1 \pm \sqrt{5}}{4}$$

The solution set is $\left\{ \frac{-1 - \sqrt{5}}{4}, \frac{-1 + \sqrt{5}}{4} \right\}$.

56. $\qquad 2x^2 = 1 - 2x$

$2x^2 + 2x - 1 = 0$

$a = 2, \quad b = 2, \quad c = -1$

$$x = \frac{-2 \pm \sqrt{2^2 - 4(2)(-1)}}{2(2)} = \frac{-2 \pm \sqrt{4 + 8}}{4}$$

$$= \frac{-2 \pm \sqrt{12}}{4} = \frac{-2 \pm 2\sqrt{3}}{4} = \frac{-1 \pm \sqrt{3}}{2}$$

The solution set is $\left\{ \frac{-1 - \sqrt{3}}{2}, \frac{-1 + \sqrt{3}}{2} \right\}$.

57. $\qquad 4x^2 = 9x$

$4x^2 - 9x = 0$

$x(4x - 9) = 0$

$x = 0 \quad \text{or} \quad 4x - 9 = 0$

$x = 0 \quad \text{or} \qquad x = \frac{9}{4}$

The solution set is $\left\{ 0, \frac{9}{4} \right\}$.

58. $5x = 4x^2$

$0 = 4x^2 - 5x$

$0 = x(4x - 5)$

$x = 0 \quad \text{or} \quad 4x - 5 = 0$

$x = 0 \quad \text{or} \qquad x = \frac{5}{4}$

The solution set is $\left\{ 0, \frac{5}{4} \right\}$.

59. $9t^2 - 6t + 1 = 0$

$a = 9, \quad b = -6, \quad c = 1$

$$t = \frac{-(-6) \pm \sqrt{(-6)^2 - 4(9)(1)}}{2(9)}$$

$$= \frac{6 \pm \sqrt{36 - 36}}{18} = \frac{6 \pm 0}{18} = \frac{1}{3}$$

The solution set is $\left\{ \frac{1}{3} \right\}$.

60. $4u^2 - 6u + 9 = 0$

$a = 4, \quad b = -6, \quad c = 9$

$$u = \frac{-(-6) \pm \sqrt{(-6)^2 - 4(4)(9)}}{2(4)}$$

$$= \frac{6 \pm \sqrt{36 - 144}}{8} = \frac{6 \pm \sqrt{-108}}{8}$$

No real solution.

61. $\frac{3}{4}x^2 - \frac{1}{4}x - \frac{1}{2} = 0$

$4\left(\frac{3}{4}x^2 - \frac{1}{4}x - \frac{1}{2}\right) = 4(0)$

$3x^2 - x - 2 = 0$

$a = 3, \quad b = -1, \quad c = -2$

$x = \dfrac{-(-1) \pm \sqrt{(-1)^2 - 4(3)(-2)}}{2(3)}$

$= \dfrac{1 \pm \sqrt{1 + 24}}{6} = \dfrac{1 \pm \sqrt{25}}{6} = \dfrac{1 \pm 5}{6}$

$x = \dfrac{1+5}{6} \quad \text{or} \quad x = \dfrac{1-5}{6}$

$x = \dfrac{6}{6} \quad \text{or} \quad x = \dfrac{-4}{6}$

$x = 1 \quad \text{or} \quad x = -\dfrac{2}{3}$

The solution set is $\left\{-\dfrac{2}{3}, 1\right\}$.

62. $\frac{2}{3}x^2 - x - 3 = 0$

$3\left(\frac{2}{3}x^2 - x - 3\right) = 3(0)$

$2x^2 - 3x - 9 = 0$

$a = 2, \quad b = -3, \quad c = -9$

$x = \dfrac{-(-3) \pm \sqrt{(-3)^2 - 4(2)(-9)}}{2(2)}$

$= \dfrac{3 \pm \sqrt{9 + 72}}{4} = \dfrac{3 \pm \sqrt{81}}{4} = \dfrac{3 \pm 9}{4}$

$x = \dfrac{3+9}{4} \quad \text{or} \quad x = \dfrac{3-9}{4}$

$x = \dfrac{12}{4} \quad \text{or} \quad x = \dfrac{-6}{4}$

$x = 3 \quad \text{or} \quad x = -\dfrac{3}{2}$

The solution set is $\left\{-\dfrac{3}{2}, 3\right\}$.

63. $\frac{5}{3}x^2 - x = \frac{1}{3}$

$3\left(\frac{5}{3}x^2 - x\right) = 3\left(\frac{1}{3}\right)$

$5x^2 - 3x = 1$

$5x^2 - 3x - 1 = 0$

$a = 5, \quad b = -3, \quad c = -1$

$x = \dfrac{-(-3) \pm \sqrt{(-3)^2 - 4(5)(-1)}}{2(5)}$

$= \dfrac{3 \pm \sqrt{9 + 20}}{10} = \dfrac{3 \pm \sqrt{29}}{10}$

The solution set is $\left\{\dfrac{3-\sqrt{29}}{10}, \dfrac{3+\sqrt{29}}{10}\right\}$.

64. $\frac{3}{5}x^2 - x = \frac{1}{5}$

$5\left(\frac{3}{5}x^2 - x\right) = 5\left(\frac{1}{5}\right)$

$3x^2 - 5x = 1$

$3x^2 - 5x - 1 = 0$

$a = 3, \quad b = -5, \quad c = -1$

$x = \dfrac{-(-5) \pm \sqrt{(-5)^2 - 4(3)(-1)}}{2(3)}$

$= \dfrac{5 \pm \sqrt{25 + 12}}{6} = \dfrac{5 \pm \sqrt{37}}{6}$

The solution set is $\left\{\dfrac{5-\sqrt{37}}{6}, \dfrac{5+\sqrt{37}}{6}\right\}$.

65. $2x(x+2) = 3$

$2x^2 + 4x - 3 = 0$

$a = 2, \quad b = 4, \quad c = -3$

$x = \dfrac{-4 \pm \sqrt{4^2 - 4(2)(-3)}}{2(2)} = \dfrac{-4 \pm \sqrt{16 + 24}}{4}$

$= \dfrac{-4 \pm \sqrt{40}}{4} = \dfrac{-4 \pm 2\sqrt{10}}{4} = \dfrac{-2 \pm \sqrt{10}}{2}$

The solution set is $\left\{\dfrac{-2-\sqrt{10}}{2}, \dfrac{-2+\sqrt{10}}{2}\right\}$.

66. $3x(x+2) = 1$

$3x^2 + 6x - 1 = 0$

$a = 3, \quad b = 6, \quad c = -1$

$x = \dfrac{-6 \pm \sqrt{6^2 - 4(3)(-1)}}{2(3)} = \dfrac{-6 \pm \sqrt{36+12}}{6}$

$= \dfrac{-6 \pm \sqrt{48}}{6} = \dfrac{-6 \pm 4\sqrt{3}}{6} = \dfrac{-3 \pm 2\sqrt{3}}{3}$

The solution set is $\left\{ \dfrac{-3 - 2\sqrt{3}}{3}, \dfrac{-3 + 2\sqrt{3}}{3} \right\}$.

67. $4 - \dfrac{1}{x} - \dfrac{2}{x^2} = 0$

$x^2 \left(4 - \dfrac{1}{x} - \dfrac{2}{x^2} \right) = x^2 (0)$

$4x^2 - x - 2 = 0$

$a = 4, \quad b = -1, \quad c = -2$

$x = \dfrac{-(-1) \pm \sqrt{(-1)^2 - 4(4)(-2)}}{2(4)}$

$= \dfrac{1 \pm \sqrt{1+32}}{8} = \dfrac{1 \pm \sqrt{33}}{8}$

Neither of these values causes a denominator to equal zero, so the solution set is

$\left\{ \dfrac{1 - \sqrt{33}}{8}, \dfrac{1 + \sqrt{33}}{8} \right\}$.

68. $4 + \dfrac{1}{x} - \dfrac{1}{x^2} = 0$

$x^2 \left(4 + \dfrac{1}{x} - \dfrac{1}{x^2} \right) = x^2 (0)$

$4x^2 + x - 1 = 0$

$a = 4, \quad b = 1, \quad c = -1$

$x = \dfrac{-1 \pm \sqrt{1^2 - 4(4)(-1)}}{2(4)}$

$= \dfrac{-1 \pm \sqrt{1+16}}{8} = \dfrac{-1 \pm \sqrt{17}}{8}$

Neither of these values causes a denominator to equal zero, so the solution set is

$\left\{ \dfrac{-1 - \sqrt{17}}{8}, \dfrac{-1 + \sqrt{17}}{8} \right\}$.

69. $\dfrac{3x}{x-2} + \dfrac{1}{x} = 4$

$\left(\dfrac{3x}{x-2} + \dfrac{1}{x} \right) x(x-2) = 4x(x-2)$

$3x(x) + (x-2) = 4x^2 - 8x$

$3x^2 + x - 2 = 4x^2 - 8x$

$0 = x^2 - 9x + 2$

$a = 1, \quad b = -9, \quad c = 2$

$x = \dfrac{-(-9) \pm \sqrt{(-9)^2 - 4(1)(2)}}{2(1)}$

$= \dfrac{9 \pm \sqrt{81-8}}{2} = \dfrac{9 \pm \sqrt{73}}{2}$

Neither of these values causes a denominator to equal zero, so the solution set is

$\left\{ \dfrac{9 - \sqrt{73}}{2}, \dfrac{9 + \sqrt{73}}{2} \right\}$.

70. $\dfrac{2x}{x-3} + \dfrac{1}{x} = 4$

$\left(\dfrac{2x}{x-3} + \dfrac{1}{x} \right) x(x-3) = 4x(x-3)$

$2x(x) + (x-3) = 4x^2 - 12x$

$2x^2 + x - 3 = 4x^2 - 12x$

$0 = 2x^2 - 13x + 3$

$a = 2, \quad b = -13, \quad c = 3$

$x = \dfrac{-(-13) \pm \sqrt{(-13)^2 - 4(2)(3)}}{2(2)}$

$= \dfrac{13 \pm \sqrt{169-24}}{4} = \dfrac{13 \pm \sqrt{145}}{4}$

Neither of these values causes a denominator to equal zero, so the solution set is

$\left\{ \dfrac{13 - \sqrt{145}}{4}, \dfrac{13 + \sqrt{145}}{4} \right\}$.

71. $x^2 - 4.1x + 2.2 = 0$

$a = 1, \quad b = -4.1, \quad c = 2.2$

$x = \dfrac{-(-4.1) \pm \sqrt{(-4.1)^2 - 4(1)(2.2)}}{2(1)}$

$= \dfrac{4.1 \pm \sqrt{16.81 - 8.8}}{2} = \dfrac{4.1 \pm \sqrt{8.01}}{2}$

$x \approx 3.47 \quad \text{or} \quad x \approx 0.63$

The solution set is $\{0.63, \ 3.47\}$.

81

72. $x^2 + 3.9x + 1.8 = 0$

$a = 1, \quad b = 3.9, \quad c = 1.8$

$$x = \frac{-3.9 \pm \sqrt{(3.9)^2 - 4(1)(1.8)}}{2(1)}$$

$$= \frac{-3.9 \pm \sqrt{15.21 - 7.2}}{2} = \frac{-3.9 \pm \sqrt{8.01}}{2}$$

$x \approx -0.53 \ \text{ or } \ x \approx -3.37$

The solution set is $\{-3.37, -0.53\}$.

73. $x^2 + \sqrt{3}x - 3 = 0$

$a = 1, \quad b = \sqrt{3}, \quad c = -3$

$$x = \frac{-\sqrt{3} \pm \sqrt{\left(\sqrt{3}\right)^2 - 4(1)(-3)}}{2(1)}$$

$$= \frac{-\sqrt{3} \pm \sqrt{3 + 12}}{2} = \frac{-\sqrt{3} \pm \sqrt{15}}{2}$$

$x \approx 1.07 \ \text{ or } \ x \approx -2.80$

The solution set is $\{-2.80, 1.07\}$.

74. $x^2 + \sqrt{2}x - 2 = 0$

$a = 1, \quad b = \sqrt{2}, \quad c = -2$

$$x = \frac{-\sqrt{2} \pm \sqrt{\left(\sqrt{2}\right)^2 - 4(1)(-2)}}{2(1)}$$

$$= \frac{-\sqrt{2} \pm \sqrt{2 + 8}}{2} = \frac{-\sqrt{2} \pm \sqrt{10}}{2}$$

$x \approx 0.87 \ \text{ or } \ x \approx -2.29$

The solution set is $\{-2.29, 0.87\}$.

75. $\pi x^2 - x - \pi = 0$

$a = \pi, \quad b = -1, \quad c = -\pi$

$$x = \frac{-(-1) \pm \sqrt{(-1)^2 - 4(\pi)(-\pi)}}{2(\pi)}$$

$$= \frac{1 \pm \sqrt{1 + 4\pi^2}}{2\pi}$$

$x \approx 1.17 \ \text{ or } \ x \approx -0.85$

The solution set is $\{-0.85, 1.17\}$.

76. $\pi x^2 + \pi x - 2 = 0$

$a = \pi, \quad b = \pi, \quad c = -2$

$$x = \frac{-\pi \pm \sqrt{(\pi)^2 - 4(\pi)(-2)}}{2(\pi)}$$

$$= \frac{-\pi \pm \sqrt{\pi^2 + 8\pi}}{2\pi}$$

$x \approx 0.44 \ \text{ or } \ x \approx -1.44$

The solution set is $\{-1.44, \ 0.44\}$.

77. $3x^2 + 8\pi x + \sqrt{29} = 0$

$a = 3, \quad b = 8\pi, \quad c = \sqrt{29}$

$$x = \frac{-8\pi \pm \sqrt{(8\pi)^2 - 4(3)\left(\sqrt{29}\right)}}{2(3)}$$

$$= \frac{-8\pi \pm \sqrt{64\pi^2 - 12\sqrt{29}}}{6}$$

$x \approx -0.22 \ \text{ or } \ x \approx -8.16$

The solution set is $\{-8.16, -0.22\}$.

78. $\pi x^2 - 15\sqrt{2}x + 20 = 0$

$a = \pi, \quad b = -15\sqrt{2}, \quad c = 20$

$$x = \frac{-\left(-15\sqrt{2}\right) \pm \sqrt{\left(-15\sqrt{2}\right)^2 - 4(\pi)(20)}}{2(\pi)}$$

$$= \frac{15\sqrt{2} \pm \sqrt{450 - 80\pi}}{2\pi}$$

$x \approx 5.62 \ \text{ or } \ x \approx 1.13$

The solution set is $\{1.13, \ 5.62\}$.

79. $x^2 - 5 = 0$

$$x^2 = 5$$

$$x = \pm\sqrt{5}$$

The solution set is $\left\{-\sqrt{5}, \sqrt{5}\right\}$.

80. $x^2 - 6 = 0$

$$x^2 = 6$$

$$x = \pm\sqrt{6}$$

The solution set is $\left\{-\sqrt{6}, \sqrt{6}\right\}$.

82

81. $16x^2 - 8x + 1 = 0$

$(4x - 1)(4x - 1) = 0$

$4x - 1 = 0$

$x = \dfrac{1}{4}$

The solution set is $\left\{\dfrac{1}{4}\right\}$.

82. $9x^2 - 12x + 4 = 0$

$(3x - 2)(3x - 2) = 0$

$3x - 2 = 0$

$x = \dfrac{2}{3}$

The solution set is $\left\{\dfrac{2}{3}\right\}$.

83. $10x^2 - 19x - 15 = 0$

$(5x + 3)(2x - 5) = 0$

$5x + 3 = 0 \quad \text{or} \quad 2x - 5 = 0$

$x = -\dfrac{3}{5} \quad \text{or} \quad x = \dfrac{5}{2}$

The solution set is $\left\{-\dfrac{3}{5}, \dfrac{5}{2}\right\}$.

84. $6x^2 + 7x - 20 = 0$

$(3x - 4)(2x + 5) = 0$

$3x - 4 = 0 \quad \text{or} \quad 2x + 5 = 0$

$x = \dfrac{4}{3} \quad \text{or} \quad x = -\dfrac{5}{2}$

The solution set is $\left\{-\dfrac{5}{2}, \dfrac{4}{3}\right\}$.

85. $2 + z = 6z^2$

$0 = 6z^2 - z - 2$

$0 = (3z - 2)(2z + 1)$

$3z - 2 = 0 \quad \text{or} \quad 2z + 1 = 0$

$z = \dfrac{2}{3} \quad \text{or} \quad z = -\dfrac{1}{2}$

The solution set is $\left\{-\dfrac{1}{2}, \dfrac{2}{3}\right\}$.

86. $2 = y + 6y^2$

$0 = 6y^2 + y - 2$

$0 = (3y + 2)(2y - 1)$

$3y + 2 = 0 \quad \text{or} \quad 2y - 1 = 0$

$y = -\dfrac{2}{3} \quad \text{or} \quad y = \dfrac{1}{2}$

The solution set is $\left\{-\dfrac{2}{3}, \dfrac{1}{2}\right\}$.

87. $x^2 + \sqrt{2}x = \dfrac{1}{2}$

$x^2 + \sqrt{2}x - \dfrac{1}{2} = 0$

$2\left(x^2 + \sqrt{2}x - \dfrac{1}{2}\right) = 2(0)$

$2x^2 + 2\sqrt{2}x - 1 = 0$

$a = 2, \quad b = 2\sqrt{2}, \quad c = -1$

$x = \dfrac{-(2\sqrt{2}) \pm \sqrt{(2\sqrt{2})^2 - 4(2)(-1)}}{2(2)}$

$= \dfrac{-2\sqrt{2} \pm \sqrt{8 + 8}}{4} = \dfrac{-2\sqrt{2} \pm \sqrt{16}}{4}$

$= \dfrac{-2\sqrt{2} \pm 4}{4} = \dfrac{-\sqrt{2} \pm 2}{2}$

The solution set is $\left\{\dfrac{-\sqrt{2} - 2}{2}, \dfrac{-\sqrt{2} + 2}{2}\right\}$.

88. $\dfrac{1}{2}x^2 = \sqrt{2}x + 1$

$\dfrac{1}{2}x^2 - \sqrt{2}x - 1 = 0$

$2\left(\dfrac{1}{2}x^2 - \sqrt{2}x - 1\right) = 2(0)$

$x^2 - 2\sqrt{2}x - 2 = 0$

$a = 1, \quad b = -2\sqrt{2}, \quad c = -2$

$x = \dfrac{-(-2\sqrt{2}) \pm \sqrt{(-2\sqrt{2})^2 - 4(1)(-2)}}{2(1)}$

$= \dfrac{2\sqrt{2} \pm \sqrt{8 + 8}}{2} = \dfrac{2\sqrt{2} \pm \sqrt{16}}{2}$

$= \dfrac{2\sqrt{2} \pm 4}{2} = \dfrac{\sqrt{2} \pm 2}{1}$

The solution set is $\left\{\sqrt{2} - 2, \sqrt{2} + 2\right\}$.

89. $x^2 + x = 4$

$x^2 + x - 4 = 0$

$a = 1, \quad b = 1, \quad c = -4$

$$x = \frac{-(1) \pm \sqrt{(1)^2 - 4(1)(-4)}}{2(1)}$$

$$= \frac{-1 \pm \sqrt{1+16}}{2} = \frac{-1 \pm \sqrt{17}}{2}$$

The solution set is $\left\{ \dfrac{-1 - \sqrt{17}}{2}, \dfrac{-1 + \sqrt{17}}{2} \right\}$.

90. $x^2 + x = 1$

$x^2 + x - 1 = 0$

$a = 1, \quad b = 1, \quad c = -1$

$$x = \frac{-(1) \pm \sqrt{(1)^2 - 4(1)(-1)}}{2(1)}$$

$$= \frac{-1 \pm \sqrt{1+4}}{2} = \frac{-1 \pm \sqrt{5}}{2}$$

The solution set is $\left\{ \dfrac{-1 - \sqrt{5}}{2}, \dfrac{-1 + \sqrt{5}}{2} \right\}$.

91.

$$\frac{x}{x-2} + \frac{2}{x+1} = \frac{7x+1}{x^2 - x - 2}$$

$$\frac{x}{x-2} + \frac{2}{x+1} = \frac{7x+1}{(x-2)(x+1)}$$

$$\left(\frac{x}{x-2} + \frac{2}{x+1} \right)(x-2)(x+1) = \left(\frac{7x+1}{(x-2)(x+1)} \right)(x-2)(x+1)$$

$$x(x+1) + 2(x-2) = 7x+1$$

$$x^2 + x + 2x - 4 = 7x + 1$$

$$x^2 + 3x - 4 = 7x + 1$$

$$x^2 - 4x - 5 = 0$$

$$(x+1)(x-5) = 0$$

$$x + 1 = 0 \quad \text{or} \quad x - 5 = 0$$

$$x = -1 \quad \text{or} \qquad x = 5$$

The value $x = -1$ causes a denominator to equal zero, so we disregard it. Thus, the solution set is $\{5\}$.

92.

$$\frac{3x}{x+2} + \frac{1}{x-1} = \frac{4-7x}{x^2 + x - 2}$$

$$\frac{3x}{x+2} + \frac{1}{x-1} = \frac{4-7x}{(x+2)(x-1)}$$

$$\left(\frac{3x}{x+2} + \frac{1}{x-1} \right)(x+2)(x-1) = \left(\frac{4-7x}{(x+2)(x-1)} \right)(x+2)(x-1)$$

$$3x(x-1) + (x+2) = 4 - 7x$$

$$3x^2 - 3x + x + 2 = 4 - 7x$$

$$3x^2 - 2x + 2 = 4 - 7x$$

$$3x^2 + 5x - 2 = 0$$

$$(3x-1)(x+2) = 0$$

$$3x - 1 = 0 \quad \text{or} \quad x + 2 = 0$$

$$x = \frac{1}{3} \quad \text{or} \qquad x = -2$$

The value $x = -2$ causes a denominator to equal zero, so we disregard it. Thus, the solution set is $\left\{ \dfrac{1}{3} \right\}$.

93. $2x^2 - 6x + 7 = 0$

$a = 2, \quad b = -6, \quad c = 7$

$b^2 - 4ac = (-6)^2 - 4(2)(7) = 36 - 56 = -20$

Since the $b^2 - 4ac < 0$, the equation has no real solution.

94. $x^2 + 4x + 7 = 0$

$a = 1, \quad b = 4, \quad c = 7$

$b^2 - 4ac = (4)^2 - 4(1)(7) = 16 - 28 = -12$

Since the $b^2 - 4ac < 0$, the equation has no real solution.

95. $9x^2 - 30x + 25 = 0$

$a = 9, \quad b = -30, \quad c = 25$

$b^2 - 4ac = (-30)^2 - 4(9)(25) = 900 - 900 = 0$

Since $b^2 - 4ac = 0$, the equation has one repeated real solution.

96. $25x^2 - 20x + 4 = 0$

$a = 25, \quad b = -20, \quad c = 4$

$b^2 - 4ac = (-20)^2 - 4(25)(4) = 400 - 400 = 0$

Since $b^2 - 4ac = 0$, the equation has one repeated real solution.

97. $3x^2 + 5x - 8 = 0$

$a = 3, \quad b = 5, \quad c = -8$

$b^2 - 4ac = (5)^2 - 4(3)(-8) = 25 + 96 = 121$

Since $b^2 - 4ac > 0$, the equation has two unequal real solutions.

98. $2x^2 - 3x - 7 = 0$

$a = 2, \quad b = -3, \quad c = -7$

$b^2 - 4ac = (-3)^2 - 4(2)(-7) = 9 + 56 = 65$

Since $b^2 - 4ac > 0$, the equation has two unequal real solutions.

99. $20.2x^2 + 314.5x + 3467.6 = 8000$

$20.2x^2 + 314.5x - 4532.4 = 0$

$a = 20.2, \quad b = 314.5, \quad c = -4532.4$

$x = \dfrac{-(314.5) \pm \sqrt{(314.5)^2 - 4(20.2)(-4532.4)}}{2(20.2)}$

$= \dfrac{-314.5 \pm \sqrt{465,128.17}}{40.4}$

$x \approx \cancel{-24.7}$ or $x \approx 9.1$

Disregard the negative solution since we are looking beyond the 2000-2001 academic year. Thus, according to the equation, the average annual tuition-and-fee charges will be $8000 approximately 9.1 years after 2000-2001, which is roughly the academic year 2009-2010.

100. $0.14x^2 + 7.8x + 540 = 632$

$0.14x^2 + 7.8x - 92 = 0$

$a = 0.14, \quad b = 7.8, \quad c = -92$

$x = \dfrac{-(7.8) \pm \sqrt{(7.8)^2 - 4(0.14)(-92)}}{2(0.14)}$

$= \dfrac{-7.8 \pm \sqrt{112.36}}{0.28} = \dfrac{-7.8 \pm 10.6}{0.28}$

$x \approx \cancel{-65.7}$ or $x = 10$

Disregard the negative solution since we are looking beyond the year 2000. Thus, 10 years after 2000, the median weekly earnings for women 16 years and older will be $632. 10 years after 2000. This would be the year 2010.

101. Let w represent the width of window. Then $l = w + 2$ represents the length of the window.

Since the area is 143 square feet, we have:

$w(w + 2) = 143$

$w^2 + 2w - 143 = 0$

$(w + 13)(w - 11) = 0$

$w \cancel{= -13}$ or $w = 11$

Discard the negative solution since width cannot be negative. The width of the rectangular window is 11 feet and the length is 13 feet.

102. Let w represent the width of window. Then $l = w + 1$ represents the length of the window.

Since the area is 306 square centimeters, we have: $w(w + 1) = 306$

$w^2 + w - 306 = 0$

$(w + 18)(w - 17) = 0$

$w \cancel{= -18}$ or $w = 17$

Discard the negative solution since width cannot be negative. The width of the rectangular window is 17 centimeters and the length is 18 centimeters.

85

103. Let l represent the length of the rectangle.
Let w represent the width of the rectangle.
The perimeter is 26 meters and the area is 40 square meters.
$2l + 2w = 26$

$$l + w = 13 \quad \text{so} \quad w = 13 - l$$

$$lw = 40$$

$$l(13 - l) = 40$$

$$13l - l^2 = 40$$

$$l^2 - 13l + 40 = 0$$

$$(l - 8)(l - 5) = 0$$

$$l = 8 \quad \text{or} \quad l = 5$$

$$w = 5 \qquad w = 8$$

The dimensions are 5 meters by 8 meters.

104. Let r represent the radius of the circle.
Since the field is a square with area 1250 square feet, the length of a side of the square is $\sqrt{1250} = 25\sqrt{2}$ feet. The length of the diagonal is $2r$.
Use the Pythagorean Theorem to solve for r:

$$(2r)^2 = \left(25\sqrt{2}\right)^2 + \left(25\sqrt{2}\right)^2$$

$$4r^2 = 1250 + 1250$$

$$4r^2 = 2500$$

$$r^2 = 625$$

$$r = 25$$

The shortest radius setting for the sprinkler is 25 feet.

105. Let $x = $ length of side of original sheet in feet.
Length of box: $x - 2$ feet
Width of box: $x - 2$ feet
Height of box: 1 foot
$V = l \cdot w \cdot h$

$$4 = (x - 2)(x - 2)(1)$$

$$4 = x^2 - 4x + 4$$

$$0 = x^2 - 4x$$

$$0 = x(x - 4)$$

$$x = 0 \quad \text{or} \quad x = 4$$

Discard $x = 0$ since that is not a feasible length for the original sheet. Therefore, the original sheet should measure 4 feet on each side.

106. Let $x = $ width of original sheet in feet.
Length of sheet: $2x$
Length of box: $2x - 2$ feet
Width of box: $x - 2$ feet
Height of box: 1 foot
$V = l \cdot w \cdot h$

$$4 = (2x - 2)(x - 2)(1)$$

$$4 = 2x^2 - 6x + 4$$

$$0 = 2x^2 - 6x$$

$$0 = x^2 - 3x$$

$$0 = x(x - 3)$$

$$x = 0 \quad \text{or} \quad x = 3$$

Discard $x = 0$ since that is not a feasible length for the original sheet. Therefore, the original sheet is 3 feet wide and 6 feet long.

107. a. When the ball strikes the ground, the distance from the ground will be 0. Therefore, we solve

$$96 + 80t - 16t^2 = 0$$

$$-16t^2 + 80t + 96 = 0$$

$$t^2 - 5t - 6 = 0$$

$$(t - 6)(t + 1) = 0$$

$$t = 6 \quad \text{or} \quad t = -1$$

Discard the negative solution since the time of flight must be positive. The ball will strike the ground after 6 seconds.

b. When the ball passes the top of the building, it will be 96 feet from the ground. Therefore, we solve

$$96 + 80t - 16t^2 = 96$$

$$-16t^2 + 80t = 0$$

$$t^2 - 5t = 0$$

$$t(t - 5) = 0$$

$$t = 0 \quad \text{or} \quad t = 5$$

The ball is at the top of the building at time $t = 0$ when it is thrown. It will pass the top of the building on the way down after 5 seconds.

108. a. To find when the object will be 15 meters above the ground, we solve

$$-4.9t^2 + 20t = 15$$

$$-4.9t^2 + 20t - 15 = 0$$

$$a = -4.9, \ b = 20, \ c = -15$$

$$t = \frac{-20 \pm \sqrt{20^2 - 4(-4.9)(-15)}}{2(-4.9)}$$

$$= \frac{-20 \pm \sqrt{106}}{-9.8} = \frac{20 \pm \sqrt{106}}{9.8}$$

$$t \approx 0.99 \quad \text{or} \quad t \approx 3.09$$

The object will be 15 meters above the ground after about 0.99 seconds (on the way up) and about 3.09 seconds (on the way down).

b. The object will strike the ground when the distance from the ground is 0. Therefore, we solve

$$-4.9t^2 + 20t = 0$$

$$t(-4.9t + 20) = 0$$

$$t = 0 \quad \text{or} \quad -4.9t + 20 = 0$$

$$-4.9t = -20$$

$$t \approx 4.08$$

The object will strike the ground after about 4.08 seconds.

c.
$$-4.9t^2 + 20t = 100$$

$$-4.9t^2 + 20t - 100 = 0$$

$$a = -4.9, \ b = 20, \ c = -100$$

$$t = \frac{-20 \pm \sqrt{20^2 - 4(-4.9)(-100)}}{2(-4.9)}$$

$$= \frac{-20 \pm \sqrt{-1560}}{-9.8}$$

There is no real solution. The object never reaches a height of 100 meters.

109. Let x represent the number of centimeters the length and width should be reduced.
$12 - x$ = the new length, $7 - x$ = the new width.
The new volume is 90% of the old volume.
$$(12 - x)(7 - x)(3) = 0.9(12)(7)(3)$$

$$3x^2 - 57x + 252 = 226.8$$

$$3x^2 - 57x + 25.2 = 0$$

$$x^2 - 19x + 8.4 = 0$$

$$x = \frac{-(-19) \pm \sqrt{(-19)^2 - 4(1)(8.4)}}{2(1)} = \frac{19 \pm \sqrt{327.4}}{2}$$

$$x \approx 0.45 \quad \text{or} \quad x \approx 18.55$$

Since 18.55 exceeds the dimensions, it is discarded. The dimensions of the new chocolate bar are: 11.55 cm by 6.55 cm by 3 cm.

110. Let x represent the number of centimeters the length and width should be reduced.
$12 - x$ = the new length, $7 - x$ = the new width.
The new volume is 80% of the old volume.
$$(12 - x)(7 - x)(3) = 0.8(12)(7)(3)$$

$$3x^2 - 57x + 252 = 201.6$$

$$3x^2 - 57x + 50.4 = 0$$

$$x^2 - 19x + 16.8 = 0$$

$$x = \frac{-(-19) \pm \sqrt{(-19)^2 - 4(1)(16.8)}}{2(1)} = \frac{19 \pm \sqrt{293.8}}{2}$$

$$x \approx 0.93 \quad \text{or} \quad x \approx 18.07$$

Since 18.07 exceeds the dimensions, it is discarded. The dimensions of the new chocolate bar are: 11.07 cm by 6.07 cm by 3 cm.

111. Let x represent the width of the border measured in feet. The radius of the pool is 5 feet. Then $x + 5$ represents the radius of the circle, including both the pool and the border. The total area of the pool and border is
$$A_T = \pi(x + 5)^2 .$$

The area of the pool is $A_P = \pi(5)^2 = 25\pi$.
The area of the border is
$$A_B = A_T - A_P = \pi(x + 5)^2 - 25\pi .$$

Since the concrete is 3 inches or 0.25 feet thick, the volume of the concrete in the border is
$$0.25A_B = 0.25\left(\pi(x + 5)^2 - 25\pi\right)$$

Solving the volume equation:
$$0.25\left(\pi(x + 5)^2 - 25\pi\right) = 27$$

$$\pi\left(x^2 + 10x + 25 - 25\right) = 108$$

$$\pi x^2 + 10\pi x - 108 = 0$$

$$x = \frac{-10\pi \pm \sqrt{(10\pi)^2 - 4(\pi)(-108)}}{2(\pi)}$$

$$= \frac{-31.42 \pm \sqrt{100\pi^2 + 432\pi}}{6.28}$$

$$x \approx 2.71 \quad \text{or} \quad x \approx -12.71$$

Discard the negative solution. The width of the border is roughly 2.71 feet.

112. Let x represent the width of the border measured in feet. The radius of the pool is 5 feet. Then $x + 5$ represents the radius of the circle, including both the pool and the border. The total area of the pool and border is

$$A_T = \pi(x+5)^2 .$$

The area of the pool is $A_P = \pi(5)^2 = 25\pi$.

The area of the border is

$$A_B = A_T - A_P = \pi(x+5)^2 - 25\pi .$$

Since the concrete is 4 inches $= \frac{1}{3}$ foot thick, the volume of the concrete in the border is

$$\frac{1}{3}A_B = \frac{1}{3}\left(\pi(x+5)^2 - 25\pi\right)$$

Solving the volume equation:

$$\frac{1}{3}\left(\pi(x+5)^2 - 25\pi\right) = 27$$

$$\pi\left(x^2 + 10x + 25 - 25\right) = 81$$

$$\pi x^2 + 10\pi x - 81 = 0$$

$$x = \frac{-10\pi \pm \sqrt{(10\pi)^2 - 4(\pi)(-81)}}{2(\pi)}$$

$$= \frac{-31.42 \pm \sqrt{100\pi^2 + 324\pi}}{6.28}$$

$$x \approx 2.13 \text{ or } x \approx -12.13$$

Discard the negative solution. The width of the border is approximately 2.13 feet.

113. Let x represent the width of the border measured in feet.

The total area is $A_T = (6+2x)(10+2x)$.

The area of the garden is $A_G = 6 \cdot 10 = 60$.

The area of the border is

$$A_B = A_T - A_G = (6+2x)(10+2x) - 60 .$$

Since the concrete is 3 inches or 0.25 feet thick, the volume of the concrete in the border is

$$0.25 A_B = 0.25\left((6+2x)(10+2x) - 60\right)$$

Solving the volume equation:

$$0.25\left((6+2x)(10+2x) - 60\right) = 27$$

$$60 + 32x + 4x^2 - 60 = 108$$

$$4x^2 + 32x - 108 = 0$$

$$x^2 + 8x - 27 = 0$$

$$x = \frac{-8 \pm \sqrt{8^2 - 4(1)(-27)}}{2(1)} = \frac{-8 \pm \sqrt{172}}{2}$$

$$x \approx 2.56 \text{ or } x \approx -10.56$$

Discard the negative solution. The width of the border is approximately 2.56 feet.

114. Let $x =$ the width and $2x =$ the length of the patio. The height is $\frac{1}{3}$ foot and the concrete available is $8(27) = 216$ cubic feet..

$$V = lwh = x(2x) \cdot \frac{1}{3} = 216$$

$$\frac{2}{3}x^2 = 216$$

$$x^2 = 324$$

$$x = \pm 18$$

The dimensions of the patio are 18 feet by 36 feet.

115. Let $x =$ the length of a traditional 4:3 format TV.

Then $\frac{3}{4}x =$ the width of the traditional TV.

The diagonal of the 37-inch traditional TV is 37 inches, so by the Pythagorean theorem we have:

$$x^2 + \left(\frac{3}{4}x\right)^2 = 37^2$$

$$x^2 + \frac{9}{16}x^2 = 1369$$

$$16\left(x^2 + \frac{9}{16}x^2\right) = 16(1369)$$

$$16x^2 + 9x^2 = 21,904$$

$$25x^2 = 21,904$$

$$x^2 = 876.16$$

$$x = \pm\sqrt{876.16} = \pm 29.6$$

Since the length cannot be negative, the length of the traditional 37-inch TV is 29.6 inches and the width is $\frac{3}{4}(29.6) = 22.2$ inches. Thus, the area of the traditional 37-inch TV is $(29.6)(22.2) = 657.12$ square inches.

Let $y =$ the length of a 37-inch 16:9 LCD TV.

Then $\frac{9}{16}y =$ the width of the LCD TV.

The diagonal of a 37-inch LCD TV is 37 inches, so by the Pythagorean theorem we have:

$$y^2 + \left(\frac{9}{16}y\right)^2 = 37^2$$

$$y^2 + \frac{81}{256}y^2 = 1369$$

$$256\left(y^2 + \frac{81}{256}y^2\right) = 256(1369)$$

$$256y^2 + 81y^2 = 350,464$$

$$337y^2 = 350,464$$

$$y^2 = \frac{350,464}{337}$$

$$y = \pm\sqrt{\frac{350,464}{337}} \approx \pm 32.248$$

Since the length cannot be negative, the length of

the LCD TV is $\sqrt{\dfrac{350,464}{337}} \approx 32.248$ inches and the

width is $\dfrac{9}{16}\sqrt{\dfrac{350,464}{337}} \approx 18.140$ inches. Thus, the

area of the 37-inch 16:9 format LCD TV is

$$\left(\sqrt{\frac{350,464}{337}}\right)\left(\frac{9}{16}\sqrt{\frac{350,464}{337}}\right)$$

$$= \frac{197,136}{337} \approx 584.97 \text{ square inches.}$$

The traditional 4:3 format TV has the larger screen since its area is larger.

116. Let x = the length of a traditional 4:3 format TV.

Then $\dfrac{3}{4}x$ = the width of the traditional TV.

The diagonal of the 50-inch traditional TV is 50 inches, so by the Pythagorean theorem we have:

$$x^2 + \left(\frac{3}{4}x\right)^2 = 50^2$$

$$x^2 + \frac{9}{16}x^2 = 2500$$

$$16\left(x^2 + \frac{9}{16}x^2\right) = 16(2500)$$

$$16x^2 + 9x^2 = 40,000$$

$$25x^2 = 40,000$$

$$x^2 = 1600$$

$$x = \pm\sqrt{1600} = \pm 40$$

Since the length cannot be negative, the length of the traditional TV is 40 inches and the width is

$\dfrac{3}{4}(40) = 30$ inches. Thus, the area of the 50-inch

traditional TV is $(40)(30) = 1200$ square inches.

Let y = the length of a 50-inch 16:9 Plasma TV.

Then $\dfrac{9}{16}y$ = the width of the Plasma TV.

The diagonal of the 50-inch Plasma TV is 50 inches, so by the Pythagorean theorem we have:

$$y^2 + \left(\frac{9}{16}y\right)^2 = 50^2$$

$$y^2 + \frac{81}{256}y^2 = 2500$$

$$256\left(y^2 + \frac{81}{256}y^2\right) = 256(2500)$$

$$256y^2 + 81y^2 = 640,000$$

$$337y^2 = 640,000$$

$$y^2 = \frac{640,000}{337}$$

$$y = \pm\sqrt{\frac{640,000}{337}} \approx \pm 43.578$$

Since the length cannot be negative, the length of

the Plasma TV is $\sqrt{\dfrac{640,000}{337}} \approx 43.578$ inches

and the width is $\dfrac{9}{16}\sqrt{\dfrac{640,000}{337}} \approx 24.513$ inches.

Thus, the area of the 50-inch Plasma TV is

$$\left(\sqrt{\frac{640,000}{337}}\right)\left(\frac{9}{16}\sqrt{\frac{640,000}{337}}\right)$$

$$= \frac{360,000}{337} \approx 1068.25 \text{ square inches.}$$

The traditional 4:3 format TV has the larger screen since its area is larger.

117. $$\frac{1}{2}n(n+1) = 666$$

$$n(n+1) = 1332$$

$$n^2 + n - 1332 = 0$$

$$(n-36)(n+37) = 0$$

$$n = 36 \quad \text{or} \quad n = -37$$

Since the number of consecutive integers cannot be negative, we discard the negative value. We must add 36 consecutive integers, beginning at 1, in order to get a sum of 666.

118.
$$\frac{1}{2}n(n-3) = 65$$
$$n(n-3) = 130$$
$$n^2 - 3n - 130 = 0$$
$$(n-13)(n+10) = 0$$
$$n = 13 \quad \text{or} \quad n = -10$$

Since the number of sides cannot be negative, we discard the negative value. A polygon with 65 diagonals will have 13 sides.

$$\frac{1}{2}n(n-3) = 80$$
$$n(n-3) = 160$$
$$n^2 - 3n - 160 = 0$$
$$a = 1, b = -3, c = -160$$
$$n = \frac{3 \pm \sqrt{(-3)^2 - 4(1)(-160)}}{2(1)} = \frac{3 \pm \sqrt{646}}{2}$$

Neither solution is an integer, so there is no polygon that has 80 diagonals.

119. The roots of a quadratic equation are
$$x_1 = \frac{-b - \sqrt{b^2 - 4ac}}{2a} \quad \text{and} \quad x_2 = \frac{-b + \sqrt{b^2 - 4ac}}{2a}$$
$$x_1 + x_2 = \frac{-b - \sqrt{b^2 - 4ac}}{2a} + \frac{-b + \sqrt{b^2 - 4ac}}{2a}$$
$$= \frac{-b - \sqrt{b^2 - 4ac} - b + \sqrt{b^2 - 4ac}}{2a}$$
$$= \frac{-2b}{2a}$$
$$= -\frac{b}{a}$$

120. The roots of a quadratic equation are
$$x_1 = \frac{-b - \sqrt{b^2 - 4ac}}{2a} \quad \text{and} \quad x_2 = \frac{-b + \sqrt{b^2 - 4ac}}{2a}$$
$$x_1 \cdot x_2 = \left(\frac{-b - \sqrt{b^2 - 4ac}}{2a}\right)\left(\frac{-b + \sqrt{b^2 - 4ac}}{2a}\right)$$
$$= \frac{(-b)^2 - \left(\sqrt{b^2 - 4ac}\right)^2}{(2a)^2} = \frac{b^2 - b^2 + 4ac}{4a^2}$$
$$= \frac{4ac}{4a^2}$$
$$= \frac{c}{a}$$

121. In order to have one repeated solution, we need the discriminant to be 0.
$$b^2 - 4ac = 0$$
$$1^2 - 4(k)(k) = 0$$
$$1 - 4k^2 = 0$$
$$4k^2 = 1$$
$$k^2 = \frac{1}{4}$$
$$k = \pm\sqrt{\frac{1}{4}}$$
$$k = \frac{1}{2} \quad \text{or} \quad k = -\frac{1}{2}$$

122. In order to have one repeated solution, we need the discriminant to be 0.
$$b^2 - 4ac = 0$$
$$(-k)^2 - 4(1)(4) = 0$$
$$k^2 - 16 = 0$$
$$(k-4)(k+4) = 0$$
$$k = 4 \quad \text{or} \quad k = -4$$

123. For $ax^2 + bx + c = 0$:
$$x_1 = \frac{-b - \sqrt{b^2 - 4ac}}{2a} \quad \text{and} \quad x_2 = \frac{-b + \sqrt{b^2 - 4ac}}{2a}$$

For $ax^2 - bx + c = 0$:
$$x_1{}^* = \frac{-(-b) - \sqrt{(-b)^2 - 4ac}}{2a}$$
$$= \frac{b - \sqrt{b^2 - 4ac}}{2a}$$
$$= -\left(\frac{-b + \sqrt{b^2 - 4ac}}{2a}\right)$$
$$= -x_2$$

and
$$x_2{}^* = \frac{-(-b) + \sqrt{(-b)^2 - 4ac}}{2a}$$
$$= \frac{b + \sqrt{b^2 - 4ac}}{2a}$$
$$= -\left(\frac{-b - \sqrt{b^2 - 4ac}}{2a}\right)$$
$$= -x_1$$

124. For $ax^2 + bx + c = 0$:

$$x_1 = \frac{-b - \sqrt{b^2 - 4ac}}{2a} \text{ and } x_2 = \frac{-b + \sqrt{b^2 - 4ac}}{2a}$$

For $cx^2 + bx + a = 0$:

$$x_1^* = \frac{-b - \sqrt{b^2 - 4(c)(a)}}{2c} = \frac{-b - \sqrt{b^2 - 4ac}}{2c}$$

$$= \frac{-b - \sqrt{b^2 - 4ac}}{2c} \cdot \frac{-b + \sqrt{b^2 - 4ac}}{-b + \sqrt{b^2 - 4ac}}$$

$$= \frac{b^2 - \left(b^2 - 4ac\right)}{2c\left(-b + \sqrt{b^2 - 4ac}\right)} = \frac{4ac}{2c\left(-b + \sqrt{b^2 - 4ac}\right)}$$

$$= \frac{2a}{-b + \sqrt{b^2 - 4ac}}$$

$$= \frac{1}{x_2}$$

and

$$x_2^* = \frac{-b + \sqrt{b^2 - 4(c)(a)}}{2c} = \frac{-b + \sqrt{b^2 - 4ac}}{2c}$$

$$= \frac{-b + \sqrt{b^2 - 4ac}}{2c} \cdot \frac{-b - \sqrt{b^2 - 4ac}}{-b - \sqrt{b^2 - 4ac}}$$

$$= \frac{b^2 - \left(b^2 - 4ac\right)}{2c\left(-b - \sqrt{b^2 - 4ac}\right)} = \frac{4ac}{2c\left(-b - \sqrt{b^2 - 4ac}\right)}$$

$$= \frac{2a}{-b - \sqrt{b^2 - 4ac}}$$

$$= \frac{1}{x_1}$$

125. a. $x^2 = 9$ and $x = 3$ are not equivalent because they do not have the same solution set. In the first equation we can also have $x = -3$.

b. $x = \sqrt{9}$ and $x = 3$ are equivalent because $\sqrt{9} = 3$.

c. $(x-1)(x-2) = (x-1)^2$ and $x - 2 = x - 1$ are not equivalent because they do not have the same solution set.

The first equation has the solution set $\{1\}$ while the second equation has no solutions.

126. Answers will vary. Methods may include the quadratic formula, completing the square, graphing, etc.

127. Answers will vary. Knowing the discriminant allows us to know how many real solutions the equation will have.

128. Answers will vary. One possibility:

Two distinct: $x^2 - 3x - 18 = 0$

One repeated: $x^2 - 14x + 49 = 0$

No real: $x^2 + x + 4 = 0$

129. Answers will vary.

Section 1.3

1. Integers: $\{-3, 0\}$

Rationals: $\left\{-3, 0, \dfrac{6}{5}\right\}$

2. True; the set of real numbers consists of all rational and irrational numbers.

3. $\dfrac{3}{2 + \sqrt{3}} = \dfrac{3}{2 + \sqrt{3}} \cdot \dfrac{2 - \sqrt{3}}{2 - \sqrt{3}}$

$$= \dfrac{3\left(2 - \sqrt{3}\right)}{2^2 - \left(\sqrt{3}\right)^2}$$

$$= \dfrac{3\left(2 - \sqrt{3}\right)}{4 - 3}$$

$$= 3\left(2 - \sqrt{3}\right)$$

4. real; imaginary; imaginary unit

5. $\{-2i, 2i\}$

6. False; the conjugate of $2 + 5i$ is $2 - 5i$.

7. True; the set of real numbers is a subset of the set of complex numbers.

8. False; if $2 - 3i$ is a solution of a quadratic equation with real coefficients, then its conjugate, $2 + 3i$, is also a solution.

9. $(2 - 3i) + (6 + 8i) = (2 + 6) + (-3 + 8)i = 8 + 5i$

10. $(4 + 5i) + (-8 + 2i) = (4 + (-8)) + (5 + 2)i$
$$= -4 + 7i$$

11. $(-3+2i)-(4-4i)=(-3-4)+(2-(-4))i$
$$=-7+6i$$

12. $(3-4i)-(-3-4i)=(3-(-3))+(-4-(-4))i$
$$=6+0i=6$$

13. $(2-5i)-(8+6i)=(2-8)+(-5-6)i$
$$=-6-11i$$

14. $(-8+4i)-(2-2i)=(-8-2)+(4-(-2))i$
$$=-10+6i$$

15. $3(2-6i)=6-18i$

16. $-4(2+8i)=-8-32i$

17. $2i(2-3i)=4i-6i^2=4i-6(-1)=6+4i$

18. $3i(-3+4i)=-9i+12i^2=-9i+12(-1)=-12-9i$

19. $(3-4i)(2+i)=6+3i-8i-4i^2$
$$=6-5i-4(-1)$$
$$=10-5i$$

20. $(5+3i)(2-i)=10-5i+6i-3i^2$
$$=10+i-3(-1)$$
$$=13+i$$

21. $(-6+i)(-6-i)=36+6i-6i-i^2$
$$=36-(-1)$$
$$=37$$

22. $(-3+i)(3+i)=-9-3i+3i+i^2$
$$=-9+(-1)$$
$$=-10$$

23. $\dfrac{10}{3-4i}=\dfrac{10}{3-4i}\cdot\dfrac{3+4i}{3+4i}=\dfrac{30+40i}{9+12i-12i-16i^2}$
$$=\dfrac{30+40i}{9-16(-1)}=\dfrac{30+40i}{25}$$
$$=\dfrac{30}{25}+\dfrac{40}{25}i$$
$$=\dfrac{6}{5}+\dfrac{8}{5}i$$

24. $\dfrac{13}{5-12i}=\dfrac{13}{5-12i}\cdot\dfrac{5+12i}{5+12i}$
$$=\dfrac{65+156i}{25+60i-60i-144i^2}$$
$$=\dfrac{65+156i}{25-144(-1)}=\dfrac{65+156i}{169}$$
$$=\dfrac{65}{169}+\dfrac{156}{169}i$$
$$=\dfrac{5}{13}+\dfrac{12}{13}i$$

25. $\dfrac{2+i}{i}=\dfrac{2+i}{i}\cdot\dfrac{-i}{-i}=\dfrac{-2i-i^2}{-i^2}$
$$=\dfrac{-2i-(-1)}{-(-1)}=\dfrac{1-2i}{1}=1-2i$$

26. $\dfrac{2-i}{-2i}=\dfrac{2-i}{-2i}\cdot\dfrac{i}{i}=\dfrac{2i-i^2}{-2i^2}$
$$=\dfrac{2i-(-1)}{-2(-1)}=\dfrac{1+2i}{2}=\dfrac{1}{2}+i$$

27. $\dfrac{6-i}{1+i}=\dfrac{6-i}{1+i}\cdot\dfrac{1-i}{1-i}=\dfrac{6-6i-i+i^2}{1-i+i-i^2}$
$$=\dfrac{6-7i+(-1)}{1-(-1)}=\dfrac{5-7i}{2}=\dfrac{5}{2}-\dfrac{7}{2}i$$

28. $\dfrac{2+3i}{1-i}=\dfrac{2+3i}{1-i}\cdot\dfrac{1+i}{1+i}=\dfrac{2+2i+3i+3i^2}{1+i-i-i^2}$
$$=\dfrac{2+5i+3(-1)}{1-(-1)}=\dfrac{-1+5i}{2}=-\dfrac{1}{2}+\dfrac{5}{2}i$$

29. $\left(\dfrac{1}{2}+\dfrac{\sqrt{3}}{2}i\right)^2=\dfrac{1}{4}+2\left(\dfrac{1}{2}\right)\left(\dfrac{\sqrt{3}}{2}i\right)+\dfrac{3}{4}i^2$
$$=\dfrac{1}{4}+\dfrac{\sqrt{3}}{2}i+\dfrac{3}{4}(-1)=-\dfrac{1}{2}+\dfrac{\sqrt{3}}{2}i$$

30. $\left(\dfrac{\sqrt{3}}{2}-\dfrac{1}{2}i\right)^2=\dfrac{3}{4}-2\left(\dfrac{\sqrt{3}}{2}\right)\left(\dfrac{1}{2}i\right)+\dfrac{1}{4}i^2$
$$=\dfrac{3}{4}-\dfrac{\sqrt{3}}{2}i+\dfrac{1}{4}(-1)=\dfrac{1}{2}-\dfrac{\sqrt{3}}{2}i$$

31. $(1+i)^2=1+2i+i^2=1+2i+(-1)=2i$

32. $(1-i)^2=1-2i+i^2=1-2i+(-1)=-2i$

33. $i^{23} = i^{22+1} = i^{22} \cdot i = \left(i^2\right)^{11} \cdot i = (-1)^{11} i = -i$

34. $i^{14} = \left(i^2\right)^7 = (-1)^7 = -1$

35. $i^{-15} = \dfrac{1}{i^{15}} = \dfrac{1}{i^{14+1}} = \dfrac{1}{i^{14} \cdot i} = \dfrac{1}{\left(i^2\right)^7 \cdot i}$

$\qquad = \dfrac{1}{(-1)^7 i} = \dfrac{1}{-i} = \dfrac{1}{-i} \cdot \dfrac{i}{i} = \dfrac{i}{-i^2} = \dfrac{i}{-(-1)} = i$

36. $i^{-23} = \dfrac{1}{i^{23}} = \dfrac{1}{i^{22+1}} = \dfrac{1}{i^{22} \cdot i} = \dfrac{1}{\left(i^2\right)^{11} \cdot i}$

$\qquad = \dfrac{1}{(-1)^{11} i} = \dfrac{1}{-i} = \dfrac{1}{-i} \cdot \dfrac{i}{i} = \dfrac{i}{-i^2} = \dfrac{i}{-(-1)} = i$

37. $i^6 - 5 = \left(i^2\right)^3 - 5 = (-1)^3 - 5 = -1 - 5 = -6$

38. $4 + i^3 = 4 + i^2 \cdot i = 4 + (-1)i = 4 - i$

39. $6i^3 - 4i^5 = i^3\left(6 - 4i^2\right)$

$\qquad = i^2 \cdot i(6 - 4(-1)) = -1 \cdot i(10) = -10i$

40. $4i^3 - 2i^2 + 1 = 4i^2 \cdot i - 2i^2 + 1$

$\qquad = 4(-1)i - 2(-1) + 1$

$\qquad = -4i + 2 + 1$

$\qquad = 3 - 4i$

41. $(1+i)^3 = (1+i)(1+i)(1+i) = (1 + 2i + i^2)(1+i)$

$\qquad = (1 + 2i - 1)(1+i) = 2i(1+i)$

$\qquad = 2i + 2i^2 = 2i + 2(-1)$

$\qquad = -2 + 2i$

42. $(3i)^4 + 1 = 81i^4 + 1 = 81(1) + 1 = 82$

43. $i^7(1 + i^2) = i^7(1 + (-1)) = i^7(0) = 0$

44. $2i^4(1 + i^2) = 2(1)(1 + (-1)) = 2(0) = 0$

45. $i^6 + i^4 + i^2 + 1 = \left(i^2\right)^3 + \left(i^2\right)^2 + i^2 + 1$

$\qquad = (-1)^3 + (-1)^2 + (-1) + 1$

$\qquad = -1 + 1 - 1 + 1$

$\qquad = 0$

46. $i^7 + i^5 + i^3 + i = \left(i^2\right)^3 \cdot i + \left(i^2\right)^2 \cdot i + i^2 \cdot i + i$

$\qquad = (-1)^3 \cdot i + (-1)^2 \cdot i + (-1) \cdot i + i$

$\qquad = -i + i - i + i$

$\qquad = 0$

47. $\sqrt{-4} = 2i$

48. $\sqrt{-9} = 3i$

49. $\sqrt{-25} = 5i$

50. $\sqrt{-64} = 8i$

51. $\sqrt{(3 + 4i)(4i - 3)} = \sqrt{12i - 9 + 16i^2 - 12i}$

$\qquad = \sqrt{-9 + 16(-1)}$

$\qquad = \sqrt{-25}$

$\qquad = 5i$

52. $\sqrt{(4 + 3i)(3i - 4)} = \sqrt{12i - 16 + 9i^2 - 12i}$

$\qquad = \sqrt{-16 + 9(-1)}$

$\qquad = \sqrt{-25}$

$\qquad = 5i$

53. $x^2 + 4 = 0$

$\qquad x^2 = -4$

$\qquad x = \pm\sqrt{-4}$

$\qquad x = \pm 2i$

The solution set is $\{-2i, 2i\}$.

54. $x^2 - 4 = 0$

$\qquad (x+2)(x-2) = 0$

$\qquad x = -2 \text{ or } x = 2$

The solution set is $\{-2, 2\}$.

55. $x^2 - 16 = 0$

$\qquad (x+4)(x-4) = 0$

$\qquad x = -4 \text{ or } x = 4$

The solution set is $\{-4, 4\}$.

93

56. $x^2 + 25 = 0$

$x^2 = -25$

$x = \pm\sqrt{-25} = \pm 5i$

The solution set is $\{-5i, 5i\}$.

57. $x^2 - 6x + 13 = 0$

$a = 1, b = -6, c = 13,$

$b^2 - 4ac = (-6)^2 - 4(1)(13) = 36 - 52 = -16$

$x = \dfrac{-(-6) \pm \sqrt{-16}}{2(1)} = \dfrac{6 \pm 4i}{2} = 3 \pm 2i$

The solution set is $\{3 - 2i, 3 + 2i\}$.

58. $x^2 + 4x + 8 = 0$

$a = 1, b = 4, c = 8$

$b^2 - 4ac = 4^2 - 4(1)(8) = 16 - 32 = -16$

$x = \dfrac{-4 \pm \sqrt{-16}}{2(1)} = \dfrac{-4 \pm 4i}{2} = -2 \pm 2i$

The solution set is $\{-2 - 2i, -2 + 2i\}$.

59. $x^2 - 6x + 10 = 0$

$a = 1, b = -6, c = 10$

$b^2 - 4ac = (-6)^2 - 4(1)(10) = 36 - 40 = -4$

$x = \dfrac{-(-6) \pm \sqrt{-4}}{2(1)} = \dfrac{6 \pm 2i}{2} = 3 \pm i$

The solution set is $\{3 - i, 3 + i\}$.

60. $x^2 - 2x + 5 = 0$

$a = 1, b = -2, c = 5$

$b^2 - 4ac = (-2)^2 - 4(1)(5) = 4 - 20 = -16$

$x = \dfrac{-(-2) \pm \sqrt{-16}}{2(1)} = \dfrac{2 \pm 4i}{2} = 1 \pm 2i$

The solution set is $\{1 - 2i, 1 + 2i\}$.

61. $8x^2 - 4x + 1 = 0$

$a = 8, b = -4, c = 1$

$b^2 - 4ac = (-4)^2 - 4(8)(1) = 16 - 32 = -16$

$x = \dfrac{-(-4) \pm \sqrt{-16}}{2(8)} = \dfrac{4 \pm 4i}{16} = \dfrac{1}{4} \pm \dfrac{1}{4}i$

The solution set is $\left\{ \dfrac{1}{4} - \dfrac{1}{4}i, \ \dfrac{1}{4} + \dfrac{1}{4}i \right\}$.

62. $10x^2 + 6x + 1 = 0$

$a = 10, b = 6, c = 1$

$b^2 - 4ac = 6^2 - 4(10)(1) = 36 - 40 = -4$

$x = \dfrac{-6 \pm \sqrt{-4}}{2(10)} = \dfrac{-6 \pm 2i}{20} = -\dfrac{3}{10} \pm \dfrac{1}{10}i$

The solution set is $\left\{ -\dfrac{3}{10} - \dfrac{1}{10}i, \ -\dfrac{3}{10} + \dfrac{1}{10}i \right\}$.

63. $5x^2 + 1 = 2x$

$5x^2 - 2x + 1 = 0$

$a = 5, b = -2, c = 1$

$b^2 - 4ac = (-2)^2 - 4(5)(1) = 4 - 20 = -16$

$x = \dfrac{-(-2) \pm \sqrt{-16}}{2(5)} = \dfrac{2 \pm 4i}{10} = \dfrac{1}{5} \pm \dfrac{2}{5}i$

The solution set is $\left\{ \dfrac{1}{5} - \dfrac{2}{5}i, \ \dfrac{1}{5} + \dfrac{2}{5}i \right\}$.

64. $13x^2 + 1 = 6x$

$13x^2 - 6x + 1 = 0$

$a = 13, b = -6, c = 1$

$b^2 - 4ac = (-6)^2 - 4(13)(1) = 36 - 52 = -16$

$x = \dfrac{-(-6) \pm \sqrt{-16}}{2(13)} = \dfrac{6 \pm 4i}{26} = \dfrac{3}{13} \pm \dfrac{2}{13}i$

The solution set is $\left\{ \dfrac{3}{13} - \dfrac{2}{13}i, \ \dfrac{3}{13} + \dfrac{2}{13}i \right\}$.

65. $x^2 + x + 1 = 0$

$a = 1, b = 1, c = 1,$

$b^2 - 4ac = 1^2 - 4(1)(1) = 1 - 4 = -3$

$x = \dfrac{-1 \pm \sqrt{-3}}{2(1)} = \dfrac{-1 \pm \sqrt{3}i}{2} = -\dfrac{1}{2} \pm \dfrac{\sqrt{3}}{2}i$

The solution set is $\left\{ -\dfrac{1}{2} - \dfrac{\sqrt{3}}{2}i, \ -\dfrac{1}{2} + \dfrac{\sqrt{3}}{2}i \right\}$.

66. $x^2 - x + 1 = 0$

$a = 1, b = -1, c = 1$

$b^2 - 4ac = (-1)^2 - 4(1)(1) = 1 - 4 = -3$

$x = \dfrac{-(-1) \pm \sqrt{-3}}{2(1)} = \dfrac{1 \pm \sqrt{3}i}{2} = \dfrac{1}{2} \pm \dfrac{\sqrt{3}}{2}i$

The solution set is $\left\{ \dfrac{1}{2} - \dfrac{\sqrt{3}}{2}i, \ \dfrac{1}{2} + \dfrac{\sqrt{3}}{2}i \right\}$.

67. $x^3 - 8 = 0$

$(x-2)(x^2 + 2x + 4) = 0$

$x - 2 = 0 \Rightarrow x = 2$

or $x^2 + 2x + 4 = 0$

$a = 1, b = 2, c = 4$

$b^2 - 4ac = 2^2 - 4(1)(4) = 4 - 16 = -12$

$x = \dfrac{-2 \pm \sqrt{-12}}{2(1)} = \dfrac{-2 \pm 2\sqrt{3}\,i}{2} = -1 \pm \sqrt{3}i$

The solution set is $\left\{2, -1 - \sqrt{3}i, -1 + \sqrt{3}i\right\}$.

68. $x^3 + 27 = 0$

$(x+3)(x^2 - 3x + 9) = 0$

$x + 3 = 0 \Rightarrow x = -3$

or $x^2 - 3x + 9 = 0$

$a = 1, b = -3, c = 9$

$b^2 - 4ac = (-3)^2 - 4(1)(9) = 9 - 36 = -27$

$x = \dfrac{-(-3) \pm \sqrt{-27}}{2(1)} = \dfrac{3 \pm 3\sqrt{3}\,i}{2} = \dfrac{3}{2} \pm \dfrac{3\sqrt{3}}{2}i$

The solution set is $\left\{-3, \dfrac{3}{2} - \dfrac{3\sqrt{3}}{2}i, \dfrac{3}{2} + \dfrac{3\sqrt{3}}{2}i\right\}$.

69. $\qquad\qquad x^4 = 16$

$x^4 - 16 = 0$

$(x^2 - 4)(x^2 + 4) = 0$

$(x-2)(x+2)(x^2 + 4) = 0$

$x - 2 = 0$ or $x + 2 = 0$ or $x^2 + 4 = 0$

$x = 2$ or $x = -2$ or $x^2 = -4$

$x = 2$ or $x = -2$ or $x = \pm\sqrt{-4} = \pm 2i$

The solution set is $\{-2, 2, -2i, 2i\}$.

70. $\qquad\qquad x^4 = 1$

$x^4 - 1 = 0$

$(x^2 - 1)(x^2 + 1) = 0$

$(x-1)(x+1)(x^2 + 1) = 0$

$x - 1 = 0$ or $x + 1 = 0$ or $x^2 + 1 = 0$

$x = 1$ or $x = -1$ or $x^2 = -1$

$x = 1$ or $x = -1$ or $x = \pm\sqrt{-1} = \pm i$

The solution set is $\{-1, 1, -i, i\}$.

71. $x^4 + 13x^2 + 36 = 0$

$(x^2 + 9)(x^2 + 4) = 0$

$x^2 + 9 = 0$ or $x^2 + 4 = 0$

$x^2 = -9$ or $x^2 = -4$

$x = \pm\sqrt{-9}$ or $x = \pm\sqrt{-4}$

$x = \pm 3i$ or $x = \pm 2i$

The solution set is $\{-3i, 3i, -2i, 2i\}$.

72. $\qquad\qquad x^4 + 3x^2 - 4 = 0$

$(x^2 - 1)(x^2 + 4) = 0$

$(x-1)(x+1)(x^2 + 4) = 0$

$x - 1 = 0$ or $x + 1 = 0$ or $x^2 + 4 = 0$

$x = 1$ or $x = -1$ or $x^2 = -4$

$x = 1$ or $x = -1$ or $x = \pm\sqrt{-4} = \pm 2i$

The solution set is $\{-1, 1, -2i, 2i\}$.

73. $3x^2 - 3x + 4 = 0$

$a = 3, b = -3, c = 4$

$b^2 - 4ac = (-3)^2 - 4(3)(4) = 9 - 48 = -39$

The equation has two complex solutions that are conjugates of each other.

74. $2x^2 - 4x + 1 = 0$

$a = 2, b = -4, c = 1$

$b^2 - 4ac = (-4)^2 - 4(2)(1) = 16 - 8 = 8$

The equation has two unequal real number solutions.

75. $\qquad 2x^2 + 3x = 4$

$2x^2 + 3x - 4 = 0$

$a = 2, b = 3, c = -4$

$b^2 - 4ac = 3^2 - 4(2)(-4) = 9 + 32 = 41$

The equation has two unequal real solutions.

76. $\qquad x^2 + 6 = 2x$

$x^2 - 2x + 6 = 0$

$a = 1, b = -2, c = 6$

$b^2 - 4ac = (-2)^2 - 4(1)(6) = 4 - 24 = -20$

The equation has two complex solutions that are conjugates of each other.

77. $9x^2 - 12x + 4 = 0$

$a = 9, b = -12, c = 4$

$b^2 - 4ac = (-12)^2 - 4(9)(4) = 144 - 144 = 0$

The equation has a repeated real solution.

78. $4x^2 + 12x + 9 = 0$

$a = 4, b = 12, c = 9$

$b^2 - 4ac = 12^2 - 4(4)(9) = 144 - 144 = 0$

The equation has a repeated real solution.

79. The other solution is $\overline{2 + 3i} = 2 - 3i$.

80. The other solution is $\overline{4 - i} = 4 + i$.

81. $z + \overline{z} = 3 - 4i + \overline{3 - 4i} = 3 - 4i + 3 + 4i = 6$

82. $w - \overline{w} = 8 + 3i - \left(\overline{8 + 3i} \right)$

$= 8 + 3i - (8 - 3i)$

$= 8 + 3i - 8 + 3i$

$= 0 + 6i$

$= 6i$

83. $z \cdot \overline{z} = (3 - 4i)(\overline{3 - 4i})$

$= (3 - 4i)(3 + 4i)$

$= 9 + 12i - 12i - 16i^2$

$= 9 - 16(-1)$

$= 25$

84. $\overline{z - w} = \overline{3 - 4i - (8 + 3i)}$

$= \overline{3 - 4i - 8 - 3i}$

$= \overline{-5 - 7i}$

$= -5 + 7i$

85. $Z = \dfrac{V}{I} = \dfrac{18 + i}{3 - 4i} = \dfrac{18 + i}{3 - 4i} \cdot \dfrac{3 + 4i}{3 + 4i}$

$= \dfrac{54 + 72i + 3i + 4i^2}{9 + 12i - 12i - 16i^2} = \dfrac{54 + 75i - 4}{9 + 16}$

$= \dfrac{50 + 75i}{25} = 2 + 3i$

The impedance is $2 + 3i$ ohms.

86. $\dfrac{1}{Z} = \dfrac{1}{Z_1} + \dfrac{1}{Z_2} = \dfrac{1}{2 + i} + \dfrac{1}{4 - 3i} = \dfrac{(4 - 3i) + (2 + i)}{(2 + i)(4 - 3i)}$

$= \dfrac{6 - 2i}{8 - 6i + 4i - 3i^2} = \dfrac{6 - 2i}{8 - 2i + 3} = \dfrac{6 - 2i}{11 - 2i}$

So, $Z = \dfrac{11 - 2i}{6 - 2i} = \dfrac{11 - 2i}{6 - 2i} \cdot \dfrac{6 + 2i}{6 + 2i}$

$= \dfrac{66 + 22i - 12i - 4i^2}{36 + 12i - 12i - 4i^2} = \dfrac{66 + 10i + 4}{36 + 4}$

$= \dfrac{70 + 10i}{40} = \dfrac{7}{4} + \dfrac{1}{4}i$

The total impedance is $\dfrac{7}{4} + \dfrac{1}{4}i$ ohms.

87. $z + \overline{z} = (a + bi) + \overline{(a + bi)}$

$= a + bi + a - bi$

$= 2a$

$z - \overline{z} = a + bi - \overline{(a + bi)}$

$= a + bi - (a - bi)$

$= a + bi - a + bi$

$= 2bi$

88. $\overline{\overline{z}} = \overline{\overline{a + bi}} = \overline{a - bi} = a + bi = z$

89. $\overline{z + w} = \overline{(a + bi) + (c + di)}$

$= \overline{(a + c) + (b + d)i}$

$= (a + c) - (b + d)i$

$= (a - bi) + (c - di)$

$= \overline{a + bi} + \overline{c + di}$

$= \overline{z} + \overline{w}$

90. $\overline{z \cdot w} = \overline{(a + bi) \cdot (c + di)}$

$= \overline{ac + adi + bci + bdi^2}$

$= \overline{(ac - bd) + (ad + bc)i}$

$= (ac - bd) - (ad + bc)i$

$\overline{z} \cdot \overline{w} = \overline{a + bi} \cdot \overline{c + di}$

$= (a - bi)(c - di)$

$= ac - adi - bci + bdi^2$

$= (ac - bd) - (ad + bc)i$

91 – 92. Answers will vary.

Section 1.4

1. True

2. $\sqrt[3]{-8} = -2$

3. $6x^3 - 2x^2 = 2x^2(3x-1)$

4. extraneous

5. quadratic in form

6. True

7. $\sqrt{2t-1} = 1$
$$\left(\sqrt{2t-1}\right)^2 = 1^2$$
$$2t-1 = 1$$
$$2t = 2$$
$$t = 1$$
Check: $\sqrt{2(1)-1} = \sqrt{1} = 1$
The solution set is $\{1\}$.

8. $\sqrt{3t+4} = 2$
$$\left(\sqrt{3t+4}\right)^2 = 2^2$$
$$3t+4 = 4$$
$$3t = 0$$
$$t = 0$$
Check: $\sqrt{3(0)+4} = \sqrt{4} = 2$
The solution set is $\{0\}$.

9. $\sqrt{3t+4} = -6$
Since the principal square root is never negative, the equation has no real solution.

10. $\sqrt{5t+3} = -2$
Since the principal square root is never negative, the equation has no real solution.

11. $\sqrt[3]{1-2x} - 3 = 0$
$$\sqrt[3]{1-2x} = 3$$
$$\left(\sqrt[3]{1-2x}\right)^3 = 3^3$$
$$1-2x = 27$$
$$-2x = 26$$
$$x = -13$$
Check: $\sqrt[3]{1-2(-13)} - 3 = \sqrt[3]{27} - 3 = 0$
The solution set is $\{-13\}$.

12. $\sqrt[3]{1-2x} - 1 = 0$
$$\sqrt[3]{1-2x} = 1$$
$$\left(\sqrt[3]{1-2x}\right)^3 = 1^3$$
$$1-2x = 1$$
$$-2x = 0$$
$$x = 0$$
Check: $\sqrt[3]{1-2(0)} - 1 = \sqrt[3]{1} - 1 = 0$
The solution set is $\{0\}$.

13. $\sqrt[4]{5x-4} = 2$
$$\left(\sqrt[4]{5x-4}\right)^4 = 2^4$$
$$5x-4 = 16$$
$$5x = 20$$
$$x = 4$$
Check: $\sqrt[4]{5(4)-4} = \sqrt[4]{16} = 2$
The solution set is $\{4\}$.

14. $\sqrt[5]{2x-3} = -1$
$$\left(\sqrt[5]{2x-3}\right)^5 = (-1)^5$$
$$2x-3 = -1$$
$$2x = 2$$
$$x = 1$$
Check: $\sqrt[5]{2(1)-3} = \sqrt[5]{-1} = -1$
The solution set is $\{1\}$.

15. $\sqrt[5]{x^2+2x} = -1$
$$\left(\sqrt[5]{x^2+2x}\right)^5 = (-1)^5$$
$$x^2+2x = -1$$
$$x^2+2x+1 = 0$$
$$(x+1)^2 = 0$$
$$x+1 = 0$$
$$x = -1$$
Check: $\sqrt[5]{(-1)^2+2(-1)} = \sqrt[5]{1-2} = \sqrt[5]{-1} = -1$
The solution set is $\{-1\}$.

97

16. $\sqrt[4]{x^2+16} = \sqrt{5}$

$\left(\sqrt[4]{x^2+16}\right)^4 = \left(\sqrt{5}\right)^4$

$x^2 + 16 = 25$

$x^2 = 9$

$x = \pm 3$

Check -3: $\sqrt[4]{(-3)^2+16} = \sqrt[4]{9+16} = \sqrt[4]{25} = \sqrt{5}$

Check 3: $\sqrt[4]{(3)^2+16} = \sqrt[4]{9+16} = \sqrt[4]{25} = \sqrt{5}$

The solution set is $\{-3, 3\}$.

17. $x = 8\sqrt{x}$

$(x)^2 = \left(8\sqrt{x}\right)^2$

$x^2 = 64x$

$x^2 - 64x = 0$

$x(x-64) = 0$

$x = 0$ or $x = 64$

Check 0: $0 = 8\sqrt{0}$ Check 64: $64 = 8\sqrt{64}$

$0 = 0$ $64 = 64$

The solution set is $\{0, 64\}$.

18. $x = 3\sqrt{x}$

$(x)^2 = \left(3\sqrt{x}\right)^2$

$x^2 = 9x$

$x^2 - 9x = 0$

$x(x-9) = 0$

$x = 0$ or $x = 9$

Check 0: $0 = 3\sqrt{0}$ Check 9: $9 = 3\sqrt{9}$

$0 = 0$ $9 = 9$

The solution set is $\{0, 9\}$.

19. $\sqrt{15-2x} = x$

$\left(\sqrt{15-2x}\right)^2 = x^2$

$15 - 2x = x^2$

$x^2 + 2x - 15 = 0$

$(x+5)(x-3) = 0$

$x = -5$ or $x = 3$

Check -5: $\sqrt{15-2(-5)} = \sqrt{25} = 5 \neq -5$

Check 3: $\sqrt{15-2(3)} = \sqrt{9} = 3 = 3$

Disregard $x = -5$ as extraneous.

The solution set is $\{3\}$.

20. $\sqrt{12-x} = x$

$\left(\sqrt{12-x}\right)^2 = x^2$

$12 - x = x^2$

$x^2 + x - 12 = 0$

$(x+4)(x-3) = 0$

$x = -4$ or $x = 3$

Check -4: $\sqrt{12-(-4)} = \sqrt{16} = 4 \neq -4$

Check 3: $\sqrt{12-3} = \sqrt{9} = 3 = 3$

Disregard $x = -4$ as extraneous.

The solution set is $\{3\}$.

21. $x = 2\sqrt{x-1}$

$x^2 = \left(2\sqrt{x-1}\right)^2$

$x^2 = 4(x-1)$

$x^2 = 4x - 4$

$x^2 - 4x + 4 = 0$

$(x-2)^2 = 0$

$x = 2$

Check: $2 = 2\sqrt{2-1}$

$2 = 2$

The solution set is $\{2\}$.

22. $x = 2\sqrt{-x-1}$

$x^2 = \left(2\sqrt{-x-1}\right)^2$

$x^2 = 4(-x-1)$

$x^2 = -4x - 4$

$x^2 + 4x + 4 = 0$

$(x+2)^2 = 0$

$x = -2$

Check: $-2 = 2\sqrt{-(-2)-1}$

$-2 \neq 2$

The equation has no real solution.

23. $\sqrt{x^2 - x - 4} = x + 2$

$$\left(\sqrt{x^2 - x - 4}\right)^2 = (x + 2)^2$$

$$x^2 - x - 4 = x^2 + 4x + 4$$

$$-8 = 5x$$

$$-\frac{8}{5} = x$$

Check: $\sqrt{\left(-\frac{8}{5}\right)^2 - \left(-\frac{8}{5}\right) - 4} = \left(-\frac{8}{5}\right) + 2$

$$\sqrt{\frac{64}{25} + \frac{8}{5} - 4} = \frac{2}{5}$$

$$\sqrt{\frac{4}{25}} = \frac{2}{5}$$

$$\frac{2}{5} = \frac{2}{5}$$

The solution set is $\left\{-\frac{8}{5}\right\}$.

24. $\sqrt{3 - x + x^2} = x - 2$

$$\left(\sqrt{3 - x + x^2}\right)^2 = (x - 2)^2$$

$$3 - x + x^2 = x^2 - 4x + 4$$

$$3x = 1$$

$$x = \frac{1}{3}$$

Check: $\sqrt{3 - \left(\frac{1}{3}\right) + \left(\frac{1}{3}\right)^2} = \left(\frac{1}{3}\right) - 2$

$$\sqrt{3 - \frac{1}{3} + \frac{1}{9}} = -\frac{5}{3}$$

Since the principal square root is always a non-negative number; $x = \frac{1}{3}$ does not check.

Therefore this equation has no real solution.

25. $3 + \sqrt{3x + 1} = x$

$$\sqrt{3x + 1} = x - 3$$

$$\left(\sqrt{3x + 1}\right)^2 = (x - 3)^2$$

$$3x + 1 = x^2 - 6x + 9$$

$$0 = x^2 - 9x + 8$$

$$0 = (x - 1)(x - 8)$$

$$x = 1 \text{ or } x = 8$$

Check 1: $3 + \sqrt{3(1) + 1} = 3 + \sqrt{4} = 5 \neq 1$

Check 8: $3 + \sqrt{3(8) + 1} = 3 + \sqrt{25} = 8 = 8$

Discard $x = 1$ as extraneous.

The solution set is {8}.

26. $2 + \sqrt{12 - 2x} = x$

$$\sqrt{12 - 2x} = x - 2$$

$$\left(\sqrt{12 - 2x}\right)^2 = (x - 2)^2$$

$$12 - 2x = x^2 - 4x + 4$$

$$0 = x^2 - 2x - 8$$

$$(x + 2)(x - 4) = 0$$

$$x = -2 \text{ or } x = 4$$

Check -2: $2 + \sqrt{12 - 2(-2)} = 2 + \sqrt{16} = 6 \neq -2$

Check 4: $2 + \sqrt{12 - 2(4)} = 2 + \sqrt{4} = 4 = 4$

Discard $x = -2$ as extraneous.
The solution set is {4}.

27. $\sqrt{2x + 3} - \sqrt{x + 1} = 1$

$$\sqrt{2x + 3} = 1 + \sqrt{x + 1}$$

$$\left(\sqrt{2x + 3}\right)^2 = \left(1 + \sqrt{x + 1}\right)^2$$

$$2x + 3 = 1 + 2\sqrt{x + 1} + x + 1$$

$$x + 1 = 2\sqrt{x + 1}$$

$$(x + 1)^2 = \left(2\sqrt{x + 1}\right)^2$$

$$x^2 + 2x + 1 = 4(x + 1)$$

$$x^2 + 2x + 1 = 4x + 4$$

$$x^2 - 2x - 3 = 0$$

$$(x + 1)(x - 3) = 0$$

$$x = -1 \text{ or } x = 3$$

Check -1: $\sqrt{2(-1) + 3} - \sqrt{-1 + 1}$

$$= \sqrt{1} - \sqrt{0} = 1 - 0 = 1 = 1$$

Check 3: $\sqrt{2(3) + 3} - \sqrt{3 + 1}$

$$= \sqrt{9} - \sqrt{4} = 3 - 2 = 1 = 1$$

The solution set is $\{-1, 3\}$.

28. $\sqrt{3x+7}+\sqrt{x+2}=1$

$\sqrt{3x+7}=1-\sqrt{x+2}$

$\left(\sqrt{3x+7}\right)^2=\left(1-\sqrt{x+2}\right)^2$

$3x+7=1-2\sqrt{x+2}+x+2$

$2x+4=-2\sqrt{x+2}$

$-x-2=\sqrt{x+2}$

$(-x-2)^2=\left(\sqrt{x+2}\right)^2$

$x^2+4x+4=x+2$

$x^2+3x+2=0$

$(x+1)(x+2)=0$

$x=-1 \text{ or } x=-2$

Check -1: $\sqrt{3(-1)+7}+\sqrt{-1+2}$

$=\sqrt{4}+\sqrt{1}=2+1=3\neq 1$

Check -2: $\sqrt{3(-2)+7}+\sqrt{-2+2}$

$=\sqrt{1}+\sqrt{0}=1+0=1=1$

Discard $x=-1$ as extraneous.
The solution set is $\{-2\}$.

29. $\sqrt{3x+1}-\sqrt{x-1}=2$

$\sqrt{3x+1}=2+\sqrt{x-1}$

$\left(\sqrt{3x+1}\right)^2=\left(2+\sqrt{x-1}\right)^2$

$3x+1=4+4\sqrt{x-1}+x-1$

$2x-2=4\sqrt{x-1}$

$(2x-2)^2=\left(4\sqrt{x-1}\right)^2$

$4x^2-8x+4=16(x-1)$

$x^2-2x+1=4x-4$

$x^2-6x+5=0$

$(x-1)(x-5)=0$

$x=1 \text{ or } x=5$

Check 1: $\sqrt{3(1)+1}-\sqrt{1-1}$

$=\sqrt{4}-\sqrt{0}=2-0=2=2$

Check 5: $\sqrt{3(5)+1}-\sqrt{5-1}$

$=\sqrt{16}-\sqrt{4}=4-2=2=2$

The solution set is $\{1,5\}$.

30. $\sqrt{3x-5}-\sqrt{x+7}=2$

$\sqrt{3x-5}=2+\sqrt{x+7}$

$\left(\sqrt{3x-5}\right)^2=\left(2+\sqrt{x+7}\right)^2$

$3x-5=4+4\sqrt{x+7}+x+7$

$2x-16=4\sqrt{x+7}$

$(2x-16)^2=\left(4\sqrt{x+7}\right)^2$

$4x^2-64x+256=16(x+7)$

$4x^2-64x+256=16x+112$

$4x^2-80x+144=0$

$x^2-20x+36=0$

$(x-2)(x-18)=0$

$x=2 \text{ or } x=18$

Check 2: $\sqrt{3(2)-5}-\sqrt{2+7}$

$=\sqrt{1}-\sqrt{9}=1-3=-2\neq 2$

Check 18: $\sqrt{3(18)-5}-\sqrt{18+7}$

$=\sqrt{49}-\sqrt{25}=7-5=2=2$

Discard $x=2$ as extraneous.
The solution set is $\{18\}$.

31. $\sqrt{3-2\sqrt{x}}=\sqrt{x}$

$\left(\sqrt{3-2\sqrt{x}}\right)^2=\left(\sqrt{x}\right)^2$

$3-2\sqrt{x}=x$

$-2\sqrt{x}=x-3$

$\left(-2\sqrt{x}\right)^2=(x-3)^2$

$4x=x^2-6x+9$

$0=x^2-10x+9$

$0=(x-1)(x-9)$

$x=1 \text{ or } x=9$

Check 1:   Check 9:

$\sqrt{3-2\sqrt{1}}=\sqrt{1}$ $\sqrt{3-2\sqrt{9}}=\sqrt{9}$

$\sqrt{3-2}=1$ $\sqrt{3-2\cdot 3}=3$

$\sqrt{1}=1$ $\sqrt{-3}\neq 3$

$1=1$

Discard $x=9$ as extraneous.
The solution set is $\{1\}$.

32. $\sqrt{10+3\sqrt{x}} = \sqrt{x}$

$\left(\sqrt{10+3\sqrt{x}}\right)^2 = \left(\sqrt{x}\right)^2$

$10+3\sqrt{x} = x$

$3\sqrt{x} = x-10$

$\left(3\sqrt{x}\right)^2 = (x-10)^2$

$9x = x^2 - 20x + 100$

$0 = x^2 - 29x + 100$

$0 = (x-4)(x-25)$

$x = 4 \quad \text{or} \quad x = 25$

Check 4:   Check 25:

$\sqrt{10+3\sqrt{4}} = \sqrt{4}$ $\sqrt{10+3\sqrt{25}} = \sqrt{25}$

$\sqrt{10+3\cdot 2} = 2$ $\sqrt{10+3\cdot 5} = 5$

$\sqrt{16} = 2$ $\sqrt{25} = 5$

$4 \neq 2$ $5 = 5$

Discard $x = 4$ as extraneous.

The solution set is $\{25\}$.

33. $(3x+1)^{1/2} = 4$

$\left((3x+1)^{1/2}\right)^2 = (4)^2$

$3x+1 = 16$

$3x = 15$

$x = 5$

Check: $(3(5)+1)^{1/2} = 16^{1/2} = 4$

The solution set is $\{5\}$.

34. $(3x-5)^{1/2} = 2$

$\left((3x-5)^{1/2}\right)^2 = (2)^2$

$3x-5 = 4$

$3x = 9$

$x = 3$

Check: $(3(3)-5)^{1/2} = 4^{1/2} = 2$

The solution set is $\{3\}$.

35. $(5x-2)^{1/3} = 2$

$\left((5x-2)^{1/3}\right)^3 = (2)^3$

$5x-2 = 8$

$5x = 10$

$x = 2$

Check: $(5(2)-2)^{1/3} = 8^{1/3} = 2$

The solution set is $\{2\}$.

36. $(2x+1)^{1/3} = -1$

$\left((2x+1)^{1/3}\right)^3 = (-1)^3$

$2x+1 = -1$

$2x = -2$

$x = -1$

Check: $(2(-1)+1)^{1/3} = (-1)^{1/3} = -1$

The solution set is $\{-1\}$.

37. $(x^2+9)^{1/2} = 5$

$\left((x^2+9)^{1/2}\right)^2 = (5)^2$

$x^2 + 9 = 25$

$x^2 = 16$

$x = \pm\sqrt{16} = \pm 4$

Check -4: $\left((-4)^2+9\right)^{1/2} = 25^{1/2} = 5$

Check 4: $\left((4)^2+9\right)^{1/2} = 25^{1/2} = 5$

The solution set is $\{-4, 4\}$.

38. $(x^2-16)^{1/2} = 9$

$\left((x^2-16)^{1/2}\right)^2 = (9)^2$

$x^2 - 16 = 81$

$x^2 = 97$

$x = \pm\sqrt{97}$

Check $-\sqrt{97}$: $\left((-\sqrt{97})^2 - 16\right)^{1/2} = 81^{1/2} = 9$

Check $\sqrt{97}$: $\left((\sqrt{97})^2 - 16\right)^{1/2} = 81^{1/2} = 9$

The solution set is $\left\{-\sqrt{97}, \sqrt{97}\right\}$.

39. $x^{3/2} - 3x^{1/2} = 0$

$\quad x^{1/2}(x-3) = 0$

$\quad x^{1/2} = 0$ or $x - 3 = 0$

$\quad\quad x = 0$ or $\quad x = 3$

Check 0: $0^{3/2} - 3 \cdot 0^{1/2} = 0 - 0 = 0$

Check 3: $3^{3/2} - 3 \cdot 3^{1/2} = 3\sqrt{3} - 3\sqrt{3} = 0$

The solution set is $\{0, 3\}$.

40. $x^{3/4} - 9x^{1/4} = 0$

$\quad x^{1/4}(x^{1/2} - 9) = 0$

$\quad x^{1/4} = 0$ or $x^{1/2} = 9$

$\quad\quad x = 0 \quad\quad x = 81$

Check 0: $0^{3/4} - 9 \cdot 0^{1/4} = 0 - 0 = 0$

Check 81: $81^{3/4} - 9 \cdot 81^{1/4} = 27 - 27 = 0$

The solution set is $\{0, 81\}$.

41. $x^4 - 5x^2 + 4 = 0$

$\quad (x^2 - 4)(x^2 - 1) = 0$

$\quad x^2 - 4 = 0$ or $x^2 - 1 = 0$

$\quad\quad x = \pm 2$ or $x = \pm 1$

The solution set is $\{-2, -1, 1, 2\}$.

42. $x^4 - 10x^2 + 25 = 0$

$\quad (x^2 - 5)(x^2 - 5) = 0$

$\quad\quad x^2 - 5 = 0$

$\quad\quad\quad x = \pm\sqrt{5}$

The solution set is $\{-\sqrt{5}, \sqrt{5}\}$.

43. $3x^4 - 2x^2 - 1 = 0$

$\quad (3x^2 + 1)(x^2 - 1) = 0$

$\quad 3x^2 + 1 = 0$ or $x^2 - 1 = 0$

$\quad\quad 3x^2 = -1$ or $\quad x^2 = 1$

$\quad\quad$ Not real or $\quad x = \pm 1$

The solution set is $\{-1, 1\}$.

44. $2x^4 - 5x^2 - 12 = 0$

$\quad (2x^2 + 3)(x^2 - 4) = 0$

$\quad 2x^2 + 3 = 0$ or $x^2 - 4 = 0$

$\quad\quad 2x^2 = -3$ or $\quad x^2 = 4$

$\quad\quad$ Not real or $\quad x = \pm 2$

The solution set is $\{-2, 2\}$.

45. $x^6 + 7x^3 - 8 = 0$

$\quad (x^3 + 8)(x^3 - 1) = 0$

$\quad x^3 + 8 = 0$ or $x^3 - 1 = 0$

$\quad\quad x^3 = -8$ or $\quad x^3 = 1$

$\quad\quad x = -2$ or $\quad\quad x = 1$

The solution set is $\{-2, 1\}$.

46. $x^6 - 7x^3 - 8 = 0$

$\quad (x^3 - 8)(x^3 + 1) = 0$

$\quad x^3 - 8 = 0$ or $x^3 + 1 = 0$

$\quad\quad x^3 = 8$ or $\quad x^3 = -1$

$\quad\quad x = 2$ or $\quad\quad x = -1$

The solution set is $\{-1, 2\}$.

47. $(x+2)^2 + 7(x+2) + 12 = 0$

Let $u = x + 2$, so that $u^2 = (x+2)^2$.

$\quad u^2 + 7u + 12 = 0$

$\quad (u+3)(u+4) = 0$

$\quad u + 3 = 0$ or $u + 4 = 0$

$\quad\quad u = -3$ or $\quad\quad u = -4$

$\quad x + 2 = -3$ or $x + 2 = -4$

$\quad\quad x = -5$ or $\quad\quad x = -6$

The solution set is $\{-6, -5\}$.

48. $(2x+5)^2 - (2x+5) - 6 = 0$

Let $u = 2x + 5$ so that $u^2 = (2x+5)^2$.

$\quad u^2 - u - 6 = 0$

$\quad (u-3)(u+2) = 0$

$\quad u - 3 = 0$ or $\quad u + 2 = 0$

$\quad\quad u = 3$ or $\quad\quad u = -2$

$\quad 2x + 5 = 3$ or $\quad 2x + 5 = -2$

$\quad\quad x = -1$ or $\quad\quad x = -\dfrac{7}{2}$

The solution set is $\left\{-\dfrac{7}{2}, -1\right\}$.

49. $(3x+4)^2 - 6(3x+4) + 9 = 0$

Let $u = 3x+4$ so that $u^2 = (3x+4)^2$.

$u^2 - 6u + 9 = 0$

$(u-3)^2 = 0$

$u - 3 = 0$

$u = 3$

$3x + 4 = 3$

$x = -\dfrac{1}{3}$

The solution set is $\left\{-\dfrac{1}{3}\right\}$.

50. $(2-x)^2 + (2-x) - 20 = 0$

Let $u = 2-x$ so that $u^2 = (2-x)^2$.

$u^2 + u - 20 = 0$

$(u+5)(u-4) = 0$

$u + 5 = 0$ or $u - 4 = 0$

$u = -5$ or $u = 4$

$2 - x = -5$ or $2 - x = 4$

$x = 7$ or $x = -2$

The solution set is $\{-2, 7\}$.

51. $2(s+1)^2 - 5(s+1) = 3$

Let $u = s+1$ so that $u^2 = (s+1)^2$.

$2u^2 - 5u = 3$

$2u^2 - 5u - 3 = 0$

$(2u+1)(u-3) = 0$

$2u + 1 = 0$ or $u - 3 = 0$

$u = -\dfrac{1}{2}$ or $u = 3$

$s + 1 = -\dfrac{1}{2}$ or $s + 1 = 3$

$s = -\dfrac{3}{2}$ or $s = 2$

The solution set is $\left\{-\dfrac{3}{2}, 2\right\}$.

52. $3(1-y)^2 + 5(1-y) + 2 = 0$

Let $u = 1-y$ so that $u^2 = (1-y)^2$.

$3u^2 + 5u + 2 = 0$

$(3u+2)(u+1) = 0$

$3u + 2 = 0$ or $u + 1 = 0$

$u = -\dfrac{2}{3}$ or $u = -1$

$1 - y = -\dfrac{2}{3}$ or $1 - y = -1$

$y = \dfrac{5}{3}$ or $y = 2$

The solution set is $\left\{\dfrac{5}{3}, 2\right\}$.

53. $x - 4x\sqrt{x} = 0$

$x\left(1 - 4\sqrt{x}\right) = 0$

$x = 0$ or $1 - 4\sqrt{x} = 0$

$1 = 4\sqrt{x}$

$\frac{1}{4} = \sqrt{x}$

$\left(\frac{1}{4}\right)^2 = \left(\sqrt{x}\right)^2$

$\frac{1}{16} = x$

Check:

$x = 0$: $0 - 4(0)\sqrt{0} = 0$

$0 = 0$

$x = \frac{1}{16}$: $\left(\frac{1}{16}\right) - 4\left(\frac{1}{16}\right)\sqrt{\frac{1}{16}} = 0$

$\frac{1}{16} - 4\left(\frac{1}{16}\right)\left(\frac{1}{4}\right) = 0$

$\frac{1}{16} - \frac{1}{16} = 0$

$0 = 0$

The solution set is $\left\{0, \dfrac{1}{16}\right\}$.

54. $x + 8\sqrt{x} = 0$

$8\sqrt{x} = -x$

$\left(8\sqrt{x}\right)^2 = (-x)^2$

$64x = x^2$

$0 = x^2 - 64x$

$0 = x(x-64)$

$x = 0$ or $x = 64$

Check: $x = 0$: $0 + 8\sqrt{0} = 0$

$0 = 0$

$x = 64$: $64 + 8\sqrt{64} = 0$

$64 + 64 \neq 0$

The solution set is $\{0\}$.

55. $x + \sqrt{x} = 20$

Let $u = \sqrt{x}$ so that $u^2 = x$.

$$u^2 + u = 20$$
$$u^2 + u - 20 = 0$$
$$(u+5)(u-4) = 0$$
$$u + 5 = 0 \quad \text{or} \quad u - 4 = 0$$
$$u = -5 \quad \text{or} \quad u = 4$$
$$\sqrt{x} = -5 \quad \text{or} \quad \sqrt{x} = 4$$
$$\text{not possible} \quad \text{or} \quad x = 16$$

Check: $16 + \sqrt{16} = 20$
$$16 + 4 = 20$$

The solution set is $\{16\}$.

56. $x + \sqrt{x} = 6$

Let $u = \sqrt{x}$ so that $u^2 = x$.

$$u^2 + u = 6$$
$$u^2 + u - 6 = 0$$
$$(u+3)(u-2) = 0$$
$$u + 3 = 0 \quad \text{or} \quad u - 2 = 0$$
$$u = -3 \quad \text{or} \quad u = 2$$
$$\sqrt{x} = -3 \quad \text{or} \quad \sqrt{x} = 2$$
$$\text{not possible} \quad \text{or} \quad x = 4$$

Check: $4 + \sqrt{4} = 6$
$$4 + 2 = 6$$

The solution set is $\{4\}$.

57. $t^{1/2} - 2t^{1/4} + 1 = 0$

Let $u = t^{1/4}$ so that $u^2 = t^{1/2}$.

$$u^2 - 2u + 1 = 0$$
$$(u-1)^2 = 0$$
$$u - 1 = 0$$
$$u = 1$$
$$t^{1/4} = 1$$
$$t = 1$$

Check: $1^{1/2} - 2(1)^{1/4} + 1 = 0$
$$1 - 2 + 1 = 0$$
$$0 = 0$$

The solution set is $\{1\}$.

58. $z^{1/2} - 4t^{1/4} + 4 = 0$

Let $u = z^{1/4}$ so that $u^2 = z^{1/2}$.

$$u^2 - 4u + 4 = 0$$
$$(u-2)^2 = 0$$
$$u - 2 = 0$$
$$u = 2$$
$$z^{1/4} = 2$$
$$z = 16$$

Check: $16^{1/2} - 4(16)^{1/4} + 4 = 0$
$$4 - 8 + 4 = 0$$
$$0 = 0$$

The solution set is $\{16\}$.

59. $4x^{1/2} - 9x^{1/4} + 4 = 0$

Let $u = x^{1/4}$ so that $u^2 = x^{1/2}$.

$$4u^2 - 9u + 4 = 0$$
$$u = \frac{-(-9) \pm \sqrt{(-9)^2 - 4(4)(4)}}{2(4)} = \frac{9 \pm \sqrt{17}}{8}$$
$$x^{1/4} = \frac{9 \pm \sqrt{17}}{8}$$
$$x = \left(\frac{9 \pm \sqrt{17}}{8}\right)^4$$

Check $x = \left(\frac{9 + \sqrt{17}}{8}\right)^4$:

$$4\left(\left(\frac{9+\sqrt{17}}{8}\right)^4\right)^{1/2} - 9\left(\left(\frac{9+\sqrt{17}}{8}\right)^4\right)^{1/4} + 4 = 0$$

$$4\left(\frac{9+\sqrt{17}}{8}\right)^2 - 9\left(\frac{9+\sqrt{17}}{8}\right) + 4 = 0$$

$$4\frac{\left(9+\sqrt{17}\right)^2}{64} - 9\left(\frac{9+\sqrt{17}}{8}\right) + 4 = 0$$

$$64\left(4\frac{\left(9+\sqrt{17}\right)^2}{64} - 9\left(\frac{9+\sqrt{17}}{8}\right) + 4\right) = (0)(64)$$

$$4\left(9+\sqrt{17}\right)^2 - 72\left(9+\sqrt{17}\right) + 256 = 0$$

$$4\left(81 + 18\sqrt{17} + 17\right) - 72\left(9+\sqrt{17}\right) + 256 = 0$$

$$324 + 72\sqrt{17} + 68 - 648 - 72\sqrt{17} + 256 = 0$$

$$0 = 0$$

Check $x = \left(\dfrac{9-\sqrt{17}}{8}\right)^4$:

$$4\left(\left(\dfrac{9-\sqrt{17}}{8}\right)^4\right)^{1/2} - 9\left(\left(\dfrac{9-\sqrt{17}}{8}\right)^4\right)^{1/4} + 4 = 0$$

$$4\left(\dfrac{9-\sqrt{17}}{8}\right)^2 - 9\left(\dfrac{9-\sqrt{17}}{8}\right) + 4 = 0$$

$$4\left(81 - 18\sqrt{17} + 17\right) - 72\left(9 - \sqrt{17}\right) + 256 = 0$$

$$324 - 72\sqrt{17} + 68 - 648 + 72\sqrt{17} + 256 = 0$$

$$0 = 0$$

The solution set is $\left\{\left(\dfrac{9-\sqrt{17}}{8}\right)^4, \left(\dfrac{9+\sqrt{17}}{8}\right)^4\right\}$.

60. $x^{1/2} - 3x^{1/4} + 2 = 0$

Let $u = x^{1/4}$ so that $u^2 = x^{1/2}$.

$u^2 - 3u + 2 = 0$

$(u-2)(u-1) = 0$

$u = 2$ or $u = 1$

$x^{1/4} = 2$ or $x^{1/4} = 1$

$x = 16$ or $x = 1$

Check:

$x = 16$: $16^{1/2} - 3(16)^{1/4} + 2 = 0$

$4 - 6 + 2 = 0$

$0 = 0$

$x = 1$: $1^{1/2} - 3(1)^{1/4} + 2 = 0$

$1 - 3 + 2 = 0$

$0 = 0$

The solution set is $\{1, 16\}$.

61. $\sqrt[4]{5x^2 - 6} = x$

$\left(\sqrt[4]{5x^2 - 6}\right)^4 = x^4$

$5x^2 - 6 = x^4$

$0 = x^4 - 5x^2 + 6$

Let $u = x^2$ so that $u^2 = x^4$.

$0 = u^2 - 5u + 6$

$0 = (u-3)(u-2)$

$u = 3$ or $u = 2$

$x^2 = 3$ or $x^2 = 2$

$x = \pm\sqrt{3}$ or $x = \pm\sqrt{2}$

Check:

$x = -\sqrt{3}$: $\sqrt[4]{5\left(-\sqrt{3}\right)^2 - 6} = -\sqrt{3}$

$\sqrt[4]{15 - 6} = -\sqrt{3}$

$\sqrt[4]{9} \ne -\sqrt{3}$

$x = \sqrt{3}$: $\sqrt[4]{5\left(\sqrt{3}\right)^2 - 6} = \sqrt{3}$

$\sqrt[4]{15 - 6} = \sqrt{3}$

$\sqrt[4]{9} = \sqrt{3}$

$\sqrt{3} = \sqrt{3}$

$x = -\sqrt{2}$: $\sqrt[4]{5\left(-\sqrt{2}\right)^2 - 6} = -\sqrt{2}$

$\sqrt[4]{10 - 6} = -\sqrt{2}$

$\sqrt[4]{4} \ne -\sqrt{2}$

$x = \sqrt{2}$: $\sqrt[4]{5\left(\sqrt{2}\right)^2 - 6} = \sqrt{2}$

$\sqrt[4]{10 - 6} = \sqrt{2}$

$\sqrt[4]{4} = \sqrt{2}$

$\sqrt{2} = \sqrt{2}$

The solution set is $\left\{\sqrt{2}, \sqrt{3}\right\}$.

62. $\sqrt[4]{4 - 5x^2} = x$

$\left(\sqrt[4]{4 - 5x^2}\right)^4 = x^4$

$4 - 5x^2 = x^4$

$0 = x^4 + 5x^2 - 4$

Let $u = x^2$ so that $u^2 = x^4$.

$0 = u^2 + 5u - 4$

$u = \dfrac{-5 \pm \sqrt{5^2 - 4(1)(-4)}}{2} = \dfrac{-5 \pm \sqrt{41}}{2}$

$x^2 = \dfrac{-5 \pm \sqrt{41}}{2}$

$x = \pm\sqrt{\dfrac{-5 \pm \sqrt{41}}{2}}$

Since $-5 - \sqrt{41} < 0$, $x = \pm\sqrt{\dfrac{-5-\sqrt{41}}{2}}$ is not real.

Since x is a fourth root, $x = -\sqrt{\dfrac{-5+\sqrt{41}}{2}}$ is also not real. Therefore, we have only one possible solution to check: $x = \sqrt{\dfrac{-5+\sqrt{41}}{2}}$:

105

Check $x = \sqrt{\dfrac{-5+\sqrt{41}}{2}}$:

$$\sqrt[4]{4 - 5\left(\pm\sqrt{\dfrac{-5+\sqrt{41}}{2}}\right)^2} = \sqrt{\dfrac{-5+\sqrt{41}}{2}}$$

$$\sqrt[4]{4 - 5\left(\dfrac{-5+\sqrt{41}}{2}\right)} = \sqrt{\dfrac{-5+\sqrt{41}}{2}}$$

$$\sqrt[4]{\dfrac{8 - 5\left(-5+\sqrt{41}\right)}{2}} = \sqrt{\dfrac{-5+\sqrt{41}}{2}}$$

$$\sqrt[4]{\dfrac{33 - 5\sqrt{41}}{2}} = \sqrt{\dfrac{-5+\sqrt{41}}{2}}$$

$$\sqrt[4]{\dfrac{66 - 10\sqrt{41}}{4}} = \sqrt{\dfrac{-5+\sqrt{41}}{2}}$$

$$\sqrt[4]{\dfrac{25 - 10\sqrt{41} + 41}{4}} = \sqrt{\dfrac{-5+\sqrt{41}}{2}}$$

$$\sqrt[4]{\dfrac{\left(-5+\sqrt{41}\right)^2}{4}} = \sqrt{\dfrac{-5+\sqrt{41}}{2}}$$

$$\sqrt{\dfrac{-5+\sqrt{41}}{2}} = \sqrt{\dfrac{-5+\sqrt{41}}{2}}$$

The solution set is $\left\{ \sqrt{\dfrac{-5+\sqrt{41}}{2}} \right\}$.

63. $x^2 + 3x + \sqrt{x^2 + 3x} = 6$

Let $u = \sqrt{x^2 + 3x}$ so that $u^2 = x^2 + 3x$.

$$u^2 + u = 6$$
$$u^2 + u - 6 = 0$$
$$(u+3)(u-2) = 0$$

$u = -3$ or $u = 2$

$\sqrt{x^2 + 3x} = -3$ or $\sqrt{x^2 + 3x} = 2$

Not possible or $x^2 + 3x = 4$

$$x^2 + 3x - 4 = 0$$
$$(x+4)(x-1) = 0$$
$$x = -4 \text{ or } x = 1$$

Check $x = -4$:

$$(-4)^2 + 3(-4) + \sqrt{(-4)^2 + 3(-4)} = 6$$
$$16 - 12 + \sqrt{16 - 12} = 6$$
$$16 - 12 + \sqrt{4} = 6$$
$$6 = 6$$

Check $x = 1$:

$$(1)^2 + 3(1) + \sqrt{(1)^2 + 3(1)} = 6$$
$$1 + 3 + \sqrt{1+3} = 6$$
$$4 + \sqrt{4} = 6$$
$$6 = 6$$

The solution set is $\{-4,\ 1\}$.

64. $x^2 - 3x - \sqrt{x^2 - 3x} = 2$

Let $u = \sqrt{x^2 - 3x}$ so that $u^2 = x^2 - 3x$.

$$u^2 - u = 2$$
$$u^2 - u - 2 = 0$$
$$(u+1)(u-2) = 0$$

$u = -1$ or $u = 2$

$\sqrt{x^2 - 3x} = -1$ or $\sqrt{x^2 - 3x} = 2$

Not possible or $x^2 - 3x = 4$

$$x^2 - 3x - 4 = 0$$
$$(x-4)(x+1) = 0$$
$$x = 4 \text{ or } x = -1$$

Check $x = 4$:

$$(4)^2 - 3(4) - \sqrt{(4)^2 - 3(4)} = 16 - 12 - \sqrt{4}$$
$$= 4 - 2 = 2$$

Check $x = -1$:

$$(-1)^2 - 3(-1) - \sqrt{(-1)^2 - 3(-1)} = 1 + 3 - \sqrt{4}$$
$$= 4 - 2 = 2$$

The solution set is $\{-1,\ 4\}$.

65. $\dfrac{1}{(x+1)^2} = \dfrac{1}{x+1} + 2$

Let $u = \dfrac{1}{x+1}$ so that $u^2 = \left(\dfrac{1}{x+1}\right)^2$.

$$u^2 = u + 2$$
$$u^2 - u - 2 = 0$$
$$(u+1)(u-2) = 0$$

$u = -1$ or $u = 2$

$\dfrac{1}{x+1} = -1$ or $\dfrac{1}{x+1} = 2$

$1 = -x - 1$ or $1 = 2x + 2$

$x = -2$ or $-2x = 1$

$$x = -\dfrac{1}{2}$$

Check:

$x = -2$: $\dfrac{1}{(-2+1)^2} = \dfrac{1}{-2+1} + 2$

$$1 = -1 + 2$$
$$1 = 1$$

$x = -\dfrac{1}{2}$: $\dfrac{1}{\left(-\frac{1}{2}+1\right)^2} = \dfrac{1}{\left(-\frac{1}{2}+1\right)} + 2$

$$4 = 2 + 2$$
$$4 = 4$$

The solution set is $\left\{ -2, -\dfrac{1}{2} \right\}$.

66. $\dfrac{1}{(x-1)^2} + \dfrac{1}{x-1} = 12$

Let $u = \dfrac{1}{x-1}$ so that $u^2 = \left(\dfrac{1}{x-1} \right)^2$.

$$u^2 + u = 12$$
$$u^2 + u - 12 = 0$$
$$(u+4)(u-3) = 0$$

$u = -4$	or	$u = 3$
$\dfrac{1}{x-1} = -4$	or	$\dfrac{1}{x-1} = 3$
$1 = -4x + 4$	or	$1 = 3x - 3$
$4x = 3$	or	$4 = 3x$
$x = \dfrac{3}{4}$	or	$x = \dfrac{4}{3}$

Check:

$x = \dfrac{3}{4}$: $\dfrac{1}{\left(\frac{3}{4}-1\right)^2} + \dfrac{1}{\left(\frac{3}{4}-1\right)} = 12$

$$\dfrac{1}{\left(\frac{1}{16}\right)} + \dfrac{1}{\left(-\frac{1}{4}\right)} = 12$$
$$16 - 4 = 12$$
$$12 = 12$$

$x = \dfrac{4}{3}$: $\dfrac{1}{\left(\frac{4}{3}-1\right)^2} + \dfrac{1}{\left(\frac{4}{3}-1\right)} = 12$

$$\dfrac{1}{\left(\frac{1}{9}\right)} + \dfrac{1}{\left(\frac{1}{3}\right)} = 12$$
$$9 + 3 = 12$$
$$12 = 12$$

The solution set is $\left\{ \dfrac{3}{4}, \dfrac{4}{3} \right\}$.

67. $3x^{-2} - 7x^{-1} - 6 = 0$

Let $u = x^{-1}$ so that $u^2 = x^{-2}$.

$$3u^2 - 7u - 6 = 0$$
$$(3u+2)(u-3) = 0$$

$u = -\dfrac{2}{3}$	or	$u = 3$
$x^{-1} = -\dfrac{2}{3}$	or	$x^{-1} = 3$
$\left(x^{-1}\right)^{-1} = \left(-\dfrac{2}{3}\right)^{-1}$	or	$\left(x^{-1}\right)^{-1} = (3)^{-1}$
$x = -\dfrac{3}{2}$	or	$x = \dfrac{1}{3}$

Check:

$x = -\dfrac{3}{2}$: $3\left(-\dfrac{3}{2}\right)^{-2} - 7\left(-\dfrac{3}{2}\right)^{-1} - 6 = 0$

$$3\left(\dfrac{4}{9}\right) - 7\left(-\dfrac{2}{3}\right) - 6 = 0$$
$$\dfrac{4}{3} + \dfrac{14}{3} - 6 = 0$$
$$0 = 0$$

$x = \dfrac{1}{3}$: $3\left(\dfrac{1}{3}\right)^{-2} - 7\left(\dfrac{1}{3}\right)^{-1} - 6 = 0$

$$3(9) - 7(3) - 6 = 0$$
$$27 - 21 - 6 = 0$$
$$0 = 0$$

The solution set is $\left\{ -\dfrac{3}{2}, \dfrac{1}{3} \right\}$.

68. $2x^{-2} - 3x^{-1} - 4 = 0$

Let $u = x^{-1}$ so that $u^2 = x^{-2}$.

$$2u^2 - 3u - 4 = 0$$

$$u = \dfrac{-(-3) \pm \sqrt{(-3)^2 - 4(2)(-4)}}{2(2)} = \dfrac{3 \pm \sqrt{41}}{4}$$

$u = \dfrac{3+\sqrt{41}}{4}$	or	$u = \dfrac{3-\sqrt{41}}{4}$
$x^{-1} = \dfrac{3+\sqrt{41}}{4}$	or	$x^{-1} = \dfrac{3-\sqrt{41}}{4}$
$\left(x^{-1}\right)^{-1} = \left(\dfrac{3+\sqrt{41}}{4}\right)^{-1}$	or	$\left(x^{-1}\right)^{-1} = \left(\dfrac{3-\sqrt{41}}{4}\right)^{-1}$
$x = \dfrac{4}{3+\sqrt{41}}\left(\dfrac{3-\sqrt{41}}{3-\sqrt{41}}\right)$	or	$x = \dfrac{4}{3-\sqrt{41}}\left(\dfrac{3+\sqrt{41}}{3+\sqrt{41}}\right)$
$= \dfrac{12-4\sqrt{41}}{-32}$		$= \dfrac{12+4\sqrt{41}}{-32}$
$= \dfrac{-3+\sqrt{41}}{8}$		$= \dfrac{-3-\sqrt{41}}{8}$

107

Check $x = \dfrac{-3+\sqrt{41}}{8}$:

$$2\left(\dfrac{-3+\sqrt{41}}{8}\right)^{-2} - 3\left(\dfrac{-3+\sqrt{41}}{8}\right)^{-1} - 4 = 0$$

$$2\left(\dfrac{64}{\left(-3+\sqrt{41}\right)^2}\right) - 3\left(\dfrac{8}{-3+\sqrt{41}}\right) - 4 = 0$$

$$2(64) - 3(8)\left(-3+\sqrt{41}\right) - 4\left(-3+\sqrt{41}\right)^2 = 0$$

$$128 + 72 - 24\sqrt{41} - 4\left(9 - 6\sqrt{41} + 41\right) = 0$$

$$128 + 72 - 24\sqrt{41} - 36 + 24\sqrt{41} - 164 = 0$$

$$0 = 0$$

Check $x = \dfrac{-3-\sqrt{41}}{8}$:

$$2\left(\dfrac{-3-\sqrt{41}}{8}\right)^{-2} - 3\left(\dfrac{-3-\sqrt{41}}{8}\right)^{-1} - 4 = 0$$

$$2\left(\dfrac{64}{\left(-3-\sqrt{41}\right)^2}\right) - 3\left(\dfrac{8}{-3-\sqrt{41}}\right) - 4 = 0$$

$$2(64) - 3(8)\left(-3-\sqrt{41}\right) - 4\left(-3-\sqrt{41}\right)^2 = 0$$

$$128 + 72 + 24\sqrt{41} - 4\left(9 + 6\sqrt{41} + 41\right) = 0$$

$$128 + 72 + 24\sqrt{41} - 36 - 24\sqrt{41} - 164 = 0$$

$$0 = 0$$

The solution set is $\left\{\dfrac{-3-\sqrt{41}}{8}, \dfrac{-3+\sqrt{41}}{8}\right\}$.

69. $2x^{2/3} - 5x^{1/3} - 3 = 0$

Let $u = x^{1/3}$ so that $u^2 = x^{2/3}$.

$$2u^2 - 5u - 3 = 0$$

$$(2u+1)(u-3) = 0$$

$$u = -\dfrac{1}{2} \quad \text{or} \quad u = 3$$

$$x^{1/3} = -\dfrac{1}{2} \quad \text{or} \quad x^{1/3} = 3$$

$$\left(x^{1/3}\right)^3 = \left(-\dfrac{1}{2}\right)^3 \quad \text{or} \quad \left(x^{1/3}\right)^3 = (3)^3$$

$$x = -\dfrac{1}{8} \quad \text{or} \quad x = 27$$

Check $x = -\dfrac{1}{8}$: $2\left(-\dfrac{1}{8}\right)^{2/3} - 5\left(-\dfrac{1}{8}\right)^{1/3} - 3 = 0$

$$2\left(\dfrac{1}{4}\right) - 5\left(-\dfrac{1}{2}\right) - 3 = 0$$

$$\dfrac{1}{2} + \dfrac{5}{2} - 3 = 0$$

$$3 - 3 = 0$$

$$0 = 0$$

Check $x = 27$: $2(27)^{2/3} - 5(27)^{1/3} - 3 = 0$

$$2(9) - 5(3) - 3 = 0$$

$$18 - 15 - 3 = 0$$

$$3 - 3 = 0$$

$$0 = 0$$

The solution set is $\left\{-\dfrac{1}{8}, 27\right\}$.

70. $3x^{4/3} + 5x^{2/3} - 2 = 0$

Let $u = x^{2/3}$ so that $u^2 = x^{4/3}$.

$$3u^2 + 5u - 2 = 0$$

$$(3u-1)(u+2) = 0$$

$$u = \dfrac{1}{3} \quad \text{or} \quad u = -2$$

$$x^{2/3} = \dfrac{1}{3} \quad \text{or} \quad x^{2/3} = -2$$

$$\left(x^{2/3}\right)^3 = \left(\dfrac{1}{3}\right)^3 \quad \text{or} \quad \left(x^{2/3}\right)^3 = (-2)^3$$

$$x^2 = \dfrac{1}{27} \quad \text{or} \quad x^2 = -8$$

$$x = \pm\sqrt{\dfrac{1}{27}} \qquad \text{not real}$$

Check: $3\left(\pm\sqrt{\dfrac{1}{27}}\right)^{4/3} + 5\left(\pm\sqrt{\dfrac{1}{27}}\right)^{2/3} - 2 = 0$

$$3\left(\dfrac{1}{27}\right)^{2/3} + 5\left(\pm\sqrt{\dfrac{1}{27}}\right)^{1/3} - 2 = 0$$

$$3\left(\dfrac{1}{3}\right)^2 + 5\left(\dfrac{1}{3}\right) - 2 = 0$$

$$3\left(\dfrac{1}{9}\right) + \dfrac{5}{3} - 2 = 0$$

$$\dfrac{1}{3} + \dfrac{5}{3} - 2 = 0$$

$$2 - 2 = 0$$

$$0 = 0$$

Note: $\pm\sqrt{\dfrac{1}{27}} = \pm\sqrt{\dfrac{3}{81}} = \pm\dfrac{\sqrt{3}}{9}$

The solution set is $\left\{-\dfrac{\sqrt{3}}{9}, \dfrac{\sqrt{3}}{9}\right\}$.

71. $\left(\dfrac{v}{v+1}\right)^2 + \dfrac{2v}{v+1} = 8$

$\left(\dfrac{v}{v+1}\right)^2 + 2\left(\dfrac{v}{v+1}\right) = 8$

Let $u = \dfrac{v}{v+1}$ so that $u^2 = \left(\dfrac{v}{v+1}\right)^2$.

$u^2 + 2u = 8$

$u^2 + 2u - 8 = 0$

$(u+4)(u-2) = 0$

$u = -4 \quad$ or $\quad u = 2$

$\dfrac{v}{v+1} = -4 \quad$ or $\quad \dfrac{v}{v+1} = 2$

$v = -4v - 4 \quad$ or $\quad v = 2v + 2$

$v = -\dfrac{4}{5} \quad$ or $\quad v = -2$

Check $v = -\dfrac{4}{5}$: $\left(\dfrac{-\frac{4}{5}}{-\frac{4}{5}+1}\right)^2 + \dfrac{2\left(-\frac{4}{5}\right)}{\left(-\frac{4}{5}\right)+1} = 8$

$\dfrac{\left(\frac{16}{25}\right)}{\left(\frac{1}{25}\right)} + \dfrac{\left(-\frac{8}{5}\right)}{\left(\frac{1}{5}\right)} = 8$

$16 - 8 = 8$

$8 = 8$

Check $v = -2$: $\left(\dfrac{-2}{-2+1}\right)^2 + \dfrac{2(-2)}{(-2)+1} = 8$

$4 + 4 = 8$

$8 = 8$

The solution set is $\left\{-2, -\dfrac{4}{5}\right\}$.

72. $\left(\dfrac{y}{y-1}\right)^2 = 6\left(\dfrac{y}{y-1}\right) + 7$

Let $u = \dfrac{y}{y-1}$ so that $u^2 = \left(\dfrac{y}{y-1}\right)^2$.

$u^2 = 6u + 7$

$u^2 - 6u - 7 = 0$

$(u-7)(u+1) = 0$

$u = -1 \quad$ or $\quad u = 7$

$\dfrac{y}{y-1} = -1 \quad$ or $\quad \dfrac{y}{y-1} = 7$

$y = -y + 1 \quad$ or $\quad y = 7y - 7$

$2y = 1 \quad$ or $\quad -6y = -7$

$y = \dfrac{1}{2} \quad$ or $\quad y = \dfrac{7}{6}$

Check $y = \dfrac{1}{2}$: $\left(\dfrac{\frac{1}{2}}{\frac{1}{2}-1}\right)^2 = 6\left(\dfrac{\frac{1}{2}}{\frac{1}{2}-1}\right) + 7$

$\dfrac{\frac{1}{4}}{\frac{1}{4}} = 6\cdot\dfrac{\frac{1}{2}}{\left(-\frac{1}{2}\right)} + 7$

$1 = 6(-1) + 7$

$1 = 1$

Check $y = \dfrac{7}{6}$: $\left(\dfrac{\frac{7}{6}}{\frac{7}{6}-1}\right)^2 = 6\left(\dfrac{\frac{7}{6}}{\frac{7}{6}-1}\right) + 7$

$\dfrac{\left(\frac{49}{36}\right)}{\left(\frac{1}{36}\right)} = 6\left(\dfrac{\left(\frac{7}{6}\right)}{\left(\frac{1}{6}\right)}\right) + 7$

$49 = 42 + 7$

$49 = 49$

The solution set is $\left\{\dfrac{1}{2}, \dfrac{7}{6}\right\}$.

73. $x^3 - 9x = 0$

$x\left(x^2 - 9\right) = 0$

$x(x-3)(x+3) = 0$

$x = 0 \;$ or $\; x - 3 = 0 \;\; x + 3 = 0$

$\qquad\qquad\quad x = 3 \qquad\quad x = -3$

The solution set is $\{-3, 0, 3\}$.

74. $x^4 - x^2 = 0$

$x^2\left(x^2 - 1\right) = 0$

$x^2(x-1)(x+1) = 0$

$x^2 = 0 \;$ or $\; x - 1 = 0 \;$ or $\; x + 1 = 0$

$x = 0 \qquad\quad x = 1 \qquad\quad x = -1$

The solution set is $\{-1, 0, 1\}$.

75.
$$4x^3 = 3x^2$$
$$4x^3 - 3x^2 = 0$$
$$x^2(4x - 3) = 0$$
$$x^2 = 0 \quad \text{or} \quad 4x - 3 = 0$$
$$x = 0 \qquad 4x = 3$$
$$x = \frac{3}{4}$$
The solution set is $\left\{0, \dfrac{3}{4}\right\}$.

76.
$$x^5 = 4x^3$$
$$x^5 - 4x^3 = 0$$
$$x^3(x^2 - 4) = 0$$
$$x^3(x - 2)(x + 2) = 0$$
$$x^3 = 0 \quad \text{or} \quad x - 2 = 0 \quad \text{or} \quad x + 2 = 0$$
$$x = 0 \qquad x = 2 \qquad x = -2$$
The solution set is $\{-2, 0, 2\}$.

77.
$$x^3 + x^2 - 20x = 0$$
$$x(x^2 + x - 20) = 0$$
$$x(x + 5)(x - 4) = 0$$
$$x = 0 \quad \text{or} \quad x + 5 = 0 \quad \text{or} \quad x - 4 = 0$$
$$x = -5 \qquad x = 4$$
The solution set is $\{-5, 0, 4\}$.

78.
$$x^3 + 6x^2 - 7x = 0$$
$$x(x^2 + 6x - 7) = 0$$
$$x(x + 7)(x - 1) = 0$$
$$x = 0 \quad \text{or} \quad x + 7 = 0 \quad \text{or} \quad x - 1 = 0$$
$$x = -7 \qquad x = 1$$
The solution set is $\{-7, 0, 1\}$.

79.
$$x^3 + x^2 - x - 1 = 0$$
$$x^2(x + 1) - 1(x + 1) = 0$$
$$(x + 1)(x^2 - 1) = 0$$
$$(x + 1)(x - 1)(x + 1) = 0$$
$$x + 1 = 0 \quad \text{or} \quad x - 1 = 0$$
$$x = -1 \qquad x = 1$$
The solution set is $\{-1, 1\}$.

80.
$$x^3 + 4x^2 - x - 4 = 0$$
$$x^2(x + 4) - 1(x + 4) = 0$$
$$(x + 4)(x^2 - 1) = 0$$
$$(x + 4)(x - 1)(x + 1) = 0$$
$$x + 4 = 0 \quad \text{or} \quad x - 1 = 0 \quad \text{or} \quad x + 1 = 0$$
$$x = -4 \qquad x = 1 \qquad x = -1$$
The solution set is $\{-4, -1, 1\}$.

81.
$$x^3 - 3x^2 - 4x + 12 = 0$$
$$x^2(x - 3) - 4(x - 3) = 0$$
$$(x - 3)(x^2 - 4) = 0$$
$$(x - 3)(x - 2)(x + 2) = 0$$
$$x - 3 = 0 \quad \text{or} \quad x - 2 = 0 \quad \text{or} \quad x + 2 = 0$$
$$x = 3 \qquad x = 2 \qquad x = -2$$
The solution set is $\{-2, 2, 3\}$.

82.
$$x^3 - 3x^2 - x + 3 = 0$$
$$x^2(x - 3) - 1(x - 3) = 0$$
$$(x - 3)(x^2 - 1) = 0$$
$$(x - 3)(x - 1)(x + 1) = 0$$
$$x - 3 = 0 \quad \text{or} \quad x - 1 = 0 \quad \text{or} \quad x + 1 = 0$$
$$x = 3 \qquad x = 1 \qquad x = -1$$
The solution set is $\{-1, 1, 3\}$.

83.
$$2x^3 + 4 = x^2 + 8x$$
$$2x^3 - x^2 - 8x + 4 = 0$$
$$x^2(2x - 1) - 4(2x - 1) = 0$$
$$(2x - 1)(x^2 - 4) = 0$$
$$(2x - 1)(x - 2)(x + 2) = 0$$
$$2x - 1 = 0 \quad \text{or} \quad x - 2 = 0 \quad \text{or} \quad x + 2 = 0$$
$$2x = 1 \qquad x = 2 \qquad x = -2$$
$$x = \frac{1}{2}$$
The solution set is $\left\{-2, \dfrac{1}{2}, 2\right\}$.

84.
$$3x^3 + 4x^2 = 27x + 36$$
$$3x^3 + 4x^2 - 27x - 36 = 0$$
$$x^2(3x+4) - 9(3x+4) = 0$$
$$(3x+4)(x^2-9) = 0$$
$$(3x+4)(x-3)(x+3) = 0$$
$$3x+4 = 0 \quad \text{or} \quad x-3 = 0 \quad \text{or} \quad x+3 = 0$$
$$3x = -4 \qquad x = 3 \qquad x = -3$$
$$x = -\frac{4}{3}$$

The solution set is $\left\{-3, -\frac{4}{3}, 3\right\}$.

85.
$$5x^3 + 45x = 2x^2 + 18$$
$$5x^3 - 2x^2 + 45x - 18 = 0$$
$$x^2(5x-2) + 9(5x-2) = 0$$
$$(5x-2)(x^2+9) = 0$$
$$5x-2 = 0 \quad \text{or} \quad x^2+9 = 0$$
$$5x = 2 \qquad\qquad x^2 = -9$$
$$x = \frac{2}{5} \qquad\qquad \text{no real solutions}$$

The solution set is $\left\{\frac{2}{5}\right\}$.

86.
$$3x^3 + 12x = 5x^2 + 20$$
$$3x^3 - 5x^2 + 12x - 20 = 0$$
$$x^2(3x-5) + 4(3x-5) = 0$$
$$(3x-5)(x^2+4) = 0$$
$$3x-5 = 0 \quad \text{or} \quad x^2+4 = 0$$
$$3x = 5 \qquad\qquad x^2 = -4$$
$$x = \frac{5}{3} \qquad\qquad \text{no real solutions}$$

The solution set is $\left\{\frac{5}{3}\right\}$.

87. $x\left(x^2-3x\right)^{1/3} + 2\left(x^2-3x\right)^{4/3} = 0$
$$\left(x^2-3x\right)^{1/3}\left[x + 2\left(x^2-3x\right)\right] = 0$$
$$\left(x^2-3x\right)^{1/3}\left(x + 2x^2 - 6x\right) = 0$$
$$\left(x^2-3x\right)^{1/3}\left(2x^2 - 5x\right) = 0$$

$$\left(x^2-3x\right)^{1/3} = 0 \quad \text{or} \quad 2x^2 - 5x = 0$$
$$x^2 - 3x = 0 \quad \text{or} \quad 2x^2 - 5x = 0$$
$$x(x-3) = 0 \quad \text{or} \quad x(2x-5) = 0$$
$$x = 0 \text{ or } x = 3 \quad \text{or} \quad x = 0 \text{ or } x = \frac{5}{2}$$

The solution set is $\left\{0, \frac{5}{2}, 3\right\}$.

88. $3x\left(x^2+2x\right)^{1/2} - 2\left(x^2+2x\right)^{3/2} = 0$
$$\left(x^2+2x\right)^{1/2}\left[3x - 2\left(x^2+2x\right)\right] = 0$$
$$\left(x^2+2x\right)^{1/2}\left(3x - 2x^2 - 4x\right) = 0$$
$$\left(x^2+2x\right)^{1/2}\left(-2x^2 - x\right) = 0$$

$$\left(x^2+2x\right)^{1/2} = 0 \quad \text{or} \quad -2x^2 - x = 0$$
$$x^2 + 2x = 0 \quad \text{or} \quad 2x^2 + x = 0$$
$$x(x+2) = 0 \quad \text{or} \quad x(2x+1) = 0$$
$$x = 0 \text{ or } x = -2 \quad \text{or} \quad x = 0 \text{ or } x = -\frac{1}{2}$$

Check $x = 0$:
$$3\cdot 0\left(0^2 + 2\cdot 0\right)^{1/2} - 2\left(0^2 + 2\cdot 0\right)^{3/2} = 0$$
$$3\cdot 0(0)^{1/2} - 2(0)^{3/2} = 0$$
$$0 = 0$$

Check $x = -2$:
$$3(-2)\left((-2)^2 + 2(-2)\right)^{1/2} - 2\left((-2)^2 + 2(-2)\right)^{3/2} = 0$$
$$3(-2)(4-4)^{1/2} - 2(4-4)^{3/2} = 0$$
$$3(-2)(0)^{1/2} - 2(0)^{3/2} = 0$$
$$3(-2)(0) - 2(0) = 0$$
$$0 = 0$$

Check $x = -\frac{1}{2}$:
$$3\left(-\tfrac{1}{2}\right)\left(\left(-\tfrac{1}{2}\right)^2 + 2\left(-\tfrac{1}{2}\right)\right)^{1/2} - 2\left(\left(-\tfrac{1}{2}\right)^2 + 2\left(-\tfrac{1}{2}\right)\right)^{3/2} = 0$$
$$3\left(-\tfrac{1}{2}\right)\left(\tfrac{1}{4}-1\right)^{1/2} - 2\left(\tfrac{1}{4}-1\right)^{3/2} = 0$$
$$3\left(-\tfrac{1}{2}\right)\left(-\tfrac{3}{4}\right)^{1/2} - 2\left(-\tfrac{3}{4}\right)^{3/2} = 0$$
Not real

The solution set is $\{-2, 0\}$.

111

89. $x - 4x^{1/2} + 2 = 0$

Let $u = x^{1/2}$ so that $u^2 = x^2$.

$u^2 - 4u + 2 = 0$

$u = \dfrac{-(-4) \pm \sqrt{(-4)^2 - 4(1)(2)}}{2}$

$= \dfrac{4 \pm \sqrt{8}}{2} = \dfrac{4 \pm 2\sqrt{2}}{2} = 2 \pm \sqrt{2}$

$u = 2 + \sqrt{2}$ or $u = 2 - \sqrt{2}$

$x^{1/2} = 2 + \sqrt{2}$ or $x^{1/2} = 2 - \sqrt{2}$

$\left(x^{1/2}\right)^2 = \left(2 + \sqrt{2}\right)^2$ or $\left(x^{1/2}\right)^2 = \left(2 - \sqrt{2}\right)^2$

$x = \left(2 + \sqrt{2}\right)^2$ or $x = \left(2 - \sqrt{2}\right)^2$

Check $x = \left(2 + \sqrt{2}\right)^2$:

$\left(2 + \sqrt{2}\right)^2 - 4\left(2 + \sqrt{2}\right) + 2 = 0$

$4 + 4\sqrt{2} + 2 - 8 - 4\sqrt{2} + 2 = 0$

$0 = 0$

Check $x = \left(2 - \sqrt{2}\right)^2$:

$\left(2 - \sqrt{2}\right)^2 - 4\left(2 - \sqrt{2}\right) + 2 = 0$

$4 - 4\sqrt{2} + 2 - 8 + 4\sqrt{2} + 2 = 0$

$0 = 0$

The solution set is

$\left\{ \left(2 - \sqrt{2}\right)^2, \ \left(2 + \sqrt{2}\right)^2 \right\} \approx \{0.34, \ 11.66\}$.

90. $x^{2/3} + 4x^{1/3} + 2 = 0$

Let $u = x^{1/3}$ so that $u^2 = x^{2/3}$.

$u^2 + 4u + 2 = 0$

$u = \dfrac{-4 \pm \sqrt{4^2 - 4(1)(2)}}{2(1)}$

$= \dfrac{-4 \pm \sqrt{8}}{2} = \dfrac{-4 \pm 2\sqrt{2}}{2} = -2 \pm \sqrt{2}$

$u = -2 + \sqrt{2}$ or $u = -2 - \sqrt{2}$

$x^{1/3} = -2 + \sqrt{2}$ or $x^{1/3} = -2 - \sqrt{2}$

$x = \left(-2 + \sqrt{2}\right)^3$ or $x = \left(-2 - \sqrt{2}\right)^3$

Check $x = \left(-2 + \sqrt{2}\right)^3$:

$\left(\left(-2 + \sqrt{2}\right)^3\right)^{2/3} + 4\left(\left(-2 + \sqrt{2}\right)^3\right)^{1/3} + 2 = 0$

$\left(-2 + \sqrt{2}\right)^2 + 4\left(-2 + \sqrt{2}\right) + 2 = 0$

$4 - 4\sqrt{2} + 2 - 8 + 4\sqrt{2} + 2 = 0$

$0 = 0$

Check $x = \left(-2 - \sqrt{2}\right)^3$:

$\left(\left(-2 - \sqrt{2}\right)^3\right)^{2/3} + 4\left(\left(-2 - \sqrt{2}\right)^3\right)^{1/3} + 2 = 0$

$\left(-2 - \sqrt{2}\right)^2 + 4\left(-2 - \sqrt{2}\right) + 2 = 0$

$4 + 4\sqrt{2} + 2 - 8 - 4\sqrt{2} + 2 = 0$

$0 = 0$

The solution set is

$\left\{ \left(-2 - \sqrt{2}\right)^3, \ \left(-2 + \sqrt{2}\right)^3 \right\} \approx \{-39.80, \ -0.20\}$.

91. $x^4 + \sqrt{3}x^2 - 3 = 0$

Let $u = x^2$ so that $u^2 = x^4$.

$u^2 + \sqrt{3}u - 3 = 0$

$u = \dfrac{-\sqrt{3} \pm \sqrt{\left(\sqrt{3}\right)^2 - 4(1)(-3)}}{2(1)} = \dfrac{-\sqrt{3} \pm \sqrt{15}}{2}$

$u = \dfrac{-\sqrt{3} + \sqrt{15}}{2}$ or $u = \dfrac{-\sqrt{3} - \sqrt{15}}{2}$

$x^2 = \dfrac{-\sqrt{3} + \sqrt{15}}{2}$ or $x^2 = \dfrac{-\sqrt{3} - \sqrt{15}}{2}$

$x = \pm\sqrt{\dfrac{-\sqrt{3} + \sqrt{15}}{2}}$ or $x = \pm\sqrt{\dfrac{-\sqrt{3} - \sqrt{15}}{2}}$

Not real

Check $x = \sqrt{\dfrac{-\sqrt{3} + \sqrt{15}}{2}}$:

$\left(\sqrt{\dfrac{-\sqrt{3} + \sqrt{15}}{2}}\right)^4 + \sqrt{3}\left(\sqrt{\dfrac{-\sqrt{3} + \sqrt{15}}{2}}\right)^2 - 3 = 0$

$\left(\dfrac{-\sqrt{3} + \sqrt{15}}{2}\right)^2 + \sqrt{3}\left(\dfrac{-\sqrt{3} + \sqrt{15}}{2}\right) - 3 = 0$

$\dfrac{3 - 2\sqrt{3}\sqrt{15} + 15}{4} + \dfrac{\sqrt{3}\left(-\sqrt{3}\right) + \sqrt{3}\sqrt{15}}{2} - 3 = 0$

$\dfrac{18 - 2\sqrt{45}}{4} + \dfrac{-3 + \sqrt{45}}{2} - 3 = 0$

$\dfrac{9 - \sqrt{45}}{2} + \dfrac{-3 + \sqrt{45}}{2} - 3 = 0$

$\dfrac{9 - \sqrt{45} - 3 + \sqrt{45}}{2} - 3 = 0$

$3 - 3 = 0$

$0 = 0$

Check $x = -\sqrt{\dfrac{-\sqrt{3} + \sqrt{15}}{2}}$:

$$\left(-\sqrt{\frac{-\sqrt{3}+\sqrt{15}}{2}}\right)^4+\sqrt{3}\left(-\sqrt{\frac{-\sqrt{3}+\sqrt{15}}{2}}\right)^2-3=0$$

$$\left(\frac{-\sqrt{3}+\sqrt{15}}{2}\right)^2+\sqrt{3}\left(\frac{-\sqrt{3}+\sqrt{15}}{2}\right)-3=0$$

$$\frac{3-2\sqrt{3}\sqrt{15}+15}{4}+\frac{\sqrt{3}\left(-\sqrt{3}\right)+\sqrt{3}\sqrt{15}}{2}-3=0$$

$$\frac{18-2\sqrt{45}}{4}+\frac{-3+\sqrt{45}}{2}-3=0$$

$$\frac{9-\sqrt{45}}{2}+\frac{-3+\sqrt{45}}{2}-3=0$$

$$\frac{9-\sqrt{45}-3+\sqrt{45}}{2}-3=0$$

$$3-3=0$$

$$0=0$$

The solution set is

$$\left\{-\sqrt{\frac{-\sqrt{3}+\sqrt{15}}{2}},\ \sqrt{\frac{-\sqrt{3}+\sqrt{15}}{2}}\right\}\approx\{-1.03,\ 1.03\}.$$

92. $x^4+\sqrt{2}x^2-2=0$

Let $u=x^2$ so that $u^2=x^4$.

$$u^2+\sqrt{2}u-2=0$$

$$u=\frac{-\sqrt{2}\pm\sqrt{\left(\sqrt{2}\right)^2-4(1)(-2)}}{2(1)}=\frac{-\sqrt{2}\pm\sqrt{10}}{2}$$

$$u=\frac{-\sqrt{2}+\sqrt{10}}{2}\quad\text{or}\quad u=\frac{-\sqrt{2}-\sqrt{10}}{2}$$

$$x^2=\frac{-\sqrt{2}+\sqrt{10}}{2}\quad\text{or}\quad x^2=\frac{-\sqrt{2}-\sqrt{10}}{2}$$

$$x=\pm\sqrt{\frac{-\sqrt{2}+\sqrt{10}}{2}}\quad\text{or}\quad x=\pm\sqrt{\frac{-\sqrt{2}-\sqrt{10}}{2}}$$

Not real

Check $x=\sqrt{\dfrac{-\sqrt{2}+\sqrt{10}}{2}}$:

$$\left(\sqrt{\frac{-\sqrt{2}+\sqrt{10}}{2}}\right)^4+\sqrt{2}\left(\sqrt{\frac{-\sqrt{2}+\sqrt{10}}{2}}\right)^2-2=0$$

$$\left(\frac{-\sqrt{2}+\sqrt{10}}{2}\right)^2+\sqrt{2}\left(\frac{-\sqrt{2}+\sqrt{10}}{2}\right)-2=0$$

$$\frac{12-2\sqrt{20}}{4}+\frac{-2+\sqrt{20}}{2}-2=0$$

$$\frac{6-\sqrt{20}-2+\sqrt{20}}{2}-2=0$$

$$2-2=0$$

$$0=0$$

Check $x=-\sqrt{\dfrac{-\sqrt{2}+\sqrt{10}}{2}}$:

$$\left(-\sqrt{\frac{-\sqrt{2}+\sqrt{10}}{2}}\right)^4+\sqrt{2}\left(-\sqrt{\frac{-\sqrt{2}+\sqrt{10}}{2}}\right)^2-2=0$$

$$\left(\frac{-\sqrt{2}+\sqrt{10}}{2}\right)^2+\sqrt{2}\left(\frac{-\sqrt{2}+\sqrt{10}}{2}\right)-2=0$$

$$\frac{12-2\sqrt{20}}{4}+\frac{-2+\sqrt{20}}{2}-2=0$$

$$\frac{6-\sqrt{20}-2+\sqrt{20}}{2}-2=0$$

$$2-2=0$$

$$0=0$$

The solution set is

$$\left\{-\sqrt{\frac{-\sqrt{2}+\sqrt{10}}{2}},\ \sqrt{\frac{-\sqrt{2}+\sqrt{10}}{2}}\right\}\approx\{-0.93,\ 0.93\}.$$

93. $\pi(1+t)^2=\pi+1+t$

Let $u=1+t$ so that $u^2=(1+t)^2$.

$$\pi u^2=\pi+u$$

$$\pi u^2-u-\pi=0$$

$$u=\frac{-(-1)\pm\sqrt{(-1)^2-4(\pi)(-\pi)}}{2(\pi)}=\frac{1\pm\sqrt{1+4\pi^2}}{2\pi}$$

$$1+t=\frac{1\pm\sqrt{1+4\pi^2}}{2\pi}$$

$$t=-1+\frac{1\pm\sqrt{1+4\pi^2}}{2\pi}$$

Check $t=-1+\dfrac{1+\sqrt{1+4\pi^2}}{2\pi}$:

$$\pi\left(\frac{1+\sqrt{1+4\pi^2}}{2\pi}\right)^2=\pi+\frac{1+\sqrt{1+4\pi^2}}{2\pi}$$

$$\pi\left(\frac{1+2\sqrt{1+4\pi^2}+1+4\pi^2}{4\pi^2}\right)=\pi+\frac{1+\sqrt{1+4\pi^2}}{2\pi}$$

$$\frac{2+2\sqrt{1+4\pi^2}+4\pi^2}{4\pi}=\frac{2\pi^2+1+\sqrt{1+4\pi^2}}{2\pi}$$

$$\frac{1+\sqrt{1+4\pi^2}+2\pi^2}{2\pi}=\frac{2\pi^2+1+\sqrt{1+4\pi^2}}{2\pi}$$

Check $t=-1+\dfrac{1-\sqrt{1+4\pi^2}}{2\pi}$:

$$\pi\left(\frac{1-\sqrt{1+4\pi^2}}{2\pi}\right)^2 = \pi + \frac{1-\sqrt{1+4\pi^2}}{2\pi}$$

$$\pi\left(\frac{1-2\sqrt{1+4\pi^2}+1+4\pi^2}{4\pi^2}\right) = \pi + \frac{1-\sqrt{1+4\pi^2}}{2\pi}$$

$$\frac{2-2\sqrt{1+4\pi^2}+4\pi^2}{4\pi} = \frac{2\pi^2+1-\sqrt{1+4\pi^2}}{2\pi}$$

$$\frac{1-\sqrt{1+4\pi^2}+2\pi^2}{2\pi} = \frac{2\pi^2+1-\sqrt{1+4\pi^2}}{2\pi}$$

The solution set is

$$\left\{-1+\frac{1-\sqrt{1+4\pi^2}}{2\pi}, -1+\frac{1+\sqrt{1+4\pi^2}}{2\pi}\right\}$$

$$\approx \{-1.85,\ 0.17\}.$$

94. $\pi(1+r)^2 = 2 + \pi(1+r)$

Let $u = 1+r$ so that $u^2 = (1+r)^2$.

$$\pi u^2 = 2 + \pi u$$

$$\pi u^2 - \pi u - 2 = 0$$

$$u = \frac{-(-\pi) \pm \sqrt{(-\pi)^2 + 4(\pi)(-2)}}{2(\pi)}$$

$$= \frac{\pi \pm \sqrt{\pi^2 - 8\pi}}{2\pi}$$

$$1+r = \frac{\pi \pm \sqrt{\pi^2 + 8\pi}}{2\pi}$$

$$r = -1 + \frac{\pi \pm \sqrt{\pi^2 + 8\pi}}{2\pi}$$

Check $r = -1 + \dfrac{\pi + \sqrt{\pi^2 + 8\pi}}{2\pi}$:

$$\pi\left(\frac{\pi + \sqrt{\pi^2 + 8\pi}}{2\pi}\right)^2 = 2 + \pi\left(\frac{\pi + \sqrt{\pi^2 + 8\pi}}{2\pi}\right)$$

$$\pi\left(\frac{\pi^2 + 2\pi\sqrt{\pi^2 + 8\pi} + \pi^2 + 8\pi}{4\pi^2}\right) = 2 + \pi\left(\frac{\pi + \sqrt{\pi^2 + 8\pi}}{2\pi}\right)$$

$$\frac{2\pi^2 + 2\pi\sqrt{\pi^2 + 8\pi} + 8\pi}{4\pi} = 2 + \frac{\pi + \sqrt{\pi^2 + 8\pi}}{2}$$

$$\frac{\pi + \sqrt{\pi^2 + 8\pi} + 4}{2} = \frac{4 + \pi + \sqrt{\pi^2 + 8\pi}}{2}$$

Check $r = -1 + \dfrac{\pi - \sqrt{\pi^2 + 8\pi}}{2\pi}$:

$$\pi\left(\frac{\pi - \sqrt{\pi^2 + 8\pi}}{2\pi}\right)^2 = 2 + \pi\left(\frac{\pi - \sqrt{\pi^2 + 8\pi}}{2\pi}\right)$$

$$\pi\left(\frac{\pi^2 - 2\pi\sqrt{\pi^2 + 8\pi} + \pi^2 + 8\pi}{4\pi^2}\right) = 2 + \pi\left(\frac{\pi - \sqrt{\pi^2 + 8\pi}}{2\pi}\right)$$

$$\frac{2\pi^2 - 2\pi\sqrt{\pi^2 + 8\pi} + 8\pi}{4\pi} = 2 + \frac{\pi - \sqrt{\pi^2 + 8\pi}}{2}$$

$$\frac{\pi - \sqrt{\pi^2 + 8\pi} + 4}{2} = \frac{4 + \pi - \sqrt{\pi^2 + 8\pi}}{2}$$

The solution set is

$$\left\{-1+\frac{\pi - \sqrt{\pi^2 + 8\pi}}{2\pi}, -1+\frac{\pi + \sqrt{\pi^2 + 8\pi}}{2\pi}\right\}$$

$$\approx \{-1.44,\ 0.44\}.$$

95.
$$k^2 - k = 12$$
$$k^2 - k - 12 = 0$$
$$(k-4)(k+3) = 0$$

$$k = 4 \qquad \text{or} \qquad k = -3$$

$$\frac{x+3}{x-3} = 4 \qquad \text{or} \qquad \frac{x+3}{x-3} = -3$$

$$x+3 = 4x-12 \quad \text{or} \quad x+3 = -3x+9$$

$$3x = 15 \qquad \text{or} \qquad 4x = 6$$

$$x = 5 \qquad \text{or} \qquad x = \frac{6}{4} = 1.5$$

Neither of these values causes a denominator to equal zero, so the solution set is $\{1.5, 5\}$.

96.
$$k^2 - 3k = 28$$
$$k^2 - 3k - 28 = 0$$
$$(k+4)(k-7) = 0$$

$$k = -4 \qquad \text{or} \qquad k = 7$$

$$\frac{x+3}{x-4} = -4 \qquad \text{or} \qquad \frac{x+3}{x-4} = 7$$

$$x+3 = -4x+16 \quad \text{or} \quad x+3 = 7x-28$$

$$5x = 13 \qquad \text{or} \qquad -6x = -31$$

$$x = \frac{13}{5} = 2.6 \quad \text{or} \quad x = \frac{31}{6} \approx 5.17$$

Neither of these values causes a denominator to equal zero, so the solution set is

$$\left\{\frac{13}{5}, \frac{31}{6}\right\} \approx \{2.6, 5.17\}.$$

97. Solve the equation $\dfrac{\sqrt{s}}{4}+\dfrac{s}{1100}=4$.

$$\frac{s}{1100}+\frac{\sqrt{s}}{4}-4=0$$

$$(1100)\left(\frac{s}{1100}+\frac{\sqrt{s}}{4}-4\right)=(0)(1100)$$

$$s+275\sqrt{s}-4400=0$$

Let $u=\sqrt{s}$, so that $u^2=s$.

$$u^2+275u-4400=0$$

$$u=\frac{-275\pm\sqrt{275^2-4(1)(-4400)}}{2}$$

$$=\frac{-275\pm\sqrt{93,225}}{2}$$

$u\approx15.1638$ or $u\approx-290.1638$

Since $u=\sqrt{s}$, it must be positive, so

$$s=u^2\approx(15.1638)^2\approx229.94$$

The distance to the water's surface is approximately 229.94 feet.

98. $T=\sqrt[4]{\dfrac{LH^2}{25}}$

Let $T=4$ and $H=10$, and solve for L.

$$4=\sqrt[4]{\frac{L(10)^2}{25}}$$

$$4=\sqrt[4]{4L}$$

$$(4)^4=\left(\sqrt[4]{4L}\right)^4$$

$$256=4L$$

$$64=L$$

The crushing load is 64 tons.

99. $T=2\pi\sqrt{\dfrac{l}{32}}$

Let $T=16.5$ and solve for l.

$$16.5=2\pi\sqrt{\frac{l}{32}}$$

$$\frac{16.5}{2\pi}=\sqrt{\frac{l}{32}}$$

$$\left(\frac{16.5}{2\pi}\right)^2=\left(\sqrt{\frac{l}{32}}\right)^2$$

$$\left(\frac{16.5}{2\pi}\right)^2=\frac{l}{32}$$

$$l=32\left(\frac{16.5}{2\pi}\right)^2\approx220.7$$

The length was approximately 220.7 feet.

100. Answers will vary. One example: $\sqrt{x+1}=-1$.

101. Answers will vary. One example: $x-\sqrt{x}-2=0$.

102. Answers will vary.

Section 1.5

1. $x\geq-2$

2. False. -5 is to the left of -2 on the number line, so $-5>-2$.

3. negative

4. closed interval

5. multiplication properties (for inequalities)

6. True. This follows from the addition property for inequalities.

7. True. This follows from the addition property for inequalities.

8. True;. This follows from the multiplication property for inequalities.

9. False. Since both sides of the inequality are being divided by a negative number, the sense, or direction, of the inequality must be reversed. That is, $\dfrac{a}{c}>\dfrac{b}{c}$.

10. True

11. Interval: $[0,2]$
Inequality: $0\leq x\leq2$

12. Interval: $(-1,2)$
Inequality: $-1<x<2$

13. Interval: $[2,\infty)$
Inequality: $x\geq2$

14. Interval: $(-\infty,0]$
Inequality: $x\leq0$

15. Interval: $[0,3)$
Inequality: $0\leq x<3$

115

16. Interval: $(-1, 1]$

Inequality: $-1 < x \le 1$

17. a.
$$3 < 5$$
$$3 + 3 < 5 + 3$$
$$6 < 8$$

b.
$$3 < 5$$
$$3 - 5 < 5 - 5$$
$$-2 < 0$$

c.
$$3 < 5$$
$$3(3) < 3(5)$$
$$9 < 15$$

d.
$$3 < 5$$
$$-2(3) > -2(5)$$
$$-6 > -10$$

18. a.
$$2 > 1$$
$$2 + 3 > 1 + 3$$
$$5 > 4$$

b.
$$2 > 1$$
$$2 - 5 > 1 - 5$$
$$-3 > -4$$

c.
$$2 > 1$$
$$3(2) > 3(1)$$
$$6 > 3$$

d.
$$2 > 1$$
$$-2(2) < -2(1)$$
$$-4 < -2$$

19. a.
$$4 > -3$$
$$4 + 3 > -3 + 3$$
$$7 > 0$$

b.
$$4 > -3$$
$$4 - 5 > -3 - 5$$
$$-1 > -8$$

c.
$$4 > -3$$
$$3(4) > 3(-3)$$
$$12 > -9$$

d.
$$4 > -3$$
$$-2(4) < -2(-3)$$
$$-8 < 6$$

20. a.
$$-3 > -5$$
$$-3 + 3 > -5 + 3$$
$$0 > -2$$

b.
$$-3 > -5$$
$$-3 - 5 > -5 - 5$$
$$-8 > -10$$

c.
$$-3 > -5$$
$$3(-3) > 3(-5)$$
$$-9 > -15$$

d.
$$-3 > -5$$
$$-2(-3) < -2(-5)$$
$$6 < 10$$

21. a.
$$2x + 1 < 2$$
$$2x + 1 + 3 < 2 + 3$$
$$2x + 4 < 5$$

b.
$$2x + 1 < 2$$
$$2x + 1 - 5 < 2 - 5$$
$$2x - 4 < -3$$

c.
$$2x + 1 < 2$$
$$3(2x + 1) < 3(2)$$
$$6x + 3 < 6$$

d.
$$2x + 1 < 2$$
$$-2(2x + 1) > -2(2)$$
$$-4x - 2 > -4$$

22. a.
$$1 - 2x > 5$$
$$1 - 2x + 3 > 5 + 3$$
$$4 - 2x > 8$$

b.
$$1 - 2x > 5$$
$$1 - 2x - 5 > 5 - 5$$
$$-4 - 2x > 0$$

c.
$$1 - 2x > 5$$
$$3(1 - 2x) > 3(5)$$
$$3 - 6x > 15$$

d.
$$1 - 2x > 5$$
$$-2(1 - 2x) < -2(5)$$
$$-2 + 4x < -10$$

23. $[0, 4]$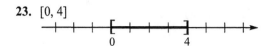

24. $(-1, 5)$

25. $[4, 6)$

26. $(-2, 0)$

27. $[4, \infty)$

28. $(-\infty, 5]$

29. $(-\infty, -4)$

30. $(1, \infty)$

31. $2 \le x \le 5$

32. $1 < x < 2$

33. $-3 < x < -2$

34. $0 \le x < 1$

35. $x \ge 4$

36. $x \le 2$

37. $x < -3$

38. $x > -8$

39. If $x < 5$, then $x - 5 < 0$.

40. If $x < -4$, then $x + 4 < 0$.

41. If $x > -4$, then $x + 4 > 0$.

42. If $x > 6$, then $x - 6 > 0$.

43. If $x \ge -4$, then $3x \ge -12$.

44. If $x \le 3$, then $2x \le 6$.

45. If $x > 6$, then $-2x < -12$.

46. If $x > -2$, then $-4x < 8$.

47. If $x \ge 5$, then $-4x \le -20$.

48. If $x \le -4$, then $-3x \ge 12$.

49. If $2x > 6$, then $x > 3$.

50. If $3x \le 12$, then $x \le 4$.

51. If $-\dfrac{1}{2}x \le 3$, then $x \ge -6$.

52. If $-\dfrac{1}{4}x > 1$, then $x < -4$.

53. $\quad x + 1 < 5$

$\quad x + 1 - 1 < 5 - 1$

$\qquad x < 4$

$\{x \mid x < 4\}$ or $(-\infty, 4)$

54. $\quad x - 6 < 1$

$\quad x - 6 + 6 < 1 + 6$

$\qquad x < 7$

The solution set is $\{x \mid x < 7\}$ or $(-\infty, 7)$.

55.
$$1 - 2x \le 3$$
$$-2x \le 2$$
$$x \ge -1$$
The solution set is $\left\{ x \mid x \ge -1 \right\}$ or $[-1, \infty)$.

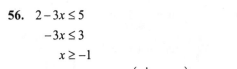

56. $2 - 3x \le 5$
$$-3x \le 3$$
$$x \ge -1$$
The solution set is $\left\{ x \mid x \ge -1 \right\}$ or $[-1, \infty)$.

57. $3x - 7 > 2$
$$3x > 9$$
$$x > 3$$
The solution set is $\left\{ x \mid x > 3 \right\}$ or $(3, \infty)$.

58. $2x + 5 > 1$
$$2x > -4$$
$$x > -2$$
The solution set is $\left\{ x \mid x > -2 \right\}$ or $(-2, \infty)$.

59. $3x - 1 \ge 3 + x$
$$2x \ge 4$$
$$x \ge 2$$
The solution set is $\left\{ x \mid x \ge 2 \right\}$ or $[2, \infty)$.

60. $2x - 2 \ge 3 + x$
$$x \ge 5$$
The solution set is $\left\{ x \mid x \ge 5 \right\}$ or $[5, \infty)$.

61. $-2(x + 3) < 8$
$$-2x - 6 < 8$$
$$-2x < 14$$
$$x > -7$$
The solution set is $\left\{ x \mid x > -7 \right\}$ or $(-7, \infty)$.

62. $-3(1 - x) < 12$
$$-3 + 3x < 12$$
$$3x < 15$$
$$x < 5$$
The solution set is $\left\{ x \mid x < 5 \right\}$ or $(-\infty, 5)$.

63. $4 - 3(1 - x) \le 3$
$$4 - 3 + 3x \le 3$$
$$3x + 1 \le 3$$
$$3x \le 2$$
$$x \le \frac{2}{3}$$
The solution set is $\left\{ x \mid x \le \frac{2}{3} \right\}$ or $\left(-\infty, \frac{2}{3} \right]$.

64. $8 - 4(2 - x) \le -2x$
$$8 - 8 + 4x \le -2x$$
$$4x \le -2x$$
$$6x \le 0$$
$$x \le 0$$
The solution set is $\left\{ x \mid x \le 0 \right\}$ or $\left(-\infty, 0 \right]$.

65. $\frac{1}{2}(x - 4) > x + 8$
$$\frac{1}{2}x - 2 > x + 8$$
$$-\frac{1}{2}x > 10$$
$$x < -20$$
The solution set is $\left\{ x \mid x < -20 \right\}$ or $(-\infty, -20)$.

118

66. $3x + 4 > \dfrac{1}{3}(x - 2)$

$3x + 4 > \dfrac{1}{3}x - \dfrac{2}{3}$

$9x + 12 > x - 2$

$8x > -14$

$x > -\dfrac{7}{4}$

The solution set is $\left\{ x \,\middle|\, x > -\dfrac{7}{4} \right\}$ or $\left(-\dfrac{7}{4}, \infty \right)$.

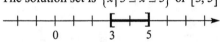

67. $\dfrac{x}{2} \ge 1 - \dfrac{x}{4}$

$2x \ge 4 - x$

$3x \ge 4$

$x \ge \dfrac{4}{3}$

The solution set is $\left\{ x \,\middle|\, x \ge \dfrac{4}{3} \right\}$ or $\left[\dfrac{4}{3}, \infty \right)$.

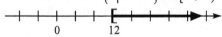

68. $\dfrac{x}{3} \ge 2 + \dfrac{x}{6}$

$2x \ge 12 + x$

$x \ge 12$

The solution set is $\left\{ x \,\middle|\, x \ge 12 \right\}$ or $[12, \infty)$.

69. $0 \le 2x - 6 \le 4$

$6 \le 2x \le 10$

$3 \le x \le 5$

The solution set is $\left\{ x \,\middle|\, 3 \le x \le 5 \right\}$ or $[3, 5]$.

70. $4 \le 2x + 2 \le 10$

$2 \le 2x \le 8$

$1 \le x \le 4$

The solution set is $\left\{ x \,\middle|\, 1 \le x \le 4 \right\}$ or $[1, 4]$.

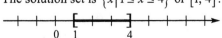

71. $-5 \le 4 - 3x \le 2$

$-9 \le -3x \le -2$

$3 \ge x \ge \dfrac{2}{3}$

The solution set is $\left\{ x \,\middle|\, \dfrac{2}{3} \le x \le 3 \right\}$ or $\left[\dfrac{2}{3}, 3 \right]$.

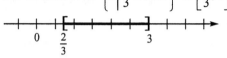

72. $-3 \le 3 - 2x \le 9$

$-6 \le -2x \le 6$

$3 \ge x \ge -3$

The solution set is $\left\{ x \,\middle|\, -3 \le x \le 3 \right\}$ or $[-3, 3]$.

73. $-3 < \dfrac{2x - 1}{4} < 0$

$-12 < 2x - 1 < 0$

$-11 < 2x < 1$

$-\dfrac{11}{2} < x < \dfrac{1}{2}$

The solution set is $\left\{ x \,\middle|\, -\dfrac{11}{2} < x < \dfrac{1}{2} \right\}$ or

$\left(-\dfrac{11}{2}, \dfrac{1}{2} \right)$.

74. $0 < \dfrac{3x + 2}{2} < 4$

$0 < 3x + 2 < 8$

$-2 < 3x < 6$

$-\dfrac{2}{3} < x < 2$

The solution set is $\left\{ x \,\middle|\, -\dfrac{2}{3} < x < 2 \right\}$ or $\left(-\dfrac{2}{3}, 2 \right)$.

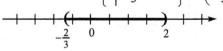

119

75. $1 < 1 - \dfrac{1}{2}x < 4$

$0 < -\dfrac{1}{2}x < 3$

$0 > x > -6$ or $-6 < x < 0$

The solution set is $\{x \mid -6 < x < 0\}$ or $(-6, 0)$.

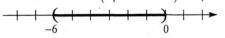

76. $0 < 1 - \dfrac{1}{3}x < 1$

$-1 < -\dfrac{1}{3}x < 0$

$3 > x > 0$ or $0 < x < 3$

The solution set is $\{x \mid 0 < x < 3\}$ or $(0, 3)$.

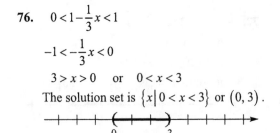

77. $(x+2)(x-3) > (x-1)(x+1)$

$x^2 - x - 6 > x^2 - 1$

$-x - 6 > -1$

$-x > 5$

$x < -5$

The solution set is $\{x \mid x < -5\}$ or $(-\infty, -5)$.

78. $(x-1)(x+1) > (x-3)(x+4)$

$x^2 - 1 > x^2 + x - 12$

$-1 > x - 12$

$-x > -11$

$x < 11$

The solution set is $\{x \mid x < 11\}$ or $(-\infty, 11)$.

79. $x(4x+3) \le (2x+1)^2$

$4x^2 + 3x \le 4x^2 + 4x + 1$

$3x \le 4x + 1$

$-x \le 1$

$x \ge -1$

The solution set is $\{x \mid x \ge -1\}$ or $[-1, \infty)$.

80. $x(9x-5) \le (3x-1)^2$

$9x^2 - 5x \le 9x^2 - 6x + 1$

$-5x \le -6x + 1$

$x \le 1$

The solution set is $\{x \mid x \le 1\}$ or $(-\infty, 1]$.

81. $\dfrac{1}{2} \le \dfrac{x+1}{3} < \dfrac{3}{4}$

$6 \le 4x + 4 < 9$

$2 \le 4x < 5$

$\dfrac{1}{2} \le x < \dfrac{5}{4}$

The solution set is $\left\{ x \mid \dfrac{1}{2} \le x < \dfrac{5}{4} \right\}$ or $\left[\dfrac{1}{2}, \dfrac{5}{4} \right)$.

82. $\dfrac{1}{3} < \dfrac{x+1}{2} \le \dfrac{2}{3}$

$2 < 3x + 3 \le 4$

$-1 < 3x \le 1$

$-\dfrac{1}{3} < x \le \dfrac{1}{3}$

The solution set is $\left\{ x \mid -\dfrac{1}{3} < x \le \dfrac{1}{3} \right\}$ or $\left(-\dfrac{1}{3}, \dfrac{1}{3} \right]$.

83. $(4x+2)^{-1} < 0$

$\dfrac{1}{4x+2} < 0$

$4x + 2 < 0$

$x < -\dfrac{1}{2}$

The solution set is $\left\{ x \mid x < -\dfrac{1}{2} \right\}$ or $\left(-\infty, -\dfrac{1}{2} \right)$.

120

84. $(2x-1)^{-1} > 0$

$$\frac{1}{2x-1} > 0$$

Since $\frac{1}{2x-1} > 0$, this means $2x-1 > 0$.

Therefore,

$2x-1 > 0$

$$x > \frac{1}{2}$$

The solution set is $\left\{ x \middle| x > \frac{1}{2} \right\}$ or $\left(\frac{1}{2}, \infty \right)$.

85. $0 < \frac{2}{x} < \frac{3}{5}$

$0 < \frac{2}{x}$ and $\frac{2}{x} < \frac{3}{5}$

Since $\frac{2}{x} > 0$, this means that $x > 0$. Therefore,

$$\frac{2}{x} < \frac{3}{5}$$

$$5x\left(\frac{2}{x}\right) < 5x\left(\frac{3}{5}\right)$$

$$10 < 3x$$

$$\frac{10}{3} < x$$

The solution set is $\left\{ x \middle| x > \frac{10}{3} \right\}$ or $\left(\frac{10}{3}, \infty \right)$.

86. $0 < \frac{4}{x} < \frac{2}{3}$

$0 < \frac{4}{x}$ and $\frac{4}{x} < \frac{2}{3}$

Since $\frac{4}{x} > 0$, this means that $x > 0$. Therefore,

$$\frac{4}{x} < \frac{2}{3}$$

$$3x\left(\frac{4}{x}\right) < 3x\left(\frac{2}{3}\right)$$

$$12 < 2x$$

$$6 < x$$

The solution set is $\left\{ x \middle| x > 6 \right\}$ or $(6, \infty)$.

87. $0 < (2x-4)^{-1} < \frac{1}{2}$

$$0 < \frac{1}{2x-4} < \frac{1}{2}$$

$0 < \frac{1}{2x-4}$ and $\frac{1}{2x-4} < \frac{1}{2}$

Since $\frac{1}{2x-4} > 0$, this means that $2x-4 > 0$.

Therefore,

$$\frac{1}{2x-4} < \frac{1}{2}$$

$$\frac{1}{2(x-2)} < \frac{1}{2}$$

$$2(x-2)\left(\frac{1}{2(x-2)}\right) < 2(x-2)\left(\frac{1}{2}\right)$$

$$1 < x-2$$

$$3 < x$$

The solution set is $\left\{ x \middle| x > 3 \right\}$ or $(3, \infty)$.

88. $0 < (3x+6)^{-1} < \frac{1}{3}$

$$0 < \frac{1}{3x+6} < \frac{1}{3}$$

$0 < \frac{1}{3x+6}$ and $\frac{1}{3x+6} < \frac{1}{3}$

Since $\frac{1}{3x+6} > 0$, this means that $3x+6 > 0$.

Therefore,

$$\frac{1}{3x+6} < \frac{1}{3}$$

$$\frac{1}{3(x+2)} < \frac{1}{3}$$

$$3(x+2)\left(\frac{1}{3(x+2)}\right) < 3(x+2)\left(\frac{1}{3}\right)$$

$$1 < x+2$$

$$-1 < x$$

The solution set is $\left\{ x \middle| x > -1 \right\}$ or $(-1, \infty)$.

89. If $-1 < x < 1$, then

$-1+4 < x+4 < 1+4$

$3 < x+4 < 5$

So, $a = 3$ and $b = 5$.

90. If $-3 < x < 2$, then
$$-3 - 6 < x - 6 < 2 - 6$$
$$-9 < x - 6 < -4$$
So, $a = -9$ and $b = -4$.

91. If $2 < x < 3$, then
$$-4(2) < -4(x) < -4(3)$$
$$-12 < -4x < -8$$
So, $a = -12$ and $b = -8$.

92. If $-4 < x < 0$, then
$$\frac{1}{2}(-4) < \frac{1}{2}(x) < \frac{1}{2}(0)$$
$$-2 < \frac{1}{2}x < 0$$
So, $a = -2$ and $b = 0$.

93. If $0 < x < 4$, then
$$2(0) < 2(x) < 2(4)$$
$$0 < 2x < 8$$
$$0 + 3 < 2x + 3 < 8 + 3$$
$$3 < 2x + 3 < 11$$
So, $a = 3$ and $b = 11$.

94. If $-3 < x < 3$, then
$$-2(-3) > -2(x) > -2(3)$$
$$6 > -2x > -6$$
$$6 + 1 > -2x + 1 > -6 + 1$$
$$7 > 1 - 2x > -5$$
$$-5 < 1 - 2x < 7$$
So, $a = -5$ and $b = 7$.

95. If $-3 < x < 0$, then
$$-3 + 4 < x + 4 < 0 + 4$$
$$1 < x + 4 < 4$$
$$1 > \frac{1}{x+4} > \frac{1}{4}$$
$$\frac{1}{4} < \frac{1}{x+4} < 1$$
So, $a = \frac{1}{4}$ and $b = 1$.

96. If $2 < x < 4$, then
$$2 - 6 < x - 6 < 4 - 6$$
$$-4 < x - 6 < -2$$
$$-\frac{1}{4} > \frac{1}{x-6} > -\frac{1}{2}$$
$$-\frac{1}{2} < \frac{1}{x-6} < -\frac{1}{4}$$
So, $a = -\frac{1}{2}$ and $b = -\frac{1}{4}$.

97. If $6 < 3x < 12$, then
$$\frac{6}{3} < \frac{3x}{3} < \frac{12}{3}$$
$$2 < x < 4$$
$$2^2 < x^2 < 4^2$$
$$4 < x^2 < 16$$
So, $a = 4$ and $b = 16$.

98. If $0 < 2x < 6$, then
$$\frac{0}{2} < \frac{2x}{2} < \frac{6}{2}$$
$$0 < x < 3$$
$$0^2 < x^2 < 3^2$$
$$0 < x^2 < 9$$
So, $a = 0$ and $b = 9$.

99. $\sqrt{3x + 6}$
We need $3x + 6 \geq 0$
$$3x \geq -6$$
$$x \geq -2$$
To the domain is $\{x | x \geq -2\}$ or $[-2, \infty)$.

100. $\sqrt{8 + 2x}$
We need $8 + 2x \geq 0$
$$2x \geq -8$$
$$x \geq -4$$
To the domain is $\{x | x \geq -4\}$ or $[-4, \infty)$.

101. $21 <$ young adult's age < 30

102. $40 \leq$ middle-aged < 60

103. a. Let $x =$ age at death.
$$x - 30 \geq 49.66$$
$$x \geq 79.66$$
Therefore, the average life expectancy for a 30-year-old male in 2005 will be greater than or equal to 79.66 years.

b. Let $x =$ age at death.
$$x - 30 \geq 53.58$$
$$x \geq 83.58$$
Therefore, the average life expectancy for a 30-year-old female in 2005 will be greater than or equal to 83.58 years.

c. By the given information, a female can expect to live $83.58 - 79.66 = 3.92$ years longer.

122

104. $V = 20T$

$80° \leq T \leq 120°$

$80° \leq \dfrac{V}{20} \leq 120°$

$1600 \leq V \leq 2400$

The volume ranges from 1600 to 2400 cubic centimeters, inclusive.

105. Let P represent the selling price and C represent the commission.

Calculating the commission:

$C = 45,000 + 0.25(P - 900,000)$

$\quad = 45,000 + 0.25P - 225,000$

$\quad = 0.25P - 180,000$

Calculate the commission range, given the price range:

$900,000 \leq P \leq 1,100,000$

$0.25(900,000) \leq 0.25P \leq 0.25(1,100,000)$

$225,000 \leq 0.25P \leq 275,000$

$225,000 - 180,000 \leq 0.25P - 180,000 \leq 275,000 - 180,000$

$45,000 \leq C \leq 95,000$

The agent's commission ranges from \$45,000 to \$95,000, inclusive.

$\dfrac{45,000}{900,000} = 0.05 = 5\%$ to $\dfrac{95,000}{1,100,000} = 0.086 = 8.6\%,$

inclusive.

As a percent of selling price, the commission ranges from 5% to 8.6%, inclusive.

106. Let C represent the commission.

Calculate the commission range:

$25 + 0.4(200) \leq C \leq 25 + 0.4(3000)$

$105 \leq C \leq 1225$

The commissions are at least \$105 and at most \$1225.

107. Let W = weekly wages and T = tax withheld.

Calculating the withholding tax range, given the range of weekly wages:

$700 \leq W \leq 900$

$700 - 620 \leq W - 620 \leq 900 - 620$

$80 \leq W - 620 \leq 280$

$0.25(80) \leq 0.25(W - 620) \leq 0.25(280)$

$20 \leq 0.25(W - 620) \leq 70$

$20 + 78.30 \leq 0.25(W - 620) + 78.30 \leq 70 + 78.30$

$98.30 \leq T \leq 148.30$

The amount withheld varies from \$98.30 to \$148.30, inclusive.

108. Let x represent the length of time Sue should exercise on the seventh day.

$200 \leq 40 + 45 + 0 + 50 + 25 + 35 + x \leq 300$

$200 \leq 195 + x \leq 300$

$5 \leq x \leq 105$

Sue will stay within the ACSM guidelines by exercising from 5 to 105 minutes.

109. Let K represent the monthly usage in kilowatt-hours and let C represent the monthly customer bill.

Calculating the bill: $C = 0.08275K + 7.58$

Calculating the range of kilowatt-hours, given the range of bills:

$63.47 \leq C \leq 214.53$

$63.47 \leq 0.08275K + 7.58 \leq 214.53$

$55.89 \leq 0.08275K \leq 206.95$

$675.41 \leq K \leq 2500.91$

The usage varies from 675.41 kilowatt-hours to 2500.91 kilowatt-hours, inclusive.

110. Let W represent the amount of water used (in thousands of gallons). Let C represent the customer charge (in dollars).

Calculating the charge:

$C = 28.84 + 2.28(W - 12)$

$\quad = 28.84 + 2.28W - 27.36$

$\quad = 2.28W + 1.48$

Calculating the range of water usage, given the range of charges:

$42.52 \leq C \leq 74.44$

$42.52 \leq 2.28W + 1.48 \leq 74.44$

$41.04 \leq 2.28W \leq 72.96$

$18 \leq W \leq 32$

The range of water usage ranged from 18,000 to 32,000 gallons.

111. Let C represent the dealer's cost and M represent the markup over dealer's cost. If the price is \$18,000, then

$18,000 = C + MC = C(1 + M)$

Solving for C yields: $C = \dfrac{18,000}{1 + M}$

Calculating the range of dealer costs, given the range of markups:

$0.12 \leq M \leq 0.18$

$1.12 \leq 1 + M \leq 1.18$

$\dfrac{1}{1.12} \geq \dfrac{1}{1 + M} \geq \dfrac{1}{1.18}$

$$\frac{18,000}{1.12} \geq \frac{18,000}{1+M} \geq \frac{18,000}{1.18}$$

$$16,071.43 \geq C \geq 15,254.24$$

The dealer's cost varies from \$15,254.24 to \$16,071.43, inclusive.

112. Let T represent the test scores of the people in the top 2.5%.

$$T > 1.96(12) + 100 = 123.52$$

People in the top 2.5% will have test scores greater than 123.52. That is, $T > 123.52$ or $(123.52, \infty)$.

113. a. Let T represent the score on the last test and G represent the course grade.

Calculating the course grade and solving for the last test:

$$G = \frac{68 + 82 + 87 + 89 + T}{5}$$

$$G = \frac{326 + T}{5}$$

$$5G = 326 + T$$

$$T = 5G - 326$$

Calculating the range of scores on the last test, given the grade range:

$$80 \leq G < 90$$

$$400 \leq 5G < 450$$

$$74 \leq 5G - 326 < 124$$

$$74 \leq T < 124$$

To get a grade of B, you need at least a 74 on the fifth test.

b. Let T represent the score on the last test and G represent the course grade.

Calculating the course grade and solving for the last test:

$$G = \frac{68 + 82 + 87 + 89 + 2T}{6}$$

$$G = \frac{326 + 2T}{6}$$

$$G = \frac{163 + T}{3}$$

$$T = 3G - 163$$

Calculating the range of scores on the last test, given the grade range:

$$80 \leq G < 90$$

$$240 \leq 3G < 270$$

$$77 \leq 3G - 163 < 107$$

$$77 \leq T < 107$$

To get a grade of B, you need at least a 77 on the fifth test.

114. Let C represent the number of calories in a serving of regular Miracle Whip®, and let F represent the grams of fat in a serving of regular Miracle Whip®.

One possibility for a "light" classification is that the 20 calories in a serving of Miracle Whip® Light is less than or equal to one-third the calories in regular Miracle Whip®. That is,

$$20 \leq \frac{1}{3}C.$$

The second possibility for a "light" classification is that the 1.5 grams of fat in a serving of Miracle Whip® Light is less than or equal to one-half the grams of fat in regular Miracle Whip®.

That is, $1.5 \leq \frac{1}{2}F$.

We have:

$$20 \leq \frac{1}{3}C \quad \text{or} \quad 1.5 \leq \frac{1}{2}F$$

$$60 \leq C \quad \text{or} \quad 3 \leq F$$

A serving of regular Miracle Whip® either contains at least 60 calories or at least 3 grams of fat, or both.

115. Since $a < b$,

$$\frac{a}{2} < \frac{b}{2} \quad \text{and} \quad \frac{a}{2} < \frac{b}{2}$$

$$\frac{a}{2} + \frac{a}{2} < \frac{a}{2} + \frac{b}{2} \quad \text{and} \quad \frac{a}{2} + \frac{b}{2} < \frac{b}{2} + \frac{b}{2}$$

$$a < \frac{a+b}{2} \quad \text{and} \quad \frac{a+b}{2} < b$$

Thus, $a < \frac{a+b}{2} < b$.

116. From problem 115, $a < \frac{a+b}{2} < b$, so

$$d\left(a, \frac{a+b}{2}\right) = \frac{a+b}{2} - a = \frac{a+b-2a}{2} = \frac{b-a}{2} \quad \text{and}$$

$$d\left(b, \frac{a+b}{2}\right) = b - \frac{a+b}{2} = \frac{2b-a-b}{2} = \frac{b-a}{2}.$$

Therefore, $\frac{a+b}{2}$ is equidistant from a and b.

117. If $0 < a < b$, then

$$ab > a^2 > 0 \quad \text{and} \quad b^2 > ab > 0$$

$$\left(\sqrt{ab}\right)^2 > a^2 \quad \text{and} \quad b^2 > \left(\sqrt{ab}\right)^2$$

$$\sqrt{ab} > a \quad \text{and} \quad b > \sqrt{ab}$$

Thus, $a < \sqrt{ab} < b$.

118. Show that $\sqrt{ab} < \dfrac{a+b}{2}$.

$$\frac{a+b}{2} - \sqrt{ab} = \frac{1}{2}\left(a - 2\sqrt{ab} + b\right)$$
$$= \frac{1}{2}\left(\sqrt{a} - \sqrt{b}\right)^2 > 0, \text{ since } a \neq b.$$

Therefore, $\sqrt{ab} < \dfrac{a+b}{2}$.

119. For $0 < a < b,\quad \dfrac{1}{h} = \dfrac{1}{2}\left(\dfrac{1}{a} + \dfrac{1}{b}\right)$

$$h \cdot \frac{1}{h} = \frac{1}{2}\left(\frac{b+a}{ab}\right) \cdot h$$
$$1 = \frac{1}{2}\left(\frac{b+a}{ab}\right) \cdot h$$
$$h = \frac{2ab}{a+b}$$

$$h - a = \frac{2ab}{a+b} - a = \frac{2ab - a(a+b)}{a+b}$$
$$= \frac{2ab - a^2 - ab}{a+b} = \frac{ab - a^2}{a+b}$$
$$= \frac{a(b-a)}{a+b} > 0$$

Therefore, $h > a$.

$$b - h = b - \frac{2ab}{a+b} = \frac{b(a+b) - 2ab}{a+b}$$
$$= \frac{ab + b^2 - 2ab}{a+b} = \frac{b^2 - ab}{a+b}$$
$$= \frac{b(b-a)}{a+b} > 0$$

Therefore, $h < b$, and we have $a < h < b$.

120. Show that $h = \dfrac{(\text{geometric mean})^2}{\text{arithmetic mean}} = \dfrac{\left(\sqrt{ab}\right)^2}{\left(\dfrac{1}{2}(a+b)\right)}$

From Problem 119, we know:

$$\frac{1}{h} = \frac{1}{2}\left(\frac{1}{a} + \frac{1}{b}\right)$$
$$\frac{2}{h} = \frac{1}{a} + \frac{1}{b} = \frac{b+a}{ab}$$
$$\frac{h}{2} = \frac{ab}{a+b}$$

$$h = 2 \cdot \frac{ab}{a+b} = \frac{\left(\sqrt{ab}\right)^2}{\left(\dfrac{1}{2}(a+b)\right)}$$

121. Since $0 < a < b$, then $a - b < 0$ and $ab > 0$.

Therefore, $\dfrac{a-b}{ab} < 0$. So,

$$\frac{a}{ab} - \frac{b}{ab} < 0$$
$$\frac{1}{b} - \frac{1}{a} < 0$$
$$\frac{1}{b} < \frac{1}{a}$$

Now, since $b > 0$, then $\dfrac{1}{b} > 0$, so we have

$$0 < \frac{1}{b} < \frac{1}{a}.$$

122. Answers will vary. One possibility:
No solution: $4x + 6 \leq 2(x-5) + 2x$
One solution: $3x + 5 \leq 2(x+3) + 1 \leq 3(x+2) - 1$

123. Since $x^2 \geq 0$, we have
$$x^2 + 1 \geq 0 + 1$$
$$x^2 + 1 \geq 1$$
Therefore, the expression $x^2 + 1$ can never be less than -5.

124 – 125. Answers will vary.

Section 1.6

1. $|-2| = 2$

2. True

3. $\{-5, 5\}$

4. $\{x \mid -5 < x < 5\}$

5. True

6. True

7. $|2x| = 6$
$2x = 6$ or $2x = -6$
$x = 3$ or $x = -3$
The solution set is $\{-3, 3\}$.

8. $|3x| = 12$

$3x = 12$ or $3x = -12$

$x = 4$ or $x = -4$

The solution set is $\{-4, 4\}$.

9. $|2x + 3| = 5$

$2x + 3 = 5$ or $2x + 3 = -5$

$2x = 2$ or $2x = -8$

$x = 1$ or $x = -4$

The solution set is $\{-4, 1\}$.

10. $|3x - 1| = 2$

$3x - 1 = 2$ or $3x - 1 = -2$

$3x = 3$ or $3x = -1$

$x = 1$ or $x = -\dfrac{1}{3}$

The solution set is $\left\{-\dfrac{1}{3}, 1\right\}$.

11. $|1 - 4t| + 8 = 13$

$|1 - 4t| = 5$

$1 - 4t = 5$ or $1 - 4t = -5$

$-4t = 4$ or $-4t = -6$

$t = -1$ or $t = \dfrac{3}{2}$

The solution set is $\left\{-1, \dfrac{3}{2}\right\}$.

12. $|1 - 2z| + 6 = 9$

$|1 - 2z| = 3$

$1 - 2z = 3$ or $1 - 2z = -3$

$-2z = 2$ or $-2z = -4$

$z = -1$ or $z = 2$

The solution set is $\{-1, 2\}$.

13. $|-2x| = |8|$

$|-2x| = 8$

$-2x = 8$ or $-2x = -8$

$x = -4$ or $x = 4$

The solution set is $\{-4, 4\}$.

14. $|-x| = |1|$

$|-x| = 1$

$-x = 1$ or $-x = -1$

The solution set is $\{-1, 1\}$.

15. $|-2|x = 4$

$2x = 4$

$x = 2$

The solution set is $\{2\}$.

16. $|3|x = 9$

$3x = 9$

$x = 3$

The solution set is $\{3\}$.

17. $\dfrac{2}{3}|x| = 9$

$|x| = \dfrac{27}{2}$

$x = \dfrac{27}{2}$ or $x = -\dfrac{27}{2}$

The solution set is $\left\{-\dfrac{27}{2}, \dfrac{27}{2}\right\}$.

18. $\dfrac{3}{4}|x| = 9$

$|x| = 12$

$x = 12$ or $x = -12$

The solution set is $\{-12, 12\}$.

19. $\left|\dfrac{x}{3} + \dfrac{2}{5}\right| = 2$

$\dfrac{x}{3} + \dfrac{2}{5} = 2$ or $\dfrac{x}{3} + \dfrac{2}{5} = -2$

$5x + 6 = 30$ or $5x + 6 = -30$

$5x = 24$ or $5x = -36$

$x = \dfrac{24}{5}$ or $x = -\dfrac{36}{5}$

The solution set is $\left\{-\dfrac{36}{5}, \dfrac{24}{5}\right\}$.

20. $\left|\dfrac{x}{2} - \dfrac{1}{3}\right| = 1$

$\dfrac{x}{2} - \dfrac{1}{3} = 1$ or $\dfrac{x}{2} - \dfrac{1}{3} = -1$

$3x - 2 = 6$ or $3x - 2 = -6$

$3x = 8$ or $3x = -4$

$x = \dfrac{8}{3}$ or $x = -\dfrac{4}{3}$

The solution set is $\left\{-\dfrac{4}{3}, \dfrac{8}{3}\right\}$.

21. $\left|u-2\right|=-\dfrac{1}{2}$

No solution, since absolute value always yields a non-negative number.

22. $\left|2-v\right|=-1$

No solution, since absolute value always yields a non-negative number.

23. $4-\left|2x\right|=3$

$-\left|2x\right|=-1$

$\left|2x\right|=1$

$2x=1$ or $2x=-1$

$x=\dfrac{1}{2}$ or $x=-\dfrac{1}{2}$

The solution set is $\left\{-\dfrac{1}{2},\dfrac{1}{2}\right\}$.

24. $5-\left|\dfrac{1}{2}x\right|=3$

$-\left|\dfrac{1}{2}x\right|=-2$

$\left|\dfrac{1}{2}x\right|=2$

$\dfrac{1}{2}x=2$ or $\dfrac{1}{2}x=-2$

$x=4$ or $x=-4$

The solution set is $\left\{-4,4\right\}$.

25. $\left|x^2-9\right|=0$

$x^2-9=0$

$x^2=9$

$x=\pm 3$

The solution set is $\left\{-3,3\right\}$.

26. $\left|x^2-16\right|=0$

$x^2-16=0$

$x^2=16$

$x=\pm 4$

The solution set is $\left\{-4,4\right\}$.

27. $\left|x^2-2x\right|=3$

$x^2-2x=3$ or $x^2-2x=-3$

$x^2-2x-3=0$ or $x^2-2x+3=0$

$(x-3)(x+1)=0$ or $x=\dfrac{2\pm\sqrt{4-12}}{2}$

$x=3$ or $x=-1$ or $x=\dfrac{2\pm\sqrt{-8}}{2}$ no real sol.

The solution set is $\left\{-1,3\right\}$.

28. $\left|x^2+x\right|=12$

$x^2+x=12$ or $x^2+x=-12$

$x^2+x-12=0$ or $x^2+x+12=0$

$(x-3)(x+4)=0$ or $x=\dfrac{-1\pm\sqrt{1-48}}{2}$

$x=3$ or $x=-4$ or $x=\dfrac{1\pm\sqrt{-47}}{2}$ no real sol.

The solution set is $\left\{-4,3\right\}$.

29. $\left|x^2+x-1\right|=1$

$x^2+x-1=1$ or $x^2+x-1=-1$

$x^2+x-2=0$ or $x^2+x=0$

$(x-1)(x+2)=0$ or $x(x+1)=0$

$x=1,x=-2$ or $x=0,x=-1$

The solution set is $\left\{-2,-1,0,1\right\}$.

30. $\left|x^2+3x-2\right|=2$

$x^2+3x-2=2$ or $x^2+3x-2=-2$

$x^2+3x=4$ or $x^2+3x=0$

$x^2+3x-4=0$ or $x(x+3)=0$

$(x+4)(x-1)=0$ or $x=0,x=-3$

$x=-4,x=1$

The solution set is $\left\{-4,-3,0,1\right\}$.

31. $\left|\dfrac{3x-2}{2x-3}\right|=2$

$\dfrac{3x-2}{2x-3}=2 \qquad$ or $\qquad \dfrac{3x-2}{2x-3}=-2$

$3x-2=2(2x-3)$ or $\quad 3x-2=-2(2x-3)$

$3x-2=4x-6 \qquad$ or $\quad 3x-2=-4x+6$

$-x=-4 \qquad$ or $\qquad 7x=8$

$x=4 \qquad$ or $\qquad x=\dfrac{8}{7}$

Neither of these values cause the denominator to equal zero, so the solution set is $\left\{\dfrac{8}{7},\,4\right\}$.

32. $\left|\dfrac{2x+1}{3x+4}\right|=1$

$\dfrac{2x+1}{3x+4}=1 \qquad$ or $\qquad \dfrac{2x+1}{3x+4}=-1$

$2x+1=1(3x+4)$ or $\quad 2x+1=-1(3x+4)$

$2x+1=3x+4 \qquad$ or $\quad 2x+1=-3x-4$

$-x=3 \qquad$ or $\qquad 5x=-5$

$x=-3 \qquad$ or $\qquad x=-1$

Neither of these values cause the denominator to equal zero, so the solution set is $\{-3,-1\}$.

33. $\left|x^2+3x\right|=\left|x^2-2x\right|$

$x^2+3x=x^2-2x \quad$ or $\quad x^2+3x=-\left(x^2-2x\right)$

$3x=-2x \qquad$ or $\quad x^2+3x=-x^2+2x$

$5x=0 \qquad$ or $\quad 2x^2+x=0$

$x=0 \qquad$ or $\quad x(2x+1)=0$

$x=0 \qquad$ or $\ x=0 \ $ or $\ x=-\dfrac{1}{2}$

The solution set is $\left\{-\dfrac{1}{2},0\right\}$.

34. $\left|x^2-2x\right|=\left|x^2+6x\right|$

$x^2-2x=x^2+6x \quad$ or $\quad x^2-2x=-\left(x^2+6x\right)$

$-2x=6x \qquad$ or $\quad x^2-2x=-x^2-6x$

$-8x=0 \qquad$ or $\quad 2x^2+4x=0$

$x=0 \qquad$ or $\quad 2x(x+2)=0$

$x=0 \qquad$ or $\ x=0$ or $x=-2$

The solution set is $\{-2,0\}$.

35. $|2x|<8$

$-8<2x<8$

$-4<x<4$

$\{x|-4<x<4\}$ or $(-4,4)$

36. $|3x|<15$

$-15<3x<15$

$-5<x<5$

$\{x|-5<x<5\}$ or $(-5,5)$

37. $|3x|>12$

$3x<-12$ or $3x>12$

$x<-4$ or $x>4$

$\{x|x<-4 \text{ or } x>4\}$ or $(-\infty,-4)\cup(4,\infty)$

38. $|2x|>6$

$2x<-6$ or $2x>6$

$x<-3$ or $x>3$

$\{x|x<-3 \text{ or } x>3\}$ or $(-\infty,-3)\cup(3,\infty)$

39. $|x-2|+2<3$

$|x-2|<1$

$-1<x-2<1$

$1<x<3$

$\{x|1<x<3\}$ or $(1,3)$

40. $|x+4|+3<5$

$|x+4|<2$

$-2<x+4<2$

$-6<x<-2$

$\{x|-6<x<-2\}$ or $(-6,-2)$

41. $|3t-2| \le 4$

$$-4 \le 3t - 2 \le 4$$
$$-2 \le 3t \le 6$$
$$-\frac{2}{3} \le t \le 2$$

$\left\{ t \left| -\frac{2}{3} \le t \le 2 \right. \right\}$ or $\left[-\frac{2}{3}, 2 \right]$

42. $|2u+5| \le 7$

$$-7 \le 2u + 5 \le 7$$
$$-12 \le 2u \le 2$$
$$-6 \le u \le 1$$

$\left\{ u \left| -6 \le u \le 1 \right. \right\}$ or $[-6, 1]$

43. $|2x-3| \ge 2$

$$2x - 3 \le -2 \ \text{ or } \ 2x - 3 \ge 2$$
$$2x \le 1 \quad \text{ or } \quad 2x \ge 5$$
$$x \le \frac{1}{2} \quad \text{ or } \quad x \ge \frac{5}{2}$$

$\left\{ x \left| x \le \frac{1}{2} \text{ or } x \ge \frac{5}{2} \right. \right\}$ or $\left(-\infty, \frac{1}{2} \right] \cup \left[\frac{5}{2}, \infty \right)$

44. $|3x+4| \ge 2$

$$3x + 4 \le -2 \ \text{ or } \ 3x + 4 \ge 2$$
$$3x \le -6 \ \text{ or } \quad 3x \ge -2$$
$$x \le -2 \ \text{ or } \quad x \ge -\frac{2}{3}$$

$\left\{ x \left| x \le -2 \text{ or } x \ge -\frac{2}{3} \right. \right\}$ or $\left(-\infty, -2 \right] \cup \left[-\frac{2}{3}, \infty \right)$

45. $|1-4x| - 7 < -2$

$$|1 - 4x| < 5$$
$$-5 < 1 - 4x < 5$$
$$-6 < -4x < 4$$
$$\frac{-6}{-4} > x > \frac{4}{-4}$$
$$\frac{3}{2} > x > -1 \quad \text{ or } \quad -1 < x < \frac{3}{2}$$

$\left\{ x \left| -1 < x < \frac{3}{2} \right. \right\}$ or $\left(-1, \frac{3}{2} \right)$

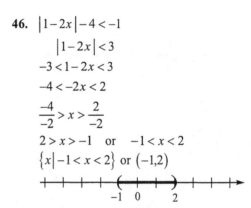

46. $|1-2x| - 4 < -1$

$$|1 - 2x| < 3$$
$$-3 < 1 - 2x < 3$$
$$-4 < -2x < 2$$
$$\frac{-4}{-2} > x > \frac{2}{-2}$$
$$2 > x > -1 \quad \text{ or } \quad -1 < x < 2$$

$\left\{ x \left| -1 < x < 2 \right. \right\}$ or $(-1, 2)$

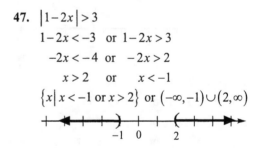

47. $|1-2x| > 3$

$$1 - 2x < -3 \ \text{ or } \ 1 - 2x > 3$$
$$-2x < -4 \ \text{ or } \ -2x > 2$$
$$x > 2 \quad \text{ or } \quad x < -1$$

$\left\{ x \left| x < -1 \text{ or } x > 2 \right. \right\}$ or $(-\infty, -1) \cup (2, \infty)$

48. $|2-3x| > 1$

$$2 - 3x < -1 \ \text{ or } \ 2 - 3x > 1$$
$$-3x < -3 \ \text{ or } \ -3x > -1$$
$$x > 1 \quad \text{ or } \quad x < \frac{1}{3}$$

$\left\{ x \left| x < \frac{1}{3} \text{ or } x > 1 \right. \right\}$ or $\left(-\infty, \frac{1}{3} \right) \cup (1, \infty)$

129

49. $\left|-4x\right|+\left|-5\right|\le 1$

$\quad\left|-4x\right|+5\le 1$

$\quad\quad\left|-4x\right|\le -4$

This is impossible since absolute value always yields a non-negative number. The inequality has no solution.

50. $\left|-x\right|-\left|4\right|\le 2$

$\quad\left|-x\right|-4\le 2$

$\quad\quad\left|-x\right|\le 6$

$\quad -6\le -x\le 6$

$\quad\quad 6\ge x\ge -6$

$\left\{x\mid -6\le x\le 6\right\}$ or $\left[-6,\,6\right]$

51. $\left|-2x\right|>\left|-3\right|$

$\quad\left|2x\right|>3$

$\quad 2x<-3\ \ \text{or}\ \ 2x>3$

$\quad x<-\dfrac{3}{2}\ \ \text{or}\ \ x>\dfrac{3}{2}$

$\left\{x\,\middle|\,x<-\dfrac{3}{2}\ \text{or}\ x>\dfrac{3}{2}\right\}$ or $\left(-\infty,\,-\dfrac{3}{2}\right)\cup\left(\dfrac{3}{2},\infty\right)$

52. $\left|-x-2\right|\ge 1$

$\quad -x-2\le -1\ \ \text{or}\ \ -x-2\ge 1$

$\quad\quad -x\le 1\quad \text{or}\quad -x\ge 3$

$\quad\quad x\ge -1\ \ \text{or}\quad x\le -3$

$\left\{x\mid x\le -3\ \text{or}\ x\ge -1\right\}$ or $\left(-\infty,\,-3\right]\cup\left[-1,\infty\right)$

53. $-\left|2x-1\right|\ge -3$

$\quad\left|2x-1\right|\le 3$

$\quad -3\le 2x-1\le 3$

$\quad -2\le 2x\le 4$

$\quad -1\le x\le 2$

$\left\{x\mid -1\le x\le 2\right\}$ or $\left[-1,\,2\right]$

54. $-\left|1-2x\right|\ge -3$

$\quad\left|1-2x\right|\le 3$

$\quad -3\le 1-2x\le 3$

$\quad -4\le -2x\le 2$

$\quad\quad 2\ge x\ge -1$

$\left\{x\mid -1\le x\le 2\right\}$ or $\left[-1,\,2\right]$

55. $\left|2x\right|<-1$

This is impossible since absolute value always yields a non-negative number. No solution.

56. $\left|3x\right|\ge 0$

Absolute value yields a non-negative number, so this inequality is true for all real numbers, $(-\infty,\infty)$.

57. $\left|5x\right|\ge -1$

Absolute value yields a non-negative number, so this inequality is true for all real numbers, $(-\infty,\infty)$.

58. $\left|6x\right|<-2$

This is impossible since absolute value always yields a non-negative number. No solution.

59. $\left|\dfrac{2x+3}{3}-\dfrac{1}{2}\right|<1$

$\quad -1<\dfrac{2x+3}{3}-\dfrac{1}{2}<1$

$\quad 6(-1)<6\left(\dfrac{2x+3}{3}-\dfrac{1}{2}\right)<6(1)$

$\quad -6<2(2x+3)-3<6$

$\quad -6<4x+6-3<6$

$\quad -6<4x+3<6$

$\quad -9<4x<3$

$\quad -\dfrac{9}{4}<x<\dfrac{3}{4}$

$\left\{x\,\middle|\,-\dfrac{9}{4}<x<\dfrac{3}{4}\right\}$ or $\left(-\dfrac{9}{4},\dfrac{3}{4}\right)$

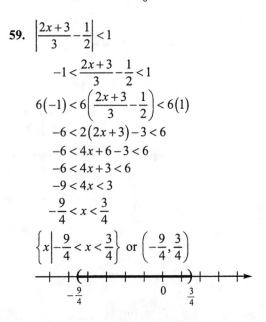

60. $3 - |x+1| < \dfrac{1}{2}$

$-|x+1| < -\dfrac{5}{2}$

$|x+1| > \dfrac{5}{2}$

$x+1 < -\dfrac{5}{2}$ or $x+1 > \dfrac{5}{2}$

$x < -\dfrac{7}{2}$ or $x > \dfrac{3}{2}$

$\left\{ x \middle| x < -\dfrac{7}{2} \text{ or } x > \dfrac{3}{2} \right\}$ or $\left(-\infty, -\dfrac{7}{2} \right) \cup \left(\dfrac{3}{2}, \infty \right)$

61. $5 + |x-1| > \dfrac{1}{2}$

$|x-1| > -\dfrac{9}{2}$

Absolute value yields a non-negative number, so this inequality is true for all real numbers, $(-\infty, \infty)$.

62. $\left| \dfrac{2x-3}{2} + \dfrac{1}{3} \right| > 1$

$\dfrac{2x-3}{2} + \dfrac{1}{3} < -1$ or $\dfrac{2x-3}{2} + \dfrac{1}{3} > 1$

$6\left(\dfrac{2x-3}{2} + \dfrac{1}{3} \right) < 6(-1)$ or $6\left(\dfrac{2x-3}{2} + \dfrac{1}{3} \right) > 6(1)$

$3(2x-3) + 2 < -6$ or $3(2x-3) + 2 > 6$

$6x - 9 + 2 < -6$ or $6x - 9 + 2 > 6$

$6x - 7 < -6$ or $6x - 7 > 6$

$6x < 1$ or $6x > 13$

$x < \dfrac{1}{6}$ or $x > \dfrac{13}{6}$

$\left\{ x \middle| x < \dfrac{1}{6} \text{ or } x > \dfrac{13}{6} \right\}$ or $\left(-\infty, \dfrac{1}{6} \right) \cup \left(\dfrac{13}{6}, \infty \right)$

63. A temperature x that differs from $98.6°$ F by at least $1.5°F$.

$|x - 98.6°| \ge 1.5°$

$x - 98.6° \le -1.5°$ or $x - 98.6° \ge 1.5°$

$x \le 97.1°$ or $x \ge 100.1°$

The temperatures that are considered unhealthy are those that are less than 97.1°F or greater than 100.1°F, inclusive.

64. A voltage x that differs from 110 volts by at most 5 volts.

$|x - 110| \le 5$

$-5 \le x - 110 \le 5$

$105 \le x \le 115$

The actual voltage is between 105 and 115 volts, inclusive.

65. The true average number of books read x should differ from 13.4 by less than 1.35 books.

$|x - 13.4| < 1.35$

$-1.35 < x - 13.4 < 1.35$

$12.05 < x < 14.75$

Gallup is 99% confident that the actual average number of books read per year is between 12.05 and 14.75 books.

66. The speed x varies from 707 mph by up to 55 mph.

a. $|x - 707| \le 55$

b. $-55 \le x - 707 \le 55$

$-55 \le x - 707 \le 55$

$652 \le x \le 762$

The speed of sound is between 652 and 762 miles per hour, depending on conditions.

67. x differs from 3 by less than $\dfrac{1}{2}$.

$|x - 3| < \dfrac{1}{2}$

$-\dfrac{1}{2} < x - 3 < \dfrac{1}{2}$

$\dfrac{5}{2} < x < \dfrac{7}{2}$

$\left\{ x \middle| \dfrac{5}{2} < x < \dfrac{7}{2} \right\}$

68. x differs from -4 by less than 1

$|x - (-4)| < 1$

$|x + 4| < 1$

$-1 < x + 4 < 1$

$-5 < x < -3$

$\{ x | -5 < x < -3 \}$

131

69. x differs from -3 by more than 2.

$$|x-(-3)|>2$$
$$|x+3|>2$$
$$x+3<-2 \text{ or } x+3>2$$
$$x<-5 \text{ or } \quad x>-1$$
$$\{x\,|\,x<-5 \text{ or } x>-1\}$$

70. x differs from 2 by more than 3.

$$|x-2|>3$$
$$x-2<-3 \text{ or } x-2>3$$
$$x<-1 \text{ or } \quad x>5$$
$$\{x\,|\,x<-1 \text{ or } x>5\}$$

71. $|x-1|<3$

$$-3<x-1<3$$
$$-3+5<(x-1)+5<3+5$$
$$2<x+4<8$$
$$a=2,\ b=8$$

72. $|x+2|<5$

$$-5<x+2<5$$
$$-5-4<(x+2)-4<5-4$$
$$-9<x-2<1$$
$$a=-9,\ b=1$$

73. $|x+4|\le 2$

$$-2\le x+4\le 2$$
$$-6\le x\le -2$$
$$-12\le 2x\le -4$$
$$-15\le 2x-3\le -7$$
$$a=-15,\ b=-7$$

74. $|x-3|\le 1$

$$-1\le x-3\le 1$$
$$2\le x\le 4$$
$$6\le 3x\le 12$$
$$7\le 3x+1\le 13$$
$$a=7,\ b=13$$

75. $|x-2|\le 7$

$$-7\le x-2\le 7$$
$$-5\le x\le 9$$
$$-15\le x-10\le -1$$
$$-\frac{1}{15}\ge \frac{1}{x-10}\ge -1$$
$$-1\le \frac{1}{x-10}\le -\frac{1}{15}$$
$$a=-1,\ b=-\frac{1}{15}$$

76. $|x+1|\le 3$

$$-3\le x+1\le 3$$
$$-4\le x\le 2$$
$$1\le x+5\le 7$$
$$1\ge \frac{1}{x+5}\ge \frac{1}{7}$$
$$\frac{1}{7}\le \frac{1}{x+5}\le 1$$
$$a=\frac{1}{7},\ b=1$$

77. Given that $a>0$, $b>0$, and $\sqrt{a}<\sqrt{b}$, show that $a<b$.

Note that $b-a=\left(\sqrt{b}+\sqrt{a}\right)\left(\sqrt{b}-\sqrt{a}\right)$.

Since $\sqrt{a}<\sqrt{b}$ means $\sqrt{b}-\sqrt{a}>0$, we have $b-a=\left(\sqrt{b}+\sqrt{a}\right)\left(\sqrt{b}-\sqrt{a}\right)>0$.

Therefore, $b-a>0$ which means $a<b$.

78. Show that $a\le |a|$.

We know $0\le |a|$. So if $a<0$, then we have $a<0\le |a|$ which means $a\le |a|$.. Now, if $a\ge 0$, then $|a|=a$. So $a\le |a|$.

79. Prove $|a+b|\le |a|+|b|$.

Note that $|a+b|^2=|a+b|\cdot|a+b|$.

<u>Case 1</u>: If $a+b\ge 0$, then $|a+b|=a+b$, so

$$|a+b|\cdot|a+b|=(a+b)(a+b)$$
$$=a^2+2ab+b^2$$
$$\le |a|^2+2|a|\cdot|b|+|b|^2$$
$$=\left(|a|+|b|\right)^2 \text{ by problem 78}$$

Thus, $\left(|a+b|\right)^2\le \left(|a|+|b|\right)^2$

$$|a+b|\le |a|+|b|.$$

<u>Case 2</u>: If $a+b<0$, then $|a+b|=-(a+b)$, so

$$|a+b|\cdot|a+b|=(-(a+b))(-(a+b))$$
$$=(a+b)(a+b)$$
$$=a^2+2ab+b^2$$
$$\le |a|^2+2|a|\cdot|b|+|b|^2$$
$$=\left(|a|+|b|\right)^2 \text{ by problem 78}$$

Thus, $\left(|a+b|\right)^2\le \left(|a|+|b|\right)^2$

$$|a+b|\le |a|+|b|$$

80. Prove $|a-b| \geq |a| - |b|$.

$|a| = |(a-b)+b| \leq |a-b| + |b|$ by the Triangle Inequality, so $|a| \leq |a-b| + |b|$ which means $|a| - |b| \leq |a-b|$. Therefore, $|a-b| \geq |a| - |b|$.

81. Given that $a > 0$,
$$x^2 < a$$
$$x^2 - a < 0$$
$$\left(x+\sqrt{a}\right)\left(x-\sqrt{a}\right) < 0$$

If $x < -\sqrt{a}$, then $x+\sqrt{a} < 0$ and $x-\sqrt{a} < -2\sqrt{a} < 0$. Therefore, $\left(x+\sqrt{a}\right)\left(x-\sqrt{a}\right) > 0$, which is a contradiction.

If $-\sqrt{a} < x < \sqrt{a}$, then $0 < x+\sqrt{a} < 2\sqrt{a}$ and $-2\sqrt{a} < x-\sqrt{a} < 0$. Therefore, $\left(x+\sqrt{a}\right)\left(x-\sqrt{a}\right) < 0$.

If $x > \sqrt{a}$, then $x+\sqrt{a} > 2\sqrt{a} > 0$ and $x-\sqrt{a} > 0$. Therefore, $\left(x+\sqrt{a}\right)\left(x-\sqrt{a}\right) > 0$, which is a contradiction. So the solution set for $x^2 < a$ is $\left\{x \middle| -\sqrt{a} < x < \sqrt{a}\right\}$.

82. Given that $a > 0$,
$$x^2 > a.$$
$$x^2 - a > 0$$
$$\left(x+\sqrt{a}\right)\left(x-\sqrt{a}\right) > 0$$
If $x < -\sqrt{a}$, then $x+\sqrt{a} < 0$ and $x-\sqrt{a} < -2\sqrt{a} < 0$. Therefore, $\left(x+\sqrt{a}\right)\left(x-\sqrt{a}\right) > 0$.

If $-\sqrt{a} < x < \sqrt{a}$, then $0 < x+\sqrt{a} < 2\sqrt{a}$ and $-2\sqrt{a} < x-\sqrt{a} < 0$ ..Therefore, $\left(x+\sqrt{a}\right)\left(x-\sqrt{a}\right) < 0$, which is a contradiction.

If $x > \sqrt{a}$, then $x+\sqrt{a} > 2\sqrt{a} > 0$ and $x-\sqrt{a} > 0$. Therefore, $\left(x+\sqrt{a}\right)\left(x-\sqrt{a}\right) > 0$.

So the solution set for $x^2 > a$ is $\left\{x \middle| x < -\sqrt{a} \text{ or } x > \sqrt{a}\right\}$.

83. $x^2 < 1$
$-\sqrt{1} < x < \sqrt{1}$
$-1 < x < 1$
The solution set is $\left\{x \middle| -1 < x < 1\right\}$.

84. $x^2 < 4$
$-\sqrt{4} < x < \sqrt{4}$
$-2 < x < 2$
The solution set is $\left\{x \middle| -2 < x < 2\right\}$.

85. $x^2 \geq 9$
$x \leq -\sqrt{9}$ or $x \geq \sqrt{9}$
$x \leq -3$ or $x \geq 3$
The solution set is $\left\{x \middle| x \leq -3 \text{ or } x \geq 3\right\}$.

86. $x^2 \geq 1$
$x \leq -\sqrt{1}$ or $x \geq \sqrt{1}$
$x \leq -1$ or $x \geq 1$
The solution set is $\left\{x \middle| x \leq -1 \text{ or } x \geq 1\right\}$.

87. $x^2 \leq 16$
$-\sqrt{16} \leq x \leq \sqrt{16}$
$-4 \leq x \leq 4$
The solution set is $\left\{x \middle| -4 \leq x \leq 4\right\}$.

88. $x^2 \leq 9$
$-\sqrt{9} \leq x \leq \sqrt{9}$
$-3 \leq x \leq 3$
The solution set is $\left\{x \middle| -3 \leq x \leq 3\right\}$.

89. $x^2 > 4$
$x < -\sqrt{4}$ or $x > \sqrt{4}$
$x < -2$ or $x > 2$
The solution set is $\left\{x \middle| x < -2 \text{ or } x > 2\right\}$.

90. $x^2 \geq 16$
$x \leq -\sqrt{16}$ or $x \geq \sqrt{16}$
$x \leq -4$ or $x \geq 4$
The solution set is $\left\{x \middle| x < -4 \text{ or } x > 4\right\}$.

133

91. $\left|3x-\left|2x+1\right|\right|=4$

$3x-\left|2x+1\right|=4$ or $3x-\left|2x+1\right|=-4$

$3x-\left|2x+1\right|=4$

$\quad 3x-4=\left|2x+1\right|$

$2x+1=3x-4$ or $2x+1=-(3x-4)$

$\quad -x=-5 \qquad$ or $\quad 2x+1=-3x+4$

$\quad\quad x=5 \qquad$ or $\qquad 5x=3$

$\quad\quad x=5 \qquad$ or $\qquad x=\dfrac{3}{5}$

or

$3x-\left|2x+1\right|=-4$

$\quad 3x+4=\left|2x+1\right|$

$2x+1=3x+4$ or $2x+1=-(3x+4)$

$\quad -x=3 \qquad$ or $\quad 2x+1=-3x-4$

$\quad x=-3 \qquad$ or $\qquad 5x=-5$

$\quad x=-3 \qquad$ or $\qquad x=-1$

The only values that check in the original equation are $x=5$ and $x=-1$.

The solution set is $\{-1,\ 5\}$.

92. $\left|x+\left|3x-2\right|\right|=2$

$x+\left|3x-2\right|=2$ or $x+\left|3x-2\right|=-2$

$x+\left|3x-2\right|=2$

$\quad \left|3x-2\right|=2-x$

$3x-2=2-x$ or $3x-2=-(2-x)$

$\quad 4x=4 \qquad$ or $\quad 3x-2=-2+x$

$\quad x=1 \qquad$ or $\qquad 2x=0$

$\quad x=1 \qquad$ or $\qquad x=0$

or

$x+\left|3x-2\right|=-2$

$\quad \left|3x-2\right|=-2-x$

$3x-2=-2-x$ or $3x-2=-(-2-x)$

$\quad 4x=0 \qquad$ or $\quad 3x-2=2+x$

$\quad x=0 \qquad$ or $\qquad 2x=4$

$\quad x=0 \qquad$ or $\qquad x=2$

The only values that check in the original equation are $x=0$ and $x=1$.

The solution set is $\{0,\ 1\}$.

93 – 95. Answers will vary.

Section 1.7

1. mathematical modeling

2. interest

3. uniform motion

4. False; the amount charged for the use of principal is the interest.

5. True; this is the uniform motion formula.

6. If there are x pounds of coffee A, then there are $100-x$ pounds of coffee B.

7. Let A represent the area of the circle and r the radius. The area of a circle is the product of π times the square of the radius: $A=\pi r^2$

8. Let C represent the circumference of a circle and r the radius. The circumference of a circle is the product of π times twice the radius: $C=2\pi r$

9. Let A represent the area of the square and s the length of a side. The area of the square is the square of the length of a side: $A=s^2$

10. Let P represent the perimeter of a square and s the length of a side. The perimeter of a square is four times the length of a side: $P=4s$

11. Let F represent the force, m the mass, and a the acceleration. Force equals the product of the mass times the acceleration: $F=ma$

12. Let P represent the pressure, F the force, and A the area. Pressure is the force per unit area: $P=\dfrac{F}{A}$

13. Let W represent the work, F the force, and d the distance. Work equals force times distance: $W=Fd$

14. Let K represent the kinetic energy, m the mass, and v the velocity. Kinetic energy is one-half the product of the mass and the square of the velocity: $K=\dfrac{1}{2}mv^2$

15. C = total variable cost in dollars, x = number of dishwashers manufactured: $C = 150x$

16. R = total revenue in dollars, x = number of dishwashers sold: $R = 250x$

17. Let x represent the amount of money invested in bonds. Then $50,000 - x$ represents the amount of money invested in CD's. Since the total interest is to be $6,000, we have:
$$0.15x + 0.07(50,000 - x) = 6,000$$
$$(100)(0.15x + 0.07(50,000 - x)) = (6,000)(100)$$
$$15x + 7(50,000 - x) = 600,000$$
$$15x + 350,000 - 7x = 600,000$$
$$8x + 350,000 = 600,000$$
$$8x = 250,000$$
$$x = 31,250$$
$31,250 should be invested in bonds at 15% and $18,750 should be invested in CD's at 7%.

18. Let x represent the amount of money invested in bonds. Then $50,000 - x$ represents the amount of money invested in CD's. Since the total interest is to be $7,000, we have:
$$0.15x + 0.07(50,000 - x) = 7,000$$
$$(100)(0.15x + 0.07(50,000 - x)) = (7,000)(100)$$
$$15x + 7(50,000 - x) = 700,000$$
$$15x + 350,000 - 7x = 700,000$$
$$8x + 350,000 = 700,000$$
$$8x = 350,000$$
$$x = 43,750$$
$43,750 should be invested in bonds at 15% and $6,250 should be invested in CD's at 7%.

19. Let x represent the amount of money loaned at 8%. Then $12,000 - x$ represents the amount of money loaned at 18%. Since the total interest is to be $1,000, we have:
$$0.08x + 0.18(12,000 - x) = 1,000$$
$$(100)(0.08x + 0.18(12,000 - x)) = (1,000)(100)$$
$$8x + 18(12,000 - x) = 100,000$$
$$8x + 216,000 - 18x = 100,000$$
$$-10x + 216,000 = 100,000$$
$$-10x = -116,000$$
$$x = 11,600$$
$11,600 is loaned at 8% and $400 is at 18%.

20. Let x represent the amount of money loaned at 16%. Then $1,000,000 - x$ represents the amount of money loaned at 19%. Since the total interest is to be $1,000,000(0.18)$, we have:
$$0.16x + 0.19(1,000,000 - x) = 1,000,000(0.18)$$
$$0.16x + 190,000 - 0.19x = 180,000$$
$$-0.03x + 190,000 = 180,000$$
$$-0.03x = -10,000$$
$$x = \frac{-10,000}{-0.03}$$
$$x = \$333,333.33$$
Wendy can lend $333,333.33 at 16%.

21. Let x represent the number of pounds of Earl Gray tea. Then $100 - x$ represents the number of pounds of Orange Pekoe tea.
$$5x + 3(100 - x) = 4.50(100)$$
$$5x + 300 - 3x = 450$$
$$2x + 300 = 450$$
$$2x = 150$$
$$x = 75$$
75 pounds of Earl Gray tea must be blended with 25 pounds of Orange Pekoe.

22. Let x represent the number of pounds of the first kind of coffee. Then $100 - x$ represents the number of pounds of the second kind of coffee.
$$2.75x + 5(100 - x) = 3.90(100)$$
$$2.75x + 500 - 5x = 390$$
$$-2.25x + 500 = 390$$
$$-2.25x = -110$$
$$x \approx 48.9$$
Approximately 49 pounds of the first kind of coffee must be blended with approximately 51 pounds of the second kind of coffee.

23. Let x represent the number of pounds of cashews. Then $x + 60$ represents the number of pounds in the mixture.
$$9x + 3.50(60) = 7.50(x + 60)$$
$$9x + 210 = 7.50x + 450$$
$$1.5x = 240$$
$$x = 160$$
160 pounds of cashews must be added to the 60 pounds of almonds.

24. Let x represent the number of caramels in the box. Then $30 - x$ represents the number of cremes in the box.

$$\text{Revenue} - \text{Cost} = \text{Profit}$$
$$12.50 - \left(0.25x + 0.45(30 - x)\right) = 3.00$$
$$12.50 - \left(0.25x + 13.5 - 0.45x\right) = 3.00$$
$$12.50 - \left(13.5 - 0.20x\right) = 3.00$$
$$12.50 - 13.50 + 0.20x = 3.00$$
$$-1.00 + 0.20x = 3.00$$
$$0.20x = 4.00$$
$$x = 20$$

The box should contain 20 caramels and 10 cremes.

25. Let r represent the speed of the current.

	Rate	Time	Distance
Upstream	$16 - r$	$\frac{20}{60} = \frac{1}{3}$	$\frac{16 - r}{3}$
Downstream	$16 + r$	$\frac{15}{60} = \frac{1}{4}$	$\frac{16 + r}{4}$

Since the distance is the same in each direction:
$$\frac{16 - r}{3} = \frac{16 + r}{4}$$
$$4(16 - r) = 3(16 + r)$$
$$64 - 4r = 48 + 3r$$
$$16 = 7r$$
$$r = \frac{16}{7} \approx 2.286$$

The speed of the current is approximately 2.286 miles per hour.

26. Let r represent the speed of the motorboat.

	Rate	Time	Distance
Upstream	$r - 3$	5	$5(r - 3)$
Downstream	$r + 3$	2.5	$2.5(r + 3)$

The distance is the same in each direction:
$$5(r - 3) = 2.5(r + 3)$$
$$5r - 15 = 2.5r + 7.5$$
$$2.5r = 22.5$$
$$r = 9$$

The speed of the motorboat is 9 miles per hour.

27. Let r represent the speed of the current.

	Rate	Time	Distance
Upstream	$15 - r$	$\frac{10}{15 - r}$	10
Downstream	$15 + r$	$\frac{10}{15 + r}$	10

Since the total time is 1.5 hours, we have:

$$\frac{10}{15 - r} + \frac{10}{15 + r} = 1.5$$
$$10(15 + r) + 10(15 - r) = 1.5(15 - r)(15 + r)$$
$$150 + 10r + 150 - 10r = 1.5(225 - r^2)$$
$$300 = 1.5(225 - r^2)$$
$$200 = 225 - r^2$$
$$r^2 - 25 = 0$$
$$(r - 5)(r + 5) = 0$$
$$r = 5 \text{ or } r = -5$$

Speed must be positive, so disregard $r = -5$. The speed of the current is 5 miles per hour.

28. Let r represent the rate of the slower car. Then $r + 10$ represents the rate of the faster car.

	Rate	Time	Distance
Slower car	r	3.5	$3.5r$
Faster car	$r + 10$	3	$3(r + 10)$

$$3.5r = 3(r + 10)$$
$$3.5r = 3r + 30$$
$$0.5r = 30$$
$$r = 60$$

The slower car travels at a rate of 60 miles per hour. The faster car travels at a rate of 70 miles per hour. The distance is $(70)(3) = 210$ miles.

29. Let r represent Karen's normal walking speed.

	Rate	Time	Distance
With walkway	$r + 2.5$	$\frac{50}{r + 2.5}$	50
Against walkway	$r - 2.5$	$\frac{50}{r - 2.5}$	50

Since the total time is 40 seconds:
$$\frac{50}{r + 2.5} + \frac{50}{r - 2.5} = 40$$
$$50(r - 2.5) + 50(r + 2.5) = 40(r - 2.5)(r + 2.5)$$
$$50r - 125 + 50r + 125 = 40(r^2 - 6.25)$$
$$100r = 40r^2 - 250$$
$$0 = 40r^2 - 100r - 250$$
$$0 = 4r^2 - 10r - 25$$
$$r = \frac{-(-10) \pm \sqrt{(-10)^2 - 4(4)(-25)}}{2(4)}$$
$$= \frac{10 \pm \sqrt{500}}{8} = \frac{10 \pm 10\sqrt{5}}{8} = \frac{5 \pm 5\sqrt{5}}{4}$$
$$r \approx 4.05 \text{ or } r \approx -1.55$$

Speed must be positive, so disregard $r \approx -1.55$. Karen' normal walking speed is approximately 4.05 feet per second.

30. Let r represent the speed of the Montparnasse walkway.

	Rate	Time	Distance
Walking with	$1.5 + r$	$\dfrac{200}{1.5 + r}$	200
Standing still	r	$\dfrac{200}{r}$	200

Walking with the walkway takes 30 seconds less time than standing still on the walkway:

$$\frac{200}{1.5 + r} = \frac{200}{r} - 30$$

$$200r = 200(1.5 + r) - 30r(r + 1.5)$$

$$200r = 300 + 200r - 30r^2 - 45r$$

$$30r^2 + 45r - 300 = 0$$

$$2r^2 + 3r - 20 = 0$$

$$(2r + 5)(r + 4) = 0$$

$$2r - 5 = 0 \quad \text{or} \quad r + 4 = 0$$

$$r = \frac{5}{2} = 2.5 \quad \text{or} \quad r = -4$$

Speed must be positive, so disregard $r = -4$.
The speed of the Montparnasse walkways is 2.5 meters per second.

31. Let w represent the width of a regulation doubles tennis court. Then $2w + 6$ represents the length. The area is 2808 square feet:

$$w(2w + 6) = 2808$$

$$2w^2 + 6w = 2808$$

$$2w^2 + 6w - 2808 = 0$$

$$w^2 + 3w - 1404 = 0$$

$$(w + 39)(w - 36) = 0$$

$$w + 39 = 0 \quad \text{or} \quad w - 36 = 0$$

$$w = -39 \quad \text{or} \quad w = 36$$

The width must be positive, so disregard $w = -39$.
The width of a regulation doubles tennis court is 36 feet and the length is $2(36) + 6 = 78$ feet.

32. Let t represent the time it takes the HP LaserJet 2420 to complete the print job alone. Then $t + 10$ represents the time it takes the HP LaserJet 1300 to complete the print job alone.

	Time to do job	Part of job done in one minute
HP LJ 2420	t	$\dfrac{1}{t}$
HP LJ 1300	$t + 10$	$\dfrac{1}{t+10}$
Together	12	$\dfrac{1}{12}$

$$\frac{1}{t} + \frac{1}{t+10} = \frac{1}{12}$$

$$12(t + 10) + 12t = t(t + 10)$$

$$12t + 120 + 12t = t^2 + 10t$$

$$0 = t^2 - 14t - 120$$

$$0 = (t - 20)(t + 6)$$

$$t - 20 = 0 \quad \text{or} \quad t + 6 = 0$$

$$t = 20 \quad \text{or} \quad t = -6$$

Time must be positive, so disregard $t = -6$.
The HP LaserJet 2420 takes 20 minutes to complete the job alone, printing $\dfrac{600}{20} = 30$ pages per minute. The HP LaserJet 1300 takes $20 + 10 = 30$ minutes to complete the job alone, printing $\dfrac{600}{30} = 20$ pages per minute.

33. Let t represent the time it takes to do the job together.

	Time to do job	Part of job done in one minute
Trent	30	$\dfrac{1}{30}$
Lois	20	$\dfrac{1}{20}$
Together	t	$\dfrac{1}{t}$

$$\frac{1}{30} + \frac{1}{20} = \frac{1}{t}$$

$$2t + 3t = 60$$

$$5t = 60$$

$$t = 12$$

Working together, the job can be done in 12 minutes.

34. Let t represent the time it takes April to do the job working alone.

	Time to do job	Part of job done in one hour
Patrice	10	$\dfrac{1}{10}$
April	t	$\dfrac{1}{t}$
Together	6	$\dfrac{1}{6}$

$$\frac{1}{10} + \frac{1}{t} = \frac{1}{6}$$

$$3t + 30 = 5t$$

$$2t = 30$$

$$t = 15$$

April would take 15 hours to paint the rooms.

35. $l =$ length of the garden
$w =$ width of the garden

a. The length of the garden is to be twice its width. Thus, $l = 2w$.
The dimensions of the fence are $l + 4$ and $w + 4$.
The perimeter is 46 feet, so:
$$2(l+4) + 2(w+4) = 46$$
$$2(2w+4) + 2(w+4) = 46$$
$$4w + 8 + 2w + 8 = 46$$
$$6w + 16 = 46$$
$$6w = 30$$
$$w = 5$$
The dimensions of the garden are 5 feet by 10 feet.

b. Area $= l \cdot w = 5 \cdot 10 = 50$ square feet

c. If the dimensions of the garden are the same, then the length and width of the fence are also the same $(l+4)$. The perimeter is 46 feet, so:
$$2(l+4) + 2(l+4) = 46$$
$$2l + 8 + 2l + 8 = 46$$
$$4l + 16 = 46$$
$$4l = 30$$
$$l = 7.5$$
The dimensions of the garden are 7.5 feet by 7.5 feet.

d. Area $= l \cdot w = 7.5(7.5) = 56.25$ square feet.

36. $l =$ length of the pond
$w =$ width of the pond

a. The pond is to be a square. Thus, $l = w$.
The dimensions of the fenced area are $w + 6$ on each side. The perimeter is 100 feet, so:
$$4(w+6) = 100$$
$$4w + 24 = 100$$
$$4w = 76$$
$$w = 19$$
The dimensions of the pond are 19 feet by 19 feet.

b. The length of the pond is to be three times the width. Thus, $l = 3w$. The dimensions of the fenced area are $w + 6$ and $l + 6$. The perimeter is 100 feet, so:

$$2(w+6) + 2(l+6) = 100$$
$$2(w+6) + 2(3w+6) = 100$$
$$2w + 12 + 6w + 12 = 100$$
$$8w + 24 = 100$$
$$8w = 76$$
$$w = 9.5$$
$$l = 3(9.5) = 28.5$$
The dimensions of the pond are 9.5 feet by 28.5 feet.

c. If the pond is circular, the diameter is d and the diameter of the circle with the pond and the deck is $d + 6$.

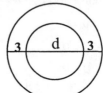

The perimeter is 100 feet, so:
$$\pi(d+6) = 100$$
$$\pi d + 6\pi = 100$$
$$\pi d = 100 - 6\pi$$
$$d = \frac{100}{\pi} - 6 \approx 25.83$$
The diameter of the pond is 25.83 feet.

d. Area$_{\text{square}} = l \cdot w = 19(19) = 361 \text{ ft}^2$.

Area$_{\text{rectangle}} = l \cdot w = 28.5(9.5) = 270.75 \text{ ft}^2$.

Area$_{\text{circle}} = \pi r^2 = \pi \left(\frac{25.83}{2}\right)^2 \approx 524 \text{ ft}^2$.

The circular pond has the largest area.

37. Let t represent the time it takes for the defensive back to catch the tight end.

	Time to run 100 yards	Time	Rate	Distance
Tight End	12 sec	t	$\frac{100}{12} = \frac{25}{3}$	$\frac{25}{3}t$
Def. Back	10 sec	t	$\frac{100}{10} = 10$	$10t$

Since the defensive back has to run 5 yards farther, we have:
$$\frac{25}{3}t + 5 = 10t$$
$$25t + 15 = 30t$$
$$15 = 5t$$
$$t = 3 \qquad \rightarrow \qquad 10t = 30$$

The defensive back will catch the tight end at the 45 yard line ($15 + 30 = 45$).

38. Let x represent the number of highway miles traveled. Then $30,000 - x$ represents the number of city miles traveled.

$$\frac{x}{40} + \frac{30,000 - x}{25} = 900$$

$$200\left(\frac{x}{40} + \frac{30,000 - x}{25}\right) = 200(900)$$

$$5x + 240,000 - 8x = 180,000$$

$$-3x + 240,000 = 180,000$$

$$-3x = -60,000$$

$$x = 20,000$$

Therese is allowed to claim 20,000 miles as a business expense.

39. Let x represent the number of gallons of pure water. Then $x + 1$ represents the number of gallons in the 60% solution.

$$(\%)(\text{gallons}) + (\%)(\text{gallons}) = (\%)(\text{gallons})$$

$$0(x) + 1(1) = 0.60(x + 1)$$

$$1 = 0.6x + 0.6$$

$$0.4 = 0.6x$$

$$x = \frac{4}{6} = \frac{2}{3}$$

$\frac{2}{3}$ gallon of pure water should be added.

40. Let x represent the number of liters to be drained and replaced with pure antifreeze.

$$(\%)(\text{liters}) + (\%)(\text{liters}) = (\%)(\text{liters})$$

$$1(x) + 0.40(15 - x) = 0.60(15)$$

$$x + 6 - 0.40x = 9$$

$$0.60x = 3$$

$$x = 5$$

5 liters should be drained and replaced with pure antifreeze.

41. Let x represent the number of ounces of water to be evaporated; the amount of salt remains the same. Therefore, we get

$$0.04(32) = 0.06(32 - x)$$

$$1.28 = 1.92 - 0.06x$$

$$0.06x = 0.64$$

$$x = \frac{0.64}{0.06} = \frac{64}{6} = \frac{32}{3} = 10\frac{2}{3}$$

$10\frac{2}{3} \approx 10.67$ ounces of water need to be evaporated.

42. Let x represent the number of gallons of water to be evaporated; the amount of salt remains the same.

$$0.03(240) = 0.05(240 - x)$$

$$7.2 = 12 - 0.05x$$

$$0.05x = 4.8$$

$$x = \frac{4.8}{0.05} = 96$$

96 gallons of water need to be evaporated.

43. Let x represent the number of grams of pure gold. Then $60 - x$ represents the number of grams of 12 karat gold to be used.

$$x + \frac{1}{2}(60 - x) = \frac{2}{3}(60)$$

$$x + 30 - 0.5x = 40$$

$$0.5x = 10$$

$$x = 20$$

20 grams of pure gold should be mixed with 40 grams of 12 karat gold.

44. Let x represent the number of atoms of oxygen. $2x$ represents the number of atoms of hydrogen. $x + 1$ represents the number of atoms of carbon.

$$x + 2x + x + 1 = 45$$

$$4x = 44$$

$$x = 11$$

There are 11 atoms of oxygen and 22 atoms of hydrogen in the sugar molecule.

45. Let t represent the time it takes for Mike to catch up with Dan. Since the distances are the same, we have:

$$\frac{1}{6}t = \frac{1}{9}(t + 1)$$

$$3t = 2t + 2$$

$$t = 2$$

Mike will pass Dan after 2 minutes, which is a distance of $\frac{1}{3}$ mile.

46. Let t represent the time of flight with the wind. The distance is the same in each direction:

$$330t = 270(5 - t)$$

$$330t = 1350 - 270t$$

$$600t = 1350$$

$$t = 2.25$$

The distance the plane can fly and still return safely is $330(2.25) = 742.5$ miles.

47. Let t represent the time the auxiliary pump needs to run. Since the two pumps are emptying one tanker, we have:

$$\frac{3}{4} + \frac{t}{9} = 1$$
$$27 + 4t = 36$$
$$4t = 9$$
$$t = \frac{9}{4} = 2.25$$

The auxiliary pump must run for 2.25 hours. It must be started at 9:45 a.m.

48. Let x represent the number of pounds of pure cement. Then $x + 20$ represents the number of pounds in the 40% mixture.

$$x + 0.25(20) = 0.40(x + 20)$$
$$x + 5 = 0.4x + 8$$
$$0.6x = 3$$
$$x = \frac{30}{6} = 5$$

5 pounds of pure cement should be added.

49. Let t represent the time for the tub to fill with the faucets on and the stopper removed. Since one tub is being filled, we have:

$$\frac{t}{15} + \left(-\frac{t}{20}\right) = 1$$
$$4t - 3t = 60$$
$$t = 60$$

60 minutes is required to fill the tub.

50. Let t be the time the 5 horsepower pump needs to run to finish emptying the pool. Since the two pumps are emptying one pool, we have:

$$\frac{t+2}{5} + \frac{2}{8} = 1$$
$$4(2+t) + 5 = 20$$
$$8 + 4t + 5 = 20$$
$$4t = 7$$
$$t = 1.75$$

The 5 horsepower pump must run for an additional 1.75 hours or 1 hour and 45 minutes to empty the pool.

51. Let t represent the time spent running. Then $5 - t$ represents the time spent biking.

	Rate	Time	Distance
Run	6	t	$6t$
Bike	25	$5-t$	$25(5-t)$

The total distance is 87 miles:
$$6t + 25(5 - t) = 87$$
$$6t + 125 - 25t = 87$$
$$-19t + 125 = 87$$
$$-19t = -38$$
$$t = 2$$

The time spent running is 2 hours, so the distance of the run is $6(2) = 12$ miles. The distance of the bicycle race is $25(5 - 2) = 75$ miles.

52. Let r represent the speed of the eastbound cyclist. Then $r + 5$ represents the speed of the westbound cyclist.

	Rate	Time	Distance
Eastbound	r	6	$6r$
Westbound	$r+5$	6	$6(r+5)$

The total distance is 246 miles:
$$6r + 6(r + 5) = 246$$
$$6r + 6r + 30 = 246$$
$$12r + 30 = 246$$
$$12r = 216$$
$$r = 18$$

The speed of the eastbound cyclist is 18 miles per hour, and the speed of the westbound cyclist is $18 + 5 = 23$ miles per hour.

53. Burke's rate is $\frac{100}{12}$ meters/sec. In 9.99 seconds, Burke will run $\frac{100}{12}(9.99) = 83.25$ meters. Lewis would win by 16.75 meters.

54. $A = 2\pi r^2 + 2\pi r h$. Since $A = 188.5$ square inches and $h = 7$ inches,

$$2\pi r^2 + 2\pi r(7) = 188.5$$
$$2\pi r^2 + 14\pi r - 188.5 = 0$$
$$r = \frac{-14\pi \pm \sqrt{(14\pi)^2 - 4(2\pi)(-188.5)}}{2(2\pi)}$$
$$= \frac{-14\pi \pm \sqrt{6671.9642}}{4\pi}$$

$r \approx 3$ or $r \approx -10$

The radius of the coffee can is approximately 3 inches.

55. Let x be the original selling price of the shirt.
Profit = Revenue − Cost
$4 = x - 0.40x - 20 \rightarrow 24 = 0.60x \rightarrow x = 40$
The original price should be \$40 to ensure a profit of \$4 after the sale.
If the sale is 50% off, the profit is:
$40 - 0.50(40) - 20 = 40 - 20 - 20 = 0$
At 50% off there will be no profit.

56. Answers will vary.

57. It is impossible to mix two solutions with a lower concentration and end up with a new solution with a higher concentration.

Algebraic Solution:
Let x = the number of liters of 25% solution.
$(\%)(\text{liters}) + (\%)(\text{liters}) = (\%)(\text{liters})$
$$0.25x + 0.48(20) = 0.58(20 + x)$$
$$0.25x + 9.6 = 10.6 + 0.58x$$
$$-0.33x = 1$$
$$x \approx -3.03 \text{ liters}$$
$$(\text{not possible})$$

58. Let t_1 and t_2 represent the times for the two segments of the trip. Since Atlanta is halfway between Chicago and Miami, the distances are equal.
$45t_1 = 55t_2$
$$t_1 = \frac{55}{45}t_2$$
$$t_1 = \frac{11}{9}t_2$$
Computing the average speed:
$$\text{Avg Speed} = \frac{\text{Distance}}{\text{Time}} = \frac{45t_1 + 55t_2}{t_1 + t_2}$$
$$= \frac{45\left(\frac{11}{9}t_2\right) + 55t_2}{\frac{11}{9}t_2 + t_2} = \frac{55t_2 + 55t_2}{\left(\frac{11t_2 + 9t_2}{9}\right)}$$
$$= \frac{110t_2}{\left(\frac{20t_2}{9}\right)} = \frac{990t_2}{20t_2}$$
$$= \frac{99}{2} = 49.5 \text{ miles per hour}$$
The average speed for the trip from Chicago to Miami is 49.5 miles per hour.

59. The time traveled with the tail wind was:
$$t = \frac{919}{550} \approx 1.67091 \text{ hours}.$$
Since they were 20 minutes $\left(\frac{1}{3} \text{ hour}\right)$ early, the time in still air would have been:
$1.67091 \text{ hrs} + 20 \text{ min} = (1.67091 + 0.33333) \text{ hrs}$
$$\approx 2.00424 \text{ hrs}$$
Thus, with no wind, the ground speed is
$\frac{919}{2.00424} \approx 458.53$. Therefore, the tail wind is
$550 - 458.53 = 91.47 \text{ knots}.$

Chapter 1 Review

1. $2 - \dfrac{x}{3} = 8$
$6 - x = 24$
$x = -18$
The solution set is $\{-18\}$.

2. $\dfrac{x}{4} - 2 = 4$
$x - 8 = 16$
$x = 24$
The solution set is $\{24\}$.

3. $-2(5 - 3x) + 8 = 4 + 5x$
$-10 + 6x + 8 = 4 + 5x$
$6x - 2 = 4 + 5x$
$x = 6$
The solution set is $\{6\}$.

4. $(6 - 3x) - 2(1 + x) = 6x$
$6 - 3x - 2 - 2x = 6x$
$-5x + 4 = 6x$
$-11x = -4$
$$x = \frac{4}{11}$$
The solution set is $\left\{\dfrac{4}{11}\right\}$.

5. $\dfrac{3x}{4} - \dfrac{x}{3} = \dfrac{1}{12}$

$9x - 4x = 1$

$5x = 1$

$x = \dfrac{1}{5}$

The solution set is $\left\{\dfrac{1}{5}\right\}$.

6. $\dfrac{4-2x}{3} + \dfrac{1}{6} = 2x$

$2(4-2x) + 1 = 12x$

$8 - 4x + 1 = 12x$

$9 = 16x$

$x = \dfrac{9}{16}$

The solution set is $\left\{\dfrac{9}{16}\right\}$.

7. $\dfrac{x}{x-1} = \dfrac{6}{5}$

$5x = 6x - 6$

$6 = x$

Since $x = 6$ does not cause a denominator to equal zero, the solution set is $\{6\}$.

8. $\dfrac{4x-5}{3-7x} = 2$

$4x - 5 = 6 - 14x$

$18x = 11$

$x = \dfrac{11}{18}$

Since $x = \dfrac{11}{18}$ does not cause a denominator to

equal zero, the solution set is $\left\{\dfrac{11}{18}\right\}$.

$\{$

9. $x(1-x) = 6$

$x - x^2 = 6$

$0 = x^2 - x + 6$

$b^2 - 4ac = (-1)^2 - 4(1)(6)$

$= 1 - 24 = -23$

Therefore, there are no real solutions.

10. $x(1+x) = 6$

$x + x^2 = 6$

$x^2 + x - 6 = 0$

$(x+3)(x-2) = 0$

$x = -3 \text{ or } x = 2$

The solution set is $\{-3, 2\}$.

11. $\dfrac{1}{2}\left(x - \dfrac{1}{3}\right) = \dfrac{3}{4} - \dfrac{x}{6}$

$(12)\left(\dfrac{1}{2}\right)\left(x - \dfrac{1}{3}\right) = \left(\dfrac{3}{4} - \dfrac{x}{6}\right)(12)$

$6x - 2 = 9 - 2x$

$8x = 11$

$x = \dfrac{11}{8}$

The solution set is $\left\{\dfrac{11}{8}\right\}$.

12. $\dfrac{1-3x}{4} = \dfrac{x+6}{3} + \dfrac{1}{2}$

$(12)\left(\dfrac{1-3x}{4}\right) = \left(\dfrac{x+6}{3} + \dfrac{1}{2}\right)(12)$

$3(1-3x) = 4(x+6) + 6$

$3 - 9x = 4x + 24 + 6$

$-13x = 27$

$x = -\dfrac{27}{13}$

The solution set is $\left\{-\dfrac{27}{13}\right\}$.

13. $(x-1)(2x+3) = 3$

$2x^2 + x - 3 = 3$

$2x^2 + x - 6 = 0$

$(2x-3)(x+2) = 0$

$x = \dfrac{3}{2} \text{ or } x = -2$

The solution set is $\left\{-2, \dfrac{3}{2}\right\}$.

14. $x(2-x) = 3(x-4)$

$2x - x^2 = 3x - 12$

$x^2 + x - 12 = 0$

$(x+4)(x-3) = 0$

$x = -4 \text{ or } x = 3$

The solution set is $\{-4, 3\}$.

142

15. $2x + 3 = 4x^2$

$$0 = 4x^2 - 2x - 3$$

$$x = \frac{-(-2) \pm \sqrt{(-2)^2 - 4(4)(-3)}}{2(4)}$$

$$= \frac{2 \pm \sqrt{52}}{8} = \frac{2 \pm 2\sqrt{13}}{8} = \frac{1 \pm \sqrt{13}}{4}$$

The solution set is $\left\{ \dfrac{1 - \sqrt{13}}{4}, \dfrac{1 + \sqrt{13}}{4} \right\}$.

16. $1 + 6x = 4x^2$

$$0 = 4x^2 - 6x - 1$$

$$x = \frac{-(-6) \pm \sqrt{(-6)^2 - 4(4)(-1)}}{2(4)}$$

$$= \frac{6 \pm \sqrt{52}}{8} = \frac{6 \pm 2\sqrt{13}}{8} = \frac{3 \pm \sqrt{13}}{4}$$

The solution set is $\left\{ \dfrac{3 - \sqrt{13}}{4}, \dfrac{3 + \sqrt{13}}{4} \right\}$.

17. $\sqrt[3]{x^2 - 1} = 2$

$$\left(\sqrt[3]{x^2 - 1} \right)^3 = (2)^3$$

$$x^2 - 1 = 8$$

$$x^2 = 9$$

$$x = \pm 3$$

Check $x = -3$:   Check $x = 3$:

$\sqrt[3]{(-3)^2 - 1} = 2$ $\sqrt[3]{(3)^2 - 1} = 2$

$\sqrt[3]{9 - 1} = 2$ $\sqrt[3]{9 - 1} = 2$

$\sqrt[3]{8} = 2$ $\sqrt[3]{8} = 2$

$2 = 2$ $2 = 2$

The solution set is $\{-3, 3\}$.

18. $\sqrt{1 + x^3} = 3$

$$\left(\sqrt{1 + x^3} \right)^2 = (3)^2$$

$$1 + x^3 = 9$$

$$x^3 = 8$$

$$x = \sqrt[3]{8} = 2$$

Check $x = 2$: $\sqrt{1 + (2)^3} = 3$

$$\sqrt{9} = 3$$

$$3 = 3$$

The solution set is $\{2\}$.

19. $x(x + 1) + 2 = 0$

$$x^2 + x + 2 = 0$$

$$x = \frac{-1 \pm \sqrt{(1)^2 - 4(1)(2)}}{2(1)} = \frac{-1 \pm \sqrt{-7}}{2}$$

No real solutions.

20. $3x^2 - x + 1 = 0$

$$x = \frac{-(-1) \pm \sqrt{(-1)^2 - 4(3)(1)}}{2(3)} = \frac{1 \pm \sqrt{-11}}{6}$$

No real solutions.

21. $x^4 - 5x^2 + 4 = 0$

$$(x^2 - 4)(x^2 - 1) = 0$$

$$x^2 - 4 = 0 \ \text{ or } \ x^2 - 1 = 0$$

$$x = \pm 2 \ \text{ or } \ x = \pm 1$$

The solution set is $\{-2, -1, 1, 2\}$.

22. $3x^4 + 4x^2 + 1 = 0$

$$(3x^2 + 1)(x^2 + 1) = 0$$

$$3x^2 + 1 = 0 \ \text{ or } \ x^2 + 1 = 0$$

$$3x^2 = -1 \ \text{ or } \ x^2 = -1$$

No real solutions.

23. $\sqrt{2x - 3} + x = 3$

$$\sqrt{2x - 3} = 3 - x$$

$$2x - 3 = 9 - 6x + x^2$$

$$x^2 - 8x + 12 = 0$$

$$(x - 2)(x - 6) = 0$$

$$x = 2 \ \text{ or } \ x = 6$$

Check $x = 2$: $\sqrt{2(2) - 3} + 2 = \sqrt{1} + 2 = 3$

Check $x = 6$: $\sqrt{2(6) - 3} + 6 = \sqrt{9} + 6 = 9 \neq 3$

The solution set is $\{2\}$.

24. $\sqrt{2x - 1} = x - 2$

$$2x - 1 = x^2 - 4x + 4$$

$$x^2 - 6x + 5 = 0$$

$$(x - 1)(x - 5) = 0$$

$$x = 1 \ \text{ or } \ x = 5$$

Check $x = 1$:   Check $x = 5$:

$\sqrt{2(1) - 1} = 1 - 2$ $\sqrt{2(5) - 1} = 5 - 2$

$1 \neq -1$ $3 = 3$

The solution set is $\{5\}$.

25. $\sqrt[4]{2x+3} = 2$

$\left(\sqrt[4]{2x+3}\right)^4 = 2^4$

$2x+3 = 16$

$2x = 13$

$x = \dfrac{13}{2}$

Check $x = \dfrac{13}{2}$:

$\sqrt[4]{2\left(\dfrac{13}{2}\right)+3} = \sqrt[4]{13+3} = \sqrt[4]{16} = 2$

The solution set is $\left\{\dfrac{13}{2}\right\}$.

26. $\sqrt[5]{3x+1} = -1$

$\left(\sqrt[5]{3x+1}\right)^5 = (-1)^5$

$3x+1 = -1$

$3x = -2$

$x = -\dfrac{2}{3}$

Check $x = -\dfrac{2}{3}$:

$\sqrt[5]{3\left(-\dfrac{2}{3}\right)+1} = \sqrt[5]{-2+1} = \sqrt[5]{-1} = -1$

The solution set is $\left\{-\dfrac{2}{3}\right\}$.

27. $\sqrt{x+1} + \sqrt{x-1} = \sqrt{2x+1}$

$\left(\sqrt{x+1} + \sqrt{x-1}\right)^2 = \left(\sqrt{2x+1}\right)^2$

$x+1 + 2\sqrt{x+1}\sqrt{x-1} + x-1 = 2x+1$

$2x + 2\sqrt{x+1}\sqrt{x-1} = 2x+1$

$2\sqrt{x+1}\sqrt{x-1} = 1$

$\left(2\sqrt{x+1}\sqrt{x-1}\right)^2 = (1)^2$

$4(x+1)(x-1) = 1$

$4x^2 - 4 = 1$

$4x^2 = 5$

$x^2 = \dfrac{5}{4}$

$x = \pm\dfrac{\sqrt{5}}{2}$

Check $x = \dfrac{\sqrt{5}}{2}$:

$\sqrt{\dfrac{\sqrt{5}}{2}+1} + \sqrt{\dfrac{\sqrt{5}}{2}-1} = \sqrt{2\left(\dfrac{\sqrt{5}}{2}\right)+1}$

$1.79890743995 = 1.79890743995$

Check $x = -\dfrac{\sqrt{5}}{2}$:

$\sqrt{-\dfrac{\sqrt{5}}{2}+1} + \sqrt{-\dfrac{\sqrt{5}}{2}-1} = \sqrt{2\left(-\dfrac{\sqrt{5}}{2}\right)+1},$

The second solution is not possible because it makes the radicand negative.

The solution set is $\left\{\dfrac{\sqrt{5}}{2}\right\}$.

28. $\sqrt{2x-1} - \sqrt{x-5} = 3$

$\sqrt{2x-1} = 3 + \sqrt{x-5}$

$\left(\sqrt{2x-1}\right)^2 = \left(3+\sqrt{x-5}\right)^2$

$2x-1 = 9 + 6\sqrt{x-5} + x-5$

$x-5 = 6\sqrt{x-5}$

$(x-5)^2 = \left(6\sqrt{x-5}\right)^2$

$x^2 - 10x + 25 = 36(x-5)$

$x^2 - 10x + 25 = 36x - 180$

$x^2 - 46x + 205 = 0$

$(x-41)(x-5) = 0$

$x = 41 \ \text{ or } \ x = 5$

Check $x = 41$:

$\sqrt{2(41)-1} - \sqrt{41-5} = \sqrt{81} - \sqrt{36} = 9-6 = 3$

Check $x = 5$:

$\sqrt{2(5)-1} - \sqrt{5-5} = \sqrt{9} - \sqrt{0} = 3-0 = 3$

The solution set is $\{5, 41\}$.

29. $2x^{1/2} - 3 = 0$

$$2x^{1/2} = 3$$

$$\left(2x^{1/2}\right)^2 = 3^2$$

$$4x = 9$$

$$x = \frac{9}{4}$$

Check $x = \frac{9}{4}$:

$$2\left(\frac{9}{4}\right)^{1/2} - 3 = 2\left(\frac{3}{2}\right) - 3 = 3 - 3 = 0$$

The solution set is $\left\{\frac{9}{4}\right\}$.

30. $3x^{1/4} - 2 = 0$

$$3x^{1/4} = 2$$

$$\left(3x^{1/4}\right)^4 = 2^4$$

$$81x = 16$$

$$x = \frac{16}{81}$$

Check $x = \frac{16}{81}$:

$$3\left(\frac{16}{81}\right)^{1/4} - 2 = 3\left(\frac{2}{3}\right) - 2 = 2 - 2 = 0$$

The solution set is $\left\{\frac{16}{81}\right\}$.

31. $x^{-6} - 7x^{-3} - 8 = 0$

Let $u = x^{-3}$ so that $u^2 = x^{-6}$.

$$u^2 - 7u - 8 = 0$$

$$(u - 8)(u + 1) = 0$$

$$u = 8 \qquad \text{or} \qquad u = -1$$

$$x^{-3} = 8 \qquad \text{or} \qquad x^{-3} = -1$$

$$\left(x^{-3}\right)^{-1/3} = (8)^{-1/3} \quad \text{or} \quad \left(x^{-3}\right)^{-1/3} = (-1)^{-1/3}$$

$$x = \frac{1}{2} \qquad \text{or} \qquad x = -1$$

Check $\frac{1}{2}$: $\left(\frac{1}{2}\right)^{-6} - 7\left(\frac{1}{2}\right)^{-3} - 8 = 64 - 56 - 8 = 0$

Check -1: $(-1)^{-6} - 7(-1)^{-3} - 8 = 1 + 7 - 8 = 0$

The solution set is $\left\{-1, \frac{1}{2}\right\}$.

32. $6x^{-1} - 5x^{-1/2} + 1 = 0$

Let $u = x^{-1/2}$ so that $u^2 = x^{-1}$.

$$6u^2 - 5u + 1 = 0$$

$$(3u - 1)(2u - 1) = 0$$

$$u = \frac{1}{3} \qquad \text{or} \qquad u = \frac{1}{2}$$

$$x^{-1/2} = \frac{1}{3} \qquad \text{or} \qquad x^{-1/2} = \frac{1}{2}$$

$$\left(x^{-1/2}\right)^{-2} = \left(\frac{1}{3}\right)^{-2} \quad \text{or} \quad \left(x^{-1/2}\right)^{-2} = \left(\frac{1}{2}\right)^{-2}$$

$$x = 9 \qquad \text{or} \qquad x = 4$$

Check $x = 9$:

$$6(9)^{-1} - 5(9)^{-1/2} + 1 = 6\left(\frac{1}{9}\right) - 5\left(\frac{1}{3}\right) + 1$$

$$= \frac{2}{3} - \frac{5}{3} + 1 = -1 + 1 = 0$$

Check $x = 4$:

$$6(4)^{-1} - 5(4)^{-1/2} + 1 = 6\left(\frac{1}{4}\right) - 5\left(\frac{1}{2}\right) + 1$$

$$= \frac{3}{2} - \frac{5}{2} + 1 = -1 + 1 = 0$$

The solution set is $\{4, 9\}$.

33.
$$x^2 + m^2 = 2mx + (nx)^2$$

$$x^2 + m^2 = 2mx + n^2x^2$$

$$x^2 - n^2x^2 - 2mx + m^2 = 0$$

$$\left(1 - n^2\right)x^2 - 2mx + m^2 = 0$$

$$x = \frac{-(-2m) \pm \sqrt{(-2m)^2 - 4\left(1 - n^2\right)m^2}}{2\left(1 - n^2\right)}$$

$$= \frac{2m \pm \sqrt{4m^2 - 4m^2 + 4m^2n^2}}{2\left(1 - n^2\right)}$$

$$= \frac{2m \pm \sqrt{4m^2n^2}}{2\left(1 - n^2\right)} = \frac{2m \pm 2mn}{2\left(1 - n^2\right)}$$

$$= \frac{2m(1 \pm n)}{2\left(1 - n^2\right)} = \frac{m(1 \pm n)}{1 - n^2}$$

$$x = \frac{m(1 + n)}{1 - n^2} = \frac{m(1 + n)}{(1 + n)(1 - n)} = \frac{m}{1 - n}$$

or

$$x = \frac{m(1 - n)}{1 - n^2} = \frac{m(1 - n)}{(1 + n)(1 - n)} = \frac{m}{1 + n}$$

The solution set is $\left\{\dfrac{m}{1 - n}, \dfrac{m}{1 + n}\right\}$, $n \ne 1$, $n \ne -1$.

34.
$$b^2x^2 + 2ax = x^2 + a^2$$
$$b^2x^2 + 2ax - x^2 - a^2 = 0$$
$$b^2x^2 - x^2 + 2ax - a^2 = 0$$
$$\left(b^2 - 1\right)x^2 + 2ax - a^2 = 0$$

$$x = \frac{-(2a) \pm \sqrt{(2a)^2 - 4\left(b^2 - 1\right)\left(-a^2\right)}}{2\left(b^2 - 1\right)}$$

$$= \frac{-2a \pm \sqrt{4a^2 + 4a^2b^2 - 4a^2}}{2\left(b^2 - 1\right)} = \frac{-2a \pm \sqrt{4a^2b^2}}{2\left(b^2 - 1\right)}$$

$$= \frac{-2a \pm 2ab}{2\left(b^2 - 1\right)} = \frac{2a(-1 \pm b)}{2\left(b^2 - 1\right)} = \frac{a(-1 \pm b)}{b^2 - 1}$$

$$x = \frac{a(-1 - b)}{b^2 - 1} = \frac{-a(b + 1)}{(b + 1)(b - 1)} = \frac{-a}{b - 1} = \frac{a}{1 - b}$$

or

$$x = \frac{a(-1 + b)}{b^2 - 1} = \frac{a(b - 1)}{(b + 1)(b - 1)} = \frac{a}{b + 1} = \frac{a}{1 + b}$$

The solution set is $\left\{\dfrac{a}{1 - b}, \dfrac{a}{1 + b}\right\}$, $b \neq 1$, $b \neq -1$.

35.
$$10a^2x^2 - 2abx - 36b^2 = 0$$
$$5a^2x^2 - abx - 18b^2 = 0$$
$$(5ax + 9b)(ax - 2b) = 0$$

$$5ax + 9b = 0 \qquad \text{or} \quad ax - 2b = 0$$
$$5ax = -9b \qquad\qquad ax = 2b$$
$$x = -\frac{9b}{5a} \qquad\qquad x = \frac{2b}{a}$$

The solution set is $\left\{-\dfrac{9b}{5a}, \dfrac{2b}{a}\right\}$, $a \neq 0$.

36.
$$\frac{1}{x - m} + \frac{1}{x - n} = \frac{2}{x}$$
$$\frac{(x - n) + (x - m)}{(x - m)(x - n)} = \frac{2}{x}$$
$$\frac{2x - m - n}{(x - m)(x - n)} = \frac{2}{x}$$
$$x(2x - m - n) = 2(x - m)(x - n)$$
$$2x^2 - xm - xn = 2x^2 - 2xn - 2xm + 2mn$$
$$xm + xn - 2mn = 0$$
$$xn + xm = 2mn$$
$$x(n + m) = 2mn$$
$$x = \frac{2mn}{n + m}$$

The solution set is $\left\{\dfrac{2mn}{n + m}\right\}$ where

$n \neq -m, x \neq m, x \neq n, x \neq 0$.

37.
$$\sqrt{x^2 + 3x + 7} - \sqrt{x^2 - 3x + 9} + 2 = 0$$
$$\sqrt{x^2 + 3x + 7} = \sqrt{x^2 - 3x + 9} - 2$$
$$\left(\sqrt{x^2 + 3x + 7}\right)^2 = \left(\sqrt{x^2 - 3x + 9} - 2\right)^2$$
$$x^2 + 3x + 7 = x^2 - 3x + 9 - 4\sqrt{x^2 - 3x + 9} + 4$$
$$6x - 6 = -4\sqrt{x^2 - 3x + 9}$$
$$\left(6(x - 1)\right)^2 = \left(-4\sqrt{x^2 - 3x + 9}\right)^2$$
$$36\left(x^2 - 2x + 1\right) = 16\left(x^2 - 3x + 9\right)$$
$$36x^2 - 72x + 36 = 16x^2 - 48x + 144$$
$$20x^2 - 24x - 108 = 0$$
$$5x^2 - 6x - 27 = 0$$
$$(5x + 9)(x - 3) = 0$$
$$x = -\frac{9}{5} \quad \text{or} \quad x = 3$$

Check $x = -\dfrac{9}{5}$:

$$\sqrt{\left(-\frac{9}{5}\right)^2 + 3\left(-\frac{9}{5}\right) + 7} - \sqrt{\left(-\frac{9}{5}\right)^2 - 3\left(-\frac{9}{5}\right) + 9} + 2$$

$$= \sqrt{\frac{81}{25} - \frac{27}{5} + 7} - \sqrt{\frac{81}{25} + \frac{27}{5} + 9} + 2$$

$$= \sqrt{\frac{81 - 135 + 175}{25}} - \sqrt{\frac{81 + 135 + 225}{25}} + 2$$

$$= \sqrt{\frac{121}{25}} - \sqrt{\frac{441}{25}} + 2 = \frac{11}{5} - \frac{21}{5} + 2 = 0$$

Check $x = 3$:

$$\sqrt{(3)^2 + 3(3) + 7} - \sqrt{(3)^2 - 3(3) + 9} + 2$$
$$= \sqrt{9 + 9 + 7} - \sqrt{9 - 9 + 9} + 2$$
$$= \sqrt{25} - \sqrt{9} + 2 = 2 + 2$$
$$= 4 \neq 0$$

The solution set is $\left\{-\dfrac{9}{5}\right\}$.

38.
$$\sqrt{x^2 + 3x + 7} - \sqrt{x^2 + 3x + 9} = 2$$
$$\sqrt{x^2 + 3x + 7} = \sqrt{x^2 + 3x + 9} + 2$$
$$\left(\sqrt{x^2 + 3x + 7}\right)^2 = \left(\sqrt{x^2 + 3x + 9} + 2\right)^2$$
$$x^2 + 3x + 7 = x^2 + 3x + 9 + 4\sqrt{x^2 + 3x + 9} + 4$$
$$-6 = 4\sqrt{x^2 + 3x + 9}$$

This is impossible since the principal square root always yields a non-negative number. Therefore, there is no real solution.

39. $|2x+3| = 7$

$2x+3 = 7$ or $2x+3 = -7$

$2x = 4$ or $\quad 2x = -10$

$x = 2$ or $\qquad x = -5$

The solution set is $\{-5, 2\}$.

40. $|3x-1| = 5$

$3x-1 = 5$ or $3x-1 = -5$

$3x = 6$ or $\quad 3x = -4$

$x = 2$ or $\qquad x = -\dfrac{4}{3}$

The solution set is $\left\{-\dfrac{4}{3}, 2\right\}$.

41. $|2-3x| + 2 = 9$

$|2-3x| = 7$

$2-3x = 7$ or $\quad 2-3x = -7$

$-3x = 5$ or $\quad -3x = -9$

$x = -\dfrac{5}{3}$ or $\qquad x = 3$

The solution set is $\left\{-\dfrac{5}{3}, 3\right\}$

42. $|1-2x| + 1 = 4$

$|1-2x| = 3$

$1-2x = 3$ or $1-2x = -3$

$2x = -2$ or $\quad 2x = 4$

$x = -1$ or $\qquad x = 2$

The solution set is $\{-1, 2\}$.

43. $\qquad 2x^3 = 3x^2$

$2x^3 - 3x^2 = 0$

$x^2(2x-3) = 0$

$x^2 = 0$ or $\quad 2x-3 = 0$

$x = 0$ or $\qquad x = \dfrac{3}{2}$

The solution set is $\left\{0, \dfrac{3}{2}\right\}$.

44. $\qquad 5x^4 = 9x^3$

$5x^4 - 9x^3 = 0$

$x^3(5x-9) = 0$

$x^3 = 0$ or $5x-9 = 0$

$x = 0$ or $\qquad x = \dfrac{9}{5}$

The solution set is $\left\{0, \dfrac{9}{5}\right\}$.

45. $\qquad 2x^3 + 5x^2 - 8x - 20 = 0$

$x^2(2x+5) - 4(2x+5) = 0$

$(2x+5)(x^2-4) = 0$

$2x+5 = 0$ or $x^2-4 = 0$

$2x = -5$ or $\quad x^2 = 4$

$x = -\dfrac{5}{2}$ or $\qquad x = \pm 2$

The solution set is $\left\{-\dfrac{5}{2}, -2, 2\right\}$.

46. $\qquad 3x^3 + 5x^2 - 3x - 5 = 0$

$x^2(3x+5) - 1(3x+5) = 0$

$(3x+5)(x^2-1) = 0$

$3x+5 = 0$ or $x^2-1 = 0$

$3x = -5$ or $\quad x^2 = 1$

$x = -\dfrac{5}{3}$ or $\qquad x = \pm 1$

The solution set is $\left\{-\dfrac{5}{3}, -1, 1\right\}$.

47. $\qquad \dfrac{2x-3}{5} + 2 \le \dfrac{x}{2}$

$2(2x-3) + 10(2) \le 5x$

$4x - 6 + 20 \le 5x$

$14 \le x$

$x \ge 14$

$\{x \mid x \ge 14\}$ or $[14, \infty)$

14

147

48. $\dfrac{5-x}{3} \le 6x-4$

$5-x \le 3(6x-4)$

$5-x \le 18x-12$

$-19x \le -17$

$x \ge \dfrac{17}{19}$

$\left\{ x \middle| x \ge \dfrac{17}{19} \right\}$ or $\left[\dfrac{17}{19}, \infty \right)$

$\dfrac{17}{19}$

49. $-9 \le \dfrac{2x+3}{-4} \le 7$

$36 \ge 2x+3 \ge -28$

$33 \ge \quad 2x \quad \ge -31$

$\dfrac{33}{2} \ge \quad x \quad \ge -\dfrac{31}{2}$

$-\dfrac{31}{2} \le \quad x \quad \le \dfrac{33}{2}$

$\left\{ x \middle| -\dfrac{31}{2} \le x \le \dfrac{33}{2} \right\}$ or $\left[-\dfrac{31}{2}, \dfrac{33}{2} \right]$

$-\dfrac{31}{2} \qquad\qquad \dfrac{33}{2}$

50. $-4 < \dfrac{2x-2}{3} < 6$

$-12 < 2x-2 < 18$

$-10 < \quad 2x \quad < 20$

$-5 < \quad x \quad < 10$

$\{x | -5 < x < 10\}$ or $(-5, 10)$

$-5 \qquad\qquad 10$

51. $2 < \dfrac{3-3x}{12} < 6$

$24 < 3-3x < 72$

$21 < \quad -3x \quad < 69$

$-7 > \quad x \quad > -23$

$\{x | -23 < x < -7\}$ or $(-23, -7)$

$-23 \qquad\qquad -7$

52. $-3 \le \dfrac{5-3x}{2} \le 6$

$-6 \le 5-3x \le 12$

$-11 \le \quad -3x \quad \le 7$

$\dfrac{11}{3} \ge \quad x \quad \ge -\dfrac{7}{3}$

$\left\{ x \middle| -\dfrac{7}{3} \le x \le \dfrac{11}{3} \right\}$ or $\left[-\dfrac{7}{3}, \dfrac{11}{3} \right]$

$-\dfrac{7}{3} \qquad\qquad \dfrac{11}{3}$

53. $\left| 3x+4 \right| < \dfrac{1}{2}$

$-\dfrac{1}{2} < 3x+4 < \dfrac{1}{2}$

$-\dfrac{9}{2} < \quad 3x \quad < -\dfrac{7}{2}$

$-\dfrac{3}{2} < \quad x \quad < -\dfrac{7}{6}$

$\left\{ x \middle| -\dfrac{3}{2} < x < -\dfrac{7}{6} \right\}$ or $\left(-\dfrac{3}{2}, -\dfrac{7}{6} \right)$

$-\dfrac{3}{2} \qquad\qquad -\dfrac{7}{6}$

54. $\left| 1-2x \right| < \dfrac{1}{3}$

$-\dfrac{1}{3} < 1-2x < \dfrac{1}{3}$

$-\dfrac{4}{3} < \quad -2x \quad < -\dfrac{2}{3}$

$\dfrac{2}{3} > \quad x \quad > \dfrac{1}{3}$

$\left\{ x \middle| \dfrac{1}{3} < x < \dfrac{2}{3} \right\}$ or $\left(\dfrac{1}{3}, \dfrac{2}{3} \right)$

$\dfrac{1}{3} \qquad\qquad \dfrac{2}{3}$

55. $\left| 2x-5 \right| \ge 9$

$2x-5 \le -9$ or $2x-5 \ge 9$

$2x \le -4$ or $\quad 2x \ge 14$

$x \le -2$ or $\quad\quad x \ge 7$

$\left\{ x \middle| x \le -2 \text{ or } x \ge 7 \right\}$ or $(-\infty, -2] \cup [7, \infty)$

$-2 \quad 7$

148

56. $|3x+1| \geq 10$

$3x+1 \leq -10$ or $3x+1 \geq 10$

$3x \leq -11$ or $\quad 3x \geq 9$

$x \leq -\dfrac{11}{3}$ or $\quad x \geq 3$

$\left\{ x \,\middle|\, x \leq -\dfrac{11}{3} \text{ or } x \geq 3 \right\}$ or $\left(-\infty, -\dfrac{11}{3} \right] \cup [3, \infty)$

57. $2 + |2 - 3x| \leq 4$

$|2 - 3x| \leq 2$

$-2 \leq 2 - 3x \leq 2$

$-4 \leq -3x \leq 0$

$\dfrac{4}{3} \geq x \geq 0$

$\left\{ x \,\middle|\, 0 \leq x \leq \dfrac{4}{3} \right\}$ or $\left[0, \dfrac{4}{3} \right]$

58. $\dfrac{1}{2} + \left| \dfrac{2x-1}{3} \right| \leq 1$

$\left| \dfrac{2x-1}{3} \right| \leq \dfrac{1}{2}$

$-\dfrac{1}{2} \leq \dfrac{2x-1}{3} \leq \dfrac{1}{2}$

$-\dfrac{3}{2} \leq 2x - 1 \leq \dfrac{3}{2}$

$-\dfrac{1}{2} \leq 2x \leq \dfrac{5}{2}$

$-\dfrac{1}{4} \leq x \leq \dfrac{5}{4}$

$\left\{ x \,\middle|\, -\dfrac{1}{4} \leq x \leq \dfrac{5}{4} \right\}$ or $\left[-\dfrac{1}{4}, \dfrac{5}{4} \right]$

59. $1 - |2 - 3x| < -4$

$-|2 - 3x| < -5$

$|2 - 3x| > 5$

$2 - 3x < -5$ or $2 - 3x > 5$

$7 < 3x$ or $\quad -3 > 3x$

$\dfrac{7}{3} < x$ or $\quad -1 > x$

$x < -1$ or $\quad x > \dfrac{7}{3}$

$\left\{ x \,\middle|\, x < -1 \text{ or } x > \dfrac{7}{3} \right\}$ or $(-\infty, -1) \cup \left(\dfrac{7}{3}, \infty \right)$

60. $1 - \left| \dfrac{2x-1}{3} \right| < -2$

$-\left| \dfrac{2x-1}{3} \right| < -3$

$\left| \dfrac{2x-1}{3} \right| > 3$

$\dfrac{2x-1}{3} < -3$ or $\dfrac{2x-1}{3} > 3$

$2x - 1 < -9$ or $2x - 1 > 9$

$2x < -8$ or $2x > 10$

$x < -4$ or $x > 5$

$\left\{ x \,\middle|\, x < -4 \text{ or } x > 5 \right\}$ or $(-\infty, -4) \cup (5, \infty)$

61. $\left(\dfrac{1}{2} \cdot 6 \right)^2 = 9$

62. $\left(\dfrac{1}{2} \cdot (-10) \right)^2 = 25$

63. $\left(\dfrac{1}{2} \cdot \left(-\dfrac{4}{3} \right) \right)^2 = \dfrac{4}{9}$

64. $\left(\dfrac{1}{2} \cdot \dfrac{4}{5} \right)^2 = \dfrac{4}{25}$

65. $(6+3i)-(2-4i)=(6-2)+(3-(-4))i=4+7i$

66. $(8-3i)+(-6+2i)=(8-6)+(-3+2)i=2-i$

67. $4(3-i)+3(-5+2i)=12-4i-15+6i=-3+2i$

68. $2(1+i)-3(2-3i)=2+2i-6+9i=-4+11i$

69. $\dfrac{3}{3+i}=\dfrac{3}{3+i}\cdot\dfrac{3-i}{3-i}=\dfrac{9-3i}{9-3i+3i-i^2}$

$\quad=\dfrac{9-3i}{10}=\dfrac{9}{10}-\dfrac{3}{10}i$

70. $\dfrac{4}{2-i}=\dfrac{4}{2-i}\cdot\dfrac{2+i}{2+i}=\dfrac{8+4i}{4+2i-2i-i^2}$

$\quad=\dfrac{8+4i}{5}=\dfrac{8}{5}+\dfrac{4}{5}i$

71. $i^{50}=i^{48}\cdot i^2=\left(i^4\right)^{12}\cdot i^2=1^{12}(-1)=-1$

72. $i^{29}=i^{28}\cdot i=\left(i^4\right)^7\cdot i=1^7\cdot i=i$

73. $(2+3i)^3=(2+3i)^2(2+3i)$

$\quad=\left(4+12i+9i^2\right)(2+3i)$

$\quad=(-5+12i)(2+3i)$

$\quad=-10-15i+24i+36i^2$

$\quad=-46+9i$

74. $(3-2i)^3=(3-2i)^2(3-2i)$

$\quad=\left(9-12i+4i^2\right)(3-2i)$

$\quad=(5-12i)(3-2i)$

$\quad=15-10i-36i+24i^2$

$\quad=-9-46i$

75. $x^2+x+1=0$

$a=1,\,b=1,\,c=1,$

$b^2-4ac=1^2-4(1)(1)=1-4=-3$

$x=\dfrac{-1\pm\sqrt{-3}}{2(1)}=\dfrac{-1\pm\sqrt{3}\,i}{2}=-\dfrac{1}{2}\pm\dfrac{\sqrt{3}}{2}i$

The solution set is $\left\{-\dfrac{1}{2}-\dfrac{\sqrt{3}}{2}i,\ -\dfrac{1}{2}+\dfrac{\sqrt{3}}{2}i\right\}.$

76. $x^2-x+1=0$

$a=1,\,b=-1,\,c=1,$

$b^2-4ac=(-1)^2-4(1)(1)=1-4=-3$

$x=\dfrac{-(-1)\pm\sqrt{-3}}{2(1)}=\dfrac{1\pm\sqrt{3}\,i}{2}=\dfrac{1}{2}\pm\dfrac{\sqrt{3}}{2}i$

The solution set is $\left\{\dfrac{1}{2}-\dfrac{\sqrt{3}}{2}i,\ \dfrac{1}{2}+\dfrac{\sqrt{3}}{2}i\right\}.$

77. $2x^2+x-2=0$

$a=2,\,b=1,\,c=-2,$

$b^2-4ac=1^2-4(2)(-2)=1+16=17$

$x=\dfrac{-1\pm\sqrt{17}}{2(2)}=\dfrac{-1\pm\sqrt{17}}{4}$

The solution set is $\left\{\dfrac{-1-\sqrt{17}}{4},\ \dfrac{-1+\sqrt{17}}{4}\right\}.$

78. $3x^2-2x-1=0$

$(3x+1)(x-1)=0$

$x=-\dfrac{1}{3}$ or $x=1$

The solution set is $\left\{-\dfrac{1}{3},\ 1\right\}.$

79. $x^2+3=x$

$x^2-x+3=0$

$a=1,\,b=-1,\,c=3,$

$b^2-4ac=(-1)^2-4(1)(3)=1-12=-11$

$x=\dfrac{-(-1)\pm\sqrt{-11}}{2(1)}=\dfrac{1\pm\sqrt{11}\,i}{2}=\dfrac{1}{2}\pm\dfrac{\sqrt{11}}{2}i$

The solution set is $\left\{\dfrac{1}{2}-\dfrac{\sqrt{11}}{2}i,\ \dfrac{1}{2}+\dfrac{\sqrt{11}}{2}i\right\}.$

80. $2x^2+1=2x$

$2x^2-2x+1=0$

$a=2,\,b=-2,\,c=1,$

$b^2-4ac=(-2)^2-4(2)(1)=4-8=-4$

$x=\dfrac{-(-2)\pm\sqrt{-4}}{2(2)}=\dfrac{2\pm2i}{4}=\dfrac{1}{2}\pm\dfrac{1}{2}i$

The solution set is $\left\{\dfrac{1}{2}-\dfrac{1}{2}i,\ \dfrac{1}{2}+\dfrac{1}{2}i\right\}.$

81. $x(1-x) = 6$

$-x^2 + x - 6 = 0$

$a = -1, b = 1, c = -6,$

$b^2 - 4ac = 1^2 - 4(-1)(-6) = 1 - 24 = -23$

$x = \dfrac{-1 \pm \sqrt{-23}}{2(-1)} = \dfrac{-1 \pm \sqrt{23}\, i}{-2} = \dfrac{1}{2} \pm \dfrac{\sqrt{23}}{2} i$

The solution set is $\left\{ \dfrac{1}{2} - \dfrac{\sqrt{23}}{2} i, \ \dfrac{1}{2} + \dfrac{\sqrt{23}}{2} i \right\}$.

82. $x(1+x) = 2$

$x^2 + x - 2 = 0$

$(x+2)(x-1) = 0$

$x = -2$ or $x = 1$

The solution set is $\{-2, 1\}$.

83. $p = 2l + 2w$

84. $c = 50,000 + 95x$

85. $I = P \cdot r \cdot t$

$I = (9000)(0.07)(1) = \$630$

86. Let x represent the amount of money invested in bonds. Then $70,000 - x$ represents the amount of money invested in CD's.

Since the total interest is to be $5000, we have:

$0.08x + 0.05(70,000 - x) = 5000$

$(100 \quad (8x + 0.05(70,000 - x)) = (5000)(100)$

$8x + 350,000 - 5x = 500,000$

$3x + 350,000 = 500,000$

$3x = 150,000$

$x = 50,000$

$50,000 should be invested in bonds at 8% and $20,000 should be invested in CD's at 5%.

87. Using $s = vt$, we have $t = 3$ and $v = 1100$.

Finding the distance s in feet:

$s = 1100(3) = 3300$

The storm is 3300 feet away.

88. $1600 \le I \le 3600$

$1600 \le \dfrac{900}{x^2} \le 3600$

$\dfrac{1}{1600} \ge \dfrac{x^2}{900} \ge \dfrac{1}{3600}$

$\dfrac{9}{16} \ge x^2 \ge \dfrac{1}{4}$

$\dfrac{3}{4} \ge x \ge \dfrac{1}{2}$

The range of distances is from 0.5 meters to 0.75 meters, inclusive.

89. Let s represent the distance the plane can travel.

	With wind	Against wind
Rate	$250 + 30 = 280$	$250 - 30 = 220$
Time	$\dfrac{(s/2)}{280}$	$\dfrac{(s/2)}{220}$
Dist.	$\dfrac{s}{2}$	$\dfrac{s}{2}$

Since the total time is at most 5 hours, we have:

$\dfrac{(s/2)}{280} + \dfrac{(s/2)}{220} \le 5$

$\dfrac{s}{560} + \dfrac{s}{440} \le 5$

$11s + 14s \le 5(6160)$

$25s \le 30,800$

$s \le 1232$

The plane can travel at most 1232 miles or 616 miles one way and return 616 miles.

90. Let s represent the distance the plane can travel.

	With wind	Against wind
Rate	$250 + 30 = 280$	$250 - 30 = 220$
Time	$\dfrac{(s/2)}{280}$	$\dfrac{(s/2)}{220}$
Dist.	$\dfrac{s}{2}$	$\dfrac{s}{2}$

Since the total time is at most 7 hours, we have:

$\dfrac{(s/2)}{280} + \dfrac{(s/2)}{220} \le 7$

$\dfrac{s}{560} + \dfrac{s}{440} \le 7$

$11s + 14s \le 7(6160)$

$25s \le 43,120$

$s \le 1724.8$

The plane can travel at most 1724.8 miles or 862.4 miles one way. This is 246.4 miles farther than in Problem 89.

91. Let t represent the time it takes the helicopter to reach the raft.

	Raft	Helicopter
Rate	5	90
Time	t	t
Dist.	$5t$	$90t$

Since the total distance is 150 miles, we have:
$5t + 90t = 150$

$\qquad 95t = 150$

$\qquad\qquad t \approx 1.58$ hours $\approx$ 1 hour and 35 minutes

The helicopter will reach the raft in about 1 hour and 35 minutes.

92. Let d represent the distance flown by the bee traveling at 3 meters per second.

$\dfrac{d}{3} = \dfrac{150 - d}{5}$ (Times needed to meet are equal.)

$5d = 450 - 3d$

$8d = 450$

$d = 56.25$ meters

$t = \dfrac{56.25}{3} = 18.75$ seconds

The bees meet for the first time after 18.75 seconds.

The bees will meet a second time on the second lap. The first bee will have traveled $150 + x$ meters and the second bee will have traveled $150 + (150 - x)$ meters.
Solving for time, we have:

$\dfrac{150 + x}{3} = \dfrac{150 + (150 - x)}{5}$

$\dfrac{150 + x}{3} = \dfrac{300 - x}{5}$

$750 + 5x = 900 - 3x$

$\qquad 8x = 150$

$\qquad\quad x = 18.75$ meters into the second lap

$\qquad t = \dfrac{168.75}{3} = 56.25$ seconds

The bees meet the second time after 56.25 seconds, or 37.5 seconds after their first meeting.

93. Let r represent the rate of the Metra train in miles per hour.

	Metra Train	Amtrak Train
Rate	r	$r + 50$
Time	3	1
Dist.	$3r$	$r + 50$

The Amtrak Train has traveled 10 fewer miles than the Metra Train.
$r + 50 = 3r - 10$

$\quad 60 = 2r$

$\quad\ \ r = 30$

The Metra Train is traveling at 30 mph, and the Amtrak Train is traveling at $30 + 50 = 80$ mph.

94. Given that $s = 1280 - 32t - 16t^2$,

a. The object hits the ground when $s = 0$.
$$0 = 1280 - 32t - 16t^2$$
$$t^2 + 2t - 80 = 0$$
$$(t + 10)(t - 8) = 0$$
$$t = -10, t = 8$$
The object hits the ground after 8 seconds.

b. After 4 seconds, the object's height is
$s = 1280 - 32(4) - 16(4)^2 = 896$ feet.

95. Let t represent the time it takes Clarissa to complete the job by herself.

	Clarissa	Shawna
Time to do job alone	t	$t + 5$
Part of job done in 1 day	$\dfrac{1}{t}$	$\dfrac{1}{t + 5}$
Time on job (days)	6	6
Part of job done by each person	$\dfrac{6}{t}$	$\dfrac{6}{t + 5}$

Since the two people paint one house, we have:

$\dfrac{6}{t} + \dfrac{6}{t + 5} = 1$

$6(t + 5) + 6t = t(t + 5)$

$6t + 30 + 6t = t^2 + 5t$

$t^2 - 7t - 30 = 0$

$(t - 10)(t + 3) = 0$

$t = 10$ or $t = -3$

It takes Clarissa 10 days to paint the house when working by herself.

96. Let t represent the time it takes the smaller pump to empty the tank.

	Small Pump	Large Pump
Time to do job alone	t	$t-4$
Part of job done in 1 hr	$\dfrac{1}{t}$	$\dfrac{1}{t-4}$
Time on job (hrs)	5	5
Part of job done by each pump	$\dfrac{5}{t}$	$\dfrac{5}{t-4}$

Since the two pumps empty one tank, we have:

$$\frac{5}{t}+\frac{5}{t-4}=1$$

$$5(t-4)+5t=t(t-4)$$

$$5t-20+5t=t^2-4t$$

$$t^2-14t+20=0$$

We can solve this equation for t by using the quadratic formula:

$$t=\frac{-(-14)\pm\sqrt{(-14)^2-4(1)(20)}}{2(1)}$$

$$=\frac{14\pm\sqrt{116}}{2}=\frac{14\pm2\sqrt{29}}{2}$$

$$=7\pm\sqrt{29}\approx7+5.385$$

$t=12.385$ or $t=1.615$ (not feasible)

It takes the small pump approximately 12.385 hours (12 hr 23 min) to empty the tank.

97. Let x represent the amount of water added.

% salt	Tot. amt.	amt. of salt
10%	64	$(0.10)(64)$
0%	x	$(0.00)(x)$
2%	$64+x$	$(0.02)(64+x)$

$$(0.10)(64)+(0.00)(x)=(0.02)(64+x)$$

$$6.4=1.28+0.02x$$

$$5.12=0.02x$$

$$x=256$$

256 ounces of water must be added.

98. Let x represent the amount of water evaporated.

% salt	Tot. amt.	amt. of salt
2%	64	$(0.02)(64)$
0%	x	$(0.00)(x)$
10%	$64-x$	$(0.10)(64-x)$

$$(0.02)(64)-(0.00)(x)=(0.10)(64-x)$$

$$1.28=6.4-0.10x$$

$$0.10x=5.12$$

$$x=51.2$$

51.2 ounces of water must be evaporated.

99. Let the length of leg $1=x$.
Then the length of leg $2=17-x$.
By the Pythagorean Theorem we have

$$x^2+(17-x)^2=(13)^2$$

$$x^2+x^2-34x+289=169$$

$$2x^2-34x+120=0$$

$$x^2-17x+60=0$$

$$(x-12)(x-5)=0$$

$$x=12\quad\text{or}\quad x=5$$

The legs are 5 centimeters and 12 centimeters long.

100. Consider the diagram

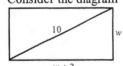

By the Pythagorean Theorem we have

$$w^2+(w+2)^2=(10)^2$$

$$w^2+w^2+4w+4=100$$

$$2w^2+4w-96=0$$

$$w^2+2w-48=0$$

$$(w+8)(w-6)=0$$

$$w=-8\quad\text{or}\quad w=6$$

The width is 6 inches and the length is $6+2=8$ inches.

101. Let x represent the amount of the 15% solution added.

% acid	tot. amt.	amt. of acid
40%	60	$(0.40)(60)$
15%	x	$(0.15)(x)$
25%	$60+x$	$(0.25)(60+x)$

$$(0.40)(60)+(0.15)(x)=(0.25)(60+x)$$

$$24+0.15x=15+0.25x$$

$$9=0.1x$$

$$x=90$$

90 cubic centimeters of the 15% solution must be added, producing 150 cubic centimeters of the 25% solution.

102. a. Consider the following diagram:

$$4(s+6) = 50$$
$$4s + 24 = 50$$
$$4s = 26$$
$$s = 6.5$$

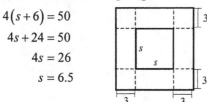

The painting is 6.5 inches by 6.5 inches.
$s + 6 = 12.5$, so the frame is 12.5 inches by 12.5 inches.

b. Consider the following diagram:

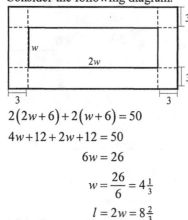

$$2(2w+6) + 2(w+6) = 50$$
$$4w + 12 + 2w + 12 = 50$$
$$6w = 26$$
$$w = \frac{26}{6} = 4\frac{1}{3}$$
$$l = 2w = 8\frac{2}{3}$$

The painting is $8\frac{2}{3}$ inches by $4\frac{1}{3}$ inches.

The frame is $14\frac{2}{3}$ inches by $10\frac{1}{3}$ inches.

103. Let t represent the time it takes the smaller pump to finish filling the tank.

	3hp Pump	8hp Pump
Time to do job alone	12	8
Part of job done in 1 hr	$\frac{1}{12}$	$\frac{1}{8}$
Time on job (hrs)	$t+4$	4
Part of job done by each pump	$\frac{t+4}{12}$	$\frac{4}{8}$

Since the two pumps fill one tank, we have:

$$\frac{t+4}{12} + \frac{4}{8} = 1$$
$$\frac{t+4}{12} = \frac{1}{2}$$
$$t + 4 = 6$$
$$t = 2$$

It takes the small pump a total of 2 more hours to fill the tank.

104. Let $w = 4$. Solve for the length:

$$l^2 = 4(l+4)$$
$$l^2 = 4l + 16$$
$$l^2 - 4l - 16 = 0$$
$$l = \frac{-(-4) + \sqrt{(-4)^2 - 4(1)(-16)}}{2(1)} = \frac{4 + \sqrt{80}}{2}$$
$$= 2 + 2\sqrt{5} \approx 6.47$$

The length of the plasterboard should be cut to a length of approximately 6.47 feet.

105. Let x represent the amount Scott receives. Then $\frac{3}{4}x$ represents the amount Alice receives and $\frac{1}{2}x$ represents the amount Tricia receives. The total amount is \$900,000, so we have:

$$x + \frac{3}{4}x + \frac{1}{2}x = 900,000$$
$$4\left(x + \frac{3}{4}x + \frac{1}{2}x\right) = 4(900,000)$$
$$4x + 3x + 2x = 3,600,000$$
$$9x = 3,600,000$$
$$x = 400,000$$

So, $\frac{3}{4}x = \frac{3}{4}(400,000) = 300,000$ and

$\frac{1}{2}x = \frac{1}{2}(400,000) = 200,000$.

Scott receives \$400,000, Alice receives \$300,000, and Tricia receives \$200,000.

106. Let x represent the number of passengers over 20. Then $20 + x$ represents the total number of passengers, and $15 - 0.1x$ represents the fare for each passenger. Solving the equation for total cost, \$482.40, we have:

$$(20 + x)(15 - 0.1x) = 482.40$$
$$300 + 13x - 0.1x^2 = 482.40$$
$$-0.1x^2 + 13x - 182.40 = 0$$
$$x^2 - 130x + 1824 = 0$$
$$(x - 114)(x - 16) = 0$$
$$x = 114 \text{ or } x = 16$$

Since the capacity of the bus is 44, we discard the 114. Therefore, $20 + 16 = 36$ people went on the trip; each person paid $15 - 0.1(16) = \$13.40$.

107. Let t represent the time it takes the older machine to complete the job by itself.

	Old copier	New copier
Time to do job alone	t	$t-1$
Part of job done in 1 hr	$\dfrac{1}{t}$	$\dfrac{1}{t-1}$
Time on job (hrs)	1.2	1.2
Part of job done by each copier	$\dfrac{1.2}{t}$	$\dfrac{1.2}{t-1}$

Since the two copiers complete one job, we have:

$$\frac{1.2}{t}+\frac{1.2}{t-1}=1$$
$$1.2(t-1)+1.2t=t(t-1)$$
$$1.2t-1.2+1.2t=t^2-t$$
$$t^2-3.4t+1.2=0$$
$$5t^2-17t+6=0$$
$$(5t-2)(t-3)=0$$
$$t=0.4 \quad\text{or}\quad t=3$$

It takes the old copier 3 hours to do the job by itself. (0.4 hour is impossible since together it takes 1.2 hours.)

108. Let r_S represent Scott's rate and let r_T represent Todd's rate. The time for Scott to run 95 meters is the same as for Todd to run 100 meters.

$$\frac{95}{r_S}=\frac{100}{r_T}$$
$$r_S=0.95r_T$$
$$d_S=t\cdot r_s=t\left(0.95r_T\right)=0.95d_T$$

If Todd starts from 5 meters behind the start:
$$d_T=105$$
$$d_S=0.95d_T=0.95(105)=99.75$$

   a. The race does not end in a tie.

   b. Todd wins the race.

   c. Todd wins by 0.25 meters.

   d. To end in a tie:
   $$100=0.95(100+x)$$
   $$100=95+0.95x$$
   $$5=0.95x$$
   $$x\approx 5.26 \text{ meters}$$

   e. $95=0.95(100)$ Therefore, the race ends in a tie.

109. The effective speed of the train (i.e., relative to the man) is $30-4=26$ miles per hour. The time is 5 sec $=\dfrac{5}{60}$ min $=\dfrac{5}{3600}$ hr $=\dfrac{1}{720}$ hr.

$$s=vt$$
$$=26\left(\frac{1}{720}\right)$$
$$=\frac{26}{720} \text{ miles}$$
$$=\frac{26}{720}\cdot 5280\approx 190.67 \text{ feet}$$

The freight train is about 190.67 feet long.

Chapter 1 Test

1.
$$\frac{2x}{3}-\frac{x}{2}=\frac{5}{12}$$
$$12\left(\frac{2x}{3}-\frac{x}{2}\right)=12\left(\frac{5}{12}\right)$$
$$8x-6x=5$$
$$2x=5$$
$$x=\frac{5}{2}$$

The solution set is $\left\{\dfrac{5}{2}\right\}$.

2.
$$x(x-1)=6$$
$$x^2-x=6$$
$$x^2-x-6=0$$
$$(x-3)(x+2)=0$$
$$x-3=0 \quad\text{or}\quad x+2=0$$
$$x=3 \quad\text{or}\qquad x=-2$$

The solution set is $\{-2, 3\}$.

3.
$$x^4-3x^2-4=0$$
$$\left(x^2-4\right)\left(x^2+1\right)=0$$
$$x^2-4=0 \quad\text{or}\quad x^2+1=0$$
$$x^2=4 \quad\text{or}\qquad x^2=-1$$
$$x=\pm 2 \quad\text{or}\qquad \text{Not real}$$

The solution set is $\{-2, 2\}$.

4. $\sqrt{2x-5}+2=4$

$\sqrt{2x-5}=2$

$\left(\sqrt{2x-5}\right)^2=(2)^2$

$2x-5=4$

$2x=9$

$x=\dfrac{9}{2}$

Check: $\sqrt{2\left(\dfrac{9}{2}\right)-5}+2=4$

$\sqrt{9-5}+2=4$

$\sqrt{4}+2=4$

$2+2=4$

$4=4$

The solution set is $\left\{\dfrac{9}{2}\right\}$.

5. $|2x-3|+7=10$

$|2x-3|=3$

$2x-3=3$ or $2x-3=-3$

$2x=6$ or $2x=0$

$x=3$ or $x=0$

The solutions set is $\{0,3\}$.

6. $3x^3+2x^2-12x-8=0$

$x^2(3x+2)-4(3x+2)=0$

$\left(x^2-4\right)(3x+2)=0$

$(x+2)(x-2)(3x+2)=0$

$x+2=0$ or $x-2=0$ or $3x+2=0$

$x=-2$ or $x=2$ or $x=-\dfrac{2}{3}$

The solution set is $\left\{-2,-\dfrac{2}{3},2\right\}$.

7. $3x^2-x+1=0$

$x=\dfrac{-(-1)\pm\sqrt{(-1)^2-4(3)(1)}}{2(3)}$

$=\dfrac{1\pm\sqrt{-11}}{6}$ (Not real)

This equation has no real solutions.

8. $-3\le\dfrac{3x-4}{2}\le6$

$2(-3)\le2\left(\dfrac{3x-4}{2}\right)\le2(6)$

$-6\le3x-4\le12$

$-2\le3x\le16$

$-\dfrac{2}{3}\le x\le\dfrac{16}{3}$

$\left\{x\left|-\dfrac{2}{3}\le x\le\dfrac{16}{3}\right.\right\}$ or $\left[-\dfrac{2}{3},\dfrac{16}{3}\right]$

9. $|3x+4|<8$

$-8<3x+4<8$

$-12<3x<4$

$-4<x<\dfrac{4}{3}$

$\left\{x\left|-4<x<\dfrac{4}{3}\right.\right\}$ or $\left(-4,\dfrac{4}{3}\right)$

10. $2+|2x-5|\ge9$

$|2x-5|\ge7$

$2x-5\le-7$ or $2x-5\ge7$

$2x\le-2$ or $2x\ge12$

$x\le-1$ or $x\ge6$

$\{x|x\le-1 \text{ or } x\ge6\}$ or $(-\infty,-1]\cup[6,\infty)$.

11. $\dfrac{-2}{3-i}=\dfrac{-2}{3-i}\cdot\dfrac{3+i}{3+i}=\dfrac{-6-2i}{9+3i-3i-i^2}=\dfrac{-6-2i}{9-(-1)}$

$=\dfrac{-6-2i}{10}=\dfrac{-3-i}{5}=-\dfrac{3}{5}-\dfrac{1}{5}i$

12. $4x^2-4x+5=0$

$x=\dfrac{-(-4)\pm\sqrt{(-4)^2-4(4)(5)}}{2(4)}$

$=\dfrac{4\pm\sqrt{-64}}{8}=\dfrac{4\pm8i}{8}=\dfrac{1}{2}\pm i$

This solution set is $\left\{\dfrac{1}{2}-i,\dfrac{1}{2}+i\right\}$.

13. Let x represent the amount of the $8-per-pound coffee.

Amt. of coffee (pounds)	Price ($)	Total $
20	4	$(20)(4)$
x	8	$(8)(x)$
$20 + x$	5	$(5)(20 + x)$

$$80 + 8x = (5)(20 + x)$$
$$80 + 8x = 100 + 5x$$
$$3x = 20$$
$$x = \frac{20}{3} = 6\frac{2}{3}$$

Add $6\frac{2}{3}$ pounds of $8/lb coffee to get $26\frac{2}{3}$ pounds of $5/lb coffee.

Chapter 1 Projects

Project I

$$P = L\left[\frac{\frac{r}{12}}{1 - \left(1 + \frac{r}{12}\right)^{-t}}\right]$$

P = monthly payment, L = loan amount, r = annual rate of interest, expressed as a decimal, t = length of loan, in months

1. a. $P = 200000\left[\dfrac{\frac{0.0658}{12}}{1 - \left(1 + \frac{0.0658}{12}\right)^{-360}}\right] \approx \$1274.68$

b. $P = 200000\left[\dfrac{\frac{0.0617}{12}}{1 - \left(1 + \frac{0.0617}{12}\right)^{-180}}\right] \approx \$1706.14$

2. Total paid $= (\text{Life of loan})(\text{Monthly payment})$

a. Total amount paid $= (360)(1274.68)$
$= \$458,884.80$

b. Total amount paid $= (180)(1706.14)$
$= \$307,105.20$

3. Interest $=$ Total paid $-$ original loan amount

a. Interest paid $= 458,884.80 - 200,000$
$= \$258,884.80$

b. Interest paid $= 307,105.20 - 200,000$
$= \$107,105.20$

4. a. $P = 200000\left[\dfrac{\frac{0.0659}{12}}{1 - \left(1 + \frac{0.0659}{12}\right)^{-360}}\right] \approx \$1276.00$

b. $P = 200000\left[\dfrac{\frac{0.0622}{12}}{1 - \left(1 + \frac{0.0622}{12}\right)^{-180}}\right] \approx \$1711.58$

5. Total paid $= (\text{Life of loan})(\text{Monthly payment})$

a. Total paid $= (360)(1276.00)$
$= \$459,360.00$

b. Total paid $= (180)(1711.58)$
$= \$308,084.40$

6. Interest $=$ Total paid $-$ original loan

a. Interest $= 459,360.00 - 200,000$
$= \$259,360.00$

b. Interest $= 308,084.40 - 200,000$
$= \$108,084.40$

7. $P = L\left[\dfrac{\frac{r}{12}}{1 - \left(1 + \frac{r}{12}\right)^{-t}}\right]$

$$L = \frac{P}{\left[\dfrac{\frac{r}{12}}{1 - \left(1 + \frac{r}{12}\right)^{-t}}\right]} = P\left[\dfrac{1 - \left(1 + \frac{r}{12}\right)^{-t}}{\frac{r}{12}}\right]$$

157

8. $L = P\left[\dfrac{1-\left(1+\dfrac{r}{12}\right)^{-t}}{\dfrac{r}{12}}\right]$

   a. $L = 1000\left[\dfrac{1-\left(1+\dfrac{0.0659}{12}\right)^{-360}}{\dfrac{0.0659}{12}}\right] \approx \$156,740.19$

   b. $L = 1000\left[\dfrac{1-\left(1+\dfrac{0.0622}{12}\right)^{-180}}{\dfrac{0.0622}{12}}\right] \approx \$116,851.28$

9. $L = P\left[\dfrac{1-\left(1+\dfrac{r}{12}\right)^{-t}}{\dfrac{r}{12}}\right]$

   a. $L = 1000\left[\dfrac{1-\left(1+\dfrac{0.0658}{12}\right)^{-360}}{\dfrac{0.0658}{12}}\right] \approx \$156,902.52$

   b. $L = 1000\left[\dfrac{1-\left(1+\dfrac{0.0617}{12}\right)^{-180}}{\dfrac{0.0617}{12}}\right] \approx \$117,223.84$

10. Answers will vary.

11. Answers will vary. (Use $P = \$1300$ and the interest rates you obtained for problem 10.)

12. Answers will vary.

13. Answers will vary.

Project II

1. $T = \dfrac{n}{Cnp + L + M}$, $n = 3$, $L = 5$, $M = 1$, $C = 0.2$

$T = \dfrac{3}{0.2(3)p+5+1} = \dfrac{3}{0.6p+6} = \dfrac{1}{0.2p+2}$

2. All of the times given in problem 1 were in seconds, so $T = 0.1$ board per second needs to used as the value for T in the equation found in problem 1.

$0.1 = \dfrac{1}{0.2p+2}$

$(0.2p+2)(0.1) = 1$

$0.02p + 0.2 = 1$

$0.02p = 0.8$

$p = 40$ parts per board

3. $T = 0.15$ board per second

$0.15 = \dfrac{1}{0.2p+2}$

$(0.2p+2)(0.15) = 1$

$0.03p + 0.3 = 1$

$0.03p = 0.7$

$p \approx 23.3$ parts per board

Thus, only 23 parts per board will work.

For problems 4 – 6, C is requested, so solve for C first:

$T = \dfrac{n}{Cnp + L + M}$

$(Cnp + L + M)T = n$

$CnpT + LT + MT = n$

$CnpT = n - LT - MT$

$C = \dfrac{n - LT - MT}{npT}$

4. $T = 0.06$, $n = 3$, $p = 100$, $M = 1$, $L = 5$

$C = \dfrac{3-5(0.06)-1(0.06)}{3(100)(0.06)} \approx 0.147$ sec

5. $T = 0.06$, $n = 3$, $p = 150$, $M = 1$, $L = 5$

$C = \dfrac{3-5(0.06)-1(0.06)}{3(150)(0.06)} \approx 0.098$ sec

6. $T = 0.06$, $n = 3$, $p = 200$, $M = 1$, $L = 5$

$C = \dfrac{3-5(0.06)-1(0.06)}{3(200)(0.06)} \approx 0.073$ sec

7. As the number of parts per board increases, the tact time decreases, if all the other factors remain constant.

Chapter 2
Graphs

Section 2.1

1. 0

2. $|5 - (-3)| = |8| = 8$

3. $\sqrt{3^2 + 4^2} = \sqrt{25} = 5$

4. $11^2 + 60^2 = 121 + 3600 = 3721 = 61^2$
   Since the sum of the squares of two of the sides of the triangle equals the square of the third side, the triangle is a right triangle.

5. abscissa (or x-coordinate); ordinate (or y-coordinate)

6. quadrants

7. midpoint

8. False; the distance between two points is never negative.

9. False; points that lie in Quadrant IV will have a positive x-coordinate and a negative y-coordinate. The point $(-1, 4)$ lies in Quadrant II.

10. True; $M = \left(\dfrac{x_1 + x_2}{2}, \dfrac{y_1 + y_2}{2} \right)$

11. (a) Quadrant II
    (b) x-axis
    (c) Quadrant III
    (d) Quadrant I
    (e) y-axis
    (f) Quadrant IV

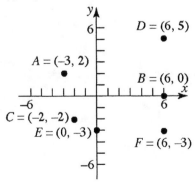

12. (a) Quadrant I
    (b) Quadrant III
    (c) Quadrant II
    (d) Quadrant I
    (e) y-axis
    (f) x-axis

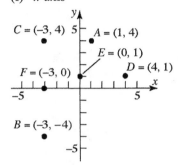

13. The points will be on a vertical line that is two units to the right of the y-axis.

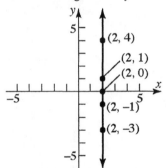

14. The points will be on a horizontal line that is three units above the x-axis.

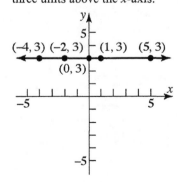

15. $d(P_1, P_2) = \sqrt{(2-0)^2 + (1-0)^2}$
    $= \sqrt{2^2 + 1^2} = \sqrt{4+1} = \sqrt{5}$

16. $d(P_1, P_2) = \sqrt{(-2-0)^2 + (1-0)^2}$
$= \sqrt{(-2)^2 + 1^2} = \sqrt{4+1} = \sqrt{5}$

17. $d(P_1, P_2) = \sqrt{(-2-1)^2 + (2-1)^2}$
$= \sqrt{(-3)^2 + 1^2} = \sqrt{9+1} = \sqrt{10}$

18. $d(P_1, P_2) = \sqrt{(2-(-1))^2 + (2-1)^2}$
$= \sqrt{3^2 + 1^2} = \sqrt{9+1} = \sqrt{10}$

19. $d(P_1, P_2) = \sqrt{(5-3)^2 + (4-(-4))^2}$
$= \sqrt{2^2 + (8)^2} = \sqrt{4+64} = \sqrt{68} = 2\sqrt{17}$

20. $d(P_1, P_2) = \sqrt{(2-(-1))^2 + (4-0)^2}$
$= \sqrt{(3)^2 + 4^2} = \sqrt{9+16} = \sqrt{25} = 5$

21. $d(P_1, P_2) = \sqrt{(6-(-3))^2 + (0-2)^2}$
$= \sqrt{9^2 + (-2)^2} = \sqrt{81+4} = \sqrt{85}$

22. $d(P_1, P_2) = \sqrt{(4-2)^2 + (2-(-3))^2}$
$= \sqrt{2^2 + 5^2} = \sqrt{4+25} = \sqrt{29}$

23. $d(P_1, P_2) = \sqrt{(6-4)^2 + (4-(-3))^2}$
$= \sqrt{2^2 + 7^2} = \sqrt{4+49} = \sqrt{53}$

24. $d(P_1, P_2) = \sqrt{(6-(-4))^2 + (2-(-3))^2}$
$= \sqrt{10^2 + 5^2} = \sqrt{100+25}$
$= \sqrt{125} = 5\sqrt{5}$

25. $d(P_1, P_2) = \sqrt{(2.3-(-0.2))^2 + (1.1-0.3)^2}$
$= \sqrt{(2.5)^2 + (0.8)^2} = \sqrt{6.25+0.64}$
$= \sqrt{6.89} \approx 2.62$

26. $d(P_1, P_2) = \sqrt{(-0.3-1.2)^2 + (1.1-2.3)^2}$
$= \sqrt{(-1.5)^2 + (-1.2)^2} = \sqrt{2.25+1.44}$
$= \sqrt{3.69} \approx 1.92$

27. $d(P_1, P_2) = \sqrt{(0-a)^2 + (0-b)^2}$
$= \sqrt{(-a)^2 + (-b)^2} = \sqrt{a^2 + b^2}$

28. $d(P_1, P_2) = \sqrt{(0-a)^2 + (0-a)^2}$
$= \sqrt{(-a)^2 + (-a)^2}$
$= \sqrt{a^2 + a^2} = \sqrt{2a^2} = |a|\sqrt{2}$

29. $A = (-2,5), \ B = (1,3), \ C = (-1,0)$
$d(A,B) = \sqrt{(1-(-2))^2 + (3-5)^2}$
$= \sqrt{3^2 + (-2)^2} = \sqrt{9+4} = \sqrt{13}$
$d(B,C) = \sqrt{(-1-1)^2 + (0-3)^2}$
$= \sqrt{(-2)^2 + (-3)^2} = \sqrt{4+9} = \sqrt{13}$
$d(A,C) = \sqrt{(-1-(-2))^2 + (0-5)^2}$
$= \sqrt{1^2 + (-5)^2} = \sqrt{1+25} = \sqrt{26}$

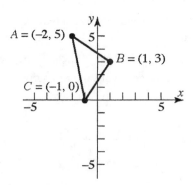

Verifying that $\triangle$ ABC is a right triangle by the Pythagorean Theorem:
$$[d(A,B)]^2 + [d(B,C)]^2 = [d(A,C)]^2$$
$$\left(\sqrt{13}\right)^2 + \left(\sqrt{13}\right)^2 = \left(\sqrt{26}\right)^2$$
$$13 + 13 = 26$$
$$26 = 26$$

The area of a triangle is $A = \frac{1}{2} \cdot bh$. In this problem,
$$A = \frac{1}{2} \cdot [d(A,B)] \cdot [d(B,C)]$$
$$= \frac{1}{2} \cdot \sqrt{13} \cdot \sqrt{13} = \frac{1}{2} \cdot 13$$
$$= \frac{13}{2} \text{ square units}$$

30. $A = (-2, 5)$, $B = (12, 3)$, $C = (10, -11)$

$d(A,B) = \sqrt{(12-(-2))^2 + (3-5)^2}$

$\qquad = \sqrt{14^2 + (-2)^2}$

$\qquad = \sqrt{196+4} = \sqrt{200}$

$\qquad = 10\sqrt{2}$

$d(B,C) = \sqrt{(10-12)^2 + (-11-3)^2}$

$\qquad = \sqrt{(-2)^2 + (-14)^2}$

$\qquad = \sqrt{4+196} = \sqrt{200}$

$\qquad = 10\sqrt{2}$

$d(A,C) = \sqrt{(10-(-2))^2 + (-11-5)^2}$

$\qquad = \sqrt{12^2 + (-16)^2}$

$\qquad = \sqrt{144+256} = \sqrt{400}$

$\qquad = 20$

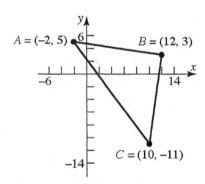

Verifying that $\triangle ABC$ is a right triangle by the Pythagorean Theorem:

$[d(A,B)]^2 + [d(B,C)]^2 = [d(A,C)]^2$

$\left(10\sqrt{2}\right)^2 + \left(10\sqrt{2}\right)^2 = (20)^2$

$\qquad 200 + 200 = 400$

$\qquad 400 = 400$

The area of a triangle is $A = \dfrac{1}{2}bh$. In this problem,

$A = \dfrac{1}{2} \cdot [d(A,B)] \cdot [d(B,C)]$

$\quad = \dfrac{1}{2} \cdot 10\sqrt{2} \cdot 10\sqrt{2}$

$\quad = \dfrac{1}{2} \cdot 100 \cdot 2$

$\quad = 100$ square units

31. $A = (-5, 3)$, $B = (6, 0)$, $C = (5, 5)$

$d(A,B) = \sqrt{(6-(-5))^2 + (0-3)^2}$

$\qquad = \sqrt{11^2 + (-3)^2} = \sqrt{121+9}$

$\qquad = \sqrt{130}$

$d(B,C) = \sqrt{(5-6)^2 + (5-0)^2}$

$\qquad = \sqrt{(-1)^2 + 5^2} = \sqrt{1+25}$

$\qquad = \sqrt{26}$

$d(A,C) = \sqrt{(5-(-5))^2 + (5-3)^2}$

$\qquad = \sqrt{10^2 + 2^2} = \sqrt{100+4}$

$\qquad = \sqrt{104}$

$\qquad = 2\sqrt{26}$

Verifying that $\triangle ABC$ is a right triangle by the Pythagorean Theorem:

$[d(A,C)]^2 + [d(B,C)]^2 = [d(A,B)]^2$

$\left(\sqrt{104}\right)^2 + \left(\sqrt{26}\right)^2 = \left(\sqrt{130}\right)^2$

$\qquad 104 + 26 = 130$

$\qquad 130 = 130$

The area of a triangle is $A = \dfrac{1}{2}bh$. In this problem,

$A = \dfrac{1}{2} \cdot [d(A,C)] \cdot [d(B,C)]$

$\quad = \dfrac{1}{2} \cdot \sqrt{104} \cdot \sqrt{26}$

$\quad = \dfrac{1}{2} \cdot 2\sqrt{26} \cdot \sqrt{26}$

$\quad = \dfrac{1}{2} \cdot 2 \cdot 26$

$\quad = 26$ square units

161

32. $A = (-6, 3),\ B = (3, -5),\ C = (-1, 5)$

$d(A,B) = \sqrt{(3-(-6))^2 + (-5-3)^2}$

$= \sqrt{9^2 + (-8)^2} = \sqrt{81+64}$

$= \sqrt{145}$

$d(B,C) = \sqrt{(-1-3)^2 + (5-(-5))^2}$

$= \sqrt{(-4)^2 + 10^2} = \sqrt{16+100}$

$= \sqrt{116} = 2\sqrt{29}$

$d(A,C) = \sqrt{(-1-(-6))^2 + (5-3)^2}$

$= \sqrt{5^2 + 2^2} = \sqrt{25+4}$

$= \sqrt{29}$

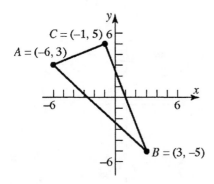

Verifying that $\triangle$ ABC is a right triangle by the Pythagorean Theorem:

$[d(A,C)]^2 + [d(B,C)]^2 = [d(A,B)]^2$

$\left(\sqrt{29}\right)^2 + \left(2\sqrt{29}\right)^2 = \left(\sqrt{145}\right)^2$

$29 + 4 \cdot 29 = 145$

$29 + 116 = 145$

$145 = 145$

The area of a triangle is $A = \dfrac{1}{2}bh$. In this problem,

$A = \dfrac{1}{2} \cdot [d(A,C)] \cdot [d(B,C)]$

$= \dfrac{1}{2} \cdot \sqrt{29} \cdot 2\sqrt{29}$

$= \dfrac{1}{2} \cdot 2 \cdot 29$

$= 29$ square units

33. $A = (4, -3),\ B = (0, -3),\ C = (4, 2)$

$d(A,B) = \sqrt{(0-4)^2 + (-3-(-3))^2}$

$= \sqrt{(-4)^2 + 0^2} = \sqrt{16+0}$

$= \sqrt{16}$

$= 4$

$d(B,C) = \sqrt{(4-0)^2 + (2-(-3))^2}$

$= \sqrt{4^2 + 5^2} = \sqrt{16+25}$

$= \sqrt{41}$

$d(A,C) = \sqrt{(4-4)^2 + (2-(-3))^2}$

$= \sqrt{0^2 + 5^2} = \sqrt{0+25}$

$= \sqrt{25}$

$= 5$

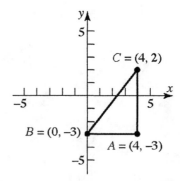

Verifying that $\triangle$ ABC is a right triangle by the Pythagorean Theorem:

$[d(A,B)]^2 + [d(A,C)]^2 = [d(B,C)]^2$

$4^2 + 5^2 = \left(\sqrt{41}\right)^2$

$16 + 25 = 41$

$41 = 41$

The area of a triangle is $A = \dfrac{1}{2}bh$. In this problem,

$A = \dfrac{1}{2} \cdot [d(A,B)] \cdot [d(A,C)]$

$= \dfrac{1}{2} \cdot 4 \cdot 5$

$= 10$ square units

34. $A = (4, -3), \quad B = (4, 1), \quad C = (2, 1)$

$$d(A, B) = \sqrt{(4-4)^2 + (1-(-3))^2}$$
$$= \sqrt{0^2 + 4^2}$$
$$= \sqrt{0 + 16}$$
$$= \sqrt{16}$$
$$= 4$$

$$d(B, C) = \sqrt{(2-4)^2 + (1-1)^2}$$
$$= \sqrt{(-2)^2 + 0^2} = \sqrt{4+0}$$
$$= \sqrt{4}$$
$$= 2$$

$$d(A, C) = \sqrt{(2-4)^2 + (1-(-3))^2}$$
$$= \sqrt{(-2)^2 + 4^2} = \sqrt{4+16}$$
$$= \sqrt{20}$$
$$= 2\sqrt{5}$$

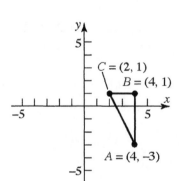

Verifying that $\triangle ABC$ is a right triangle by the Pythagorean Theorem:

$$[d(A, B)]^2 + [d(B, C)]^2 = [d(A, C)]^2$$
$$4^2 + 2^2 = (2\sqrt{5})^2$$
$$16 + 4 = 20$$
$$20 = 20$$

The area of a triangle is $A = \dfrac{1}{2} bh$. In this problem,

$$A = \frac{1}{2} \cdot [d(A, B)] \cdot [d(B, C)]$$
$$= \frac{1}{2} \cdot 4 \cdot 2$$
$$= 4 \text{ square units}$$

35. The coordinates of the midpoint are:

$$(x, y) = \left(\frac{x_1 + x_2}{2}, \frac{y_1 + y_2}{2} \right)$$
$$= \left(\frac{3+5}{2}, \frac{-4+4}{2} \right)$$
$$= \left(\frac{8}{2}, \frac{0}{2} \right)$$
$$= (4, 0)$$

36. The coordinates of the midpoint are:

$$(x, y) = \left(\frac{x_1 + x_2}{2}, \frac{y_1 + y_2}{2} \right)$$
$$= \left(\frac{-2+2}{2}, \frac{0+4}{2} \right)$$
$$= \left(\frac{0}{2}, \frac{4}{2} \right)$$
$$= (0, 2)$$

37. The coordinates of the midpoint are:

$$(x, y) = \left(\frac{x_1 + x_2}{2}, \frac{y_1 + y_2}{2} \right)$$
$$= \left(\frac{-3+6}{2}, \frac{2+0}{2} \right)$$
$$= \left(\frac{3}{2}, \frac{2}{2} \right)$$
$$= \left(\frac{3}{2}, 1 \right)$$

38. The coordinates of the midpoint are:

$$(x, y) = \left(\frac{x_1 + x_2}{2}, \frac{y_1 + y_2}{2} \right)$$
$$= \left(\frac{2+4}{2}, \frac{-3+2}{2} \right)$$
$$= \left(\frac{6}{2}, \frac{-1}{2} \right)$$
$$= \left(3, -\frac{1}{2} \right)$$

39. The coordinates of the midpoint are:

$$(x, y) = \left(\frac{x_1 + x_2}{2}, \frac{y_1 + y_2}{2} \right)$$
$$= \left(\frac{4+6}{2}, \frac{-3+1}{2} \right)$$
$$= \left(\frac{10}{2}, \frac{-2}{2} \right)$$
$$= (5, -1)$$

40. The coordinates of the midpoint are:

$$(x, y) = \left(\frac{x_1 + x_2}{2}, \frac{y_1 + y_2}{2} \right)$$

$$= \left(\frac{-4 + 2}{2}, \frac{-3 + 2}{2} \right)$$

$$= \left(\frac{-2}{2}, \frac{-1}{2} \right)$$

$$= \left(-1, -\frac{1}{2} \right)$$

41. The coordinates of the midpoint are:

$$(x, y) = \left(\frac{x_1 + x_2}{2}, \frac{y_1 + y_2}{2} \right)$$

$$= \left(\frac{-0.2 + 2.3}{2}, \frac{0.3 + 1.1}{2} \right)$$

$$= \left(\frac{2.1}{2}, \frac{1.4}{2} \right)$$

$$= (1.05, 0.7)$$

42. The coordinates of the midpoint are:

$$(x, y) = \left(\frac{x_1 + x_2}{2}, \frac{y_1 + y_2}{2} \right)$$

$$= \left(\frac{1.2 + (-0.3)}{2}, \frac{2.3 + 1.1}{2} \right)$$

$$= \left(\frac{0.9}{2}, \frac{3.4}{2} \right)$$

$$= (0.45, 1.7)$$

43. The coordinates of the midpoint are:

$$(x, y) = \left(\frac{x_1 + x_2}{2}, \frac{y_1 + y_2}{2} \right)$$

$$= \left(\frac{a + 0}{2}, \frac{b + 0}{2} \right)$$

$$= \left(\frac{a}{2}, \frac{b}{2} \right)$$

44. The coordinates of the midpoint are:

$$(x, y) = \left(\frac{x_1 + x_2}{2}, \frac{y_1 + y_2}{2} \right)$$

$$= \left(\frac{a + 0}{2}, \frac{a + 0}{2} \right)$$

$$= \left(\frac{a}{2}, \frac{a}{2} \right)$$

45. Consider points of the form $(2, y)$ that are a distance of 5 units from the point $(-2, -1)$.

$$d = \sqrt{(x_2 - x_1)^2 + (y_2 - y_1)^2}$$

$$= \sqrt{(-2 - 2)^2 + (-1 - y)^2}$$

$$= \sqrt{(-4)^2 + (-1 - y)^2}$$

$$= \sqrt{16 + 1 + 2y + y^2}$$

$$= \sqrt{y^2 + 2y + 17}$$

$$5 = \sqrt{y^2 + 2y + 17}$$

$$5^2 = \left(\sqrt{y^2 + 2y + 17} \right)^2$$

$$25 = y^2 + 2y + 17$$

$$0 = y^2 + 2y - 8$$

$$0 = (y + 4)(y - 2)$$

$$y + 4 = 0 \quad \text{or} \quad y - 2 = 0$$

$$y = -4 \qquad\qquad y = 2$$

Thus, the points $(2, -4)$ and $(2, 2)$ are a distance of 5 units from the point $(-2, -1)$.

46. Consider points of the form $(x, -3)$ that are a distance of 13 units from the point $(1, 2)$.

$$d = \sqrt{(x_2 - x_1)^2 + (y_2 - y_1)^2}$$

$$= \sqrt{(1 - x)^2 + (2 - (-3))^2}$$

$$= \sqrt{x^2 - 2x + 1 + (5)^2}$$

$$= \sqrt{x^2 - 2x + 1 + 25}$$

$$= \sqrt{x^2 - 2x + 26}$$

$$13 = \sqrt{x^2 - 2x + 26}$$

$$13^2 = \left(\sqrt{x^2 - 2x + 26} \right)^2$$

$$169 = x^2 - 2x + 26$$

$$0 = x^2 - 2x - 143$$

$$0 = (x - 13)(x + 11)$$

$$x - 13 = 0 \quad \text{or} \quad x + 11 = 0$$

$$x = 13 \qquad\qquad x = -11$$

Thus, the points $(13, -3)$ and $(-11, -3)$ are a distance of 13 units from the point $(1, 2)$.

47. Points on the x-axis have a y-coordinate of 0. Thus, we consider points of the form $(x,0)$ that are a distance of 5 units from the point $(4,-3)$.

$$d = \sqrt{(x_2 - x_1)^2 + (y_2 - y_1)^2}$$
$$= \sqrt{(4-x)^2 + (-3-0)^2}$$
$$= \sqrt{16 - 8x + x^2 + (-3)^2}$$
$$= \sqrt{16 - 8x + x^2 + 9}$$
$$= \sqrt{x^2 - 8x + 25}$$
$$5 = \sqrt{x^2 - 8x + 25}$$
$$5^2 = \left(\sqrt{x^2 - 8x + 25}\right)^2$$
$$25 = x^2 - 8x + 25$$
$$0 = x^2 - 8x$$
$$0 = x(x-8)$$
$$x = 0 \quad \text{or} \quad x - 8 = 0$$
$$x = 8$$

Thus, the points $(0,0)$ and $(8,0)$ are on the x-axis and a distance of 5 units from the point $(4,-3)$.

48. Points on the y-axis have an x-coordinate of 0. Thus, we consider points of the form $(0,y)$ that are a distance of 5 units from the point $(4,4)$.

$$d = \sqrt{(x_2 - x_1)^2 + (y_2 - y_1)^2}$$
$$= \sqrt{(4-0)^2 + (4-y)^2}$$
$$= \sqrt{4^2 + 16 - 8y + y^2}$$
$$= \sqrt{16 + 16 - 8y + y^2}$$
$$= \sqrt{y^2 - 8y + 32}$$
$$5 = \sqrt{y^2 - 8y + 32}$$
$$5^2 = \left(\sqrt{y^2 - 8y + 32}\right)^2$$
$$25 = y^2 - 8y + 32$$
$$0 = y^2 - 8y + 7$$
$$0 = (y-7)(y-1)$$
$$y - 7 = 0 \quad \text{or} \quad y - 1 = 0$$
$$y = 7 \qquad\qquad y = 1$$

Thus, the points $(0,7)$ and $(0,1)$ are on the y-axis and a distance of 5 units from the point $(4,4)$.

49. $M = (x,y) = \left(\dfrac{x_1 + x_2}{2}, \dfrac{y_1 + y_2}{2}\right)$.

$P_1 = (x_1, y_1) = (-3, 6)$ and $(x,y) = (-1,4)$, so

$$x = \frac{x_1 + x_2}{2} \quad \text{and} \quad y = \frac{y_1 + y_2}{2}$$
$$-1 = \frac{-3 + x_2}{2} \qquad\qquad 4 = \frac{6 + y_2}{2}$$
$$-2 = -3 + x_2 \qquad\qquad 8 = 6 + y_2$$
$$1 = x_2 \qquad\qquad\qquad 2 = y_2$$

Thus, $P_2 = (1, 2)$.

50. $M = (x,y) = \left(\dfrac{x_1 + x_2}{2}, \dfrac{y_1 + y_2}{2}\right)$.

$P_2 = (x_2, y_2) = (7,-2)$ and $(x,y) = (5,-4)$, so

$$x = \frac{x_1 + x_2}{2} \quad \text{and} \quad y = \frac{y_1 + y_2}{2}$$
$$5 = \frac{x_1 + 7}{2} \qquad\qquad -4 = \frac{y_1 + (-2)}{2}$$
$$10 = x_1 + 7 \qquad\qquad -8 = y_1 + (-2)$$
$$3 = x_1 \qquad\qquad\qquad -6 = y_1$$

Thus, $P_1 = (3,-6)$.

51. The midpoint of AB is: $D = \left(\dfrac{0+6}{2}, \dfrac{0+0}{2}\right)$
$$= (3, 0)$$

The midpoint of AC is: $E = \left(\dfrac{0+4}{2}, \dfrac{0+4}{2}\right)$
$$= (2, 2)$$

The midpoint of BC is: $F = \left(\dfrac{6+4}{2}, \dfrac{0+4}{2}\right)$
$$= (5, 2)$$

$$d(C,D) = \sqrt{(0-4)^2 + (3-4)^2}$$
$$= \sqrt{(-4)^2 + (-1)^2} = \sqrt{16+1} = \sqrt{17}$$
$$d(B,E) = \sqrt{(2-6)^2 + (2-0)^2}$$
$$= \sqrt{(-4)^2 + 2^2} = \sqrt{16+4}$$
$$= \sqrt{20} = 2\sqrt{5}$$
$$d(A,F) = \sqrt{(2-0)^2 + (5-0)^2}$$
$$= \sqrt{2^2 + 5^2} = \sqrt{4+25}$$
$$= \sqrt{29}$$

52. Let $P_1 = (0, 0)$, $P_2 = (0, 4)$, $P = (x, y)$

$$d(P_1, P_2) = \sqrt{(0-0)^2 + (4-0)^2}$$
$$= \sqrt{16} = 4$$

$$d(P_1, P) = \sqrt{(x-0)^2 + (y-0)^2}$$
$$= \sqrt{x^2 + y^2} = 4$$
$$\rightarrow x^2 + y^2 = 16$$

$$d(P_2, P) = \sqrt{(x-0)^2 + (y-4)^2}$$
$$= \sqrt{x^2 + (y-4)^2} = 4$$
$$\rightarrow x^2 + (y-4)^2 = 16$$

Therefore,

$$y^2 = (y-4)^2$$
$$y^2 = y^2 - 8y + 16$$
$$8y = 16$$
$$y = 2$$

which gives

$$x^2 + 2^2 = 16$$
$$x^2 = 12$$
$$x = \pm 2\sqrt{3}$$

Two triangles are possible. The third vertex is $\left(-2\sqrt{3}, 2\right)$ or $\left(2\sqrt{3}, 2\right)$.

53. Let $P_1 = (0, 0)$, $P_2 = (0, s)$, $P_3 = (s, 0)$, and $P_4 = (s, s)$.

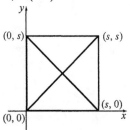

The points P_1 and P_4 are endpoints of one diagonal and the points P_2 and P_3 are the endpoints of the other diagonal.

$$M_{1,4} = \left(\frac{0+s}{2}, \frac{0+s}{2}\right) = \left(\frac{s}{2}, \frac{s}{2}\right)$$

$$M_{2,3} = \left(\frac{0+s}{2}, \frac{s+0}{2}\right) = \left(\frac{s}{2}, \frac{s}{2}\right)$$

The midpoints of the diagonals are the same. Therefore, the diagonals of a square intersect at their midpoints.

54. Let $P_1 = (0, 0)$, $P_2 = (a, 0)$, and $P_3 = \left(\frac{a}{2}, \frac{\sqrt{3}\,a}{2}\right)$. To show that these vertices form an equilateral triangle, we need to show that the distance between any pair of points is the same constant value.

$$d(P_1, P_2) = \sqrt{(x_2 - x_1)^2 + (y_2 - y_1)^2}$$
$$= \sqrt{(a-0)^2 + (0-0)^2} = \sqrt{a^2} = |a|$$

$$d(P_2, P_3) = \sqrt{(x_2 - x_1)^2 + (y_2 - y_1)^2}$$
$$= \sqrt{\left(\frac{a}{2} - a\right)^2 + \left(\frac{\sqrt{3}\,a}{2} - 0\right)^2}$$
$$= \sqrt{\frac{a^2}{4} + \frac{3a^2}{4}} = \sqrt{\frac{4a^2}{4}} = \sqrt{a^2} = |a|$$

$$d(P_1, P_3) = \sqrt{(x_2 - x_1)^2 + (y_2 - y_1)^2}$$
$$= \sqrt{\left(\frac{a}{2} - 0\right)^2 + \left(\frac{\sqrt{3}\,a}{2} - 0\right)^2}$$
$$= \sqrt{\frac{a^2}{4} + \frac{3a^2}{4}} = \sqrt{\frac{4a^2}{4}} = \sqrt{a^2} = |a|$$

Since all three distances have the same constant value, the triangle is an equilateral triangle. Now find the midpoints:

$$P_4 = M_{P_1 P_2} = \left(\frac{0+a}{2}, \frac{0+0}{2}\right) = \left(\frac{a}{2}, 0\right)$$

$$P_5 = M_{P_2 P_3} = \left(\frac{a + \frac{a}{2}}{2}, \frac{0 + \frac{\sqrt{3}\,a}{2}}{2}\right) = \left(\frac{3a}{4}, \frac{\sqrt{3}\,a}{4}\right)$$

$$P_6 = M_{P_1 P_3} = \left(\frac{0 + \frac{a}{2}}{2}, \frac{0 + \frac{\sqrt{3}a}{2}}{2}\right) = \left(\frac{a}{4}, \frac{\sqrt{3}\,a}{4}\right)$$

$$d(P_4, P_5) = \sqrt{\left(\frac{3a}{4} - \frac{a}{2}\right)^2 + \left(\frac{\sqrt{3}\,a}{4} - 0\right)^2}$$
$$= \sqrt{\left(\frac{a}{4}\right)^2 + \left(\frac{\sqrt{3}\,a}{4}\right)^2}$$
$$= \sqrt{\frac{a^2}{16} + \frac{3a^2}{16}} = \frac{|a|}{2}$$

$$d(P_4, P_6) = \sqrt{\left(\frac{a}{4} - \frac{a}{2}\right)^2 + \left(\frac{\sqrt{3}\,a}{4} - 0\right)^2}$$

$$= \sqrt{\left(-\frac{a}{4}\right)^2 + \left(\frac{\sqrt{3}\,a}{4}\right)^2}$$

$$= \sqrt{\frac{a^2}{16} + \frac{3a^2}{16}} = \frac{|a|}{2}$$

$$d(P_5, P_6) = \sqrt{\left(\frac{3a}{4} - \frac{a}{4}\right)^2 + \left(\frac{\sqrt{3}\,a}{4} - \frac{\sqrt{3}\,a}{4}\right)^2}$$

$$= \sqrt{\left(\frac{a}{2}\right)^2 + 0^2}$$

$$= \sqrt{\frac{a^2}{4}} = \frac{|a|}{2}$$

Since the sides are the same length, the triangle is equilateral.

55. $d(P_1, P_2) = \sqrt{(-4-2)^2 + (1-1)^2}$

$$= \sqrt{(-6)^2 + 0^2}$$

$$= \sqrt{36}$$

$$= 6$$

$$d(P_2, P_3) = \sqrt{(-4-(-4))^2 + (-3-1)^2}$$

$$= \sqrt{0^2 + (-4)^2}$$

$$= \sqrt{16}$$

$$= 4$$

$$d(P_1, P_3) = \sqrt{(-4-2)^2 + (-3-1)^2}$$

$$= \sqrt{(-6)^2 + (-4)^2}$$

$$= \sqrt{36+16}$$

$$= \sqrt{52}$$

$$= 2\sqrt{13}$$

Since $[d(P_1, P_2)]^2 + [d(P_2, P_3)]^2 = [d(P_1, P_3)]^2$, the triangle is a right triangle.

56. $d(P_1, P_2) = \sqrt{(6-(-1))^2 + (2-4)^2}$

$$= \sqrt{7^2 + (-2)^2}$$

$$= \sqrt{49+4}$$

$$= \sqrt{53}$$

$$d(P_2, P_3) = \sqrt{(4-6)^2 + (-5-2)^2}$$

$$= \sqrt{(-2)^2 + (-7)^2}$$

$$= \sqrt{4+49}$$

$$= \sqrt{53}$$

$$d(P_1, P_3) = \sqrt{(4-(-1))^2 + (-5-4)^2}$$

$$= \sqrt{5^2 + (-9)^2}$$

$$= \sqrt{25+81}$$

$$= \sqrt{106}$$

Since $[d(P_1, P_2)]^2 + [d(P_2, P_3)]^2 = [d(P_1, P_3)]^2$, the triangle is a right triangle.

Since $d(P_1, P_2) = d(P_2, P_3)$, the triangle is isosceles.

Therefore, the triangle is an isosceles right triangle.

57. $d(P_1, P_2) = \sqrt{(0-(-2))^2 + (7-(-1))^2}$

$$= \sqrt{2^2 + 8^2} = \sqrt{4+64} = \sqrt{68}$$

$$= 2\sqrt{17}$$

$$d(P_2, P_3) = \sqrt{(3-0)^2 + (2-7)^2}$$

$$= \sqrt{3^2 + (-5)^2} = \sqrt{9+25}$$

$$= \sqrt{34}$$

$$d(P_1, P_3) = \sqrt{(3-(-2))^2 + (2-(-1))^2}$$

$$= \sqrt{5^2 + 3^2} = \sqrt{25+9}$$

$$= \sqrt{34}$$

Since $d(P_2, P_3) = d(P_1, P_3)$, the triangle is isosceles.

Since $[d(P_1, P_3)]^2 + [d(P_2, P_3)]^2 = [d(P_1, P_2)]^2$, the triangle is also a right triangle.

Therefore, the triangle is an isosceles right triangle.

58. $d(P_1, P_2) = \sqrt{(-4-7)^2 + (0-2)^2}$

$\qquad = \sqrt{(-11)^2 + (-2)^2}$

$\qquad = \sqrt{121 + 4} = \sqrt{125}$

$\qquad = 5\sqrt{5}$

$d(P_2, P_3) = \sqrt{(4-(-4))^2 + (6-0)^2}$

$\qquad = \sqrt{8^2 + 6^2} = \sqrt{64 + 36}$

$\qquad = \sqrt{100}$

$\qquad = 10$

$d(P_1, P_3) = \sqrt{(4-7)^2 + (6-2)^2}$

$\qquad = \sqrt{(-3)^2 + 4^2} = \sqrt{9 + 16}$

$\qquad = \sqrt{25}$

$\qquad = 5$

Since $\left[d(P_1, P_3)\right]^2 + \left[d(P_2, P_3)\right]^2 = \left[d(P_1, P_2)\right]^2$, the triangle is a right triangle.

59. Using the Pythagorean Theorem:

$$90^2 + 90^2 = d^2$$

$$8100 + 8100 = d^2$$

$$16200 = d^2$$

$$d = \sqrt{16200} = 90\sqrt{2} \approx 127.28 \text{ feet}$$

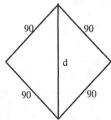

60. Using the Pythagorean Theorem:

$$60^2 + 60^2 = d^2$$

$$3600 + 3600 = d^2 \rightarrow 7200 = d^2$$

$$d = \sqrt{7200} = 60\sqrt{2} \approx 84.85 \text{ feet}$$

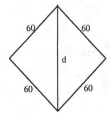

61. a. First: (90, 0), Second: (90, 90), Third: (0, 90)

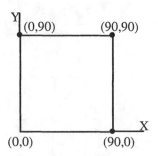

b. Using the distance formula:

$$d = \sqrt{(310-90)^2 + (15-90)^2}$$

$$= \sqrt{220^2 + (-75)^2} = \sqrt{54025}$$

$$= 5\sqrt{2161} \approx 232.43 \text{ feet}$$

c. Using the distance formula:

$$d = \sqrt{(300-0)^2 + (300-90)^2}$$

$$= \sqrt{300^2 + 210^2} = \sqrt{134100}$$

$$= 30\sqrt{149} \approx 366.20 \text{ feet}$$

62. a. First: (60, 0), Second: (60, 60) Third: (0, 60)

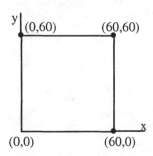

b. Using the distance formula:

$$d = \sqrt{(180-60)^2 + (20-60)^2}$$

$$= \sqrt{120^2 + (-40)^2} = \sqrt{16000}$$

$$= 40\sqrt{10} \approx 126.49 \text{ feet}$$

c. Using the distance formula:

$$d = \sqrt{(220-0)^2 + (220-60)^2}$$

$$= \sqrt{220^2 + 160^2} = \sqrt{74000}$$

$$= 20\sqrt{185} \approx 272.03 \text{ feet}$$

63. The Neon heading east moves a distance $30t$ after t hours. The truck heading south moves a distance $40t$ after t hours. Their distance apart after t hours is:

$$d = \sqrt{(30t)^2 + (40t)^2}$$
$$= \sqrt{900t^2 + 1600t^2}$$
$$= \sqrt{2500t^2}$$
$$= 50t \text{ miles}$$

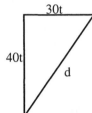

64. $\dfrac{15 \text{ miles}}{1 \text{ hr}} \cdot \dfrac{5280 \text{ ft}}{1 \text{ mile}} \cdot \dfrac{1 \text{ hr}}{3600 \text{ sec}} = 22 \text{ ft/sec}$

$$d = \sqrt{100^2 + (22t)^2}$$
$$= \sqrt{10000 + 484t^2} \text{ feet}$$

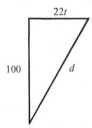

65. a. The shortest side is between $P_1 = (2.6, 1.5)$ and $P_2 = (2.7, 1.7)$. The estimate for the desired intersection point is:

$$\left(\frac{x_1 + x_2}{2}, \frac{y_1 + y_2}{2}\right) = \left(\frac{2.6 + 2.7}{2}, \frac{1.5 + 1.7}{2}\right)$$
$$= \left(\frac{5.3}{2}, \frac{3.2}{2}\right)$$
$$= (2.65, 1.6)$$

b. Using the distance formula:

$$d = \sqrt{(2.65 - 1.4)^2 + (1.6 - 1.3)^2}$$
$$= \sqrt{(1.25)^2 + (0.3)^2}$$
$$= \sqrt{1.5625 + 0.09}$$
$$= \sqrt{1.6525}$$
$$\approx 1.285 \text{ units}$$

66. Let $P_1 = (2002, 204)$ and $P_2 = (2006, 312)$. The midpoint is:

$$(x, y) = \left(\frac{x_1 + x_2}{2}, \frac{y_1 + y_2}{2}\right)$$
$$= \left(\frac{2002 + 2006}{2}, \frac{204 + 312}{2}\right)$$
$$= \left(\frac{4008}{2}, \frac{516}{2}\right)$$
$$= (2004, 258)$$

The estimate is that net sales of Wal-Mart Stores, Inc. in 2004 was $258 billion which is $2 billion off from the reported value.

Section 2.2

1. $2(x + 3) - 1 = -7$
$$2(x + 3) = -6$$
$$x + 3 = -3$$
$$x = -6$$
The solution set is $\{-6\}$.

2. $x^2 - 9 = 0$
$$x^2 = 9$$
$$x = \pm\sqrt{9}$$
$$x = \pm 3$$
The solution set is $\{-3, 3\}$.

3. intercepts

4. $y = 0$

5. y-axis

6. 4

7. $(-3, 4)$

8. True

9. False; the y-coordinate of a point at which the graph crosses or touches the x-axis is always 0. The x-coordinate of such a point is an x-intercept.

169

10. False; a graph can be symmetric with respect to both coordinate axes (in such cases it will also be symmetric with respect to the origin).

For example: $x^2 + y^2 = 1$

11. $y = x^4 - \sqrt{x}$

$0 = 0^4 - \sqrt{0}$ $\quad 1 = 1^4 - \sqrt{1}$ $\quad 0 = (-1)^4 - \sqrt{-1}$

$0 = 0$ $\qquad 1 \neq 0$ $\qquad 0 \neq 1 - \sqrt{-1}$

The point (0, 0) is on the graph of the equation.

12. $y = x^3 - 2\sqrt{x}$

$0 = 0^3 - 2\sqrt{0}$ $\quad 1 = 1^3 - 2\sqrt{1}$ $\quad -1 = 1^3 - 2\sqrt{1}$

$0 = 0$ $\qquad 1 \neq -1$ $\qquad -1 = -1$

The points (0, 0) and (1, −1) are on the graph of the equation.

13. $y^2 = x^2 + 9$

$3^2 = 0^2 + 9$ $\quad 0^2 = 3^2 + 9$ $\quad 0^2 = (-3)^2 + 9$

$9 = 9$ $\qquad 0 \neq 18$ $\qquad 0 \neq 18$

The point (0, 3) is on the graph of the equation.

14. $y^3 = x + 1$

$2^3 = 1 + 1$ $\quad 1^3 = 0 + 1$ $\quad 0^3 = -1 + 1$

$8 \neq 2$ $\qquad 1 = 1$ $\qquad 0 = 0$

The points (0, 1) and (−1, 0) are on the graph of the equation.

15. $x^2 + y^2 = 4$

$0^2 + 2^2 = 4$ $\quad (-2)^2 + 2^2 = 4$ $\quad \left(\sqrt{2}\right)^2 + \left(\sqrt{2}\right)^2 = 4$

$4 = 4$ $\qquad 8 \neq 4$ $\qquad 4 = 4$

(0, 2) and $\left(\sqrt{2}, \sqrt{2}\right)$ are on the graph of the equation.

16. $x^2 + 4y^2 = 4$

$0^2 + 4 \cdot 1^2 = 4$ $\quad 2^2 + 4 \cdot 0^2 = 4$ $\quad 2^2 + 4\left(\frac{1}{2}\right)^2 = 4$

$4 = 4$ $\qquad 4 = 4$ $\qquad 5 \neq 4$

The points (0, 1) and (2, 0) are on the graph of the equation.

17. $y = x + 2$

x-intercept: $\qquad$ y-intercept:

$0 = x + 2$ $\qquad y = 0 + 2$

$-2 = x$ $\qquad y = 2$

The intercepts are $(-2, 0)$ and $(0, 2)$.

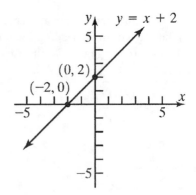

18. $y = x - 6$

x-intercept: $\qquad$ y-intercept:

$0 = x - 6$ $\qquad y = 0 - 6$

$6 = x$ $\qquad y = -6$

The intercepts are $(6, 0)$ and $(0, -6)$.

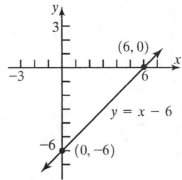

19. $y = 2x + 8$

x-intercept: $\qquad$ y-intercept:

$0 = 2x + 8$ $\qquad y = 2(0) + 8$

$2x = -8$ $\qquad y = 8$

$x = -4$

The intercepts are $(-4, 0)$ and $(0, 8)$.

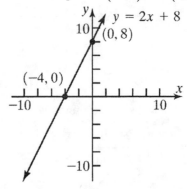

170

20. $y = 3x - 9$

x-intercept: $\qquad$ y-intercept:

$\quad 0 = 3x - 9 \qquad\qquad y = 3(0) - 9$

$\quad 3x = 9 \qquad\qquad\qquad y = -9$

$\quad\ x = 3$

The intercepts are $(3, 0)$ and $(0, -9)$.

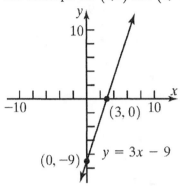

21. $y = x^2 - 1$

x-intercepts: $\qquad$ y-intercept:

$\quad 0 = x^2 - 1 \qquad\qquad y = 0^2 - 1$

$\quad x^2 = 1 \qquad\qquad\qquad y = -1$

$\quad\ x = \pm 1$

The intercepts are $(-1, 0)$, $(1, 0)$, and $(0, -1)$.

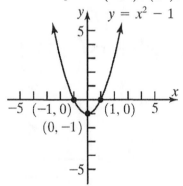

22. $y = x^2 - 9$

x-intercepts: $\qquad$ y-intercept:

$\quad 0 = x^2 - 9 \qquad\qquad y = 0^2 - 9$

$\quad x^2 = 9 \qquad\qquad\qquad y = -9$

$\quad\ x = \pm 3$

The intercepts are $(-3, 0)$, $(3, 0)$, and $(0, -9)$.

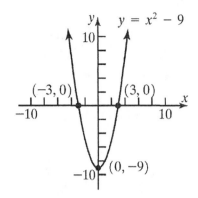

23. $y = -x^2 + 4$

x-intercepts: $\qquad$ y-intercepts:

$\quad 0 = -x^2 + 4 \qquad\qquad y = -(0)^2 + 4$

$\quad x^2 = 4 \qquad\qquad\qquad\ y = 4$

$\quad\ x = \pm 2$

The intercepts are $(-2, 0)$, $(2, 0)$, and $(0, 4)$.

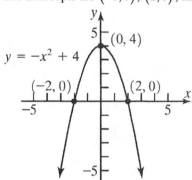

24. $y = -x^2 + 1$

x-intercepts: $\qquad$ y-intercept:

$\quad 0 = -x^2 + 1 \qquad\qquad y = -(0)^2 + 1$

$\quad x^2 = 1 \qquad\qquad\qquad\ y = 1$

$\quad\ x = \pm 1$

The intercepts are $(-1, 0)$, $(1, 0)$, and $(0, 1)$.

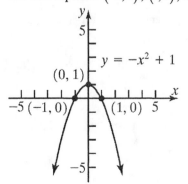

25. $2x + 3y = 6$

x-intercepts: y-intercept:

$2x + 3(0) = 6$ $2(0) + 3y = 6$

$2x = 6$ $3y = 6$

$x = 3$ $y = 2$

The intercepts are $(3,0)$ and $(0,2)$.

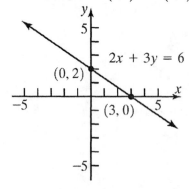

26. $5x + 2y = 10$

x-intercepts: y-intercept:

$5x + 2(0) = 10$ $5(0) + 2y = 10$

$5x = 10$ $2y = 10$

$x = 2$ $y = 5$

The intercepts are $(2,0)$ and $(0,5)$.

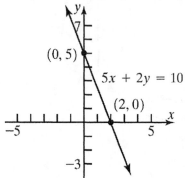

27. $9x^2 + 4y = 36$

x-intercepts: y-intercept:

$9x^2 + 4(0) = 36$ $9(0)^2 + 4y = 36$

$9x^2 = 36$ $4y = 36$

$x^2 = 4$ $y = 9$

$x = \pm 2$

The intercepts are $(-2,0)$, $(2,0)$, and $(0,9)$.

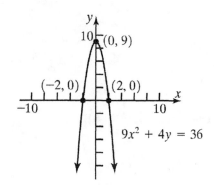

28. $4x^2 + y = 4$

x-intercepts: y-intercept:

$4x^2 + 0 = 4$ $4(0)^2 + y = 4$

$4x^2 = 4$ $y = 4$

$x^2 = 1$

$x = \pm 1$

The intercepts are $(-1,0)$, $(1,0)$, and $(0,4)$.

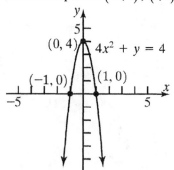

29.

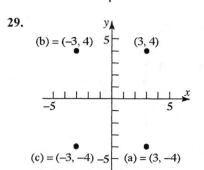

30.

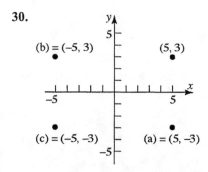

172

31.

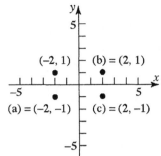

32.

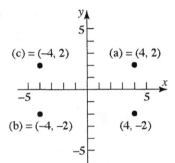

33.

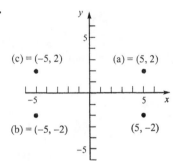

34.

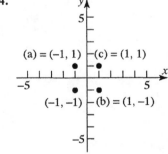

35.

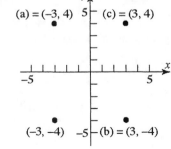

36.

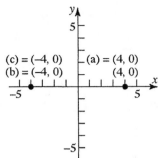

37.

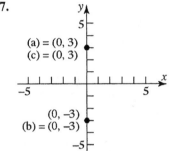

38.

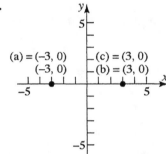

39. **a.** Intercepts: $(-1, 0)$ and $(1, 0)$

    b. Symmetric with respect to the *x*-axis, *y*-axis, and the origin.

40. **a.** Intercepts: $(0, 1)$

    b. Not symmetric to the *x*-axis, the *y*-axis, nor the origin

41. **a.** Intercepts: $\left(-\frac{\pi}{2}, 0\right)$, $(0, 1)$, and $\left(\frac{\pi}{2}, 0\right)$

    b. Symmetric with respect to the *y*-axis.

42. **a.** Intercepts: $(-2, 0)$, $(0, -3)$, and $(2, 0)$

    b. Symmetric with respect to the *y*-axis.

43. **a.** Intercepts: $(0, 0)$

    b. Symmetric with respect to the *x*-axis.

173

44. a. Intercepts: $(-2,0)$, $(0,2)$, $(0,-2)$, and $(2,0)$

    b. Symmetric with respect to the *x*-axis, *y*-axis, and the origin.

45. a. Intercepts: $(-2,0)$, $(0,0)$, and $(2,0)$

    b. Symmetric with respect to the origin.

46. a. Intercepts: $(-4,0)$, $(0,0)$, and $(4,0)$

    b. Symmetric with respect to the origin.

47. a. Intercepts: $(-1,0)$, $(0,-1)$, $(1,0)$

    b. Symmetric with respect to the *y*-axis.

48. a. Intercepts: $(0,0)$

    b. Symmetric with respect to the origin.

49. a. Intercepts: none

    b. Symmetric with respect to the origin.

50. a. Intercepts: none

    b. Symmetric with respect to the *x*-axis.

51.

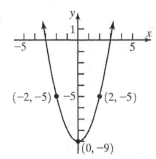

52.

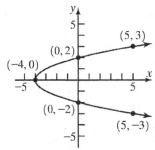

53.

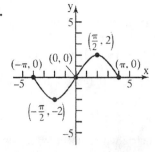

54.

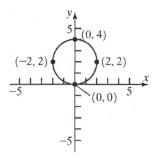

55. $y^2 = x + 4$

x-intercepts: *y*-intercepts:

$0^2 = x + 4$ $y^2 = 0 + 4$

$-4 = x$ $y^2 = 4$

                            $y = \pm 2$

The intercepts are $(-4,0)$, $(0,-2)$ and $(0,2)$.

Test *x*-axis symmetry: Let $y = -y$

$(-y)^2 = x + 4$

   $y^2 = x + 4$ same

Test *y*-axis symmetry: Let $x = -x$

$y^2 = -x + 4$ different

Test origin symmetry: Let $x = -x$ and $y = -y$.

$(-y)^2 = -x + 4$

   $y^2 = -x + 4$ different

Therefore, the graph will have *x*-axis symmetry.

56. $y^2 = x + 9$

x-intercepts: *y*-intercepts:

$(0)^2 = -x + 9$ $y^2 = 0 + 9$

$0 = -x + 9$ $y^2 = 9$

$x = 9$ $y = \pm 3$

The intercepts are $(-9,0)$, $(0,-3)$ and $(0,3)$.

Test *x*-axis symmetry: Let $y = -y$

$(-y)^2 = x + 9$

   $y^2 = x + 9$ same

Test *y*-axis symmetry: Let $x = -x$

$y^2 = -x + 9$ different

Test origin symmetry: Let $x = -x$ and $y = -y$.

$(-y)^2 = -x + 9$

   $y^2 = -x + 9$ different

Therefore, the graph will have *x*-axis symmetry.

57. $y = \sqrt[3]{x}$

x-intercepts: *y*-intercepts:

$0 = \sqrt[3]{x}$ $y = \sqrt[3]{0} = 0$

$0 = x$

The only intercept is $(0,0)$.

Test *x*-axis symmetry: Let $y = -y$

$-y = \sqrt[3]{x}$ different

Test *y*-axis symmetry: Let $x = -x$

$y = \sqrt[3]{-x} = -\sqrt[3]{x}$ different

Test origin symmetry: Let $x = -x$ and $y = -y$

$-y = \sqrt[3]{-x} = -\sqrt[3]{x}$

$\quad y = \sqrt[3]{x}$ same

Therefore, the graph will have origin symmetry.

58. $y = \sqrt[5]{x}$

x-intercepts: *y*-intercepts:

$0 = \sqrt[3]{x}$ $y = \sqrt[5]{0} = 0$

$0 = x$

The only intercept is $(0,0)$.

Test *x*-axis symmetry: Let $y = -y$

$-y = \sqrt[5]{x}$ different

Test *y*-axis symmetry: Let $x = -x$

$y = \sqrt[5]{-x} = -\sqrt[5]{x}$ different

Test origin symmetry: Let $x = -x$ and $y = -y$

$-y = \sqrt[5]{-x} = -\sqrt[5]{x}$

$\quad y = \sqrt[5]{x}$ same

Therefore, the graph will have origin symmetry.

59. $x^2 + y - 9 = 0$

x-intercepts: *y*-intercepts:

$x^2 - 9 = 0$ $0^2 + y - 9 = 0$

$\quad x^2 = 9$ $y = 9$

$\quad x = \pm 3$

The intercepts are $(-3,0)$, $(3,0)$, and $(0,9)$.

Test *x*-axis symmetry: Let $y = -y$

$x^2 - y - 9 = 0$ different

Test *y*-axis symmetry: Let $x = -x$

$(-x)^2 + y - 9 = 0$

$x^2 + y - 9 = 0$ same

Test origin symmetry: Let $x = -x$ and $y = -y$

$(-x)^2 - y - 9 = 0$

$x^2 - y - 9 = 0$ different

Therefore, the graph will have *y*-axis symmetry.

60. $x^2 - y - 4 = 0$

x-intercepts: *y*-intercept:

$x^2 - 0 - 4 = 0$ $0^2 - y - 4 = 0$

$\quad x^2 = 4$ $-y = 4$

$\quad x = \pm 2$ $y = -4$

The intercepts are $(-2,0)$, $(2,0)$, and $(0,-4)$.

Test *x*-axis symmetry: Let $y = -y$

$x^2 - (-y) - 4 = 0$

$x^2 + y - 4 = 0$ different

Test *y*-axis symmetry: Let $x = -x$

$(-x)^2 - y - 4 = 0$

$x^2 - y - 4 = 0$ same

Test origin symmetry: Let $x = -x$ and $y = -y$

$(-x)^2 - (-y) - 4 = 0$

$x^2 + y - 4 = 0$ different

Therefore, the graph will have *y*-axis symmetry.

61. $9x^2 + 4y^2 = 36$

x-intercepts: *y*-intercepts:

$9x^2 + 4(0)^2 = 36$ $9(0)^2 + 4y^2 = 36$

$\quad 9x^2 = 36$ $4y^2 = 36$

$\quad x^2 = 4$ $y^2 = 9$

$\quad x = \pm 2$ $y = \pm 3$

The intercepts are $(-2,0), (2,0), (0,-3)$, and $(0,3)$.

Test *x*-axis symmetry: Let $y = -y$

$9x^2 + 4(-y)^2 = 36$

$9x^2 + 4y^2 = 36$ same

Test *y*-axis symmetry: Let $x = -x$

$9(-x)^2 + 4y^2 = 36$

$9x^2 + 4y^2 = 36$ same

Test origin symmetry: Let $x = -x$ and $y = -y$

$9(-x)^2 + 4(-y)^2 = 36$

$9x^2 + 4y^2 = 36$ same

Therefore, the graph will have *x*-axis, *y*-axis, and origin symmetry.

175

62. $4x^2 + y^2 = 4$

    x-intercepts: *y*-intercepts:

    $4x^2 + 0^2 = 4$ $4(0)^2 + y^2 = 4$

        $4x^2 = 4$ $y^2 = 4$

         $x^2 = 1$ $y = \pm 2$

         $x = \pm 1$

    The intercepts are $(-1,0)$, $(1,0)$, $(0,-2)$, and $(0,2)$.

    Test *x*-axis symmetry: Let $y = -y$

    $4x^2 + (-y)^2 = 4$

      $4x^2 + y^2 = 4$ same

    Test *y*-axis symmetry: Let $x = -x$

    $4(-x)^2 + y^2 = 4$

      $4x^2 + y^2 = 4$ same

    Test origin symmetry: Let $x = -x$ and $y = -y$

    $4(-x)^2 + (-y)^2 = 4$

      $4x^2 + y^2 = 4$ same

    Therefore, the graph will have *x*-axis, *y*-axis, and origin symmetry.

63. $y = x^3 - 27$

    x-intercepts: *y*-intercepts:

    $0 = x^3 - 27$ $y = 0^3 - 27$

    $x^3 = 27$ $y = -27$

    $x = 3$

    The intercepts are $(3,0)$ and $(0,-27)$.

    Test *x*-axis symmetry: Let $y = -y$

    $-y = x^3 - 27$ different

    Test *y*-axis symmetry: Let $x = -x$

    $y = (-x)^3 - 27$

    $y = -x^3 - 27$ different

    Test origin symmetry: Let $x = -x$ and $y = -y$

    $-y = (-x)^3 - 27$

    $y = x^3 + 27$ different

    Therefore, the graph has none of the indicated symmetries.

64. $y = x^4 - 1$

    x-intercepts: *y*-intercepts:

    $0 = x^4 - 1$ $y = 0^4 - 1$

    $x^4 = 1$ $y = -1$

    $x = \pm 1$

    The intercepts are $(-1,0)$, $(1,0)$, and $(0,-1)$.

    Test *x*-axis symmetry: Let $y = -y$

    $-y = x^4 - 1$ different

    Test *y*-axis symmetry: Let $x = -x$

    $y = (-x)^4 - 1$

    $y = x^4 - 1$ same

    Test origin symmetry: Let $x = -x$ and $y = -y$

    $-y = (-x)^4 - 1$

    $-y = x^4 - 1$ different

    Therefore, the graph will have *y*-axis symmetry.

65. $y = x^2 - 3x - 4$

    x-intercepts: *y*-intercepts:

    $0 = x^2 - 3x - 4$ $y = 0^2 - 3(0) - 4$

    $0 = (x - 4)(x + 1)$ $y = -4$

    $x = 4$ or $x = -1$

    The intercepts are $(4,0)$, $(-1,0)$, and $(0,-4)$.

    Test *x*-axis symmetry: Let $y = -y$

    $-y = x^2 - 3x - 4$ different

    Test *y*-axis symmetry: Let $x = -x$

    $y = (-x)^2 - 3(-x) - 4$

    $y = x^2 + 3x - 4$ different

    Test origin symmetry: Let $x = -x$ and $y = -y$

    $-y = (-x)^2 - 3(-x) - 4$

    $-y = x^2 + 3x - 4$ different

    Therefore, the graph has none of the indicated symmetries.

66. $y = x^2 + 4$

    x-intercepts: *y*-intercepts:

    $0 = x^2 + 4$ $y = 0^2 + 4$

    $x^2 = -4$ $y = 4$

       no real solution

The only intercept is $(0, 4)$.

Test *x*-axis symmetry: Let $y = -y$

$-y = x^2 + 4$ different

Test *y*-axis symmetry: Let $x = -x$

$y = (-x)^2 + 4$

$y = x^2 + 4$ same

Test origin symmetry: Let $x = -x$ and $y = -y$

$-y = (-x)^2 + 4$

$-y = x^2 + 4$ different

Therefore, the graph will have *y*-axis symmetry.

67. $y = \dfrac{3x}{x^2 + 9}$

    x-intercepts: *y*-intercepts:

    $0 = \dfrac{3x}{x^2 + 9}$ $y = \dfrac{3(0)}{0^2 + 9} = \dfrac{0}{9} = 0$

    $3x = 0$

      $x = 0$

The only intercept is $(0, 0)$.

Test *x*-axis symmetry: Let $y = -y$

$-y = \dfrac{3x}{x^2 + 9}$ different

Test *y*-axis symmetry: Let $x = -x$

$y = \dfrac{3(-x)}{(-x)^2 + 9}$

$y = -\dfrac{3x}{x^2 + 9}$ different

Test origin symmetry: Let $x = -x$ and $y = -y$

$-y = \dfrac{3(-x)}{(-x)^2 + 9}$

$-y = -\dfrac{3x}{x^2 + 9}$

$y = \dfrac{3x}{x^2 + 9}$ same

Therefore, the graph has origin symmetry.

68. $y = \dfrac{x^2 - 4}{2x}$

    x-intercepts: *y*-intercepts:

    $0 = \dfrac{x^2 - 4}{2x}$ $y = \dfrac{0^2 - 4}{2(0)} = \dfrac{-4}{0}$

    $x^2 - 4 = 0$ undefined

    $x^2 = 4$

    $x = \pm 2$

The intercepts are $(-2, 0)$ and $(2, 0)$.

Test *x*-axis symmetry: Let $y = -y$

$-y = \dfrac{x^2 - 4}{2x}$ different

Test *y*-axis symmetry: Let $x = -x$

$y = \dfrac{(-x)^2 - 4}{2(-x)}$

$y = -\dfrac{x^2 - 4}{2x}$ different

Test origin symmetry: Let $x = -x$ and $y = -y$

$-y = \dfrac{(-x)^2 - 4}{2(-x)}$

$-y = \dfrac{x^2 - 4}{-2x}$

$y = \dfrac{x^2 - 4}{2x}$ same

Therefore, the graph has origin symmetry.

69. $y = \dfrac{-x^3}{x^2 - 9}$

    x-intercepts: *y*-intercepts:

    $0 = \dfrac{-x^3}{x^2 - 9}$ $y = \dfrac{-0^3}{0^2 - 9} = \dfrac{0}{-9} = 0$

    $-x^3 = 0$

      $x = 0$

The only intercept is $(0, 0)$.

Test *x*-axis symmetry: Let $y = -y$

$-y = \dfrac{-x^3}{x^2 - 9}$

$y = \dfrac{x^3}{x^2 - 9}$ different

177

Test *y*-axis symmetry: Let $x = -x$

$$y = \frac{-(-x)^3}{(-x)^2 - 9}$$

$$y = \frac{x^3}{x^2 - 9} \quad \text{different}$$

Test origin symmetry: Let $x = -x$ and $y = -y$

$$-y = \frac{-(-x)^3}{(-x)^2 - 9}$$

$$-y = \frac{x^3}{x^2 - 9}$$

$$y = \frac{-x^3}{x^2 - 9} \quad \text{same}$$

Therefore, the graph has origin symmetry.

70. $y = \dfrac{x^4 + 1}{2x^5}$

x-intercepts:

$$0 = \frac{x^4 + 1}{2x^5}$$

$$x^4 = -1$$

no real solution

y-intercepts:

$$y = \frac{0^4 + 1}{2(0)^5} = \frac{1}{0}$$

undefined

There are no intercepts for the graph of this equation.

Test *x*-axis symmetry: Let $y = -y$

$$-y = \frac{x^4 + 1}{2x^5} \quad \text{different}$$

Test *y*-axis symmetry: Let $x = -x$

$$y = \frac{(-x)^4 + 1}{2(-x)^5}$$

$$y = \frac{x^4 + 1}{-2x^5} \quad \text{different}$$

Test origin symmetry: Let $x = -x$ and $y = -y$

$$-y = \frac{(-x)^4 + 1}{2(-x)^5}$$

$$-y = \frac{x^4 + 1}{-2x^5}$$

$$y = \frac{x^4 + 1}{2x^5} \quad \text{same}$$

Therefore, the graph has origin symmetry.

71. $y = x^3$

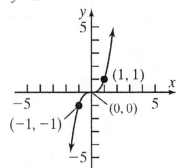

72. $x = y^2$

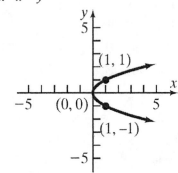

73. $y = \sqrt{x}$

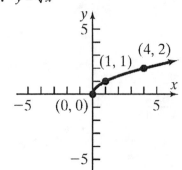

74. $y = \dfrac{1}{x}$

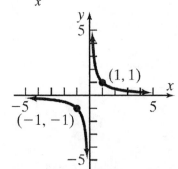

75. If the point $(3, b)$ is on the graph of $y = 4x + 1$,

then we have $b = 4(3) + 1 = 12 + 1 = 13$

Thus, $b = 13$.

76. If the point $(-2, b)$ is on the graph of

$2x + 3y = 2$, then we have

$$2(-2) + 3(b) = 2$$
$$-4 + 3b = 2$$
$$3b = 6$$
$$b = 2$$

Thus, $b = 2$.

77. If the point $(a, 4)$ is on the graph of

$y = x^2 + 3x$, then we have

$$4 = a^2 + 3a$$
$$0 = a^2 + 3a - 4$$
$$0 = (a + 4)(a - 1)$$
$$a + 4 = 0 \quad \text{or} \quad a - 1 = 0$$
$$a = -4 \qquad \quad a = 1$$

Thus, $a = -4$ or $a = 1$.

78. If the point $(a, -5)$ is on the graph of

$y = x^2 + 6x$, then we have

$$-5 = a^2 + 6a$$
$$0 = a^2 + 6a + 5$$
$$0 = (a + 5)(a + 1)$$
$$a + 5 = 0 \quad \text{or} \quad a + 1 = 0$$
$$a = -5 \qquad \quad a = -1$$

Thus, $a = -5$ or $a = -1$.

79. For a graph with origin symmetry, if the point (a, b) is on the graph, then so is the point $(-a, -b)$. Since the point $(1, 2)$ is on the graph of an equation with origin symmetry, the point $(-1, -2)$ must also be on the graph.

80. For a graph with y-axis symmetry, if the point (a, b) is on the graph, then so is the point $(-a, b)$. Since 6 is an x-intercept in this case, the point $(6, 0)$ is on the graph of the equation. Due to the y-axis symmetry, the point $(-6, 0)$ must also be on the graph. Therefore, -6 is another x-intercept.

81. For a graph with origin symmetry, if the point (a, b) is on the graph, then so is the point $(-a, -b)$. Since -4 is an x-intercept in this case, the point $(-4, 0)$ is on the graph of the equation. Due to the origin symmetry, the point $(4, 0)$ must also be on the graph. Therefore, 4 is another x-intercept.

82. For a graph with x-axis symmetry, if the point (a, b) is on the graph, then so is the point $(a, -b)$. Since 2 is a y-intercept in this case, the point $(0, 2)$ is on the graph of the equation. Due to the x-axis symmetry, the point $(0, -2)$ must also be on the graph. Therefore, -2 is another y-intercept.

83. a. $\left(x^2 + y^2 - x\right)^2 = x^2 + y^2$

x-intercepts:

$$\left(x^2 + (0)^2 - x\right)^2 = x^2 + (0)^2$$
$$\left(x^2 - x\right)^2 = x^2$$
$$x^4 - 2x^3 + x^2 = x^2$$
$$x^4 - 2x^3 = 0$$
$$x^3(x - 2) = 0$$
$$x^3 = 0 \quad \text{or} \quad x - 2 = 0$$
$$x = 0 \qquad \qquad x = 2$$

y-intercepts:

$$\left((0)^2 + y^2 - 0\right)^2 = (0)^2 + y^2$$
$$\left(y^2\right)^2 = y^2$$
$$y^4 = y^2$$
$$y^4 - y^2 = 0$$
$$y^2\left(y^2 - 1\right) = 0$$
$$y^2 = 0 \quad \text{or} \quad y^2 - 1 = 0$$
$$y = 0 \qquad \qquad y^2 = 1$$
$$y = \pm 1$$

The intercepts are $(0, 0)$, $(2, 0)$, $(0, -1)$, and $(0, 1)$.

b. Test *x*-axis symmetry: Let $y = -y$

$$\left(x^2 + (-y)^2 - x\right)^2 = x^2 + (-y)^2$$

$$\left(x^2 + y^2 - x\right)^2 = x^2 + y^2 \quad \text{same}$$

Test *y*-axis symmetry: Let $x = -x$

$$\left((-x)^2 + y^2 - (-x)\right)^2 = (-x)^2 + y^2$$

$$\left(x^2 + y^2 + x\right)^2 = x^2 + y^2 \quad \text{different}$$

Test origin symmetry: Let $x = -x$ and $y = -y$

$$\left((-x)^2 + (-y)^2 - (-x)\right)^2 = (-x)^2 + (-y)^2$$

$$\left(x^2 + y^2 + x\right)^2 = x^2 + y^2 \quad \text{different}$$

Thus, the graph will have *x*-axis symmetry.

84. a. $16y^2 = 120x - 225$

x-intercepts:

$$16y^2 = 120(0) - 225$$

$$16y^2 = -225$$

$$y^2 = -\frac{225}{16}$$

no real solution

y-intercepts:

$$16(0)^2 = 120x - 225$$

$$0 = 120x - 225$$

$$-120x = -225$$

$$x = \frac{-225}{-120} = \frac{15}{8}$$

The only intercept is $\left(\frac{15}{8}, 0\right)$.

b. Test *x*-axis symmetry: Let $y = -y$

$$16(-y)^2 = 120x - 225$$

$$16y^2 = 120x - 225 \quad \text{same}$$

Test *y*-axis symmetry: Let $x = -x$

$$16y^2 = 120(-x) - 225$$

$$16y^2 = -120x - 225 \quad \text{different}$$

Test origin symmetry: Let $x = -x$ and $y = -y$

$$16(-y)^2 = 120(-x) - 225$$

$$16y^2 = -120x - 225 \quad \text{different}$$

Thus, the graph will have *x*-axis symmetry.

85. a.

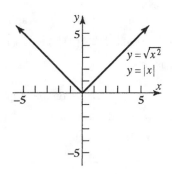

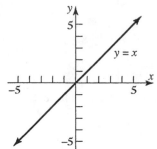

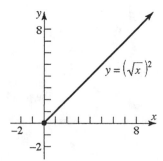

b. Since $\sqrt{x^2} = |x|$ for all x, the graphs of $y = \sqrt{x^2}$ and $y = |x|$ are the same.

c. For $y = \left(\sqrt{x}\right)^2$, the domain of the variable x is $x \geq 0$; for $y = x$, the domain of the variable x is all real numbers. Thus, $\left(\sqrt{x}\right)^2 = x$ only for $x \geq 0$.

d. For $y = \sqrt{x^2}$, the range of the variable y is $y \geq 0$; for $y = x$, the range of the variable y is all real numbers. Also, $\sqrt{x^2} = x$ only if $x \geq 0$. Otherwise, $\sqrt{x^2} = -x$.

86. Answers will vary. A complete graph presents enough of the graph to the viewer so they can "see" the rest of the graph as an obvious continuation of what is shown.

87. Answers will vary. One example:

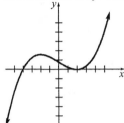

88. Answers will vary

89. Answers will vary

90. Answers will vary.
Case 1: Graph has x-axis and y-axis symmetry, show origin symmetry.
(x, y) on graph $\rightarrow (x, -y)$ on graph
(from x-axis symmetry)
$(x, -y)$ on graph $\rightarrow (-x, -y)$ on graph
(from y-axis symmetry)
Since the point $(-x, -y)$ is also on the graph, the graph has origin symmetry.

Case 2: Graph has x-axis and origin symmetry, show y-axis symmetry.
(x, y) on graph $\rightarrow (x, -y)$ on graph
(from x-axis symmetry)
$(x, -y)$ on graph $\rightarrow (-x, y)$ on graph
(from origin symmetry)
Since the point $(-x, y)$ is also on the graph, the graph has y-axis symmetry.

Case 3: Graph has y-axis and origin symmetry, show x-axis symmetry.
(x, y) on graph $\rightarrow (-x, y)$ on graph
(from y-axis symmetry)
$(-x, y)$ on graph $\rightarrow (x, -y)$ on graph
(from origin symmetry)
Since the point $(x, -y)$ is also on the graph, the graph has x-axis symmetry.

Section 2.3

1. undefined; 0

2. 3; 2
x-intercept: $\quad 2x + 3(0) = 6$
$$2x = 6$$
$$x = 3$$
y-intercept: $\quad 2(0) + 3y = 6$
$$3y = 6$$
$$y = 2$$

3. $y = b$; y-intercept

4. True

5. False; the slope is $\frac{3}{2}$.
$$2y = 3x + 5$$
$$y = \frac{3}{2}x + \frac{5}{2}$$

6. True; $2(1) + (2) \overset{?}{=} 4$
$$2 + 2 \overset{?}{=} 4$$
$$4 = 4 \quad \text{True}$$

7. $m_1 = m_2$; y-intercepts; $m_1 \cdot m_2 = -1$

8. 2

9. $-\dfrac{1}{2}$

10. False; perpendicular lines have slopes that are opposite-reciprocals of each other.

11. a. Slope $= \dfrac{1-0}{2-0} = \dfrac{1}{2}$

    b. If x increases by 2 units, y will increase by 1 unit.

12. a. Slope $= \dfrac{1-0}{-2-0} = -\dfrac{1}{2}$

    b. If x increases by 2 units, y will decrease by 1 unit.

13. a. Slope $= \dfrac{1-2}{1-(-2)} = -\dfrac{1}{3}$

b. If x increases by 3 units, y will decrease by 1 unit.

14. a. Slope $= \dfrac{2-1}{2-(-1)} = \dfrac{1}{3}$

b. If x increases by 3 units, y will increase by 1 unit.

15. Slope $= \dfrac{y_2 - y_1}{x_2 - x_1} = \dfrac{0-3}{4-2} = -\dfrac{3}{2}$

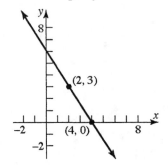

16. Slope $= \dfrac{y_2 - y_1}{x_2 - x_1} = \dfrac{4-2}{3-4} = \dfrac{2}{-1} = -2$

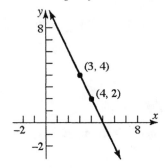

17. Slope $= \dfrac{y_2 - y_1}{x_2 - x_1} = \dfrac{1-3}{2-(-2)} = \dfrac{-2}{4} = -\dfrac{1}{2}$

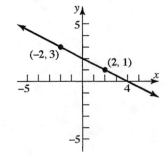

18. Slope $= \dfrac{y_2 - y_1}{x_2 - x_1} = \dfrac{3-1}{2-(-1)} = \dfrac{2}{3}$

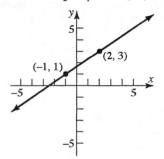

19. Slope $= \dfrac{y_2 - y_1}{x_2 - x_1} = \dfrac{-1-(-1)}{2-(-3)} = \dfrac{0}{5} = 0$

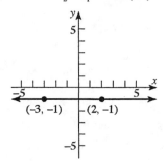

20. Slope $= \dfrac{y_2 - y_1}{x_2 - x_1} = \dfrac{2-2}{-5-4} = \dfrac{0}{-9} = 0$

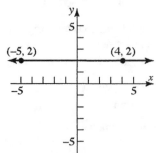

21. Slope $= \dfrac{y_2 - y_1}{x_2 - x_1} = \dfrac{-2-2}{-1-(-1)} = \dfrac{-4}{0}$ undefined.

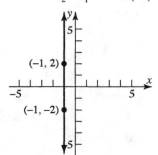

22. Slope $= \dfrac{y_2 - y_1}{x_2 - x_1} = \dfrac{2-0}{2-2} = \dfrac{2}{0}$ undefined.

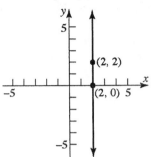

23. $P = (1, 2); m = 3$

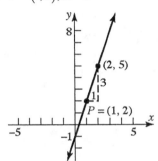

24. $P = (2, 1); m = 4$

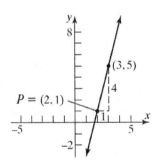

25. $P = (2, 4); m = -\dfrac{3}{4}$

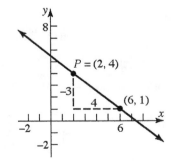

26. $P = (1, 3); m = -\dfrac{2}{5}$

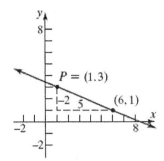

27. $P = (-1, 3); m = 0$

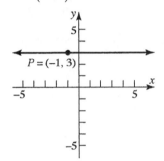

28. $P = (2, -4); m = 0$

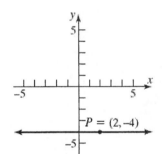

29. $P = (0, 3);$ slope undefined

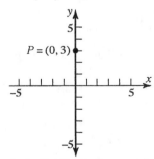

(note: the line is the y-axis)

183

30. $P = (-2, 0)$; slope undefined

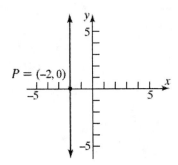

31. Slope $= 4 = \dfrac{4}{1}$; point: $(1, 2)$

If x increases by 1 unit, then y increases by 4 units.
Answers will vary. Three possible points are:
$x = 1 + 1 = 2$ and $y = 2 + 4 = 6$
$\quad (2, 6)$
$x = 2 + 1 = 3$ and $y = 6 + 4 = 10$
$\quad (3, 10)$
$x = 3 + 1 = 4$ and $y = 10 + 4 = 14$
$\quad (4, 14)$

32. Slope $= 2 = \dfrac{2}{1}$; point: $(-2, 3)$

If x increases by 1 unit, then y increases by 2 units.
Answers will vary. Three possible points are:
$x = -2 + 1 = -1$ and $y = 3 + 2 = 5$
$\quad (-1, 5)$
$x = -1 + 1 = 0$ and $y = 5 + 2 = 7$
$\quad (0, 7)$
$x = 0 + 1 = 1$ and $y = 7 + 2 = 9$
$\quad (1, 9)$

33. Slope $= -\dfrac{3}{2} = \dfrac{-3}{2}$; point: $(2, -4)$

If x increases by 2 units, then y decreases by 3 units.
Answers will vary. Three possible points are:
$x = 2 + 2 = 4$ and $y = -4 - 3 = -7$
$\quad (4, -7)$
$x = 4 + 2 = 6$ and $y = -7 - 3 = -10$
$\quad (6, -10)$
$x = 6 + 2 = 8$ and $y = -10 - 3 = -13$
$\quad (8, -13)$

34. Slope $= \dfrac{4}{3}$; point: $(-3, 2)$

If x increases by 3 units, then y increases by 4 units.
Answers will vary. Three possible points are:
$x = -3 + 3 = 0$ and $y = 2 + 4 = 6$
$\quad (0, 6)$
$x = 0 + 3 = 3$ and $y = 6 + 4 = 10$
$\quad (3, 10)$
$x = 3 + 3 = 6$ and $y = 10 + 4 = 14$
$\quad (6, 14)$

35. Slope $= -2 = \dfrac{-2}{1}$; point: $(-2, -3)$

If x increases by 1 unit, then y decreases by 2 units.
Answers will vary. Three possible points are:
$x = -2 + 1 = -1$ and $y = -3 - 2 = -5$
$\quad (-1, -5)$
$x = -1 + 1 = 0$ and $y = -5 - 2 = -7$
$\quad (0, -7)$
$x = 0 + 1 = 1$ and $y = -7 - 2 = -9$
$\quad (1, -9)$

36. Slope $= -1 = \dfrac{-1}{1}$; point: $(4, 1)$

If x increases by 1 unit, then y decreases by 1 unit.
Answers will vary. Three possible points are:
$x = 4 + 1 = 5$ and $y = 1 - 1 = 0$
$\quad (5, 0)$
$x = 5 + 1 = 6$ and $y = 0 - 1 = -1$
$\quad (6, -1)$
$x = 6 + 1 = 7$ and $y = -1 - 1 = -2$
$\quad (7, -2)$

37. (0, 0) and (2, 1) are points on the line.
Slope $= \dfrac{1 - 0}{2 - 0} = \dfrac{1}{2}$

y-intercept is 0; using $y = mx + b$:
$$y = \frac{1}{2}x + 0$$
$$2y = x$$
$$0 = x - 2y$$
$$x - 2y = 0 \text{ or } y = \frac{1}{2}x$$

38. $(0, 0)$ and $(-2, 1)$ are points on the line.

Slope $= \dfrac{1-0}{-2-0} = \dfrac{1}{-2} = -\dfrac{1}{2}$

y-intercept is 0; using $y = mx + b$:

$y = -\dfrac{1}{2}x + 0$

$2y = -x$

$x + 2y = 0$

$x + 2y = 0$ or $y = -\dfrac{1}{2}x$

39. $(-1, 3)$ and $(1, 1)$ are points on the line.

Slope $= \dfrac{1-3}{1-(-1)} = \dfrac{-2}{2} = -1$

Using $y - y_1 = m(x - x_1)$

$y - 1 = -1(x - 1)$

$y - 1 = -x + 1$

$y = -x + 2$

$x + y = 2$ or $y = -x + 2$

40. $(-1, 1)$ and $(2, 2)$ are points on the line.

Slope $= \dfrac{2-1}{2-(-1)} = \dfrac{1}{3}$

Using $y - y_1 = m(x - x_1)$

$y - 1 = \dfrac{1}{3}\left(x - (-1)\right)$

$y - 1 = \dfrac{1}{3}(x + 1)$

$y - 1 = \dfrac{1}{3}x + \dfrac{1}{3}$

$y = \dfrac{1}{3}x + \dfrac{4}{3}$

$x - 3y = -4$ or $y = \dfrac{1}{3}x + \dfrac{4}{3}$

41. $y - y_1 = m(x - x_1),\ m = 2$

$y - 3 = 2(x - 3)$

$y - 3 = 2x - 6$

$y = 2x - 3$

$2x - y = 3$ or $y = 2x - 3$

42. $y - y_1 = m(x - x_1),\ m = -1$

$y - 2 = -1(x - 1)$

$y - 2 = -x + 1$

$y = -x + 3$

$x + y = 3$ or $y = -x + 3$

43. $y - y_1 = m(x - x_1),\ m = -\dfrac{1}{2}$

$y - 2 = -\dfrac{1}{2}(x - 1)$

$y - 2 = -\dfrac{1}{2}x + \dfrac{1}{2}$

$y = -\dfrac{1}{2}x + \dfrac{5}{2}$

$x + 2y = 5$ or $y = -\dfrac{1}{2}x + \dfrac{5}{2}$

44. $y - y_1 = m(x - x_1),\ m = 1$

$y - 1 = 1(x - (-1))$

$y - 1 = x + 1$

$y = x + 2$

$x - y = -2$ or $y = x + 2$

45. Slope $= 3$; containing $(-2, 3)$

$y - y_1 = m(x - x_1)$

$y - 3 = 3(x - (-2))$

$y - 3 = 3x + 6$

$y = 3x + 9$

$3x - y = -9$ or $y = 3x + 9$

46. Slope $= 2$; containing the point $(4, -3)$

$y - y_1 = m(x - x_1)$

$y - (-3) = 2(x - 4)$

$y + 3 = 2x - 8$

$y = 2x - 11$

$2x - y = 11$ or $y = 2x - 11$

47. Slope $= -\dfrac{2}{3}$; containing $(1, -1)$

$y - y_1 = m(x - x_1)$

$y - (-1) = -\dfrac{2}{3}(x - 1)$

$y + 1 = -\dfrac{2}{3}x + \dfrac{2}{3}$

$y = -\dfrac{2}{3}x - \dfrac{1}{3}$

$2x + 3y = -1$ or $y = -\dfrac{2}{3}x - \dfrac{1}{3}$

185

48. Slope $=\dfrac{1}{2}$; containing the point $(3, 1)$

$$y - y_1 = m(x - x_1)$$

$$y - 1 = \frac{1}{2}(x - 3)$$

$$y - 1 = \frac{1}{2}x - \frac{3}{2}$$

$$y = \frac{1}{2}x - \frac{1}{2}$$

$$x - 2y = 1 \ \text{ or } \ y = \frac{1}{2}x - \frac{1}{2}$$

49. Containing $(1, 3)$ and $(-1, 2)$

$$m = \frac{2 - 3}{-1 - 1} = \frac{-1}{-2} = \frac{1}{2}$$

$$y - y_1 = m(x - x_1)$$

$$y - 3 = \frac{1}{2}(x - 1)$$

$$y - 3 = \frac{1}{2}x - \frac{1}{2}$$

$$y = \frac{1}{2}x + \frac{5}{2}$$

$$x - 2y = -5 \ \text{ or } \ y = \frac{1}{2}x + \frac{5}{2}$$

50. Containing the points $(-3, 4)$ and $(2, 5)$

$$m = \frac{5 - 4}{2 - (-3)} = \frac{1}{5}$$

$$y - y_1 = m(x - x_1)$$

$$y - 5 = \frac{1}{5}(x - 2)$$

$$y - 5 = \frac{1}{5}x - \frac{2}{5}$$

$$y = \frac{1}{5}x + \frac{23}{5}$$

$$x - 5y = -23 \ \text{ or } \ y = \frac{1}{5}x + \frac{23}{5}$$

51. Slope $= -3$; y-intercept $= 3$

$$y = mx + b$$

$$y = -3x + 3$$

$$3x + y = 3 \ \text{ or } \ y = -3x + 3$$

52. Slope $= -2$; y-intercept $= -2$

$$y = mx + b$$

$$y = -2x + (-2)$$

$$2x + y = -2 \ \text{ or } \ y = -2x - 2$$

53. x-intercept $= 2$; y-intercept $= -1$
Points are $(2, 0)$ and $(0, -1)$

$$m = \frac{-1 - 0}{0 - 2} = \frac{-1}{-2} = \frac{1}{2}$$

$$y = mx + b$$

$$y = \frac{1}{2}x - 1$$

$$x - 2y = 2 \ \text{ or } \ y = \frac{1}{2}x - 1$$

54. x-intercept $= -4$; y-intercept $= 4$
Points are $(-4, 0)$ and $(0, 4)$

$$m = \frac{4 - 0}{0 - (-4)} = \frac{4}{4} = 1$$

$$y = mx + b$$

$$y = 1x + 4$$

$$y = x + 4$$

$$x - y = -4 \ \text{ or } \ y = x + 4$$

55. Slope undefined; containing the point $(2, 4)$
This is a vertical line.
$x = 2$ No slope-intercept form.

56. Slope undefined; containing the point $(3, 8)$
This is a vertical line.
$x = 3$ No slope-intercept form.

57. Horizontal lines have slope $m = 0$ and take the form $y = b$. Therefore, the horizontal line passing through the point $(-3, 2)$ is $y = 2$.

58. Vertical lines have an undefined slope and take the form $x = a$. Therefore, the vertical line passing through the point $(4, -5)$ is $x = 4$.

59. Parallel to $y = 2x$; Slope $= 2$
Containing $(-1, 2)$

$$y - y_1 = m(x - x_1)$$

$$y - 2 = 2(x - (-1))$$

$$y - 2 = 2x + 2 \rightarrow y = 2x + 4$$

$$2x - y = -4 \ \text{ or } \ y = 2x + 4$$

60. Parallel to $y = -3x$; Slope $= -3$; Containing the point $(-1, 2)$

$$y - y_1 = m(x - x_1)$$

$$y - 2 = -3(x - (-1))$$

$$y - 2 = -3x - 3 \rightarrow y = -3x - 1$$

$$3x + y = -1 \ \text{ or } \ y = -3x - 1$$

186

61. Parallel to $2x - y = -2$; Slope = 2
Containing the point $(0, 0)$
$$y - y_1 = m(x - x_1)$$
$$y - 0 = 2(x - 0)$$
$$y = 2x$$
$2x - y = 0$ or $y = 2x$

62. Parallel to $x - 2y = -5$;
Slope $= \dfrac{1}{2}$; Containing the point $(0, 0)$
$$y - y_1 = m(x - x_1)$$
$$y - 0 = \frac{1}{2}(x - 0) \rightarrow y = \frac{1}{2}x$$
$x - 2y = 0$ or $y = \dfrac{1}{2}x$

63. Parallel to $x = 5$; Containing $(4, 2)$
This is a vertical line.
$x = 4$ No slope-intercept form.

64. Parallel to $y = 5$; Containing the point $(4, 2)$
This is a horizontal line. Slope = 0
$y = 2$

65. Perpendicular to $y = \dfrac{1}{2}x + 4$; Containing $(1, -2)$
Slope of perpendicular = -2
$$y - y_1 = m(x - x_1)$$
$$y - (-2) = -2(x - 1)$$
$$y + 2 = -2x + 2 \rightarrow y = -2x$$
$2x + y = 0$ or $y = -2x$

66. Perpendicular to $y = 2x - 3$; Containing the point $(1, -2)$
Slope of perpendicular $= -\dfrac{1}{2}$
$$y - y_1 = m(x - x_1)$$
$$y - (-2) = -\frac{1}{2}(x - 1)$$
$$y + 2 = -\frac{1}{2}x + \frac{1}{2} \rightarrow y = -\frac{1}{2}x - \frac{3}{2}$$
$x + 2y = -3$ or $y = -\dfrac{1}{2}x - \dfrac{3}{2}$

67. Perpendicular to $2x + y = 2$; Containing the point $(-3, 0)$
Slope of perpendicular $= \dfrac{1}{2}$
$$y - y_1 = m(x - x_1)$$
$$y - 0 = \frac{1}{2}(x - (-3)) \rightarrow y = \frac{1}{2}x + \frac{3}{2}$$
$x - 2y = -3$ or $y = \dfrac{1}{2}x + \dfrac{3}{2}$

68. Perpendicular to $x - 2y = -5$; Containing the point $(0, 4)$
Slope of perpendicular $= -2$
$$y = mx + b$$
$$y = -2x + 4$$
$2x + y = 4$ or $y = -2x + 4$

69. Perpendicular to $x = 8$; Containing $(3, 4)$
Slope of perpendicular = 0 (horizontal line)
$y = 4$

70. Perpendicular to $y = 8$;
Containing the point $(3, 4)$
Slope of perpendicular is undefined (vertical line). $x = 3$ No slope-intercept form.

71. $y = 2x + 3$; Slope = 2; y-intercept = 3

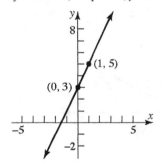

72. $y = -3x + 4$; Slope = -3; y-intercept = 4

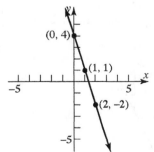

187

73. $\frac{1}{2}y = x - 1$; $y = 2x - 2$

Slope = 2; y-intercept = -2

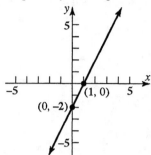

74. $\frac{1}{3}x + y = 2$; $y = -\frac{1}{3}x + 2$

Slope = $-\frac{1}{3}$; y-intercept = 2

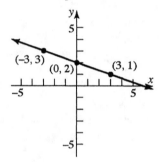

75. $y = \frac{1}{2}x + 2$; Slope = $\frac{1}{2}$; y-intercept = 2

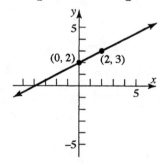

76. $y = 2x + \frac{1}{2}$; Slope = 2; y-intercept = $\frac{1}{2}$

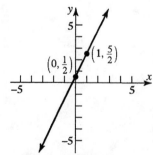

77. $x + 2y = 4$; $2y = -x + 4 \rightarrow y = -\frac{1}{2}x + 2$

Slope = $-\frac{1}{2}$; y-intercept = 2

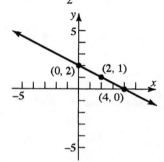

78. $-x + 3y = 6$; $3y = x + 6 \rightarrow y = \frac{1}{3}x + 2$

Slope = $\frac{1}{3}$; y-intercept = 2

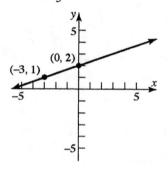

79. $2x - 3y = 6$; $-3y = -2x + 6 \rightarrow y = \frac{2}{3}x - 2$

Slope = $\frac{2}{3}$; y-intercept = -2

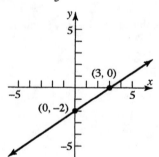

80. $3x + 2y = 6$; $2y = -3x + 6 \rightarrow y = -\dfrac{3}{2}x + 3$

Slope $= -\dfrac{3}{2}$; y-intercept $= 3$

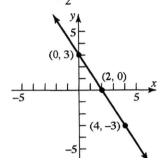

81. $x + y = 1$; $y = -x + 1$
Slope $= -1$; y-intercept $= 1$

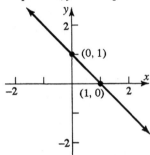

82. $x - y = 2$; $y = x - 2$
Slope $= 1$; y-intercept $= -2$

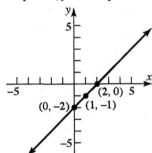

83. $x = -4$; Slope is undefined
y-intercept - none

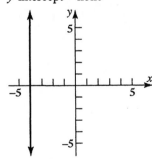

84. $y = -1$; Slope $= 0$; y-intercept $= -1$

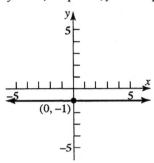

85. $y = 5$; Slope $= 0$; y-intercept $= 5$

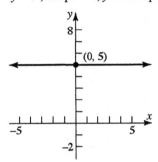

86. $x = 2$; Slope is undefined
y-intercept - none

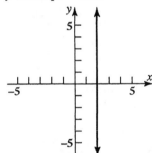

87. $y - x = 0$; $y = x$
Slope $= 1$; y-intercept $= 0$

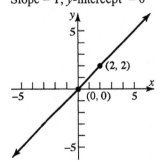

88. $x + y = 0$; $y = -x$

Slope $= -1$; y-intercept $= 0$

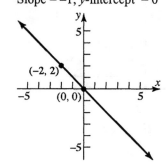

89. $2y - 3x = 0$; $2y = 3x \rightarrow y = \dfrac{3}{2}x$

Slope $= \dfrac{3}{2}$; y-intercept $= 0$

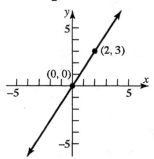

90. $3x + 2y = 0$; $2y = -3x \rightarrow y = -\dfrac{3}{2}x$

Slope $= -\dfrac{3}{2}$; y-intercept $= 0$

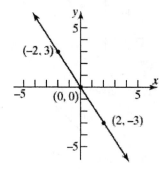

91. a. x-intercept: $2x + 3(0) = 6$

$$2x = 6$$
$$x = 3$$

The point $(3, 0)$ is on the graph.

y-intercept: $2(0) + 3y = 6$

$$3y = 6$$
$$y = 2$$

The point $(0, 2)$ is on the graph.

b.

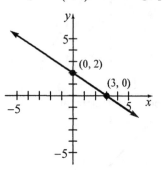

92. a. x-intercept: $3x - 2(0) = 6$

$$3x = 6$$
$$x = 2$$

The point $(2, 0)$ is on the graph.

y-intercept: $3(0) - 2y = 6$

$$-2y = 6$$
$$y = -3$$

The point $(0, -3)$ is on the graph.

b.

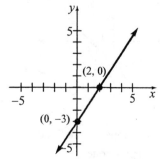

190

93. a. x-intercept: $-4x+5(0)=40$

$$-4x=40$$
$$x=-10$$

The point $(-10,0)$ is on the graph.

y-intercept: $-4(0)+5y=40$

$$5y=40$$
$$y=8$$

The point $(0,8)$ is on the graph.

b.

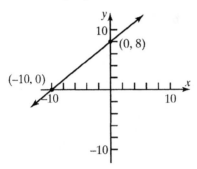

94. a. x-intercept: $6x-4(0)=24$

$$6x=24$$
$$x=4$$

The point $(4,0)$ is on the graph.

y-intercept: $6(0)-4y=24$

$$-4y=24$$
$$y=-6$$

The point $(0,-6)$ is on the graph.

b.

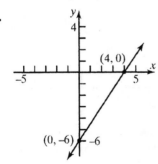

95. a. x-intercept: $7x+2(0)=21$

$$7x=21$$
$$x=3$$

The point $(3,0)$ is on the graph.

y-intercept: $7(0)+2y=21$

$$2y=21$$
$$y=\frac{21}{2}$$

The point $\left(0,\dfrac{21}{2}\right)$ is on the graph.

b.

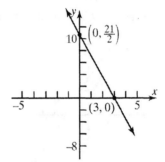

96. a. x-intercept: $5x+3(0)=18$

$$5x=18$$
$$x=\frac{18}{5}$$

The point $\left(\dfrac{18}{5},0\right)$ is on the graph.

y-intercept: $5(0)+3y=18$

$$3y=18$$
$$y=6$$

The point $(0,6)$ is on the graph.

b.

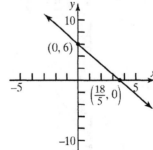

97. a. *x*-intercept: $\dfrac{1}{2}x + \dfrac{1}{3}(0) = 1$

$$\dfrac{1}{2}x = 1$$

$$x = 2$$

The point $(2,0)$ is on the graph.

y-intercept: $\dfrac{1}{2}(0) + \dfrac{1}{3}y = 1$

$$\dfrac{1}{3}y = 1$$

$$y = 3$$

The point $(0,3)$ is on the graph.

b.

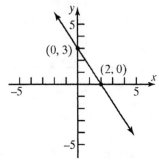

98. a. *x*-intercept: $x - \dfrac{2}{3}(0) = 4$

$$x = 4$$

The point $(4,0)$ is on the graph.

y-intercept: $(0) - \dfrac{2}{3}y = 4$

$$-\dfrac{2}{3}y = 4$$

$$y = -6$$

The point $(0,-6)$ is on the graph.

b.

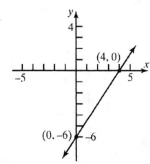

99. a. *x*-intercept: $0.2x - 0.5(0) = 1$

$$0.2x = 1$$

$$x = 5$$

The point $(5,0)$ is on the graph.

y-intercept: $0.2(0) - 0.5y = 1$

$$-0.5y = 1$$

$$y = -2$$

The point $(0,-2)$ is on the graph.

b.

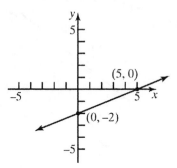

100. a. *x*-intercept: $-0.3x + 0.4(0) = 1.2$

$$-0.3x = 1.2$$

$$x = -4$$

The point $(-4,0)$ is on the graph.

y-intercept: $-0.3(0) + 0.4y = 1.2$

$$0.4y = 1.2$$

$$y = 3$$

The point $(0,3)$ is on the graph.

b.

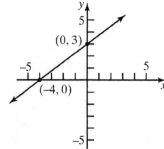

101. The equation of the *x*-axis is $y = 0$. (The slope is 0 and the *y*-intercept is 0.)

102. The equation of the *y*-axis is $x = 0$. (The slope is undefined.)

103. The slopes are the same but the *y*-intercepts are different. Therefore, the two lines are parallel.

104. The slopes are opposite-reciprocals. That is, their product is -1. Therefore, the lines are perpendicular.

105. The slopes are different and their product does not equal -1. Therefore, the lines are neither parallel nor perpendicular.

106. The slopes are different and their product does not equal -1 (in fact, the signs are the same so the product is positive). Therefore, the lines are neither parallel nor perpendicular.

107. Intercepts: $(0,2)$ and $(-2,0)$. Thus, slope $= 1$.
$y = x + 2$ or $x - y = -2$

108. Intercepts: $(0,1)$ and $(1,0)$. Thus, slope $= -1$.
$y = -x + 1$ or $x + y = 1$

109. Intercepts: $(3,0)$ and $(0,1)$. Thus, slope $= -\dfrac{1}{3}$.
$y = -\dfrac{1}{3}x + 1$ or $x + 3y = 3$

110. Intercepts: $(0,-1)$ and $(-2,0)$. Thus,
slope $= -\dfrac{1}{2}$.
$y = -\dfrac{1}{2}x - 1$ or $x + 2y = -2$

111. $P_1 = (-2,5)$, $P_2 = (1,3)$: $m_1 = \dfrac{5-3}{-2-1} = \dfrac{2}{-3} = -\dfrac{2}{3}$

$P_2 = (1,3)$, $P_3 = (-1,0)$: $m_2 = \dfrac{3-0}{1-(-1)} = \dfrac{3}{2}$

Since $m_1 \cdot m_2 = -1$, the line segments $\overline{P_1 P_2}$ and $\overline{P_2 P_3}$ are perpendicular. Thus, the points P_1, P_2, and P_3 are vertices of a right triangle.

112. $P_1 = (1,-1)$, $P_2 = (4,1)$, $P_3 = (2,2)$, $P_4 = (5,4)$
$m_{12} = \dfrac{1-(-1)}{4-1} = \dfrac{2}{3}$; $m_{24} = \dfrac{4-1}{5-4} = 3$;
$m_{34} = \dfrac{4-2}{5-2} = \dfrac{2}{3}$; $m_{13} = \dfrac{2-(-1)}{2-1} = 3$
Each pair of opposite sides are parallel (same slope) and adjacent sides are not perpendicular. Therefore, the vertices are for a parallelogram.

113. $P_1 = (-1,0)$, $P_2 = (2,3)$, $P_3 = (1,-2)$, $P_4 = (4,1)$
$m_{12} = \dfrac{3-0}{2-(-1)} = \dfrac{3}{3} = 1$; $m_{24} = \dfrac{1-3}{4-2} = -1$;
$m_{34} = \dfrac{1-(-2)}{4-1} = \dfrac{3}{3} = 1$; $m_{13} = \dfrac{-2-0}{1-(-1)} = -1$
Opposite sides are parallel (same slope) and adjacent sides are perpendicular (product of slopes is -1). Therefore, the vertices are for a rectangle.

114. $P_1 = (0,0)$, $P_2 = (1,3)$, $P_3 = (4,2)$, $P_4 = (3,-1)$
$m_{12} = \dfrac{3-0}{1-0} = 3$; $m_{23} = \dfrac{2-3}{4-1} = -\dfrac{1}{3}$;
$m_{34} = \dfrac{-1-2}{3-4} = 3$; $m_{14} = \dfrac{-1-0}{3-0} = -\dfrac{1}{3}$
$d_{12} = \sqrt{(1-0)^2 + (3-0)^2} = \sqrt{1+9} = \sqrt{10}$
$d_{23} = \sqrt{(4-1)^2 + (2-3)^2} = \sqrt{9+1} = \sqrt{10}$
$d_{34} = \sqrt{(3-4)^2 + (-1-2)^2} = \sqrt{1+9} = \sqrt{10}$
$d_{14} = \sqrt{(3-0)^2 + (-1-0)^2} = \sqrt{9+1} = \sqrt{10}$
Opposite sides are parallel (same slope) and adjacent sides are perpendicular (product of slopes is -1). In addition, the length of all four sides is the same. Therefore, the vertices are for a square.

115. Let $x =$ number of miles driven, and let $C =$ cost in dollars.
Total cost = (cost per mile)(number of miles) + fixed cost
$C = 0.20x + 29$
When $x = 110$, $C = (0.20)(110) + 29 = \$51.00$.
When $x = 230$, $C = (0.20)(230) + 29 = \$75.00$.

116. Let $x =$ number of pairs of jeans manufactured, and let $C =$ cost in dollars.
Total cost = (cost per pair)(number of pairs) + fixed cost
$C = 8x + 500$
When $x = 400$, $C = (8)(400) + 500 = \$3700$.
When $x = 740$, $C = (8)(740) + 500 = \$6420$.

117. Let $x =$ number newspapers delivered, and let $C =$ cost in dollars.
Total cost = (delivery cost per paper)(number of papers delivered) + fixed cost
$C = 0.53x + 1,070,000$

193

118. Let x = profit in dollars, and let S = salary in dollars.
Weekly salary = (% share of profit)(profit) + weekly pay
$S = 0.05x + 375$

119. a. $C = 0.08275x + 7.58$; $0 \le x \le 400$

b.

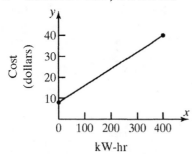

c. For 100 kWh,
$C = 0.08275(100) + 7.58 = \$15.86$

d. For 300 kWh,
$C = 0.08725(300) + 7.58 = \$32.41$

e. For each usage increase of 1 kWh, the monthly charge increases by \$0.08275 (that is, 8.275 cents).

120. a. $C = 0.1007x + 5.17$; $0 \le x \le 1000$

b.

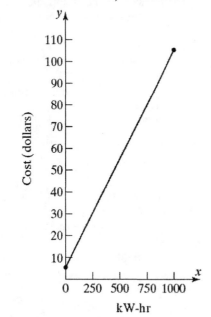

c. For 200 kWh,
$C = 0.1007(200) + 5.17 = \$25.31$

d. For 500 kWh,
$C = 0.1007(500) + 5.17 = \$55.52$

e. For each usage increase of 1 kWh, the monthly charge increases by \$0.1007 (that is, 10.07 cents).

121. $(°C, °F) = (0, 32)$; $(°C, °F) = (100, 212)$

$$\text{slope } = \frac{212 - 32}{100 - 0} = \frac{180}{100} = \frac{9}{5}$$

$$°F - 32 = \frac{9}{5}(°C - 0)$$

$$°F - 32 = \frac{9}{5}(°C)$$

$$°C = \frac{5}{9}(°F - 32)$$

If $°F = 70$, then

$$°C = \frac{5}{9}(70 - 32) = \frac{5}{9}(38)$$

$$°C \approx 21.1°$$

122. a. $K = °C + 273$

b. $°C = \frac{5}{9}(°F - 32)$

$$K = \frac{5}{9}(°F - 32) + 273$$

$$K = \frac{5}{9}°F - \frac{160}{9} + 273$$

$$K = \frac{5}{9}°F + \frac{2297}{9}$$

$$K = \frac{1}{9}\left(5°F + 2297\right)$$

123. a. The y-intercept is $(0, 30)$, so $b = 30$. Since the ramp drops 2 inches for every 25 inches of run, the slope is $m = \frac{-2}{25} = -\frac{2}{25}$. Thus, the equation is $y = -\frac{2}{25}x + 30$.

b. Let $y = 0$.

$$0 = -\frac{2}{25}x + 30$$

$$\frac{2}{25}x = 30$$

$$\frac{25}{2}\left(\frac{2}{25}x\right) = \frac{25}{2}(30)$$

$$x = 375$$

The x-intercept is $(375, 0)$. This means that the ramp meets the floor 375 inches (or 31.25 feet) from the base of the platform.

c. No. From part (b), the run is 31.25 feet which exceeds the required maximum of 30 feet.

d. First, design requirements state that the maximum slope is a drop of 1 inch for each 12 inches of run. This means $|m| \le \dfrac{1}{12}$.

Second, the run is restricted to be no more than 30 feet = 360 inches. For a rise of 30 inches, this means the minimum slope is $\dfrac{30}{360} = \dfrac{1}{12}$. That is, $|m| \ge \dfrac{1}{12}$. Thus, the only possible slope is $|m| = \dfrac{1}{12}$. The diagram indicates that the slope is negative. Therefore, the only slope that can be used to obtain the 30-inch rise and still meet design requirements is $m = -\dfrac{1}{12}$. In words, for every 12 inches of run, the ramp must drop *exactly* 1 inch.

124. a. The year 1998 corresponds to $x = 0$, and the year 2005 corresponds to $x = 7$. Therefore, the points (0, 42) and (7, 22) are on the line. Thus, $m = \dfrac{22 - 42}{7 - 0} = -\dfrac{20}{7}$. The y-intercept is (0, 42), so $b = 42$ and the equation is

$$y = -\frac{20}{7}x + 42$$

b. x-intercept: $\qquad 0 = -\dfrac{20}{7}x + 42$

$$\frac{20}{7}x = 42$$

$$\frac{7}{20}\left(\frac{20}{7}x\right) = \frac{7}{20}(42)$$

$$x = 14.7$$

y-intercept: $y = -\dfrac{20}{7}(0) + 42 = 42$

The intercepts are (14.7, 0) and (0, 42).

c. The y-intercept represents the percentage of teens in 1998 who had recently used cigarettes. The x-intercept represents the number of years after 1998 when 0% of teens will have recently used cigarettes.

d. The year 2019 corresponds to $x = 21$.

$$y = -\frac{20}{7}(21) + 42 = -60 + 42 = -18$$

This prediction is not reasonable because the percent cannot be negative.

125. a. Let x = number of boxes to be sold, and A = money, in dollars, spent on advertising. We have the points

$(x_1, A_1) = (100,000, 40,000)$;

$(x_2, A_2) = (200,000, 60,000)$

$$\text{slope } = \frac{60,000 - 40,000}{200,000 - 100,000}$$

$$= \frac{20,000}{100,000} = \frac{1}{5}$$

$$A - 40,000 = \frac{1}{5}(x - 100,000)$$

$$A - 40,000 = \frac{1}{5}x - 20,000$$

$$A = \frac{1}{5}x + 20,000$$

b. If $x = 300,000$, then

$$A = \frac{1}{5}(300,000) + 20,000 = \$80,000$$

c. Each additional box sold requires an additional $0.20 in advertising.

126. Find the slope of the line containing (a, b) and (b, a):

$$\text{slope} = \frac{a - b}{b - a} = -1$$

The slope of the line $y = x$ is 1.

Since $-1 \cdot 1 = -1$, the line containing the points (a, b) and (b, a) is perpendicular to the line $y = x$.

The midpoint of (a, b) and (b, a) is

$$M = \left(\frac{a + b}{2}, \frac{b + a}{2}\right).$$

Since the coordinates are the same, the midpoint lies on the line $y = x$.

Note: $\dfrac{a + b}{2} = \dfrac{b + a}{2}$

127. $2x - y = C$

Graph the lines:

$2x - y = -4$

$2x - y = 0$

$2x - y = 2$

All the lines have the same slope, 2. The lines are parallel.

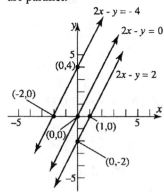

128. Refer to Figure 47.

length of $\overline{OA} = d(O, A) = \sqrt{1 + m_1^2}$

length of $\overline{OB} = d(O, B) = \sqrt{1 + m_2^2}$

length of $\overline{AB} = d(A, B) = m_1 - m_2$

Now consider the equation

$$\left(\sqrt{1 + m_1^2}\right)^2 + \left(\sqrt{1 + m_2^2}\right)^2 = \left(m_1 - m_2\right)^2$$

If this equation is valid, then $\triangle AOB$ is a right triangle with right angle at vertex O.

$$\left(\sqrt{1 + m_1^2}\right)^2 + \left(\sqrt{1 + m_2^2}\right)^2 = \left(m_1 - m_2\right)^2$$

$$1 + m_1^2 + 1 + m_2^2 = m_1^2 - 2m_1 m_2 + m_2^2$$

$$2 + m_1^2 + m_2^2 = m_1^2 - 2m_1 m_2 + m_2^2$$

But we are assuming that $m_1 m_2 = -1$, so we have

$$2 + m_1^2 + m_2^2 = m_1^2 - 2(-1) + m_2^2$$

$$2 + m_1^2 + m_2^2 = m_1^2 + 2 + m_2^2$$

$$0 = 0$$

Therefore, by the converse of the Pythagorean Theorem, $\triangle AOB$ is a right triangle with right angle at vertex O. Thus Line 1 is perpendicular to Line 2.

129. (b), (c), (e) and (g)

The line has positive slope and positive y-intercept.

130. (a), (c), and (g)

The line has negative slope and positive y-intercept.

131. (c)

The equation $x - y = -2$ has slope 1 and y-intercept $(0, 2)$. The equation $x - y = 1$ has slope 1 and y-intercept $(0, -1)$. Thus, the lines are parallel with positive slopes. One line has a positive y-intercept and the other with a negative y-intercept.

132. (d)

The equation $y - 2x = 2$ has slope 2 and y-intercept $(0, 2)$. The equation $x + 2y = -1$ has slope $-\dfrac{1}{2}$ and y-intercept $\left(0, -\dfrac{1}{2}\right)$. The lines are perpendicular since $2\left(-\dfrac{1}{2}\right) = -1$. One line has a positive y-intercept and the other with a negative y-intercept.

133 – 135. Answers will vary.

136. No, the equation of a vertical line cannot be written in slope-intercept form because the slope is undefined.

137. No, a line does not need to have both an x-intercept and a y-intercept. Vertical and horizontal lines have only one intercept (unless they are a coordinate axis). Every line must have at least one intercept.

138. Two lines with equal slopes and equal y-intercepts are coinciding lines (i.e. the same).

139. Two lines that have the same x-intercept and y-intercept (assuming the x-intercept is not 0) are the same line since a line is uniquely defined by two distinct points.

140. No. Two lines with the same slope and different x-intercepts are distinct parallel lines and have no points in common.

Assume Line 1 has equation $y = mx + b_1$ and Line 2 has equation $y = mx + b_2$,

Line 1 has x-intercept $-\dfrac{b_1}{m}$ and y-intercept b_1.

Line 2 has x-intercept $-\dfrac{b_2}{m}$ and y-intercept b_2.

Assume also that Line 1 and Line 2 have unequal x-intercepts.

If the lines have the same y-intercept, then $b_1 = b_2$.

$$b_1 = b_2 \Rightarrow \frac{b_1}{m} = \frac{b_2}{m} \Rightarrow -\frac{b_1}{m} = -\frac{b_2}{m}$$

But $-\dfrac{b_1}{m} = -\dfrac{b_2}{m} \Rightarrow$ Line 1 and Line 2 have the same x-intercept, which contradicts the original assumption that the lines have unequal x-intercepts. Therefore, Line 1 and Line 2 cannot have the same y-intercept.

141. Yes. Two distinct lines with the same y-intercept, but different slopes, can have the same x-intercept if the x-intercept is $x = 0$.

Assume Line 1 has equation $y = m_1 x + b$ and Line 2 has equation $y = m_2 x + b$,

Line 1 has x-intercept $-\dfrac{b}{m_1}$ and y-intercept b.

Line 2 has x-intercept $-\dfrac{b}{m_2}$ and y-intercept b.

Assume also that Line 1 and Line 2 have unequal slopes, that is $m_1 \neq m_2$.

If the lines have the same x-intercept, then

$$-\frac{b}{m_1} = -\frac{b}{m_2}.$$

$$-\frac{b}{m_1} = -\frac{b}{m_2}$$
$$-m_2 b = -m_1 b$$
$$-m_2 b + m_1 b = 0$$

But $-m_2 b + m_1 b = 0 \Rightarrow b(m_1 - m_2) = 0$
$$\Rightarrow b = 0$$
$$\text{or } m_1 - m_2 = 0 \Rightarrow m_1 = m_2$$

Since we are assuming that $m_1 \neq m_2$, the only way that the two lines can have the same x-intercept is if $b = 0$.

142. Answers will vary.

Section 2.4

1. add; 25

2. $(x-2)^2 = 9$
$$x - 2 = \pm\sqrt{9}$$
$$x - 2 = \pm 3$$
$$x = 2 \pm 3$$
$$x = 5 \quad \text{or} \quad x = -1$$
The solution set is $\{-1, 5\}$.

3. False. For example, $x^2 + y^2 + 2x + 2y + 8 = 0$ is not a circle. It has no real solutions.

4. radius

5. True; $r^2 = 9 \rightarrow r = 3$

6. False; the center of the circle $(x+3)^2 + (y-2)^2 = 13$ is $(-3, 2)$.

7. Center = $(2, 1)$
Radius = distance from $(0,1)$ to $(2,1)$
$$= \sqrt{(2-0)^2 + (1-1)^2} = \sqrt{4} = 2$$
Equation: $(x-2)^2 + (y-1)^2 = 4$

8. Center = $(1, 2)$
Radius = distance from $(1,0)$ to $(1,2)$
$$= \sqrt{(1-1)^2 + (2-0)^2} = \sqrt{4} = 2$$
Equation: $(x-1)^2 + (y-2)^2 = 4$

9. Center = midpoint of $(1, 2)$ and $(4, 2)$
$$= \left(\frac{1+4}{2}, \frac{2+2}{2}\right) = \left(\frac{5}{2}, 2\right)$$
Radius = distance from $\left(\frac{5}{2}, 2\right)$ to $(4,2)$
$$= \sqrt{\left(4 - \frac{5}{2}\right)^2 + (2-2)^2} = \sqrt{\frac{9}{4}} = \frac{3}{2}$$
Equation: $\left(x - \frac{5}{2}\right)^2 + (y-2)^2 = \frac{9}{4}$

10. Center = midpoint of $(0, 1)$ and $(2, 3)$
$$= \left(\frac{0+2}{2}, \frac{1+3}{2}\right) = (1, 2)$$
Radius = distance from $(1, 2)$ to $(2,3)$
$$= \sqrt{(2-1)^2 + (3-2)^2} = \sqrt{2}$$
Equation: $(x-1)^2 + (y-2)^2 = 2$

11. $(x-h)^2 + (y-k)^2 = r^2$

$(x-0)^2 + (y-0)^2 = 2^2$

$x^2 + y^2 = 4$

General form: $x^2 + y^2 - 4 = 0$

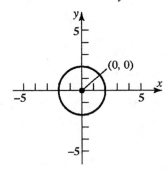

12. $(x-h)^2 + (y-k)^2 = r^2$

$(x-0)^2 + (y-0)^2 = 3^2$

$x^2 + y^2 = 9$

General form: $x^2 + y^2 - 9 = 0$

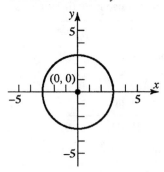

13. $(x-h)^2 + (y-k)^2 = r^2$

$(x-0)^2 + (y-2)^2 = 2^2$

$x^2 + (y-2)^2 = 4$

General form: $x^2 + y^2 - 4y + 4 = 4$

$x^2 + y^2 - 4y = 0$

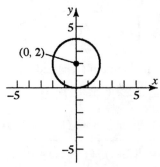

14. $(x-h)^2 + (y-k)^2 = r^2$

$(x-1)^2 + (y-0)^2 = 3^2$

$(x-1)^2 + y^2 = 9$

General form: $x^2 - 2x + 1 + y^2 = 9$

$x^2 + y^2 - 2x - 8 = 0$

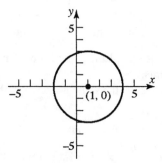

15. $(x-h)^2 + (y-k)^2 = r^2$

$(x-4)^2 + (y-(-3))^2 = 5^2$

$(x-4)^2 + (y+3)^2 = 25$

General form:

$x^2 - 8x + 16 + y^2 + 6y + 9 = 25$

$x^2 + y^2 - 8x + 6y = 0$

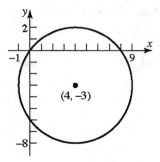

16. $(x-h)^2 + (y-k)^2 = r^2$

$(x-2)^2 + (y-(-3))^2 = 4^2$

$(x-2)^2 + (y+3)^2 = 16$

General form: $x^2 - 4x + 4 + y^2 + 6y + 9 = 16$

$x^2 + y^2 - 4x + 6y - 3 = 0$

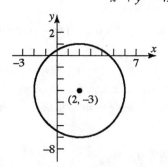

198

17. $(x-h)^2 + (y-k)^2 = r^2$

$(x-(-2))^2 + (y-1)^2 = 4^2$

$(x+2)^2 + (y-1)^2 = 16$

General form: $x^2 + 4x + 4 + y^2 - 2y + 1 = 16$

$x^2 + y^2 + 4x - 2y - 11 = 0$

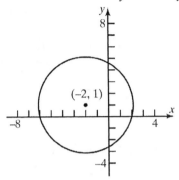

(−2, 1)

18. $(x-h)^2 + (y-k)^2 = r^2$

$(x-(-5))^2 + (y-(-2))^2 = 7^2$

$(x+5)^2 + (y+2)^2 = 49$

General form: $x^2 + 10x + 25 + y^2 + 4y + 4 = 49$

$x^2 + y^2 + 10x + 4y - 20 = 0$

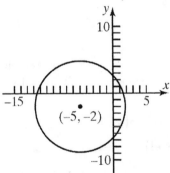

(−5, −2)

19. $(x-h)^2 + (y-k)^2 = r^2$

$\left(x - \dfrac{1}{2}\right)^2 + (y-0)^2 = \left(\dfrac{1}{2}\right)^2$

$\left(x - \dfrac{1}{2}\right)^2 + y^2 = \dfrac{1}{4}$

General form: $x^2 - x + \dfrac{1}{4} + y^2 = \dfrac{1}{4}$

$x^2 + y^2 - x = 0$

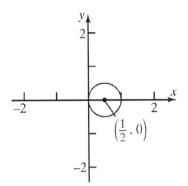

$\left(\dfrac{1}{2}, 0\right)$

20. $(x-h)^2 + (y-k)^2 = r^2$

$(x-0)^2 + \left(y - \left(-\dfrac{1}{2}\right)\right)^2 = \left(\dfrac{1}{2}\right)^2$

$x^2 + \left(y + \dfrac{1}{2}\right)^2 = \dfrac{1}{4}$

General form: $x^2 + y^2 + y + \dfrac{1}{4} = \dfrac{1}{4}$

$x^2 + y^2 + y = 0$

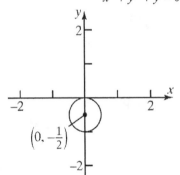

$\left(0, -\dfrac{1}{2}\right)$

21. $x^2 + y^2 = 4$

$x^2 + y^2 = 2^2$

a. Center: $(0,0)$; Radius $= 2$

b.

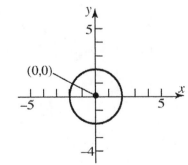

(0,0)

199

c. *x*-intercepts: $x^2 + (0)^2 = 4$

$$x^2 = 4$$

$$x = \pm\sqrt{4} = \pm 2$$

y-intercepts: $(0)^2 + y^2 = 4$

$$y^2 = 4$$

$$y = \pm\sqrt{4} = \pm 2$$

The intercepts are $(-2, 0), (2, 0), (0, -2),$ and $(0, 2)$.

22. $x^2 + (y-1)^2 = 1$

$$x^2 + (y-1)^2 = 1^2$$

a. Center: $(0, 1)$; Radius $= 1$

b.

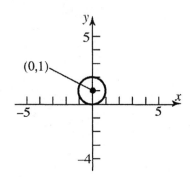

c. *x*-intercepts: $x^2 + (0-1)^2 = 1$

$$x^2 + 1 = 1$$

$$x^2 = 0$$

$$x = \pm\sqrt{0} = 0$$

y-intercepts: $(0)^2 + (y-1)^2 = 1$

$$(y-1)^2 = 1$$

$$y - 1 = \pm\sqrt{1}$$

$$y - 1 = \pm 1$$

$$y = 1 \pm 1$$

$$y = 2 \quad \text{or} \quad y = 0$$

The intercepts are $(0, 0)$ and $(0, 2)$.

23. $2(x-3)^2 + 2y^2 = 8$

$$(x-3)^2 + y^2 = 4$$

a. Center: $(3, 0)$; Radius $= 2$

b.

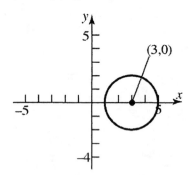

c. *x*-intercepts: $(x-3)^2 + (0)^2 = 4$

$$(x-3)^2 = 4$$

$$x - 3 = \pm\sqrt{4}$$

$$x - 3 = \pm 2$$

$$x = 3 \pm 2$$

$$x = 5 \quad \text{or} \quad x = 1$$

y-intercepts: $(0-3)^2 + y^2 = 4$

$$(-3)^2 + y^2 = 4$$

$$9 + y^2 = 4$$

$$y^2 = -5$$

No real solution.

The intercepts are $(1, 0)$ and $(5, 0)$.

24. $3(x+1)^2 + 3(y-1)^2 = 6$

$$(x+1)^2 + (y-1)^2 = 2$$

a. Center: $(-1, 1)$; Radius $= \sqrt{2}$

b.

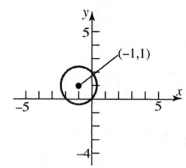

c. x-intercepts: $(x+1)^2 + (0-1)^2 = 2$

$$(x+1)^2 + (-1)^2 = 2$$
$$(x+1)^2 + 1 = 2$$
$$(x+1)^2 = 1$$
$$x+1 = \pm\sqrt{1}$$
$$x+1 = \pm 1$$
$$x = -1 \pm 1$$
$$x = 0 \quad \text{or} \quad x = -2$$

y-intercepts: $(0+1)^2 + (y-1)^2 = 2$

$$(1)^2 + (y-1)^2 = 2$$
$$1 + (y-1)^2 = 2$$
$$(y-1)^2 = 1$$
$$y-1 = \pm\sqrt{1}$$
$$y-1 = \pm 1$$
$$y = 1 \pm 1$$
$$y = 2 \quad \text{or} \quad y = 0$$

The intercepts are $(-2, 0), (0, 0),$ and $(0, 2)$.

25. $x^2 + y^2 - 2x - 4y - 4 = 0$

$$x^2 - 2x + y^2 - 4y = 4$$
$$(x^2 - 2x + 1) + (y^2 - 4y + 4) = 4 + 1 + 4$$
$$(x-1)^2 + (y-2)^2 = 3^2$$

a. Center: $(1, 2)$; Radius $= 3$

b.

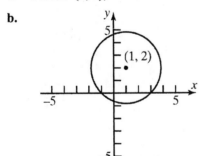

c. x-intercepts: $(x-1)^2 + (0-2)^2 = 3^2$

$$(x-1)^2 + (-2)^2 = 3^2$$
$$(x-1)^2 + 4 = 9$$
$$(x-1)^2 = 5$$
$$x-1 = \pm\sqrt{5}$$
$$x = 1 \pm \sqrt{5}$$

y-intercepts: $(0-1)^2 + (y-2)^2 = 3^2$

$$(-1)^2 + (y-2)^2 = 3^2$$
$$1 + (y-2)^2 = 9$$
$$(y-2)^2 = 8$$
$$y-2 = \pm\sqrt{8}$$
$$y-2 = \pm 2\sqrt{2}$$
$$y = 2 \pm 2\sqrt{2}$$

The intercepts are $\left(1-\sqrt{5}, 0\right), \left(1+\sqrt{5}, 0\right),$

$\left(0, 2-2\sqrt{2}\right),$ and $\left(0, 2+2\sqrt{2}\right)$.

26. $x^2 + y^2 + 4x + 2y - 20 = 0$

$$x^2 + 4x + y^2 + 2y = 20$$
$$(x^2 + 4x + 4) + (y^2 + 2y + 1) = 20 + 4 + 1$$
$$(x+2)^2 + (y+1)^2 = 5^2$$

a. Center: $(-2, -1)$; Radius $= 5$

b.

c. x-intercepts: $(x+2)^2 + (0+1)^2 = 5^2$

$$(x+2)^2 + 1 = 25$$
$$(x+2)^2 = 24$$
$$x+2 = \pm\sqrt{24}$$
$$x+2 = \pm 2\sqrt{6}$$
$$x = -2 \pm 2\sqrt{6}$$

y-intercepts: $(0+2)^2 + (y+1)^2 = 5^2$

$$4 + (y+1)^2 = 25$$
$$(y+1)^2 = 21$$
$$y+1 = \pm\sqrt{21}$$
$$y = -1 \pm \sqrt{21}$$

The intercepts are $\left(-2-2\sqrt{6}, 0\right),$

$\left(-2+2\sqrt{6}, 0\right), \left(0, -1-\sqrt{21}\right),$ and

$\left(0, -1+\sqrt{21}\right)$.

201

27.
$$x^2 + y^2 + 4x - 4y - 1 = 0$$
$$x^2 + 4x + y^2 - 4y = 1$$
$$(x^2 + 4x + 4) + (y^2 - 4y + 4) = 1 + 4 + 4$$
$$(x + 2)^2 + (y - 2)^2 = 3^2$$

a. Center: $(-2, 2)$; Radius $= 3$

b.

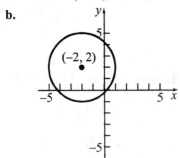

c. *x*-intercepts: $(x + 2)^2 + (0 - 2)^2 = 3^2$
$$(x + 2)^2 + 4 = 9$$
$$(x + 2)^2 = 5$$
$$x + 2 = \pm\sqrt{5}$$
$$x = -2 \pm \sqrt{5}$$

y-intercepts: $(0 + 2)^2 + (y - 2)^2 = 3^2$
$$4 + (y - 2)^2 = 9$$
$$(y - 2)^2 = 5$$
$$y - 2 = \pm\sqrt{5}$$
$$y = 2 \pm \sqrt{5}$$

The intercepts are $\left(-2 - \sqrt{5}, 0\right)$,

$\left(-2 + \sqrt{5}, 0\right)$, $\left(0, 2 - \sqrt{5}\right)$, and $\left(0, 2 + \sqrt{5}\right)$.

28.
$$x^2 + y^2 - 6x + 2y + 9 = 0$$
$$x^2 - 6x + y^2 + 2y = -9$$
$$(x^2 - 6x + 9) + (y^2 + 2y + 1) = -9 + 9 + 1$$
$$(x - 3)^2 + (y + 1)^2 = 1^2$$

a. Center: $(3, -1)$; Radius $= 1$

b.

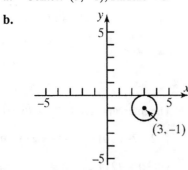

c. *x*-intercepts: $(x - 3)^2 + (0 + 1)^2 = 1^2$
$$(x - 3)^2 + 1 = 1$$
$$(x - 3)^2 = 0$$
$$x - 3 = 0$$
$$x = 3$$

y-intercepts: $(0 - 3)^2 + (y + 1)^2 = 1^2$
$$9 + (y + 1)^2 = 1$$
$$(y + 1)^2 = -8$$
No real solution.
The intercept only intercept is $(3, 0)$.

29.
$$x^2 + y^2 - x + 2y + 1 = 0$$
$$x^2 - x + y^2 + 2y = -1$$
$$\left(x^2 - x + \frac{1}{4}\right) + (y^2 + 2y + 1) = -1 + \frac{1}{4} + 1$$
$$\left(x - \frac{1}{2}\right)^2 + (y + 1)^2 = \left(\frac{1}{2}\right)^2$$

a. Center: $\left(\frac{1}{2}, -1\right)$; Radius $= \frac{1}{2}$

b.

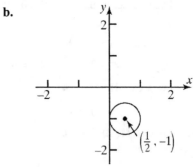

c. *x*-intercepts: $\left(x - \frac{1}{2}\right)^2 + (0 + 1)^2 = \left(\frac{1}{2}\right)^2$
$$\left(x - \frac{1}{2}\right)^2 + 1 = \frac{1}{4}$$
$$\left(x - \frac{1}{2}\right)^2 = -\frac{3}{4}$$
No real solutions

y-intercepts: $\left(0 - \frac{1}{2}\right)^2 + (y + 1)^2 = \left(\frac{1}{2}\right)^2$
$$\frac{1}{4} + (y + 1)^2 = \frac{1}{4}$$
$$(y + 1)^2 = 0$$
$$y + 1 = 0$$
$$y = -1$$
The only intercept is $(0, -1)$.

30.
$$x^2 + y^2 + x + y - \frac{1}{2} = 0$$
$$x^2 + x + y^2 + y = \frac{1}{2}$$
$$\left(x^2 + x + \frac{1}{4}\right) + \left(y^2 + y + \frac{1}{4}\right) = \frac{1}{2} + \frac{1}{4} + \frac{1}{4}$$
$$\left(x + \frac{1}{2}\right)^2 + \left(y + \frac{1}{2}\right)^2 = 1^2$$

a. Center: $\left(-\frac{1}{2}, -\frac{1}{2}\right)$; Radius = 1

b.

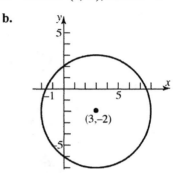

c. x-intercepts: $\left(x + \frac{1}{2}\right)^2 + \left(0 + \frac{1}{2}\right)^2 = 1^2$
$$\left(x + \frac{1}{2}\right)^2 + \frac{1}{4} = 1$$
$$\left(x + \frac{1}{2}\right)^2 = \frac{3}{4}$$
$$x + \frac{1}{2} = \pm\frac{\sqrt{3}}{2}$$
$$x = \frac{-1 \pm \sqrt{3}}{2}$$

y-intercepts: $\left(0 + \frac{1}{2}\right)^2 + \left(y + \frac{1}{2}\right)^2 = 1^2$
$$\frac{1}{4} + \left(y + \frac{1}{2}\right)^2 = 1$$
$$\left(y + \frac{1}{2}\right)^2 = \frac{3}{4}$$
$$y + \frac{1}{2} = \pm\frac{\sqrt{3}}{2}$$
$$y = \frac{-1 \pm \sqrt{3}}{2}$$

The intercepts are $\left(\frac{-1-\sqrt{3}}{2}, 0\right)$, $\left(\frac{-1+\sqrt{3}}{2}, 0\right)$,
$\left(0, \frac{-1-\sqrt{3}}{2}\right)$, and $\left(0, \frac{-1+\sqrt{3}}{2}\right)$.

31.
$$2x^2 + 2y^2 - 12x + 8y - 24 = 0$$
$$x^2 + y^2 - 6x + 4y = 12$$
$$x^2 - 6x + y^2 + 4y = 12$$
$$(x^2 - 6x + 9) + (y^2 + 4y + 4) = 12 + 9 + 4$$
$$(x - 3)^2 + (y + 2)^2 = 5^2$$

a. Center: $(3, -2)$; Radius = 5

b.

c. x-intercepts: $(x - 3)^2 + (0 + 2)^2 = 5^2$
$$(x - 3)^2 + 4 = 25$$
$$(x - 3)^2 = 21$$
$$x - 3 = \pm\sqrt{21}$$
$$x = 3 \pm \sqrt{21}$$

y-intercepts: $(0 - 3)^2 + (y + 2)^2 = 5^2$
$$9 + (y + 2)^2 = 25$$
$$(y + 2)^2 = 16$$
$$y + 2 = \pm 4$$
$$y = -2 \pm 4$$
$$y = 2 \quad \text{or} \quad y = -6$$

The intercepts are $\left(3 - \sqrt{21}, 0\right)$, $\left(3 + \sqrt{21}, 0\right)$,
$(0, -6)$, and $(0, 2)$.

32. a.
$$2x^2 + 2y^2 + 8x + 7 = 0$$
$$2x^2 + 8x + 2y^2 = -7$$
$$x^2 + 4x + y^2 = -\frac{7}{2}$$
$$(x^2 + 4x + 4) + y^2 = -\frac{7}{2} + 4$$
$$(x + 2)^2 + y^2 = \frac{1}{2}$$
$$(x + 2)^2 + y^2 = \left(\frac{\sqrt{2}}{2}\right)^2$$

Center: $(-2, 0)$; Radius = $\frac{\sqrt{2}}{2}$

203

b.

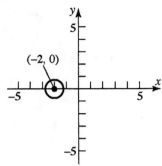

$(-2, 0)$

c. x-intercepts: $(x+2)^2 + (0)^2 = \dfrac{1}{2}$

$$(x+2)^2 = \dfrac{1}{2}$$

$$x+2 = \pm\sqrt{\dfrac{1}{2}}$$

$$x+2 = \pm\dfrac{\sqrt{2}}{2}$$

$$x = -2 \pm \dfrac{\sqrt{2}}{2}$$

y-intercepts: $(0+2)^2 + y^2 = \dfrac{1}{2}$

$$4 + y^2 = \dfrac{1}{2}$$

$$y^2 = -\dfrac{7}{2}$$

No real solutions.

The intercepts are $\left(-2 - \dfrac{\sqrt{2}}{2}, 0\right)$ and

$\left(-2 + \dfrac{\sqrt{2}}{2}, 0\right)$.

33. $\quad 2x^2 + 8x + 2y^2 = 0$

$$x^2 + 4x + y^2 = 0$$

$$x^2 + 4x + 4 + y^2 = 0 + 4$$

$$(x+2)^2 + y^2 = 2^2$$

a. Center: $(-2, 0)$; Radius: $r = 2$

b.

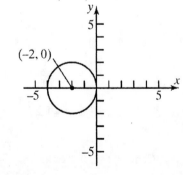

$(-2, 0)$

c. x-intercepts: $(x+2)^2 + (0)^2 = 2^2$

$$(x+2)^2 = 4$$

$$(x+2)^2 = \pm\sqrt{4}$$

$$x+2 = \pm 2$$

$$x = -2 \pm 2$$

$$x = 0 \quad \text{or} \quad x = -4$$

y-intercepts: $(0+2)^2 + y^2 = 2^2$

$$4 + y^2 = 4$$

$$y^2 = 0$$

$$y = 0$$

The intercepts are $(-4, 0)$ and $(0, 0)$.

34. $\quad 3x^2 + 3y^2 - 12y = 0$

$$x^2 + y^2 - 4y = 0$$

$$x^2 + y^2 - 4y + 4 = 0 + 4$$

$$x^2 + (y-2)^2 = 4$$

a. Center: $(0, 2)$; Radius: $r = 2$

b.

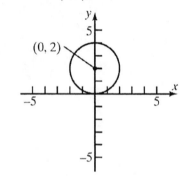

$(0, 2)$

c. x-intercepts: $x^2 + (0-2)^2 = 4$

$$x^2 + 4 = 4$$

$$x^2 = 0$$

$$x = 0$$

y-intercepts: $0^2 + (y-2)^2 = 4$

$$(y-2)^2 = 4$$

$$y - 2 = \pm\sqrt{4}$$

$$y - 2 = \pm 2$$

$$y = 2 \pm 2$$

$$y = 4 \quad \text{or} \quad y = 0$$

The intercepts are $(0, 0)$ and $(0, 4)$.

204

35. Center at (0, 0); containing point (–2, 3).

$r = \sqrt{(-2-0)^2 + (3-0)^2} = \sqrt{4+9} = \sqrt{13}$

Equation: $(x-0)^2 + (y-0)^2 = \left(\sqrt{13}\right)^2$

$x^2 + y^2 = 13$

36. Center at (1, 0); containing point (–3, 2).

$r = \sqrt{(-3-1)^2 + (2-0)^2} = \sqrt{16+4} = \sqrt{20} = 2\sqrt{5}$

Equation: $(x-1)^2 + (y-0)^2 = \left(\sqrt{20}\right)^2$

$(x-1)^2 + y^2 = 20$

37. Center at (2, 3); tangent to the *x*-axis.

$r = 3$

Equation: $(x-2)^2 + (y-3)^2 = 3^2$

$(x-2)^2 + (y-3)^2 = 9$

38. Center at (–3, 1); tangent to the *y*-axis.

$r = 3$

Equation: $(x+3)^2 + (y-1)^2 = 3^2$

$(x+3)^2 + (y-1)^2 = 9$

39. Endpoints of a diameter are (1, 4) and (–3, 2). The center is at the midpoint of that diameter:

Center: $\left(\dfrac{1+(-3)}{2}, \dfrac{4+2}{2}\right) = (-1, 3)$

Radius: $r = \sqrt{(1-(-1))^2 + (4-3)^2} = \sqrt{4+1} = \sqrt{5}$

Equation: $(x-(-1))^2 + (y-3)^2 = \left(\sqrt{5}\right)^2$

$(x+1)^2 + (y-3)^2 = 5$

40. Endpoints of a diameter are (4, 3) and (0, 1). The center is at the midpoint of that diameter:

Center: $\left(\dfrac{4+0}{2}, \dfrac{3+1}{2}\right) = (2, 2)$

Radius: $r = \sqrt{(4-2)^2 + (3-2)^2} = \sqrt{4+1} = \sqrt{5}$

Equation: $(x-2)^2 + (y-2)^2 = \left(\sqrt{5}\right)^2$

$(x-2)^2 + (y-2)^2 = 5$

41. Center at (–1, 3); tangent to the line *y* = 2. This means that the circle contains the point (–1, 2), so the radius is *r* = 1.

Equation: $(x+1)^2 + (y-3)^2 = (1)^2$

$(x+1)^2 + (y-3)^2 = 1$

42. Center at (4, –2); tangent to the line *x* = 1. This means that the circle contains the point (1, –2), so the radius is *r* = 3.

Equation: $(x-4)^2 + (y+2)^2 = (3)^2$

$(x-4)^2 + (y+2)^2 = 9$

43. (c); Center: $(1, -2)$; Radius = 2

44. (d); Center: $(-3, 3)$; Radius = 3

45. (b); Center: $(-1, 2)$; Radius = 2

46. (a); Center: $(-3, 3)$; Radius = 3

47. Let the upper-right corner of the square be the point (x, y). The circle and the square are both centered about the origin. Because of symmetry, we have that $x = y$ at the upper-right corner of the square. Therefore, we get

$x^2 + y^2 = 9$

$x^2 + x^2 = 9$

$2x^2 = 9$

$x^2 = \dfrac{9}{2}$

$x = \sqrt{\dfrac{9}{2}} = \dfrac{3\sqrt{2}}{2}$

The length of one side of the square is $2x$. Thus, the area is

$A = s^2 = \left(2 \cdot \dfrac{3\sqrt{2}}{2}\right)^2 = \left(3\sqrt{2}\right)^2 = 18$ square units.

48. The area of the shaded region is the area of the circle, less the area of the square. Let the upper-right corner of the square be the point (x, y).

The circle and the square are both centered about the origin. Because of symmetry, we have that $x = y$ at the upper-right corner of the square. Therefore, we get

$$x^2 + y^2 = 36$$
$$x^2 + x^2 = 36$$
$$2x^2 = 36$$
$$x^2 = 18$$
$$x = 3\sqrt{2}$$

The length of one side of the square is $2x$. Thus, the area of the square is $\left(2 \cdot 3\sqrt{2}\right)^2 = 72$ square units. From the equation of the circle, we have $r = 6$. The area of the circle is

$$\pi r^2 = \pi(6)^2 = 36\pi \text{ square units.}$$

Therefore, the area of the shaded region is $A = 36\pi - 72$ square units.

49. The diameter of the Ferris wheel was 250 feet, so the radius was 125 feet. The maximum height was 264 feet, so the center was at a height of $264 - 125 = 139$ feet above the ground. Since the center of the wheel is on the y-axis, it is the point (0, 139). Thus, an equation for the wheel is:

$$(x - 0)^2 + (y - 139)^2 = 125^2$$
$$x^2 + (y - 139)^2 = 15,625$$

50. The diameter of the wheel is 153 meters, so the radius is 76.5 meters. The maximum height is 160 meters, so the center of the wheel is at a height of $160 - 76.5 = 83.5$ meters above the ground. Since the center of the wheel is on the y-axis, it is the point (0, 83.5). Thus, an equation for the wheel is:

$$(x - 0)^2 + (y - 83.5)^2 = 76.5^2$$
$$x^2 + (y - 83.5)^2 = 5852.25$$

51.
$$x^2 + y^2 + 2x + 4y - 4091 = 0$$
$$x^2 + 2x + y^2 + 4y - 4091 = 0$$
$$x^2 + 2x + 1 + y^2 + 4y + 4 = 4091 + 5$$
$$(x + 1)^2 + (y + 2)^2 = 4096$$

The circle representing Earth has center $(-1, -2)$ and radius $= \sqrt{4096} = 64$.
So the radius of the satellite's orbit is $64 + 0.6 = 64.6$ units.
The equation of the orbit is
$$(x + 1)^2 + (y + 2)^2 = (64.6)^2$$
$$x^2 + y^2 + 2x + 4y - 4168.16 = 0$$

52. a.
$$x^2 + (mx + b)^2 = r^2$$
$$x^2 + m^2 x^2 + 2bmx + b^2 = r^2$$
$$(1 + m^2)x^2 + 2bmx + b^2 - r^2 = 0$$

There is one solution if and only if the discriminant is zero.

$$(2bm)^2 - 4(1 + m^2)(b^2 - r^2) = 0$$
$$4b^2 m^2 - 4b^2 + 4r^2 - 4b^2 m^2 + 4m^2 r^2 = 0$$
$$-4b^2 + 4r^2 + 4m^2 r^2 = 0$$
$$-b^2 + r^2 + m^2 r^2 = 0$$
$$r^2(1 + m^2) = b^2$$

b. Using the quadratic formula, the result from part (a), and knowing that the discriminant is zero, we get:

$$(1 + m^2)x^2 + 2bmx + b^2 - r^2 = 0$$

$$x = \frac{-2bm}{2(1 + m^2)} = \frac{-bm}{\left(\dfrac{b^2}{r^2}\right)} = \frac{-bmr^2}{b^2} = \frac{-mr^2}{b}$$

$$y = m\left(\frac{-mr^2}{b}\right) + b$$

$$= \frac{-m^2 r^2}{b} + b = \frac{-m^2 r^2 + b^2}{b} = \frac{r^2}{b}$$

c. The slope of the tangent line is m. The slope of the line joining the point of tangency and the center is:

$$\frac{\left(\dfrac{r^2}{b} - 0\right)}{\left(\dfrac{-mr^2}{b} - 0\right)} = \frac{r^2}{b} \cdot \frac{b}{-mr^2} = -\frac{1}{m}$$

Therefore, the tangent line is perpendicular to the line containing the center of the circle and the point of tangency.

53. $x^2 + y^2 = 9$

Center: $(0, 0)$

Slope from center to $\left(1, 2\sqrt{2}\right)$ is

$$\frac{2\sqrt{2} - 0}{1 - 0} = \frac{2\sqrt{2}}{1} = 2\sqrt{2}.$$

Slope of the tangent line is $\dfrac{-1}{2\sqrt{2}} = -\dfrac{\sqrt{2}}{4}$.

Equation of the tangent line is:

$$y - 2\sqrt{2} = -\frac{\sqrt{2}}{4}(x - 1)$$

$$y - 2\sqrt{2} = -\frac{\sqrt{2}}{4}x + \frac{\sqrt{2}}{4}$$

$$4y - 8\sqrt{2} = -\sqrt{2}\,x + \sqrt{2}$$

$$\sqrt{2}\,x + 4y = 9\sqrt{2}$$

$$\sqrt{2}\,x + 4y - 9\sqrt{2} = 0$$

54. $x^2 + y^2 - 4x + 6y + 4 = 0$

$$(x^2 - 4x + 4) + (y^2 + 6y + 9) = -4 + 4 + 9$$

$$(x - 2)^2 + (y + 3)^2 = 9$$

Center: $(2, -3)$

Slope from center to $\left(3, 2\sqrt{2} - 3\right)$ is

$$\frac{2\sqrt{2} - 3 - (-3)}{3 - 2} = \frac{2\sqrt{2}}{1} = 2\sqrt{2}$$

Slope of the tangent line is: $\dfrac{-1}{2\sqrt{2}} = -\dfrac{\sqrt{2}}{4}$

Equation of the tangent line:

$$y - \left(2\sqrt{2} - 3\right) = -\frac{\sqrt{2}}{4}(x - 3)$$

$$y - 2\sqrt{2} + 3 = -\frac{\sqrt{2}}{4}x + \frac{3\sqrt{2}}{4}$$

$$4y - 8\sqrt{2} + 12 = -\sqrt{2}x + 3\sqrt{2}$$

$$\sqrt{2}x + 4y - 11\sqrt{2} + 12 = 0$$

55. Let (h, k) be the center of the circle.

$$x - 2y + 4 = 0$$

$$2y = x + 4$$

$$y = \frac{1}{2}x + 2$$

The slope of the tangent line is $\dfrac{1}{2}$. The slope from (h, k) to $(0, 2)$ is -2.

$$\frac{2 - k}{0 - h} = -2$$

$$2 - k = 2h$$

The other tangent line is $y = 2x - 7$, and it has slope 2.

The slope from (h, k) to $(3, -1)$ is $-\dfrac{1}{2}$.

$$\frac{-1 - k}{3 - h} = -\frac{1}{2}$$

$$2 + 2k = 3 - h$$

$$2k = 1 - h$$

$$h = 1 - 2k$$

Solve the two equations in h and k:

$$2 - k = 2(1 - 2k)$$

$$2 - k = 2 - 4k$$

$$3k = 0$$

$$k = 0$$

$$h = 1 - 2(0) = 1$$

The center of the circle is $(1, 0)$.

56. Find the centers of the two circles:

$$x^2 + y^2 - 4x + 6y + 4 = 0$$

$$(x^2 - 4x + 4) + (y^2 + 6y + 9) = -4 + 4 + 9$$

$$(x - 2)^2 + (y + 3)^2 = 9$$

Center: $(2, -3)$

$$x^2 + y^2 + 6x + 4y + 9 = 0$$

$$(x^2 + 6x + 9) + (y^2 + 4y + 4) = -9 + 9 + 4$$

$$(x + 3)^2 + (y + 2)^2 = 4$$

Center: $(-3, -2)$

Find the slope of the line containing the centers:

$$m = \frac{-2 - (-3)}{-3 - 2} = -\frac{1}{5}$$

Find the equation of the line containing the centers:

$$y + 3 = -\frac{1}{5}(x - 2)$$

$$5y + 15 = -x + 2$$

$$x + 5y = -13$$

$$x + 5y + 13 = 0$$

57. Consider the following diagram:

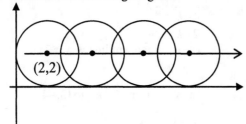

(2,2)

Therefore, the path of the center of the circle has the equation $y = 2$.

58.
$$C = 2\pi r$$
$$6\pi = 2\pi r$$
$$\frac{6\pi}{2\pi} = \frac{2\pi r}{2\pi}$$
$$3 = r$$
The radius is 3 units long.

59. (b), (c), (e) and (g)
We need $h, k > 0$ and $(0,0)$ on the graph.

60. (b), (e) and (g)
We need $h < 0$, $k = 0$, and $|h| > r$.

61. Answers will vary.

Section 2.5

1. $y = kx$

2. False. If y varies directly with x, then $y = kx$, where k is a constant.

3. $y = kx$
$$2 = 10k$$
$$k = \frac{2}{10} = \frac{1}{5}$$
$$y = \frac{1}{5}x$$

4. $v = kt$
$$16 = 2k$$
$$8 = k$$
$$v = 8t$$

5. $A = kx^2$
$$4\pi = k(2)^2$$
$$4\pi = 4k$$
$$\pi = k$$
$$A = \pi x^2$$

6. $V = kx^3$
$$36\pi = k(3)^3$$
$$36\pi = 27k$$
$$k = \frac{36\pi}{27} = \frac{4}{3}\pi$$
$$V = \frac{4}{3}\pi x^3$$

7. $F = \dfrac{k}{d^2}$
$$10 = \frac{k}{5^2}$$
$$10 = \frac{k}{25}$$
$$k = 250$$
$$F = \frac{250}{d^2}$$

8. $y = \dfrac{k}{\sqrt{x}}$
$$4 = \frac{k}{\sqrt{9}}$$
$$4 = \frac{k}{3}$$
$$k = 12$$
$$y = \frac{12}{\sqrt{x}}$$

9. $z = k\left(x^2 + y^2\right)$
$$5 = k\left(3^2 + 4^2\right)$$
$$5 = k(25)$$
$$k = \frac{5}{25} = \frac{1}{5}$$
$$z = \frac{1}{5}\left(x^2 + y^2\right)$$

10. $T = k\left(\sqrt[3]{x}\right)\left(d^2\right)$

$18 = k\left(\sqrt[3]{8}\right)\left(3^2\right)$

$18 = k(18)$

$1 = k$

$T = \left(\sqrt[3]{x}\right)\left(d^2\right)$

11. $M = \dfrac{kd^2}{\sqrt{x}}$

$24 = \dfrac{k\left(4^2\right)}{\sqrt{9}}$

$24 = \dfrac{16k}{3}$

$k = 24\left(\dfrac{3}{16}\right) = \dfrac{9}{2}$

$M = \dfrac{9d^2}{2\sqrt{x}}$

12. $z = k\left(x^3 + y^2\right)$

$1 = k\left(2^3 + 3^2\right)$

$1 = k(17)$

$k = \dfrac{1}{17}$

$z = \dfrac{1}{17}\left(x^3 + y^2\right)$

13. $T^2 = \dfrac{ka^3}{d^2}$

$2^2 = \dfrac{k\left(2^3\right)}{4^2}$

$4 = \dfrac{k(8)}{16}$

$4 = \dfrac{k}{2}$

$k = 8$

$T^2 = \dfrac{8a^3}{d^2}$

14. $z^3 = k\left(x^2 + y^2\right)$

$2^3 = k\left(9^2 + 4^2\right)$

$8 = k(97)$

$k = \dfrac{8}{97}$

$z^3 = \dfrac{8}{97}\left(x^2 + y^2\right)$

15. $V = \dfrac{4\pi}{3}r^3$

16. $c^2 = a^2 + b^2$

17. $A = \dfrac{1}{2}bh$

18. $p = 2(l + w)$

19. $F = \left(6.67 \times 10^{-11}\right)\left(\dfrac{mM}{d^2}\right)$

20. $T = \dfrac{2\pi}{\sqrt{32}}\sqrt{l}$

21. $\qquad p = kB$

$\qquad 6.49 = k(1000)$

$0.00649 = k$

Therefore we have the linear equation
$p = 0.00649B$.

If $B = 145000$, then
$p = 0.00649(145000) = \$941.05$.

22. $\qquad p = kB$

$\qquad 8.99 = k(1000)$

$0.00899 = k$

Therefore we have the linear equation
$p = 0.00899B$.

If $B = 175000$, then
$p = 0.00899(175000) = \$1573.25$.

23. $s = kt^2$

$16 = k(1)^2$

$k = 16$

Therefore, we have equation $s = 16t^2$.

If $t = 3$ seconds, then $s = 16(3)^2 = 144$ feet.

If $s = 64$ feet, then

$64 = 16t^2$

$t^2 = 4$

$t = \pm 2$

Time must be positive, so we disregard $t = -2$.
It takes 2 seconds to fall 64 feet.

24. $v = kt$

$64 = k(2)$

$k = 32$

Therefore, we have the linear equation $v = 32t$.
If $t = 3$ seconds, then $v = 32(3) = 96$ ft/sec.

25. $E = kW$

$3 = k(20)$

$k = \dfrac{3}{20}$

Therefore, we have the linear equation $E = \dfrac{3}{20}W$.

If $W = 15$, then $E = \dfrac{3}{20}(15) = 2.25$.

26. $R = \dfrac{k}{l}$

$256 = \dfrac{k}{48}$

$k = 12,288$

Therefore, we have the equation $R = \dfrac{12,288}{l}$.

If $R = 576$, then

$576 = \dfrac{12,288}{l}$

$576l = 12,288$

$l = \dfrac{12,288}{576} = \dfrac{64}{3}$ inches

27. $R = kg$

$47.40 = k(12)$

$3.95 = k$

Therefore, we have the linear equation $R = 3.95g$.

If $g = 10.5$, then $R = (3.95)(10.5) \approx \$41.48$.

28. $C = kA$

$23.75 = k(5)$

$4.75 = k$

Therefore, we have the linear equation $C = 4.75A$.
If $A = 3.5$, then $C = (4.75)(3.5) = \$16.63$.

29. $D = \dfrac{k}{p}$

a. $D = 156$, $p = 2.75$;

$156 = \dfrac{k}{2.75}$

$k = 429$

So, $D = \dfrac{429}{p}$.

b. $D = \dfrac{429}{3} = 143$ bags of candy

30. $t = \dfrac{k}{s}$

a. $t = 40$, $s = 30$;

$40 = \dfrac{k}{30}$

$k = 1200$

So, we have the equation $t = \dfrac{1200}{s}$.

b. $t = \dfrac{1200}{40} = 30$ minutes

31. $V = \dfrac{k}{P}$

$V = 600, P = 150$;

$600 = \dfrac{k}{150}$

$k = 90,000$

So, we have the equation $V = \dfrac{90,000}{P}$

If $P = 200$, then $V = \dfrac{90,000}{200} = 450$ cm^3.

32. $i = \dfrac{k}{R}$

If $i = 30, R = 8$, then $30 = \dfrac{k}{8}$ and $k = 240$.

So, we have the equation $i = \dfrac{240}{R}$.

If $R = 10$, then $i = \dfrac{240}{10} = 24$ amperes.

33. $W = \dfrac{k}{d^2}$

If $W = 125, d = 3960$ then

$125 = \dfrac{k}{3960^2}$ and $k = 1{,}960{,}200{,}000$

So, we have the equation $W = \dfrac{1{,}960{,}200{,}000}{d}$.

At the top of Mt. McKinley, we have

$d = 3960 + 3.8 = 3963.8$, so

$W = \dfrac{1{,}960{,}200{,}000}{(3963.8)^2} \approx 124.76$ pounds.

34. $I = \dfrac{k}{d^2}$

If $I = 0.075, d = 2$, then

$0.075 = \dfrac{k}{2^2}$ and $k = 0.3$.

So, we have the equation $I = \dfrac{0.3}{d^2}$.

If $d = 5$, then $I = \dfrac{0.3}{5^2} = 0.012$ foot-candles.

35. $V = \pi r^2 h$

36. $V = \dfrac{\pi}{3} r^2 h$

37. $W = \dfrac{k}{d^2}$

$55 = \dfrac{k}{3960^2}$

$k = 862{,}488{,}000$

So, we have the equation $W = \dfrac{862{,}488{,}000}{d^2}$.

If $d = 3965$, then

$W = \dfrac{862{,}488{,}000}{3965^2} \approx 54.86$ pounds.

38. $F = kAv^2$

$11 = k(20)(22)^2$

$11 = 9860k$

$k = \dfrac{11}{9680} = \dfrac{1}{880}$

So, we have the equation $F = \dfrac{1}{880} Av^2$.

If $A = 47.125$ and $v = 36.5$, then

$F = \dfrac{1}{880}(47.125)(36.5)^2 \approx 71.34$ pounds.

39. $h = ksd^3$

$36 = k(75)(2)^3$

$36 = 600k$

$0.06 = k$

So, we have the equation $h = 0.06sd^3$.

If $h = 45$ and $s = 125$, then

$45 = (0.06)(125)d^3$

$45 = 7.5d^3$

$6 = d^3$

$d = \sqrt[3]{6} \approx 1.82$ inches

40. $V = \dfrac{kT}{P}$

$100 = \dfrac{k(300)}{15}$

$100 = 20k$

$5 = k$

So, we have the equation $V = \dfrac{5T}{P}$.

If $V = 80$ and $T = 310$, then

$80 = \dfrac{5(310)}{P}$

$80P = 1550$

$P = \dfrac{1550}{80} = 19.375$ atmospheres

41. $K = kmv^2$

$1250 = k(25)(10)^2$

$1250 = 2500k$

$k = 0.5$

So, we have the equation $K = 0.5mv^2$.

If $m = 25$ and $v = 15$, then

$K = 0.5(25)(15)^2 = 2812.5$ Joules

42. $R = \dfrac{kl}{d^2}$

$1.24 = \dfrac{k(432)}{(4)^2}$

$1.24 = 27k$

$k = \dfrac{1.24}{27}$

So, we have the equation $R = \dfrac{1.24l}{27d^2}$.

If $R = 1.44$ and $d = 3$, then

$1.44 = \dfrac{1.24l}{27(3)^2}$

$1.44 = \dfrac{1.24l}{243}$

$349.92 = 1.24l$

$l = \dfrac{349.92}{1.24} \approx 282.2$ feet

43. $S = \dfrac{kpd}{t}$

$100 = \dfrac{k(25)(5)}{0.75}$

$75 = 125k$

$0.6 = k$

So, we have the equation $S = \dfrac{0.6pd}{t}$.

If $p = 40$, $d = 8$, and $t = 0.50$, then

$S = \dfrac{0.6(40)(8)}{0.50} = 384$ psi.

44. $S = \dfrac{kwt^2}{l}$

$750 = \dfrac{k(4)(2)^2}{8}$

$750 = 2k$

$375 = k$

So, we have the equation $S = \dfrac{375wt^2}{l}$.

If $l = 10$, $w = 6$, and $t = 2$, then

$S = \dfrac{375(6)(2)^2}{10} = 900$ pounds.

45 – 48. Answers will vary.

Chapter 2 Review Exercises

1. $P_1 = (0,0)$ and $P_2 = (4,2)$

a. $d(P_1, P_2) = \sqrt{(4-0)^2 + (2-0)^2}$
$= \sqrt{16+4} = \sqrt{20} = 2\sqrt{5}$

b. The coordinates of the midpoint are:

$(x, y) = \left(\dfrac{x_1 + x_2}{2}, \dfrac{y_1 + y_2}{2} \right)$

$= \left(\dfrac{0+4}{2}, \dfrac{0+2}{2} \right) = \left(\dfrac{4}{2}, \dfrac{2}{2} \right) = (2,1)$

c. slope $= \dfrac{\Delta y}{\Delta x} = \dfrac{2-0}{4-0} = \dfrac{2}{4} = \dfrac{1}{2}$

d. For each run of 2, there is a rise of 1.

2. $P_1 = (0,0)$ and $P_2 = (-4,6)$

a. $d(P_1, P_2) = \sqrt{(-4-0)^2 + (6-0)^2}$
$= \sqrt{16+36} = \sqrt{52} = 2\sqrt{13}$

b. The coordinates of the midpoint are:

$(x, y) = \left(\dfrac{x_1 + x_2}{2}, \dfrac{y_1 + y_2}{2} \right)$

$= \left(\dfrac{0+(-4)}{2}, \dfrac{0+6}{2} \right) = \left(\dfrac{-4}{2}, \dfrac{6}{2} \right) = (-2,3)$

c. slope $= \dfrac{\Delta y}{\Delta x} = \dfrac{6-0}{-4-0} = \dfrac{6}{-4} = -\dfrac{3}{2}$

d. For each run of 2, there is a rise of –3.

3. $P_1 = (1,-1)$ and $P_2 = (-2,3)$

a. $d(P_1, P_2) = \sqrt{(-2-1)^2 + (3-(-1))^2}$
$= \sqrt{9+16} = \sqrt{25} = 5$

b. The coordinates of the midpoint are:

$(x, y) = \left(\dfrac{x_1 + x_2}{2}, \dfrac{y_1 + y_2}{2} \right)$

$= \left(\dfrac{1+(-2)}{2}, \dfrac{-1+3}{2} \right)$

$= \left(\dfrac{-1}{2}, \dfrac{2}{2} \right) = \left(-\dfrac{1}{2}, 1 \right)$

c. slope $= \dfrac{\Delta y}{\Delta x} = \dfrac{3-(-1)}{-2-1} = \dfrac{4}{-3} = -\dfrac{4}{3}$

d. For each run of 3, there is a rise of –4.

4. $P_1 = (-2, 2)$ and $P_2 = (1, 4)$

  a. $d(P_1, P_2) = \sqrt{(1 - (-2))^2 + (4 - 2)^2}$
  $$= \sqrt{9 + 4} = \sqrt{13}$$

  b. $(x, y) = \left(\dfrac{x_1 + x_2}{2}, \dfrac{y_1 + y_2}{2} \right)$
  $$= \left(\dfrac{-2 + 1}{2}, \dfrac{2 + 4}{2} \right)$$
  $$= \left(-\dfrac{1}{2}, \dfrac{6}{2} \right) = \left(-\dfrac{1}{2}, 3 \right)$$

  c. slope $= \dfrac{\Delta y}{\Delta x} = \dfrac{4 - 2}{1 - (-2)} = \dfrac{2}{3}$

  d. For each run of 3, there is a rise of 2.

5. $P_1 = (4, -4)$ and $P_2 = (4, 8)$

  a. $d(P_1, P_2) = \sqrt{(4 - 4)^2 + (8 - (-4))^2}$
  $$= \sqrt{0 + 144} = \sqrt{144} = 12$$

  b. The coordinates of the midpoint are:
  $$(x, y) = \left(\dfrac{x_1 + x_2}{2}, \dfrac{y_1 + y_2}{2} \right)$$
  $$= \left(\dfrac{4 + 4}{2}, \dfrac{-4 + 8}{2} \right) = \left(\dfrac{8}{2}, \dfrac{4}{2} \right) = (4, 2)$$

  c. slope $= \dfrac{\Delta y}{\Delta x} = \dfrac{8 - (-4)}{4 - 4} = \dfrac{12}{0}$, undefined

  d. An undefined slope means the points lie on a vertical line. There is no change in x.

6. $P_1 = (-3, 4)$ and $P_2 = (2, 4)$

  a. $d(P_1, P_2) = \sqrt{(2 - (-3))^2 + (4 - 4)^2}$
  $$= \sqrt{25 + 0} = \sqrt{25} = 5$$

  b. The coordinates of the midpoint are:
  $$(x, y) = \left(\dfrac{x_1 + x_2}{2}, \dfrac{y_1 + y_2}{2} \right)$$
  $$= \left(\dfrac{-3 + 2}{2}, \dfrac{4 + 4}{2} \right) = \left(-\dfrac{1}{2}, \dfrac{8}{2} \right) = \left(-\dfrac{1}{2}, 4 \right)$$

  c. slope $= \dfrac{\Delta y}{\Delta x} = \dfrac{4 - 4}{2 - (-3)} = \dfrac{0}{5} = 0$

  d. A slope of zero means the points lie on a horizontal line. There is no change in y.

7. $y = x^2 + 4$

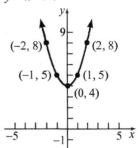

8. x-intercepts: $-4, 0, 2$; y-intercepts: $-2, 0, 2$
  Intercepts: $(-4, 0), (0, 0), (2, 0), (0, -2), (0, 2)$

9. $2x = 3y^2$

x-intercepts:	y-intercepts:
$2x = 3(0)^2$	$2(0) = 3y^2$
$2x = 0$	$0 = y^2$
$x = 0$	$y = 0$

  The only intercept is $(0, 0)$.

  <u>Test x-axis symmetry</u>: Let $y = -y$
  $$2x = 3(-y)^2$$
  $$2x = 3y^2 \quad \text{same}$$
  <u>Test y-axis symmetry</u>: Let $x = -x$
  $$2(-x) = 3y^2$$
  $$-2x = 3y^2 \quad \text{different}$$
  <u>Test origin symmetry</u>: Let $x = -x$ and $y = -y$.
  $$2(-x) = 3(-y)^2$$
  $$-2x = 3y^2 \quad \text{different}$$
  Therefore, the graph will have x-axis symmetry.

10. $y = 5x$

x-intercepts:	y-intercepts:
$0 = 5x$	$y = 5(0)$
$0 = x$	$y = 0$

  The only intercept is $(0, 0)$.

  <u>Test x-axis symmetry</u>: Let $y = -y$
  $$-y = 5x$$
  $$y = -5x \quad \text{different}$$
  <u>Test y-axis symmetry</u>: Let $x = -x$
  $$y = 5(-x)$$
  $$y = -5x \quad \text{different}$$
  <u>Test origin symmetry</u>: Let $x = -x$ and $y = -y$.
  $$-y = 5(-x)$$
  $$y = 5x \quad \text{same}$$
  Therefore, the graph will have origin symmetry.

11. $x^2 + 4y^2 = 16$

x-intercepts:

$x^2 + 4(0)^2 = 16$

$x^2 = 16$

$x = \pm 4$

y-intercepts:

$(0)^2 + 4y^2 = 16$

$4y^2 = 16$

$y^2 = 4$

$y = \pm 2$

The intercepts are $(-4, 0)$, $(4, 0)$, $(0, -2)$, and $(0, 2)$.

Test x-axis symmetry: Let $y = -y$

$x^2 + 4(-y)^2 = 16$

$x^2 + 4y^2 = 16$ same

Test y-axis symmetry: Let $x = -x$

$(-x)^2 + 4y^2 = 16$

$x^2 + 4y^2 = 16$ same

Test origin symmetry: Let $x = -x$ and $y = -y$.

$(-x)^2 + 4(-y)^2 = 16$

$x^2 + 4y^2 = 16$ same

Therefore, the graph will have x-axis, y-axis, and origin symmetry.

12. $9x^2 - y^2 = 9$

x-intercepts:

$9x^2 - (0)^2 = 9$

$9x^2 = 9$

$x^2 = 1$

$x = \pm 1$

y-intercepts:

$9(0)^2 - y^2 = 9$

$-y^2 = 9$

$y^2 = -9$

no real solutions

The intercepts are $(-1, 0)$ and $(1, 0)$.

Test x-axis symmetry: Let $y = -y$

$9x^2 - (-y)^2 = 9$

$9x^2 - y^2 = 9$ same

Test y-axis symmetry: Let $x = -x$

$9(-x)^2 - y^2 = 9$

$9x^2 - y^2 = 9$ same

Test origin symmetry: Let $x = -x$ and $y = -y$.

$9(-x)^2 - (-y)^2 = 9$

$9x^2 - y^2 = 9$ same

Therefore, the graph will have x-axis, y-axis, and origin symmetry.

13. $y = x^4 + 2x^2 + 1$

x-intercepts:

$0 = x^4 + 2x^2 + 1$

$0 = (x^2 + 1)(x^2 + 1)$

$x^2 + 1 = 0$

$x^2 = -1$

no real solutions

y-intercepts:

$y = (0)^4 + 2(0)^2 + 1$

$= 1$

The only intercept is $(0, 1)$.

Test x-axis symmetry: Let $y = -y$

$-y = x^4 + 2x^2 + 1$

$y = -x^4 - 2x^2 - 1$ different

Test y-axis symmetry: Let $x = -x$

$y = (-x)^4 + 2(-x)^2 + 1$

$y = x^4 + 2x^2 + 1$ same

Test origin symmetry: Let $x = -x$ and $y = -y$.

$-y = (-x)^4 + 2(-x)^2 + 1$

$-y = x^4 + 2x^2 + 1$

$y = -x^4 - 2x^2 - 1$ different

Therefore, the graph will have y-axis symmetry.

14. $y = x^3 - x$

x-intercepts:

$0 = x^3 - x$

$0 = x(x^2 - 1)$

$0 = x(x + 1)(x - 1)$

$x = 0, x = -1, x = 1$

y-intercepts:

$y = (0)^3 - 0$

$= 0$

The intercepts are $(-1, 0)$, $(0, 0)$, and $(1, 0)$.

Test x-axis symmetry: Let $y = -y$

$-y = x^3 - x$

$y = -x^3 + x$ different

Test y-axis symmetry: Let $x = -x$

$y = (-x)^3 - (-x)$

$y = -x^3 + x$ different

Test origin symmetry: Let $x = -x$ and $y = -y$.

$-y = (-x)^3 - (-x)$

$-y = -x^3 + x$

$y = x^3 - x$ same

Therefore, the graph will have origin symmetry.

15. $x^2 + x + y^2 + 2y = 0$

  x-intercepts: $x^2 + x + (0)^2 + 2(0) = 0$
  $$x^2 + x = 0$$
  $$x(x+1) = 0$$
  $$x = 0, \ x = -1$$

  y-intercepts: $(0)^2 + 0 + y^2 + 2y = 0$
  $$y^2 + 2y = 0$$
  $$y(y+2) = 0$$
  $$y = 0, \ y = -2$$

  The intercepts are $(-1, 0)$, $(0, 0)$, and $(0, -2)$.

  <u>Test x-axis symmetry</u>: Let $y = -y$

  $x^2 + x + (-y)^2 + 2(-y) = 0$
  $x^2 + x + y^2 - 2y = 0$ different

  <u>Test y-axis symmetry</u>: Let $x = -x$

  $(-x)^2 + (-x) + y^2 + 2y = 0$
  $x^2 - x + y^2 + 2y = 0$ different

  <u>Test origin symmetry</u>: Let $x = -x$ and $y = -y$.

  $(-x)^2 + (-x) + (-y)^2 + 2(-y) = 0$
  $x^2 - x + y^2 - 2y = 0$ different

  The graph has none of the indicated symmetries.

16. $x^2 + 4x + y^2 - 2y = 0$

  x-intercepts: $x^2 + 4x + (0)^2 - 2(0) = 0$
  $$x^2 + 4x = 0$$
  $$x(x+4) = 0$$
  $$x = 0, \ x = -4$$

  y-intercepts: $(0)^2 + 4(0) + y^2 - 2y = 0$
  $$y^2 - 2y = 0$$
  $$y(y-2) = 0$$
  $$y = 0, \ y = 2$$

  The intercepts are $(-4, 0)$, $(0, 0)$, and $(0, 2)$.

  <u>Test x-axis symmetry</u>: Let $y = -y$

  $x^2 + 4x + (-y)^2 - 2(-y) = 0$
  $x^2 + 4x + y^2 + 2y = 0$ different

  <u>Test y-axis symmetry</u>: Let $x = -x$

  $(-x)^2 + 4(-x) + y^2 - 2y = 0$
  $x^2 - 4x + y^2 - 2y = 0$ different

  <u>Test origin symmetry</u>: Let $x = -x$ and $y = -y$.

  $(-x)^2 + 4(-x) + (-y)^2 - 2(-y) = 0$
  $x^2 - 4x + y^2 + 2y = 0$ different

  The graph has none of the indicated symmetries.

17. $(x-h)^2 + (y-k)^2 = r^2$
  $$\left(x - (-2)\right)^2 + (y-3)^2 = 4^2$$
  $$(x+2)^2 + (y-3)^2 = 16$$

18. $(x-h)^2 + (y-k)^2 = r^2$
  $$(x-3)^2 + (y-4)^2 = 4^2$$
  $$(x-3)^2 + (y-4)^2 = 16$$

19. $(x-h)^2 + (y-k)^2 = r^2$
  $$\left(x - (-1)\right)^2 + \left(y - (-2)\right)^2 = 1^2$$
  $$(x+1)^2 + (y+2)^2 = 1$$

20. $(x-h)^2 + (y-k)^2 = r^2$
  $$(x-2)^2 + \left(y - (-4)\right)^2 = 3^2$$
  $$(x-2)^2 + (y+4)^2 = 9$$

21. $x^2 + (y-1)^2 = 4$
  $$x^2 + (y-1)^2 = 2^2$$

  Center: $(0,1)$; Radius $= 2$

  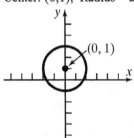

  x-intercepts: $x^2 + (0-1)^2 = 4$
  $$x^2 + 1 = 4$$
  $$x^2 = 3$$
  $$x = \pm\sqrt{3}$$

  y-intercepts: $0^2 + (y-1)^2 = 4$
  $$(y-1)^2 = 4$$
  $$y - 1 = \pm 2$$
  $$y = 1 \pm 2$$
  $$y = 3 \ \text{or} \ y = -1$$

  The intercepts are $\left(-\sqrt{3}, 0\right)$, $\left(\sqrt{3}, 0\right)$, $(0, -1)$,
  and $(0, 3)$.

22. $(x+2)^2 + y^2 = 9$

$(x+2)^2 + y^2 = 3^2$

Center: (–2, 0); Radius = 3

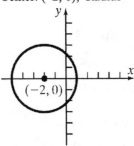

x-intercepts: $(x+2)^2 + 0^2 = 9$

$(x+2)^2 = 9$

$x+2 = \pm 3$

$x = -2 \pm 3$

$x = 1$ or $x = -5$

y-intercepts: $(0+2)^2 + y^2 = 9$

$4 + y^2 = 9$

$y^2 = 5$

$y = \pm\sqrt{5}$

The intercepts are $(-5, 0)$, $(1, 0)$, $\left(0, -\sqrt{5}\right)$, and $\left(0, \sqrt{5}\right)$.

23. $x^2 + y^2 - 2x + 4y - 4 = 0$

$x^2 - 2x + y^2 + 4y = 4$

$\left(x^2 - 2x + 1\right) + \left(y^2 + 4y + 4\right) = 4 + 1 + 4$

$(x-1)^2 + (y+2)^2 = 3^2$

Center: (1, –2) Radius = 3

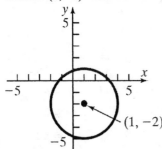

x-intercepts: $(x-1)^2 + (0+2)^2 = 3^2$

$(x-1)^2 + 4 = 9$

$(x-1)^2 = 5$

$x-1 = \pm\sqrt{5}$

$x = 1 \pm \sqrt{5}$

y-intercepts: $(0-1)^2 + (y+2)^2 = 3^2$

$1 + (y+2)^2 = 9$

$(y+2)^2 = 8$

$y+2 = \pm\sqrt{8}$

$y+2 = \pm 2\sqrt{2}$

$y = -2 \pm 2\sqrt{2}$

The intercepts are $\left(1-\sqrt{5}, 0\right)$, $\left(1+\sqrt{5}, 0\right)$, $\left(0, -2-2\sqrt{2}\right)$, and $\left(0, -2+2\sqrt{2}\right)$.

24. $x^2 + y^2 + 4x - 4y - 1 = 0$

$x^2 + 4x + y^2 - 4y = 1$

$\left(x^2 + 4x + 4\right) + \left(y^2 - 4y + 4\right) = 1 + 4 + 4$

$(x+2)^2 + (y-2)^2 = 3^2$

Center: (–2, 2) Radius = 3

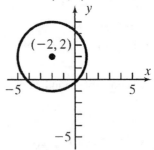

x-intercepts: $(x+2)^2 + (0-2)^2 = 3^2$

$(x+2)^2 + 4 = 9$

$(x+2)^2 = 5$

$x+2 = \pm\sqrt{5}$

$x = -2 \pm \sqrt{5}$

y-intercepts: $(0+2)^2 + (y-2)^2 = 3^2$

$4 + (y-2)^2 = 9$

$(y-2)^2 = 5$

$y-2 = \pm\sqrt{5}$

$y = 2 \pm \sqrt{5}$

The intercepts are $\left(-2-\sqrt{5}, 0\right)$, $\left(-2+\sqrt{5}, 0\right)$, $\left(0, 2-\sqrt{5}\right)$, and $\left(0, 2+\sqrt{5}\right)$.

25.
$$3x^2 + 3y^2 - 6x + 12y = 0$$
$$x^2 + y^2 - 2x + 4y = 0$$
$$x^2 - 2x + y^2 + 4y = 0$$
$$\left(x^2 - 2x + 1\right) + \left(y^2 + 4y + 4\right) = 1 + 4$$
$$(x-1)^2 + (y+2)^2 = \left(\sqrt{5}\right)^2$$

Center: $(1, -2)$ Radius $= \sqrt{5}$

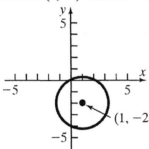

x-intercepts: $(x-1)^2 + (0+2)^2 = \left(\sqrt{5}\right)^2$
$$(x-1)^2 + 4 = 5$$
$$(x-1)^2 = 1$$
$$x - 1 = \pm 1$$
$$x = 1 \pm 1$$
$$x = 2 \quad \text{or} \quad x = 0$$

y-intercepts: $(0-1)^2 + (y+2)^2 = \left(\sqrt{5}\right)^2$
$$1 + (y+2)^2 = 5$$
$$(y+2)^2 = 4$$
$$y + 2 = \pm 2$$
$$y = -2 \pm 2$$
$$y = 0 \quad \text{or} \quad y = -4$$

The intercepts are $(0, 0)$, $(2, 0)$, and $(0, -4)$.

26.
$$2x^2 + 2y^2 - 4x = 0$$
$$x^2 + y^2 - 2x = 0$$
$$x^2 - 2x + y^2 = 0$$
$$\left(x^2 - 2x + 1\right) + y^2 = 1$$
$$(x-1)^2 + y^2 = 1^2$$

Center: $(1, 0)$ Radius $= 1$

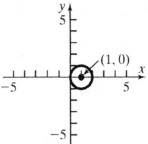

x-intercepts: $(x-1)^2 + 0^2 = 1^2$
$$(x-1)^2 = 1$$
$$x - 1 = \pm 1$$
$$x = 1 \pm 1$$
$$x = 2 \quad \text{or} \quad x = 0$$

y-intercepts: $(0-1)^2 + y^2 = y^2$
$$1 + y^2 = 1$$
$$y^2 = 0$$
$$y = 0$$

The intercepts are $(0, 0)$, and $(2, 0)$.

27. Slope $= -2$; containing $(3, -1)$
$$y - y_1 = m(x - x_1)$$
$$y - (-1) = -2(x - 3)$$
$$y + 1 = -2x + 6$$
$$y = -2x + 5 \quad \text{or} \quad 2x + y = 5$$

28. Slope $= 0$; containing the point $(-5, 4)$
$$y - y_1 = m(x - x_1)$$
$$y - 4 = 0(x - (-5))$$
$$y - 4 = 0$$
$$y = 4$$

29. vertical; containing $(-3, 4)$
Vertical lines have equations of the form $x = a$, where a is the x-intercept. Now, a vertical line containing the point $(-3, 4)$ must have an x-intercept of -3, so the equation of the line is $x = -3$. The equation does not have a slope-intercept form.

30. x-intercept $= 2$; containing the point $(4, -5)$
Points are $(2, 0)$ and $(4, -5)$.

$$m = \frac{-5-0}{4-2} = -\frac{5}{2}$$

$$y - y_1 = m(x - x_1)$$

$$y - 0 = -\frac{5}{2}(x - 2)$$

$$y = -\frac{5}{2}x + 5 \quad \text{or} \quad 5x + 2y = 10$$

31. y-intercept $= -2$; containing $(5, -3)$
Points are $(5, -3)$ and $(0, -2)$

$$m = \frac{-2-(-3)}{0-5} = \frac{1}{-5} = -\frac{1}{5}$$

$$y = mx + b$$

$$y = -\frac{1}{5}x - 2 \quad \text{or} \quad x + 5y = -10$$

32. Containing the points $(3, -4)$ and $(2, 1)$

$$m = \frac{1-(-4)}{2-3} = \frac{5}{-1} = -5$$

$$y - y_1 = m(x - x_1)$$

$$y - (-4) = -5(x - 3)$$

$$y + 4 = -5x + 15$$

$$y = -5x + 11 \quad \text{or} \quad 5x + y = 11$$

33. Parallel to $2x - 3y = -4$

$$2x - 3y = -4$$

$$-3y = -2x - 4$$

$$\frac{-3y}{-3} = \frac{-2x - 4}{-3}$$

$$y = \frac{2}{3}x + \frac{4}{3}$$

Slope $= \frac{2}{3}$; containing $(-5, 3)$

$$y - y_1 = m(x - x_1)$$

$$y - 3 = \frac{2}{3}(x - (-5))$$

$$y - 3 = \frac{2}{3}(x + 5)$$

$$y - 3 = \frac{2}{3}x + \frac{10}{3}$$

$$y = \frac{2}{3}x + \frac{19}{3} \quad \text{or} \quad 2x - 3y = -19$$

34. Parallel to $x + y = 2$

$$x + y = 2$$

$$y = -x + 2$$

Slope $= -1$; containing $(1, -3)$

$$y - y_1 = m(x - x_1)$$

$$y - (-3) = -1(x - 1)$$

$$y + 3 = -x + 1$$

$$y = -x - 2 \quad \text{or} \quad x + y = -2$$

35. Perpendicular to $x + y = 2$

$$x + y = 2$$

$$y = -x + 2$$

The slope of this line is -1, so the slope of a line perpendicular to it is 1.
Slope $= 1$; containing $(4, -3)$

$$y - y_1 = m(x - x_1)$$

$$y - (-3) = 1(x - 4)$$

$$y + 3 = x - 4$$

$$y = x - 7 \quad \text{or} \quad x - y = 7$$

36. Perpendicular to $3x - y = -4$

$$3x - y = -4$$

$$y = 3x + 4$$

The slope of this line is 3, so the slope of a line perpendicular to it is $-\frac{1}{3}$.

Slope $= -\frac{1}{3}$; containing $(-2, 4)$

$$y - y_1 = m(x - x_1)$$

$$y - 4 = -\frac{1}{3}(x - (-2))$$

$$y - 4 = -\frac{1}{3}x - \frac{2}{3}$$

$$y = -\frac{1}{3}x + \frac{10}{3} \quad \text{or} \quad x + 3y = 10$$

37. $4x - 5y = -20$

$$-5y = -4x - 20$$

$$y = \frac{4}{5}x + 4$$

slope $= \frac{4}{5}$; y-intercept $= 4$

x-intercept: Let $y = 0$.

$$4x - 5(0) = -20$$

$$4x = -20$$

$$x = -5$$

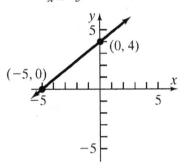

38. $3x + 4y = 12$

$$4y = -3x + 12$$

$$y = -\frac{3}{4}x + 3$$

slope $= -\frac{3}{4}$; y-intercept $= 3$

x-intercept: Let $y = 0$.

$$3x + 4(0) = 12$$

$$3x = 12$$

$$x = 4$$

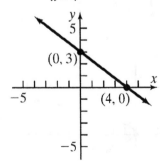

39. $\frac{1}{2}x - \frac{1}{3}y = -\frac{1}{6}$

$$-\frac{1}{3}y = -\frac{1}{2}x - \frac{1}{6}$$

$$y = \frac{3}{2}x + \frac{1}{2}$$

slope $= \frac{3}{2}$; y-intercept $= \frac{1}{2}$

x-intercept: Let $y = 0$.

$$\frac{1}{2}x - \frac{1}{3}(0) = -\frac{1}{6}$$

$$\frac{1}{2}x = -\frac{1}{6}$$

$$x = -\frac{1}{3}$$

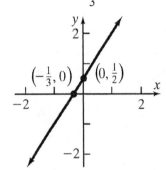

40. $-\frac{3}{4}x + \frac{1}{2}y = 0$

$$\frac{1}{2}y = \frac{3}{4}x$$

$$y = \frac{3}{2}x$$

slope $= \frac{3}{2}$; y-intercept $= 0$

x-intercept: Let $y = 0$.

$$-\frac{3}{4}x + \frac{1}{2}(0) = 0$$

$$-\frac{3}{4}x = 0$$

$$x = 0$$

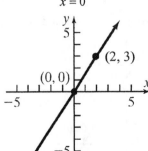

41. $2x - 3y = 12$

x-intercept:	*y*-intercept:
$2x - 3(0) = 12$	$2(0) - 3y = 12$
$2x = 12$	$-3y = 12$
$x = 6$	$y = -4$

The intercepts are $(6, 0)$ and $(0, -4)$.

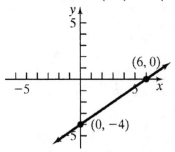

42. $x - 2y = 8$

x-intercept:	*y*-intercept:
$x - 2(0) = 8$	$0 - 2y = 8$
$x = 8$	$y = -4$

The intercepts are $(8, 0)$ and $(0, -4)$.

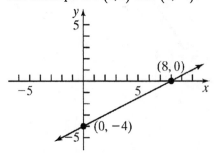

43. $\dfrac{1}{2}x + \dfrac{1}{3}y = 2$

x-intercept:	*y*-intercept:
$\dfrac{1}{2}x + \dfrac{1}{3}(0) = 2$	$\dfrac{1}{2}(0) + \dfrac{1}{3}y = 2$
$\dfrac{1}{2}x = 2$	$\dfrac{1}{3}y = 2$
$x = 4$	$y = 6$

The intercepts are $(4, 0)$ and $(0, 6)$.

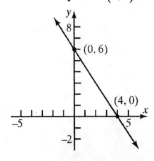

44. $\dfrac{1}{3}x - \dfrac{1}{4}y = 1$

x-intercept:	*y*-intercept:
$\dfrac{1}{3}x - \dfrac{1}{4}(0) = 1$	$\dfrac{1}{3}(0) - \dfrac{1}{4}y = 1$
$\dfrac{1}{3}x = 1$	$-\dfrac{1}{4}y = 1$
$x = 3$	$y = -4$

The intercepts are $(3, 0)$ and $(0, -4)$.

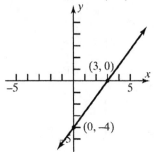

45. $y = x^3$

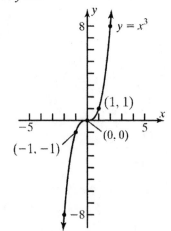

46. $y = \sqrt{x}$

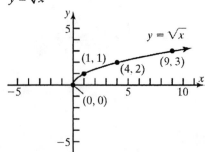

47. slope $= \dfrac{2}{3}$, containing the point (1,2)

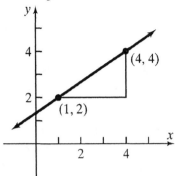

48. Find the distance between each pair of points.

$d_{A,B} = \sqrt{(1-3)^2 + (1-4)^2} = \sqrt{4+9} = \sqrt{13}$

$d_{B,C} = \sqrt{(-2-1)^2 + (3-1)^2} = \sqrt{9+4} = \sqrt{13}$

$d_{A,C} = \sqrt{(-2-3)^2 + (3-4)^2} = \sqrt{25+1} = \sqrt{26}$

Since $AB = BC$, triangle ABC is isosceles.

49. Given the points $A = (-2, 0)$, $B = (-4, 4)$, and $C = (8, 5)$.

  a. Find the distance between each pair of points.

$d(A,B) = \sqrt{(-4-(-2))^2 + (4-0)^2}$

$\quad = \sqrt{4+16}$

$\quad = \sqrt{20} = 2\sqrt{5}$

$d(B,C) = \sqrt{(8-(-4))^2 + (5-4)^2}$

$\quad = \sqrt{144+1}$

$\quad = \sqrt{145}$

$d(A,C) = \sqrt{(8-(-2))^2 + (5-0)^2}$

$\quad = \sqrt{100+25}$

$\quad = \sqrt{125} = 5\sqrt{5}$

$\left[d(A,B)\right]^2 + \left[d(A,C)\right]^2 = \left[d(B,C)\right]^2$

$\left(\sqrt{20}\right)^2 + \left(\sqrt{125}\right)^2 = \left(\sqrt{145}\right)^2$

$20 + 125 = 145$

$145 = 145$

The Pythagorean Theorem is satisfied, so this is a right triangle.

  b. Find the slopes:

$m_{AB} = \dfrac{4-0}{-4-(-2)} = \dfrac{4}{-2} = -2$

$m_{BC} = \dfrac{5-4}{8-(-4)} = \dfrac{1}{12}$

$m_{AC} = \dfrac{5-0}{8-(-2)} = \dfrac{5}{10} = \dfrac{1}{2}$

Since $m_{AB} \cdot m_{AC} = -2 \cdot \dfrac{1}{2} = -1$, the sides AB and AC are perpendicular and the triangle is a right triangle.

50. Endpoints of the diameter are $(-3, 2)$ and $(5, -6)$. The center is at the midpoint of the diameter:

Center: $\left(\dfrac{-3+5}{2}, \dfrac{2+(-6)}{2}\right) = (1, -2)$

Radius: $r = \sqrt{(1-(-3))^2 + (-2-2)^2}$

$\quad = \sqrt{16+16}$

$\quad = \sqrt{32} = 4\sqrt{2}$

Equation: $(x-1)^2 + (y+2)^2 = \left(4\sqrt{2}\right)^2$

$(x-1)^2 + (y+2)^2 = 32$

51. slope of $\overline{AB} = \dfrac{1-5}{6-2} = -1$

slope of $\overline{AC} = \dfrac{-1-5}{8-2} = -1$

slope of $\overline{BC} = \dfrac{-1-1}{8-6} = -1$

Therefore, the points lie on a line.

52. $\quad p = kB$

$854 = k(130,000)$

$k = \dfrac{854}{130,000} = \dfrac{427}{65,000}$

Therefore, we have the equation $p = \dfrac{427}{65,000} B$.

If $B = 165,000$, then

$p = \dfrac{427}{65,000}(165,000) = \$1083.92$.

53. $R = kg$

$46.67 = k(13)$

$k = \dfrac{46.67}{13} = 3.59$

Therefore, we have the equation

$R = 3.59g$.

If $g = 11.2$, then $p = 3.59(11.2) \approx \$40.21$.

54. $w = \dfrac{k}{d^2}$

$200 = \dfrac{k}{3960^2}$

$k = (200)(3960^2) = 3{,}136{,}320{,}000$

Therefore, we have the equation

$w = \dfrac{3{,}136{,}320{,}000}{d^2}$.

If $d = 3960 + 1 = 3961$ miles, then

$w = \dfrac{3{,}136{,}320{,}000}{3961^2} \approx 199.9$ pounds.

55. $T^2 = ka^3$

$365^2 = (k)(93)^3$

$k = \dfrac{365^2}{93^3}$

Therefore, we have the equation

$T^2 = \dfrac{365^2}{93^3} a^3$.

If $T = 88$ days, then

$88^2 = \left(\dfrac{365^2}{93^3}\right)(a)^3$

$a^3 = (88^2)\left(\dfrac{93^3}{365^2}\right)$

$a = \sqrt[3]{(88^2)\left(\dfrac{93^3}{365^2}\right)} \approx 36$ million miles

56. Answers will vary.

57. a. The graph of $x = 0$ is a vertical line passing through the origin. That is, $x = 0$ is the equation of the *y*-axis.

b. The grapy of $y = 0$ is a horizontal line passing through the origin. That is, $y = 0$ is the equation of the *x*-axis.

c. $x + y = 0$

$y = -x$

The graph of $x + y = 0$ is line passing through the origin with slope $= -1$.

d. $xy = 0$

$y = 0$ or $x = 0$

The graph of $xy = 0$ consists of the coordinate axes.

e. $x^2 + y^2 = 0$

$y = 0$ and $x = 0$

The graph of $x^2 + y^2 = 0$ is consists of the origin.

58. Set the axes so that the field's maximum dimension is along the *x*-axis.

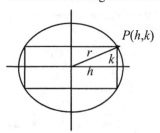

Let $2h = width$, $2k = height$, therefore the point farthest from the origin has coordinates $P(h, k)$. So the distance from the origin to point P is

$r = \sqrt{h^2 + k^2}$ = the radius of the circle .

Using 1 sprinkler arm:

If we place the sprinkler at the origin, we get a circle with equation $x^2 + y^2 = r^2$, where $r = \sqrt{h^2 + k^2}$. So how much excess land is being watered ? The area of the field $=$

$A_F = 4hk$.

The area of the circular water pattern

$A_C = \pi r^2 = \pi\left(\sqrt{h^2 + k^2}\right)^2 = \pi\left(h^2 + k^2\right)$.

Therefore the amount of excess land being

watered $= A_C - A_F = \pi\left(h^2 + k^2\right) - 4hk$.

Using 2 sprinkler arms:

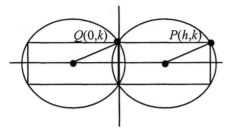

We want to place the sprinklers so that they overlap as little as possible while watering the entire field. The equation of the circle with center on the positive x-axis that passes through the point $P(h,k)$ and $Q(0,k)$ is

$$\left(x-\frac{h}{2}\right)^2 + y^2 = \sqrt{\frac{1}{4}h^2 + k^2}\,,\text{ since the center is}$$

$\left(\dfrac{h}{2},0\right)$, and the radius is $\sqrt{\dfrac{1}{4}h^2 + k^2}$.

The case for the other side is similar. Thus, the sprinklers should have their centers at $\left(-\dfrac{h}{2},0\right)$

and $\left(\dfrac{h}{2},0\right)$, with the arm lengths set at

$\sqrt{\dfrac{1}{4}h^2 + k^2}$.

Each sprinkler waters the same area, so the total area watered is

$$A_C = 2\pi r^2 = 2\pi\left(\sqrt{\frac{1}{4}h^2 + k^2}\right)^2 = 2\pi\left(\frac{1}{4}h^2 + k^2\right).$$

The amount of excess land being watered is

$$A_C - A_F = 2\pi\left(\frac{1}{4}h^2 + k^2\right) - 4hk .$$

Comparison:

In order to determine when to switch from 1 sprinkler to 2 sprinklers, we want to determine when 2 sprinklers water less excess land than 1 sprinkler waters. That is, we want to solve:

$$2\pi\left(\frac{1}{4}h^2 + k^2\right) - 4hk < \pi\left(h^2 + k^2\right) - 4hk .$$

$$2\pi\left(\frac{1}{4}h^2 + k^2\right) - 4hk < \pi\left(h^2 + k^2\right) - 4hk$$

$$\frac{\pi}{2}h^2 + 2\pi\,k^2 - 4hk < \pi\,h^2 + \pi\,k^2 - 4hk$$

$$\frac{\pi}{2}h^2 + 2\pi\,k^2 < \pi\,h^2 + \pi\,k^2$$

$$\frac{1}{2}h^2 + 2\,k^2 < h^2 + k^2$$

$$k^2 < \frac{1}{2}h^2$$

$$k < \sqrt{\frac{1}{2}}h$$

$$h > \sqrt{2}k$$

So 2 sprinklers is the better choice when the longer dimension of the rectangle exceeds the shorter dimension by a factor of more than $\sqrt{2} \approx 1.414$.

Chapter 2 Test

1. $d(P_1,P_2) = \sqrt{\left(5-(-1)\right)^2 + \left(-1-3\right)^2}$

$$= \sqrt{6^2 + (-4)^2}$$

$$= \sqrt{36 + 16}$$

$$= \sqrt{52} = 2\sqrt{13}$$

2. The coordinates of the midpoint are:

$$(x,y) = \left(\frac{x_1 + x_2}{2}, \frac{y_1 + y_2}{2}\right)$$

$$= \left(\frac{-1+5}{2}, \frac{3+(-1)}{2}\right)$$

$$= \left(\frac{4}{2}, \frac{2}{2}\right)$$

$$= (2,1)$$

3. **a.** $m = \dfrac{y_2 - y_1}{x_2 - x_1} = \dfrac{-1-3}{5-(-1)} = \dfrac{-4}{6} = -\dfrac{2}{3}$

   b. If x increases by 3 units, y will decrease by 2 units.

4. $y = x^2 - 9$

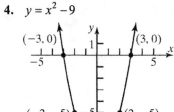

5. $y^2 = x$

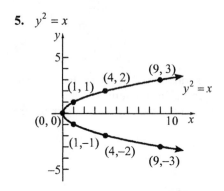

6. $x^2 + y = 9$

x-intercepts: y-intercept:

$x^2 + 0 = 9$ $(0)^2 + y = 9$

$\quad x^2 = 9$ $\quad\quad y = 9$

$\quad x = \pm 3$

The intercepts are $(-3, 0)$, $(3, 0)$, and $(0, 9)$.

Test x-axis symmetry: Let $y = -y$

$x^2 + (-y) = 9$

$\quad x^2 - y = 9$ different

Test y-axis symmetry: Let $x = -x$

$(-x)^2 + y = 9$

$\quad x^2 + y = 9$ same

Test origin symmetry: Let $x = -x$ and $y = -y$

$(-x)^2 + (-y) = 9$

$\quad x^2 - y = 9$ different

Therefore, the graph will have y-axis symmetry.

7. Slope $= -2$; containing $(3, -4)$

$$y - y_1 = m(x - x_1)$$
$$y - (-4) = -2(x - 3)$$
$$y + 4 = -2x + 6$$
$$y = -2x + 2$$

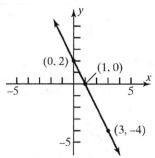

8. $(x - h)^2 + (y - k)^2 = r^2$

$$(x - 4)^2 + (y - (-3))^2 = 5^2$$
$$(x - 4)^2 + (y + 3)^2 = 25$$

General form: $(x - 4)^2 + (y + 3)^2 = 25$

$$x^2 - 8x + 16 + y^2 + 6y + 9 = 25$$
$$x^2 + y^2 - 8x + 6y = 0$$

9. $x^2 + y^2 + 4x - 2y - 4 = 0$

$$x^2 + 4x + y^2 - 2y = 4$$
$$(x^2 + 4x + 4) + (y^2 - 2y + 1) = 4 + 4 + 1$$
$$(x + 2)^2 + (y - 1)^2 = 3^2$$

Center: $(-2, 1)$; Radius $= 3$

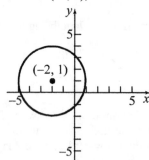

224

10. $2x + 3y = 6$

$$3y = -2x + 6$$

$$y = -\frac{2}{3}x + 2$$

Parallel line
Any line parallel to $2x + 3y = 6$ has slope

$m = -\frac{2}{3}$. The line contains $(1, -1)$:

$$y - y_1 = m(x - x_1)$$

$$y - (-1) = -\frac{2}{3}(x - 1)$$

$$y + 1 = -\frac{2}{3}x + \frac{2}{3}$$

$$y = -\frac{2}{3}x - \frac{1}{3}$$

Perpendicular line
Any line perpendicular to $2x + 3y = 6$ has slope

$m = \frac{3}{2}$. The line contains $(0, 3)$:

$$y - y_1 = m(x - x_1)$$

$$y - 3 = \frac{3}{2}(x - 0)$$

$$y - 3 = \frac{3}{2}x$$

$$y = \frac{3}{2}x + 3$$

11. Let R = the resistance, l = length, and r = radius.

Then $R = k \cdot \dfrac{l}{r^2}$. Now, $R = 10$ ohms, when

$l = 50$ feet and $r = 6 \times 10^{-3}$ inch, so

$$10 = k \cdot \frac{50}{\left(6 \times 10^{-3}\right)^2}$$

$$k = 10 \cdot \frac{\left(6 \times 10^{-3}\right)^2}{50} = 7.2 \times 10^{-6}$$

Therefore, we have the equation

$$R = \left(7.2 \times 10^{-6}\right)\frac{l}{r^2}.$$

If $l = 100$ feet and $r = 7 \times 10^{-3}$ inch, then

$$R = \left(7.2 \times 10^{-6}\right)\frac{100}{\left(7 \times 10^{-3}\right)^2} \approx 14.69 \text{ ohms.}$$

Chapter 2 Cumulative Review

1. $3x - 5 = 0$

$$3x = 5$$

$$x = \frac{5}{3}$$

The solution set is $\left\{\dfrac{5}{3}\right\}$.

2. $\qquad x^2 - x - 12 = 0$

$$(x - 4)(x + 3) = 0$$

$$x = 4 \text{ or } x = -3$$

The solution set is $\{-3, 4\}$.

3. $\qquad 2x^2 - 5x - 3 = 0$

$$(2x + 1)(x - 3) = 0$$

$$x = -\frac{1}{2} \text{ or } x = 3$$

The solution set is $\left\{-\dfrac{1}{2}, 3\right\}$.

4. $x^2 - 2x - 2 = 0$

$$x = \frac{-(-2) \pm \sqrt{(-2)^2 - 4(1)(-2)}}{2(1)}$$

$$= \frac{2 \pm \sqrt{4 + 8}}{2}$$

$$= \frac{2 \pm \sqrt{12}}{2}$$

$$= \frac{2 \pm 2\sqrt{3}}{2}$$

$$= 1 \pm \sqrt{3}$$

The solution set is $\left\{1 - \sqrt{3}, 1 + \sqrt{3}\right\}$.

5. $x^2 + 2x + 5 = 0$

$$x = \frac{-2 \pm \sqrt{2^2 - 4(1)(5)}}{2(1)}$$

$$= \frac{-2 \pm \sqrt{4 - 20}}{2}$$

$$= \frac{-2 \pm \sqrt{-16}}{2}$$

No real solutions

225

6. $\sqrt{2x+1} = 3$

$\left(\sqrt{2x+1}\right)^2 = 3^2$

$2x+1 = 9$

$2x = 8$

$x = 4$

Check: $\sqrt{2(4)+1} = 3$?

$\sqrt{9} = 3$?

$3 = 3$ True

The solution set is $\{4\}$.

7. $|x-2| = 1$

$x-2 = 1$ or $x-2 = -1$

$x = 3$ $\qquad$ $x = 1$

The solution set is $\{1,3\}$.

8. $\sqrt{x^2+4x} = 2$

$\left(\sqrt{x^2+4x}\right)^2 = 2^2$

$x^2 + 4x = 4$

$x^2 + 4x - 4 = 0$

$x = \dfrac{-4 \pm \sqrt{4^2 - 4(1)(-4)}}{2(1)} = \dfrac{-4 \pm \sqrt{16+16}}{2}$

$= \dfrac{-4 \pm \sqrt{32}}{2} = \dfrac{-4 \pm 4\sqrt{2}}{2} = -2 \pm 2\sqrt{2}$

Check $x = -2 + 2\sqrt{2}$:

$\sqrt{\left(-2+2\sqrt{2}\right)^2 + 4\left(-2+2\sqrt{2}\right)} = 2$?

$\sqrt{4 - 8\sqrt{2} + 8 - 8 + 8\sqrt{2}} = 2$?

$\sqrt{4} = 2$ True

Check $x = -2 - 2\sqrt{2}$:

$\sqrt{\left(-2-2\sqrt{2}\right)^2 + 4\left(-2-2\sqrt{2}\right)} = 2$?

$\sqrt{4 + 8\sqrt{2} + 8 - 8 - 8\sqrt{2}} = 2$?

$\sqrt{4} = 2$ True

The solution set is $\left\{-2 - 2\sqrt{2}, -2 + 2\sqrt{2}\right\}$.

9. $x^2 = -9$

$x = \pm\sqrt{-9}$

$x = \pm 3i$

The solution set is $\{-3i, 3i\}$.

10. $x^2 - 2x + 5 = 0$

$x = \dfrac{-(-2) \pm \sqrt{(-2)^2 - 4(1)(5)}}{2(1)} = \dfrac{2 \pm \sqrt{4-20}}{2}$

$= \dfrac{2 \pm \sqrt{-16}}{2} = \dfrac{2 \pm 4i}{2} = 1 \pm 2i$

The solution set is $\{1 - 2i, 1 + 2i\}$.

11. $2x - 3 \le 7$

$2x \le 10$

$x \le 5$

$\{x \mid x \le 5\}$ or $(-\infty, 5]$

12. $-1 < x + 4 < 5$

$-5 < x < 1$

$\{x \mid -5 < x < 1\}$ or $(-5, 1)$

13. $|x - 2| \le 1$

$-1 \le x - 2 \le 1$

$1 \le x \le 3$

$\{x \mid 1 \le x \le 3\}$ or $[1, 3]$

14. $|2 + x| > 3$

$2 + x < -3$ or $2 + x > 3$

$x < -5$ or $\qquad$ $x > 1$

$\{x \mid x < -5 \text{ or } x > 1\}$ or $(-\infty, -5) \cup (1, \infty)$

15. $d(P, Q) = \sqrt{(-1-4)^2 + (3-(-2))^2}$

$= \sqrt{(-5)^2 + (5)^2}$

$= \sqrt{25 + 25}$

$= \sqrt{50} = 5\sqrt{2}$

Midpoint $= \left(\dfrac{-1+4}{2}, \dfrac{3+(-2)}{2}\right) = \left(\dfrac{3}{2}, \dfrac{1}{2}\right)$

16. $y = x^3 - 3x + 1$

    a. $(-2, -1)$:

       $(-2)^3 - (3)(-2) + 1 = -8 + 6 + 1 = -1$

       $(-2, -1)$ is on the graph.

    b. $(2, 3)$:

       $(2)^3 - (3)(2) + 1 = 8 - 6 + 1 = 3$

       $(2, 3)$ is on the graph.

    c. $(3, 1)$:

       $(3)^3 - (3)(3) + 1 = 27 - 9 + 1 = 19 \neq 1$

       $(3, 1)$ is not on the graph.

17. $y = x^3$

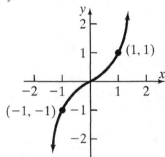

18. The points $(-1, 4)$ and $(2, -2)$ are on the line.

$$\text{Slope} = \frac{-2 - 4}{2 - (-1)} = \frac{-6}{3} = -2$$

$$y - y_1 = m(x - x_1)$$
$$y - 4 = -2(x - (-1))$$
$$y - 4 = -2(x + 1)$$
$$y = -2x - 2 + 4$$
$$y = -2x + 2$$

19. Perpendicular to $y = 2x + 1$; Contains $(3, 5)$

$$\text{Slope of perpendicular} = -\frac{1}{2}$$

$$y - y_1 = m(x - x_1)$$
$$y - 5 = -\frac{1}{2}(x - 3)$$
$$y - 5 = -\frac{1}{2}x + \frac{3}{2}$$
$$y = -\frac{1}{2}x + \frac{13}{2}$$

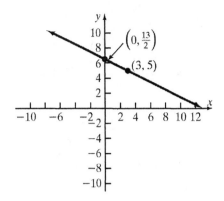

20.
$$x^2 + y^2 - 4x + 8y - 5 = 0$$
$$x^2 - 4x + y^2 + 8y = 5$$
$$(x^2 - 4x + 4) + (y^2 + 8y + 16) = 5 + 4 + 16$$
$$(x - 2)^2 + (y + 4)^2 = 25$$
$$(x - 2)^2 + (y + 4)^2 = 5^2$$

Center: $(2, -4)$; Radius = 5

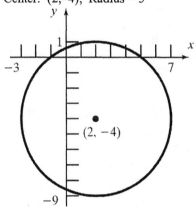

Chapter 2 Project

1. <u>Men:</u> Let $(x_1, y_1) = (1992, 2.22)$ and $(x_2, y_2) = (1996, 2.21)$.

$$m = \frac{y_2 - y_1}{x_2 - x_1} = \frac{2.21 - 2.22}{1996 - 1992} = \frac{-0.01}{4} = -0.0025$$

$$y - y_1 = m(x - x_1)$$
$$y - 2.22 = -0.0025(x - 1992)$$
$$y - 2.22 = -0.0025x + 4.98$$
$$y = -0.0025x + 7.20$$

Women: Let $(x_1, y_1) = (1992, 2.54)$ and $(x_2, y_2) = (1996, 2.43)$.

$m = \dfrac{y_2 - y_1}{x_2 - x_1} = \dfrac{2.43 - 2.54}{1996 - 1992} = \dfrac{-0.11}{4} = -0.0275$

$y - y_1 = m(x - x_1)$

$y - 2.54 = -0.0275(x - 1992)$

$y - 2.54 = -0.0275x + 54.78$

$y = -0.0275x + 57.32$

2. Men: The slope $m = -0.0025$ indicates that the winning times for men in the Olympic marathon are decreasing at an average rate of 0.0025 hour per year.

   Women: The slope $m = -0.0275$ indicates that the winning times for women in the Olympic marathon are decreasing at an average rate of 0.0275 hour per year.

   The y-intercepts do not have reasonable interpretations. In this case, the y-intercepts would indicate the winning times of the marathons in the year 0, which is not reasonable because it is too far away from the data on which our equations are based.

3. Men: If $x = 2004$, then
   $y = -0.0025(2004) + 7.20 = 2.19$ hours. This compares reasonably well to the actual result of 2.18 hours.

   Women: If $x = 2004$, then
   $y = -0.0275(2004) + 57.32 = 2.21$ hours. This does not compare well to the actual result of 2.44 hours.

4. (1) Men: Let $(x_1, y_1) = (1996, 2.21)$ and $(x_2, y_2) = (2000, 2.17)$.

   $m = \dfrac{y_2 - y_1}{x_2 - x_1} = \dfrac{2.17 - 2.21}{2000 - 1996} = \dfrac{-0.04}{4} = -0.01$

   $y - y_1 = m(x - x_1)$

   $y - 2.21 = -0.01(x - 1996)$

   $y - 2.21 = -0.01x + 19.96$

   $y = -0.01x + 22.17$

Women: Let $(x_1, y_1) = (1996, 2.43)$ and $(x_2, y_2) = (2000, 2.39)$.

$m = \dfrac{y_2 - y_1}{x_2 - x_1} = \dfrac{2.39 - 2.43}{2000 - 1996} = \dfrac{-0.04}{4} = -0.01$

$y - y_1 = m(x - x_1)$

$y - 2.39 = -0.01(x - 1996)$

$y - 2.39 = -0.01x + 19.96$

$y = -0.01x + 22.35$

(2) Men: The slope $m = -0.01$ indicates that the winning times for men in the Olympic marathon are decreasing at a rate of 0.01 hour per year.

   Women: The slope $m = -0.01$ indicates that the winning times for women in the Olympic marathon are decreasing at a rate of 0.01 hour per year.

   The y-intercepts do not have reasonable interpretations. In this case, the y-intercepts would indicate the winning times of the marathons in the year 0, which is not reasonable because it is too far away from the data on which our equations are based.

(3) Men: If $x = 2004$, then
   $y = -0.01(2004) + 22.17 = 2.13$ hours. This prediction is not extremely accurate, but it does compare reasonably well to the actual result of 2.18 hours.

   Women: If $x = 2004$, then
   $y = -0.01(2004) + 22.35 = 2.31$ hours. This does not compare well to the actual result of 2.44 hours.

5. No. The year 2104 is too far away from the data on which our equations are based.

6. Answers will vary.

Chapter 3

Functions and Their Graphs

Section 3.1

1. $(-1, 3)$

2. $3(-2)^2 - 5(-2) + \dfrac{1}{(-2)} = 3(4) - 5(-2) - \dfrac{1}{2}$

$$= 12 + 10 - \dfrac{1}{2}$$

$$= \dfrac{43}{2} \quad \text{or} \quad 21\tfrac{1}{2} \quad \text{or} \quad 21.5$$

3. We must not allow the denominator to be 0.
$x + 4 \neq 0 \Rightarrow x \neq -4$; Domain: $\{x \mid x \neq -4\}$.

4. $3 - 2x > 5$

$-2x > 2$

$x < -1$

Solution set: $\{x \mid x < -1\}$ or $(-\infty, -1)$

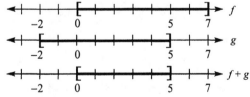

5. independent; dependent

6. range

7. $[0, 5]$

We need the intersection of the intervals $[0, 7]$
and $[-2, 5]$. That is, domain of $f \cap$ domain of g.

8. $\neq$; f, g

9. $(g - f)(x)$ or $g(x) - f(x)$

10. False; every function is a relation, but not every relation is a function. For example, the relation $x^2 + y^2 = 1$ is not a function.

11. True

12. True

13. False; if the domain is not specified, we assume it is the largest set of real numbers for which the value of f is a real number.

14. False; the domain of $f(x) = \dfrac{x^2 - 4}{x}$ is $\{x \mid x \neq 0\}$.

15. Function
Domain: {Elvis, Colleen, Kaleigh, Marissa}
Range: {Jan. 8, Mar. 15, Sept. 17}

16. Not a function

17. Not a function

18. Function
Domain: {Less than 9th grade, 9th-12th grade, High School Graduate, Some College, College Graduate}
Range: {$18,120, $23,251, $36,055, $45,810, $67,165}

19. Not a function

20. Function
Domain: {−2, −1, 3, 4}
Range: {3, 5, 7, 12}

21. Function
Domain: {1, 2, 3, 4}
Range: {3}

22. Function
Domain: {0, 1, 2, 3}
Range: {−2, 3, 7}

23. Not a function

24. Not a function

25. Function
Domain: {−2, −1, 0, 1}
Range: {0, 1, 4}

26. Function
Domain: {−2, −1, 0, 1}
Range: {3, 4, 16}

27. Graph $y = x^2$. The graph passes the vertical line test. Thus, the equation represents a function.

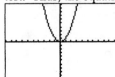

28. Graph $y = x^3$. The graph passes the vertical line test. Thus, the equation represents a function.

29. Graph $y = \dfrac{1}{x}$. The graph passes the vertical line test. Thus, the equation represents a function.

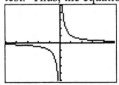

30. Graph $y = |x|$. The graph passes the vertical line test. Thus, the equation represents a function.

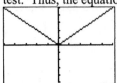

31. $y^2 = 4 - x^2$

Solve for y: $y = \pm\sqrt{4 - x^2}$

For $x = 0$, $y = \pm 2$. Thus, (0, 2) and (0, –2) are on the graph. This is not a function, since a distinct x-value corresponds to two different y-values.

32. $y = \pm\sqrt{1 - 2x}$

For $x = 0$, $y = \pm 1$. Thus, (0, 1) and (0, –1) are on the graph. This is not a function, since a distinct x-value corresponds to two different y-values.

33. $x = y^2$

Solve for y: $y = \pm\sqrt{x}$

For $x = 1$, $y = \pm 1$. Thus, (1, 1) and (1, –1) are on the graph. This is not a function, since a distinct x-value corresponds to two different y-values.

34. $x + y^2 = 1$

Solve for y: $y = \pm\sqrt{1 - x}$

For $x = 0$, $y = \pm 1$. Thus, (0, 1) and (0, –1) are on the graph. This is not a function, since a distinct x-value corresponds to two different y-values.

35. Graph $y = 2x^2 - 3x + 4$. The graph passes the vertical line test. Thus, the equation represents a function.

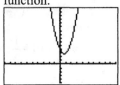

36. Graph $y = \dfrac{3x - 1}{x + 2}$. The graph passes the vertical line test. Thus, the equation represents a function.

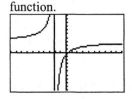

37. $2x^2 + 3y^2 = 1$

Solve for y: $2x^2 + 3y^2 = 1$

$$3y^2 = 1 - 2x^2$$

$$y^2 = \frac{1 - 2x^2}{3}$$

$$y = \pm\sqrt{\frac{1 - 2x^2}{3}}$$

For $x = 0$, $y = \pm\sqrt{\dfrac{1}{3}}$. Thus, $\left(0, \sqrt{\dfrac{1}{3}}\right)$ and $\left(0, -\sqrt{\dfrac{1}{3}}\right)$ are on the graph. This is not a function, since a distinct x-value corresponds to two different y-values.

38. $x^2 - 4y^2 = 1$

Solve for y: $x^2 - 4y^2 = 1$

$$4y^2 = x^2 - 1$$

$$y^2 = \frac{x^2 - 1}{4}$$

$$y = \frac{\pm\sqrt{x^2 - 1}}{2}$$

For $x = \sqrt{2}$, $y = \pm\frac{1}{2}$. Thus, $\left(\sqrt{2}, \frac{1}{2}\right)$ and

$\left(\sqrt{2}, -\frac{1}{2}\right)$ are on the graph. This is not a

function, since a distinct x-value corresponds to two different y-values.

39. $f(x) = 3x^2 + 2x - 4$

a. $f(0) = 3(0)^2 + 2(0) - 4 = -4$

b. $f(1) = 3(1)^2 + 2(1) - 4 = 3 + 2 - 4 = 1$

c. $f(-1) = 3(-1)^2 + 2(-1) - 4 = 3 - 2 - 4 = -3$

d. $f(-x) = 3(-x)^2 + 2(-x) - 4 = 3x^2 - 2x - 4$

e. $-f(x) = -\left(3x^2 + 2x - 4\right) = -3x^2 - 2x + 4$

f. $f(x+1) = 3(x+1)^2 + 2(x+1) - 4$

$$= 3\left(x^2 + 2x + 1\right) + 2x + 2 - 4$$

$$= 3x^2 + 6x + 3 + 2x + 2 - 4$$

$$= 3x^2 + 8x + 1$$

g. $f(2x) = 3(2x)^2 + 2(2x) - 4 = 12x^2 + 4x - 4$

h. $f(x+h) = 3(x+h)^2 + 2(x+h) - 4$

$$= 3\left(x^2 + 2xh + h^2\right) + 2x + 2h - 4$$

$$= 3x^2 + 6xh + 3h^2 + 2x + 2h - 4$$

40. $f(x) = -2x^2 + x - 1$

a. $f(0) = -2(0)^2 + 0 - 1 = -1$

b. $f(1) = -2(1)^2 + 1 - 1 = -2$

c. $f(-1) = -2(-1)^2 + (-1) - 1 = -4$

d. $f(-x) = -2(-x)^2 + (-x) - 1 = -2x^2 - x - 1$

e. $-f(x) = -\left(-2x^2 + x - 1\right) = 2x^2 - x + 1$

f. $f(x+1) = -2(x+1)^2 + (x+1) - 1$

$$= -2\left(x^2 + 2x + 1\right) + x + 1 - 1$$

$$= -2x^2 - 4x - 2 + x$$

$$= -2x^2 - 3x - 2$$

g. $f(2x) = -2(2x)^2 + (2x) - 1 = -8x^2 + 2x - 1$

h. $f(x+h) = -2(x+h)^2 + (x+h) - 1$

$$= -2\left(x^2 + 2xh + h^2\right) + x + h - 1$$

$$= -2x^2 - 4xh - 2h^2 + x + h - 1$$

41. $f(x) = \dfrac{x}{x^2 + 1}$

a. $f(0) = \dfrac{0}{0^2 + 1} = \dfrac{0}{1} = 0$

b. $f(1) = \dfrac{1}{1^2 + 1} = \dfrac{1}{2}$

c. $f(-1) = \dfrac{-1}{(-1)^2 + 1} = \dfrac{-1}{1+1} = -\dfrac{1}{2}$

d. $f(-x) = \dfrac{-x}{(-x)^2 + 1} = \dfrac{-x}{x^2 + 1}$

e. $-f(x) = -\left(\dfrac{x}{x^2 + 1}\right) = \dfrac{-x}{x^2 + 1}$

f. $f(x+1) = \dfrac{x+1}{(x+1)^2 + 1}$

$$= \dfrac{x+1}{x^2 + 2x + 1 + 1}$$

$$= \dfrac{x+1}{x^2 + 2x + 2}$$

g. $f(2x) = \dfrac{2x}{(2x)^2 + 1} = \dfrac{2x}{4x^2 + 1}$

h. $f(x+h) = \dfrac{x+h}{(x+h)^2 + 1} = \dfrac{x+h}{x^2 + 2xh + h^2 + 1}$

231

42. $f(x) = \dfrac{x^2 - 1}{x + 4}$

   a. $f(0) = \dfrac{0^2 - 1}{0 + 4} = \dfrac{-1}{4} = -\dfrac{1}{4}$

   b. $f(1) = \dfrac{1^2 - 1}{1 + 4} = \dfrac{0}{5} = 0$

   c. $f(-1) = \dfrac{(-1)^2 - 1}{-1 + 4} = \dfrac{0}{3} = 0$

   d. $f(-x) = \dfrac{(-x)^2 - 1}{-x + 4} = \dfrac{x^2 - 1}{-x + 4}$

   e. $-f(x) = -\left(\dfrac{x^2 - 1}{x + 4}\right) = \dfrac{-x^2 + 1}{x + 4}$

   f. $f(x + 1) = \dfrac{(x + 1)^2 - 1}{(x + 1) + 4}$

         $= \dfrac{x^2 + 2x + 1 - 1}{x + 5} = \dfrac{x^2 + 2x}{x + 5}$

   g. $f(2x) = \dfrac{(2x)^2 - 1}{2x + 4} = \dfrac{4x^2 - 1}{2x + 4}$

   h. $f(x + h) = \dfrac{(x + h)^2 - 1}{(x + h) + 4} = \dfrac{x^2 + 2xh + h^2 - 1}{x + h + 4}$

43. $f(x) = |x| + 4$

   a. $f(0) = |0| + 4 = 0 + 4 = 4$

   b. $f(1) = |1| + 4 = 1 + 4 = 5$

   c. $f(-1) = |-1| + 4 = 1 + 4 = 5$

   d. $f(-x) = |-x| + 4 = |x| + 4$

   e. $-f(x) = -(|x| + 4) = -|x| - 4$

   f. $f(x + 1) = |x + 1| + 4$

   g. $f(2x) = |2x| + 4 = 2|x| + 4$

   h. $f(x + h) = |x + h| + 4$

44. $f(x) = \sqrt{x^2 + x}$

   a. $f(0) = \sqrt{0^2 + 0} = \sqrt{0} = 0$

   b. $f(1) = \sqrt{1^2 + 1} = \sqrt{2}$

   c. $f(-1) = \sqrt{(-1)^2 + (-1)} = \sqrt{1 - 1} = \sqrt{0} = 0$

   d. $f(-x) = \sqrt{(-x)^2 + (-x)} = \sqrt{x^2 - x}$

   e. $-f(x) = -\left(\sqrt{x^2 + x}\right) = -\sqrt{x^2 + x}$

   f. $f(x + 1) = \sqrt{(x + 1)^2 + (x + 1)}$

         $= \sqrt{x^2 + 2x + 1 + x + 1}$

         $= \sqrt{x^2 + 3x + 2}$

   g. $f(2x) = \sqrt{(2x)^2 + 2x} = \sqrt{4x^2 + 2x}$

   h. $f(x + h) = \sqrt{(x + h)^2 + (x + h)}$

         $= \sqrt{x^2 + 2xh + h^2 + x + h}$

45. $f(x) = \dfrac{2x + 1}{3x - 5}$

   a. $f(0) = \dfrac{2(0) + 1}{3(0) - 5} = \dfrac{0 + 1}{0 - 5} = -\dfrac{1}{5}$

   b. $f(1) = \dfrac{2(1) + 1}{3(1) - 5} = \dfrac{2 + 1}{3 - 5} = \dfrac{3}{-2} = -\dfrac{3}{2}$

   c. $f(-1) = \dfrac{2(-1) + 1}{3(-1) - 5} = \dfrac{-2 + 1}{-3 - 5} = \dfrac{-1}{-8} = \dfrac{1}{8}$

   d. $f(-x) = \dfrac{2(-x) + 1}{3(-x) - 5} = \dfrac{-2x + 1}{-3x - 5} = \dfrac{2x - 1}{3x + 5}$

   e. $-f(x) = -\left(\dfrac{2x + 1}{3x - 5}\right) = \dfrac{-2x - 1}{3x - 5}$

   f. $f(x + 1) = \dfrac{2(x + 1) + 1}{3(x + 1) - 5} = \dfrac{2x + 2 + 1}{3x + 3 - 5} = \dfrac{2x + 3}{3x - 2}$

   g. $f(2x) = \dfrac{2(2x) + 1}{3(2x) - 5} = \dfrac{4x + 1}{6x - 5}$

   h. $f(x + h) = \dfrac{2(x + h) + 1}{3(x + h) - 5} = \dfrac{2x + 2h + 1}{3x + 3h - 5}$

46. $f(x) = 1 - \dfrac{1}{(x+2)^2}$

a. $f(0) = 1 - \dfrac{1}{(0+2)^2} = 1 - \dfrac{1}{4} = \dfrac{3}{4}$

b. $f(1) = 1 - \dfrac{1}{(1+2)^2} = 1 - \dfrac{1}{9} = \dfrac{8}{9}$

c. $f(-1) = 1 - \dfrac{1}{(-1+2)^2} = 1 - \dfrac{1}{1} = 0$

d. $f(-x) = 1 - \dfrac{1}{(-x+2)^2} = 1 - \dfrac{1}{(2-x)^2}$

e. $-f(x) = -\left(1 - \dfrac{1}{(x+2)^2}\right) = \dfrac{1}{(x+2)^2} - 1$

f. $f(x+1) = 1 - \dfrac{1}{(x+1+2)^2} = 1 - \dfrac{1}{(x+3)^2}$

g. $f(2x) = 1 - \dfrac{1}{(2x+2)^2} = 1 - \dfrac{1}{4(x+1)^2}$

h. $f(x+h) = 1 - \dfrac{1}{(x+h+2)^2}$

47. $f(x) = -5x + 4$

Domain: $\{x \mid x \text{ is any real number}\}$

48. $f(x) = x^2 + 2$

Domain: $\{x \mid x \text{ is any real number}\}$

49. $f(x) = \dfrac{x}{x^2 + 1}$

Domain: $\{x \mid x \text{ is any real number}\}$

50. $f(x) = \dfrac{x^2}{x^2 + 1}$

Domain: $\{x \mid x \text{ is any real number}\}$

51. $g(x) = \dfrac{x}{x^2 - 16}$

$x^2 - 16 \neq 0$

$x^2 \neq 16 \Rightarrow x \neq \pm 4$

Domain: $\{x \mid x \neq -4, x \neq 4\}$

52. $h(x) = \dfrac{2x}{x^2 - 4}$

$x^2 - 4 \neq 0$

$x^2 \neq 4 \Rightarrow x \neq \pm 2$

Domain: $\{x \mid x \neq -2, x \neq 2\}$

53. $F(x) = \dfrac{x-2}{x^3 + x}$

$x^3 + x \neq 0$

$x(x^2 + 1) \neq 0$

$x \neq 0, \quad x^2 \neq -1$

Domain: $\{x \mid x \neq 0\}$

54. $G(x) = \dfrac{x+4}{x^3 - 4x}$

$x^3 - 4x \neq 0$

$x(x^2 - 4) \neq 0$

$x \neq 0, \quad x^2 \neq 4$

$x \neq 0, \quad x \neq \pm 2$

Domain: $\{x \mid x \neq -2, x \neq 0, x \neq 2\}$

55. $h(x) = \sqrt{3x - 12}$

$3x - 12 \geq 0$

$3x \geq 12$

$x \geq 4$

Domain: $\{x \mid x \geq 4\}$

56. $G(x) = \sqrt{1 - x}$

$1 - x \geq 0$

$-x \geq -1$

$x \leq 1$

Domain: $\{x \mid x \leq 1\}$

57. $f(x) = \dfrac{4}{\sqrt{x - 9}}$

$x - 9 > 0$

$x > 9$

Domain: $\{x \mid x > 9\}$

58. $f(x) = \dfrac{x}{\sqrt{x-4}}$

$x - 4 > 0$

$x > 4$

Domain: $\{x \mid x > 4\}$

59. $p(x) = \sqrt{\dfrac{2}{x-1}} = \dfrac{\sqrt{2}}{\sqrt{x-1}}$

$x - 1 > 0$

$x > 1$

Domain: $\{x \mid x > 1\}$

60. $q(x) = \sqrt{-x-2}$

$-x - 2 \geq 0$

$-x \geq 2$

$x \leq -2$

Domain: $\{x \mid x \leq -2\}$

61. $f(x) = 3x + 4 \qquad g(x) = 2x - 3$

a. $(f + g)(x) = 3x + 4 + 2x - 3 = 5x + 1$

Domain: $\{x \mid x \text{ is any real number}\}$.

b. $(f - g)(x) = (3x + 4) - (2x - 3)$

$= 3x + 4 - 2x + 3$

$= x + 7$

Domain: $\{x \mid x \text{ is any real number}\}$.

c. $(f \cdot g)(x) = (3x + 4)(2x - 3)$

$= 6x^2 - 9x + 8x - 12$

$= 6x^2 - x - 12$

Domain: $\{x \mid x \text{ is any real number}\}$.

d. $\left(\dfrac{f}{g}\right)(x) = \dfrac{3x + 4}{2x - 3}$

$2x - 3 \neq 0 \Rightarrow 2x \neq 3 \Rightarrow x \neq \dfrac{3}{2}$

Domain: $\left\{x \mid x \neq \dfrac{3}{2}\right\}$.

e. $(f + g)(3) = 5(3) + 1 = 15 + 1 = 16$

f. $(f - g)(4) = 4 + 7 = 11$

g. $(f \cdot g)(2) = 6(2)^2 - 2 - 12 = 24 - 2 - 12 = 10$

h. $\left(\dfrac{f}{g}\right)(1) = \dfrac{3(1) + 4}{2(1) - 3} = \dfrac{3 + 4}{2 - 3} = \dfrac{7}{-1} = -7$

62. $f(x) = 2x + 1 \qquad g(x) = 3x - 2$

a. $(f + g)(x) = 2x + 1 + 3x - 2 = 5x - 1$

Domain: $\{x \mid x \text{ is any real number}\}$.

b. $(f - g)(x) = (2x + 1) - (3x - 2)$

$= 2x + 1 - 3x + 2$

$= -x + 3$

Domain: $\{x \mid x \text{ is any real number}\}$.

c. $(f \cdot g)(x) = (2x + 1)(3x - 2)$

$= 6x^2 - 4x + 3x - 2$

$= 6x^2 - x - 2$

Domain: $\{x \mid x \text{ is any real number}\}$.

d. $\left(\dfrac{f}{g}\right)(x) = \dfrac{2x + 1}{3x - 2}$

$3x - 2 \neq 0$

$3x \neq 2 \Rightarrow x \neq \dfrac{2}{3}$

Domain: $\left\{x \mid x \neq \dfrac{2}{3}\right\}$.

e. $(f + g)(3) = 5(3) - 1 = 15 - 1 = 14$

f. $(f - g)(4) = -4 + 3 = -1$

g. $(f \cdot g)(2) = 6(2)^2 - 2 - 2$

$= 6(4) - 2 - 2$

$= 24 - 2 - 2 = 20$

h. $\left(\dfrac{f}{g}\right)(1) = \dfrac{2(1) + 1}{3(1) - 2} = \dfrac{2 + 1}{3 - 2} = \dfrac{3}{1} = 3$

63. $f(x) = x - 1 \qquad g(x) = 2x^2$

a. $(f + g)(x) = x - 1 + 2x^2 = 2x^2 + x - 1$

Domain: $\{x \mid x \text{ is any real number}\}$.

b. $(f - g)(x) = (x - 1) - (2x^2)$

$= x - 1 - 2x^2$

$= -2x^2 + x - 1$

Domain: $\{x \mid x \text{ is any real number}\}$.

c. $(f \cdot g)(x) = (x - 1)(2x^2) = 2x^3 - 2x^2$

Domain: $\{x \mid x \text{ is any real number}\}$.

d. $\left(\dfrac{f}{g}\right)(x) = \dfrac{x-1}{2x^2}$

Domain: $\{x \mid x \neq 0\}$.

e. $(f+g)(3) = 2(3)^2 + 3 - 1$
$\quad\quad = 2(9) + 3 - 1$
$\quad\quad = 18 + 3 - 1 = 20$

f. $(f-g)(4) = -2(4)^2 + 4 - 1$
$\quad\quad = -2(16) + 4 - 1$
$\quad\quad = -32 + 4 - 1 = -29$

g. $(f \cdot g)(2) = 2(2)^3 - 2(2)^2$
$\quad\quad = 2(8) - 2(4)$
$\quad\quad = 16 - 8 = 8$

h. $\left(\dfrac{f}{g}\right)(1) = \dfrac{1-1}{2(1)^2} = \dfrac{0}{2(1)} = \dfrac{0}{2} = 0$

64. $f(x) = 2x^2 + 3 \quad\quad g(x) = 4x^3 + 1$

a. $(f+g)(x) = 2x^2 + 3 + 4x^3 + 1$
$\quad\quad = 4x^3 + 2x^2 + 4$
Domain: $\{x \mid x \text{ is any real number}\}$.

b. $(f-g)(x) = \left(2x^2 + 3\right) - \left(4x^3 + 1\right)$
$\quad\quad = 2x^2 + 3 - 4x^3 - 1$
$\quad\quad = -4x^3 + 2x^2 + 2$
Domain: $\{x \mid x \text{ is any real number}\}$.

c. $(f \cdot g)(x) = \left(2x^2 + 3\right)\left(4x^3 + 1\right)$
$\quad\quad = 8x^5 + 12x^3 + 2x^2 + 3$
Domain: $\{x \mid x \text{ is any real number}\}$.

d. $\left(\dfrac{f}{g}\right)(x) = \dfrac{2x^2 + 3}{4x^3 + 1}$

$4x^3 + 1 \neq 0$

$4x^3 \neq -1$

$x^3 \neq -\dfrac{1}{4} \Rightarrow x \neq \sqrt[3]{-\dfrac{1}{4}} = -\dfrac{\sqrt[3]{2}}{2}$

Domain: $\left\{x \mid x \neq -\dfrac{\sqrt[3]{2}}{2}\right\}$.

e. $(f+g)(3) = 4(3)^3 + 2(3)^2 + 4$
$\quad\quad = 4(27) + 2(9) + 4$
$\quad\quad = 108 + 18 + 4 = 130$

f. $(f-g)(4) = -4(4)^3 + 2(4)^2 + 2$
$\quad\quad = -4(64) + 2(16) + 2$
$\quad\quad = -256 + 32 + 2 = -222$

g. $(f \cdot g)(2) = 8(2)^5 + 12(2)^3 + 2(2)^2 + 3$
$\quad\quad = 8(32) + 12(8) + 2(4) + 3$
$\quad\quad = 256 + 96 + 8 + 3 = 363$

h. $\left(\dfrac{f}{g}\right)(1) = \dfrac{2(1)^2 + 3}{4(1)^3 + 1} = \dfrac{2(1) + 3}{4(1) + 1} = \dfrac{2+3}{4+1} = \dfrac{5}{5} = 1$

65. $f(x) = \sqrt{x} \quad\quad g(x) = 3x - 5$

a. $(f+g)(x) = \sqrt{x} + 3x - 5$
Domain: $\{x \mid x \geq 0\}$.

b. $(f-g)(x) = \sqrt{x} - (3x - 5) = \sqrt{x} - 3x + 5$
Domain: $\{x \mid x \geq 0\}$.

c. $(f \cdot g)(x) = \sqrt{x}(3x - 5) = 3x\sqrt{x} - 5\sqrt{x}$
Domain: $\{x \mid x \geq 0\}$.

d. $\left(\dfrac{f}{g}\right)(x) = \dfrac{\sqrt{x}}{3x - 5}$

$x \geq 0$ and $3x - 5 \neq 0$

$\quad\quad 3x \neq 5 \Rightarrow x \neq \dfrac{5}{3}$

Domain: $\left\{x \mid x \geq 0 \text{ and } x \neq \dfrac{5}{3}\right\}$.

e. $(f+g)(3) = \sqrt{3} + 3(3) - 5$
$\quad\quad = \sqrt{3} + 9 - 5 = \sqrt{3} + 4$

f. $(f-g)(4) = \sqrt{4} - 3(4) + 5$
$\quad\quad = 2 - 12 + 5 = -5$

g. $(f \cdot g)(2) = 3(2)\sqrt{2} - 5\sqrt{2}$
$\quad\quad = 6\sqrt{2} - 5\sqrt{2} = \sqrt{2}$

h. $\left(\dfrac{f}{g}\right)(1) = \dfrac{\sqrt{1}}{3(1) - 5} = \dfrac{1}{3 - 5} = \dfrac{1}{-2} = -\dfrac{1}{2}$

235

66. $f(x) = |x|$ $g(x) = x$

   a. $(f+g)(x) = |x| + x$

    Domain: $\{x \mid x \text{ is any real number}\}$.

   b. $(f-g)(x) = |x| - x$

    Domain: $\{x \mid x \text{ is any real number}\}$.

   c. $(f \cdot g)(x) = |x| \cdot x = x|x|$

    Domain: $\{x \mid x \text{ is any real number}\}$.

   d. $\left(\dfrac{f}{g}\right)(x) = \dfrac{|x|}{x}$

    Domain: $\{x \mid x \neq 0\}$.

   e. $(f+g)(3) = |3| + 3 = 3 + 3 = 6$

   f. $(f-g)(4) = |4| - 4 = 4 - 4 = 0$

   g. $(f \cdot g)(2) = 2|2| = 2 \cdot 2 = 4$

   h. $\left(\dfrac{f}{g}\right)(1) = \dfrac{|1|}{1} = \dfrac{1}{1} = 1$

67. $f(x) = 1 + \dfrac{1}{x}$ $g(x) = \dfrac{1}{x}$

   a. $(f+g)(x) = 1 + \dfrac{1}{x} + \dfrac{1}{x} = 1 + \dfrac{2}{x}$

    Domain: $\{x \mid x \neq 0\}$.

   b. $(f-g)(x) = 1 + \dfrac{1}{x} - \dfrac{1}{x} = 1$

    Domain: $\{x \mid x \neq 0\}$.

   c. $(f \cdot g)(x) = \left(1 + \dfrac{1}{x}\right)\dfrac{1}{x} = \dfrac{1}{x} + \dfrac{1}{x^2}$

    Domain: $\{x \mid x \neq 0\}$.

   d. $\left(\dfrac{f}{g}\right)(x) = \dfrac{1 + \dfrac{1}{x}}{\dfrac{1}{x}} = \dfrac{\dfrac{x+1}{x}}{\dfrac{1}{x}} = \dfrac{x+1}{x} \cdot \dfrac{x}{1} = x + 1$

    Domain: $\{x \mid x \neq 0\}$.

   e. $(f+g)(3) = 1 + \dfrac{2}{3} = \dfrac{5}{3}$

   f. $(f-g)(4) = 1$

   g. $(f \cdot g)(2) = \dfrac{1}{2} + \dfrac{1}{(2)^2} = \dfrac{1}{2} + \dfrac{1}{4} = \dfrac{3}{4}$

   h. $\left(\dfrac{f}{g}\right)(1) = 1 + 1 = 2$

68. $f(x) = \sqrt{x-1}$ $g(x) = \sqrt{4-x}$

   a. $(f+g)(x) = \sqrt{x-1} + \sqrt{4-x}$

    $x - 1 \geq 0$ and $4 - x \geq 0$

     $x \geq 1$ and $-x \geq -4$

      $x \leq 4$

    Domain: $\{x \mid 1 \leq x \leq 4\}$.

   b. $(f-g)(x) = \sqrt{x-1} - \sqrt{4-x}$

    $x - 1 \geq 0$ and $4 - x \geq 0$

     $x \geq 1$ and $-x \geq -4$

      $x \leq 4$

    Domain: $\{x \mid 1 \leq x \leq 4\}$.

   c. $(f \cdot g)(x) = \left(\sqrt{x-1}\right)\left(\sqrt{4-x}\right)$

          $= \sqrt{-x^2 + 5x - 4}$

    $x - 1 \geq 0$ and $4 - x \geq 0$

     $x \geq 1$ and $-x \geq -4$

      $x \leq 4$

    Domain: $\{x \mid 1 \leq x \leq 4\}$.

   d. $\left(\dfrac{f}{g}\right)(x) = \dfrac{\sqrt{x-1}}{\sqrt{4-x}} = \sqrt{\dfrac{x-1}{4-x}}$

    $x - 1 \geq 0$ and $4 - x > 0$

     $x \geq 1$ and $-x > -4$

      $x < 4$

    Domain: $\{x \mid 1 \leq x < 4\}$.

   e. $(f+g)(3) = \sqrt{3-1} + \sqrt{4-3}$

          $= \sqrt{2} + \sqrt{1} = \sqrt{2} + 1$

   f. $(f-g)(4) = \sqrt{4-1} - \sqrt{4-4}$

          $= \sqrt{3} - \sqrt{0} = \sqrt{3} - 0 = \sqrt{3}$

   g. $(f \cdot g)(2) = \sqrt{-(2)^2 + 5(2) - 4}$

          $= \sqrt{-4 + 10 - 4} = \sqrt{2}$

   h. $\left(\dfrac{f}{g}\right)(1) = \sqrt{\dfrac{1-1}{4-1}} = \sqrt{\dfrac{0}{3}} = \sqrt{0} = 0$

69. $f(x) = \dfrac{2x+3}{3x-2} \qquad g(x) = \dfrac{4x}{3x-2}$

a. $(f+g)(x) = \dfrac{2x+3}{3x-2} + \dfrac{4x}{3x-2}$

$\qquad = \dfrac{2x+3+4x}{3x-2} = \dfrac{6x+3}{3x-2}$

$3x-2 \neq 0$

$\qquad 3x \neq 2 \Rightarrow x \neq \dfrac{2}{3}$

Domain: $\left\{ x \mid x \neq \dfrac{2}{3} \right\}.$

b. $(f-g)(x) = \dfrac{2x+3}{3x-2} - \dfrac{4x}{3x-2}$

$\qquad = \dfrac{2x+3-4x}{3x-2} = \dfrac{-2x+3}{3x-2}$

$3x-2 \neq 0$

$\qquad 3x \neq 2 \Rightarrow x \neq \dfrac{2}{3}$

Domain: $\left\{ x \mid x \neq \dfrac{2}{3} \right\}.$

c. $(f \cdot g)(x) = \left(\dfrac{2x+3}{3x-2} \right)\left(\dfrac{4x}{3x-2} \right) = \dfrac{8x^2+12x}{(3x-2)^2}$

$3x-2 \neq 0$

$\qquad 3x \neq 2 \Rightarrow x \neq \dfrac{2}{3}$

Domain: $\left\{ x \mid x \neq \dfrac{2}{3} \right\}.$

d. $\left(\dfrac{f}{g} \right)(x) = \dfrac{\dfrac{2x+3}{3x-2}}{\dfrac{4x}{3x-2}} = \dfrac{2x+3}{3x-2} \cdot \dfrac{3x-2}{4x} = \dfrac{2x+3}{4x}$

$3x-2 \neq 0 \quad$ and $\quad x \neq 0$

$\qquad 3x \neq 2$

$\qquad x \neq \dfrac{2}{3}$

Domain: $\left\{ x \mid x \neq \dfrac{2}{3} \text{ and } x \neq 0 \right\}.$

e. $(f+g)(3) = \dfrac{6(3)+3}{3(3)-2} = \dfrac{18+3}{9-2} = \dfrac{21}{7} = 3$

f. $(f-g)(4) = \dfrac{-2(4)+3}{3(4)-2} = \dfrac{-8+3}{12-2} = \dfrac{-5}{10} = -\dfrac{1}{2}$

g. $(f \cdot g)(2) = \dfrac{8(2)^2 + 12(2)}{(3(2)-2)^2}$

$\qquad = \dfrac{8(4)+24}{(6-2)^2} = \dfrac{32+24}{(4)^2} = \dfrac{56}{16} = \dfrac{7}{2}$

h. $\left(\dfrac{f}{g} \right)(1) = \dfrac{2(1)+3}{4(1)} = \dfrac{2+3}{4} = \dfrac{5}{4}$

70. $f(x) = \sqrt{x+1} \qquad g(x) = \dfrac{2}{x}$

a. $(f+g)(x) = \sqrt{x+1} + \dfrac{2}{x}$

$x+1 \geq 0 \quad$ and $\quad x \neq 0$

$\qquad x \geq -1$

Domain: $\left\{ x \mid x \geq -1, \text{ and } x \neq 0 \right\}.$

b. $(f-g)(x) = \sqrt{x+1} - \dfrac{2}{x}$

$x+1 \geq 0 \quad$ and $\quad x \neq 0$

$\qquad x \geq -1$

Domain: $\left\{ x \mid x \geq -1, \text{ and } x \neq 0 \right\}.$

c. $(f \cdot g)(x) = \sqrt{x+1} \cdot \dfrac{2}{x} = \dfrac{2\sqrt{x+1}}{x}$

$x+1 \geq 0 \quad$ and $\quad x \neq 0$

$\qquad x \geq -1$

Domain: $\left\{ x \mid x \geq -1, \text{ and } x \neq 0 \right\}.$

d. $\left(\dfrac{f}{g} \right)(x) = \dfrac{\sqrt{x+1}}{\dfrac{2}{x}} = \dfrac{x\sqrt{x+1}}{2}$

$x+1 \geq 0 \quad$ and $\quad x \neq 0$

$\qquad x \geq -1$

Domain: $\left\{ x \mid x \geq -1, \text{ and } x \neq 0 \right\}.$

e. $(f+g)(3) = \sqrt{3+1} + \dfrac{2}{3} = \sqrt{4} + \dfrac{2}{3} = 2 + \dfrac{2}{3} = \dfrac{8}{3}$

f. $(f-g)(4) = \sqrt{4+1} - \dfrac{2}{4} = \sqrt{5} - \dfrac{1}{2}$

g. $(f \cdot g)(2) = \dfrac{2\sqrt{2+1}}{2} = \dfrac{2\sqrt{3}}{2} = \sqrt{3}$

h. $\left(\dfrac{f}{g} \right)(1) = \dfrac{1\sqrt{1+1}}{2} = \dfrac{\sqrt{2}}{2}$

71. $f(x) = 3x + 1 \qquad (f+g)(x) = 6 - \dfrac{1}{2}x$

$6 - \dfrac{1}{2}x = 3x + 1 + g(x)$

$5 - \dfrac{7}{2}x = g(x)$

$g(x) = 5 - \dfrac{7}{2}x$

72. $f(x) = \dfrac{1}{x} \qquad \left(\dfrac{f}{g}\right)(x) = \dfrac{x+1}{x^2 - x}$

$\dfrac{x+1}{x^2 - x} = \dfrac{\frac{1}{x}}{g(x)}$

$g(x) = \dfrac{\frac{1}{x}}{\frac{x+1}{x^2 - x}} = \dfrac{1}{x} \cdot \dfrac{x^2 - x}{x+1}$

$= \dfrac{1}{x} \cdot \dfrac{x(x-1)}{x+1} = \dfrac{x-1}{x+1}$

73. $f(x) = 4x + 3$

$\dfrac{f(x+h) - f(x)}{h} = \dfrac{4(x+h) + 3 - (4x+3)}{h}$

$= \dfrac{4x + 4h + 3 - 4x - 3}{h}$

$= \dfrac{4h}{h} = 4$

74. $f(x) = -3x + 1$

$\dfrac{f(x+h) - f(x)}{h} = \dfrac{-3(x+h) + 1 - (-3x+1)}{h}$

$= \dfrac{-3x - 3h + 1 + 3x - 1}{h}$

$= \dfrac{-3h}{h} = -3$

75. $f(x) = x^2 - x + 4$

$\dfrac{f(x+h) - f(x)}{h}$

$= \dfrac{(x+h)^2 - (x+h) + 4 - (x^2 - x + 4)}{h}$

$= \dfrac{x^2 + 2xh + h^2 - x - h + 4 - x^2 + x - 4}{h}$

$= \dfrac{2xh + h^2 - h}{h}$

$= 2x + h - 1$

76. $f(x) = x^2 + 5x - 1$

$\dfrac{f(x+h) - f(x)}{h}$

$= \dfrac{(x+h)^2 + 5(x+h) - 1 - (x^2 + 5x - 1)}{h}$

$= \dfrac{x^2 + 2xh + h^2 + 5x + 5h - 1 - x^2 - 5x + 1}{h}$

$= \dfrac{2xh + h^2 + 5h}{h} = 2x + h + 5$

77. $f(x) = 3x^2 - 2x + 6$

$\dfrac{f(x+h) - f(x)}{h}$

$= \dfrac{\left[3(x+h)^2 - 2(x+h) + 6\right] - \left[3x^2 - 2x + 6\right]}{h}$

$= \dfrac{3(x^2 + 2xh + h^2) - 2x - 2h + 6 - 3x^2 + 2x - 6}{h}$

$= \dfrac{3x^2 + 6xh + 3h^2 - 2h - 3x^2}{h} = \dfrac{6xh + 3h^2 - 2h}{h}$

$= 6x + 3h - 2$

78. $f(x) = 4x^2 + 5x - 7$

$\dfrac{f(x+h) - f(x)}{h}$

$= \dfrac{\left[4(x+h)^2 + 5(x+h) - 7\right] - \left[4x^2 + 5x - 7\right]}{h}$

$= \dfrac{4(x^2 + 2xh + h^2) + 5x + 5h - 7 - 4x^2 - 5x + 7}{h}$

$= \dfrac{4x^2 + 8xh + 4h^2 + 5h - 4x^2}{h} = \dfrac{8xh + 4h^2 + 5h}{h}$

$= 8x + 4h + 5$

79. $f(x) = x^3 - 2$

$\dfrac{f(x+h) - f(x)}{h}$

$= \dfrac{(x+h)^3 - 2 - (x^3 - 2)}{h}$

$= \dfrac{x^3 + 3x^2 h + 3xh^2 + h^3 - 2 - x^3 + 2}{h}$

$= \dfrac{3x^2 h + 3xh^2 + h^3}{h} = 3x^2 + 3xh + h^2$

80. $f(x) = \dfrac{1}{x+3}$

$$\dfrac{f(x+h)-f(x)}{h} = \dfrac{\dfrac{1}{x+h+3}-\dfrac{1}{x+3}}{h}$$

$$= \dfrac{\dfrac{x+3-(x+3+h)}{(x+h+3)(x+3)}}{h}$$

$$= \left(\dfrac{x+3-x-3-h}{(x+h+3)(x+3)}\right)\left(\dfrac{1}{h}\right)$$

$$= \left(\dfrac{-h}{(x+h+3)(x+3)}\right)\left(\dfrac{1}{h}\right)$$

$$= \dfrac{-1}{(x+h+3)(x+3)}$$

81. $f(x) = 2x^3 + Ax^2 + 4x - 5$ and $f(2) = 5$

$$f(2) = 2(2)^3 + A(2)^2 + 4(2) - 5$$
$$5 = 16 + 4A + 8 - 5$$
$$5 = 4A + 19$$
$$-14 = 4A$$
$$A = \dfrac{-14}{4} = -\dfrac{7}{2}$$

82. $f(x) = 3x^2 - Bx + 4$ and $f(-1) = 12$:

$$f(-1) = 3(-1)^2 - B(-1) + 4$$
$$12 = 3 + B + 4$$
$$B = 5$$

83. $f(x) = \dfrac{3x+8}{2x-A}$ and $f(0) = 2$

$$f(0) = \dfrac{3(0)+8}{2(0)-A}$$
$$2 = \dfrac{8}{-A}$$
$$-2A = 8$$
$$A = -4$$

84. $f(x) = \dfrac{2x-B}{3x+4}$ and $f(2) = \dfrac{1}{2}$

$$f(2) = \dfrac{2(2)-B}{3(2)+4}$$
$$\dfrac{1}{2} = \dfrac{4-B}{10}$$
$$5 = 4 - B$$
$$B = -1$$

85. $f(x) = \dfrac{2x-A}{x-3}$ and $f(4) = 0$

$$f(4) = \dfrac{2(4)-A}{4-3}$$
$$0 = \dfrac{8-A}{1}$$
$$0 = 8 - A$$
$$A = 8$$

f is undefined when $x = 3$.

86. $f(x) = \dfrac{x-B}{x-A}, f(2) = 0$ and $f(1)$ is undefined

$$1 - A = 0 \implies A = 1$$
$$f(2) = \dfrac{2-B}{2-1}$$
$$0 = \dfrac{2-B}{1}$$
$$0 = 2 - B$$
$$B = 2$$

87. Let x represent the length of the rectangle. Then, $\dfrac{x}{2}$ represents the width of the rectangle since the length is twice the width. The function for the area is: $A(x) = x \cdot \dfrac{x}{2} = \dfrac{x^2}{2} = \dfrac{1}{2}x^2$

88. Let x represent the length of one of the two equal sides. The function for the area is:
$$A(x) = \dfrac{1}{2} \cdot x \cdot x = \dfrac{1}{2}x^2$$

89. Let x represent the number of hours worked. The function for the gross salary is:
$$G(x) = 10x$$

90. Let x represent the number of items sold. The function for the gross salary is:
$$G(x) = 10x + 100$$

91. a. P is the dependent variable; a is the independent variable

b. $P(20) = 0.015(20)^2 - 4.962(20) + 290.580$
$= 6 - 99.24 + 290.580$
$= 197.34$
In 2005 there are 197.34 million people who are 20 years of age or older.

c. $P(0) = 0.015(0)^2 - 4.962(0) + 290.580$
$= 290.580$
In 2005 there are 290.580 million people.

92. a. N is the dependent variable; r is the independent variable

b. $N(3) = -1.44(3)^2 + 14.52(3) - 14.96$
$= -12.96 + 43.56 - 14.96$
$= 15.64$
In 2005, there are 15.64 million housing units with 3 rooms.

93. a. $H(1) = 20 - 4.9(1)^2$
$= 20 - 4.9 = 15.1$ meters
$H(1.1) = 20 - 4.9(1.1)^2$
$= 20 - 4.9(1.21)$
$= 20 - 5.929 = 14.071$ meters
$H(1.2) = 20 - 4.9(1.2)^2$
$= 20 - 4.9(1.44)$
$= 20 - 7.056 = 12.944$ meters
$H(1.3) = 20 - 4.9(1.3)^2$
$= 20 - 4.9(1.69)$
$= 20 - 8.281 = 11.719$ meters

b. $H(x) = 15$:
$15 = 20 - 4.9x^2$
$-5 = -4.9x^2$
$x^2 \approx 1.0204$
$x \approx 1.01$ seconds
$H(x) = 10$:
$10 = 20 - 4.9x^2$
$-10 = -4.9x^2$
$x^2 \approx 2.0408$
$x \approx 1.43$ seconds

$H(x) = 5$:
$5 = 20 - 4.9x^2$
$-15 = -4.9x^2$
$x^2 \approx 3.0612$
$x \approx 1.75$ seconds

c. $H(x) = 0$
$0 = 20 - 4.9x^2$
$-20 = -4.9x^2$
$x^2 \approx 4.0816$
$x \approx 2.02$ seconds

94. a. $H(1) = 20 - 13(1)^2 = 20 - 13 = 7$ meters
$H(1.1) = 20 - 13(1.1)^2 = 20 - 13(1.21)$
$= 20 - 15.73 = 4.27$ meters
$H(1.2) = 20 - 13(1.2)^2 = 20 - 13(1.44)$
$= 20 - 18.72 = 1.28$ meters

b. $H(x) = 15$
$15 = 20 - 13x^2$
$-5 = -13x^2$
$x^2 \approx 0.3846$
$x \approx 0.62$ seconds
$H(x) = 10$
$10 = 20 - 13x^2$
$-10 = -13x^2$
$x^2 \approx 0.7692$
$x \approx 0.88$ seconds
$H(x) = 5$
$5 = 20 - 13x^2$
$-15 = -13x^2$
$x^2 \approx 1.1538$
$x \approx 1.07$ seconds

c. $H(x) = 0$
$0 = 20 - 13x^2$
$-20 = -13x^2$
$x^2 \approx 1.5385$
$x \approx 1.24$ seconds

240

95. $C(x) = 100 + \dfrac{x}{10} + \dfrac{36,000}{x}$

   a. $C(500) = 100 + \dfrac{500}{10} + \dfrac{36,000}{500}$

      $= 100 + 50 + 72$

      $= \$222$

   b. $C(450) = 100 + \dfrac{450}{10} + \dfrac{36,000}{450}$

      $= 100 + 45 + 80$

      $= \$225$

   c. $C(600) = 100 + \dfrac{600}{10} + \dfrac{36,000}{600}$

      $= 100 + 60 + 60$

      $= \$220$

   d. $C(400) = 100 + \dfrac{400}{10} + \dfrac{36,000}{400}$

      $= 100 + 40 + 90$

      $= \$230$

96. $A(x) = 4x\sqrt{1-x^2}$

   a. $A\left(\dfrac{1}{3}\right) = 4 \cdot \dfrac{1}{3}\sqrt{1 - \left(\dfrac{1}{3}\right)^2} = \dfrac{4}{3}\sqrt{\dfrac{8}{9}} = \dfrac{4}{3} \cdot \dfrac{2\sqrt{2}}{3}$

      $= \dfrac{8\sqrt{2}}{9} \approx 1.26 \text{ ft}^2$

   b. $A\left(\dfrac{1}{2}\right) = 4 \cdot \dfrac{1}{2}\sqrt{1 - \left(\dfrac{1}{2}\right)^2} = 2\sqrt{\dfrac{3}{4}} = 2 \cdot \dfrac{\sqrt{3}}{2}$

      $= \sqrt{3} \approx 1.73 \text{ ft}^2$

   c. $A\left(\dfrac{2}{3}\right) = 4 \cdot \dfrac{2}{3}\sqrt{1 - \left(\dfrac{2}{3}\right)^2} = \dfrac{8}{3}\sqrt{\dfrac{5}{9}} = \dfrac{8}{3} \cdot \dfrac{\sqrt{5}}{3}$

      $= \dfrac{8\sqrt{5}}{9} \approx 1.99 \text{ ft}^2$

97. $R(x) = \left(\dfrac{L}{P}\right)(x) = \dfrac{L(x)}{P(x)}$

98. $T(x) = (V+P)(x) = V(x) + P(x)$

99. $H(x) = (P \cdot I)(x) = P(x) \cdot I(x)$

100. $N(x) = (I-T)(x) = I(x) - T(x)$

101. **a.** $P(x) = R(x) - C(x)$

      $= \left(-1.2x^2 + 220x\right) - \left(0.05x^3 - 2x^2 + 65x + 500\right)$

      $= -1.2x^2 + 220x - 0.05x^3 + 2x^2 - 65x - 500$

      $= -0.05x^3 + 0.8x^2 + 155x - 500$

   b. $P(15) = -0.05(15)^3 + 0.8(15)^2 + 155(15) - 500$

      $= -168.75 + 180 + 2325 - 500$

      $= \$1836.25$

   c. When 15 hundred cell phones are sold, the profit is \$1836.25.

102. **a.** $P(x) = R(x) - C(x)$

      $= 30x - \left(0.1x^2 + 7x + 400\right)$

      $= 30x - 0.1x^2 - 7x - 400$

      $= -0.1x^2 + 23x - 400$

   b. $P(30) = -0.1(30)^2 + 23(30) - 400$

      $= -90 + 690 - 400$

      $= \$200$

   c. When 30 clocks are sold, the profit is \$200.

103. **a.** $h(x) = 2x$

      $h(a+b) = 2(a+b) = 2a + 2b$

          $= h(a) + h(b)$

      $h(x) = 2x$ has the property.

   b. $g(x) = x^2$

      $g(a+b) = (a+b)^2 = a^2 + 2ab + b^2$

      Since

      $a^2 + 2ab + b^2 \neq a^2 + b^2 = g(a) + g(b)$,

      $g(x) = x^2$ does not have the property.

   c. $F(x) = 5x - 2$

      $F(a+b) = 5(a+b) - 2 = 5a + 5b - 2$

      Since

      $5a + 5b - 2 \neq 5a - 2 + 5b - 2 = F(a) + F(b)$,

      $F(x) = 5x - 2$ does not have the property.

d. $G(x) = \dfrac{1}{x}$

$$G(a+b) = \frac{1}{a+b} \neq \frac{1}{a} + \frac{1}{b} = G(a) + G(b)$$

$G(x) = \dfrac{1}{x}$ does not have the property.

104. No. The domain of f is $\{x \mid x \text{ is any real number}\}$, but the domain of g is $\{x \mid x \neq -1\}$.

105. Answers will vary.

Section 3.2

1. $x^2 + 4y^2 = 16$

x-intercepts:

$x^2 + 4(0)^2 = 16$

$x^2 = 16$

$x = \pm 4 \Rightarrow (-4, 0), (4, 0)$

y-intercepts:

$(0)^2 + 4y^2 = 16$

$4y^2 = 16$

$y^2 = 4$

$y = \pm 2 \Rightarrow (0, -2), (0, 2)$

2. False; $x = 2y - 2$

$-2 = 2y - 2$

$0 = 2y$

$0 = y$

The point $(-2, 0)$ is on the graph.

3. vertical

4. $f(5) = -3$

5. $f(x) = ax^2 + 4$

$a(-1)^2 + 4 = 2 \Rightarrow a = -2$

6. False; it would fail the vertical line test.

7. False; e.g. $y = \dfrac{1}{x}$.

8. True

9. a. $f(0) = 3$ since $(0, 3)$ is on the graph.

$f(-6) = -3$ since $(-6, -3)$ is on the graph.

b. $f(6) = 0$ since $(6, 0)$ is on the graph.

$f(11) = 1$ since $(11, 1)$ is on the graph.

c. $f(3)$ is positive since $f(3) \approx 3.7$.

d. $f(-4)$ is negative since $f(-4) \approx -1$.

e. $f(x) = 0$ when $x = -3$, $x = 6$, and $x = 10$.

f. $f(x) > 0$ when $-3 < x < 6$, and $10 < x \leq 11$.

g. The domain of f is $\{x \mid -6 \leq x \leq 11\}$ or $[-6, 11]$.

h. The range of f is $\{y \mid -3 \leq y \leq 4\}$ or $[-3, 4]$.

i. The *x*-intercepts are -3, 6, and 10.

j. The *y*-intercept is 3.

k. The line $y = \dfrac{1}{2}$ intersects the graph 3 times.

l. The line $x = 5$ intersects the graph 1 time.

m. $f(x) = 3$ when $x = 0$ and $x = 4$.

n. $f(x) = -2$ when $x = -5$ and $x = 8$.

10. a. $f(0) = 0$ since $(0, 0)$ is on the graph.

$f(6) = 0$ since $(6, 0)$ is on the graph.

b. $f(2) = -2$ since $(2, -2)$ is on the graph.

$f(-2) = 1$ since $(-2, 1)$ is on the graph.

c. $f(3)$ is negative since $f(3) \approx -1$.

d. $f(-1)$ is positive since $f(-1) \approx 1.0$.

e. $f(x) = 0$ when $x = 0$, $x = 4$, and $x = 6$.

f. $f(x) < 0$ when $0 < x < 4$.

g. The domain of f is $\{x \mid -4 \leq x \leq 6\}$ or $[-4, 6]$.

h. The range of f is $\{y \mid -2 \leq y \leq 3\}$ or $[-2, 3]$.

i. The *x*-intercepts are 0, 4, and 6.

j. The *y*-intercept is 0.

k. The line $y = -1$ intersects the graph 2 times.

 l. The line $x = 1$ intersects the graph 1 time.

 m. $f(x) = 3$ when $x = 5$.

 n. $f(x) = -2$ when $x = 2$.

11. Not a function since vertical lines will intersect the graph in more than one point.

12. Function

 a. Domain: $\{x \mid x \text{ is any real number}\}$;

  Range: $\{y \mid y > 0\}$

 b. Intercepts: $(0, 1)$

 c. None

13. Function

 a. Domain: $\{x \mid -\pi \le x \le \pi\}$;

  Range: $\{y \mid -1 \le y \le 1\}$

 b. Intercepts: $\left(-\dfrac{\pi}{2}, 0\right)$, $\left(\dfrac{\pi}{2}, 0\right)$, $(0, 1)$

 c. Symmetry about y-axis.

14. Function

 a. Domain: $\{x \mid -\pi \le x \le \pi\}$;

  Range: $\{y \mid -1 \le y \le 1\}$

 b. Intercepts: $(-\pi, 0)$, $(\pi, 0)$, $(0, 0)$

 c. Symmetry about the origin.

15. Not a function since vertical lines will intersect the graph in more than one point.

16. Not a function since vertical lines will intersect the graph in more than one point.

17. Function

 a. Domain: $\{x \mid x > 0\}$;

  Range: $\{y \mid y \text{ is any real number}\}$

 b. Intercepts: $(1, 0)$

 c. None

18. Function

 a. Domain: $\{x \mid 0 \le x \le 4\}$;

  Range: $\{y \mid 0 \le y \le 3\}$

 b. Intercepts: $(0, 0)$

 c. None

19. Function

 a. Domain: $\{x \mid x \text{ is any real number}\}$;

  Range: $\{y \mid y \le 2\}$

 b. Intercepts: $(-3, 0)$, $(3, 0)$, $(0, 2)$

 c. Symmetry about y-axis.

20. Function

 a. Domain: $\{x \mid x \ge -3\}$;

  Range: $\{y \mid y \ge 0\}$

 b. Intercepts: $(-3, 0)$, $(2, 0)$, $(0, 2)$

 c. None

21. Function

 a. Domain: $\{x \mid x \text{ is any real number}\}$;

  Range: $\{y \mid y \ge -3\}$

 b. Intercepts: $(1, 0)$, $(3, 0)$, $(0, 9)$

 c. None

22. Function

 a. Domain: $\{x \mid x \text{ is any real number}\}$;

  Range: $\{y \mid y \le 5\}$

 b. Intercepts: $(-1, 0)$, $(2, 0)$, $(0, 4)$

 c. None

23. $f(x) = 2x^2 - x - 1$

 a. $f(-1) = 2(-1)^2 - (-1) - 1 = 2$

  The point $(-1, 2)$ is on the graph of f.

 b. $f(-2) = 2(-2)^2 - (-2) - 1 = 9$

  The point $(-2, 9)$ is on the graph of f.

c. Solve for x:

$$-1 = 2x^2 - x - 1$$

$$0 = 2x^2 - x$$

$$0 = x(2x-1) \Rightarrow x = 0, x = \frac{1}{2}$$

$(0,-1)$ and $\left(\frac{1}{2},-1\right)$ are on the graph of f.

d. The domain of f is $\{x \mid x \text{ is any real number}\}$.

e. x-intercepts:

$$f(x)=0 \Rightarrow 2x^2 - x - 1 = 0$$

$$(2x+1)(x-1) = 0 \Rightarrow x = -\frac{1}{2}, x = 1$$

$\left(-\frac{1}{2},0\right)$ and $(1,0)$

f. y-intercept:

$$f(0) = 2(0)^2 - 0 - 1 = -1 \Rightarrow (0,-1)$$

24. $f(x) = -3x^2 + 5x$

a. $f(-1) = -3(-1)^2 + 5(-1) = -8 \neq 2$

The point $(-1,2)$ is not on the graph of f.

b. $f(-2) = -3(-2)^2 + 5(-2) = -22$

The point $(-2,-22)$ is on the graph of f.

c. Solve for x:

$$-2 = -3x^2 + 5x \Rightarrow 3x^2 - 5x - 2 = 0$$

$$(3x+1)(x-2) = 0 \Rightarrow x = -\frac{1}{3}, x = 2$$

$(2,-2)$ and $\left(-\frac{1}{3},-2\right)$ on the graph of f.

d. The domain of f is $\{x \mid x \text{ is any real number}\}$.

e. x-intercepts:

$$f(x)=0 \Rightarrow -3x^2 + 5x = 0$$

$$x(-3x+5) = 0 \Rightarrow x = 0, x = \frac{5}{3}$$

$(0,0)$ and $\left(\frac{5}{3},0\right)$

f. y-intercept:

$$f(0) = -3(0)^2 + 5(0) = 0 \Rightarrow (0,0)$$

25. $f(x) = \dfrac{x+2}{x-6}$

a. $f(3) = \dfrac{3+2}{3-6} = -\dfrac{5}{3} \neq 14$

The point $(3,14)$ is not on the graph of f.

b. $f(4) = \dfrac{4+2}{4-6} = \dfrac{6}{-2} = -3$

The point $(4,-3)$ is on the graph of f.

c. Solve for x:

$$2 = \frac{x+2}{x-6}$$

$$2x - 12 = x + 2$$

$$x = 14$$

$(14, 2)$ is a point on the graph of f.

d. The domain of f is $\{x \mid x \neq 6\}$.

e. x-intercepts:

$$f(x)=0 \Rightarrow \frac{x+2}{x-6} = 0$$

$$x + 2 = 0 \Rightarrow x = -2 \Rightarrow (-2,0)$$

f. y-intercept: $f(0) = \dfrac{0+2}{0-6} = -\dfrac{1}{3} \Rightarrow \left(0,-\dfrac{1}{3}\right)$

26. $f(x) = \dfrac{x^2 + 2}{x+4}$

a. $f(1) = \dfrac{1^2 + 2}{1+4} = \dfrac{3}{5}$

The point $\left(1, \dfrac{3}{5}\right)$ is on the graph of f.

b. $f(0) = \dfrac{0^2 + 2}{0+4} = \dfrac{2}{4} = \dfrac{1}{2}$

The point $\left(0, \dfrac{1}{2}\right)$ is on the graph of f.

c. Solve for x:

$$\frac{1}{2} = \frac{x^2 + 2}{x+4} \Rightarrow x + 4 = 2x^2 + 4$$

$$0 = 2x^2 - x$$

$$x(2x-1) = 0 \Rightarrow x = 0 \text{ or } x = \frac{1}{2}$$

$\left(0, \dfrac{1}{2}\right)$ and $\left(\dfrac{1}{2}, \dfrac{1}{2}\right)$ are on the graph of f.

d. The domain of f is $\{x \mid x \neq -4\}$.

e. x-intercepts:

$$f(x) = 0 \Rightarrow \frac{x^2+2}{x+4} = 0 \Rightarrow x^2 + 2 = 0$$

This is impossible, so there are no x-intercepts.

f. y-intercept:

$$f(0) = \frac{0^2+2}{0+4} = \frac{2}{4} = \frac{1}{2} \Rightarrow \left(0, \frac{1}{2}\right)$$

27. $f(x) = \dfrac{2x^2}{x^4+1}$

a. $f(-1) = \dfrac{2(-1)^2}{(-1)^4+1} = \dfrac{2}{2} = 1$

The point $(-1, 1)$ is on the graph of f.

b. $f(2) = \dfrac{2(2)^2}{(2)^4+1} = \dfrac{8}{17}$

The point $\left(2, \dfrac{8}{17}\right)$ is on the graph of f.

c. Solve for x:

$$1 = \frac{2x^2}{x^4+1}$$
$$x^4 + 1 = 2x^2$$
$$x^4 - 2x^2 + 1 = 0$$
$$(x^2 - 1)^2 = 0$$
$$x^2 - 1 = 0 \Rightarrow x = \pm 1$$

$(1,1)$ and $(-1,1)$ are on the graph of f.

d. The domain of f is $\{x \mid x \text{ is any real number}\}$.

e. x-intercept:

$$f(x) = 0 \Rightarrow \frac{2x^2}{x^4+1} = 0$$
$$2x^2 = 0 \Rightarrow x = 0 \Rightarrow (0,0)$$

f. y-intercept:

$$f(0) = \frac{2(0)^2}{0^4+1} = \frac{0}{0+1} = 0 \Rightarrow (0,0)$$

28. $f(x) = \dfrac{2x}{x-2}$

a. $f\left(\dfrac{1}{2}\right) = \dfrac{2\left(\frac{1}{2}\right)}{\frac{1}{2}-2} = \dfrac{1}{-\frac{3}{2}} = -\dfrac{2}{3}$

The point $\left(\dfrac{1}{2}, -\dfrac{2}{3}\right)$ is on the graph of f.

b. $f(4) = \dfrac{2(4)}{4-2} = \dfrac{8}{2} = 4$

The point $(4, 4)$ is on the graph of f.

c. Solve for x:

$$1 = \frac{2x}{x-2} \Rightarrow x - 2 = 2x \Rightarrow -2 = x$$

$(-2, 1)$ is a point on the graph of f.

d. The domain of f is $\{x \mid x \neq 2\}$.

e. x-intercept:

$$f(x) = 0 \Rightarrow \frac{2x}{x-2} = 0 \Rightarrow 2x = 0$$
$$\Rightarrow x = 0 \Rightarrow (0,0)$$

f. y-intercept: $f(0) = \dfrac{0}{0-2} = 0 \Rightarrow (0,0)$

29. $h(x) = -\dfrac{44x^2}{v^2} + x + 6$

a. $h(8) = -\dfrac{44(8)^2}{28^2} + (8) + 6$

$$= -\frac{2816}{784} + 14$$
$$\approx 10.4 \text{ feet}$$

b. $h(12) = -\dfrac{44(12)^2}{28^2} + (12) + 6$

$$= -\frac{6336}{784} + 18$$
$$\approx 9.9 \text{ feet}$$

245

c. From part (a) we know the point $(8, 10.4)$ is on the graph and from part (b) we know the point $(12, 9.9)$ is on the graph. We could evaluate the function at several more values of x (e.g. $x = 0$, $x = 15$, and $x = 20$) to obtain additional points.

$$h(0) = -\frac{44(0)^2}{28^2} + (0) + 6 = 6$$

$$h(15) = -\frac{44(15)^2}{28^2} + (15) + 6 \approx 8.4$$

$$h(20) = -\frac{44(20)^2}{28^2} + (20) + 6 \approx 3.6$$

Some additional points are $(0, 6)$, $(15, 8.4)$ and $(20, 3.6)$. The complete graph is given below.

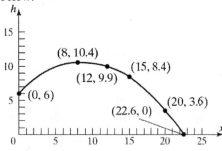

d. $h(15) = -\frac{44(15)^2}{28^2} + (15) + 6 \approx 8.4$ feet

No; when the ball is 15 feet in front of the foul line, it will be below the hoop. Therefore it cannot go through the hoop.

In order for the ball to pass through the hoop, we need to have $h(15) = 10$.

$$10 = -\frac{44(15)^2}{v^2} + (15) + 6$$

$$-11 = -\frac{44(15)^2}{v^2}$$

$$v^2 = 4(225)$$

$$v^2 = 900$$

$$v = 30 \text{ ft/sec}$$

The ball must be shot with an initial velocity of 30 feet per second in order to go through the hoop.

30. $h(x) = -\frac{136x^2}{v^2} + 2.7x + 3.5$

a. We want $h(15) = 10$.

$$-\frac{136(15)^2}{v^2} + 2.7(15) + 3.5 = 10$$

$$-\frac{30,600}{v^2} = -34$$

$$v^2 = 900$$

$$v = 30 \text{ ft/sec}$$

The ball needs to be thrown with an initial velocity of 30 feet per second.

b. $h(x) = -\frac{126x^2}{30^2} + 2.7x + 3.5$

which simplifies to

$$h(x) = -\frac{34}{225}x^2 + 2.7x + 3.5$$

c. Using the velocity from part (b),

$$h(9) = -\frac{34}{225}(9)^2 + 2.7(9) + 3.5 = 15.56 \text{ ft}$$

The ball will be 15.56 feet above the floor when it has traveled 9 feet in front of the foul line.

d. Select several values for x and use these to find the corresponding values for h. Use the results to form ordered pairs (x, h). Plot the points and connect with a smooth curve.

$$h(0) = -\frac{34}{225}(0)^2 + 2.7(0) + 3.5 = 3.5 \text{ ft}$$

$$h(5) = -\frac{34}{225}(5)^2 + 2.7(5) + 3.5 \approx 13.2 \text{ ft}$$

$$h(15) = -\frac{24}{225}(15)^2 + 2.7(15) + 3.5 \approx 10 \text{ ft}$$

Thus, some points on the graph are $(0, 3.5)$, $(5, 13.2)$, and $(15, 10)$. The complete graph is given below.

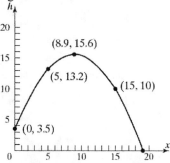

31. $h(x) = \dfrac{-32x^2}{130^2} + x$

    a. $h(100) = \dfrac{-32(100)^2}{130^2} + 100$

            $= \dfrac{-320,000}{16,900} + 100 \approx 81.07$ feet

    b. $h(300) = \dfrac{-32(300)^2}{130^2} + 300$

            $= \dfrac{-2,880,000}{16,900} + 300 \approx 129.59$ feet

    c. $h(500) = \dfrac{-32(500)^2}{130^2} + 500$

            $= \dfrac{-8,000,000}{16,900} + 500 \approx 26.63$ feet

    d. Solving $h(x) = \dfrac{-32x^2}{130^2} + x = 0$

        $\dfrac{-32x^2}{130^2} + x = 0$

        $x\left(\dfrac{-32x}{130^2} + 1\right) = 0$

        $x = 0$ or $\dfrac{-32x}{130^2} + 1 = 0$

                         $1 = \dfrac{32x}{130^2}$

                    $130^2 = 32x$

                     $x = \dfrac{130^2}{32} = 528.13$ feet

    Therefore, the golf ball travels 528.13 feet.

    e. $y_1 = \dfrac{-32x^2}{130^2} + x$

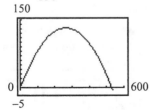

    f. Use INTERSECT on the graphs of

        $y_1 = \dfrac{-32x^2}{130^2} + x$ and $y_2 = 90$.

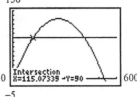

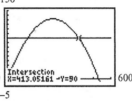

    The ball reaches a height of 90 feet twice. The first time is when the ball has traveled approximately 115.07 feet, and the second time is when the ball has traveled about 413.05 feet.

    g. The ball travels approximately 275 feet before it reaches its maximum height of approximately 131.8 feet.

X	Y1
200	124.26
225	129.14
250	131.66
275	131.8
300	129.59
325	125
350	118.05

X=275

    h. The ball travels approximately 264 feet before it reaches its maximum height of approximately 132.03 feet.

X	Y1
260	132
261	132.01
262	132.02
263	132.03
264	132.03
265	132.03
266	132.02

Y1=132.029112426

X	Y1
260	132
261	132.01
262	132.02
263	132.03
264	132.03
265	132.03
266	132.02

Y1=132.031242604

X	Y1
260	132
261	132.01
262	132.02
263	132.03
264	132.03
265	132.03
266	132.02

Y1=132.029585799

32. $A(x) = 4x\sqrt{1-x^2}$

    a. Domain of $A(x) = 4x\sqrt{1-x^2}$; we know that x must be greater than or equal to zero, since x represents a length. We also need $1 - x^2 \geq 0$, since this expression occurs under a square root. In fact, to avoid Area = 0, we require

        $x > 0$ and $1 - x^2 > 0$.

        Solve: $1 - x^2 > 0$

            $(1+x)(1-x) > 0$

        Case1: $1 + x > 0$ and $1 - x > 0$

               $x > -1$ and $x < 1$

                (i.e. $-1 < x < 1$)

        Case2: $1 + x < 0$ and $1 - x < 0$

               $x < -1$ and $x > 1$

                (which is impossible)

    Therefore the domain of A is $\{x \mid 0 < x < 1\}$.

    b. Graphing $A(x) = 4x\sqrt{1-x^2}$

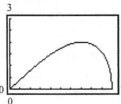

    c. When $x = 0.7$ feet, the cross-sectional area is maximized at approximately 1.9996 square feet. Therefore, the length of the base of the beam should be 1.4 feet in order to maximize the cross-sectional area.

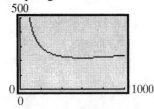

33. $C(x) = 100 + \dfrac{x}{10} + \dfrac{36000}{x}$

    a. Graphing:

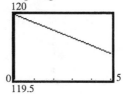

b. TblStart = 0; ΔTbl = 50

X	Y1
0	ERROR
50	825
100	470
150	355
200	300
250	269
300	250

Y1☐100+X/10+360...

c. The cost per passenger is minimized to about \$220 when the ground speed is roughly 600 miles per hour.

X	Y1
450	225
500	222
550	220.45
600	220
650	220.38
700	221.43
750	223

X=600

34. $W(h) = m\left(\dfrac{4000}{4000+h}\right)^2$

    a. $h = 14110$ feet ≈ 2.67 miles ;

        $W(2.67) = 120\left(\dfrac{4000}{4000+2.67}\right)^2 \approx 119.84$

    On Pike's Peak, Amy will weigh about 119.84 pounds.

    b. Graphing:

    c. Create a TABLE:

X	Y1		X	Y1
0	120		2	119.88
.5	119.97		2.5	119.85
1	119.94		3	119.82
1.5	119.91		3.5	119.79
2	119.88		4	119.76
2.5	119.85		4.5	119.73
3	119.82		5	119.7

X=0   X=5

The weight W will vary from 120 pounds to about 119.7 pounds.

    d. By refining the table, Amy will weigh 119.95 lbs at a height of about 0.83 miles (4382 feet).

X	Y1		X	Y1
.5	119.97		.8	119.95
.6	119.96		.81	119.95
.7	119.96		.82	119.95
.8	119.95		.83	119.95
.9	119.95		.84	119.95
1	119.94		.85	119.95
1.1	119.93		.86	119.95

X=.8   Y1=119.950215496

    e. Yes, 4382 feet is reasonable.

35. **a.** $(f+g)(2) = f(2) + g(2) = 2 + 1 = 3$

b. $(f+g)(4) = f(4) + g(4) = 1 + (-3) = -2$

c. $(f-g)(6) = f(6) - g(6) = 0 - 1 = -1$

d. $(g-f)(6) = g(6) - f(6) = 1 - 0 = 1$

e. $(f \cdot g)(2) = f(2) \cdot g(2) = 2(1) = 2$

f. $\left(\dfrac{f}{g}\right)(4) = \dfrac{f(4)}{g(4)} = \dfrac{1}{-3} = -\dfrac{1}{3}$

36. Answers will vary. From a graph, the domain can be found by visually locating the x-values for which the graph is defined. The range can be found in a similar fashion by visually locating the *y*-values for which the function is defined.

If an equation is given, the domain can be found by locating any restricted values and removing them from the set of real numbers. The range can be found by using known properties of the graph of the equation, or estimated by means of a table of values.

37. The graph of a function can have any number of x-intercepts. The graph of a function can have at most one *y*-intercept (otherwise the graph would fail the vertical line test).

38. Yes, the graph of a single point is the graph of a function since it would pass the vertical line test. The equation of such a function would be something like the following: $f(x) = 2$, where $x = 7$.

39. (a) III; (b) IV; (c) I; (d) V; (e) II

40. (a) II; (b) V; (c) IV; (d) III; (e) I

41.

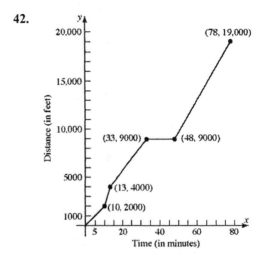

42.

43. **a.** 2 hours elapsed; Kevin was between 0 and 3 miles from home.

b. 0.5 hours elapsed; Kevin was 3 miles from home.

c. 0.3 hours elapsed; Kevin was between 0 and 3 miles from home.

d. 0.2 hours elapsed; Kevin was at home.

e. 0.9 hours elapsed; Kevin was between 0 and 2.8 miles from home.

f. 0.3 hours elapsed; Kevin was 2.8 miles from home.

g. 1.1 hours elapsed; Kevin was between 0 and 2.8 miles from home.

h. The farthest distance Kevin is from home is 3 miles.

i. Kevin returned home 2 times.

44. **a.** Michael travels fastest between 7 and 7.4 minutes. That is, $(7, 7.4)$.

b. Michael's speed is zero between 4.2 and 6 minutes. That is, $(4.2, 6)$.

c. Between 0 and 2 minutes, Michael's speed increased from 0 to 30 miles/hour.

d. Between 4.2 and 6 minutes, Michael was stopped (i.e, his speed was 0 miles/hour).

e. Between 7 and 7.4 minutes, Michael was traveling at a steady rate of 50 miles/hour.

f. Michael's speed is constant between 2 and 4 minutes, between 4.2 and 6 minutes, between 7 and 7.4 minutes, and between 7.6 and 8 minutes. That is, on the intervals (2, 4), (4.2, 6), (7, 7.4), and (7.6, 8).

249

45. Answers (graphs) will vary. Points of the form $(5, y)$ and of the form $(x, 0)$ cannot be on the graph of the function.

46. The only such function is $f(x) = 0$ because it is the only function for which $f(x) = -f(x)$. Any other such graph would fail the vertical line test.

Section 3.3

1. $2 < x < 5$

2. slope $= \dfrac{\Delta y}{\Delta x} = \dfrac{8-3}{3-(-2)} = \dfrac{5}{5} = 1$

3. x-axis: $y \to -y$

$(-y) = 5x^2 - 1$

$-y = 5x^2 - 1$

$y = -5x^2 + 1$ different

y-axis: $x \to -x$

$y = 5(-x)^2 - 1$

$y = 5x^2 - 1$ same

origin: $x \to -x$ and $y \to -y$

$(-y) = 5(-x)^2 - 1$

$-y = 5x^2 - 1$

$y = -5x^2 + 1$ different

The equation has symmetry with respect to the y-axis only.

4. $y - y_1 = m(x - x_1)$

$y - (-2) = 5(x - 3)$

$y + 2 = 5(x - 3)$

5. $y = x^2 - 9$

x-intercepts:

$0 = x^2 - 9$

$x^2 = 9 \to x = \pm 3$

y-intercept:

$y = (0)^2 - 9 = -9$

The intercepts are $(-3, 0)$, $(3, 0)$, and $(0, -9)$.

6. increasing

7. even; odd

8. True

9. True

10. False; odd functions are symmetric with respect to the origin. Even functions are symmetric with respect to the y-axis.

11. Yes

12. No, it is increasing.

13. No, it only increases on (5, 10).

14. Yes

15. f is increasing on the intervals $(-8, -2)$, $(0, 2)$, $(5, \infty)$.

16. f is decreasing on the intervals: $(-\infty, -8)$, $(-2, 0)$, $(2, 5)$.

17. Yes. The local maximum at $x = 2$ is 10.

18. No. There is a local minimum at $x = 5$; the local minimum is 0.

19. f has local maxima at $x = -2$ and $x = 2$. The local maxima are 6 and 10, respectively.

20. f has local minima at $x = -8$, $x = 0$ and $x = 5$. The local minima are –4, 0, and 0, respectively.

21. a. Intercepts: (–2, 0), (2, 0), and (0, 3).

b. Domain: $\{x | -4 \le x \le 4\}$ or $[-4, 4]$;

Range: $\{y | 0 \le y \le 3\}$ or $[0, 3]$.

c. Increasing: (–2, 0) and (2, 4);
Decreasing: (–4, –2) and (0, 2).

d. Since the graph is symmetric with respect to the y-axis, the function is <u>even</u>.

22. a. Intercepts: (–1, 0), (1, 0), and (0, 2).

b. Domain: $\{x | -3 \le x \le 3\}$ or $[-3, 3]$;

Range: $\{y | 0 \le y \le 3\}$ or $[0, 3]$.

c. Increasing: (–1, 0) and (1, 3);
Decreasing: (–3, –1) and (0, 1).

d. Since the graph is symmetric with respect to the y-axis, the function is <u>even</u>.

23. a. Intercepts: $(0, 1)$.

    b. Domain: $\{x \mid x \text{ is any real number}\}$;

       Range: $\{y \mid y > 0\}$ or $(0, \infty)$.

    c. Increasing: $(-\infty, \infty)$; Decreasing: never.

    d. Since the graph is not symmetric with respect to the y-axis or the origin, the function is <u>neither</u> even nor odd.

24. a. Intercepts: $(1, 0)$.

    b. Domain: $\{x \mid x > 0\}$ or $(0, \infty)$;

       Range: $\{y \mid y \text{ is any real number}\}$.

    c. Increasing: $(0, \infty)$; Decreasing: never.

    d. Since the graph is not symmetric with respect to the y-axis or the origin, the function is <u>neither</u> even nor odd.

25. a. Intercepts: $(-\pi, 0)$, $(\pi, 0)$, and $(0, 0)$.

    b. Domain: $\{x \mid -\pi \le x \le \pi\}$ or $[-\pi, \pi]$;

       Range: $\{y \mid -1 \le y \le 1\}$ or $[-1, 1]$.

    c. Increasing: $\left(-\dfrac{\pi}{2}, \dfrac{\pi}{2}\right)$;

       Decreasing: $\left(-\pi, -\dfrac{\pi}{2}\right)$ and $\left(\dfrac{\pi}{2}, \pi\right)$.

    d. Since the graph is symmetric with respect to the origin, the function is <u>odd</u>.

26. a. Intercepts: $\left(-\dfrac{\pi}{2}, 0\right)$, $\left(\dfrac{\pi}{2}, 0\right)$, and $(0, 1)$.

    b. Domain: $\{x \mid -\pi \le x \le \pi\}$ or $[-\pi, \pi]$;

       Range: $\{y \mid -1 \le y \le 1\}$ or $[-1, 1]$.

    c. Increasing: $(-\pi, 0)$; Decreasing: $(0, \pi)$.

    d. Since the graph is symmetric with respect to the y-axis, the function is <u>even</u>.

27. a. Intercepts: $\left(\dfrac{1}{3}, 0\right)$, $\left(\dfrac{5}{2}, 0\right)$, and $\left(0, \dfrac{1}{2}\right)$.

    b. Domain: $\{x \mid -3 \le x \le 3\}$ or $[-3, 3]$;

       Range: $\{y \mid -1 \le y \le 2\}$ or $[-1, 2]$.

    c. Increasing: $(2, 3)$; Decreasing: $(-1, 1)$;

       Constant: $(-3, -1)$ and $(1, 2)$

    d. Since the graph is not symmetric with respect to the y-axis or the origin, the function is <u>neither</u> even nor odd.

28. a. Intercepts: $(-2.3, 0)$, $(3, 0)$, and $(0, 1)$.

    b. Domain: $\{x \mid -3 \le x \le 3\}$ or $[-3, 3]$;

       Range: $\{y \mid -2 \le y \le 2\}$ or $[-2, 2]$.

    c. Increasing: $(-3, -2)$ and $(0, 2)$;

       Decreasing: $(2, 3)$; Constant: $(-2, 0)$.

    d. Since the graph is not symmetric with respect to the y-axis or the origin, the function is <u>neither</u> even nor odd.

29. a. f has a local maximum of 3 at $x = 0$.

    b. f has a local minimum of 0 at both $x = -2$ and $x = 2$.

30. a. f has a local maximum of 2 at $x = 0$.

    b. f has a local minimum of 0 at both $x = -1$ and $x = 1$.

31. a. f has a local maximum of 1 at $x = \dfrac{\pi}{2}$.

    b. f has a local minimum of -1 at $x = -\dfrac{\pi}{2}$.

32. a. f has a local maximum of 1 at $x = 0$.

    b. f has a local minimum of -1 both at $x = -\pi$ and $x = \pi$.

33. $f(x) = 4x^3$

    $f(-x) = 4(-x)^3 = -4x^3 = -f(x)$

    Therefore, f is odd.

34. $f(x) = 2x^4 - x^2$

    $f(-x) = 2(-x)^4 - (-x)^2 = 2x^4 - x^2 = f(x)$

    Therefore, f is even.

35. $g(x) = -3x^2 - 5$

    $g(-x) = -3(-x)^2 - 5 = -3x^2 - 5 = g(x)$

    Therefore, g is even.

36. $h(x) = 3x^3 + 5$

$h(-x) = 3(-x)^3 + 5 = -3x^3 + 5$

h is neither even nor odd.

37. $F(x) = \sqrt[3]{x}$

$F(-x) = \sqrt[3]{-x} = -\sqrt[3]{x} = -F(x)$

Therefore, F is odd.

38. $G(x) = \sqrt{x}$

$G(-x) = \sqrt{-x}$

G is neither even nor odd.

39. $f(x) = x + |x|$

$f(-x) = -x + |-x| = -x + |x|$

f is neither even nor odd.

40. $f(x) = \sqrt[3]{2x^2 + 1}$

$f(-x) = \sqrt[3]{2(-x)^2 + 1} = \sqrt[3]{2x^2 + 1} = f(x)$

Therefore, f is even.

41. $g(x) = \dfrac{1}{x^2}$

$g(-x) = \dfrac{1}{(-x)^2} = \dfrac{1}{x^2} = g(x)$

Therefore, g is even.

42. $h(x) = \dfrac{x}{x^2 - 1}$

$h(-x) = \dfrac{-x}{(-x)^2 - 1} = \dfrac{-x}{x^2 - 1} = -h(x)$

Therefore, h is odd.

43. $h(x) = \dfrac{-x^3}{3x^2 - 9}$

$h(-x) = \dfrac{-(-x)^3}{3(-x)^2 - 9} = \dfrac{x^3}{3x^2 - 9} = -h(x)$

Therefore, h is odd.

44. $F(x) = \dfrac{2x}{|x|}$

$F(-x) = \dfrac{2(-x)}{|-x|} = \dfrac{-2x}{|x|} = -F(x)$

Therefore, F is odd.

45. $f(x) = x^3 - 3x + 2$ on the interval $(-2, 2)$

Use MAXIMUM and MINIMUM on the graph of $y_1 = x^3 - 3x + 2$.

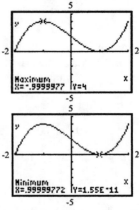

local maximum at: $(-1, 4)$;

local minimum at: $(1, 0)$

f is increasing on: $(-2, -1)$ and $(1, 2)$;

f is decreasing on: $(-1, 1)$

46. $f(x) = x^3 - 3x^2 + 5$ on the interval $(-1, 3)$

Use MAXIMUM and MINIMUM on the graph of $y_1 = x^3 - 3x^2 + 5$.

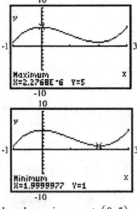

local maximum at: $(0, 5)$;

local minimum at: $(2, 1)$

f is increasing on: $(-1, 0)$ and $(2, 3)$;

f is decreasing on: $(0, 2)$

47. $f(x) = x^5 - x^3$ on the interval $(-2, 2)$

Use MAXIMUM and MINIMUM on the graph of $y_1 = x^5 - x^3$.

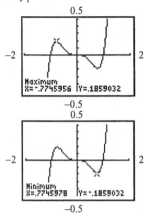

local maximum at: $(-0.77, 0.19)$;

local minimum at: $(0.77, -0.19)$;

f is increasing on: $(-2, -0.77)$ and $(0.77, 2)$;

f is decreasing on: $(-0.77, 0.77)$

48. $f(x) = x^4 - x^2$ on the interval $(-2, 2)$

Use MAXIMUM and MINIMUM on the graph of $y_1 = x^4 - x^2$.

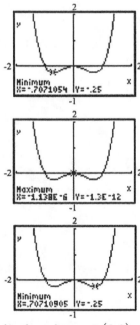

local maximum at: $(0, 0)$;

local minimum at: $(-0.71, -0.25)$, $(0.71, -0.25)$

f is increasing on: $(-0.71, 0)$ and $(0.71, 2)$;

f is decreasing on: $(-2, -0.71)$ and $(0, 0.71)$

49. $f(x) = -0.2x^3 - 0.6x^2 + 4x - 6$ on the interval $(-6, 4)$

Use MAXIMUM and MINIMUM on the graph of $y_1 = -0.2x^3 - 0.6x^2 + 4x - 6$.

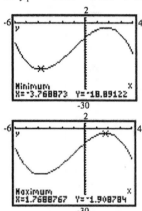

local maximum at: $(1.77, -1.91)$;

local minimum at: $(-3.77, -18.89)$

f is increasing on: $(-3.77, 1.77)$;

f is decreasing on: $(-6, -3.77)$ and $(1.77, 4)$

50. $f(x) = -0.4x^3 + 0.6x^2 + 3x - 2$ on the interval $(-4, 5)$

Use MAXIMUM and MINIMUM on the graph of $y_1 = -0.4x^3 + 0.6x^2 + 3x - 2$.

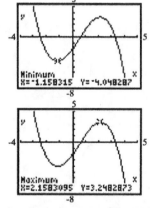

local maximum at: $(2.16, 3.25)$;

local minimum at: $(-1.16, -4.05)$

f is increasing on: $(-1.16, 2.16)$;

f is decreasing on: $(-4, -1.16)$ and $(2.16, 5)$

253

51. $f(x) = 0.25x^4 + 0.3x^3 - 0.9x^2 + 3$ on the interval $(-3, 2)$

Use MAXIMUM and MINIMUM on the graph of $y_1 = 0.25x^4 + 0.3x^3 - 0.9x^2 + 3$.

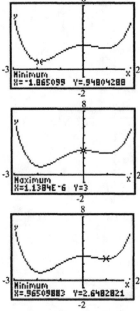

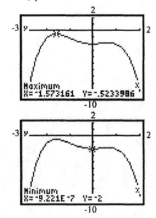

local maximum at: $(0, 3)$;

local minimum at: $(-1.87, 0.95)$, $(0.97, 2.65)$

f is increasing on: $(-1.87, 0)$ and $(0.97, 2)$;

f is decreasing on: $(-3, -1.87)$ and $(0, 0.97)$

52. $f(x) = -0.4x^4 - 0.5x^3 + 0.8x^2 - 2$ on the interval $(-3, 2)$

Use MAXIMUM and MINIMUM on the graph of $y_1 = -0.4x^4 - 0.5x^3 + 0.8x^2 - 2$.

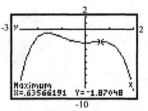

local maxima at: $(-1.57, -0.52)$, $(0.64, -1.87)$;

local minimum at: $(0, -2)$

f is increasing on: $(-3, -1.57)$ and $(0, 0.64)$;

f is decreasing on: $(-1.57, 0)$ and $(0.64, 2)$

53. $f(x) = -2x^2 + 4$

a. Average rate of change of f from $x = 0$ to $x = 2$

$$\frac{f(2) - f(0)}{2 - 0} = \frac{(-2(2)^2 + 4) - (-2(0)^2 + 4)}{2}$$
$$= \frac{(-4) - (4)}{2} = \frac{-8}{2} = -4$$

b. Average rate of change of f from $x = 1$ to $x = 3$:

$$\frac{f(3) - f(1)}{3 - 1} = \frac{(-2(3)^2 + 4) - (-2(1)^2 + 4)}{2}$$
$$= \frac{(-14) - (2)}{2} = \frac{-16}{2} = -8$$

c. Average rate of change of f from $x = 1$ to $x = 4$:

$$\frac{f(4) - f(1)}{4 - 1} = \frac{(-2(4)^2 + 4) - (-2(1)^2 + 4)}{3}$$
$$= \frac{(-28) - (2)}{3} = \frac{-30}{3} = -10$$

54. $f(x) = -x^3 + 1$

a. Average rate of change of f from $x = 0$ to $x = 2$:

$$\frac{f(2) - f(0)}{2 - 0} = \frac{(-(2)^3 + 1) - (-(0)^3 + 1)}{2}$$
$$= \frac{-7 - 1}{2} = \frac{-8}{2} = -4$$

b. Average rate of change of f from $x = 1$ to $x = 3$:

$$\frac{f(3) - f(1)}{3 - 1} = \frac{(-(3)^3 + 1) - (-(1)^3 + 1)}{2}$$
$$= \frac{-26 - (0)}{2} = \frac{-26}{2} = -13$$

c. Average rate of change of f from $x = -1$ to $x = 1$:

$$\frac{f(1) - f(-1)}{1 - (-1)} = \frac{\left(-(1)^3 + 1\right) - \left(-(-1)^3 + 1\right)}{2}$$

$$= \frac{0 - 2}{2} = \frac{-2}{2} = -1$$

55. $g(x) = x^3 - 2x + 1$

a. Average rate of change of g from $x = -3$ to $x = -2$:

$$\frac{g(-2) - g(-3)}{-2 - (-3)}$$

$$= \frac{\left[(-2)^3 - 2(-2) + 1\right] - \left[(-3)^3 - 2(-3) + 1\right]}{1}$$

$$= \frac{(-3) - (-20)}{1} = \frac{17}{1} = 17$$

b. Average rate of change of g from $x = -1$ to $x = 1$:

$$\frac{g(1) - g(-1)}{1 - (-1)}$$

$$= \frac{\left[(1)^3 - 2(1) + 1\right] - \left[(-1)^3 - 2(-1) + 1\right]}{2}$$

$$= \frac{(0) - (2)}{2} = \frac{-2}{2} = -1$$

c. Average rate of change of g from $x = 1$ to $x = 3$:

$$\frac{g(3) - g(1)}{3 - 1}$$

$$= \frac{\left[(3)^3 - 2(3) + 1\right] - \left[(1)^3 - 2(1) + 1\right]}{2}$$

$$= \frac{(22) - (0)}{2} = \frac{22}{2} = 11$$

56. $h(x) = x^2 - 2x + 3$

a. Average rate of change of h from $x = -1$ to $x = 1$:

$$\frac{h(1) - h(-1)}{1 - (-1)}$$

$$= \frac{\left[(1)^2 - 2(1) + 3\right] - \left[(-1)^2 - 2(-1) + 3\right]}{2}$$

$$= \frac{(2) - (6)}{2} = \frac{-4}{2} = -2$$

b. Average rate of change of h from $x = 0$ to $x = 2$:

$$\frac{h(2) - h(0)}{2 - 0}$$

$$= \frac{\left[(2)^2 - 2(2) + 3\right] - \left[(0)^2 - 2(0) + 3\right]}{2}$$

$$= \frac{(3) - (3)}{2} = \frac{0}{2} = 0$$

c. Average rate of change of h from $x = 2$ to $x = 5$:

$$\frac{h(5) - h(2)}{5 - 2}$$

$$= \frac{\left[(5)^2 - 2(5) + 3\right] - \left[(2)^2 - 2(2) + 3\right]}{3}$$

$$= \frac{(18) - (3)}{3} = \frac{15}{3} = 5$$

57. $f(x) = 5x - 2$

a. Average rate of change of f from 1 to 3:

$$\frac{\Delta y}{\Delta x} = \frac{f(3) - f(1)}{3 - 1} = \frac{13 - 3}{3 - 1} = \frac{10}{2} = 5$$

Thus, the average rate of change of f from 1 to 3 is 5.

b. From (a), the slope of the secant line joining $\left(1, f(1)\right)$ and $\left(3, f(3)\right)$ is 5. We use the point-slope form to find the equation of the secant line:

$$y - y_1 = m_{\text{sec}}(x - x_1)$$

$$y - 3 = 5(x - 1)$$

$$y - 3 = 5x - 5$$

$$y = 5x - 2$$

58. $f(x) = -4x + 1$

a. Average rate of change of f from 2 to 5:

$$\frac{\Delta y}{\Delta x} = \frac{f(5) - f(2)}{5 - 2} = \frac{-19 - (-7)}{5 - 2}$$

$$= \frac{-12}{3} = -4$$

Therefore, the average rate of change of f from 2 to 5 is -4.

b. From (a), the slope of the secant line joining $(2, f(2))$ and $(5, f(5))$ is -4. We use the point-slope form to find the equation of the secant line:

$$y - y_1 = m_{sec}(x - x_1)$$
$$y - (-7) = -4(x - 2)$$
$$y + 7 = -4x + 8$$
$$y = -4x + 1$$

59. $g(x) = x^2 - 2$

  a. Average rate of change of g from -2 to 1:
  $$\frac{\Delta y}{\Delta x} = \frac{g(1) - g(-2)}{1 - (-2)} = \frac{-1 - 2}{1 - (-2)} = \frac{-3}{3} = -1$$
  Therefore, the average rate of change of g from -2 to 1 is -1.

  b. From (a), the slope of the secant line joining $(-2, g(-2))$ and $(1, g(1))$ is -1. We use the point-slope form to find the equation of the secant line:
  $$y - y_1 = m_{sec}(x - x_1)$$
  $$y - 2 = -1(x - (-2))$$
  $$y - 2 = -x - 2$$
  $$y = -x$$

60. $g(x) = x^2 + 1$

  a. Average rate of change of g from -1 to 2:
  $$\frac{\Delta y}{\Delta x} = \frac{g(2) - g(-1)}{2 - (-1)} = \frac{5 - 2}{2 - (-1)} = \frac{3}{3} = 1$$
  Therefore, the average rate of change of g from -1 to 2 is 1.

  b. From (a), the slope of the secant line joining $(-1, g(-1))$ and $(2, g(2))$ is 1. We use the point-slope form to find the equation of the secant line:
  $$y - y_1 = m_{sec}(x - x_1)$$
  $$y - 2 = 1(x - (-1))$$
  $$y - 2 = x + 1$$
  $$y = x + 3$$

61. $h(x) = x^2 - 2x$

  a. Average rate of change of h from 2 to 4:
  $$\frac{\Delta y}{\Delta x} = \frac{h(4) - h(2)}{4 - 2} = \frac{8 - 0}{4 - 2} = \frac{8}{2} = 4$$
  Therefore, the average rate of change of h from 2 to 4 is 4.

b. From (a), the slope of the secant line joining $(2, h(2))$ and $(4, h(4))$ is 4. We use the point-slope form to find the equation of the secant line:

$$y - y_1 = m_{sec}(x - x_1)$$
$$y - 0 = 4(x - 2)$$
$$y = 4x - 8$$

62. $h(x) = -2x^2 + x$

  a. Average rate of change from 0 to 3:
  $$\frac{\Delta y}{\Delta x} = \frac{h(3) - h(0)}{3 - 0} = \frac{-15 - 0}{3 - 0}$$
  $$= \frac{-15}{3} = -5$$
  Therefore, the average rate of change of h from 0 to 3 is -5.

  b. From (a), the slope of the secant line joining $(0, h(0))$ and $(3, h(3))$ is -5. We use the point-slope form to find the equation of the secant line:
  $$y - y_1 = m_{sec}(x - x_1)$$
  $$y - 0 = -5(x - 0)$$
  $$y = -5x$$

63. a. length $= 24 - 2x$; width $= 24 - 2x$; height $= x$
  $$V(x) = x(24 - 2x)(24 - 2x) = x(24 - 2x)^2$$

  b. $V(3) = 3(24 - 2(3))^2 = 3(18)^2$
  $$= 3(324) = 972 \text{ cu.in.}$$

  c. $V(10) = 10(24 - 2(10))^2 = 10(4)^2$
  $$= 10(16) = 160 \text{ cu.in.}$$

  d. $y_1 = x(24 - 2x)^2$

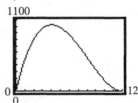

  Use MAXIMUM.

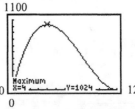

  The volume is largest when $x = 4$ inches.

64. a. Let A = amount of material,
x = length of the base, h = height, and
V = volume.

$$V = x^2 h = 10 \Rightarrow h = \frac{10}{x^2}$$

Total Area $A = \left(\text{Area}_{\text{base}}\right) + (4)\left(\text{Area}_{\text{side}}\right)$

$$= x^2 + 4xh$$

$$= x^2 + 4x\left(\frac{10}{x^2}\right)$$

$$= x^2 + \frac{40}{x}$$

$$A(x) = x^2 + \frac{40}{x}$$

b. $A(1) = 1^2 + \dfrac{40}{1} = 1 + 40 = 41 \text{ ft}^2$

c. $A(2) = 2^2 + \dfrac{40}{2} = 4 + 20 = 24 \text{ ft}^2$

d. $y_1 = x^2 + \dfrac{40}{x}$

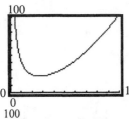

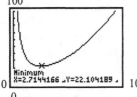

The amount of material is least when
$x = 2.71$ ft.

65. a. $s(t) = -16t^2 + 80t + 6$

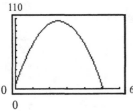

b. Use MAXIMUM. The maximum height
occurs when $t = 2.5$ seconds.

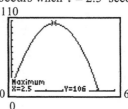

c. From the graph, the maximum height is 106
feet.

66. a. $y = s(t) = -17.28t^2 + 100t$

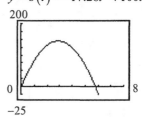

b. Use the Maximum option on the CALC
menu.

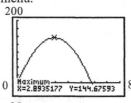

The object reaches its maximum height after
about 2.89 seconds.

c. From the graph in part (b), the maximum
height is about 144.68 feet.

d. $s(t) = -16t^2 + 100t$

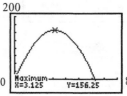

On Earth, the object would reach a
maximum height of 156.25 feet after 3.125
seconds. The maximum height is slightly
higher than on Saturn.

67. $\overline{C}(x) = 0.3x^2 + 21x - 251 + \dfrac{2500}{x}$

   a. $y_1 = 0.3x^2 + 21x - 251 + \dfrac{2500}{x}$

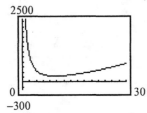

   b. Use MINIMUM. Rounding to the nearest whole number, the average cost is minimized when approximately 10 lawnmowers are produced per hour.

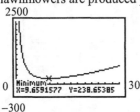

   c. The minimum average cost is approximately $239 per mower.

68. **a.** $C(t) = -.002t^4 + .039t^3 - .285t^2 + .766t + .085$

   Graph the function on a graphing utility and use the Maximum option from the CALC menu.

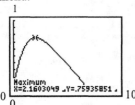

   The concentration will be highest after about 2.16 hours.

   b. Enter the function in Y1 and 0.5 in Y2. Graph the two equations in the same window and use the Intersect option from the CALC menu.

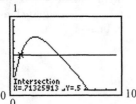

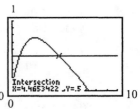

After taking the medication, the woman can feed her child within the first 0.71 hours (about 42 minutes) or after 4.47 hours (about 4 hours 28 minutes) have elapsed.

69. **a.** avg. rate of change $= \dfrac{P(2.5) - P(0)}{2.5 - 0}$

$$= \dfrac{0.18 - 0.09}{2.5 - 0}$$

$$= \dfrac{0.09}{2.5}$$

$$= 0.036 \text{ gram per hour}$$

On overage, the population is increasing at a rate of 0.036 gram per hour from 0 to 2.5 hours.

   b. avg. rate of change $= \dfrac{P(6) - P(4.5)}{6 - 4.5}$

$$= \dfrac{0.50 - 0.35}{6 - 4.5}$$

$$= \dfrac{0.15}{1.5}$$

$$= 0.1 \text{ gram per hour}$$

On overage, the population is increasing at a rate of 0.1 gram per hour from 4.5 to 6 hours.

   c. The average rate of change is increasing as time passes. This indicates that the population is increasing at an increasing rate.

70. **a.** avg. rate of change $= \dfrac{P(2000) - P(1998)}{2000 - 1998}$

$$= \dfrac{27.6 - 20.7}{2000 - 1998}$$

$$= \dfrac{6.9}{2}$$

$$= 3.45 \text{ percentage points per year}$$

On overage, the percentage of returns that are e-filed is increasing at a rate of 3.45 percentage points per year from 1998 to 2000.

b. avg. rate of change $= \dfrac{P(2003)-P(2001)}{2003-2001}$

$= \dfrac{40.2-30.7}{2003-2001}$

$= \dfrac{9.5}{2}$

$= 4.75$ percentage points per year

On overage, the percentage of returns that are e-filed is increasing at a rate of 4.75 percentage points per year from 2001 to 2003.

c. avg. rate of change $= \dfrac{P(2006)-P(2004)}{2006-2004}$

$= \dfrac{57.1-46.5}{2006-2004}$

$= \dfrac{10.6}{2}$

$= 5.3$ percentage points per year

On overage, the percentage of returns that are e-filed is increasing at a rate of 5.3 percentage points per year from 2004 to 2006.

d. The average rate of change is increasing as time passes. This indicates that the percentage of e-filers is increasing at an increasing rate.

71. $f(x)=x^2$

a. Average rate of change of f from $x=0$ to $x=1$:

$\dfrac{f(1)-f(0)}{1-0} = \dfrac{1^2-0^2}{1} = \dfrac{1}{1} = 1$

b. Average rate of change of f from $x=0$ to $x=0.5$:

$\dfrac{f(0.5)-f(0)}{0.5-0} = \dfrac{(0.5)^2-0^2}{0.5} = \dfrac{0.25}{0.5} = 0.5$

c. Average rate of change of f from $x=0$ to $x=0.1$:

$\dfrac{f(0.1)-f(0)}{0.1-0} = \dfrac{(0.1)^2-0^2}{0.1} = \dfrac{0.01}{0.1} = 0.1$

d. Average rate of change of f from $x=0$ to $x=0.01$:

$\dfrac{f(0.01)-f(0)}{0.01-0} = \dfrac{(0.01)^2-0^2}{0.01}$

$= \dfrac{0.0001}{0.01} = 0.01$

e. Average rate of change of f from $x=0$ to $x=0.001$:

$\dfrac{f(0.001)-f(0)}{0.001-0} = \dfrac{(0.001)^2-0^2}{0.001}$

$= \dfrac{0.000001}{0.001} = 0.001$

f. Graphing the secant lines:

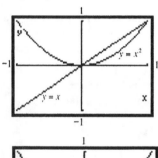

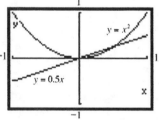

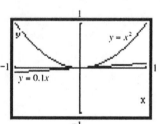

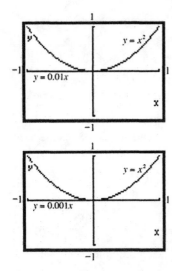

g. The secant lines are beginning to look more and more like the tangent line to the graph of f at the point where $x = 0$.

h. The slopes of the secant lines are getting smaller and smaller. They seem to be approaching the number zero.

72. $f(x) = x^2$

a. Average rate of change of f from $x = 1$ to $x = 2$:

$$\frac{f(2) - f(1)}{2 - 1} = \frac{2^2 - 1^2}{1} = \frac{3}{1} = 3$$

b. Average rate of change of f from $x = 1$ to $x = 1.5$:

$$\frac{f(1.5) - f(1)}{1.5 - 1} = \frac{(1.5)^2 - 1^2}{0.5} = \frac{1.25}{0.5} = 2.5$$

c. Average rate of change of f from $x = 1$ to $x = 1.1$:

$$\frac{f(1.1) - f(1)}{1.1 - 1} = \frac{(1.1)^2 - 1^2}{0.1} = \frac{0.21}{0.1} = 2.1$$

d. Average rate of change of f from $x = 1$ to $x = 1.01$:

$$\frac{f(1.01) - f(1)}{1.01 - 1} = \frac{(1.01)^2 - 1^2}{0.01} = \frac{0.0201}{0.01} = 2.01$$

e. Average rate of change of f from $x = 1$ to $x = 1.001$:

$$\frac{f(1.001) - f(1)}{1.001 - 1} = \frac{(1.001)^2 - 1^2}{0.001}$$

$$= \frac{0.002001}{0.001} = 2.001$$

f. Graphing the secant lines:

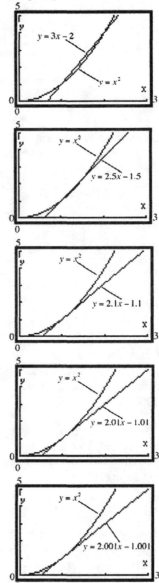

g. The secant lines are beginning to look more and more like the tangent line to the graph of f at the point where $x = 1$.

h. The slopes of the secant lines are getting smaller and smaller. They seem to be approaching the number 2.

73. $f(x) = 2x + 5$

a. $m_{sec} = \dfrac{f(x + h) - f(x)}{h}$

$$= \frac{2(x + h) + 5 - 2x - 5}{h} = \frac{2h}{h} = 2$$

260

b. When $x = 1$:

$h = 0.5 \Rightarrow m_{\sec} = 2$

$h = 0.1 \Rightarrow m_{\sec} = 2$

$h = 0.01 \Rightarrow m_{\sec} = 2$

as $h \to 0$, $m_{\sec} \to 2$

c. Using the point $(1, f(1)) = (1, 7)$ and slope,

$m = 2$, we get the secant line:

$y - 7 = 2(x - 1)$

$y - 7 = 2x - 2$

$y = 2x + 5$

d. Graphing:

The graph and the secant line coincide.

74. $f(x) = -3x + 2$

a. $m_{\sec} = \dfrac{f(x+h) - f(x)}{h}$

$= \dfrac{-3(x+h) + 2 - (-3x+2)}{h} = \dfrac{-3h}{h} = -3$

b. When $x = 1$,

$h = 0.5 \Rightarrow m_{\sec} = -3$

$h = 0.1 \Rightarrow m_{\sec} = -3$

$h = 0.01 \Rightarrow m_{\sec} = -3$

as $h \to 0$, $m_{\sec} \to -3$

c. Using point $(1, f(1)) = (1, -1)$ and

slope $= -3$, we get the secant line:

$y - (-1) = -3(x - 1)$

$y + 1 = -3x + 3$

$y = -3x + 2$

d. Graphing:

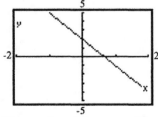

The graph and the secant line coincide.

75. $f(x) = x^2 + 2x$

a. $m_{\sec} = \dfrac{f(x+h) - f(x)}{h}$

$= \dfrac{(x+h)^2 + 2(x+h) - (x^2 + 2x)}{h}$

$= \dfrac{x^2 + 2xh + h^2 + 2x + 2h - x^2 - 2x}{h}$

$= \dfrac{2xh + h^2 + 2h}{h}$

$= 2x + h + 2$

b. When $x = 1$,

$h = 0.5 \Rightarrow m_{\sec} = 2 \cdot 1 + 0.5 + 2 = 4.5$

$h = 0.1 \Rightarrow m_{\sec} = 2 \cdot 1 + 0.1 + 2 = 4.1$

$h = 0.01 \Rightarrow m_{\sec} = 2 \cdot 1 + 0.01 + 2 = 4.01$

as $h \to 0$, $m_{\sec} \to 2 \cdot 1 + 0 + 2 = 4$

c. Using point $(1, f(1)) = (1, 3)$ and

slope $= 4.01$, we get the secant line:

$y - 3 = 4.01(x - 1)$

$y - 3 = 4.01x - 4.01$

$y = 4.01x - 1.01$

d. Graphing:

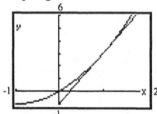

76. $f(x) = 2x^2 + x$

a. $m_{\sec} = \dfrac{f(x+h) - f(x)}{h}$

$= \dfrac{2(x+h)^2 + (x+h) - (2x^2 + x)}{h}$

$= \dfrac{2(x^2 + 2xh + h^2) + x + h - 2x^2 - x}{h}$

$= \dfrac{2x^2 + 4xh + 2h^2 + x + h - 2x^2 - x}{h}$

$= \dfrac{4xh + 2h^2 + h}{h}$

$= 4x + 2h + 1$

b. When $x = 1$,
$$h = 0.5 \Rightarrow m_{sec} = 4 \cdot 1 + 2(0.5) + 1 = 6$$
$$h = 0.1 \Rightarrow m_{sec} = 4 \cdot 1 + 2(0.1) + 1 = 5.2$$
$$h = 0.01 \Rightarrow m_{sec} = 4 \cdot 1 + 2(0.01) + 1 = 5.02$$
as $h \to 0$, $m_{sec} \to 4 \cdot 1 + 2(0) + 1 = 5$

c. Using point $(1, f(1)) = (1, 3)$ and
slope = 5.02, we get the secant line:
$$y - 3 = 5.02(x - 1)$$
$$y - 3 = 5.02x - 5.02$$
$$y = 5.02x - 2.02$$

d. Graphing:

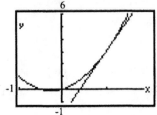

77. $f(x) = 2x^2 - 3x + 1$

a. $m_{sec} = \dfrac{f(x+h) - f(x)}{h}$

$$= \frac{2(x+h)^2 - 3(x+h) + 1 - (2x^2 - 3x + 1)}{h}$$

$$= \frac{2(x^2 + 2xh + h^2) - 3x - 3h + 1 - 2x^2 + 3x - 1}{h}$$

$$= \frac{2x^2 + 4xh + 2h^2 - 3x - 3h + 1 - 2x^2 + 3x - 1}{h}$$

$$= \frac{4xh + 2h^2 - 3h}{h}$$

$$= 4x + 2h - 3$$

b. When $x = 1$,
$$h = 0.5 \Rightarrow m_{sec} = 4 \cdot 1 + 2(0.5) - 3 = 2$$
$$h = 0.1 \Rightarrow m_{sec} = 4 \cdot 1 + 2(0.1) - 3 = 1.2$$
$$h = 0.01 \Rightarrow m_{sec} = 4 \cdot 1 + 2(0.01) - 3 = 1.02$$
as $h \to 0$, $m_{sec} \to 4 \cdot 1 + 2(0) - 3 = 1$

c. Using point $(1, f(1)) = (1, 0)$ and
slope = 1.02, we get the secant line:
$$y - 0 = 1.02(x - 1)$$
$$y = 1.02x - 1.02$$

d. Graphing:

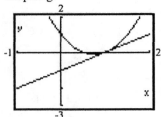

78. $f(x) = -x^2 + 3x - 2$

a. $m_{sec} = \dfrac{f(x+h) - f(x)}{h}$

$$= \frac{-(x+h)^2 + 3(x+h) - 2 - (-x^2 + 3x - 2)}{h}$$

$$= \frac{-(x^2 + 2xh + h^2) + 3x + 3h - 2 + x^2 - 3x + 2}{h}$$

$$= \frac{-x^2 - 2xh - h^2 + 3x + 3h - 2 + x^2 - 3x + 2}{h}$$

$$= \frac{-2xh - h^2 + 3h}{h}$$

$$= -2x - h + 3$$

b. When $x = 1$,
$$h = 0.5 \Rightarrow m_{sec} = -2 \cdot 1 - 0.5 + 3 = 0.5$$
$$h = 0.1 \Rightarrow m_{sec} = -2 \cdot 1 - 0.1 + 3 = 0.9$$
$$h = 0.01 \Rightarrow m_{sec} = -2 \cdot 1 - 0.01 + 3 = 0.99$$
as $h \to 0$, $m_{sec} \to -2 \cdot 1 - 0 + 3 = 1$

c. Using point $(1, f(1)) = (1, 0)$ and
slope = 0.99, we get the secant line:
$$y - 0 = 0.99(x - 1)$$
$$y = 0.99x - 0.99$$

d. Graphing:

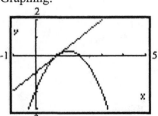

79. $f(x) = \dfrac{1}{x}$

   a. $m_{sec} = \dfrac{f(x+h) - f(x)}{h}$

$$= \dfrac{\left(\dfrac{1}{x+h} - \dfrac{1}{x}\right)}{h} = \dfrac{\left(\dfrac{x - (x+h)}{(x+h)x}\right)}{h}$$

$$= \left(\dfrac{x - x - h}{(x+h)x}\right)\left(\dfrac{1}{h}\right) = \left(\dfrac{-h}{(x+h)x}\right)\left(\dfrac{1}{h}\right)$$

$$= -\dfrac{1}{(x+h)x}$$

   b. When $x = 1$,

$$h = 0.5 \Rightarrow m_{sec} = -\dfrac{1}{(1+0.5)(1)}$$

$$= -\dfrac{1}{1.5} = -\dfrac{2}{3} \approx -0.667$$

$$h = 0.1 \Rightarrow m_{sec} = -\dfrac{1}{(1+0.1)(1)}$$

$$= -\dfrac{1}{1.1} = -\dfrac{10}{11} \approx -0.909$$

$$h = 0.01 \Rightarrow m_{sec} = -\dfrac{1}{(1+0.01)(1)}$$

$$= -\dfrac{1}{1.01} = -\dfrac{100}{101} \approx -0.990$$

as $h \to 0$, $\quad m_{sec} \to -\dfrac{1}{(1+0)(1)} = -\dfrac{1}{1} = -1$

   c. Using point $(1, f(1)) = (1, 1)$ and

slope $= -\dfrac{100}{101}$, we get the secant line:

$$y - 1 = -\dfrac{100}{101}(x - 1)$$

$$y - 1 = -\dfrac{100}{101}x + \dfrac{100}{101}$$

$$y = -\dfrac{100}{101}x + \dfrac{201}{101}$$

   d. Graphing:

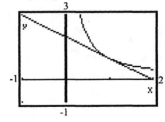

80. $f(x) = \dfrac{1}{x^2}$

   a. $m_{sec} = \dfrac{f(x+h) - f(x)}{h}$

$$= \dfrac{\left(\dfrac{1}{(x+h)^2} - \dfrac{1}{x^2}\right)}{h}$$

$$= \dfrac{\left(\dfrac{x^2 - (x+h)^2}{(x+h)^2 x^2}\right)}{h}$$

$$= \left(\dfrac{x^2 - (x^2 + 2xh + h^2)}{(x+h)^2 x^2}\right)\left(\dfrac{1}{h}\right)$$

$$= \left(\dfrac{-2xh - h^2}{(x+h)^2 x^2}\right)\left(\dfrac{1}{h}\right)$$

$$= \dfrac{-2x - h}{(x+h)^2 x^2} = \dfrac{-2x - h}{(x^2 + 2xh + h^2)x^2}$$

   b. When $x = 1$,

$$h = 0.5 \Rightarrow m_{sec} = \dfrac{-2 \cdot 1 - 0.5}{(1+0.5)^2 1^2} = -\dfrac{10}{9} \approx -1.1111$$

$$h = 0.1 \Rightarrow m_{sec} = \dfrac{-2 \cdot 1 - 0.1}{(1+0.1)^2 1^2} = -\dfrac{210}{121} \approx -1.7355$$

$$h = 0.01 \Rightarrow m_{sec} = \dfrac{-2 \cdot 1 - 0.01}{(1+0.01)^2 1^2}$$

$$= -\dfrac{20,100}{10,201} \approx -1.9704$$

as $h \to 0$, $m_{sec} \to \dfrac{-2 \cdot 1 - 0}{(1+0)^2 1^2} = -2$

   c. Using point $(1, f(1)) = (1, 1)$ and

slope $= -1.9704$, we get the secant line:

$$y - 1 = -1.9704(x - 1)$$

$$y - 1 = -1.9704x + 1.9704$$

$$y = -1.9704x + 2.9704$$

   d. Graphing:

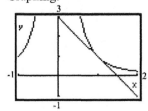

81. Answers will vary. One possibility follows:

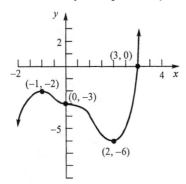

82. Answers will vary. See solution to Problem 81 for one possibility.

83. A function that is increasing on an interval can have at most one x-intercept on the interval. The graph of f could not "turn" and cross it again or it would start to decrease.

84. An increasing function is a function whose graph goes up as you read from left to right.

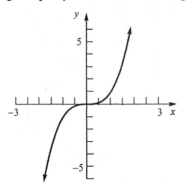

A decreasing function is a function whose graph goes down as you read from left to right.

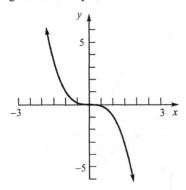

85. To be an even function we need $f(-x) = f(x)$ and to be an odd function we need $f(-x) = -f(x)$. In order for a function be both even and odd, we would need $f(x) = -f(x)$. This is only possible if $f(x) = 0$.

86. The graph of $y = 5$ is a horizontal line.

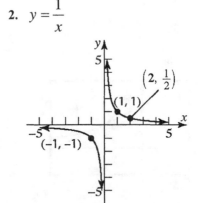

The local maximum is $y = 5$ and it occurs at each x-value in the interval.

Section 3.4

1. $y = \sqrt{x}$

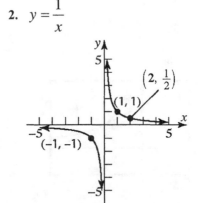

2. $y = \dfrac{1}{x}$

3. $y = x^3 - 8$

y-intercept:

Let $x = 0$, then $y = (0)^3 - 8 = -8$.

x-intercept:

Let $y = 0$, then $0 = x^3 - 8$

$$x^3 = 8$$
$$x = 2$$

The intercepts are $(0, -8)$ and $(2, 0)$.

4. $(-\infty, 0)$

5. piecewise-defined

6. True

7. False; the cube root function is odd and increasing on the interval $(-\infty, \infty)$.

8. False; the domain and range of the reciprocal function are both the set of real numbers except for 0.

9. C

10. A

11. E

12. G

13. B

14. D

15. F

16. H

17. $f(x) = x$

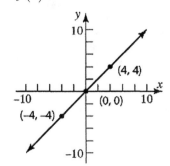

18. $f(x) = x^2$

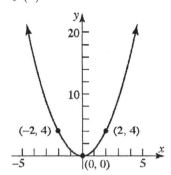

19. $f(x) = x^3$

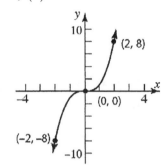

20. $f(x) = \sqrt{x}$

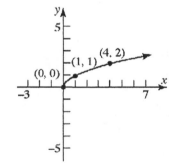

21. $f(x) = \dfrac{1}{x}$

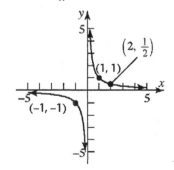

22. $f(x) = |x|$

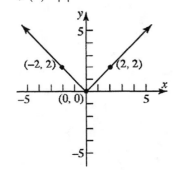

23. $f(x) = \sqrt[3]{x}$

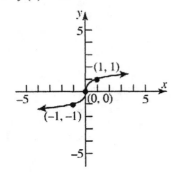

24. $f(x) = 3$

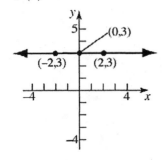

25. a. $f(-2) = (-2)^2 = 4$

b. $f(0) = 2$

c. $f(2) = 2(2) + 1 = 5$

26. a. $f(-2) = -3(-2) = 6$

b. $f(-1) = 0$

c. $f(0) = 2(0)^2 + 1 = 1$

27. a. $f(0) = 2(0) - 4 = -4$

b. $f(1) = 2(1) - 4 = -2$

c. $f(2) = 2(2) - 4 = 0$

d. $f(3) = (3)^3 - 2 = 25$

28. a. $f(-1) = (-1)^3 = -1$

b. $f(0) = (0)^3 = 0$

c. $f(1) = 3(1) + 2 = 5$

d. $f(3) = 3(3) + 2 = 11$

29. $f(x) = \begin{cases} 2x & \text{if } x \neq 0 \\ 1 & \text{if } x = 0 \end{cases}$

a. Domain: $\{x \mid x \text{ is any real number}\}$

b. x-intercept: none
   y-intercept:
   $f(0) = 1$

   The only intercept is $(0, 1)$.

c. Graph:

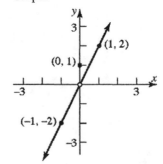

d. Range: $\{y \mid y \neq 0\}$; $(-\infty, 0)$ or $(0, \infty)$

30. $f(x) = \begin{cases} 3x & \text{if } x \neq 0 \\ 4 & \text{if } x = 0 \end{cases}$

    a. Domain: $\{x \mid x \text{ is any real number}\}$

    b. x-intercept: none

        y-intercept: $f(0) = 4$

        The only intercept is $(0, 4)$.

    c. Graph:

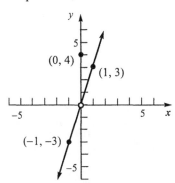

    d. Range: $\{y \mid y \neq 0\}$; $(-\infty, 0)$ or $(0, \infty)$

31. $f(x) = \begin{cases} -2x + 3 & \text{if } x < 1 \\ 3x - 2 & \text{if } x \geq 1 \end{cases}$

    a. Domain: $\{x \mid x \text{ is any real number}\}$

    b. x-intercept: none

        y-intercept: $f(0) = -2(0) + 3 = 3$

        The only intercept is $(0, 3)$.

    c. Graph:

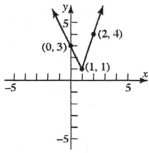

    d. Range: $\{y \mid y \geq 1\}$; $[1, \infty)$

32. $f(x) = \begin{cases} x + 3 & \text{if } x < -2 \\ -2x - 3 & \text{if } x \geq -2 \end{cases}$

    a. Domain: $\{x \mid x \text{ is any real number}\}$

    b. $x + 3 = 0 \qquad -2x - 3 = 0$

         $x = -3 \qquad\quad -2x = 3$

                          $x = -\dfrac{3}{2}$

        x-intercepts: $-3, -\dfrac{3}{2}$

        y-intercept: $f(0) = -2(0) - 3 = -3$

        The intercepts are $(-3, 0)$, $\left(-\dfrac{3}{2}, 0\right)$, and

        $(0, -3)$.

    c. Graph:

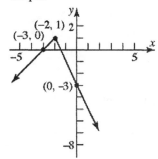

    d. Range: $\{y \mid y \leq 1\}$; $(-\infty, 1]$

33. $f(x) = \begin{cases} x + 3 & \text{if } -2 \leq x < 1 \\ 5 & \text{if } x = 1 \\ -x + 2 & \text{if } x > 1 \end{cases}$

    a. Domain: $\{x \mid x \geq -2\}$; $[-2, \infty)$

    b. $x + 3 = 0 \qquad -x + 2 = 0$

         $x = -3 \qquad\quad -x = -2$

        (not in domain) $\qquad x = 2$

        x-intercept: 2

        y-intercept: $f(0) = 0 + 3 = 3$

        The intercepts are $(2, 0)$ and $(0, 3)$.

c. Graph:

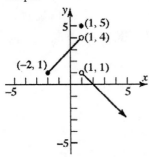

d. Range: $\{y \mid y < 4 \text{ and } y = 5\}$;

$(-\infty, 4) \cup \{5\}$

34. $f(x) = \begin{cases} 2x+5 & \text{if } -3 \le x < 0 \\ -3 & \text{if } x = 0 \\ -5x & \text{if } x > 0 \end{cases}$

a. Domain: $\{x \mid x \ge -3\}$; $[-3, \infty)$

b. $2x + 5 = 0 \qquad -5x = 0$

$2x = -5 \qquad x = 0$

$x = -\dfrac{5}{2}$ (not in domain of piece)

x-intercept: $-\dfrac{5}{2}$

y-intercept: $f(0) = -3$

The intercepts are $\left(-\dfrac{5}{2}, 0\right)$ and $(0, -3)$.

c. Graph:

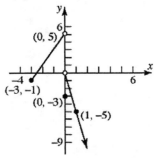

d. Range: $\{y \mid y < 5\}$; $(-\infty, 5)$

35. $f(x) = \begin{cases} 1+x & \text{if } x < 0 \\ x^2 & \text{if } x \ge 0 \end{cases}$

a. Domain: $\{x \mid x \text{ is any real number}\}$

b. $1 + x = 0 \qquad x^2 = 0$

$x = -1 \qquad x = 0$

x-intercepts: $-1, 0$

y-intercept: $f(0) = 0^2 = 0$

The intercepts are $(-1, 0)$ and $(0, 0)$.

c. Graph:

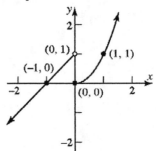

d. Range: $\{y \mid y \text{ is any real number}\}$

36. $f(x) = \begin{cases} \dfrac{1}{x} & \text{if } x < 0 \\ \sqrt[3]{x} & \text{if } x \ge 0 \end{cases}$

a. Domain: $\{x \mid x \text{ is any real number}\}$

b. $\dfrac{1}{x} = 0 \qquad\qquad \sqrt[3]{x} = 0$

(no solution) $\qquad x = 0$

x-intercept: 0

y-intercept: $f(0) = \sqrt[3]{0} = 0$

The only intercept is $(0, 0)$.

c. Graph:

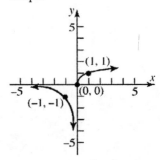

d. Range: $\{y \mid y \text{ is any real number}\}$

37. $f(x) = \begin{cases} |x| & \text{if } -2 \le x < 0 \\ x^3 & \text{if } x > 0 \end{cases}$

   a. Domain: $\{x \mid -2 \le x < 0 \text{ and } x > 0\}$ or

      $\{x \mid x \ge -2, x \ne 0\}$; $[-2, 0) \cup (0, \infty)$.

   b. *x*-intercept: none
There are no *x*-intercepts since there are no
values for *x* such that $f(x) = 0$.

     y-intercept:
There is no *y*-intercept since $x = 0$ is not in
the domain.

   c. Graph:

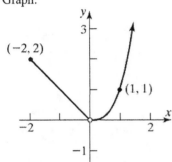

   d. Range: $\{y \mid y > 0\}$; $(0, \infty)$

38. $f(x) = \begin{cases} 2-x & \text{if } -3 \le x < 1 \\ \sqrt{x} & \text{if } x > 1 \end{cases}$

   a. Domain: $\{x \mid -3 \le x < 1 \text{ and } x > 1\}$ or

      $\{x \mid x \ge -3, x \ne 1\}$; $[-3, 1) \cup (1, \infty)$.

   b. $\quad 2 - x = 0 \qquad \sqrt{x} = 0$

       $x = 2 \qquad\quad x = 0$

                (not in domain of piece)

     no *x*-intercepts

     y-intercept: $f(0) = 2 - 0 = 2$

     The intercept is $(0, 2)$.

c. Graph:

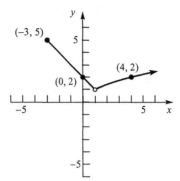

   d. Range: $\{y \mid y > 1\}$; $(1, \infty)$

39. $f(x) = 2\,\text{int}(x)$

   a. Domain: $\{x \mid x \text{ is any real number}\}$

   b. *x*-intercepts:
All values for *x* such that $0 \le x < 1$.

     y-intercept: $f(0) = 2\,\text{int}(0) = 0$

     The intercepts are all ordered pairs $(x, 0)$
when $0 \le x < 1$.

   c. Graph:

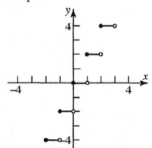

   d. Range: $\{y \mid y \text{ is an even integer}\}$

40. $f(x) = \text{int}(2x)$

   a. Domain: $\{x \mid x \text{ is any real number}\}$

   b. *x*-intercepts:

     All values for *x* such that $0 \le x < \dfrac{1}{2}$.

     y-intercept: $f(0) = \text{int}(2(0)) = \text{int}(0) = 0$

     The intercepts are all ordered pairs $(x, 0)$

     when $0 \le x < \dfrac{1}{2}$.

269

c. Graph:

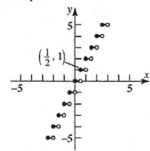

d. Range: $\{y\mid y \text{ is an integer}\}$

41. Answers may vary. One possibility follows:

$$f(x) = \begin{cases} -x & \text{if } -1 \le x \le 0 \\ \dfrac{1}{2}x & \text{if } 0 < x \le 2 \end{cases}$$

42. Answers may vary. One possibility follows:

$$f(x) = \begin{cases} x & \text{if } -1 \le x \le 0 \\ 1 & \text{if } 0 < x \le 2 \end{cases}$$

43. Answers may vary. One possibility follows:

$$f(x) = \begin{cases} -x & \text{if } x \le 0 \\ -x+2 & \text{if } 0 < x \le 2 \end{cases}$$

44. Answers may vary. One possibility follows:

$$f(x) = \begin{cases} 2x+2 & \text{if } -1 \le x \le 0 \\ x & \text{if } x > 0 \end{cases}$$

45. a. $f(1.2) = \text{int}(2(1.2)) = \text{int}(2.4) = 2$

b. $f(1.6) = \text{int}(2(1.6)) = \text{int}(3.2) = 3$

c. $f(-1.8) = \text{int}(2(-1.8)) = \text{int}(-3.6) = -4$

46. a. $f(1.2) = \text{int}\left(\dfrac{1.2}{2}\right) = \text{int}(0.6) = 0$

b. $f(1.6) = \text{int}\left(\dfrac{1.6}{2}\right) = \text{int}(0.8) = 0$

c. $f(-1.8) = \text{int}\left(\dfrac{-1.8}{2}\right) = \text{int}(-0.9) = -1$

47. $C = \begin{cases} 35 & \text{if } 0 < x \le 300 \\ 0.40x - 85 & \text{if } x > 300 \end{cases}$

a. $C(200) = \$35.00$

b. $C(365) = 0.40(365) - 85 = \$61.00$

c. $C(301) = 0.40(301) - 85 = \$35.40$

48. $F(x) = \begin{cases} 3 & \text{if } 0 < x \le 3 \\ 5\,\text{int}(x+1)+1 & \text{if } 3 < x < 9 \\ 50 & \text{if } 9 \le x \le 24 \end{cases}$

a. $F(2) = 3$

Parking for 2 hours costs \$3.

b. $F(7) = 5\,\text{int}(7+1)+1 = 41$

Parking for 7 hours costs \$41.

c. $F(15) = 50$

Parking for 15 hours costs \$50.

d. $24 \text{ min} \cdot \dfrac{1 \text{ hr}}{60 \text{ min}} = 0.4 \text{ hr}$

$F(8.4) = 5\,\text{int}(8.4+1)+1 = 5(9)+1 = 46$

Parking for 8 hours and 24 minutes costs \$46.

49. a. Charge for 50 therms:

$C = 9.45 + 0.7958(50) + 0.36375(50)$

$\quad = \$67.43$

b. Charge for 500 therms:

$C = 9.45 + 0.36375(50) + 0.11445(450)$

$\quad + 0.7958(500)$

$\quad = \$477.04$

c. For $0 \le x \le 50$:

$C = 9.45 + 0.36375x + 0.7958x$

$\quad = 1.15955x + 9.45$

For $x > 50$:

$C = 9.45 + 0.36375(50) + 0.11445(x - 50)$

$\quad + 0.7958x$

$\quad = 9.45 + 18.1875 + 0.11445x - 5.7225$

$\quad + 0.7958x$

$\quad = 0.91025x + 21.915$

The monthly charge function:

$C = \begin{cases} 1.15955x + 9.45 & \text{for } 0 \le x \le 50 \\ 0.91025x + 21.915 & \text{for } x > 50 \end{cases}$

d. Graph:

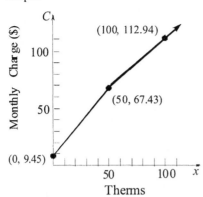

50. a. Charge for 40 therms:

$$C = 8.85 + 0.1557(20) + 0.0663(20)$$
$$+ 0.66(40)$$
$$= \$39.69$$

b. Charge for 202 therms:

$$C = 8.85 + 0.1557(20) + 0.0663(30)$$
$$+ 0.0519(152) + 0.66(202)$$
$$= \$155.16$$

c. For $0 \le x \le 20$:

$$C = 8.85 + 0.1557x + 0.66x$$
$$= 8.85 + 0.8157x$$

For $20 < x \le 50$:

$$C = 8.85 + 0.1557(20) + 0.0663(x - 20)$$
$$+ 0.66x$$
$$= 8.85 + 3.114 + 0.0663x - 1.326$$
$$+ 0.66x$$
$$= 10.638 + 0.7263x$$

For $x > 50$:

$$C = 8.85 + 0.1557(20) + 0.0663(30)$$
$$+ 0.0519(x - 50) + 0.66x$$
$$= 8.85 + 3.114 + 1.989 + 0.0519x - 2.595$$
$$+ 0.66x$$
$$= 11.358 + 0.7119x$$

The monthly charge function:

$$C(x) = \begin{cases} 0.8157x + 8.85 & \text{if } 0 \le x \le 20 \\ 0.7263x + 10.638 & \text{if } 20 < x \le 50 \\ 0.7119x + 11.358 & \text{if } x > 50 \end{cases}$$

d. Graph:

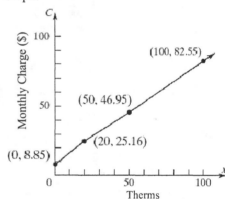

51. For schedule X:

$$f(x) = \begin{cases} 0.10x & \text{if } 0 < x \le 7550 \\ 755.00 + 0.15(x - 7550) & \text{if } 7550 < x \le 30,650 \\ 4220.00 + 0.25(x - 30,650) & \text{if } 30,650 < x \le 74,200 \\ 15,107.50 + 0.28(x - 74,200) & \text{if } 74,200 < x \le 154,800 \\ 37,675.50 + 0.33(x - 154,800) & \text{if } 154,800 < x \le 336,550 \\ 97,653.00 + 0.35(x - 336,550) & \text{if } x > 336,550 \end{cases}$$

52. For Schedule $Y - 1$:

$$f(x) = \begin{cases} 0.10x & \text{if } 0 < x \le 15,100 \\ 1510.00 + 0.15(x - 15,100) & \text{if } 15,100 < x \le 61,300 \\ 8440.00 + 0.25(x - 61,300) & \text{if } 61,300 < x \le 123,700 \\ 24,040.00 + 0.28(x - 123,700) & \text{if } 123,700 < x \le 188,450 \\ 42,176.00 + 0.33(x - 188,450) & \text{if } 188,450 < x \le 336,550 \\ 91,043.00 + 0.35(x - 336,550) & \text{if } x > 336,550 \end{cases}$$

53. a. Let x represent the number of miles and C be the cost of transportation.

$$C(x) = \begin{cases} 0.50x & \text{if } 0 \le x \le 100 \\ 0.50(100) + 0.40(x-100) & \text{if } 100 < x \le 400 \\ 0.50(100) + 0.40(300) + 0.25(x-400) & \text{if } 400 < x \le 800 \\ 0.50(100) + 0.40(300) + 0.25(400) + 0(x-800) & \text{if } 800 < x \le 960 \end{cases}$$

$$C(x) = \begin{cases} 0.50x & \text{if } 0 \le x \le 100 \\ 10 + 0.40x & \text{if } 100 < x \le 400 \\ 70 + 0.25x & \text{if } 400 < x \le 800 \\ 270 & \text{if } 800 < x \le 960 \end{cases}$$

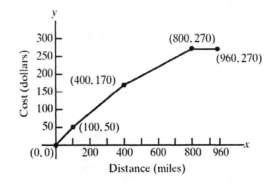

b. For hauls between 100 and 400 miles the cost is: $C(x) = 10 + 0.40x$.

c. For hauls between 400 and 800 miles the cost is: $C(x) = 70 + 0.25x$.

54. Let x = number of days car is used. The cost of renting is given by

$$C(x) = \begin{cases} 95 & \text{if } x = 7 \\ 119 & \text{if } 7 < x \le 8 \\ 143 & \text{if } 8 < x \le 9 \\ 167 & \text{if } 9 < x \le 10 \\ 190 & \text{if } 10 < x \le 14 \end{cases}$$

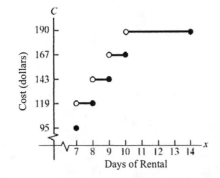

55. Let x = the amount of the bill in dollars. The minimum payment due is given by

$$f(x) = \begin{cases} x & \text{if } x < 10 \\ 10 & \text{if } 10 \le x < 500 \\ 30 & \text{if } 500 \le x < 1000 \\ 50 & \text{if } 1000 \le x < 1500 \\ 70 & \text{if } x \ge 1500 \end{cases}$$

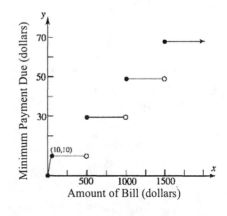

272

56. Let x = the balance of the bill in dollars. The monthly interest charge is given by

$$g(x) = \begin{cases} 0.015x & \text{if } 0 \le x \le 1000 \\ 15 + 0.01(x - 1000) & \text{if } x > 1000 \end{cases}$$

$$= \begin{cases} 0.015x & \text{if } 0 \le x \le 1000 \\ 5 + 0.01x & \text{if } x > 1000 \end{cases}$$

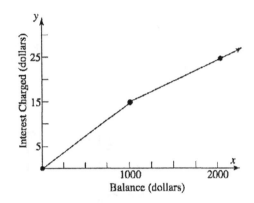

57. a. $W = 10°C$

b. $W = 33 - \dfrac{(10.45 + 10\sqrt{5} - 5)(33 - 10)}{22.04} \approx 4°C$

c. $W = 33 - \dfrac{(10.45 + 10\sqrt{15} - 15)(33 - 10)}{22.04} \approx -3°C$

d. $W = 33 - 1.5958(33 - 10) = -4°C$

e. When $0 \le v < 1.79$, the wind speed is so small that there is no effect on the temperature.

f. When the wind speed exceeds 20, the wind chill depends only on the temperature.

58. a. $W = -10°C$

b. $W = 33 - \dfrac{\left(10.45 + 10\sqrt{5} - 5\right)\left(33 - (-10)\right)}{22.04}$

$\approx -21°C$

c. $W = 33 - \dfrac{\left(10.45 + 10\sqrt{15} - 15\right)\left(33 - (-10)\right)}{22.04}$

$\approx -34°C$

d. $W = 33 - 1.5958\left(33 - (-10)\right) = -36°C$

59. Let x = the number of ounces and $C(x)$ = the postage due.

For $0 < x \le 1$: $C(x) = \$0.39$

For $1 < x \le 2$: $C(x) = 0.39 + 0.24 = \$0.63$

For $2 < x \le 3$: $C(x) = 0.39 + 2(0.24) = \$0.87$

For $3 < x \le 4$: $C(x) = 0.39 + 3(0.24) = \$1.11$

$\vdots$

For $12 < x \le 13$: $C(x) = 0.39 + 12(0.24) = \$3.27$

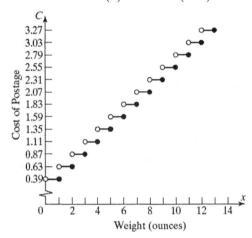

60. Each graph is that of $y = x^2$, but shifted vertically.

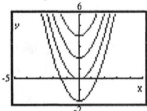

If $y = x^2 + k$, $k > 0$, the shift is up k units; if $y = x^2 - k$, $k > 0$, the shift is down k units. The graph of $y = x^2 - 4$ is the same as the graph of $y = x^2$, but shifted down 4 units. The graph of $y = x^2 + 5$ is the graph of $y = x^2$, but shifted up 5 units.

61. Each graph is that of $y = x^2$, but shifted horizontally.

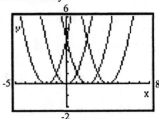

If $y = (x-k)^2$, $k > 0$, the shift is to the right k units; if $y = (x+k)^2$, $k > 0$, the shift is to the left k units. The graph of $y = (x+4)^2$ is the same as the graph of $y = x^2$, but shifted to the left 4 units. The graph of $y = (x-5)^2$ is the graph of $y = x^2$, but shifted to the right 5 units.

62. Each graph is that of $y = |x|$, but either compressed or stretched vertically.

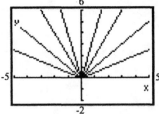

If $y = k|x|$ and $k > 1$, the graph is stretched vertically; if $y = k|x|$ and $0 < k < 1$, the graph is compressed vertically. The graph of $y = \frac{1}{4}|x|$ is the same as the graph of $y = |x|$, but compressed vertically. The graph of $y = 5|x|$ is the same as the graph of $y = |x|$, but stretched vertically.

63. The graph of $y = -x^2$ is the reflection of the graph of $y = x^2$ about the x-axis.

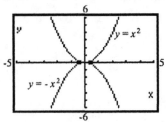

The graph of $y = -|x|$ is the reflection of the graph of $y = |x|$ about the x-axis.

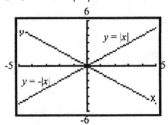

Multiplying a function by -1 causes the graph to be a reflection about the x-axis of the original function's graph.

64. The graph of $y = \sqrt{-x}$ is the reflection about the y-axis of the graph of $y = \sqrt{x}$.

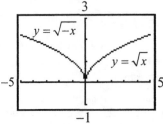

The same type of reflection occurs when graphing $y = 2x+1$ and $y = 2(-x)+1$.

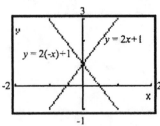

The graph of $y = f(-x)$ is the reflection about the y-axis of the graph of $y = f(x)$.

65. The graph of $y = (x-1)^3 + 2$ is a shifting of the graph of $y = x^3$ one unit to the right and two units up. Yes, the result could be predicted.

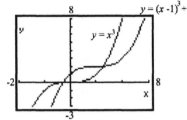

66. The graphs of $y = x^n$, n a positive even integer, are all U-shaped and open upward. All go through the points $(-1, 1)$, $(0, 0)$, and $(1, 1)$. As n increases, the graph of the function is narrower for $|x| > 1$ and flatter for $|x| < 1$.

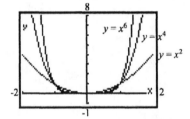

67. The graphs of $y = x^n$, n a positive odd integer, all have the same general shape. All go through the points $(-1, -1)$, $(0, 0)$, and $(1, 1)$. As n increases, the graph of the function increases at a greater rate for $|x| > 1$ and is flatter around 0 for $|x| < 1$.

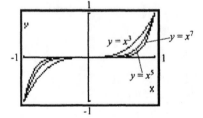

68. $f(x) = \begin{cases} 1 & \text{if } x \text{ is rational} \\ 0 & \text{if } x \text{ is irrational} \end{cases}$

Yes, it is a function.

Domain = $\{x \mid x \text{ is any real number}\}$

Range = $\{0, 1\}$

y-intercept: $x = 0 \Rightarrow x$ is rational $\Rightarrow y = 1$ So the y-intercept is $(0, 1)$.

x-intercept: $y = 0 \Rightarrow x$ is irrational So the graph has infinitely many x-intercepts, namely, there is an x-intercept at each irrational value of x.

$f(-x) = 1 = f(x)$ when x is rational;

$f(-x) = 0 = f(x)$ when x is irrational.

Thus, f is even.

The graph of f consists of 2 infinite clusters of distinct points, extending horizontally in both directions. One cluster is located 1 unit above the x-axis, and the other is located along the x-axis.

69. For $0 < x < 1$, the graph of $y = x^r$, r rational and $r > 0$, flattens down toward the x-axis as r gets bigger. For $x > 1$, the graph of $y = x^r$ increases at a greater rate as r gets bigger.

Section 3.5

1. horizontal; right

2. y

3. -5, -2, and 2 (shift left three units)

4. True; the graph of $y = -f(x)$ is the reflection about the x-axis of the graph of $y = f(x)$.

5. False; to obtain the graph of $y = f(x+2) - 3$ you shift the graph of $y = f(x)$ to the *left* 2 units and down 3 units.

6. True; to obtain the graph of $y = 2f(x)$ we multiply the y-coordinates of the graph of $y = f(x)$ by 2. Since the y-coordinate of x-intercepts is 0 and $2 \cdot 0 = 0$, multiplying by a constant does not change the x-intercepts.

7. B

8. E

9. H

10. D

11. I

12. A

13. L

275

14. C

15. F

16. J

17. G

18. K

19. $y = (x-4)^3$

20. $y = (x+4)^3$

21. $y = x^3 + 4$

22. $y = x^3 - 4$

23. $y = (-x)^3 = -x^3$

24. $y = -x^3$

25. $y = 4x^3$

26. $y = \left(\dfrac{1}{4}x\right)^3 = \dfrac{1}{64}x^3$

27. (1) $y = \sqrt{x} + 2$

    (2) $y = -\left(\sqrt{x} + 2\right)$

    (3) $y = -\left(\sqrt{-x} + 2\right) = -\sqrt{-x} - 2$

28. (1) $y = -\sqrt{x}$

    (2) $y = -\sqrt{x-3}$

    (3) $y = -\sqrt{x-3} - 2$

29. (1) $y = -\sqrt{x}$

    (2) $y = -\sqrt{x} + 2$

    (3) $y = -\sqrt{x+3} + 2$

30. (1) $y = \sqrt{x} + 2$

    (2) $y = \sqrt{-x} + 2$

    (3) $y = \sqrt{-(x+3)} + 2 = \sqrt{-x-3} + 2$

31. (c); To go from $y = f(x)$ to $y = -f(x)$ we reflect about the *x*-axis. This means we change the sign of the *y*-coordinate for each point on the graph of $y = f(x)$. Thus, the point $(3, 0)$ would remain the same.

32. (d); To go from $y = f(x)$ to $y = f(-x)$, we reflect each point on the graph of $y = f(x)$ about the *y*-axis. This means we change the sign of the *x*-coordinate for each point on the graph of $y = f(x)$. Thus, the point $(3,0)$ would become $(-3,0)$.

33. (c); To go from $y = f(x)$ to $y = 2f(x)$, we multiply the *y*-coordinate of each point on the graph of $y = f(x)$ by 2. Thus, the point $(0,3)$ would become $(0,6)$.

34. (a); To go from $y = f(x)$ to $y = \dfrac{1}{2}f(x)$, we multiply the *y*-coordinate of each point on the graph of $y = f(x)$ by $\dfrac{1}{2}$. Thus, the point $(3,0)$ would remain $(3,0)$.

35. $f(x) = x^2 - 1$

Using the graph of $y = x^2$, vertically shift downward 1 unit.

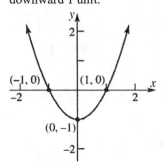

36. $f(x) = x^2 + 4$

Using the graph of $y = x^2$, vertically shift upward 4 units.

276

37. $g(x) = x^3 + 1$

Using the graph of $y = x^3$, vertically shift upward 1 unit.

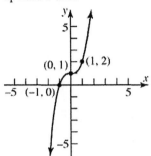

38. $g(x) = x^3 - 1$

Using the graph of $y = x^3$, vertically shift downward 1 unit.

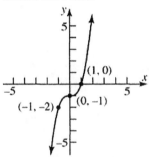

39. $h(x) = \sqrt{x - 2}$

Using the graph of $y = \sqrt{x}$, horizontally shift to the right 2 units.

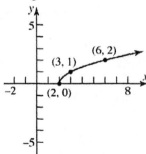

40. $h(x) = \sqrt{x + 1}$

Using the graph of $y = \sqrt{x}$, horizontally shift to the left 1 unit.

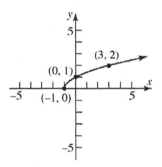

41. $f(x) = (x - 1)^3 + 2$

Using the graph of $y = x^3$, horizontally shift to the right 1 unit $\left[y = (x - 1)^3 \right]$, then vertically shift up 2 units $\left[y = (x - 1)^3 + 2 \right]$.

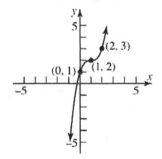

42. $f(x) = (x + 2)^3 - 3$

Using the graph of $y = x^3$, horizontally shift to the left 2 units $\left[y = (x + 2)^3 \right]$, then vertically shift down 3 units $\left[y = (x + 2)^3 - 3 \right]$.

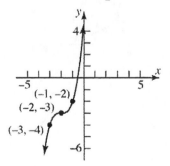

43. $g(x) = 4\sqrt{x}$

Using the graph of $y = \sqrt{x}$, vertically stretch by a factor of 4.

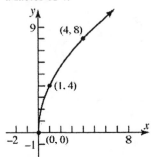

44. $g(x) = \dfrac{1}{2}\sqrt{x}$

Using the graph of $y = \sqrt{x}$, vertically compress by a factor of $\dfrac{1}{2}$.

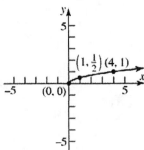

45. $h(x) = \dfrac{1}{2x} = \left(\dfrac{1}{2}\right)\left(\dfrac{1}{x}\right)$

Using the graph of $y = \dfrac{1}{x}$, vertically compress

by a factor of $\dfrac{1}{2}$.

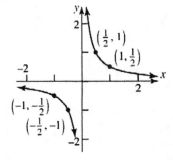

46. $h(x) = 3\sqrt[3]{x}$

Using the graph of $y = \sqrt[3]{x}$, vertically stretch by a factor of 3.

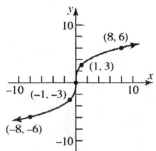

47. $f(x) = -\sqrt[3]{x}$

Using the graph of $y = \sqrt[3]{x}$, reflect the graph about the x-axis.

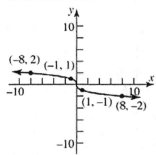

48. $f(x) = -\sqrt{x}$

Using the graph of $y = \sqrt{x}$, reflect the graph about the x-axis.

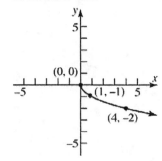

49. $g(x) = \sqrt[3]{-x}$

Using the graph of $y = \sqrt[3]{x}$, reflect the graph about the y-axis.

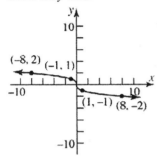

50. $g(x) = -\dfrac{1}{x}$

Using the graph of $y = \dfrac{1}{x}$, reflect the graph about the x-axis.

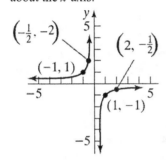

51. $h(x) = -x^3 + 2$

Using the graph of $y = x^3$, reflect the graph about the x-axis $\left[y = -x^3 \right]$, then shift vertically upward 2 units $\left[y = -x^3 + 2 \right]$.

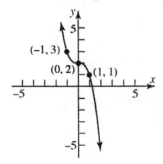

52. $h(x) = \dfrac{1}{-x} + 2$

Using the graph of $y = \dfrac{1}{x}$, reflect the graph about the y-axis $\left[y = \dfrac{1}{-x} \right]$, then shift vertically upward 2 units $\left[y = \dfrac{1}{-x} + 2 \right]$.

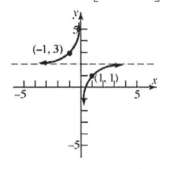

53. $f(x) = 2(x+1)^2 - 3$

Using the graph of $y = x^2$, horizontally shift to the left 1 unit $\left[y = (x+1)^2 \right]$, vertically stretch by a factor of 2 $\left[y = 2(x+1)^2 \right]$, and then vertically shift downward 3 units $\left[y = 2(x+1)^2 - 3 \right]$.

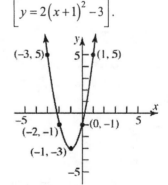

54. $f(x) = 3(x-2)^2 + 1$

Using the graph of $y = x^2$, horizontally shift to

the right 2 units $\left[y = (x-2)^2 \right]$, vertically

stretch by a factor of 3 $\left[y = 3(x-2)^2 \right]$, and then

vertically shift upward 1 unit

$\left[y = 3(x-2)^2 + 1 \right]$.

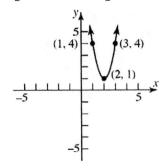

55. $g(x) = \sqrt{x-2} + 1$

Using the graph of $y = \sqrt{x}$, horizontally shift to

the right 2 units $\left[y = \sqrt{x-2} \right]$ and vertically

shift upward 1 unit $\left[y = \sqrt{x-2} + 1 \right]$.

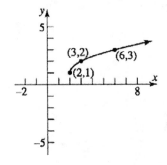

56. $g(x) = |x+1| - 3$

Using the graph of $y = |x|$, horizontally shift to

the left 1 unit $\left[y = |x+1| \right]$ and vertically shift

downward 3 units $\left[y = |x+1| - 3 \right]$.

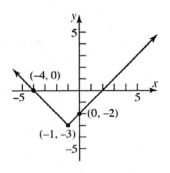

57. $h(x) = \sqrt{-x} - 2$

Using the graph of $y = \sqrt{x}$, reflect the graph

about the y-axis $\left[y = \sqrt{-x} \right]$ and vertically shift

downward 2 units $\left[y = \sqrt{-x} - 2 \right]$.

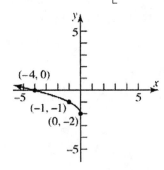

58. $h(x) = \dfrac{4}{x} + 2 = 4\left(\dfrac{1}{x}\right) + 2$

Stretch the graph of $y = \dfrac{1}{x}$ vertically by a factor

of 4 $\left[y = 4 \cdot \dfrac{1}{x} = \dfrac{4}{x} \right]$ and vertically shift upward 2

units $\left[y = \dfrac{4}{x} + 2 \right]$.

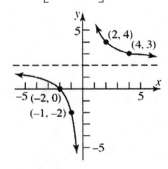

59. $f(x) = -(x+1)^3 - 1$

Using the graph of $y = x^3$, horizontally shift to

the left 1 unit $\left[y = (x+1)^3 \right]$, reflect the graph

about the x-axis $\left[y = -(x+1)^3 \right]$, and vertically

shift downward 1 unit $\left[y = -(x+1)^3 - 1 \right]$.

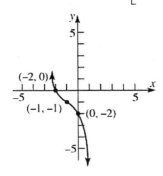

60. $f(x) = -4\sqrt{x-1}$

Using the graph of $y = \sqrt{x}$, horizontally shift to

the right 1 unit $\left[y = \sqrt{x-1} \right]$, reflect the graph

about the x-axis $\left[y = -\sqrt{x-1} \right]$, and stretch

vertically by a factor of 4 $\left[y = -4\sqrt{x-1} \right]$.

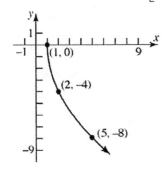

61. $g(x) = 2|1-x| = 2|-(-1+x)| = 2|x-1|$

Using the graph of $y = |x|$, horizontally shift to

the right 1 unit $\left[y = |x-1| \right]$, and vertically

stretch by a factor or 2 $\left[y = 2|x-1| \right]$.

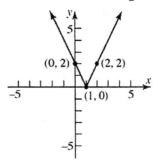

62. $g(x) = 4\sqrt{2-x} = 4\sqrt{-(x-2)}$

Using the graph of $y = \sqrt{x}$, reflect the graph

about the y-axis $\left[y = \sqrt{-x} \right]$, horizontally shift

to the right 2 units $\left[y = \sqrt{-(x-2)} \right]$, and

vertically stretch by a factor of 4

$\left[y = 4\sqrt{-(x-2)} \right]$.

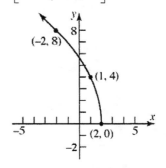

63. $h(x) = 2\operatorname{int}(x-1)$

Using the graph of $y = \operatorname{int}(x)$, horizontally shift to the right 1 unit $\left[y = \operatorname{int}(x-1)\right]$, and vertically stretch by a factor of 2 $\left[y = 2\operatorname{int}(x-1)\right]$.

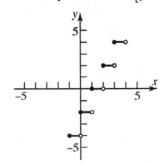

64. $h(x) = \operatorname{int}(-x)$

Reflect the graph of $y = \operatorname{int}(x)$ about the y-axis.

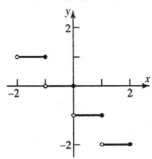

65. a. $F(x) = f(x) + 3$

Shift up 3 units.

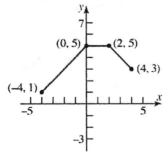

b. $G(x) = f(x+2)$

Shift left 2 units.

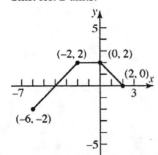

c. $P(x) = -f(x)$

Reflect about the x-axis.

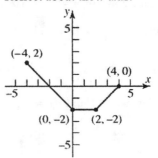

d. $H(x) = f(x+1) - 2$

Shift left 1 unit and shift down 2 units.

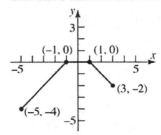

e. $Q(x) = \dfrac{1}{2}f(x)$

Compress vertically by a factor of $\dfrac{1}{2}$.

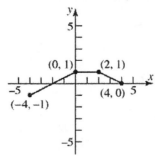

f. $g(x) = f(-x)$

Reflect about the y-axis.

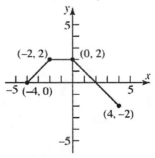

g. $h(x) = f(2x)$

Compress horizontally by a factor of $\dfrac{1}{2}$.

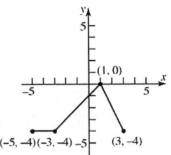

66. a. $F(x) = f(x) + 3$

Shift up 3 units.

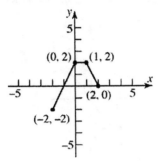

b. $G(x) = f(x+2)$

Shift left 2 units.

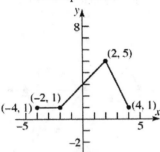

c. $P(x) = -f(x)$

Reflect about the *x*-axis.

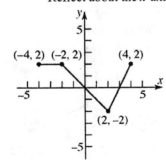

d. $H(x) = f(x+1) - 2$

Shift left 1 unit and shift down 2 units.

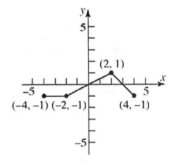

e. $Q(x) = \dfrac{1}{2}f(x)$

Compress vertically by a factor of $\dfrac{1}{2}$.

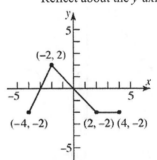

f. $g(x) = f(-x)$

Reflect about the *y*-axis.

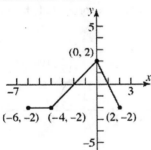

g. $h(x) = f(2x)$

Compress horizontally by a factor of $\dfrac{1}{2}$.

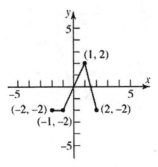

283

67. a. $F(x) = f(x) + 3$
Shift up 3 units.

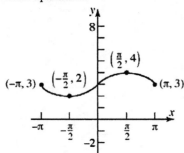

b. $G(x) = f(x+2)$
Shift left 2 units.

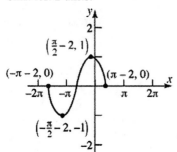

c. $P(x) = -f(x)$
Reflect about the *x*-axis.

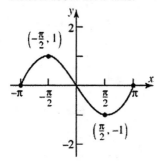

d. $H(x) = f(x+1) - 2$
Shift left 1 unit and shift down 2 units.

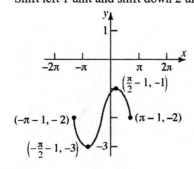

e. $Q(x) = \frac{1}{2} f(x)$

Compress vertically by a factor of $\frac{1}{2}$.

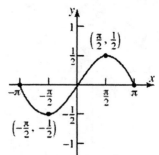

f. $g(x) = f(-x)$
Reflect about the *y*-axis.

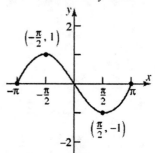

g. $h(x) = f(2x)$

Compress horizontally by a factor of $\frac{1}{2}$.

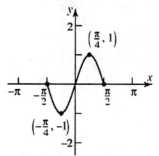

68. a. $F(x) = f(x) + 3$
Shift up 3 units.

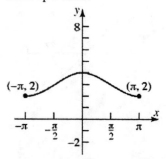

284

b. $G(x) = f(x+2)$
Shift left 2 units.

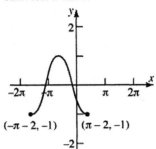

c. $P(x) = -f(x)$
Reflect about the *x*-axis.

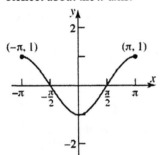

d. $H(x) = f(x+1) - 2$
Shift left 1 unit and shift down 2 units.

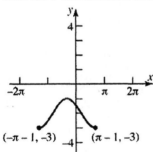

e. $Q(x) = \dfrac{1}{2} f(x)$

Compress vertically by a factor of $\dfrac{1}{2}$.

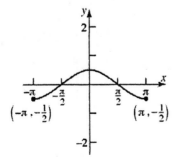

f. $g(x) = f(-x)$
Reflect about the *y*-axis.

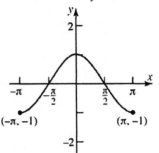

g. $h(x) = f(2x)$

Compress horizontally by a factor of $\dfrac{1}{2}$.

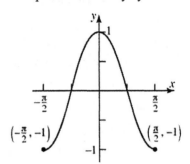

69. a. The graph of $y = f(x+2)$ is the same as the graph of $y = f(x)$, but shifted 2 units to the left. Therefore, the *x*-intercepts are -7 and 1.

b. The graph of $y = f(x-2)$ is the same as the graph of $y = f(x)$, but shifted 2 units to the right. Therefore, the *x*-intercepts are -3 and 5.

c. The graph of $y = 4f(x)$ is the same as the graph of $y = f(x)$, but stretched vertically by a factor of 4. Therefore, the *x*-intercepts are still -5 and 3 since the *y*-coordinate of each is 0.

d. The graph of $y = f(-x)$ is the same as the graph of $y = f(x)$, but reflected about the y-axis. Therefore, the *x*-intercepts are 5 and -3.

285

70. a. The graph of $y = f(x+4)$ is the same as the graph of $y = f(x)$, but shifted 4 units to the left. Therefore, the x-intercepts are -12 and -3.

  b. The graph of $y = f(x-3)$ is the same as the graph of $y = f(x)$, but shifted 3 units to the right. Therefore, the x-intercepts are -5 and 4.

  c. The graph of $y = 2f(x)$ is the same as the graph of $y = f(x)$, but stretched vertically by a factor of 2. Therefore, the x-intercepts are still -8 and 1 since the y-coordinate of each is 0.

  d. The graph of $y = f(-x)$ is the same as the graph of $y = f(x)$, but reflected about the y-axis. Therefore, the x-intercepts are 8 and -1.

71. a. The graph of $y = f(x+2)$ is the same as the graph of $y = f(x)$, but shifted 2 units to the left. Therefore, the graph of $f(x+2)$ is increasing on the interval $(-3,3)$.

  b. The graph of $y = f(x-5)$ is the same as the graph of $y = f(x)$, but shifted 5 units to the right. Therefore, the graph of $f(x-5)$ is increasing on the interval $(4,10)$.

  c. The graph of $y = -f(x)$ is the same as the graph of $y = f(x)$, but reflected about the x-axis. Therefore, we can say that the graph of $y = -f(x)$ must be *decreasing* on the interval $(-1,5)$.

  d. The graph of $y = f(-x)$ is the same as the graph of $y = f(x)$, but reflected about the y-axis. Therefore, we can say that the graph of $y = f(-x)$ must be *decreasing* on the interval $(-5,1)$.

72. a. The graph of $y = f(x+2)$ is the same as the graph of $y = f(x)$, but shifted 2 units to the left. Therefore, the graph of $f(x+2)$ is decreasing on the interval $(-4,5)$.

  b. The graph of $y = f(x-5)$ is the same as the graph of $y = f(x)$, but shifted 5 units to the right. Therefore, the graph of $f(x-5)$ is decreasing on the interval $(3,12)$.

  c. The graph of $y = -f(x)$ is the same as the graph of $y = f(x)$, but reflected about the x-axis. Therefore, we can say that the graph of $y = -f(x)$ must be *increasing* on the interval $(-2,7)$.

  d. The graph of $y = f(-x)$ is the same as the graph of $y = f(x)$, but reflected about the y-axis. Therefore, we can say that the graph of $y = f(-x)$ must be *increasing* on the interval $(-7,2)$.

73. a. $y = |f(x)|$

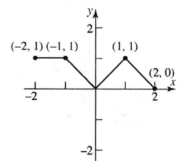

  b. $y = f(|x|)$

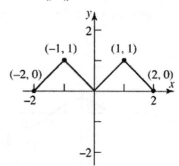

74. a. $y = |f(x)|$

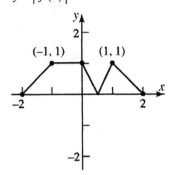

b. $y = f(|x|)$

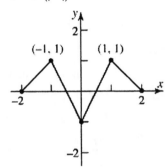

75. $f(x) = x^2 + 2x$

$f(x) = (x^2 + 2x + 1) - 1$

$f(x) = (x+1)^2 - 1$

Using $f(x) = x^2$, shift left 1 unit and shift down 1 unit.

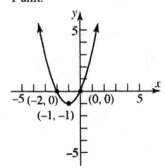

76. $f(x) = x^2 - 6x$

$f(x) = (x^2 - 6x + 9) - 9$

$f(x) = (x-3)^2 - 9$

Using $f(x) = x^2$, shift right 3 units and shift down 9 units.

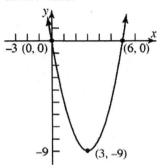

77. $f(x) = x^2 - 8x + 1$

$f(x) = \left(x^2 - 8x + 16\right) + 1 - 16$

$f(x) = (x-4)^2 - 15$

Using $f(x) = x^2$, shift right 4 units and shift down 15 units.

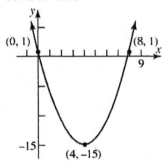

78. $f(x) = x^2 + 4x + 2$

$f(x) = \left(x^2 + 4x + 4\right) + 2 - 4$

$f(x) = (x+2)^2 - 2$

Using $f(x) = x^2$, shift left 2 units and shift down 2 units.

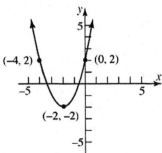

79. $f(x) = x^2 + x + 1$

$$f(x) = \left(x^2 + x + \frac{1}{4}\right) + 1 - \frac{1}{4}$$

$$f(x) = \left(x + \frac{1}{2}\right)^2 + \frac{3}{4}$$

Using $f(x) = x^2$, shift left $\frac{1}{2}$ unit and shift up $\frac{3}{4}$ unit.

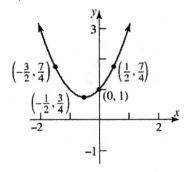

80. $f(x) = x^2 - x + 1$

$$f(x) = \left(x^2 - x + \frac{1}{4}\right) + 1 - \frac{1}{4}$$

$$f(x) = \left(x - \frac{1}{2}\right)^2 + \frac{3}{4}$$

Using $f(x) = x^2$, shift right $\frac{1}{2}$ unit and shift up $\frac{3}{4}$ unit.

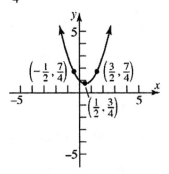

81. $f(x) = 2x^2 - 12x + 19$

$$= 2\left(x^2 - 6x\right) + 19$$

$$= 2\left(x^2 - 6x + 9\right) + 19 - 18$$

$$= 2(x - 3)^2 + 1$$

Using $f(x) = x^2$, shift right 3 units, vertically stretch by a factor of 2, and then shift up 1 unit.

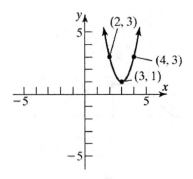

82. $f(x) = 3x^2 + 6x + 1$

$$= 3\left(x^2 + 2x\right) + 1$$

$$= 3\left(x^2 + 2x + 1\right) + 1 - 3$$

$$= 3(x + 1)^2 - 2$$

Using $f(x) = x^2$, shift left 1 unit, vertically stretch by a factor of 3, and shift down 2 units.

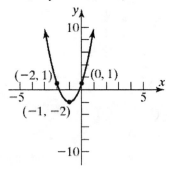

83. $f(x) = -3x^2 - 12x - 17$

$$= -3\left(x^2 + 4x\right) - 17$$

$$= -3\left(x^2 + 4x + 4\right) - 17 + 12$$

$$= -3(x + 2)^2 - 5$$

Using $f(x) = x^2$, shift left 2 units, stretch vertically by a factor of 3, reflect about the x-axis, and shift down 5 units.

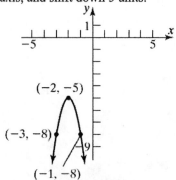

84. $f(x) = -2x^2 - 12x - 13$

$\quad\quad = -2(x^2 + 6x) - 13$

$\quad\quad = -2(x^2 + 6x + 9) - 13 + 18$

$\quad\quad = -2(x + 3)^2 + 5$

Using $f(x) = x^2$, shift left 3 units, stretch vertically by a factor of 2, reflect about the *x*-axis, and shift up 5 units.

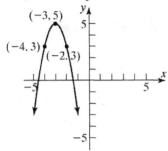

85. $y = (x - c)^2$

If $c = 0$, $y = x^2$.

If $c = 3$, $y = (x - 3)^2$; shift right 3 units.

If $c = -2$, $y = (x + 2)^2$; shift left 2 units.

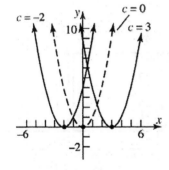

86. $y = x^2 + c$

If $c = 0$, $y = x^2$.

If $c = 3$, $y = x^2 + 3$; shift up 3 units.

If $c = -2$, $y = x^2 - 2$; shift down 2 units.

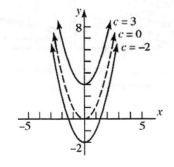

87. a. From the graph, the thermostat is set at 72°F during the daytime hours. The thermostat appears to be set at 65°F overnight.

b. To graph $y = T(t) - 2$, the graph of $T(t)$ should be shifted down 2 units. This change will lower the temperature in the house by 2 degrees.

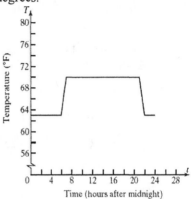

c. To graph $y = T(t + 1)$, the graph of $T(t)$ should be shifted left one unit. This change will cause the program to switch between the daytime temperature and overnight temperature one hour sooner. The home will begin warming up at 5am instead of 6am and will begin cooling down at 8pm instead of 9pm.

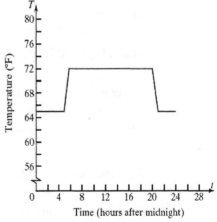

88. a. $R(0) = 170.7(0)^2 + 1373(0) + 1080 = 1080$

The estimated worldwide music revenue for 2005 is $1080 million.

$R(3) = 170.7(3)^2 + 1373(3) + 1080$
$= 6735.3$

The estimated worldwide music revenue for 2008 is $6735.3 million.

$R(5) = 170.7(5)^2 + 1373(5) + 1080$
$= 12,212.5$

The estimated worldwide music revenue for 2010 is $12,212.5 million.

b. $r(x) = R(x-5)$

$= 170.7(x-5)^2 + 1373(x-5) + 1080$

$= 170.7(x^2 - 10x + 25) + 1373(x-5)$
$+ 1080$

$= 170.7x^2 - 1707x + 4267.5 + 1373x$
$- 6865 + 1080$

$= 170.7x^2 - 334x - 1517.5$

c. The graph of $r(x)$ is the graph of $R(x)$ shifted 5 units to the left. Thus, $r(x)$ represents the estimated worldwide music revenue, x years after 2000.

$r(5) = 170.7(5)^2 - 334(5) - 1517.5 = 1080$

The estimated worldwide music revenue for 2005 is $1080 million.

$r(8) = 170.7(8)^2 - 334(8) - 1517.5$
$= 6735.3$

The estimated worldwide music revenue for 2008 is $6735.3 million.

$r(10) = 170.7(10)^2 - 334(10) - 1517.5$
$= 12,212.5$

The estimated worldwide music revenue for 2010 is $12,212.5 million.

d. In $r(x)$, x represents the number of years after 2000 (see the previous part).

e. Answers will vary. One advantage might be that it is easier to determine what value should be substituted for x when using $r(x)$ instead of $R(x)$ to estimate worldwide music revenue.

89. $F = \dfrac{9}{5}C + 32$

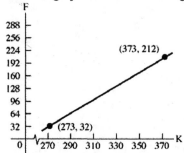

$F = \dfrac{9}{5}(K - 273) + 32$

Shift the graph 273 units to the right.

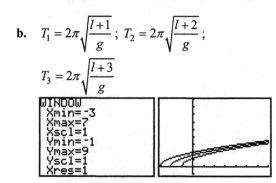

90. a. $T = 2\pi\sqrt{\dfrac{l}{g}}$

```
WINDOW
Xmin=-1
Xmax=9
Xscl=1
Ymin=-1
Ymax=9
Yscl=1
Xres=1
```

b. $T_1 = 2\pi\sqrt{\dfrac{l+1}{g}}$; $T_2 = 2\pi\sqrt{\dfrac{l+2}{g}}$;

$T_3 = 2\pi\sqrt{\dfrac{l+3}{g}}$

```
WINDOW
Xmin=-3
Xmax=7
Xscl=1
Ymin=-1
Ymax=9
Yscl=1
Xres=1
```

c. As the length of the pendulum increases, the period increases.

290

d. $T_1 = 2\pi\sqrt{\dfrac{2l}{g}}$; $T_2 = 2\pi\sqrt{\dfrac{3l}{g}}$; $T_3 = 2\pi\sqrt{\dfrac{4l}{g}}$

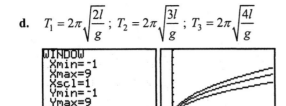

e. If the length of the pendulum is multiplied by k, the period is multiplied by $\sqrt{k}$.

91. a. $p(x) = -0.05x^2 + 100x - 2000$

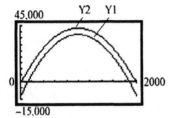

b. Select the 10% tax since the profits are higher.

c. The graph of Y1 is obtained by shifting the graph of $p(x)$ vertically down 10,000 units. The graph of Y2 is obtained by multiplying the y-coordinate of the graph of $p(x)$ by 0.9. Thus, Y2 is the graph of $p(x)$ vertically compressed by a factor of 0.9.

d. Select the 10% tax since the graph of $Y1 = 0.9p(x) \geq Y2 = -0.05x^2 + 100x - 6800$ for all x in the domain.

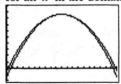

92. The graph of $y = 4f(x)$ is a vertical stretch of the graph of f by a factor of 4, while the graph of $y = f(4x)$ is a horizontal compression of the graph of f by a factor of $\frac{1}{4}$.

Section 3.6

1. a. The distance d from P to the origin is $d = \sqrt{x^2 + y^2}$. Since P is a point on the graph of $y = x^2 - 8$, we have:
$$d(x) = \sqrt{x^2 + (x^2 - 8)^2} = \sqrt{x^4 - 15x^2 + 64}$$

b. $d(0) = \sqrt{0^4 - 15(0)^2 + 64} = \sqrt{64} = 8$

c. $d(1) = \sqrt{(1)^4 - 15(1)^2 + 64}$
$= \sqrt{1 - 15 + 64} = \sqrt{50} = 5\sqrt{2} \approx 7.07$

d.

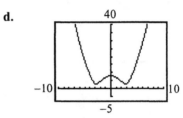

e. d is smallest when $x \approx -2.74$ or when $x \approx 2.74$.

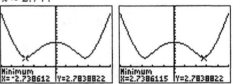

2. a. The distance d from P to $(0, -1)$ is $d = \sqrt{x^2 + (y+1)^2}$. Since P is a point on the graph of $y = x^2 - 8$, we have:
$$d(x) = \sqrt{x^2 + (x^2 - 8 + 1)^2}$$
$$= \sqrt{x^2 + (x^2 - 7)^2} = \sqrt{x^4 - 13x^2 + 49}$$

b. $d(0) = \sqrt{0^4 - 13(0)^2 + 49} = \sqrt{49} = 7$

c. $d(-1) = \sqrt{(-1)^4 - 13(-1)^2 + 49} = \sqrt{37} \approx 6.08$

d.

291

e. *d* is smallest when $x \approx -2.55$ or when $x \approx 2.55$.

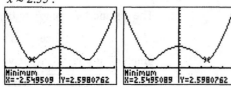

3. a. The distance *d* from *P* to the point (1, 0) is $d = \sqrt{(x-1)^2 + y^2}$. Since *P* is a point on the graph of $y = \sqrt{x}$, we have:

$$d(x) = \sqrt{(x-1)^2 + \left(\sqrt{x}\right)^2} = \sqrt{x^2 - x + 1}$$

where $x \geq 0$.

b.

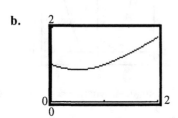

c. *d* is smallest when $x = \frac{1}{2}$.

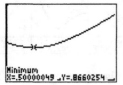

4. a. The distance *d* from *P* to the origin is $d = \sqrt{x^2 + y^2}$. Since *P* is a point on the graph of $y = \frac{1}{x}$, we have:

$$d(x) = \sqrt{x^2 + \left(\frac{1}{x}\right)^2} = \sqrt{x^2 + \frac{1}{x^2}} = \sqrt{\frac{x^4 + 1}{x^2}}$$

$$= \frac{\sqrt{x^2 + 1}}{|x|}$$

b.

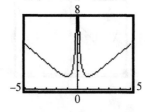

c. *d* is smallest when $x = -1$ or $x = 1$.

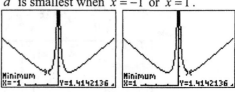

5. By definition, a triangle has area $A = \frac{1}{2}bh$, *b* = base, *h* = height. From the figure, we know that $b = x$ and $h = y$. Expressing the area of the triangle as a function of *x*, we have:

$$A(x) = \frac{1}{2}xy = \frac{1}{2}x\left(x^3\right) = \frac{1}{2}x^4.$$

6. By definition, a triangle has area $A = \frac{1}{2}bh$, *b*=base, *h* = height. Because one vertex of the triangle is at the origin and the other is on the *x*-axis, we know that $b = x$ and $h = y$. Expressing the area of the triangle as a function of *x*, we have:

$$A(x) = \frac{1}{2}xy = \frac{1}{2}x\left(9 - x^2\right) = \frac{9}{2}x - \frac{1}{2}x^3.$$

7. a. $A(x) = xy = x\left(16 - x^2\right) = -x^3 + 16x$

b. Domain: $\left\{x \mid 0 < x < 4\right\}$

c. The area is largest when $x \approx 2.31$.

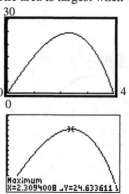

8. a. $A(x) = 2xy = 2x\sqrt{4 - x^2}$

b. $p(x) = 2(2x) + 2(y) = 4x + 2\sqrt{4 - x^2}$

c. Graphing the area equation:

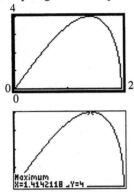

The area is largest when $x \approx 1.41$.

d. Graphing the perimeter equation:

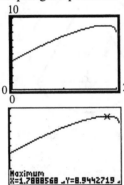

The perimeter is largest when $x \approx 1.79$.

9. a. In Quadrant I, $x^2 + y^2 = 4 \rightarrow y = \sqrt{4 - x^2}$

$A(x) = (2x)(2y) = 4x\sqrt{4 - x^2}$

b. $p(x) = 2(2x) + 2(2y) = 4x + 4\sqrt{4 - x^2}$

c. Graphing the area equation:

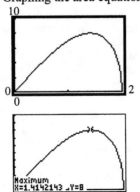

The area is largest when $x \approx 1.41$.

d. Graphing the perimeter equation:

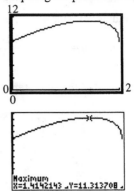

The perimeter is largest when $x \approx 1.41$.

10. a. $A(r) = (2r)(2r) = 4r^2$

b. $p(r) = 4(2r) = 8r$

11. a. $C =$ circumference, $A =$ total area,
$r =$ radius, $x =$ side of square

$C = 2\pi r = 10 - 4x \implies r = \dfrac{5 - 2x}{\pi}$

Total Area $=$ area$_{\text{square}}$ $+$ area$_{\text{circle}}$ $= x^2 + \pi r^2$

$A(x) = x^2 + \pi\left(\dfrac{5 - 2x}{\pi}\right)^2 = x^2 + \dfrac{25 - 20x + 4x^2}{\pi}$

b. Since the lengths must be positive, we have:
$10 - 4x > 0$ and $x > 0$
$-4x > -10$ and $x > 0$
$x < 2.5$ and $x > 0$
Domain: $\{x \mid 0 < x < 2.5\}$

c. The total area is smallest when $x \approx 1.40$ meters.

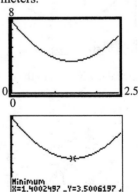

293

12. a. C = circumference, A = total area,
r = radius, x = side of equilateral triangle

$$C = 2\pi r = 10 - 3x \Rightarrow r = \frac{10 - 3x}{2\pi}$$

The height of the equilateral triangle is $\frac{\sqrt{3}}{2}x$.

Total Area = area$_{\text{triangle}}$ + area$_{\text{circle}}$

$$= \frac{1}{2}x\left(\frac{\sqrt{3}}{2}x\right) + \pi r^2$$

$$A(x) = \frac{\sqrt{3}}{4}x^2 + \pi\left(\frac{10 - 3x}{2\pi}\right)^2$$

$$= \frac{\sqrt{3}}{4}x^2 + \frac{100 - 60x + 9x^2}{4\pi}$$

b. Since the lengths must be positive, we have:
$10 - 3x > 0$ and $x > 0$
$-3x > -10$ and $x > 0$
$x < \frac{10}{3}$ and $x > 0$

Domain: $\left\{x \mid 0 < x < \frac{10}{3}\right\}$

c. The area is smallest when $x \approx 2.08$ meters.

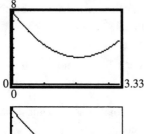

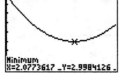

13. a. Since the wire of length x is bent into a circle, the circumference is x. Therefore, $C(x) = x$.

b. Since $C = x = 2\pi r$, $r = \frac{x}{2\pi}$.

$$A(x) = \pi r^2 = \pi\left(\frac{x}{2\pi}\right)^2 = \frac{x^2}{4\pi}.$$

14. a. Since the wire of length x is bent into a square, the perimeter is x. Therefore, $P(x) = x$.

b. Since $P = x = 4s$, $s = \frac{1}{4}x$, we have

$$A(x) = s^2 = \left(\frac{1}{4}x\right)^2 = \frac{1}{16}x^2.$$

15. a. A = area, r = radius; diameter = $2r$
$$A(r) = (2r)(r) = 2r^2$$

b. p = perimeter
$$p(r) = 2(2r) + 2r = 6r$$

16. C = circumference, r = radius;
x = length of a side of the triangle

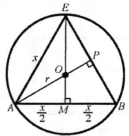

Since $\triangle ABC$ is equilateral, $EM = \frac{\sqrt{3}x}{2}$.

Therefore, $OM = \frac{\sqrt{3}x}{2} - OE = \frac{\sqrt{3}x}{2} - r$

In $\triangle OAM$, $r^2 = \left(\frac{x}{2}\right)^2 + \left(\frac{\sqrt{3}x}{2} - r\right)^2$

$$r^2 = \frac{x^2}{4} + \frac{3}{4}x^2 - \sqrt{3}rx + r^2$$

$$\sqrt{3}rx = x^2$$

$$r = \frac{x}{\sqrt{3}}$$

Therefore, the circumference of the circle is

$$C(x) = 2\pi r = 2\pi\left(\frac{x}{\sqrt{3}}\right) = \frac{2\pi\sqrt{3}}{3}x$$

17. Area of the equilateral triangle

$$A = \frac{1}{2}x \cdot \frac{\sqrt{3}}{2}x = \frac{\sqrt{3}}{4}x^2$$

From problem 16, we have $r^2 = \frac{x^2}{3}$.

Area inside the circle, but outside the triangle:

$$A(x) = \pi r^2 - \frac{\sqrt{3}}{4}x^2$$

$$= \pi \frac{x^2}{3} - \frac{\sqrt{3}}{4}x^2 = \left(\frac{\pi}{3} - \frac{\sqrt{3}}{4}\right)x^2$$

18. $d^2 = d_1^{\,2} + d_2^{\,2}$

$$d^2 = (30t)^2 + (40t)^2$$

$$d(t) = \sqrt{900t^2 + 1600t^2} = \sqrt{2500t^2} = 50t$$

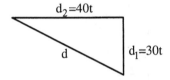

19. a. $d^2 = d_1^{\,2} + d_2^{\,2}$

$$d^2 = (2-30t)^2 + (3-40t)^2$$

$$d(t) = \sqrt{(2-30t)^2 + (3-40t)^2}$$

$$= \sqrt{4 - 120t + 900t^2 + 9 - 240t + 1600t^2}$$

$$= \sqrt{2500t^2 - 360t + 13}$$

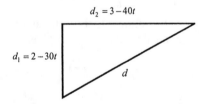

b. The distance is smallest at $t \approx 0.07$ hours.

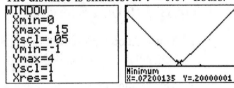

20. r = radius of cylinder, h = height of cylinder, V = volume of cylinder

$$r^2 + \left(\frac{h}{2}\right)^2 = R^2 \Rightarrow r^2 + \frac{h^2}{4} = R^2 \Rightarrow r^2 = R^2 - \frac{h^2}{4}$$

$$V = \pi r^2 h$$

$$V(h) = \pi\left(R^2 - \frac{h^2}{4}\right)h = \pi h\left(R^2 - \frac{h^2}{4}\right)$$

21. r = radius of cylinder, h = height of cylinder, V = volume of cylinder

By similar triangles: $\dfrac{H}{R} = \dfrac{H-h}{r}$

$$Hr = R(H-h)$$

$$Hr = RH - Rh$$

$$Rh = RH - Hr$$

$$h = \frac{RH - Hr}{R} = \frac{H(R-r)}{R}$$

$$V = \pi r^2 h = \pi r^2\left(\frac{H(R-r)}{R}\right) = \frac{\pi H(R-r)r^2}{R}$$

22. a. The total cost of installing the cable along the road is $500x$. If cable is installed x miles along the road, there are $5-x$ miles between the road to the house and where the cable ends along the road.

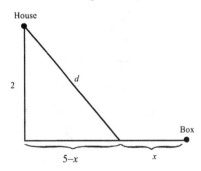

$$d = \sqrt{(5-x)^2 + 2^2}$$

$$= \sqrt{25 - 10x + x^2 + 4} = \sqrt{x^2 - 10x + 29}$$

The total cost of installing the cable is:

$$C(x) = 500x + 700\sqrt{x^2 - 10x + 29}$$

Domain: $\left\{x \mid 0 \le x \le 5\right\}$

295

b. $C(1) = 500(1) + 700\sqrt{1^2 - 10(1) + 29}$

$= 500 + 700\sqrt{20} = \$3630.50$

c. $C(3) = 500(3) + 700\sqrt{3^2 - 10(3) + 29}$

$= 1500 + 700\sqrt{8} = \$3479.90$

d.

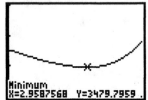

e. Using MINIMUM, the graph indicates that $x \approx 2.96$ miles results in the least cost.

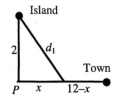

23. a. The time on the boat is given by $\dfrac{d_1}{3}$. The time on land is given by $\dfrac{12 - x}{5}$.

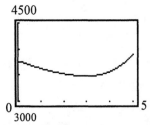

$d_1 = \sqrt{x^2 + 2^2} = \sqrt{x^2 + 4}$

The total time for the trip is:

$T(x) = \dfrac{12 - x}{5} + \dfrac{d_1}{3} = \dfrac{12 - x}{5} + \dfrac{\sqrt{x^2 + 4}}{3}$

b. Domain: $\{x \mid 0 \le x \le 12\}$

c. $T(4) = \dfrac{12 - 4}{5} + \dfrac{\sqrt{4^2 + 4}}{3}$

$= \dfrac{8}{5} + \dfrac{\sqrt{20}}{3} \approx 3.09$ hours

d. $T(8) = \dfrac{12 - 8}{5} + \dfrac{\sqrt{8^2 + 4}}{3}$

$= \dfrac{4}{5} + \dfrac{\sqrt{68}}{3} \approx 3.55$ hours

24. Consider the diagrams shown below.

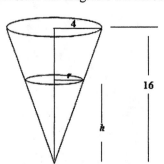

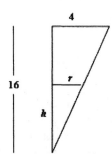

There is a pair of similar triangles in the diagram. Since the smaller triangle is similar to the larger triangle, we have the proportion

$\dfrac{r}{h} = \dfrac{4}{16} \Rightarrow \dfrac{r}{h} = \dfrac{1}{4} \Rightarrow r = \dfrac{1}{4}h$

Substituting into the volume formula for the conical portion of water gives

$V(h) = \dfrac{1}{3}\pi r^2 h = \dfrac{1}{3}\pi\left(\dfrac{1}{4}h\right)^2 h = \dfrac{1}{48}\pi h^3$.

Chapter 3 Review Exercises

1. This relation represents a function.
Domain = {−1, 2, 4}; Range = {0, 3}.

2. This relation does not represent a function, since 4 is paired with two different values.

3. $f(x) = \dfrac{3x}{x^2 - 1}$

a. $f(2) = \dfrac{3(2)}{(2)^2 - 1} = \dfrac{6}{4 - 1} = \dfrac{6}{3} = 2$

296

b. $f(-2) = \dfrac{3(-2)}{(-2)^2 - 1} = \dfrac{-6}{4-1} = \dfrac{-6}{3} = -2$

c. $f(-x) = \dfrac{3(-x)}{(-x)^2 - 1} = \dfrac{-3x}{x^2 - 1}$

d. $-f(x) = -\left(\dfrac{3x}{x^2 - 1}\right) = \dfrac{-3x}{x^2 - 1}$

e. $f(x-2) = \dfrac{3(x-2)}{(x-2)^2 - 1}$

$= \dfrac{3x-6}{x^2 - 4x + 4 - 1} = \dfrac{3(x-2)}{x^2 - 4x + 3}$

f. $f(2x) = \dfrac{3(2x)}{(2x)^2 - 1} = \dfrac{6x}{4x^2 - 1}$

4. $f(x) = \dfrac{x^2}{x+1}$

a. $f(2) = \dfrac{2^2}{2+1} = \dfrac{4}{3}$

b. $f(-2) = \dfrac{(-2)^2}{-2+1} = \dfrac{4}{-1} = -4$

c. $f(-x) = \dfrac{(-x)^2}{-x+1} = \dfrac{x^2}{-x+1}$

d. $-f(x) = -\dfrac{x^2}{x+1} = \dfrac{-x^2}{x+1}$

e. $f(x-2) = \dfrac{(x-2)^2}{(x-2)+1} = \dfrac{(x-2)^2}{x-1}$

f. $f(2x) = \dfrac{(2x)^2}{(2x)+1} = \dfrac{4x^2}{2x+1}$

5. $f(x) = \sqrt{x^2 - 4}$

a. $f(2) = \sqrt{2^2 - 4} = \sqrt{4-4} = \sqrt{0} = 0$

b. $f(-2) = \sqrt{(-2)^2 - 4} = \sqrt{4-4} = \sqrt{0} = 0$

c. $f(-x) = \sqrt{(-x)^2 - 4} = \sqrt{x^2 - 4}$

d. $-f(x) = -\sqrt{x^2 - 4}$

e. $f(x-2) = \sqrt{(x-2)^2 - 4}$

$= \sqrt{x^2 - 4x + 4 - 4}$

$= \sqrt{x^2 - 4x}$

f. $f(2x) = \sqrt{(2x)^2 - 4} = \sqrt{4x^2 - 4}$

$= \sqrt{4\left(x^2 - 1\right)} = 2\sqrt{x^2 - 1}$

6. $f(x) = \left| x^2 - 4 \right|$

a. $f(2) = \left| 2^2 - 4 \right| = \left| 4 - 4 \right| = \left| 0 \right| = 0$

b. $f(-2) = \left| (-2)^2 - 4 \right| = \left| 4 - 4 \right| = \left| 0 \right| = 0$

c. $f(-x) = \left| (-x)^2 - 4 \right| = \left| x^2 - 4 \right|$

d. $-f(x) = -\left| x^2 - 4 \right|$

e. $f(x-2) = \left| (x-2)^2 - 4 \right|$

$= \left| x^2 - 4x + 4 - 4 \right|$

$= \left| x^2 - 4x \right|$

f. $f(2x) = \left| (2x)^2 - 4 \right| = \left| 4x^2 - 4 \right|$

$= \left| 4\left(x^2 - 1\right) \right| = 4\left| x^2 - 1 \right|$

7. $f(x) = \dfrac{x^2 - 4}{x^2}$

a. $f(2) = \dfrac{2^2 - 4}{2^2} = \dfrac{4-4}{4} = \dfrac{0}{4} = 0$

b. $f(-2) = \dfrac{(-2)^2 - 4}{(-2)^2} = \dfrac{4-4}{4} = \dfrac{0}{4} = 0$

c. $f(-x) = \dfrac{(-x)^2 - 4}{(-x)^2} = \dfrac{x^2 - 4}{x^2}$

d. $-f(x) = -\left(\dfrac{x^2 - 4}{x^2}\right) = \dfrac{4 - x^2}{x^2} = -\dfrac{x^2 - 4}{x^2}$

e. $f(x-2) = \dfrac{(x-2)^2 - 4}{(x-2)^2} = \dfrac{x^2 - 4x + 4 - 4}{(x-2)^2}$

$= \dfrac{x^2 - 4x}{(x-2)^2} = \dfrac{x(x-4)}{(x-2)^2}$

f. $f(2x) = \dfrac{(2x)^2 - 4}{(2x)^2} = \dfrac{4x^2 - 4}{4x^2}$

$= \dfrac{4(x^2 - 1)}{4x^2} = \dfrac{x^2 - 1}{x^2}$

8. $f(x) = \dfrac{x^3}{x^2 - 9}$

a. $f(2) = \dfrac{2^3}{2^2 - 9} = \dfrac{8}{4 - 9} = \dfrac{8}{-5} = -\dfrac{8}{5}$

b. $f(2) = \dfrac{(-2)^3}{(-2)^2 - 9} = \dfrac{-8}{4 - 9} = \dfrac{-8}{-5} = \dfrac{8}{5}$

c. $f(-x) = \dfrac{(-x)^3}{(-x)^2 - 9} = \dfrac{-x^3}{x^2 - 9}$

d. $-f(x) = -\dfrac{x^3}{x^2 - 9} = \dfrac{-x^3}{x^2 - 9}$

e. $f(x - 2) = \dfrac{(x - 2)^3}{(x - 2)^2 - 9}$

$= \dfrac{(x - 2)^3}{x^2 - 4x + 4 - 9}$

$= \dfrac{(x - 2)^3}{x^2 - 4x - 5}$

f. $f(2x) = \dfrac{(2x)^3}{(2x)^2 - 9} = \dfrac{8x^3}{4x^2 - 9}$

9. $f(x) = \dfrac{x}{x^2 - 9}$

The denominator cannot be zero:

$x^2 - 9 \neq 0$

$(x + 3)(x - 3) \neq 0$

$x \neq -3$ or 3

Domain: $\{x \mid x \neq -3, x \neq 3\}$

10. $f(x) = \dfrac{3x^2}{x - 2}$

The denominator cannot be zero:

$x - 2 \neq 0$

$x \neq 2$

Domain: $\{x \mid x \neq 2\}$

11. $f(x) = \sqrt{2 - x}$

The radicand must be non-negative:

$2 - x \geq 0$

$x \leq 2$

Domain: $\{x \mid x \leq 2\}$ or $(-\infty, 2]$

12. $f(x) = \sqrt{x + 2}$

The radicand must be non-negative:

$x + 2 \geq 0$

$x \geq -2$

Domain: $\{x \mid x \geq -2\}$ or $[-2, \infty)$

13. $f(x) = \dfrac{\sqrt{x}}{|x|}$

The radicand must be non-negative and the denominator cannot be zero: $x > 0$

Domain: $\{x \mid x > 0\}$ or $(0, \infty)$

14. $g(x) = \dfrac{|x|}{x}$

The denominator cannot be zero:

$x \neq 0$

Domain: $\{x \mid x \neq 0\}$

15. $f(x) = \dfrac{x}{x^2 + 2x - 3}$

The denominator cannot be zero:

$x^2 + 2x - 3 \neq 0$

$(x + 3)(x - 1) \neq 0$

$x \neq -3$ or 1

Domain: $\{x \mid x \neq -3, x \neq 1\}$

16. $F(x) = \dfrac{1}{x^2 - 3x - 4}$

The denominator cannot be zero:

$x^2 - 3x - 4 \neq 0$

$(x + 1)(x - 4) \neq 0$

$x \neq -1$ or 4

Domain: $\{x \mid x \neq -1, x \neq 4\}$

17. $f(x) = 2 - x \quad g(x) = 3x + 1$

$(f + g)(x) = f(x) + g(x)$

$\qquad = 2 - x + 3x + 1 = 2x + 3$

Domain: $\{x \mid x \text{ is any real number}\}$

$(f - g)(x) = f(x) - g(x)$

$\qquad = 2 - x - (3x + 1)$

$\qquad = 2 - x - 3x - 1$

$\qquad = -4x + 1$

Domain: $\{x \mid x \text{ is any real number}\}$

$(f \cdot g)(x) = f(x) \cdot g(x)$

$\qquad = (2 - x)(3x + 1)$

$\qquad = 6x + 2 - 3x^2 - x$

$\qquad = -3x^2 + 5x + 2$

Domain: $\{x \mid x \text{ is any real number}\}$

$\left(\dfrac{f}{g}\right)(x) = \dfrac{f(x)}{g(x)} = \dfrac{2 - x}{3x + 1}$

$3x + 1 \neq 0$

$\qquad 3x \neq -1 \Rightarrow x \neq -\dfrac{1}{3}$

Domain: $\left\{x \mid x \neq -\dfrac{1}{3}\right\}$

18. $f(x) = 2x - 1 \quad g(x) = 2x + 1$

$(f + g)(x) = f(x) + g(x)$

$\qquad = 2x - 1 + 2x + 1$

$\qquad = 4x$

Domain: $\{x \mid x \text{ is any real number}\}$

$(f - g)(x) = f(x) - g(x)$

$\qquad = 2x - 1 - (2x + 1)$

$\qquad = 2x - 1 - 2x - 1$

$\qquad = -2$

Domain: $\{x \mid x \text{ is any real number}\}$

$(f \cdot g)(x) = f(x) \cdot g(x)$

$\qquad = (2x - 1)(2x + 1)$

$\qquad = 4x^2 - 1$

Domain: $\{x \mid x \text{ is any real number}\}$

$\left(\dfrac{f}{g}\right)(x) = \dfrac{f(x)}{g(x)} = \dfrac{2x - 1}{2x + 1}$

$2x + 1 \neq 0 \Rightarrow 2x \neq -1 \Rightarrow x \neq -\dfrac{1}{2}$

Domain: $\left\{x \mid x \neq -\dfrac{1}{2}\right\}$

19. $f(x) = 3x^2 + x + 1 \qquad g(x) = 3x$

$(f + g)(x) = f(x) + g(x)$

$\qquad = 3x^2 + x + 1 + 3x$

$\qquad = 3x^2 + 4x + 1$

Domain: $\{x \mid x \text{ is any real number}\}$

$(f - g)(x) = f(x) - g(x)$

$\qquad = 3x^2 + x + 1 - 3x$

$\qquad = 3x^2 - 2x + 1$

Domain: $\{x \mid x \text{ is any real number}\}$

$(f \cdot g)(x) = f(x) \cdot g(x)$

$\qquad = (3x^2 + x + 1)(3x)$

$\qquad = 9x^3 + 3x^2 + 3x$

Domain: $\{x \mid x \text{ is any real number}\}$

$\left(\dfrac{f}{g}\right)(x) = \dfrac{f(x)}{g(x)} = \dfrac{3x^2 + x + 1}{3x}$

$3x \neq 0 \Rightarrow x \neq 0$

Domain: $\{x \mid x \neq 0\}$

299

20. $f(x) = 3x \qquad g(x) = 1 + x + x^2$

$(f + g)(x) = f(x) + g(x)$

$\qquad = 3x + 1 + x + x^2$

$\qquad = x^2 + 4x + 1$

Domain: $\{x \mid x \text{ is any real number}\}$

$(f - g)(x) = f(x) - g(x)$

$\qquad = 3x - \left(1 + x + x^2\right)$

$\qquad = -x^2 + 2x - 1$

Domain: $\{x \mid x \text{ is any real number}\}$

$(f \cdot g)(x) = f(x) \cdot g(x)$

$\qquad = (3x)\left(1 + x + x^2\right)$

$\qquad = 3x + 3x^2 + 3x^3$

Domain: $\{x \mid x \text{ is any real number}\}$

$\left(\dfrac{f}{g}\right)(x) = \dfrac{f(x)}{g(x)} = \dfrac{3x}{1 + x + x^2}$

$1 + x + x^2 \neq 0$

$x^2 + x + 1 \neq 0$

Since the discriminant is $1^2 - 4(1)(1) = -3 < 0$,

$x^2 + x + 1$ will never equal 0.

Domain: $\{x \mid x \text{ is any real number}\}$

21. $f(x) = \dfrac{x+1}{x-1} \qquad g(x) = \dfrac{1}{x}$

$(f + g)(x) = f(x) + g(x)$

$\qquad = \dfrac{x+1}{x-1} + \dfrac{1}{x} = \dfrac{x(x+1) + 1(x-1)}{x(x-1)}$

$\qquad = \dfrac{x^2 + x + x - 1}{x(x-1)} = \dfrac{x^2 + 2x - 1}{x(x-1)}$

Domain: $\{x \mid x \neq 0, x \neq 1\}$

$(f - g)(x) = f(x) - g(x)$

$\qquad = \dfrac{x+1}{x-1} - \dfrac{1}{x} = \dfrac{x(x+1) - 1(x-1)}{x(x-1)}$

$\qquad = \dfrac{x^2 + x - x + 1}{x(x-1)} = \dfrac{x^2 + 1}{x(x-1)}$

Domain: $\{x \mid x \neq 0, x \neq 1\}$

$(f \cdot g)(x) = f(x) \cdot g(x) = \left(\dfrac{x+1}{x-1}\right)\left(\dfrac{1}{x}\right) = \dfrac{x+1}{x(x-1)}$

Domain: $\{x \mid x \neq 0, x \neq 1\}$

$\left(\dfrac{f}{g}\right)(x) = \dfrac{f(x)}{g(x)} = \dfrac{\dfrac{x+1}{x-1}}{\dfrac{1}{x}} = \left(\dfrac{x+1}{x-1}\right)\left(\dfrac{x}{1}\right) = \dfrac{x(x+1)}{x-1}$

Domain: $\{x \mid x \neq 0, x \neq 1\}$

22. $f(x) = \dfrac{1}{x-3} \qquad g(x) = \dfrac{3}{x}$

$(f + g)(x) = f(x) + g(x)$

$\qquad = \dfrac{1}{x-3} + \dfrac{3}{x} = \dfrac{x + 3(x-3)}{x(x-3)}$

$\qquad = \dfrac{x + 3x - 9}{x(x-3)} = \dfrac{4x - 9}{x(x-3)}$

Domain: $\{x \mid x \neq 0, x \neq 3\}$

$(f - g)(x) = f(x) - g(x) = \dfrac{1}{x-3} - \dfrac{3}{x}$

$\qquad = \dfrac{x - 3(x-3)}{x(x-3)} = \dfrac{x - 3x + 9}{x(x-3)}$

$\qquad = \dfrac{-2x + 9}{x(x-3)}$

Domain: $\{x \mid x \neq 0, x \neq 3\}$

$(f \cdot g)(x) = f(x) \cdot g(x) = \left(\dfrac{1}{x-3}\right)\left(\dfrac{3}{x}\right) = \dfrac{3}{x(x-3)}$

Domain: $\{x \mid x \neq 0, x \neq 3\}$

$\left(\dfrac{f}{g}\right)(x) = \dfrac{f(x)}{g(x)} = \dfrac{\dfrac{1}{x-3}}{\dfrac{3}{x}}$

$\qquad = \left(\dfrac{1}{x-3}\right)\left(\dfrac{x}{3}\right)$

$\qquad = \dfrac{x}{3(x-3)}$

Domain: $\{x \mid x \neq 0, x \neq 3\}$

23. $f(x) = -2x^2 + x + 1$

$$\frac{f(x+h) - f(x)}{h}$$

$$= \frac{-2(x+h)^2 + (x+h) + 1 - (-2x^2 + x + 1)}{h}$$

$$= \frac{-2(x^2 + 2xh + h^2) + x + h + 1 + 2x^2 - x - 1}{h}$$

$$= \frac{-2x^2 - 4xh - 2h^2 + x + h + 1 + 2x^2 - x - 1}{h}$$

$$= \frac{-4xh - 2h^2 + h}{h} = \frac{h(-4x - 2h + 1)}{h}$$

$$= -4x - 2h + 1$$

24. $f(x) = 3x^2 - 2x + 4$

$$\frac{f(x+h) - f(x)}{h}$$

$$= \frac{3(x+h)^2 - 2(x+h) + 4 - (3x^2 - 2x + 4)}{h}$$

$$= \frac{3(x^2 + 2xh + h^2) - 2x - 2h + 4 - 3x^2 + 2x - 4}{h}$$

$$= \frac{3x^2 + 6xh + 3h^2 - 2x - 2h + 4 - 3x^2 + 2x - 4}{h}$$

$$= \frac{6xh + 3h^2 - 2h}{h} = \frac{h(6x + 3h - 2)}{h}$$

$$= 6x + 3h - 2$$

25. a. Domain: $\{x \mid -4 \le x \le 3\}$; $[-4, 3]$

Range: $\{y \mid -3 \le y \le 3\}$; $[-3, 3]$

b. x-intercept: $(0, 0)$; y-intercept: $(0, 0)$

c. $f(-2) = -1$

d. $f(x) = -3$ when $x = -4$

e. $f(x) > 0$ when $0 < x \le 3$

f. To graph $y = f(x - 3)$, shift the graph of f horizontally 3 units to the right.

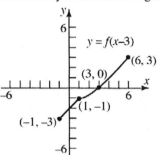

g. To graph $y = f\left(\frac{1}{2}x\right)$, stretch the graph of f horizontally by a factor of 2.

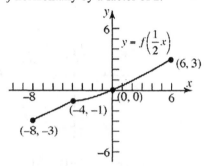

h. To graph $y = -f(x)$, reflect the graph of f vertically about the y-axis.

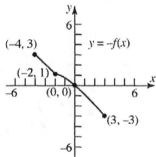

26. a. Domain: $\{x \mid -5 \le x \le 4\}$; $[-5, 4]$

Range: $\{y \mid -3 \le y \le 1\}$; $[-3, 1]$

b. $g(-1) = 1$

c. x-intercepts: $0, 4$; y-intercept: 0

d. $g(x) = -3$ when $x = 3$

e. $g(x) > 0$ when $-5 \le x < 0$

f. To graph $y = g(x-2)$, shift the graph of g horizontally 2 units to the right.

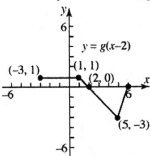

g. To graph $y = g(x)+1$, shift the graph of g vertically up 1 unit.

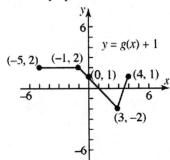

h. To graph $y = 2g(x)$, stretch the graph of g vertically by a factor of 2.

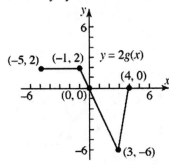

27. a. Domain: $\{x \mid -4 \le x \le 4\}$; $[-4, 4]$
Range: $\{y \mid -3 \le y \le 1\}$; $[-3, 1]$

b. Increasing: $(-4, -1)$ and $(3, 4)$;
Decreasing: $(-1, 3)$

c. Local minimum is -3 when $x = 3$;
Local maximum is 1 when $x = -1$.
Note that $x = 4$ and $x = -4$ do not yield local extrema because there is no open interval that contains either value.

d. The graph is not symmetric with respect to the x-axis, the y-axis or the origin.

e. The function is neither even nor odd.

f. x-intercepts: $-2, 0, 4$,
y-intercept: 0

28. a. Domain: $\{x \mid x \text{ is any real number}\}$
Range: $\{y \mid y \text{ is any real number}\}$

b. Increasing: $(-\infty, -2)$ and $(2, \infty)$;
Decreasing: $(-2, 2)$

c. Local minimum is -1 at $x = 2$;
Local maximum is 1 at $x = -2$

d. The graph is symmetric with respect to the origin.

e. The function is odd.

f. x-intercepts: $-3, 0, 3$;
y-intercept: 0

29. $f(x) = x^3 - 4x$
$f(-x) = (-x)^3 - 4(-x) = -x^3 + 4x$
$\qquad = -\left(x^3 - 4x\right) = -f(x)$
f is odd.

30. $g(x) = \dfrac{4 + x^2}{1 + x^4}$
$g(-x) = \dfrac{4 + (-x)^2}{1 + (-x)^4} = \dfrac{4 + x^2}{1 + x^4} = g(x)$
g is even.

31. $h(x) = \dfrac{1}{x^4} + \dfrac{1}{x^2} + 1$
$h(-x) = \dfrac{1}{(-x)^4} + \dfrac{1}{(-x)^2} + 1 = \dfrac{1}{x^4} + \dfrac{1}{x^2} + 1 = h(x)$
h is even.

32. $F(x) = \sqrt{1 - x^3}$
$F(-x) = \sqrt{1 - (-x)^3} = \sqrt{1 + x^3} \ne F(x)$ or $-F(x)$
F is neither even nor odd.

33. $G(x) = 1 - x + x^3$

$$G(-x) = 1 - (-x) + (-x)^3$$
$$= 1 + x - x^3 \neq -G(x) \text{ or } G(x)$$

G is neither even nor odd.

34. $H(x) = 1 + x + x^2$

$$H(-x) = 1 + (-x) + (-x)^2$$
$$= 1 - x + x^2 \neq -H(x) \text{ or } H(x)$$

H is neither even nor odd.

35. $f(x) = \dfrac{x}{1 + x^2}$

$$f(-x) = \frac{-x}{1 + (-x)^2} = \frac{-x}{1 + x^2} = -f(x)$$

f is odd.

36. $g(x) = \dfrac{1 + x^2}{x^3}$

$$g(-x) = \frac{1 + (-x)^2}{(-x)^3} = \frac{1 + x^2}{-x^3} = -\frac{1 + x^2}{x^3} = -g(x)$$

g is odd.

37. $f(x) = 2x^3 - 5x + 1$ on the interval $(-3, 3)$

Use MAXIMUM and MINIMUM on the graph of $y_1 = 2x^3 - 5x + 1$.

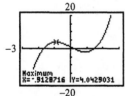 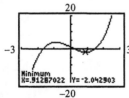

local maximum at: $(-0.91, 4.04)$;

local minimum at: $(0.91, -2.04)$;

f is increasing on: $(-3, -0.91)$ and $(0.91, 3)$;

f is decreasing on: $(-0.91, 0.91)$.

38. $f(x) = -x^3 + 3x - 5$ on the interval $(-3, 3)$

Use MAXIMUM and MINIMUM on the graph of $y_1 = -x^3 + 3x - 5$.

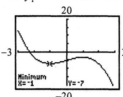 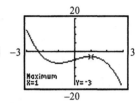

local maximum at: $(1, -3)$;

local minimum at: $(-1, -7)$;

f is increasing on: $(-1, 1)$;

f is decreasing on: $(-3, -1)$ and $(1, 3)$.

39. $f(x) = 2x^4 - 5x^3 + 2x + 1$ on the interval $(-2, 3)$

Use MAXIMUM and MINIMUM on the graph of $y_1 = 2x^4 - 5x^3 + 2x + 1$.

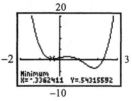 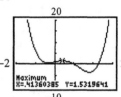

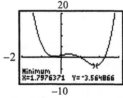

local maximum at: $(0.41, 1.53)$;

local minima at: $(-0.34, 0.54)$ and $(1.80, -3.56)$;

f is increasing on: $(-0.34, 0.41)$ and $(1.80, 3)$;

f is decreasing on: $(-2, -0.34)$ and $(0.41, 1.80)$.

40. $f(x) = -x^4 + 3x^3 - 4x + 3$ on the interval $(-2, 3)$
Use MAXIMUM and MINIMUM on the graph
of $y_1 = -x^4 + 3x^3 - 4x + 3$.

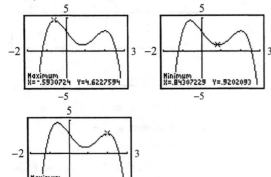

local maxima at: $(-0.59, 4.62)$ and $(2, 3)$;
local minimum at: $(0.84, 0.92)$;
f is increasing on: $(-2, -0.59)$ and $(0.84, 2)$;
f is decreasing on: $(-0.59, 0.84)$ and $(2, 3)$.

41. $f(x) = 8x^2 - x$

a. $\dfrac{f(2) - f(1)}{2 - 1} = \dfrac{8(2)^2 - 2 - [8(1)^2 - 1]}{1}$
$= 32 - 2 - (7) = 23$

b. $\dfrac{f(1) - f(0)}{1 - 0} = \dfrac{8(1)^2 - 1 - [8(0)^2 - 0]}{1}$
$= 8 - 1 - (0) = 7$

c. $\dfrac{f(4) - f(2)}{4 - 2} = \dfrac{8(4)^2 - 4 - [8(2)^2 - 2]}{2}$
$= \dfrac{128 - 4 - (30)}{2} = \dfrac{94}{2} = 47$

42. $f(x) = 2x^3 + x$

a. $\dfrac{f(2) - f(1)}{2 - 1} = \dfrac{2(2)^3 + 2 - \left(2(1)^3 + 1\right)}{1}$
$= 16 + 2 - (3) = 15$

b. $\dfrac{f(1) - f(0)}{1 - 0} = \dfrac{2(1)^3 + 1 - \left(2(0)^3 + 0\right)}{1}$
$= 2 + 1 - (0) = 3$

c. $\dfrac{f(4) - f(2)}{4 - 2} = \dfrac{2(4)^3 + 4 - (2(2)^3 + 2)}{2}$
$= \dfrac{128 + 4 - (18)}{2} = \dfrac{114}{2} = 57$

43. $f(x) = 2 - 5x$
$\dfrac{f(3) - f(2)}{3 - 2} = \dfrac{[2 - 5(3)] - [2 - 5(2)]}{3 - 2}$
$= \dfrac{(2 - 15) - (2 - 10)}{1}$
$= -13 - (-8) = -5$

44. $f(x) = 2x^2 + 7$
$\dfrac{f(3) - f(2)}{3 - 2} = \dfrac{\left[2(3)^2 + 7\right] - \left[2(2)^2 + 7\right]}{3 - 2}$
$= \dfrac{(18 + 7) - (8 + 7)}{1}$
$= 25 - 15 = 10$

45. $f(x) = 3x - 4x^2$
$\dfrac{f(3) - f(2)}{3 - 2} = \dfrac{\left[3(3) - 4(3)^2\right] - \left[3(2) - 4(2)^2\right]}{3 - 2}$
$= \dfrac{(9 - 36) - (6 - 16)}{1}$
$= -27 + 10 = -17$

46. $f(x) = x^2 - 3x + 2$
$\dfrac{f(3) - f(2)}{3 - 2} = \dfrac{\left[(3)^2 - 3(3) + 2\right] - \left[(2)^2 - 3(2) + 2\right]}{3 - 2}$
$= \dfrac{(9 - 9 + 2) - (4 - 6 + 2)}{1}$
$= 2 - 0 = 2$

47. The graph does not pass the Vertical Line Test and is therefore not a function.

48. The graph passes the Vertical Line Test and is therefore a function.

49. The graph passes the Vertical Line Test and is therefore a function.

50. The graph passes the Vertical Line Test and is therefore a function.

51. $f(x) = |x|$

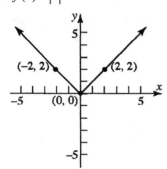

52. $f(x) = \sqrt[3]{x}$

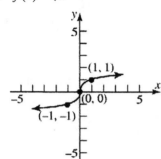

53. $f(x) = \sqrt{x}$

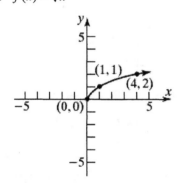

54. $f(x) = \dfrac{1}{x}$

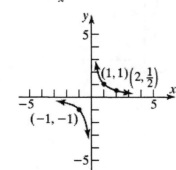

55. $F(x) = |x| - 4$. Using the graph of $y = |x|$, vertically shift the graph downward 4 units.

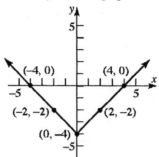

Intercepts: $(-4, 0)$, $(4, 0)$, $(0, -4)$

Domain: $\{x \mid x \text{ is any real number}\}$

Range: $\{y \mid y \geq -4\}$ or $[-4, \infty)$

56. $f(x) = |x| + 4$. Using the graph of $y = |x|$, vertically shift the graph upward 4 units.

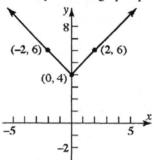

Intercepts: $(0, 4)$

Domain: $\{x \mid x \text{ is any real number}\}$

Range: $\{y \mid y \geq 4\}$ or $[4, \infty)$

57. $g(x) = -2|x|$. Reflect the graph of $y = |x|$ about the x-axis and vertically stretch the graph by a factor of 2.

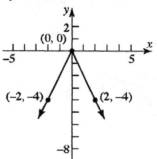

Intercepts: $(0, 0)$

Domain: $\{x \mid x \text{ is any real number}\}$

Range: $\{y \mid y \leq 0\}$ or $(-\infty, 0]$

58. $g(x) = \frac{1}{2}|x|$. Using the graph of $y = |x|$, vertically shrink the graph by a factor of $\frac{1}{2}$.

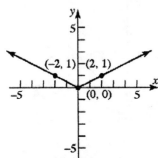

Intercepts: $(0, 0)$

Domain: $\{x \mid x \text{ is any real number}\}$

Range: $\{y \mid y \geq 0\}$ or $[0, \infty)$

59. $h(x) = \sqrt{x-1}$. Using the graph of $y = \sqrt{x}$, horizontally shift the graph to the right 1 unit.

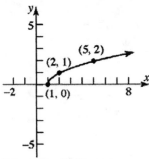

Intercept: $(1, 0)$

Domain: $\{x \mid x \geq 1\}$ or $[1, \infty)$

Range: $\{y \mid y \geq 0\}$ or $[0, \infty)$

60. $h(x) = \sqrt{x} - 1$. Using the graph of $y = \sqrt{x}$, vertically shift the graph downward 1 unit.

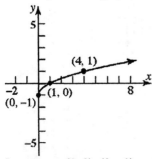

Intercepts: $(1, 0), (0, -1)$

Domain: $\{x \mid x \geq 0\}$ or $[0, \infty)$

Range: $\{y \mid y \geq -1\}$ or $[-1, \infty)$

61. $f(x) = \sqrt{1-x} = \sqrt{-(x-1)}$. Reflect the graph of $y = \sqrt{x}$ about the y-axis and horizontally shift the graph to the right 1 unit.

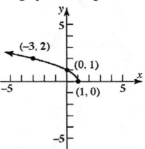

Intercepts: $(1, 0), (0, 1)$

Domain: $\{x \mid x \leq 1\}$ or $(-\infty, 1]$

Range: $\{y \mid y \geq 0\}$ or $[0, \infty)$

62. $f(x) = -\sqrt{x+3}$. Using the graph of $y = \sqrt{x}$, horizontally shift the graph to the left 3 units, and reflect on the x-axis.

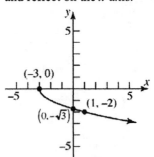

Intercepts: $(-3, 0), \left(0, -\sqrt{3}\right)$

Domain: $\{x \mid x \geq -3\}$ or $[-3, \infty)$

Range: $\{y \mid y \leq 0\}$ or $(-\infty, 0]$

63. $h(x) = (x-1)^2 + 2$. Using the graph of $y = x^2$, horizontally shift the graph to the right 1 unit and vertically shift the graph up 2 units.

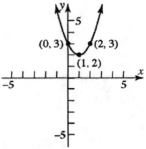

Intercepts: $(0, 3)$

Domain: $\{x \mid x \text{ is any real number}\}$

Range: $\{y \mid y \geq 2\}$ or $[2, \infty)$

64. $h(x) = (x+2)^2 - 3$. Using the graph of $y = x^2$, horizontally shift the graph to the left 2 units and vertically shift the graph down 3 units.

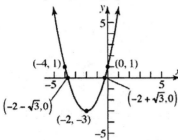

Intercepts: $(0, 1)$, $\left(-2+\sqrt{3}, 0\right)$, $\left(-2-\sqrt{3}, 0\right)$

Domain: $\{x \mid x \text{ is any real number}\}$

Range: $\{y \mid y \geq -3\}$ or $[-3, \infty)$

65. $g(x) = 3(x-1)^3 + 1$. Using the graph of $y = x^3$, horizontally shift the graph to the right 1 unit vertically stretch the graph by a factor of 3, and vertically shift the graph up 1 unit.

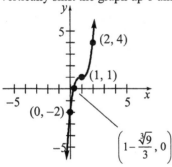

Intercepts: $(0, -2)$, $\left(1 - \dfrac{\sqrt[3]{9}}{3}, 0\right) \approx (0.3, 0)$

Domain: $\{x \mid x \text{ is any real number}\}$

Range: $\{y \mid y \text{ is any real number}\}$

66. $g(x) = -2(x+2)^3 - 8$

Using the graph of $y = x^3$, horizontally shift the graph to the left 2 units, vertically stretch the graph by a factor of 2, reflect about the x-axis, and vertically shift the graph down 8 units.

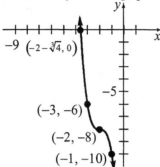

Intercepts: $(0, -24)$, $\left(-2 - \sqrt[3]{4}, 0\right) \approx (-3.6, 0)$

Domain: $\{x \mid x \text{ is any real number}\}$

Range: $\{y \mid y \text{ is any real number}\}$

67. $f(x) = \begin{cases} 3x & \text{if } -2 < x \leq 1 \\ x+1 & \text{if } x > 1 \end{cases}$

a. Domain: $\{x \mid x > -2\}$ or $(-2, \infty)$

b. x-intercept: $(0, 0)$

   y-intercept: $(0, 0)$

c. Graph:

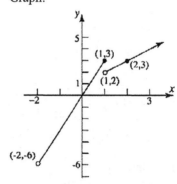

d. Range: $\{y \mid y > -6\}$ or $(-6, \infty)$

68. $f(x) = \begin{cases} x-1 & \text{if } -3 < x < 0 \\ 3x-1 & \text{if } x \geq 0 \end{cases}$

a. Domain: $\{x \mid x > -3\}$ or $(-3, \infty)$

b. x-intercept: $\left(\dfrac{1}{3}, 0\right)$

   y-intercept: $(0, -1)$

c. Graph:

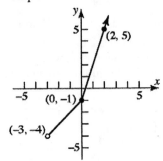

d. Range: $\{y > -4\}$ or $(-4, \infty)$

69. $f(x) = \begin{cases} x & \text{if } -4 \leq x < 0 \\ 1 & \text{if } x = 0 \\ 3x & \text{if } x > 0 \end{cases}$

a. Domain: $\{x \mid x \geq -4\}$ or $[-4, \infty)$

b. x-intercept: none
y-intercept: $(0, 1)$

c. Graph:

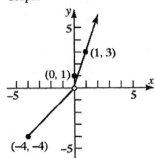

d. Range: $\{y \mid y \geq -4, y \neq 0\}$

70. $f(x) = \begin{cases} x^2 & \text{if } -2 \leq x \leq 2 \\ 2x - 1 & \text{if } x > 2 \end{cases}$

a. Domain: $\{x \mid x \geq -2\}$ or $[-2, \infty)$

b. x-intercept: $(0, 0)$
y-intercept: $(0, 0)$

c. Graph:

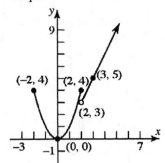

d. Range: $\{y \mid y \geq 0\}$ or $[0, \infty)$

71. $f(x) = \dfrac{Ax + 5}{6x - 2}$ and $f(1) = 4$

$\dfrac{A(1) + 5}{6(1) - 2} = 4$

$\dfrac{A + 5}{4} = 4$

$A + 5 = 16$

$A = 11$

72. $g(x) = \dfrac{A}{x} + \dfrac{8}{x^2}$ and $g(-1) = 0$

$\dfrac{A}{-1} + \dfrac{8}{(-1)^2} = 0$

$-A + 8 = 0$

$A = 8$

73. $S = 4\pi r^2$; $V = \dfrac{4}{3}\pi r^3$

Let $R = 2r$, S_2 = new surface area, and V_2 = new volume.

$S_2 = 4\pi R^2$

$\quad = 4\pi (2r)^2 = 4\pi \left(4r^2\right) = 4\left(4\pi r^2\right) = 4S$

$V_2 = \dfrac{4}{3}\pi R^3$

$\quad = \dfrac{4}{3}\pi (2r)^3 = \dfrac{4}{3}\pi \left(8r^3\right) = 8\left(\dfrac{4}{3}\pi r^3\right) = 8V$

Thus, if the radius of the sphere doubles, the surface area is 4 times as large and the volume is 8 times as large as for the original sphere.

74. **a.** The printed region is a rectangle. Its area is given by
$A = (\text{length})(\text{width}) = (11-2x)(8.5-2x)$
$A(x) = (11-2x)(8.5-2x)$

b. For the domain of $A(x) = (11-2x)(8.5-2x)$ recall that the dimensions of a rectangle must be non-negative.
$x \geq 0$ and $11-2x > 0$ and $8.5-2x > 0$
$\qquad\qquad -2x > -11 \qquad -2x > 8.5$
$\qquad\qquad x < 5.5 \qquad\qquad x < 4.25$
The domain is given by $0 \leq x < 4.25$.
The range of $A(x) = (11-2x)(8.5-2x)$ is given by $A(4.25) < A \leq A(0) \Rightarrow$
$0 < A \leq 93.5$.

c. $A(1) = (11-2(1))(8.5-2(1))$
$\qquad = 9 \cdot 6.5 = 58.5$ in^2
$A(1.2) = (11-2(1.2))(8.5-2(1.2))$
$\qquad = 8.6 \cdot 6.1 = 52.46$ in^2
$A(1.5) = (11-2(1.5))(8.5-2(1.5))$
$\qquad = 8 \cdot 5.5 = 44$ in^2

d. $y_1 = (11-2x)(8.5-2x)$

e. Using TRACE,
$A \approx 70$ when $x \approx 0.643$ inches
$\qquad A = 50$ when $x \approx 1.28$ inches

75. **a.** We are given that the volume is 100 cubic feet, so we have
$V = \pi r^2 h = 100 \Rightarrow h = \dfrac{100}{\pi r^2}$
The amount of material needed to construct the drum is the surface area of the barrel. The cylindrical body of the barrel can be viewed as a rectangle whose dimensions are given by

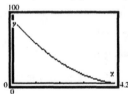

$A = \text{area}_{\text{top}} + \text{area}_{\text{bottom}} + \text{area}_{\text{body}}$
$\qquad = \pi r^2 + \pi r^2 + 2\pi rh = 2\pi r^2 + 2\pi rh$
$A(r) = 2\pi r^2 + 2\pi r\left(\dfrac{100}{\pi r^2}\right) = 2\pi r^2 + \dfrac{200}{r}$

b. $A(3) = 2\pi(3)^2 + \dfrac{200}{3}$
$\qquad = 18\pi + \dfrac{200}{3} \approx 123.22$ ft^2

c. $A(4) = 2\pi(4)^2 + \dfrac{200}{4}$
$\qquad = 32\pi + 50 \approx 150.53$ ft^2

d. $A(5) = 2\pi(5)^2 + \dfrac{200}{5}$
$\qquad = 50\pi + 40 \approx 197.08$ ft^2

e. Graphing:

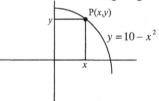

The surface area is smallest when $r \approx 2.52$ feet.

76. **a.** Consider the following diagram:

The area of the rectangle is $A = xy$. Thus, the area function for the rectangle is:
$A(x) = x(10-x^2) = -x^3 + 10x$

b. The maximum value occurs at the vertex:

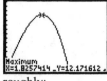

The maximum area is roughly:
$A(1.83) = -(1.83)^3 + 10(1.83)$
$\qquad \approx 12.17$ square units

309

Chapter 3 Test

1. a. $\{(2,5),(4,6),(6,7),(8,8)\}$

This relation is a function because there are no ordered pairs that have the same first element and different second elements.

Domain: $\{2,4,6,8\}$

Range: $\{5,6,7,8\}$

b. $\{(1,3),(4,-2),(-3,5),(1,7)\}$

This relation is not a function because there are two ordered pairs that have the same first element but different second elements.

c. This relation is not a function because the graph fails the vertical line test.

d. This relation is a function because it passes the vertical line test.

Domain: $\{x \mid x \text{ is any real number}\}$

Range: $\{y \mid y \geq 2\}$ or $[2, \infty)$

2. $f(x) = \sqrt{4 - 5x}$

The function tells us to take the square root of $4 - 5x$. Only nonnegative numbers have real square roots so we need $4 - 5x \geq 0$.

$$4 - 5x \geq 0$$
$$4 - 5x - 4 \geq 0 - 4$$
$$-5x \geq -4$$
$$\frac{-5x}{-5} \leq \frac{-4}{-5}$$
$$x \leq \frac{4}{5}$$

Domain: $\left\{x \mid x \leq \frac{4}{5}\right\}$ or $\left(-\infty, \frac{4}{5}\right]$

$$f(-1) = \sqrt{4 - 5(-1)} = \sqrt{4 + 5} = \sqrt{9} = 3$$

3. $g(x) = \dfrac{x + 2}{|x + 2|}$

The function tells us to divide $x + 2$ by $|x + 2|$. Division by 0 is undefined, so the denominator can never equal 0. This means that $x \neq -2$.

Domain: $\{x \mid x \neq -2\}$

$$g(-1) = \frac{(-1) + 2}{|(-1) + 2|} = \frac{1}{|1|} = 1$$

4. $h(x) = \dfrac{x - 4}{x^2 + 5x - 36}$

The function tells us to divide $x - 4$ by $x^2 + 5x - 36$. Since division by 0 is not defined, we need to exclude any values which make the denominator 0.

$$x^2 + 5x - 36 = 0$$
$$(x + 9)(x - 4) = 0$$
$$x = -9 \text{ or } x = 4$$

Domain: $\{x \mid x \neq -9, x \neq 4\}$

(note: there is a common factor of $x - 4$ but we must determine the domain prior to simplifying)

$$h(-1) = \frac{(-1) - 4}{(-1)^2 + 5(-1) - 36} = \frac{-5}{-40} = \frac{1}{8}$$

5. a. To find the domain, note that all the points on the graph will have an x-coordinate between -5 and 5, inclusive. To find the range, note that all the points on the graph will have a y-coordinate between -3 and 3, inclusive.

Domain: $\{x \mid -5 \leq x \leq 5\}$ or $[-5, 5]$

Range: $\{y \mid -3 \leq y \leq 3\}$ or $[-3, 3]$

b. The intercepts are $(0,2)$, $(-2,0)$, and $(2,0)$.

x-intercepts: $-2, 2$

y-intercept: 2

c. $f(1)$ is the value of the function when $x = 1$. According to the graph, $f(1) = 3$.

d. Since $(-5,-3)$ and $(3,-3)$ are the only points on the graph for which $y = f(x) = -3$, we have $f(x) = -3$ when $x = -5$ and $x = 3$.

e. To solve $f(x) < 0$, we want to find x-values such that the graph is below the x-axis. The graph is below the x-axis for values in the domain that are less than -2 and greater than 2. Therefore, the solution set is $\{x \mid -5 \leq x < -2 \text{ or } 2 < x \leq 5\}$. In interval notation we would write the solution set as $[-5, -2) \cup (2, 5]$.

6. $f(x) = -x^4 + 2x^3 + 4x^2 - 2$

We set Xmin = −5 and Xmax = 5. The standard Ymin and Ymax will not be good enough to see the whole picture so some adjustment must be made.

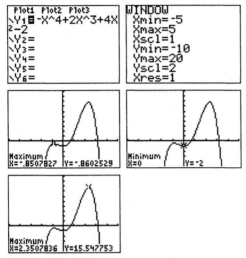

We see that the graph has a local maximum of −0.86 (rounded to two places) when $x = -0.85$ and another local maximum of 15.55 when $x = 2.35$. There is a local minimum of −2 when $x = 0$. Thus, we have

Local maxima: $f(-0.85) \approx -0.86$

$$f(2.35) \approx 15.55$$

Local minima: $f(0) = -2$

The function is increasing on the intervals $(-5, -0.85)$ and $(0, 2.35)$ and decreasing on the intervals $(-0.85, 0)$ and $(2.35, 5)$.

7. a. $f(x) = \begin{cases} 2x+1 & x < -1 \\ x-4 & x \geq -1 \end{cases}$

To graph the function, we graph each "piece". First we graph the line $y = 2x + 1$ but only keep the part for which $x < -1$. Then we plot the line $y = x - 4$ but only keep the part for which $x \geq -1$.

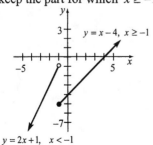

$y = 2x + 1, \quad x < -1$

b. To find the intercepts, notice that the only piece that hits either axis is $y = x - 4$.

$y = x - 4$	$y = x - 4$
$y = 0 - 4$	$0 = x - 4$
$y = -4$	$4 = x$

The intercepts are $(0, -4)$ and $(4, 0)$.

c. To find $g(-5)$ we first note that $x = -5$ so we must use the first "piece" because $-5 < -1$.
$$g(-5) = 2(-5) + 1 = -10 + 1 = -9$$

d. To find $g(2)$ we first note that $x = 2$ so we must use the second "piece" because $2 \geq -1$.
$$g(2) = 2 - 4 = -2$$

8. The average rate of change from 3 to 4 is given by

$$\frac{\Delta y}{\Delta x} = \frac{f(4) - f(3)}{4 - 3}$$

$$= \frac{\left(3(4)^2 - 2(4) + 4\right) - \left(3(3)^2 - 2(3) + 4\right)}{4 - 3}$$

$$= \frac{44 - 25}{4 - 3} = \frac{19}{1} = 19$$

9. a. $f - g = \left(2x^2 + 1\right) - \left(3x - 2\right)$

$$= 2x^2 + 1 - 3x + 2 = 2x^2 - 3x + 3$$

b. $f \cdot g = \left(2x^2 + 1\right)\left(3x - 2\right) = 6x^3 - 4x^2 + 3x - 2$

c. $f(x + h) - f(x)$

$$= \left(2(x + h)^2 + 1\right) - \left(2x^2 + 1\right)$$

$$= \left(2\left(x^2 + 2xh + h^2\right) + 1\right) - \left(2x^2 + 1\right)$$

$$= 2x^2 + 4xh + 2h^2 + 1 - 2x^2 - 1$$

$$= 4xh + 2h^2$$

10. a. The basic function is $y = x^3$ so we start with the graph of this function.

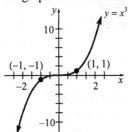

Next we shift this graph 1 unit to the left to obtain the graph of $y = (x+1)^3$.

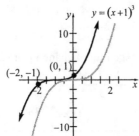

Next we reflect this graph about the x-axis to obtain the graph of $y = -(x+1)^3$.

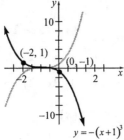

Next we stretch this graph vertically by a factor of 2 to obtain the graph of $y = -2(x+1)^3$.

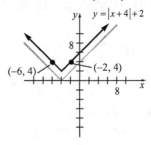

The last step is to shift this graph up 3 units to obtain the graph of $y = -2(x+1)^3 + 3$.

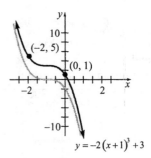

b. The basic function is $y = |x|$ so we start with the graph of this function.

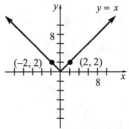

Next we shift this graph 4 units to the left to obtain the graph of $y = |x+4|$.

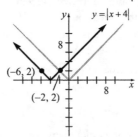

Next we shift this graph up 2 units to obtain the graph of $y = |x+4| + 2$.

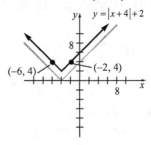

11. a. $r(x) = -0.115x^2 + 1.183x + 5.623$

For the years 1992 to 2004, we have values of x between 0 and 12. Therefore, we can let Xmin = 0 and Xmax = 12. Since r is the interest rate as a percent, we can try letting Ymin = 0 and Ymax = 10.

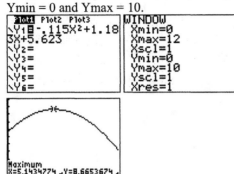

The highest rate during this period appears to be 8.67%, occurring in 1997 ($x \approx 5$).

b. For 2010, we have $x = 2010 - 1992 = 18$.

$$r(18) = -0.115(18)^2 + 1.183(18) + 5.623$$
$$= -10.343$$

$$\boxed{\begin{array}{l} Y_1(18) \\ \quad\quad\quad -10.343 \end{array}}$$

The model predicts that the interest rate will be -10.343%. This is not a reasonable value since it implies that the bank would be paying interest to the borrower.

12. a. Let x = width of the rink in feet. Then the length of the rectangular portion is given by $2x - 20$. The radius of the semicircular portions is half the width, or $r = \dfrac{x}{2}$.

To find the volume, we first find the area of the surface and multiply by the thickness of the ice. The two semicircles can be combined to form a complete circle, so the area is given by

$$A = l \cdot w + \pi r^2$$
$$= (2x - 20)(x) + \pi\left(\frac{x}{2}\right)^2$$
$$= 2x^2 - 20x + \frac{\pi x^2}{4}$$

We have expressed our measures in feet so we need to convert the thickness to feet as well.

$$0.75 \text{ in} \cdot \frac{1 \text{ ft}}{12 \text{ in}} = \frac{0.75}{12} \text{ ft} = \frac{1}{16} \text{ ft}$$

Now we multiply this by the area to obtain the volume. That is,

$$V(x) = \frac{1}{16}\left(2x^2 - 20x + \frac{\pi x^2}{4}\right)$$
$$V(x) = \frac{x^2}{8} - \frac{5x}{4} + \frac{\pi x^2}{64}$$

b. If the rink is 90 feet wide, then we have $x = 90$.

$$V(90) = \frac{90^2}{8} - \frac{5(90)}{4} + \frac{\pi(90)^2}{64} \approx 1297.61$$

The volume of ice is roughly 1297.61 ft^3.

Chapter 3 Cumulative Review

1.
$$3x - 8 = 10$$
$$3x - 8 + 8 = 10 + 8$$
$$3x = 18$$
$$\frac{3x}{3} = \frac{18}{3}$$
$$x = 6$$

The solution set is $\{6\}$.

2.
$$3x^2 - x = 0$$
$$x(3x - 1) = 0$$
$$x = 0 \quad \text{or} \quad 3x - 1 = 0$$
$$3x = 1$$
$$x = \frac{1}{3}$$

The solution set is $\left\{0, \dfrac{1}{3}\right\}$.

3.
$$x^2 - 8x - 9 = 0$$
$$(x - 9)(x + 1) = 0$$
$$x - 9 = 0 \quad \text{or} \quad x + 1 = 0$$
$$x = 9 \quad\quad\quad x = -1$$

The solution set is $\{-1, 9\}$.

4. $6x^2 - 5x + 1 = 0$

$(3x - 1)(2x - 1) = 0$

$3x - 1 = 0 \quad \text{or} \quad 2x - 1 = 0$

$3x = 1 \qquad\qquad 2x = 1$

$x = \dfrac{1}{3} \qquad\qquad x = \dfrac{1}{2}$

The solution set is $\left\{\dfrac{1}{3}, \dfrac{1}{2}\right\}$.

5. $|2x + 3| = 4$

$2x + 3 = -4 \quad \text{or} \quad 2x + 3 = 4$

$2x = -7 \qquad\qquad 2x = 1$

$x = -\dfrac{7}{2} \qquad\qquad x = \dfrac{1}{2}$

The solution set is $\left\{-\dfrac{7}{2}, \dfrac{1}{2}\right\}$.

6. $\sqrt{2x + 3} = 2$

$\left(\sqrt{2x + 3}\right)^2 = 2^2$

$2x + 3 = 4$

$2x = 1$

$x = \dfrac{1}{2}$

Check:

$\sqrt{2\left(\dfrac{1}{2}\right) + 3} \overset{?}{=} 2$

$\sqrt{1 + 3} \overset{?}{=} 2$

$\sqrt{4} \overset{?}{=} 2$

$2 = 2 \ \checkmark$

The solution set is $\left\{\dfrac{1}{2}\right\}$.

7. $2 - 3x > 6$

$-3x > 4$

$x < -\dfrac{4}{3}$

Solution set: $\left\{x \mid x < -\dfrac{4}{3}\right\}$

Interval notation: $\left(-\infty, -\dfrac{4}{3}\right)$

8. $|2x - 5| < 3$

$-3 < 2x - 5 < 3$

$2 < 2x < 8$

$1 < x < 4$

Solution set: $\left\{x \mid 1 < x < 4\right\}$

Interval notation: $(1, 4)$

9. $|4x + 1| \geq 7$

$4x + 1 \leq -7 \quad \text{or} \quad 4x + 1 \geq 7$

$4x \leq -8 \qquad\qquad 4x \geq 6$

$x \leq -2 \qquad\qquad x \geq \dfrac{3}{2}$

Solution set: $\left\{x \mid x \leq -2 \ \text{or} \ x \geq \dfrac{3}{2}\right\}$

Interval notation: $\left(-\infty, -2\right] \cup \left[\dfrac{3}{2}, \infty\right)$

10. a. $d = \sqrt{(x_2 - x_1)^2 + (y_2 - y_1)^2}$

$= \sqrt{(3 - (-2))^2 + (-5 - (-3))^2}$

$= \sqrt{(3 + 2)^2 + (-5 + 3)^2}$

$= \sqrt{5^2 + (-2)^2} = \sqrt{25 + 4}$

$= \sqrt{29}$

b. $M = \left(\dfrac{x_1 + x_2}{2}, \dfrac{y_1 + y_2}{2}\right)$

$= \left(\dfrac{-2+3}{2}, \dfrac{-3+(-5)}{2}\right)$

$= \left(\dfrac{1}{2}, -4\right)$

c. $m = \dfrac{y_2 - y_1}{x_2 - x_1} = \dfrac{-5-(-3)}{3-(-2)} = \dfrac{-2}{5} = -\dfrac{2}{5}$

11. $3x - 2y = 12$

x-intercept:

$3x - 2(0) = 12$

$3x = 12$

$x = 4$

The point $(4,0)$ is on the graph.

y-intercept:

$3(0) - 2y = 12$

$-2y = 12$

$y = -6$

The point $(0,-6)$ is on the graph.

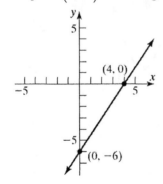

12. $x = y^2$

y	$x = y^2$	(x,y)
-2	$x = (-2)^2 = 4$	$(4,-2)$
-1	$x = (-1)^2 = 1$	$(1,-1)$
0	$x = 0^2 = 0$	$(0,0)$
1	$x = 1^2 = 1$	$(1,1)$
2	$x = 2^2 = 4$	$(4,2)$

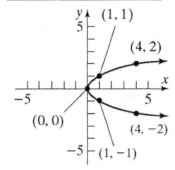

13. $x^2 + (y-3)^2 = 16$

This is the equation of a circle with radius $r = \sqrt{16} = 4$ and center at $(0,3)$. Starting at the center we can obtain some points on the graph by moving 4 units up, down, left, and right. The corresponding points are $(0,7)$, $(0,-1)$, $(-4,3)$, and $(4,3)$, respectively.

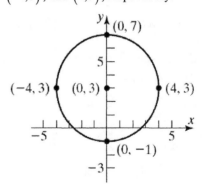

315

14. $y = \sqrt{x}$

x	$y = \sqrt{x}$	(x, y)
0	$y = \sqrt{0} = 0$	$(0, 0)$
1	$y = \sqrt{1} = 1$	$(1, 1)$
4	$y = \sqrt{4} = 2$	$(4, 2)$

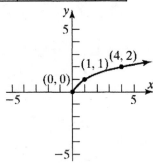

15. $3x^2 - 4y = 12$

x-intercepts:

$3x^2 - 4(0) = 12$

$3x^2 = 12$

$x^2 = 4$

$x = \pm 2$

y-intercept:

$3(0)^2 - 4y = 12$

$-4y = 12$

$y = -3$

The intercepts are $(-2, 0)$, $(2, 0)$, and $(0, -3)$.

Check x-axis symmetry:

$3x^2 - 4(-y) = 12$

$3x^2 + 4y = 12$ different

Check y-axis symmetry:

$3(-x)^2 - 4y = 12$

$3x^2 - 4y = 12$ same

Check origin symmetry:

$3(-x)^2 - 4(-y) = 12$

$3x^2 + 4y = 12$ different

The graph of the equation has y-axis symmetry.

16. First we find the slope:

$$m = \frac{8 - 4}{6 - (-2)} = \frac{4}{8} = \frac{1}{2}$$

Next we use the slope and the given point $(6, 8)$ in the point-slope form of the equation of a line:

$y - y_1 = m(x - x_1)$

$y - 8 = \frac{1}{2}(x - 6)$

$y - 8 = \frac{1}{2}x - 3$

$y = \frac{1}{2}x + 5$

17. $f(x) = (x + 2)^2 - 3$

Starting with the graph of $y = x^2$, shift the graph 2 units to the left $\left[y = (x + 2)^2 \right]$ and down 3 units $\left[y = (x + 2)^2 - 3 \right]$.

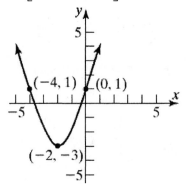

18. $f(x) = \dfrac{1}{x}$

x	$y = \dfrac{1}{x}$	(x, y)
-1	$y = \dfrac{1}{-1} = -1$	$(-1, -1)$
1	$y = \dfrac{1}{1} = 1$	$(1, 1)$
2	$y = \dfrac{1}{2}$	$\left(2, \dfrac{1}{2}\right)$

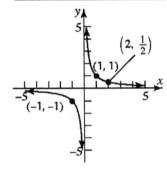

19. $f(x) = \begin{cases} 2 - x & \text{if } x \le 2 \\ |x| & \text{if } x > 2 \end{cases}$

Graph the line $y = 2 - x$ for $x \le 2$. Two points on the graph are $(0, 2)$ and $(2, 0)$.

Graph the line $y = x$ for $x > 2$. There is a hole in the graph at $x = 2$.

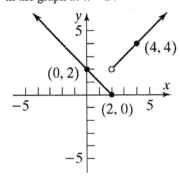

Chapter 3 Projects

Project I

1. Plan A1: Total cost = $39.99 x 24 = $959.76
   Plan A2: Total cost = $59.99 x 24 = $1439.76
   Plan B1: Total cost = $39.99 x 24 = $959.76
   Plan B2: Total cost = $49.99 x 24 = $ 1199.76
   Plan C1: Total cost = $59.99 x 24 = $1439.76
   Plan C2: Total cost = $69.99 x 24 = $1679.76

2. <u>400 Anytime; 200 MTM; 4500 NW</u>
   All plans allow for 4500 night and weekend minutes free and at least 400 Anytime minutes. Although company B does not offer MTM minutes, the combined Anytime and MTM minutes does not exceed the base amount. Thus, the cost of usage is just the monthly fee.

   A1: $39.99
   A2: $59.99
   B1: $39.99
   B2: $49.99
   C1: $59.99
   C2: $69.99
   The best plan here is either plan A1 or B1 at $39.99.

   <u>400 Anytime; 200 MTM; 5500 NW</u>
   The only plan that changes price from above when the night and weekend minutes increase to 5500 is A1. It only has 5000 free night and weekend minutes.

   A1: $39.99 + 0.45(450) = $242.49

   The best plan is B1. (Note: plan A1 only charges for 450 minutes because there were still 50 Anytime minutes remaining)

   <u>500 Anytime; 1000MTM; 2000 NW</u>
   All plans allow for at least 2000 night and weekend minutes free and at least 400 Anytime minutes. Company B does not offer MTM minutes

   A1: $39.99 + $0.45(50) = $62.49
   A2: $59.99
   B1: $39.99 + $0.40(900) = $399.99
   B2: $49.99 + $0.40(500) = $249.99
   C1: $59.99
   C2: $69.99
   The best plan here is either plan A2 or C1 at $59.99.

3. For 850 minutes,
A1: $39.99 + 0.45(400) = \$219.99$
A2: $59.99
B1: $39.99 + 0.40(250) = \$139.99$
B2: $49.99
C1: $59.99 + 5(300/50) = \$89.99$
C2: $69.99 + 5(50/50) = \$74.99$
The best priced plan is B2 at $49.99.

For 1050 minutes:
A1: $39.99 + 0.45(600) = \$309.99$
A2: $59.99 + 0.40(150) = \$119.99$
B1: $39.99 + 0.40(450) = \$219.99$
B2: $49.99 + 0.40(50) = \$69.99$
C1: $59.99 + 5(500/50) = \$109.99$
C2: $69.99 + 5(250/50) = \$94.99$
The best priced plan is B2 at $69.99.

4. $\text{Monthly} \atop \text{cost} = \text{Base} \atop \text{Price} + \left(\text{charge per} \atop \text{minute}\right)\left(\text{\# of min. over} \atop \text{those included}\right)$

A1: $C(x) = \begin{cases} 39.99 & 0 \le x \le 450 \\ 0.45x - 162.51 & x > 450 \end{cases}$

A2: $C(x) = \begin{cases} 59.99 & 0 \le x \le 900 \\ 0.40x - 300.01 & x > 900 \end{cases}$

B1: $C(x) = \begin{cases} 39.99 & 0 \le x \le 600 \\ 0.40x - 200.01 & x > 600 \end{cases}$

B2: $C(x) = \begin{cases} 49.99 & 0 \le x \le 1000 \\ 0.40x - 350.01 & x > 1000 \end{cases}$

C1:

$C(x) = \begin{cases} 59.99 & 0 \le x \le 550 \\ 59.99 + 5\{\text{int}[(x-550)/50]+1\} & 550 < x < 1050 \\ 0.10x + 4.99 & x \ge 1050 \end{cases}$

C2:

$C(x) = \begin{cases} 69.99 & 0 \le x \le 800 \\ 69.99 + 5\{\text{int}[(x-800)/50]+1\} & 800 < x < 1300 \\ 0.10x - 10.01 & x \ge 1300 \end{cases}$

5. Graph for plan A1:

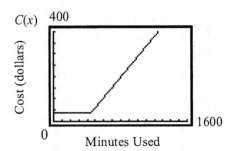

Graph for plan A2:

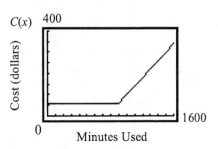

Graph for plan B1:

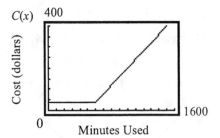

Graph for plan B2:

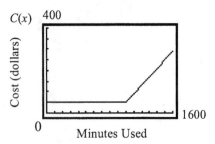

318

Graph for plan C1:

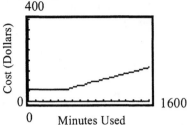

Close-up of middle portion to show steps:

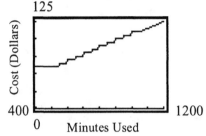

Graph for plan C2:

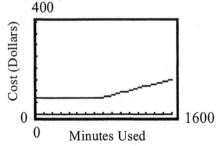

Close-up of middle portion to show steps:

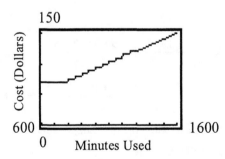

6. A1: $\dfrac{\$39.99}{450\,\text{min}} = \$0.089/\text{min}$

    A2: $\dfrac{\$59.99}{900\,\text{min}} = \$0.067/\text{min}$

    A2 is the better plan.

B1: $\dfrac{\$39.99}{600\,\text{min}} = \$0.067/\text{min}$

    B2: $\dfrac{\$49.99}{1000\,\text{min}} = \$0.050/\text{min}$

    B2 is the better plan.

C1: $\dfrac{\$59.99}{550\,\text{min}} = \$0.109/\text{min}$

    C2: $\dfrac{\$69.99}{800\,\text{min}} = \$0.087/\text{min}$

    C2 is the better plan.

7. Out of A2, B2, and C2, the best plan to choose is B2 since its \$/min rate is best.

8. Answers will vary.

Project II

1. Silver: $C(x) = 20 + 0.16(x - 200) = 0.16x - 12$

$$C(x) = \begin{cases} 20 & 0 \le x \le 200 \\ 0.16x - 12 & x > 200 \end{cases}$$

    Gold: $C(x) = 50 + 0.08(x - 1000) = 0.08x - 30$

$$C(x) = \begin{cases} 50.00 & 0 \le x \le 1000 \\ 0.08x - 30 & x > 1000 \end{cases}$$

    Platinum: $C(x) = 100 + 0.04(x - 3000)$

$$= 0.04x - 20$$

$$C(x) = \begin{cases} 100.00 & 0 \le x \le 3000 \\ 0.04x - 20 & x > 3000 \end{cases}$$

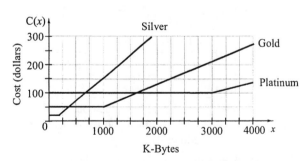

3. Let y = #K-bytes of service over the plan minimum.

    Silver: $20 + 0.16y \le 50$

$$0.16y \le 30$$

$$y \le 187.5$$

    Silver is the best up to $187.5 + 200 = 387.5$ K-bytes of service.

Gold: $50 + 0.08y \le 100$

$$0.08y \le 50$$

$$y \le 625$$

Gold is the best from 387.5 K-bytes to $625 + 1000 = 1625$ K-bytes of service.

Platinum: Platinum will be the best if more than 1625 K-bytes is needed.

4. Answers will vary.

Project III

1.

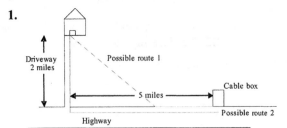

2.

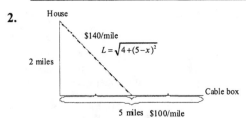

$$C(x) = 100x + 140L$$

$$C(x) = 100x + 140\sqrt{4 + (5 - x)^2}$$

3.

x	$C(x)$
0	$100(0) + 140\sqrt{4 + 25} \approx \$753.92$
1	$100(1) + 140\sqrt{4 + 16} \approx \$726.10$
2	$100(2) + 140\sqrt{4 + 9} \approx \$704.78$
3	$100(3) + 140\sqrt{4 + 4} \approx \$695.98$
4	$100(4) + 140\sqrt{4 + 1} \approx \$713.05$
5	$100(5) + 140\sqrt{4 + 0} = \$780.00$

The choice where the cable goes 3 miles down the road then cutting up to the house seems to yield the lowest cost.

4. Since all of the costs are less than $800, there would be a profit made with any of the plans.

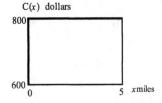

Using the MINIMUM function on a graphing calculator, the minimum occurs at $x \approx 2.96$.

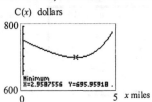

The minimum cost occurs when the cable runs for 2.96 mile along the road.

6. $C(4.5) = 100(4.5) + 140\sqrt{4 + (5 - 4.5)^2}$

$$\approx \$738.62$$

The cost for the Steven's cable would be $738.62.

7. $5000(738.62) = \$3,693,100$ State legislated
$5000(695.96) = \$3,479,800$ cheapest cost
It will cost the company $213,300 more.

Project IV

1. $A = \pi r^2$

2. $r = 2.2t$

3. $r = 2.2(2) = 4.4$ ft

$$r = 2.2(2.5) = 5.5 \text{ ft}$$

4. $A = \pi(4.4)^2 = 60.82 \text{ ft}^2$

$$A = \pi(5.5)^2 = 95.03 \text{ ft}^2$$

5. $A = \pi(2.2t)^2 = 4.84\pi t^2$

6. $A = 4.84\pi(2)^2 = 60.82 \text{ ft}^2$

$$A = 4.84\pi(2.5)^2 = 95.03 \text{ ft}^2$$

7. $\dfrac{A(2.5) - A(2)}{2.5 - 2} = \dfrac{95.03 - 60.82}{0.5} = 68.42 \text{ ft/hr}$

8. $\dfrac{A(3.5) - A(3)}{3.5 - 3} = \dfrac{186.27 - 136.85}{0.5} = 98.84 \text{ ft/hr}$

9. The average rate of change is increasing.

10. 150 yds = 450 ft

$$r = 2.2t$$

$$t = \frac{450}{2.2} = 204.5 \text{ hours}$$

11. 6 miles = 31680 ft
Therefore, we need a radius of 15,840 ft.

$$t = \frac{15,840}{2.2} = 7200 \text{ hours}$$

Chapter 4
Linear and Quadratic Functions

Section 4.1

1. From the equation $y = 2x - 3$, we see that the y-intercept is -3. Thus, the point $(0, -3)$ is on the graph. We can obtain a second point by choosing a value for x and finding the corresponding value for y. Let $x = 1$, then $y = 2(1) - 3 = -1$. Thus, the point $(1, -1)$ is also on the graph. Plotting the two points and connecting with a line yields the graph below.

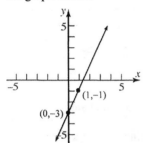

2. $m = \dfrac{y_2 - y_1}{x_2 - x_1} = \dfrac{3 - 5}{-1 - 2} = \dfrac{-2}{-3} = \dfrac{2}{3}$

3. $f(2) = 3(2)^2 - 2 = 10$

   $f(4) = 3(4)^2 - 2 = 46$

   $\dfrac{\Delta y}{\Delta x} = \dfrac{f(4) - f(2)}{4 - 2} = \dfrac{46 - 10}{4 - 2} = \dfrac{36}{2} = 18$

4. $60x - 900 = -15x + 2850$

   $75x - 900 = 2850$

   $75x = 3750$

   $x = 50$

   The solution set is $\{50\}$.

5. $f(-2) = (-2)^2 - 4 = 4 - 4 = 0$

6. True

7. slope; y-intercept

8. -4; 3

9. positive

10. True

11. False. If x increases by 3, then y increases by 2.

12. False. The y-intercept is 8. The average rate of change is 2 (the slope).

13. $f(x) = 2x + 3$

    a. Slope = 2; y-intercept = 3

    b. Plot the point $(0, 3)$. Use the slope to find an additional point by moving 1 unit to the right and 2 units up.

    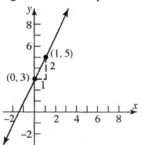

    c. average rate of change = 2

    d. increasing

14. $g(x) = 5x - 4$

    a. Slope = 5; y-intercept = -4

    b. Plot the point $(0, -4)$. Use the slope to find an additional point by moving 1 unit to the right and 5 units up.

    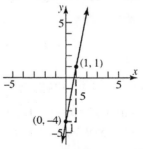

    c. average rate of change = 5

    d. increasing

321

15. $h(x) = -3x + 4$

   a. Slope $= -3$; y-intercept $= 4$

   b. Plot the point $(0, 4)$. Use the slope to find an additional point by moving 1 unit to the right and 3 units down.

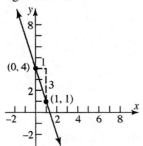

   c. average rate of change $= -3$

   d. decreasing

16. $p(x) = -x + 6$

   a. Slope $= -1$; y-intercept $= 6$

   b. Plot the point $(0, 6)$. Use the slope to find an additional point by moving 1 unit to the right and 1 unit down.

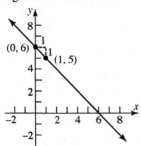

   c. average rate of change $= -1$

   d. decreasing

17. $f(x) = \dfrac{1}{4}x - 3$

   a. Slope $= \dfrac{1}{4}$; y-intercept $= -3$

   b. Plot the point $(0, -3)$. Use the slope to find an additional point by moving 4 units to the right and 1 unit up.

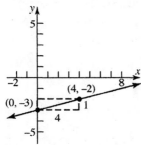

   c. average rate of change $= \dfrac{1}{4}$

   d. increasing

18. $h(x) = -\dfrac{2}{3}x + 4$

   a. Slope $= -\dfrac{2}{3}$; y-intercept $= 4$

   b. Plot the point $(0, 4)$. Use the slope to find an additional point by moving 3 units to the right and 2 units down.

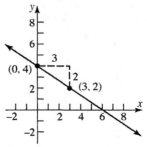

   c. average rate of change $= -\dfrac{2}{3}$

   d. decreasing

19. $F(x) = 4$

   a. Slope $= 0$; y-intercept $= 4$

   b. Plot the point $(0, 4)$ and draw a horizontal line through it.

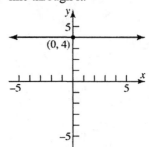

   c. average rate of change $= 0$

   d. constant

20. $G(x) = -2$

   a. Slope = 0; y-intercept = -2

   b. Plot the point $(0, -2)$ and draw a horizontal line through it.

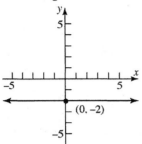

   c. average rate of change = 0

   d. constant

21.

x	$y = f(x)$	Avg. rate of change $= \dfrac{\Delta y}{\Delta x}$
-2	4	
-1	1	$\dfrac{1-4}{-1-(-2)} = \dfrac{-3}{1} = -3$
0	-2	$\dfrac{-2-1}{0-(-1)} = \dfrac{-3}{1} = -3$
1	-5	$\dfrac{-5-(-2)}{1-0} = \dfrac{-3}{1} = -3$
2	-8	$\dfrac{-8-(-5)}{2-1} = \dfrac{-3}{1} = -3$

This is a linear function with slope = -3, since the average rate of change is constant at -3.

22.

x	$y = f(x)$	Avg. rate of change $= \dfrac{\Delta y}{\Delta x}$
-2	$\dfrac{1}{4}$	
-1	$\dfrac{1}{2}$	$\dfrac{\left(\frac{1}{2}-\frac{1}{4}\right)}{-1-(-2)} = \dfrac{\frac{1}{4}}{1} = \dfrac{1}{4}$
0	1	$\dfrac{\left(1-\frac{1}{2}\right)}{0-(-1)} = \dfrac{\frac{1}{2}}{1} = \dfrac{1}{2}$
1	2	
2	4	

This is not a linear function since the average rate of change is not constant.

23.

x	$y = f(x)$	Avg. rate of change $= \dfrac{\Delta y}{\Delta x}$
-2	-8	
-1	-3	$\dfrac{-3-(-8)}{-1-(-2)} = \dfrac{5}{1} = 5$
0	0	$\dfrac{0-(-3)}{0-(-1)} = \dfrac{3}{1} = 3$
1	1	
2	0	

This is not a linear function, since the average rate of change is not constant.

24.

x	$y = f(x)$	Avg. rate of change $= \dfrac{\Delta y}{\Delta x}$
-2	-4	
-1	0	$\dfrac{0-(-4)}{-1-(-2)} = \dfrac{4}{1} = 4$
0	4	$\dfrac{4-0}{0-(-1)} = \dfrac{4}{1} = 4$
1	8	$\dfrac{8-4}{1-0} = \dfrac{4}{1} = 4$
2	12	$\dfrac{12-8}{2-1} = \dfrac{4}{1} = 4$

This is a linear function with slope = 4, since the average rate of change is constant at 4.

25.

x	$y = f(x)$	Avg. rate of change $= \dfrac{\Delta y}{\Delta x}$
-2	-26	
-1	-4	$\dfrac{-4-(-26)}{-1-(-2)} = \dfrac{22}{1} = 22$
0	2	$\dfrac{2-(-4)}{0-(-1)} = \dfrac{6}{1} = 6$
1	-2	
2	-10	

This is not a linear function, since the average rate of change is not constant.

26.

x	$y = f(x)$	Avg. rate of change $= \dfrac{\Delta y}{\Delta x}$
−2	−4	
−1	−3.5	$\dfrac{-3.5-(-4)}{-1-(-2)} = \dfrac{0.5}{1} = 0.5$
0	−3	$\dfrac{-3-(-3.5)}{0-(-1)} = \dfrac{0.5}{1} = 0.5$
1	−2.5	$\dfrac{-2.5-(-3)}{1-0} = \dfrac{0.5}{1} = 0.5$
2	−2	$\dfrac{-2-(-2.5)}{2-1} = \dfrac{0.5}{1} = 0.5$

This is a linear function, since the average rate of change is constant at 0.5

27.

x	$y = f(x)$	Avg. rate of change $= \dfrac{\Delta y}{\Delta x}$
−2	8	
−1	8	$\dfrac{8-8}{-1-(-2)} = \dfrac{0}{1} = 0$
0	8	$\dfrac{8-8}{0-(-1)} = \dfrac{0}{1} = 0$
1	8	$\dfrac{8-8}{1-0} = \dfrac{0}{1} = 0$
2	8	$\dfrac{8-8}{2-1} = \dfrac{0}{1} = 0$

This is a linear function with slope = 0, since the average rate of change is constant at 0.

28.

x	$y = f(x)$	Avg. rate of change $= \dfrac{\Delta y}{\Delta x}$
−2	0	
−1	1	$\dfrac{1-0}{-1-(-2)} = \dfrac{1}{1} = 1$
0	4	$\dfrac{4-1}{0-(-1)} = \dfrac{3}{1} = 3$
1	9	
2	16	

This is not a linear function, since the average rate of change is not constant.

29. $f(x) = 4x - 1; \quad g(x) = -2x + 5$

   a. $f(x) = 0$

   $4x - 1 = 0$

   $x = \dfrac{1}{4}$

   b. $f(x) > 0$

   $4x - 1 > 0$

   $x > \dfrac{1}{4}$

   The solution set is $\left\{ x \middle| x > \dfrac{1}{4} \right\}$ or $\left(\dfrac{1}{4}, \infty \right)$.

   c. $f(x) = g(x)$

   $4x - 1 = -2x + 5$

   $6x = 6$

   $x = 1$

   d. $f(x) \le g(x)$

   $4x - 1 \le -2x + 5$

   $6x \le 6$

   $x \le 1$

   The solution set is $\left\{ x \middle| x \le 1 \right\}$ or $(-\infty, 1]$.

   e.

   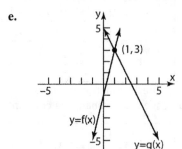

30. $f(x) = 3x + 5; \quad g(x) = -2x + 15$

   a. $f(x) = 0$

   $3x + 5 = 0$

   $x = -\dfrac{5}{3}$

   b. $f(x) < 0$

   $3x + 5 < 0$

   $x < -\dfrac{5}{3}$

   The solution set is $\left\{ x \middle| x < -\dfrac{5}{3} \right\}$ or $\left(-\infty, -\dfrac{5}{3} \right)$.

c. $f(x) = g(x)$

$3x + 5 = -2x + 15$

$5x = 10$

$x = 2$

d. $f(x) \geq g(x)$

$3x + 5 \geq -2x + 15$

$5x \geq 10$

$x \geq 2$

The solution set is $\{x | x \geq 2\}$ or $[2, \infty)$.

e.

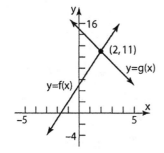

31. a. The point $(40, 50)$ is on the graph of $y = f(x)$, so the solution to $f(x) = 50$ is $x = 40$.

b. The point $(88, 80)$ is on the graph of $y = f(x)$, so the solution to $f(x) = 80$ is $x = 88$.

c. The point $(-40, 0)$ is on the graph of $y = f(x)$, so the solution to $f(x) = 0$ is $x = -40$.

d. The y-coordinates of the graph of $y = f(x)$ are above 50 when the x-coordinates are larger than 40. Thus, the solution to $f(x) > 50$ is $\{x | x > 40\}$ or $(40, \infty)$.

e. The y-coordinates of the graph of $y = f(x)$ are below 80 when the x-coordinates are smaller than 88. Thus, the solution to $f(x) \leq 80$ is $\{x | x \leq 88\}$ or $(-\infty, 88]$.

f. The y-coordinates of the graph of $y = f(x)$ are between 0 and 80 when the x-coordinates are between −40 and 88. Thus, the solution to $0 < f(x) < 80$ is $\{x | -40 < x < 88\}$ or $(-40, 88)$.

32. a. The point $(5, 20)$ is on the graph of $y = g(x)$, so the solution to $g(x) = 20$ is $x = 5$.

b. The point $(-15, 60)$ is on the graph of $y = g(x)$, so the solution to $g(x) = 60$ is $x = -15$.

c. The point $(15, 0)$ is on the graph of $y = g(x)$, so the solution to $g(x) = 0$ is $x = 15$.

d. The y-coordinates of the graph of $y = g(x)$ are above 20 when the x-coordinates are smaller than 5. Thus, the solution to $g(x) > 20$ is $\{x | x < 5\}$ or $(-\infty, 5)$.

e. The y-coordinates of the graph of $y = f(x)$ are below 60 when the x-coordinates are larger than −15. Thus, the solution to $g(x) \leq 60$ is $\{x | x \geq -15\}$ or $[-15, \infty)$.

f. The y-coordinates of the graph of $y = f(x)$ are between 0 and 60 when the x-coordinates are between −15 and 15. Thus, the solution to $0 < f(x) < 60$ is $\{x | -15 < x < 15\}$ or $(-15, 15)$.

33. a. $f(x) = g(x)$ when their graphs intersect. Thus, $x = -4$.

b. $f(x) \leq g(x)$ when the graph of f is above the graph of g. Thus, the solution is $\{x | x < -4\}$ or $(-\infty, -4)$.

34. a. $f(x) = g(x)$ when their graphs intersect. Thus, $x = 2$.

b. $f(x) \leq g(x)$ when the graph of f is below or intersects the graph of g. Thus, the solution is $\{x | x \leq 2\}$ or $(-\infty, 2]$.

35. a. $f(x) = g(x)$ when their graphs intersect. Thus, $x = -6$.

b. $g(x) \leq f(x) < h(x)$ when the graph of f is above or intersects the graph of g and below the graph of h. Thus, the solution is $\{x | -6 \leq x < 5\}$ or $[-6, 5)$.

36. a. $f(x) = g(x)$ when their graphs intersect.
Thus, $x = 7$.

b. $g(x) \le f(x) < h(x)$ when the graph of f is above or intersects the graph of g and below the graph of h. Thus, the solution is $\{x | -4 \le x < 7\}$ or $[-4, 7)$.

37. $C(x) = 0.25x + 35$

a. $C(40) = 0.25(40) + 35 = \$45$.

b. Solve $C(x) = 0.25x + 35 = 80$
$$0.25x + 35 = 80$$
$$0.25x = 45$$
$$x = \frac{45}{0.25} = 180 \text{ miles}$$

c. Solve $C(x) = 0.25x + 35 \le 100$
$$0.25x + 35 \le 100$$
$$0.25x \le 65$$
$$x \le \frac{65}{0.25} = 260 \text{ miles}$$

38. $C(x) = 0.38x + 5$

a. $C(50) = 0.38(50) + 5 = \$24$.

b. Solve $C(x) = 0.38x + 5 = 29.32$
$$0.38x + 5 = 29.32$$
$$0.38x = 24.32$$
$$x = \frac{24.32}{0.38} = 64 \text{ minutes}$$

c. Solve $C(x) = 0.38x + 5 \le 60$
$$0.38x + 5 \le 60$$
$$0.38x \le 55$$
$$x \le \frac{55}{0.38} \approx 144 \text{ minutes}$$

39. $B(t) = 19.25t + 585.72$

a. $B(10) = 19.25(10) + 585.72 = \$778.22$

b. Solve $B(t) = 19.25t + 585.72 = 893.72$
$$19.25t + 585.72 = 893.72$$
$$19.25t = 308$$
$$t = \frac{308}{19.25} = 16 \text{ years}$$
Therefore the average monthly benefit will be $893.72 in the year 2006.

c. Solve $B(t) = 19.25t + 585.72 > 1000$
$$19.25t + 585.72 > 1000$$
$$19.25t > 414.28$$
$$t > \frac{414.28}{19.25} \approx 21.52 \text{ years}$$
Therefore the average monthly benefit will exceed $1000 in the year 2012.

40. $E(t) = 26t + 411$

a. $E(10) = 26(10) + 411 = \$671$ billion.

b. Solve $E(t) = 26t + 411 = 879$
$$26t + 411 = 879$$
$$26t = 468$$
$$t = \frac{468}{26} = 18 \text{ years}$$
Therefore the total private expenditure will be $879 billion in the year 2008.

c. Solve $E(t) = 26t + 411 > 1000$
$$26t + 411 > 1000$$
$$26t > 589$$
$$t > \frac{589}{26} \approx 22.65 \text{ years}$$
Therefore the total private expenditure will exceed $1 trillion in about the year 2013.

41. $S(p) = -200 + 50p; \quad D(p) = 1000 - 25p$

a. Solve $S(p) = D(p)$.
$$-200 + 50p = 1000 - 25p$$
$$75p = 1200$$
$$p = \frac{1200}{75} = 16$$
$$S(16) = -200 + 50(16) = 600$$
Thus, the equilibrium price is $16, and the equilibrium quantity is 600 T-shirts.

b. Solve $D(p) > S(p)$.
$$1000 - 25p > -200 + 50p$$
$$1200 > 75p$$
$$\frac{1200}{75} > p$$
$$16 > p$$
The demand will exceed supply when the price is less than $16 (but still greater than $0).

c. The price will eventually be increased.

42. $S(p) = -2000 + 3000p$; $D(p) = 10000 - 1000p$

   a. Solve $S(p) = D(p)$.
   $$-2000 + 3000p = 10000 - 1000p$$
   $$4000p = 12000$$
   $$p = \frac{12000}{4000} = 3$$
   $$S(3) = -2000 + 3000(3) = 7000$$
   Thus, the equilibrium price is $3, and the equilibrium quantity is 7000 hot dogs.

   b. Solve $D(p) < S(p)$.
   $$10000 - 1000p < -2000 + 3000p$$
   $$12000 < 4000p$$
   $$\frac{12000}{4000} < p$$
   $$3 < p$$
   The demand will be less than the supply when the price is greater than $3.

   c. The price will eventually be decreased.

43. a. We are told that the tax function T is for adjusted gross incomes x between $7,300 and $29,700, inclusive. Thus, the domain is $\{x \mid 7,300 \le x \le 29,700\}$ or $[7300, \ 29700]$.

   b. $T(18000) = 0.15(18000 - 7300) + 730 = 2335$
   If a single filer's adjusted gross income is $18,000, then his or her tax bill will be $2335.

   c. The independent variable is adjusted gross income, x. The dependent variable is the tax bill, T.

   d. Evaluate T at $x = 7300$, 18000, and 29700.
   $$T(7300) = 0.15(7300 - 7300) + 730$$
   $$= 730$$
   $$T(18000) = 0.15(18000 - 7300) + 730$$
   $$= 2335$$
   $$T(29700) = 0.15(29700 - 7300) + 730$$
   $$= 4090$$
   Thus, the points $(7300, 730)$, $(18000, 2335)$, and $(29700, 4090)$ are on the graph.

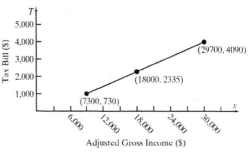

   e. We must solve $T(x) = 2860$.
   $$0.15(x - 7300) + 730 = 2860$$
   $$0.15x - 1095 + 730 = 2860$$
   $$0.15x - 365 = 2860$$
   $$0.15x = 3225$$
   $$x = 21,500$$
   A single filer with an adjusted gross income of $21,500 will have a tax bill of $2860.

44. a. The independent variable is payroll, p. The payroll tax only applies if the payroll is $128 million or more. Thus, the domain of T is $\{p \mid p \ge 128\}$ or $[128, \ \infty)$.

   b. $T(160) = 0.225(160 - 128) = 7.2$
   The luxury tax whose payroll is $160 million would be $7.2 million.

   c. Evaluate T at $p = 128$, 200, and 300 million.
   $$T(128) = 0.225(128 - 128) = 0$$
   $$T(200) = 0.225(200 - 128) = 16.2 \text{ million}$$
   $$T(300) = 0.225(300 - 128) = 38.7 \text{ million}$$

   Thus, the points $(128 \text{ million, } 0)$, $(200 \text{ million, } 16.2 \text{ million})$, and $(300 \text{ million, } 38.7 \text{ million})$ are on the graph.

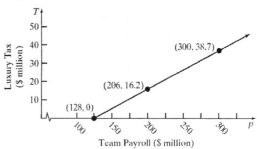

d. We must solve $T(p) = 11.7$.

$$0.225(p - 128) = 11.7$$
$$0.225p - 28.8 = 11.7$$
$$0.225p = 40.5$$
$$p = 180$$

If the luxury tax is $11.7 million, then the payroll of the team is $180 million.

45. $R(x) = 8x; \ C(x) = 4.5x + 17500$

   a. Solve $R(x) = C(x)$.

$$8x = 4.5x + 17500$$
$$3.5x = 17500$$
$$x = \frac{17500}{3.5} = 5000$$

The break-even point occurs when the company sells 5000 units.

   b. Solve $R(x) > C(x)$

$$8x > 4.5x + 17500$$
$$3.5x > 17500$$
$$x > \frac{17500}{3.5} = 5000$$

The company makes a profit if it sells more than 5000 units.

46. $R(x) = 12x; \ C(x) = 10x + 15000$

   a. Solve $R(x) = C(x)$

$$12x = 10x + 15000$$
$$2x = 15000$$
$$x = \frac{15000}{2} = 7500$$

The break-even point occurs when the company sells 7500 units.

   b. Solve $R(x) > C(x)$

$$12x > 10x + 15000$$
$$2x > 15000$$
$$x > \frac{15000}{2} = 7500$$

The company makes a profit if it sells more than 7500 units.

47. a. Consider the data points (x, y), where $x =$ the age in years of the computer and $y =$ the value in dollars of the computer. So we have the points $(0, 3000)$ and $(3, 0)$. The slope formula yields:

$$m = \frac{\Delta y}{\Delta x} = \frac{0 - 3000}{3 - 0} = \frac{-3000}{3} = -1000$$

The y-intercept is $(0, 3000)$, so $b = 3000$. Therefore, the linear function is $V(x) = mx + b = -1000x + 3000$.

   b. The graph of $V(x) = -1000x + 3000$

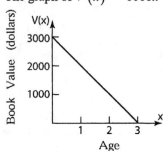

   c. $V(2) = -1000(2) + 3000 = 1000$

The computer's value after 2 years will be $1000.

   d. Solve $V(x) = 2000$

$$-1000x + 3000 = 2000$$
$$-1000x = -1000$$
$$x = 1$$

The computer will be worth $2000 after 1 year.

48. a. Consider the data points (x, y), where $x =$ the age in years of the machine and $y =$ the value in dollars of the machine. So we have the points $(0, 120000)$ and $(10, 0)$. The slope formula yields:

$$m = \frac{\Delta y}{\Delta x} = \frac{0 - 120000}{10 - 0} = \frac{-120000}{10} = -12000$$

The y-intercept is $(0, 120000)$, so $b = 120000$.

Therefore, the linear function is $V(x) = mx + b = -12,000x + 120,000$.

b. The graph of $V(x) = -12,000x + 120,000$

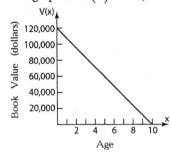

c. $V(4) = -12000(4) + 120000 = 72000$

The machine's value after 4 years is given by $72,000.

d. Solve $V(x) = 72000$.

$$-12000x + 120000 = 72000$$
$$-12000x = -48000$$
$$x = 4$$

The machine will be worth $72,000 after 4 years.

49. a. Let x = the number of bicycles manufactured. We can use the cost function $C(x) = mx + b$, with $m = 90$ and $b = 1800$. Therefore $C(x) = 90x + 1800$

b. The graph of $C(x) = 90x + 1800$

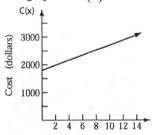

c. The cost of manufacturing 14 bicycles is given by $C(14) = 90(14) + 1800 = \$3060$.

d. Solve $C(x) = 90x + 1800 = 3780$

$$90x + 1800 = 3780$$
$$90x = 1980$$
$$x = 22$$

So 22 bicycles could be manufactured for $3780.

50. a. The new daily fixed cost is

$$1800 + \frac{100}{20} = \$1805$$

b. Let x = the number of bicycles manufactured. We can use the cost function $C(x) = mx + b$, with $m = 90$ and $b = 1805$.

Therefore $C(x) = 90x + 1805$

c. The graph of $C(x) = 90x + 1805$

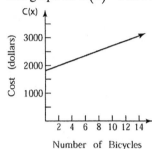

d. The cost of manufacturing 14 bicycles is given by $C(14) = 90(14) + 1805 = \$3065$.

e. Solve $C(x) = 90x + 1805 = 3780$

$$90x + 1805 = 3780$$
$$90x = 1975$$
$$x \approx 21.94$$

So approximately 21 bicycles could be manufactured for $3780.

51. a. Let x = number of miles driven, and let C = cost in dollars. Total cost = (cost per mile)(number of miles) + fixed cost

$$C(x) = 0.07x + 29$$

b. $C(110) = (0.07)(110) + 29 = \$36.70$
$C(230) = (0.07)(230) + 29 = \$45.10$

52. a. Let x = number of minutes used, and let C = cost in dollars. Total cost = (cost per minute)(number of minutes) + fixed cost

$$C(x) = 0.05x + 5$$

b. $C(105) = (0.05)(105) + 5 = \$10.25$
$C(180) = (0.05)(180) + 5 = \$14$

53. The graph shown has a positive slope and a positive y-intercept. Therefore, the function from (d) and (e) might have the graph shown.

54. The graph shown has a negative slope and a positive y-intercept. Therefore, the function from (b) and (e) might have the graph shown.

329

55. A linear function $f(x) = mx + b$ will be odd provided $f(-x) = -f(x)$.

That is, provided $m(-x) + b = -(mx + b)$.

$$-mx + b = -mx - b$$
$$b = -b$$
$$2b = 0$$
$$b = 0$$

So a linear function $f(x) = mx + b$ will be odd provided $b = 0$.

A linear function $f(x) = mx + b$ will be even provided $f(-x) = f(x)$.

That is, provided $m(-x) + b = mx + b$.

$$-mx + b = mx + b$$
$$-mxb = mx$$
$$0 = 2mx$$
$$m = 0$$

So a linear function $f(x) = mx + b$ will be even provided $m = 0$.

Section 4.2

1. scatter diagram

2. True

3. Linear relation, $m > 0$

4. Nonlinear relation

5. Linear relation, $m < 0$

6. Linear relation, $m > 0$

7. Nonlinear relation

8. Nonlinear relation

9. a.

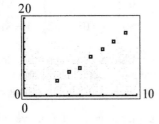

b. Answers will vary. We select (3, 4) and (9, 16). The slope of the line containing these points is: $m = \dfrac{16 - 4}{9 - 3} = \dfrac{12}{6} = 2$.

The equation of the line is:
$$y - y_1 = m(x - x_1)$$
$$y - 4 = 2(x - 3)$$
$$y - 4 = 2x - 6$$
$$y = 2x - 2$$

c.

d. Using the LINear REGression program, the line of best fit is: $y = 2.0357x - 2.3571$

e.

10. a.

b. Answers will vary. We select (3, 0) and (13, 11). The slope of the line containing these points is: $m = \dfrac{11 - 0}{13 - 3} = \dfrac{11}{10}$.

The equation of the line is:
$$y - y_1 = m(x - x_1)$$
$$y - 0 = \frac{11}{10}(x - 3)$$
$$y = \frac{11}{10}x - \frac{33}{10}$$

c.

d. Using the LINear REGression program, the line of best fit is: $y = 1.1286x - 3.8619$

e.

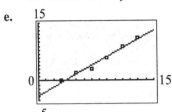

11. a.

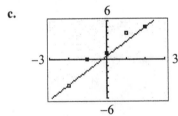

b. Answers will vary. We select $(-2, -4)$ and $(2, 5)$. The slope of the line containing these points is: $m = \dfrac{5 - (-4)}{2 - (-2)} = \dfrac{9}{4}$.

The equation of the line is:
$$y - y_1 = m(x - x_1)$$
$$y - (-4) = \frac{9}{4}(x - (-2))$$
$$y + 4 = \frac{9}{4}x + \frac{9}{2}$$
$$y = \frac{9}{4}x + \frac{1}{2}$$

c.

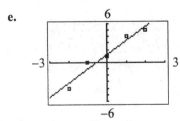

d. Using the LINear REGression program, the line of best fit is: $y = 2.2x + 1.2$

e.

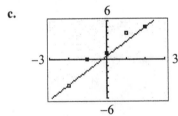

12. a.

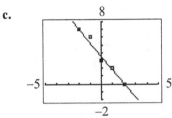

b. Answers will vary. We select $(-2, 7)$ and $(2, 0)$. The slope of the line containing these points is: $m = \dfrac{0 - 7}{2 - (-2)} = \dfrac{-7}{4} = -\dfrac{7}{4}$.

The equation of the line is:
$$y - y_1 = m(x - x_1)$$
$$y - 7 = -\frac{7}{4}(x - (-2))$$
$$y - 7 = -\frac{7}{4}x - \frac{7}{2}$$
$$y = -\frac{7}{4}x + \frac{7}{2}$$

c.

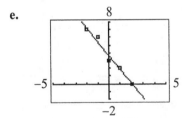

d. Using the LINear REGression program, the line of best fit is: $y = -1.8x + 3.6$

e.

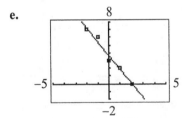

13. a.

331

b. Answers will vary. We select (–20,100) and (–10,140). The slope of the line containing these points is:

$$m = \frac{140-100}{-10-(-20)} = \frac{40}{10} = 4$$

The equation of the line is:

$$y - y_1 = m(x - x_1)$$
$$y - 100 = 4(x - (-20))$$
$$y - 100 = 4x + 80$$
$$y = 4x + 180$$

c.

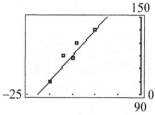

d. Using the LINear REGression program, the line of best fit is: $y = 3.8613x + 180.2920$

e.

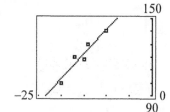

14. a.

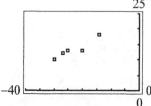

b. Selection of points will vary. We select (–30, 10) and (–14, 18). The slope of the line containing these points is:

$$m = \frac{18-10}{-14-(-30)} = \frac{8}{16} = \frac{1}{2}$$

The equation of the line is:

$$y - y_1 = m(x - x_1)$$
$$y - 10 = \frac{1}{2}(x - (-30))$$
$$y - 10 = \frac{1}{2}x + 15$$
$$y = \frac{1}{2}x + 25$$

c.

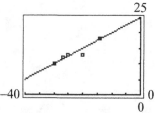

d. Using the LINear REGression program, the line of best fit is: $y = 0.4421x + 23.4559$

e.

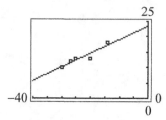

15. a.

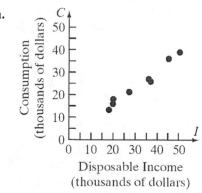

b. Answers will vary. We select (18, 13) and (50, 39). The slope of the line containing these points is: $m = \frac{39-13}{50-18} = \frac{26}{32} = \frac{13}{16}$

The equation of the line is:

$$C - C_1 = m(I - I_1)$$
$$C - 13 = \frac{13}{16}(I - 18)$$
$$C - 13 = \frac{13}{16}I - \frac{117}{8}$$
$$C = \frac{13}{16}I - \frac{13}{8}$$

c. As disposable income increases by $1000, consumption increases by

$$\frac{13}{16} \cdot 1000 = \$812.50.$$

d. Let $I = 42$ in the equation found in part (b).

$$C = \frac{13}{16}(42) - \frac{13}{8} = 32.5$$

The consumption of a family whose disposable income is $42,000 should be $32,500.

e. Using the LINear REGression program, the line of best fit is: $C = 0.7549I + 0.6266$. The correlation coefficient is: $r \approx 0.987$.

16. a. First create a table showing the disposable income and savings:

$I(000)$	$S(000)$
20	$20 - 16 = 4$
20	$20 - 18 = 2$
18	$18 - 13 = 5$
27	$27 - 21 = 6$
36	$36 - 27 = 9$
37	$37 - 26 = 11$
45	$45 - 36 = 9$
50	$50 - 39 = 11$

Now graph the data in the table using I as the independent variable and S as the dependent variable.

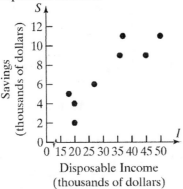

b. Answers will vary. We select (18, 5) and (50, 11). The slope of the line containing these points is: $m = \dfrac{11 - 5}{50 - 18} = \dfrac{6}{32} = \dfrac{3}{16}$.

The equation of the line is:
$$S - S_1 = m(I - I_1)$$
$$S - 5 = \frac{3}{16}(I - 18)$$
$$S - 5 = \frac{3}{16}I - \frac{27}{8}$$
$$S = \frac{3}{16}I + \frac{13}{8}$$

c. As disposable income increases by $1000, savings increases by $\dfrac{3}{16} \cdot 1000 = \$187.50$.

d. Let $I = 42$ in the equation found in part (b).
$$C = \frac{3}{16}(42) + \frac{13}{8} = 9.5$$
The savings of a family whose disposable income is $42,000 should be $9,500.

e. Using the LINear REGression program, the line of best fit is: $C = 0.2451I - 0.6266$. The correlation coefficient is: $r \approx 0.891$.

17. a.

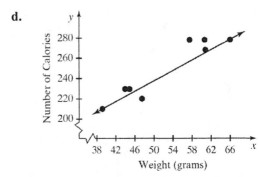

b. Linear.

c. Answers will vary. We will use the points $(39.52, 210)$ and $(66.45, 280)$.
$$m = \frac{280 - 210}{66.45 - 39.52} = \frac{70}{26.93} \approx 2.5993316$$
$$y - 210 = 2.5993316(x - 39.52)$$
$$y - 210 = 2.5993316x - 102.7255848$$
$$y = 2.599x + 107.274$$

d.

e. $x = 62.3$: $y = 2.599(62.3) + 107.274 \approx 269$
We predict that a candy bar weighing 62.3 grams will contain 269 calories.

f. If the weight of a candy bar is increased by 1 gram, then the number of calories will increase by 2.599.

18. a. No, the relation does not represent a function. Several x-coordinates are paired with multiple y-coordinates. For example, the x-coordinate 42.3 is paired with the two different y-coordinates 87 and 82.

333

b.

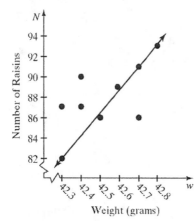

Weight (grams)

c. Answers will vary. We will use the points $(42.3, 82)$ and $(42.8, 93)$.

$$m = \frac{93-82}{42.8-42.3} = \frac{11}{0.5} = 22$$

$$N - N_1 = m(w - w_1)$$

$$N - 82 = 22(w - 42.3)$$

$$N - 82 = 22w - 930.6$$

$$N = 22w - 848.6$$

d.

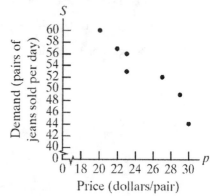

Weight (grams)

e. $N(w) = 22w - 848.6$

f. $N(42.5) = 22(42.5) - 848.6 = 86.4$

We predict that approximately 86 raisins will be in a box weighing 42.5 grams.

g. If the weight is increased by one gram, then the number of raisins will increase by 22.

19. a.

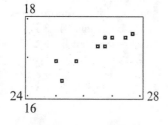

b. Using the LINear REGression program, the line of best fit is: $C(H) = 0.3734H + 7.3268$

c. For each 1 inch increase in height, the circumference increases by 0.3734 inch.

d. $C(26) = 0.3734(26) + 7.3268 \approx 17.0$ inches

e. To find the height, we solve the following equation:

$$17.4 = 0.3734H + 7.3268$$

$$10.0732 = 0.3734H$$

$$26.98 \approx H$$

A child with a head circumference of 17.4 inches would have a height of about 26.98 inches.

20. a.

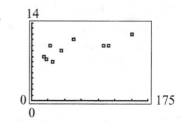

b. Using the LINear REGression program, the line of best fit is: $L(G) = 0.0261G + 7.8738$

c. For each 1 day increase in Gestation period, the life expectancy increases by 0.0261 years (about 9.5 days).

d. $L(89) = 0.0261(89) + 7.8738 \approx 10.2$ years

21. a. The relation is not a function because 23 is paired with both 56 and 53.

b.

Demand (pairs of jeans sold per day)

Price (dollars/pair)

c. Using the LINear REGression program, the line of best fit is: $D = -1.3355p + 86.1974$.

The correlation coefficient is: $r \approx -0.9491$.

d. As the price of the jeans increases by $1, the demand for the jeans decreases by about 1.34 pairs per day.

334

e. $D(p) = -1.3355p + 86.1974$

f. Domain: $\{p \mid 0 < p \le 64\}$

Note that the p-intercept is roughly 64.54 and that the number of pairs of jeans in demand cannot be negative.

g. $D(28) = -1.3355(28) + 86.1974 \approx 48.8034$

Demand is about 49 pairs.

22. a. The relation is not a function because 24 is paired with both 343 and 341.

b.
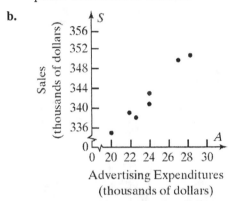

c. Using the LINear REGression program, the line of best fit is: $S = 2.0667A + 292.8869$. The correlation coefficient is: $r \approx 0.9833$.

d. As the advertising expenditure increases by 1000, the sales increase by about 2067.

e. $S(A) = 2.0667A + 292.8869$

f. Domain: $\{A \mid A \ge 0\}$

g. $S(25) = 2.0667(25) + 292.8869 \approx 344.5544$

Sales are about $344,554$.

23.
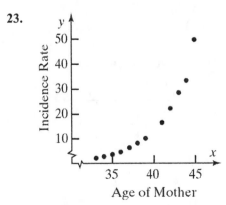

The data do not follow a linear pattern so it would not make sense to find the line of best fit.

24. Using the ordered pairs $(1, 5)$ and $(3, 8)$, the line of best fit is $y = 1.5x + 3.5$ or $y = \dfrac{3}{2}x + \dfrac{7}{2}$.

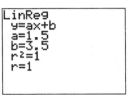

The correlation coefficient is $r = 1$. This makes sense because two points completely determine a line.

25. A correlation coefficient of 0 implies that the data do not have a linear relationship.

Section 4.3

1. $y = x^2 - 9$

To find the y-intercept, let $x = 0$:

$y = 0^2 - 9 = -9$.

To find the x-intercept(s), let $y = 0$:

$x^2 - 9 = 0$

$x^2 = 9$

$x = \pm\sqrt{9} = \pm 3$

The intercepts are $(0, -9)$, $(-3, 0)$, and $(3, 0)$.

2. $2x^2 + 7x - 4 = 0$

$(2x - 1)(x + 4) = 0$

$2x - 1 = 0 \quad$ or $\quad x + 4 = 0$

$2x = 1 \quad$ or $\qquad x = -4$

$x = \dfrac{1}{2} \quad$ or $\qquad x = -4$

The solution set is $\left\{-4, \dfrac{1}{2}\right\}$..

3. $\left(\dfrac{1}{2} \cdot (-5)\right)^2 = \dfrac{25}{4}$

4. right; 4

5. parabola

6. axis (or axis of symmetry)

7. $-\dfrac{b}{2a}$

335

8. True; $a = 2 > 0$.

9. True; $-\dfrac{b}{2a} = -\dfrac{4}{2(-1)} = 2$

10. True

11. C

12. E

13. F

14. A

15. G

16. B

17. H

18. D

19. $f(x) = \dfrac{1}{4}x^2$

Using the graph of $y = x^2$, compress vertically by a factor of $\dfrac{1}{4}$.

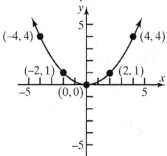

20. $f(x) = 2x^2$

Using the graph of $y = x^2$, stretch vertically by a factor of 2.

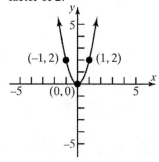

21. $f(x) = \dfrac{1}{4}x^2 - 2$

Using the graph of $y = x^2$, compress vertically by a factor of 2, then shift down 2 units.

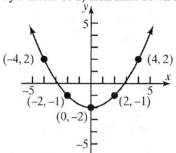

22. $f(x) = 2x^2 - 3$

Using the graph of $y = x^2$, stretch vertically by a factor of 2, then shift down 3 units.

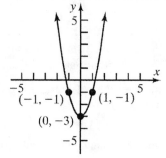

23. $f(x) = \dfrac{1}{4}x^2 + 2$

Using the graph of $y = x^2$, compress vertically by a factor of $\dfrac{1}{4}$, then shift up 2 units.

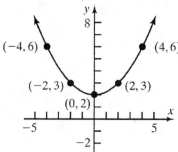

24. $f(x) = 2x^2 + 4$

Using the graph of $y = x^2$, stretch vertically by a factor of 2, then shift up 4 units.

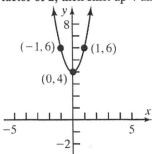

25. $f(x) = \frac{1}{4}x^2 + 1$

Using the graph of $y = x^2$, compress vertically by a factor of $\frac{1}{4}$, then shift up 1 unit.

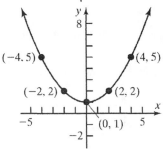

26. $f(x) = -2x^2 - 2$

Using the graph of $y = x^2$, stretch vertically by a factor of 2, reflect across the *x*-axis, then shift down 2 units.

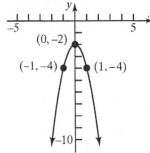

27. $f(x) = x^2 + 4x + 2$

$$= (x^2 + 4x + 4) + 2 - 4$$

$$= (x + 2)^2 - 2$$

Using the graph of $y = x^2$, shift left 2 units, then shift down 2 units.

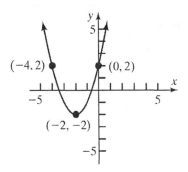

28. $f(x) = x^2 - 6x - 1$

$$= (x^2 - 6x + 9) - 1 - 9$$

$$= (x - 3)^2 - 10$$

Using the graph of $y = x^2$, shift right 3 units, then shift down 10 units.

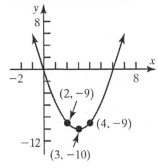

29. $f(x) = 2x^2 - 4x + 1$

$$= 2(x^2 - 2x) + 1$$

$$= 2(x^2 - 2x + 1) + 1 - 2$$

$$= 2(x - 1)^2 - 1$$

Using the graph of $y = x^2$, shift right 1 unit, stretch vertically by a factor of 2, then shift down 1 unit.

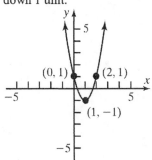

337

30. $f(x) = 3x^2 + 6x$

$= 3\left(x^2 + 2x\right)$

$= 3(x^2 + 2x + 1) - 3$

$= 3(x+1)^2 - 3$

Using the graph of $y = x^2$, shift left 1 unit, stretch vertically by a factor of 3, then shift down 3 units.

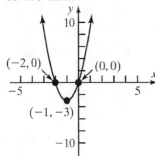

31. $f(x) = -x^2 - 2x$

$= -\left(x^2 + 2x\right)$

$= -(x^2 + 2x + 1) + 1$

$= -(x+1)^2 + 1$

Using the graph of $y = x^2$, shift left 1 unit, reflect across the x-axis, then shift up 1 unit.

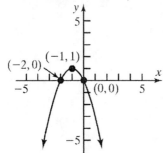

32. $f(x) = -2x^2 + 6x + 2$

$= -2\left(x^2 - 3x\right) + 2$

$= -2\left(x^2 - 3x + \dfrac{9}{4}\right) + 2 + \dfrac{9}{2}$

$= -2\left(x - \dfrac{3}{2}\right)^2 + \dfrac{13}{2}$

Using the graph of $y = x^2$, shift right $\dfrac{3}{2}$ units, reflect about the x-axis, stretch vertically by a factor of 2, then shift up $\dfrac{13}{2}$ units.

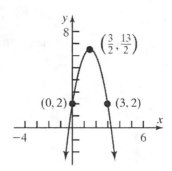

33. $f(x) = \dfrac{1}{2}x^2 + x - 1$

$= \dfrac{1}{2}\left(x^2 + 2x\right) - 1$

$= \dfrac{1}{2}\left(x^2 + 2x + 1\right) - 1 - \dfrac{1}{2}$

$= \dfrac{1}{2}(x+1)^2 - \dfrac{3}{2}$

Using the graph of $y = x^2$, shift left 1 unit, compress vertically by a factor of $\dfrac{1}{2}$, then shift down $\dfrac{3}{2}$ units.

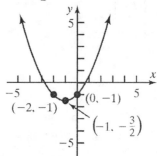

34. $f(x) = \dfrac{2}{3}x^2 + \dfrac{4}{3}x - 1$

$= \dfrac{2}{3}\left(x^2 + 2x\right) - 1$

$= \dfrac{2}{3}\left(x^2 + 2x + 1\right) - 1 - \dfrac{2}{3}$

$= \dfrac{2}{3}(x+1)^2 - \dfrac{5}{3}$

Using the graph of $y = x^2$, shift left 1 unit, compress vertically by a factor of $\dfrac{2}{3}$, then shift down $\dfrac{5}{3}$ unit.

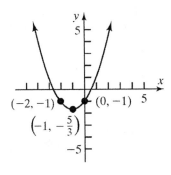

35. a. For $f(x) = x^2 + 2x$, $a = 1$, $b = 2$, $c = 0$.
Since $a = 1 > 0$, the graph opens up.
The x-coordinate of the vertex is
$$x = \frac{-b}{2a} = \frac{-(2)}{2(1)} = \frac{-2}{2} = -1.$$
The y-coordinate of the vertex is
$$f\left(\frac{-b}{2a}\right) = f(-1) = (-1)^2 + 2(-1) = 1 - 2 = -1.$$
Thus, the vertex is $(-1, -1)$.
The axis of symmetry is the line $x = -1$.
The discriminant is
$b^2 - 4ac = (2)^2 - 4(1)(0) = 4 > 0$, so the graph
has two x-intercepts.
The x-intercepts are found by solving:
$$x^2 + 2x = 0$$
$$x(x + 2) = 0$$
$$x = 0 \text{ or } x = -2$$
The x-intercepts are -2 and 0.
The y-intercept is $f(0) = 0$.

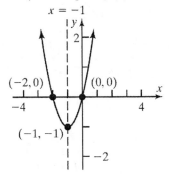

b. The domain is $(-\infty, \infty)$.
The range is $[-1, \infty)$.

c. Decreasing on $(-\infty, -1)$.
Increasing on $(-1, \infty)$.

36. a. For $f(x) = x^2 - 4x$, $a = 1$, $b = -4$, $c = 0$.
Since $a = 1 > 0$, the graph opens up.
The x-coordinate of the vertex is
$$x = \frac{-b}{2a} = \frac{-(-4)}{2(1)} = \frac{4}{2} = 2.$$
The y-coordinate of the vertex is
$$f\left(\frac{-b}{2a}\right) = f(2) = (2)^2 - 4(2) = 4 - 8 = -4.$$
Thus, the vertex is $(2, -4)$.
The axis of symmetry is the line $x = 2$.
The discriminant is:
$b^2 - 4ac = (-4)^2 - 4(1)(0) = 16 > 0$, so the
graph has two x-intercepts.
The x-intercepts are found by solving:
$$x^2 - 4x = 0$$
$$x(x - 4) = 0$$
$$x = 0 \text{ or } x = 4.$$
The x-intercepts are 0 and 4.
The y-intercept is $f(0) = 0$.

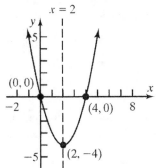

b. The domain is $(-\infty, \infty)$.
The range is $[-4, \infty)$.

c. Decreasing on $(-\infty, 2)$.
Increasing on $(2, \infty)$.

37. a. For $f(x) = -x^2 - 6x$, $a = -1$, $b = -6$,
$c = 0$. Since $a = -1 < 0$, the graph opens
down. The x-coordinate of the vertex is
$$x = \frac{-b}{2a} = \frac{-(-6)}{2(-1)} = \frac{6}{-2} = -3.$$
The y-coordinate of the vertex is
$$f\left(\frac{-b}{2a}\right) = f(-3) = -(-3)^2 - 6(-3)$$
$$= -9 + 18 = 9.$$
Thus, the vertex is $(-3, 9)$.
The axis of symmetry is the line $x = -3$.

The discriminant is:

$b^2 - 4ac = (-6)^2 - 4(-1)(0) = 36 > 0$,

so the graph has two x-intercepts.
The x-intercepts are found by solving:

$-x^2 - 6x = 0$

$-x(x + 6) = 0$

$x = 0$ or $x = -6$.

The x-intercepts are -6 and 0.
The y-intercepts are $f(0) = 0$.

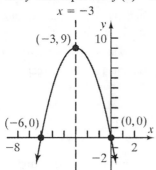

b. The domain is $(-\infty, \infty)$.
The range is $(-\infty, 9]$.

c. Increasing on $(-\infty, -3)$.
Decreasing on $(-3, \infty)$.

38. a. For $f(x) = -x^2 + 4x$, $a = -1$, $b = 4$, $c = 0$.
Since $a = -1 < 0$, the graph opens down.
The x-coordinate of the vertex is

$x = \dfrac{-b}{2a} = \dfrac{-4}{2(-1)} = \dfrac{-4}{-2} = 2$.

The y-coordinate of the vertex is

$f\left(\dfrac{-b}{2a}\right) = f(2)$

$= -(2)^2 + 4(2)$

$= 4$.

Thus, the vertex is $(2, 4)$.
The axis of symmetry is the line $x = 2$.
The discriminant is:

$b^2 - 4ac = 4^2 - 4(-1)(0) = 16 > 0$,

so the graph has two x-intercepts.
The x-intercepts are found by solving:

$-x^2 + 4x = 0$

$-x(x - 4) = 0$

$x = 0$ or $x = 4$.

The x-intercepts are 0 and 4.
The y-intercept is $f(0) = 0$.

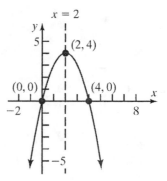

b. The domain is $(-\infty, \infty)$.
The range is $(-\infty, 4]$.

c. Increasing on $(-\infty, 2)$.
Decreasing on $(2, \infty)$.

39. a. For $f(x) = 2x^2 - 8x$, $a = 2$, $b = -8$, $c = 0$.
Since $a = 2 > 0$, the graph opens up.
The x-coordinate of the vertex is

$x = \dfrac{-b}{2a} = \dfrac{-(-8)}{2(2)} = \dfrac{8}{4} = 2$.

The y-coordinate of the vertex is

$f\left(\dfrac{-b}{2a}\right) = f(2) = 2(2)^2 - 8(2) = 8 - 16 = -8$.

Thus, the vertex is $(2, -8)$.
The axis of symmetry is the line $x = 2$.
The discriminant is:

$b^2 - 4ac = (-8)^2 - 4(2)(0) = 64 > 0$,

so the graph has two x-intercepts.
The x-intercepts are found by solving:

$2x^2 - 8x = 0$

$2x(x - 4) = 0$

$x = 0$ or $x = 4$.

The x-intercepts are 0 and 4.
The y-intercepts is $f(0) = 0$.

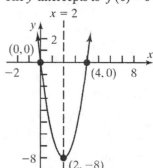

b. The domain is $(-\infty, \infty)$. The range is $[-8, \infty)$.

c. Decreasing on $(-\infty, 2)$. Increasing on $(2, \infty)$.

340

40. a. For $f(x) = 3x^2 + 18x$, $a = 3$, $b = 18$, $c = 0$.
Since $a = 3 > 0$, the graph opens up.
The x-coordinate of the vertex is
$$x = \frac{-b}{2a} = \frac{-18}{2(3)} = \frac{-18}{6} = -3.$$
The y-coordinate of the vertex is
$$f\left(\frac{-b}{2a}\right) = f(-3) = 3(-3)^2 + 18(-3)$$
$$= 27 - 54 = -27.$$
Thus, the vertex is $(-3, -27)$.
The axis of symmetry is the line $x = -3$.
The discriminant is:
$$b^2 - 4ac = (18)^2 - 4(3)(0) = 324 > 0,$$
so the graph has two x-intercepts.
The x-intercepts are found by solving:
$$3x^2 + 18x = 0$$
$$3x(x + 6) = 0$$
$$x = 0 \text{ or } x = -6.$$
The x-intercepts are 0 and -6.
The y-intercept is $f(0) = 0$.

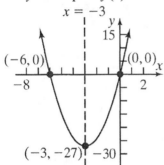

b. The domain is $(-\infty, \infty)$.
The range is $[-27, \infty)$.

c. Decreasing on $(-\infty, -3)$.
Increasing on $(-3, \infty)$.

41. a. For $f(x) = x^2 + 2x - 8$, $a = 1$, $b = 2$, $c = -8$.
Since $a = 1 > 0$, the graph opens up.
The x-coordinate of the vertex is
$$x = \frac{-b}{2a} = \frac{-2}{2(1)} = \frac{-2}{2} = -1.$$
The y-coordinate of the vertex is
$$f\left(\frac{-b}{2a}\right) = f(-1) = (-1)^2 + 2(-1) - 8$$
$$= 1 - 2 - 8 = -9.$$
Thus, the vertex is $(-1, -9)$.
The axis of symmetry is the line $x = -1$.

The discriminant is:
$$b^2 - 4ac = 2^2 - 4(1)(-8) = 4 + 32 = 36 > 0,$$
so the graph has two x-intercepts.
The x-intercepts are found by solving:
$$x^2 + 2x - 8 = 0$$
$$(x + 4)(x - 2) = 0$$
$$x = -4 \text{ or } x = 2.$$
The x-intercepts are -4 and 2.
The y-intercept is $f(0) = -8$.

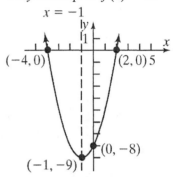

b. The domain is $(-\infty, \infty)$.
The range is $[-9, \infty)$.

c. Decreasing on $(-\infty, -1)$.
Increasing on $(-1, \infty)$.

42. a. For $f(x) = x^2 - 2x - 3$, $a = 1$, $b = -2$,
$c = -3$.
Since $a = 1 > 0$, the graph opens up.
The x-coordinate of the vertex is
$$x = \frac{-b}{2a} = \frac{-(-2)}{2(1)} = \frac{2}{2} = 1.$$

The y-coordinate of the vertex is
$$f\left(\frac{-b}{2a}\right) = f(1) = 1^2 - 2(1) - 3 = -4.$$

Thus, the vertex is $(1, -4)$.
The axis of symmetry is the line $x = 1$.
The discriminant is:
$$b^2 - 4ac = (-2)^2 - 4(1)(-3) = 4 + 12 = 16 > 0,$$
so the graph has two x-intercepts.
The x-intercepts are found by solving:
$$x^2 - 2x - 3 = 0$$
$$(x + 1)(x - 3) = 0$$
$$x = -1 \text{ or } x = 3.$$
The x-intercepts are -1 and 3.
The y-intercept is $f(0) = -3$.

341

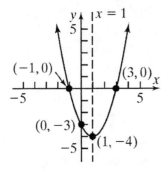

b. The domain is $(-\infty, \infty)$. The range is $[-4, \infty)$.

c. Decreasing on $(-\infty, 1)$. Increasing on $(1, \infty)$.

43. a. For $f(x) = x^2 + 2x + 1$, $a = 1$, $b = 2$, $c = 1$.
Since $a = 1 > 0$, the graph opens up.
The x-coordinate of the vertex is
$$x = \frac{-b}{2a} = \frac{-2}{2(1)} = \frac{-2}{2} = -1.$$
The y-coordinate of the vertex is
$$f\left(\frac{-b}{2a}\right) = f(-1)$$
$$= (-1)^2 + 2(-1) + 1 = 1 - 2 + 1 = 0.$$
Thus, the vertex is $(-1, 0)$.
The axis of symmetry is the line $x = -1$.

The discriminant is:
$$b^2 - 4ac = 2^2 - 4(1)(1) = 4 - 4 = 0,$$
so the graph has one x-intercept.
The x-intercept is found by solving:
$$x^2 + 2x + 1 = 0$$
$$(x + 1)^2 = 0$$
$$x = -1.$$
The x-intercept is -1.
The y-intercept is $f(0) = 1$.

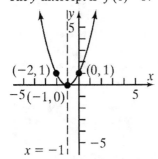

b. The domain is $(-\infty, \infty)$.
The range is $[0, \infty)$.

c. Decreasing on $(-\infty, -1)$.
Increasing on $(-1, \infty)$.

44. a. For $f(x) = x^2 + 6x + 9$, $a = 1$, $b = 6$, $c = 9$.
Since $a = 1 > 0$, the graph opens up.
The x-coordinate of the vertex is
$$x = \frac{-b}{2a} = \frac{-6}{2(1)} = \frac{-6}{2} = -3.$$
The y-coordinate of the vertex is
$$f\left(\frac{-b}{2a}\right) = f(-3)$$
$$= (-3)^2 + 6(-3) + 9 = 9 - 18 + 9 = 0.$$
Thus, the vertex is $(-3, 0)$.
The axis of symmetry is the line $x = -3$.
The discriminant is:
$$b^2 - 4ac = 6^2 - 4(1)(9) = 36 - 36 = 0,$$
so the graph has one x-intercept.
The x-intercept is found by solving:
$$x^2 + 6x + 9 = 0$$
$$(x + 3)^2 = 0$$
$$x = -3.$$
The x-intercept is -3.
The y-intercept is $f(0) = 9$.

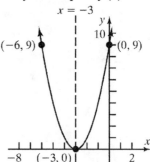

b. The domain is $(-\infty, \infty)$. The range is $[0, \infty)$.

c. Decreasing on $(-\infty, -3)$.
Increasing on $(-3, \infty)$.

45. a. For $f(x) = 2x^2 - x + 2$, $a = 2$, $b = -1$, $c = 2$.
Since $a = 2 > 0$, the graph opens up.
The x-coordinate of the vertex is
$$x = \frac{-b}{2a} = \frac{-(-1)}{2(2)} = \frac{1}{4}.$$
The y-coordinate of the vertex is
$$f\left(\frac{-b}{2a}\right) = f\left(\frac{1}{4}\right) = 2\left(\frac{1}{4}\right)^2 - \frac{1}{4} + 2$$
$$= \frac{1}{8} - \frac{1}{4} + 2 = \frac{15}{8}.$$
Thus, the vertex is $\left(\frac{1}{4}, \frac{15}{8}\right)$.

The axis of symmetry is the line $x = \frac{1}{4}$.

The discriminant is:

$b^2 - 4ac = (-1)^2 - 4(2)(2) = 1 - 16 = -15$,

so the graph has no x-intercepts.

The y-intercept is $f(0) = 2$.

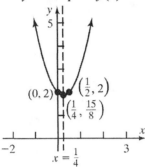

b. The domain is $(-\infty, \infty)$. The range is $\left[\frac{15}{8}, \infty\right)$.

c. Decreasing on $\left(-\infty, \frac{1}{4}\right)$. Increasing on $\left(\frac{1}{4}, \infty\right)$.

46. a. For $f(x) = 4x^2 - 2x + 1$, $a = 4$, $b = -2$, $c = 1$.

Since $a = 4 > 0$, the graph opens up.

The x-coordinate of the vertex is

$x = \dfrac{-b}{2a} = \dfrac{-(-2)}{2(4)} = \dfrac{2}{8} = \dfrac{1}{4}$.

The y-coordinate of the vertex is

$f\left(\dfrac{-b}{2a}\right) = f\left(\dfrac{1}{4}\right) = 4\left(\dfrac{1}{4}\right)^2 - 2\left(\dfrac{1}{4}\right) + 1$

$= \dfrac{1}{4} - \dfrac{1}{2} + 1 = \dfrac{3}{4}$.

Thus, the vertex is $\left(\dfrac{1}{4}, \dfrac{3}{4}\right)$.

The axis of symmetry is the line $x = \frac{1}{4}$.

The discriminant is:

$b^2 - 4ac = (-2)^2 - 4(4)(1) = 4 - 16 = -12$,

so the graph has no x-intercepts.

The y-intercept is $f(0) = 1$.

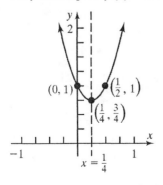

b. The domain is $(-\infty, \infty)$.

The range is $\left[\frac{3}{4}, \infty\right)$.

c. Decreasing on $\left(-\infty, \frac{1}{4}\right)$.

Increasing on $\left(\frac{1}{4}, \infty\right)$.

47. a. For $f(x) = -2x^2 + 2x - 3$, $a = -2$, $b = 2$, $c = -3$. Since $a = -2 < 0$, the graph opens down.

The x-coordinate of the vertex is

$x = \dfrac{-b}{2a} = \dfrac{-(2)}{2(-2)} = \dfrac{-2}{-4} = \dfrac{1}{2}$.

The y-coordinate of the vertex is

$f\left(\dfrac{-b}{2a}\right) = f\left(\dfrac{1}{2}\right) = -2\left(\dfrac{1}{2}\right)^2 + 2\left(\dfrac{1}{2}\right) - 3$

$= -\dfrac{1}{2} + 1 - 3 = -\dfrac{5}{2}$.

Thus, the vertex is $\left(\dfrac{1}{2}, -\dfrac{5}{2}\right)$.

The axis of symmetry is the line $x = \dfrac{1}{2}$.

The discriminant is:

$b^2 - 4ac = 2^2 - 4(-2)(-3) = 4 - 24 = -20$,

so the graph has no x-intercepts.

The y-intercept is $f(0) = -3$.

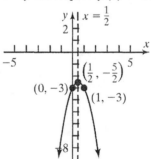

b. The domain is $(-\infty, \infty)$.

The range is $\left(-\infty, -\dfrac{5}{2}\right]$.

c. Increasing on $\left(-\infty, \dfrac{1}{2}\right)$.

Decreasing on $\left(\dfrac{1}{2}, \infty\right)$.

48. **a.** For $f(x) = -3x^2 + 3x - 2$, $a = -3$, $b = 3$,

$c = -2$. Since $a = -3 < 0$, the graph opens down.

The x-coordinate of the vertex is

$$x = \frac{-b}{2a} = \frac{-3}{2(-3)} = \frac{-3}{-6} = \frac{1}{2}.$$

The y-coordinate of the vertex is

$$f\left(\frac{-b}{2a}\right) = f\left(\frac{1}{2}\right) = -3\left(\frac{1}{2}\right)^2 + 3\left(\frac{1}{2}\right) - 2$$

$$= -\frac{3}{4} + \frac{3}{2} - 2 = -\frac{5}{4}.$$

Thus, the vertex is $\left(\frac{1}{2}, -\frac{5}{4}\right)$.

The axis of symmetry is the line $x = \frac{1}{2}$.

The discriminant is:

$$b^2 - 4ac = 3^2 - 4(-3)(-2) = 9 - 24 = -15,$$

so the graph has no x-intercepts.
The y-intercept is $f(0) = -2$.

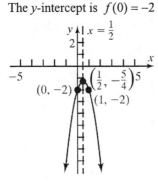

b. The domain is $(-\infty, \infty)$.

The range is $\left(-\infty, -\frac{5}{4}\right]$.

c. Increasing on $\left(-\infty, \frac{1}{2}\right)$.

Decreasing on $\left(\frac{1}{2}, \infty\right)$.

49. **a.** For $f(x) = 3x^2 + 6x + 2$, $a = 3$, $b = 6$,

$c = 2$. Since $a = 3 > 0$, the graph opens up.
The x-coordinate of the vertex is

$$x = \frac{-b}{2a} = \frac{-6}{2(3)} = \frac{-6}{6} = -1.$$

The y-coordinate of the vertex is

$$f\left(\frac{-b}{2a}\right) = f(-1) = 3(-1)^2 + 6(-1) + 2$$

$$= 3 - 6 + 2 = -1.$$

Thus, the vertex is $(-1, -1)$.
The axis of symmetry is the line $x = -1$.
The discriminant is:

$$b^2 - 4ac = 6^2 - 4(3)(2) = 36 - 24 = 12,$$

so the graph has two x-intercepts.
The x-intercepts are found by solving:

$$3x^2 + 6x + 2 = 0$$

$$x = \frac{-b \pm \sqrt{b^2 - 4ac}}{2a}$$

$$= \frac{-6 \pm \sqrt{12}}{6} = \frac{-6 \pm 2\sqrt{3}}{6} = \frac{-3 \pm \sqrt{3}}{3}$$

The x-intercepts are $-1 - \frac{\sqrt{3}}{3}$ and $-1 + \frac{\sqrt{3}}{3}$.

The y-intercept is $f(0) = 2$.

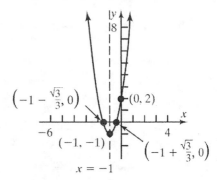

b. The domain is $(-\infty, \infty)$.

The range is $[-1, \infty)$.

c. Decreasing on $(-\infty, -1)$.

Increasing on $(-1, \infty)$.

50. **a.** For $f(x) = 2x^2 + 5x + 3$, $a = 2$, $b = 5$,

$c = 3$. Since $a = 2 > 0$, the graph opens up.
The x-coordinate of the vertex is

$$x = \frac{-b}{2a} = \frac{-5}{2(2)} = -\frac{5}{4}.$$

The y-coordinate of the vertex is

$$f\left(\frac{-b}{2a}\right) = f\left(-\frac{5}{4}\right)$$

$$= 2\left(-\frac{5}{4}\right)^2 + 5\left(-\frac{5}{4}\right) + 3$$

$$= \frac{25}{8} - \frac{25}{4} + 3$$

$$= -\frac{1}{8}.$$

Thus, the vertex is $\left(-\frac{5}{4}, -\frac{1}{8}\right)$.

The axis of symmetry is the line $x = -\dfrac{5}{4}$.

The discriminant is:
$$b^2 - 4ac = 5^2 - 4(2)(3) = 25 - 24 = 1,$$

so the graph has two x-intercepts.
The x-intercepts are found by solving:
$$2x^2 + 5x + 3 = 0$$
$$(2x+3)(x+1) = 0$$
$$x = -\dfrac{3}{2} \text{ or } x = -1.$$

The x-intercepts are $-\dfrac{3}{2}$ and -1.

The y-intercept is $f(0) = 3$.

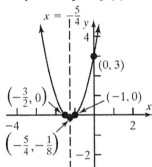

b. The domain is $(-\infty, \infty)$.

The range is $\left[-\dfrac{1}{8}, \infty\right)$.

c. Decreasing on $\left(-\infty, -\dfrac{5}{4}\right)$.

Increasing on $\left(-\dfrac{5}{4}, \infty\right)$.

51. a. For $f(x) = -4x^2 - 6x + 2$, $a = -4$, $b = -6$, $c = 2$. Since $a = -4 < 0$, the graph opens down.
The x-coordinate of the vertex is
$$x = \dfrac{-b}{2a} = \dfrac{-(-6)}{2(-4)} = \dfrac{6}{-8} = -\dfrac{3}{4}.$$
The y-coordinate of the vertex is
$$f\left(\dfrac{-b}{2a}\right) = f\left(-\dfrac{3}{4}\right) = -4\left(-\dfrac{3}{4}\right)^2 - 6\left(-\dfrac{3}{4}\right) + 2$$
$$= -\dfrac{9}{4} + \dfrac{9}{2} + 2 = \dfrac{17}{4}.$$
Thus, the vertex is $\left(-\dfrac{3}{4}, \dfrac{17}{4}\right)$.

The axis of symmetry is the line $x = -\dfrac{3}{4}$.

The discriminant is:
$$b^2 - 4ac = (-6)^2 - 4(-4)(2) = 36 + 32 = 68,$$

so the graph has two x-intercepts.
The x-intercepts are found by solving:
$$-4x^2 - 6x + 2 = 0$$
$$x = \dfrac{-b \pm \sqrt{b^2 - 4ac}}{2a} = \dfrac{-(-6) \pm \sqrt{68}}{2(-4)}$$
$$= \dfrac{6 \pm \sqrt{68}}{-8} = \dfrac{6 \pm 2\sqrt{17}}{-8} = \dfrac{3 \pm \sqrt{17}}{-4}$$

The x-intercepts are $\dfrac{-3 + \sqrt{17}}{4}$ and $\dfrac{-3 - \sqrt{17}}{4}$.

The y-intercept is $f(0) = 2$.

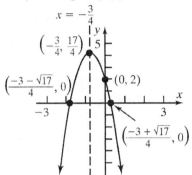

b. The domain is $(-\infty, \infty)$.

The range is $\left(-\infty, \dfrac{17}{4}\right]$.

c. Decreasing on $\left(-\dfrac{3}{4}, \infty\right)$.

Increasing on $\left(-\infty, -\dfrac{3}{4}\right)$.

52. a. For $f(x) = 3x^2 - 8x + 2$, $a = 3$, $b = -8$, $c = 2$.
Since $a = 3 > 0$, the graph opens up.
The x-coordinate of the vertex is
$$x = \dfrac{-b}{2a} = \dfrac{-(-8)}{2(3)} = \dfrac{8}{6} = \dfrac{4}{3}.$$
The y-coordinate of the vertex is
$$f\left(\dfrac{-b}{2a}\right) = f\left(\dfrac{4}{3}\right) = 3\left(\dfrac{4}{3}\right)^2 - 8\left(\dfrac{4}{3}\right) + 2$$
$$= \dfrac{16}{3} - \dfrac{32}{3} + 2 = -\dfrac{10}{3}.$$
Thus, the vertex is $\left(\dfrac{4}{3}, -\dfrac{10}{3}\right)$.

The axis of symmetry is the line $x = \dfrac{4}{3}$.

345

The discriminant is:

$b^2 - 4ac = (-8)^2 - 4(3)(2) = 64 - 24 = 40$,

so the graph has two x-intercepts.

The x-intercepts are found by solving:

$3x^2 - 8x + 2 = 0$

$x = \dfrac{-b \pm \sqrt{b^2 - 4ac}}{2a} = \dfrac{-(-8) \pm \sqrt{40}}{2(3)}$

$= \dfrac{8 \pm \sqrt{40}}{6} = \dfrac{8 \pm 2\sqrt{10}}{6} = \dfrac{4 \pm \sqrt{10}}{3}$

The x-intercepts are $\dfrac{4 + \sqrt{10}}{3}$ and $\dfrac{4 - \sqrt{10}}{3}$.

The y-intercept is $f(0) = 2$.

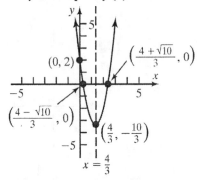

b. The domain is $(-\infty, \infty)$.

The range is $\left[-\dfrac{10}{3}, \infty \right)$.

c. Decreasing on $\left(-\infty, \dfrac{4}{3} \right)$.

Increasing on $\left(\dfrac{4}{3}, \infty \right)$.

53. Consider the form $y = a(x - h)^2 + k$. From the graph we know that the vertex is $(-1, -2)$ so we have $h = -1$ and $k = -2$. The graph also passes through the point $(x, y) = (0, -1)$. Substituting these values for x, y, h, and k, we can solve for a:

$-1 = a(0 - (-1))^2 + (-2)$

$-1 = a(1)^2 - 2$

$-1 = a - 2$

$1 = a$

The quadratic function is

$f(x) = (x + 1)^2 - 2 = x^2 + 2x - 1$.

54. Consider the form $y = a(x - h)^2 + k$. From the graph we know that the vertex is $(2, 1)$ so we have $h = 2$ and $k = 1$. The graph also passes through the point $(x, y) = (0, 5)$. Substituting these values for x, y, h, and k, we can solve for a:

$5 = a(0 - 2)^2 + 1$

$5 = a(-2)^2 + 1$

$5 = 4a + 1$

$4 = 4a$

$1 = a$

The quadratic function is

$f(x) = (x - 2)^2 + 1 = x^2 - 4x + 5$.

55. Consider the form $y = a(x - h)^2 + k$. From the graph we know that the vertex is $(-3, 5)$ so we have $h = -3$ and $k = 5$. The graph also passes through the point $(x, y) = (0, -4)$. Substituting these values for x, y, h, and k, we can solve for a:

$-4 = a(0 - (-3))^2 + 5$

$-4 = a(3)^2 + 5$

$-4 = 9a + 5$

$-9 = 9a$

$-1 = a$

The quadratic function is

$f(x) = -(x + 3)^2 + 5 = -x^2 - 6x - 4$.

56. Consider the form $y = a(x - h)^2 + k$. From the graph we know that the vertex is $(2, 3)$ so we have $h = 2$ and $k = 3$. The graph also passes through the point $(x, y) = (0, -1)$. Substituting these values for x, y, h, and k, we can solve for a:

$-1 = a(0 - 2)^2 + 3$

$-1 = a(-2)^2 + 3$

$-1 = 4a + 3$

$-4 = 4a$

$-1 = a$

The quadratic function is

$f(x) = -(x - 2)^2 + 3 = -x^2 + 4x - 1$.

57. Consider the form $y = a(x-h)^2 + k$. From the graph we know that the vertex is $(1, -3)$ so we have $h = 1$ and $k = -3$. The graph also passes through the point $(x, y) = (3, 5)$. Substituting these values for x, y, h, and k, we can solve for a:

$5 = a(3-1)^2 + (-3)$

$5 = a(2)^2 - 3$

$5 = 4a - 3$

$8 = 4a$

$2 = a$

The quadratic function is

$f(x) = 2(x-1)^2 - 3 = 2x^2 - 4x - 1$.

58. Consider the form $y = a(x-h)^2 + k$. From the graph we know that the vertex is $(-2, 6)$ so we have $h = -2$ and $k = 6$. The graph also passes through the point $(x, y) = (-4, -2)$. Substituting these values for x, y, h, and k, we can solve for a:

$-2 = a(-4-(-2))^2 + 6$

$-2 = a(-2)^2 + 6$

$-2 = 4a + 6$

$-8 = 4a$

$-2 = a$

The quadratic function is

$f(x) = -2(x+2)^2 + 6 = -2x^2 - 8x - 2$.

59. For $f(x) = 2x^2 + 12x$, $a = 2$, $b = 12$, $c = 0$. Since $a = 2 > 0$, the graph opens up, so the vertex is a minimum point. The minimum occurs at $x = \dfrac{-b}{2a} = \dfrac{-12}{2(2)} = \dfrac{-12}{4} = -3$.

The minimum value is

$f(-3) = 2(-3)^2 + 12(-3) = 18 - 36 = -18$.

60. For $f(x) = -2x^2 + 12x$, $a = -2$, $b = 12$, $c = 0$, . Since $a = -2 < 0$, the graph opens down, so the vertex is a maximum point. The maximum occurs at $x = \dfrac{-b}{2a} = \dfrac{-12}{2(-2)} = \dfrac{-12}{-4} = 3$.

The maximum value is

$f(3) = -2(3)^2 + 12(3) = -18 + 36 = 18$.

61. For $f(x) = 2x^2 + 12x - 3$, $a = 2$, $b = 12$, $c = -3$. Since $a = 2 > 0$, the graph opens up, so the vertex is a minimum point. The minimum occurs at $x = \dfrac{-b}{2a} = \dfrac{-12}{2(2)} = \dfrac{-12}{4} = -3$. The minimum value is

$f(-3) = 2(-3)^2 + 12(-3) - 3 = 18 - 36 - 3 = -21$.

62. For $f(x) = 4x^2 - 8x + 3$, $a = 4$, $b = -8$, $c = 3$. Since $a = 4 > 0$, the graph opens up, so the vertex is a minimum point. The minimum occurs at $x = \dfrac{-b}{2a} = \dfrac{-(-8)}{2(4)} = \dfrac{8}{8} = 1$. The minimum value is

$f(1) = 4(1)^2 - 8(1) + 3 = 4 - 8 + 3 = -1$.

63. For $f(x) = -x^2 + 10x - 4$, $a = -1$, $b = 10$, $c = -4$. Since $a = -1 < 0$, the graph opens down, so the vertex is a maximum point. The maximum occurs at $x = \dfrac{-b}{2a} = \dfrac{-10}{2(-1)} = \dfrac{-10}{-2} = 5$. The maximum value is

$f(5) = -(5)^2 + 10(5) - 4 = -25 + 50 - 4 = 21$.

64. For $f(x) = -2x^2 + 8x + 3$, $a = -2$, $b = 8$, $c = 3$. Since $a = -2 < 0$, the graph opens down, so the vertex is a maximum point. The maximum occurs at $x = \dfrac{-b}{2a} = \dfrac{-8}{2(-2)} = \dfrac{-8}{-4} = 2$. The maximum value is

$f(2) = -2(2)^2 + 8(2) + 3 = -8 + 16 + 3 = 11$.

65. For $f(x) = -3x^2 + 12x + 1$, $a = -3$, $b = 12$, $c = 1$. Since $a = -3 < 0$, the graph opens down, so the vertex is a maximum point. The maximum occurs at $x = \dfrac{-b}{2a} = \dfrac{-12}{2(-3)} = \dfrac{-12}{-6} = 2$. The maximum value is $f(2) = -3(2)^2 + 12(2) + 1 = -12 + 24 + 1 = 13$.

66. For $f(x) = 4x^2 - 4x$, $a = 4$, $b = -4$, $c = 0$. Since $a = 4 > 0$, the graph opens up, so the vertex is a minimum point. The minimum occurs at $x = \dfrac{-b}{2a} = \dfrac{-(-4)}{2(4)} = \dfrac{4}{8} = \dfrac{1}{2}$. The minimum value is

$f\left(\dfrac{1}{2}\right) = 4\left(\dfrac{1}{2}\right)^2 - 4\left(\dfrac{1}{2}\right) = 1 - 2 = -1$.

67. Use the form $f(x) = a(x-h)^2 + k$.

The vertex is $(0, 2)$, so $h = 0$ and $k = 2$.

$f(x) = a(x-0)^2 + 2 = ax^2 + 2$.

Since the graph passes through $(1, 8)$, $f(1) = 8$.

$f(x) = ax^2 + 2$

$8 = a(1)^2 + 2$

$8 = a + 2$

$6 = a$

$f(x) = 6x^2 + 2$.

$a = 6, b = 0, c = 2$

68. Use the form $f(x) = a(x-h)^2 + k$.

The vertex is $(1, 4)$, so $h = 1$ and $k = 4$.

$f(x) = a(x-1)^2 + 4$.

Since the graph passes through $(-1, -8)$,

$f(-1) = -8$.

$-8 = a(-1-1)^2 + 4$

$-8 = a(-2)^2 + 4$

$-8 = 4a + 4$

$-12 = 4a$

$-3 = a$

$f(x) = -3(x-1)^2 + 4$

$= -3(x^2 - 2x + 1) + 4$

$= -3x^2 + 6x - 3 + 4$

$= -3x^2 + 6x + 1$

$a = -3, b = 6, c = 1$

69. a and d.

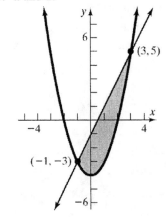

b. $f(x) = g(x)$

$2x - 1 = x^2 - 4$

$0 = x^2 - 2x - 3$

$0 = (x+1)(x-3)$

$x + 1 = 0$ or $x - 3 = 0$

$x = -1$ $\qquad$ $x = 3$

The solution set is $\{-1, 3\}$.

c. $f(-1) = 2(-1) - 1 = -2 - 1 = -3$

$g(-1) = (-1)^2 - 4 = 1 - 4 = -3$

$f(3) = 2(3) - 1 = 6 - 1 = 5$

$g(3) = (3)^2 - 4 = 9 - 4 = 5$

Thus, the graphs of f and g intersect at the points $(-1, -3)$ and $(3, 5)$.

70. a and d.

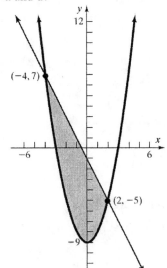

b. $f(x) = g(x)$

$-2x - 1 = x^2 - 9$

$0 = x^2 + 2x - 8$

$0 = (x+4)(x-2)$

$x + 4 = 0$ or $x - 2 = 0$

$x = -4$ $\qquad$ $x = 2$

The solution set is $\{-4, 2\}$.

c. $f(-4) = -2(-4) - 1 = 8 - 1 = 7$

$g(-4) = (-4)^2 - 9 = 16 - 9 = 7$

$f(2) = -2(2) - 1 = -4 - 1 = -5$

$g(2) = (2)^2 - 9 = 4 - 9 = -5$

Thus, the graphs of f and g intersect at the points $(-4, 7)$ and $(2, -5)$.

71. a and d.

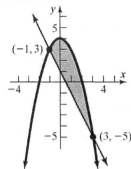

b. $f(x) = g(x)$

$-x^2 + 4 = -2x + 1$

$0 = x^2 - 2x - 3$

$0 = (x+1)(x-3)$

$x+1 = 0 \quad \text{or} \quad x-3 = 0$

$x = -1 \qquad x = 3$

The solution set is $\{-1, 3\}$.

c. $f(1) = -(-1)^2 + 4 = -1 + 4 = 3$

$g(1) = -2(-1) + 1 = 2 + 1 = 3$

$f(3) = -(3)^2 + 4 = -9 + 4 = -5$

$g(3) = -2(3) + 1 = -6 + 1 = -5$

Thus, the graphs of f and g intersect at the points $(-1, 3)$ and $(3, -5)$.

72. a and d.

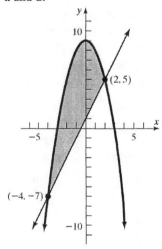

b. $f(x) = g(x)$

$-x^2 + 9 = 2x + 1$

$0 = x^2 + 2x - 8$

$0 = (x+4)(x-2)$

$x+4 = 0 \quad \text{or} \quad x-2 = 0$

$x = -4 \qquad x = 2$

The solution set is $\{-4, 2\}$.

c. $f(-4) = -(-4)^2 + 9 = -16 + 9 = -7$

$g(-4) = 2(-4) + 1 = -8 + 1 = -7$

$f(2) = -(2)^2 + 9 = -4 + 9 = 5$

$g(2) = 2(2) + 1 = 4 + 1 = 5$

Thus, the graphs of f and g intersect at the points $(-4, -7)$ and $(2, 5)$.

73. a and d.

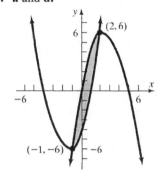

b. $f(x) = g(x)$

$-x^2 + 5x = x^2 + 3x - 4$

$0 = 2x^2 - 2x - 4$

$0 = x^2 - x - 2$

$0 = (x+1)(x-2)$

$x+1 = 0 \quad \text{or} \quad x-2 = 0$

$x = -1 \qquad x = 2$

The solution set is $\{-1, 2\}$.

c. $f(-1) = -(-1)^2 + 5(-1) = -1 - 5 = -6$

$g(-1) = (-1)^2 + 3(-1) - 4 = 1 - 3 - 4 = -6$

$f(2) = -(2)^2 + 5(2) = -4 + 10 = 6$

$g(2) = 2^2 + 3(2) - 4 = 4 + 6 - 4 = 6$

Thus, the graphs of f and g intersect at the points $(-1, -6)$ and $(2, 6)$.

74. a and d.

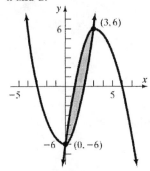

b.
$$f(x) = g(x)$$
$$-x^2 + 7x - 6 = x^2 + x - 6$$
$$0 = 2x^2 - 6x$$
$$0 = 2x(x - 3)$$
$$2x = 0 \quad \text{or} \quad x - 3 = 0$$
$$x = 0 \qquad\qquad x = 3$$

The solution set is $\{0, 3\}$.

c. $f(0) = -(0)^2 + 7(0) - 6 = -6$

$g(0) = 0^2 + 0 - 6 = -6$

$f(3) = -(3)^2 + 7(3) - 6 = -9 + 21 - 6 = 6$

$g(3) = 3^2 + 3 - 6 = 9 + 3 - 6 = 6$

Thus, the graphs of f and g intersect at the points $(0, -6)$ and $(3, 6)$.

75. a. For $a = 1$:
$$f(x) = a(x - r_1)(x - r_2)$$
$$= 1(x - (-3))(x - 1)$$
$$= (x + 3)(x - 1) = x^2 + 2x - 3$$

For $a = 2$:
$$f(x) = 2(x - (-3))(x - 1)$$
$$= 2(x + 3)(x - 1)$$
$$= 2(x^2 + 2x - 3) = 2x^2 + 4x - 6$$

For $a = -2$:
$$f(x) = -2(x - (-3))(x - 1)$$
$$= -2(x + 3)(x - 1)$$
$$= -2(x^2 + 2x - 3) = -2x^2 - 4x + 6$$

For $a = 5$:
$$f(x) = 5(x - (-3))(x - 1)$$
$$= 5(x + 3)(x - 1)$$
$$= 5(x^2 + 2x - 3) = 5x^2 + 10x - 15$$

b. The x-intercepts are not affected by the value of a. The y-intercept is multiplied by the value of a.

c. The axis of symmetry is unaffected by the value of a. For this problem, the axis of symmetry is $x = -1$ for all values of a.

d. The x-coordinate of the vertex is not affected by the value of a. The y-coordinate of the vertex is multiplied by the value of a.

e. The x-coordinate of the vertex is the mean of the x-intercepts.

76. a. For $a = 1$:
$$f(x) = 1(x - (-5))(x - 3)$$
$$= (x + 5)(x - 3) = x^2 + 2x - 15$$

For $a = 2$:
$$f(x) = 2(x - (-5))(x - 3)$$
$$= 2(x + 5)(x - 3)$$
$$= 2(x^2 + 2x - 15) = 2x^2 + 4x - 30$$

For $a = -2$:
$$f(x) = -2(x - (-5))(x - 3)$$
$$= -2(x + 5)(x - 3)$$
$$= -2(x^2 + 2x - 15) = -2x^2 - 4x + 30$$

For $a = 5$:
$$f(x) = 5(x - (-5))(x - 3)$$
$$= 5(x + 5)(x - 3)$$
$$= 5(x^2 + 2x - 15) = 5x^2 + 10x - 75$$

b. The x-intercepts are not affected by the value of a. The y-intercept is multiplied by the value of a.

c. The axis of symmetry is unaffected by the value of a. For this problem, the axis of symmetry is $x = -1$ for all values of a.

d. The x-coordinate of the vertex is not affected by the value of a. The y-coordinate of the vertex is multiplied by the value of a.

e. The x-coordinate of the vertex is the mean of the x-intercepts.

77. a. $x = -\dfrac{b}{2a} = -\dfrac{4}{2(1)} = -2$

$y = f(-2) = (-2)^2 + 4(-2) - 21 = -25$

The vertex is $(-2, -25)$.

b.
$$f(x) = 0$$
$$x^2 + 4x - 21 = 0$$
$$(x+7)(x-3) = 0$$
$$x + 7 = 0 \quad \text{or} \quad x - 3 = 0$$
$$x = -7 \qquad\qquad x = 3$$
The *x*-intercepts of *f* are $(-7, 0)$ and $(3, 0)$.

c.
$$f(x) = -21$$
$$x^2 + 4x - 21 = -21$$
$$x^2 + 4x = 0$$
$$x(x+4) = 0$$
$$x = 0 \quad \text{or} \quad x + 4 = 0$$
$$x = -4$$
The solutions $f(x) = -21$ are -4 and 0.
Thus, the points $(-4, -21)$ and $(0, -21)$ are on the graph of *f*.

d.

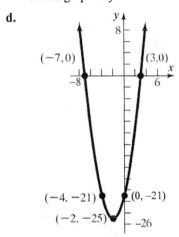

78. a.
$$x = -\frac{b}{2a} = -\frac{2}{2(1)} = -1$$
$$y = f(-1) = (-1)^2 + 2(-1) - 8 = -9$$
The vertex is $(-1, -9)$.

b.
$$f(x) = 0$$
$$x^2 + 2x - 8 = 0$$
$$(x+4)(x-2) = 0$$
$$x + 4 = 0 \quad \text{or} \quad x - 2 = 0$$
$$x = -4 \qquad\qquad x = 2$$
The *x*-intercepts of *f* are $(-4, 0)$ and $(2, 0)$.

c.
$$f(x) = -8$$
$$x^2 + 2x - 8 = -8$$
$$x^2 + 2x = 0$$
$$x(x+2) = 0$$
$$x = 0 \quad \text{or} \quad x + 2 = 0$$
$$x = -2$$
The solutions $f(x) = -8$ are -2 and 0. Thus, the points $(-2, -8)$ and $(0, -8)$ are on the graph of *f*.

d.

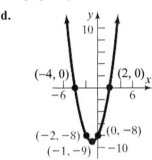

79. Let (x, y) represent a point on the line $y = x$. Then the distance from (x, y) to the point $(3, 1)$ is
$$d = \sqrt{(x-3)^2 + (y-1)^2}.$$ Since $y = x$, we can replace the *y* variable with *x* so that we have the distance expressed as a function of *x*:
$$d(x) = \sqrt{(x-3)^2 + (x-1)^2}$$
$$= \sqrt{x^2 - 6x + 9 + x^2 - 2x + 1}$$
$$= \sqrt{2x^2 - 8x + 10}$$
Squaring both sides of this function, we obtain
$$[d(x)]^2 = 2x^2 - 8x + 10.$$
Now, the expression on the right is quadratic. Since $a = 2 > 0$, it has a minimum. Finding the *x*-coordinate of the minimum point of $[d(x)]^2$ will also give us the *x*-coordinate of the minimum of
$d(x)$: $x = \dfrac{-b}{2a} = \dfrac{-(-8)}{2(2)} = \dfrac{8}{4} = 2$. So, 2 is the *x*-coordinate of the point on the line $y = x$ that is closest to the point $(3, 1)$. Since $y = x$, the *y*-coordinate is also 2. Thus, the point is $(2, 2)$ is the point on the line $y = x$ that is closest to $(3, 1)$.

351

80. Let (x, y) represent a point on the line $y = x + 1$. Then the distance from (x, y) to the point $(4, 1)$ is $d = \sqrt{(x-4)^2 + (y-1)^2}$. Replacing the y variable with $x + 1$, we find the distance expressed as a function of x:

$$d(x) = \sqrt{(x-4)^2 + ((x+1)-1)^2}$$
$$= \sqrt{x^2 - 8x + 16 + x^2}$$
$$= \sqrt{2x^2 - 8x + 16}$$

Squaring both sides of this function, we obtain $[d(x)]^2 = 2x^2 - 8x + 16$.

Now, the expression on the right is quadratic. Since $a = 2 > 0$, it has a minimum. Finding the x-coordinate of the minimum point of $[d(x)]^2$ will also give us the x-coordinate of the minimum of $d(x)$: $x = \dfrac{-b}{2a} = \dfrac{-(-8)}{2(2)} = \dfrac{8}{4} = 2$. So, 2 is the x-coordinate of the point on the line $y = x + 1$ that is closest to the point $(4, 1)$. The y-coordinate is $y = 2 + 1 = 3$. Thus, the point is $(2, 3)$ is the point on the line $y = x + 1$ that is closest to $(4, 1)$.

81. $R(p) = -4p^2 + 4000p$, $a = -4, b = 4000, c = 0$.

Since $a = -4 < 0$ the graph is a parabola that opens down, so the vertex is a maximum point. The maximum occurs at $p = \dfrac{-b}{2a} = \dfrac{-4000}{2(-4)} = 500$.

Thus, the unit price should be \$500 for maximum revenue. The maximum revenue is

$$R(500) = -4(500)^2 + 4000(500)$$
$$= -1000000 + 2000000$$
$$= \$1,000,000$$

82. $R(p) = -\dfrac{1}{2}p^2 + 1900p$, $a = -\dfrac{1}{2}, b = 1900, c = 0$.

Since $a = -\dfrac{1}{2} < 0$, the graph is a parabola that opens down, so the vertex is a maximum point. The maximum occurs at

$p = \dfrac{-b}{2a} = \dfrac{-1900}{2(-1/2)} = \dfrac{-1900}{-1} = 1900$. Thus, the

unit price should be \$1900 for maximum revenue. The maximum revenue is

$$R(1900) = -\dfrac{1}{2}(1900)^2 + 1900(1900)$$
$$= -1805000 + 3610000$$
$$= \$1,805,000$$

83. a. $C(x) = x^2 - 140x + 7400$,

$a = 1, b = -140, c = 7400$. Since $a = 1 > 0$, the graph opens up, so the vertex is a minimum point. The minimum marginal cost occurs at $x = \dfrac{-b}{2a} = \dfrac{-(-140)}{2(1)} = \dfrac{140}{2} = 70$ mp3 players produced.

b. The minimum marginal cost is

$$f\left(\dfrac{-b}{2a}\right) = f(70) = (70)^2 - 140(70) + 7400$$
$$= 4900 - 9800 + 7400$$
$$= \$2500$$

84. a. $C(x) = 5x^2 - 200x + 4000$,

$a = 5, b = -200, c = 4000$. Since $a = 5 > 0$, the graph opens up, so the vertex is a minimum point. The minimum marginal cost occurs at $x = \dfrac{-b}{2a} = \dfrac{-(-200)}{2(5)} = \dfrac{200}{10} = 20$ thousand cell phones manufactured.

b. The minimum marginal cost is

$$f\left(\dfrac{-b}{2a}\right) = f(20) = 5(20)^2 - 200(20) + 4000$$
$$= 2000 - 4000 + 4000$$
$$= \$2000$$

85. a. $a = -3.24, b = 242.1, c = -738.4$

The maximum number of hunters occurs when the income level is

$$x = \dfrac{-b}{2a} = \dfrac{-242.1}{2(-3.24)} = \dfrac{-242.1}{-6.48} \approx 37.4 \text{ years old}$$

The number of hunters this old is:

$$H(37.4) = -3.24(37.4)^2 + 242.1(37.4) - 738.4$$
$$\approx 3784 \text{ hunters}$$

b. The maximum occurs when $x = 37.4$, so the function increases on the interval $(0, 37.4)$ and decreases on the interval $(37.4, \infty)$. Therefore, the number of hunters is decreasing for individuals who are between ages 40 and 45 years of age.

352

86. a. $a = -0.008, b = 0.815, c = -9.983$

The maximum number of hunters occurs when the income level is

$$x = \frac{-b}{2a} = \frac{-0.815}{2(-0.008)} = \frac{-0.815}{-0.016} \approx 50.9 \text{ years old.}$$

The percentage for this age is:

$$P(50.9) = -0.008(50.9)^2 + 0.815(50.9) - 9.983$$
$$\approx 10.8\%$$

b. The maximum occurs when $x = 51$, so the function increases on the interval $(0, 51)$ and decreases on the interval $(51, \infty)$.

Therefore, the percentage of Americans who have earned advanced degrees if increasing for individuals who are between ages 40 and 50 years of age.

87. a. $M(23) = 1.00(23)^2 - 136.74(23) + 4764.89$
$$\approx 2149 \text{ male murder victims}$$

b. $1.00x^2 - 136.74x + 4764.89 = 1456$
$$1.00x^2 - 136.74x + 3308.89 = 0$$
$$a = 1.00, b = -136.74, c = 3308.89$$

$$x = \frac{-(-136.74) \pm \sqrt{(-136.74)^2 - 4(1.00)(3308.89)}}{2(1.00)}$$

$$= \frac{136.74 \pm \sqrt{5462.2676}}{2}$$

$$\approx \frac{136.74 \pm 73.91}{2}$$

$$x \approx 31.4 \text{ or } x \approx 105.3$$

Disregard 105.3 since it falls outside the domain for the function $(20 \le x < 90)$. Thus, the number of male murder victims is 1456 for 31.4 year olds.

c. A minimum occurs when
$$x = \frac{-b}{2a} = \frac{-(-136.74)}{2(1.00)} = \frac{136.74}{2} = 68.37,$$

so the function decreases on the interval $(20, 68.37)$ and increases on the interval $(68.37, 90)$. As age increases between 20 and 65, the number of murder victims decreases.

88. a. $H(45) = 0.004(45)^2 - 0.197(45) + 54.06$
$$\approx 4.6\%$$

b. Solve for x:
$$H(x) = 0.004x^2 - 0.197x + 5.406 = 10$$
$$0.004x^2 - 0.197x + 5.406 = 10$$
$$0.004x^2 - 0.197x - 4.594 = 0$$
$$a = 0.004, b = -0.197, c = -4.594$$

$$x = \frac{-b \pm \sqrt{b^2 - 4ac}}{2a}$$

$$= \frac{-(-0.197) \pm \sqrt{(-0.197)^2 - 4(0.004)(-4.594)}}{2(0.004)}$$

$$= \frac{0.197 \pm \sqrt{0.112313}}{0.008} \approx \frac{0.197 \pm 0.335}{0.008}$$

$$\approx 66.5 \text{ or } -17.25, \text{ which is not practical}$$

The only practical solution is $x \approx 66.5$ years old.

c.

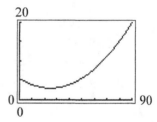

d. Initially, as age increases (between the ages of 0 and 20.6 years), the percentage of income spent on healthcare decreases, but then (after the age of 20.6 years) the percentage increases as age increases.

89. a. $R(x) = 75x - 0.2x^2$
$$a = -0.2, b = 75, c = 0$$

The maximum revenue occurs when
$$x = \frac{-b}{2a} = \frac{-75}{2(-0.2)} = \frac{-75}{-0.4} = 187.5$$

The maximum revenue occurs when $x = 187$ or $x = 188$ watches.

The maximum revenue is:
$$R(187) = 75(187) - 0.2(187)^2 = \$7031.20$$
$$R(188) = 75(188) - 0.2(188)^2 = \$7031.20$$

b. $P(x) = R(x) - C(x)$
$$= 75x - 0.2x^2 - (32x + 1750)$$
$$= -0.2x^2 + 43x - 1750$$

c. $P(x) = -0.2x^2 + 43x - 1750$

$a = -0.2, b = 43, c = -1750$

$$x = \frac{-b}{2a} = \frac{-43}{2(-0.2)} = \frac{-43}{-0.4} = 107.5$$

The maximum profit occurs when $x = 107$ or $x = 108$ watches.
The maximum profit is:

$$P(107) = -0.2(107)^2 + 43(107) - 1750$$
$$= \$561.20$$

$$P(108) = -0.2(108)^2 + 43(108) - 1750$$
$$= \$561.20$$

d. Answers will vary.

90. a. $R(x) = 9.5x - 0.04x^2$

$a = -0.04, b = 9.5, c = 0$

The maximum revenue occurs when

$$x = \frac{-b}{2a} = \frac{-9.5}{2(-0.04)} = \frac{-9.5}{-0.08}$$

$$= 118.75 \approx 119 \text{ boxes of candy}$$

The maximum revenue is:

$$R(119) = 9.5(119) - 0.04(119)^2 = \$564.06$$

b. $P(x) = R(x) - C(x)$

$$= 9.5x - 0.04x^2 - (1.25x + 250)$$

$$= -0.04x^2 + 8.25x - 250$$

c. $P(x) = -0.04x^2 + 8.25x - 250$

$a = -0.04, b = 8.25, c = -250$

The maximum profit occurs when

$$x = \frac{-b}{2a} = \frac{-8.25}{2(-0.04)} = \frac{-8.25}{-0.08}$$

$$= 103.125 \approx 103 \text{ boxes of candy}$$

The maximum profit is:

$$P(103) = -0.04(103)^2 + 8.25(103) - 250$$

$$= \$175.39$$

d. Answers will vary.

91. If x is even, then ax^2 and bx are even. When two even numbers are added to an odd number the result is odd. Thus, $f(x)$ is odd. If x is odd, then ax^2 and bx are odd. The sum of three odd numbers is an odd number. Thus, $f(x)$ is odd.

92. Answers will vary.

93. $y = x^2 + 2x - 3$; $y = x^2 + 2x + 1$; $y = x^2 + 2x$

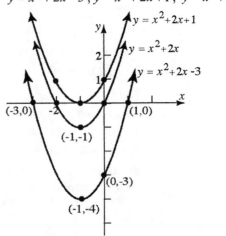

Each member of this family will be a parabola with the following characteristics:
(i) opens upwards since a > 0;

(ii) vertex occurs at $x = -\dfrac{b}{2a} = -\dfrac{2}{2(1)} = -1$;

(iii) There is at least one x-intercept since $b^2 - 4ac \geq 0$.

94. $y = x^2 - 4x + 1$; $y = x^2 + 1$; $y = x^2 + 4x + 1$

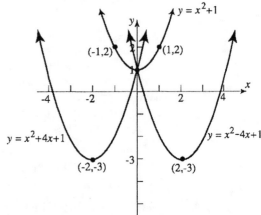

Each member of this family will be a parabola with the following characteristics:
(i) opens upwards since $a > 0$
(ii) y-intercept occurs at (0, 1).

95. The graph of the quadratic function $f(x) = ax^2 + bx + c$ will not have any x-intercepts whenever $b^2 - 4ac < 0$.

96. By completing the square on the quadratic function $f(x) = ax^2 + bx + c$ we obtain the

equation $y = a\left(x + \dfrac{b}{2a}\right)^2 + c - \dfrac{b^2}{4a}$. We can then draw the graph by applying transformations to the graph of the basic parabola $y = x^2$, which opens up. When $a > 0$, the basic parabola will either be stretched or compressed vertically. When $a < 0$, the basic parabola will either be stretched or compressed vertically as well as reflected across the x-axis. Therefore, when $a > 0$, the graph of $f(x) = ax^2 + bx + c$ will open up, and when $a < 0$, the graph of $f(x) = ax^2 + bx + c$ will open down.

97. No. We know that the graph of a quadratic function $f(x) = ax^2 + bx + c$ is a parabola with vertex $\left(-\dfrac{b}{2a}, f\left(-\dfrac{b}{2a}\right)\right)$. If $a > 0$, then the vertex is a minimum point, so the range is $\left[f\left(-\dfrac{b}{2a}\right), \infty\right)$. If $a < 0$, then the vertex is a maximum point, so the range is $\left(-\infty, f\left(-\dfrac{b}{2a}\right)\right]$. Therefore, it is impossible for the range to be $\left(-\infty, \infty\right)$.

98. Two quadratic functions can intersect 0, 1, or 2 times.

Section 4.4

1. $R = 3x$

2. $y = 1.7826x + 4.0652$

```
LinReg
y=ax+b
a=1.782608696
b=4.065217391
r²=.9585174626
r=.9790390506
```

3. a. $R(x) = x\left(-\dfrac{1}{6}x + 100\right) = -\dfrac{1}{6}x^2 + 100x$

b. $R(200) = -\dfrac{1}{6}(200)^2 + 100(200)$

$= \dfrac{-20000}{3} + 20000$

$= \dfrac{40000}{3} \approx \$13,333.33$

c. $x = \dfrac{-b}{2a} = \dfrac{-100}{2\left(-\frac{1}{6}\right)} = \dfrac{-100}{\left(-\frac{1}{3}\right)} = \dfrac{300}{1} = 300$

The maximum revenue is

$R(300) = -\dfrac{1}{6}(300)^2 + 100(300)$

$= -15000 + 30000$

$= \$15,000$

d. $p = -\dfrac{1}{6}(300) + 100 = -50 + 100 = \$50$

4. a. $R(x) = x\left(-\dfrac{1}{3}x + 100\right) = -\dfrac{1}{3}x^2 + 100x$

b. $R(100) = -\dfrac{1}{3}(100)^2 + 100(100)$

$= \dfrac{-10000}{3} + 10000$

$= \dfrac{20000}{3} \approx \$6,666.67$

c. $x = \dfrac{-b}{2a} = \dfrac{-100}{2\left(-\frac{1}{3}\right)} = \dfrac{-100}{\left(-\frac{2}{3}\right)} = \dfrac{300}{2} = 150$

The maximum revenue is

$R(150) = -\dfrac{1}{3}(150)^2 + 100(150)$

$= -7500 + 15000$

$= \$7,500$

d. $p = -\dfrac{1}{3}(150) + 100 = -50 + 100 = \$50$

5. a. If $x = -5p + 100$, then $p = \dfrac{100 - x}{5}$.

$R(x) = x\left(\dfrac{100 - x}{5}\right) = -\dfrac{1}{5}x^2 + 20x$

b. $R(15) = -\dfrac{1}{5}(15)^2 + 20(15)$

$= -45 + 300$

$= \$255$

c. $x = \dfrac{-b}{2a} = \dfrac{-20}{2\left(-\frac{1}{5}\right)} = \dfrac{-20}{\left(-\frac{2}{5}\right)} = \dfrac{100}{2} = 50$

The maximum revenue is

$R(50) = -\dfrac{1}{5}(50)^2 + 20(50)$

$= -500 + 1000 = \$500$

d. $p = \dfrac{100-50}{5} = \dfrac{50}{5} = \$10$

6. a. If $x = -20p + 500$, then $p = \dfrac{500-x}{20}$.

$R(x) = x\left(\dfrac{500-x}{20}\right) = -\dfrac{1}{20}x^2 + 25x$

b. $R(20) = -\dfrac{1}{20}(20)^2 + 25(20)$

$= -20 + 500$

$= \$480$

c. $x = \dfrac{-b}{2a} = \dfrac{-25}{2\left(-\frac{1}{20}\right)} = \dfrac{-25}{\left(-\frac{1}{10}\right)} = \dfrac{250}{1} = 250$.

The maximum revenue is

$R(250) = -\dfrac{1}{20}(250)^2 + 25(250)$

$= -3125 + 6250$

$= \$3125$

d. $p = \dfrac{500-250}{20} = \dfrac{250}{20} = \$12.50$

7. a. Let $w =$ width and $l =$ length of the rectangular area.
Solving $P = 2w + 2l = 400$ for l:

$l = \dfrac{400-2w}{2} = 200 - w$.

Then $A(w) = (200-w)w = 200w - w^2$

$= -w^2 + 200w$

b. $w = \dfrac{-b}{2a} = \dfrac{-200}{2(-1)} = \dfrac{-200}{-2} = 100$ yards

c. $A(100) = -100^2 + 200(100)$

$= -10000 + 20000$

$= 10,000$ yd^2

8. a. Let $x =$ width and $y =$ width of the rectangle.
Solving $P = 2x + 2y = 3000$ for y:

$y = \dfrac{3000-2x}{2} = 1500 - x$.

Then $A(x) = (1500-x)x$

$= 1500x - x^2$

$= -x^2 + 1500x$.

b. $x = \dfrac{-b}{2a} = \dfrac{-1500}{2(-1)} = \dfrac{-1500}{-2} = 750$ feet

c. $A(750) = -750^2 + 1500(750)$

$= -562500 + 1125000$

$= 562,500$ ft^2

9. Let $x =$ width and $y =$ length of the rectangle.
Solving $P = 2x + y = 4000$ for y:

$y = 4000 - 2x$.

Then $A(x) = (4000-2x)x$

$= 4000x - 2x^2$

$= -2x^2 + 4000x$

$x = \dfrac{-b}{2a} = \dfrac{-4000}{2(-2)} = \dfrac{-4000}{-4} = 1000$ meters

maximizes area.

$A(1000) = -2(1000)^2 + 4000(1000)$.

$= -2000000 + 4000000$

$= 2,000,000$

The largest area that can be enclosed is 2,000,000 square meters.

10. Let $x =$ width and $y =$ length of the rectangle.
$2x + y = 2000$

$y = 2000 - 2x$

Then $A(x) = (2000-2x)x$

$= 2000x - 2x^2$

$= -2x^2 + 2000x$

$x = \dfrac{-b}{2a} = \dfrac{-2000}{2(-2)} = \dfrac{-2000}{-4} = 500$ meters

maximizes area.

$A(500) = -2(500)^2 + 2000(500)$

$= -500,000 + 1,000,000$

$= 500,000$

The largest area that can be enclosed is 500,000 square meters.

11. $h(x) = \dfrac{-32x^2}{(50)^2} + x + 200 = -\dfrac{8}{625}x^2 + x + 200$

a. $a = -\dfrac{8}{625}, b = 1, c = 200.$

The maximum height occurs when
$$x = \frac{-b}{2a} = \frac{-1}{2(-8/625)} = \frac{625}{16} \approx 39 \text{ feet from}$$
base of the cliff.

b. The maximum height is
$$h\left(\frac{625}{16}\right) = \frac{-8}{625}\left(\frac{625}{16}\right)^2 + \frac{625}{16} + 200$$
$$= \frac{7025}{32} \approx 219.5 \text{ feet.}$$

c. Solving when $h(x) = 0$:
$$-\frac{8}{625}x^2 + x + 200 = 0$$
$$x = \frac{-1 \pm \sqrt{1^2 - 4(-8/625)(200)}}{2(-8/625)}$$
$$x \approx \frac{-1 \pm \sqrt{11.24}}{-0.0256}$$

$x \approx -91.90$ or $x \approx 170$
Since the distance cannot be negative, the projectile strikes the water approximately 170 feet from the base of the cliff.

d.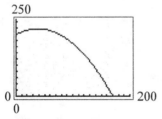

e. Using the MAXIMUM function
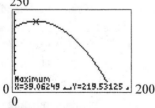

Using the ZERO function
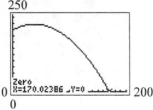

f. $-\dfrac{8}{625}x^2 + x + 200 = 100$

$$-\frac{8}{625}x^2 + x + 100 = 0$$

$$x = \frac{\sqrt{1^2 - 4(-8/625)(100)}}{2(-8/625)} = \frac{-1 \pm \sqrt{6.12}}{-0.0256}$$

$x \approx -57.57$ or $x \approx 135.70$
Since the distance cannot be negative, the projectile is 100 feet above the water when it is approximately 135.7 feet from the base of the cliff.

12. a. $h(x) = \dfrac{-32x^2}{(100)^2} + x = -\dfrac{2}{625}x^2 + x$

$a = -\dfrac{2}{625}, b = 1, c = 0.$

The maximum height occurs when
$$x = \frac{-b}{2a} = \frac{-1}{2(-2/625)} = \frac{625}{4} = 156.25 \text{ feet}$$

b. The maximum height is
$$h\left(\frac{625}{4}\right) = \frac{-2}{625}\left(\frac{625}{4}\right)^2 + \frac{625}{4}$$
$$= \frac{625}{8} = 78.125 \text{ feet}$$

c. Solving when $h(x) = 0$:
$$-\frac{2}{625}x^2 + x = 0$$
$$x\left(-\frac{2}{625}x + 1\right) = 0$$
$$x = 0 \quad \text{or} \quad -\frac{2}{625}x + 1 = 0$$
$$x = 0 \quad \text{or} \quad 1 = \frac{2}{625}x$$
$$x = 0 \quad \text{or} \quad x = \frac{625}{2} = 312.5$$

Since the distance cannot be zero, the projectile lands 312.5 feet from where it was fired.

d.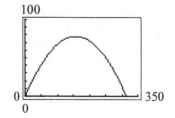

e. Using the MAXIMUM function

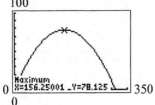

Using the ZERO function

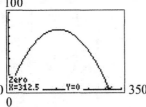

f. Solving when $h(x) = 50$:

$$-\frac{2}{625}x^2 + x = 50$$

$$-\frac{2}{625}x^2 + x - 50 = 0$$

$$x = \frac{-1 \pm \sqrt{1^2 - 4(-2/625)(-50)}}{2(-2/625)}$$

$$= \frac{-1 \pm \sqrt{0.36}}{-0.0064} \approx \frac{-1 \pm 0.6}{-0.0064}$$

$$x = 62.5 \text{ or } x = 250$$

The projectile is 50 feet above the ground 62.5 feet and 250 feet from where it was fired.

13. Locate the origin at the point where the cable touches the road. Then the equation of the parabola is of the form: $y = ax^2$, where $a > 0$. Since the point $(200, 75)$ is on the parabola, we can find the constant a:

Since $75 = a(200)^2$, then $a = \frac{75}{200^2} = 0.001875$.

When $x = 100$, we have:

$y = 0.001875(100)^2 = 18.75$ meters.

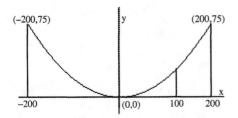

14. Locate the origin at the point directly under the highest point of the arch. Then the equation of the parabola is of the form:

$y = -ax^2 + k$, where $a > 0$. Since the maximum height is 25 feet, when $x = 0$, $y = k = 25$. Since the point $(60, 0)$ is on the parabola, we can find the constant a: Since $0 = -a(60)^2 + 25$ then

$a = \frac{25}{60^2}$. The equation of the parabola is:

$y = -\frac{25}{60^2}x^2 + 25$.

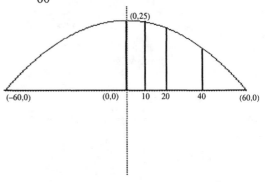

At $x = 10$:

$$y = -\frac{25}{60^2}(10)^2 + 25 = -\frac{25}{36} + 25 \approx 24.3 \text{ ft.}$$

At $x = 20$:

$$y = -\frac{25}{60^2}(20)^2 + 25 = -\frac{25}{9} + 25 \approx 22.2 \text{ ft.}$$

At $x = 40$:

$$y = -\frac{25}{60^2}(40)^2 + 25 = -\frac{100}{9} + 25 \approx 13.9 \text{ ft.}$$

15. Let x = the depth of the gutter and y = the width of the gutter.

Then $A = xy$ is the cross-sectional area of the gutter. Since the aluminum sheets for the gutter are 12 inches wide, we have $2x + y = 12$. Solving for y: $y = 12 - 2x$. The area is to be maximized, so: $A = xy = x(12 - 2x) = -2x^2 + 12x$. This equation is a parabola opening down; thus, it has a maximum when $x = \frac{-b}{2a} = \frac{-12}{2(-2)} = \frac{-12}{-4} = 3$.

Thus, a depth of 3 inches produces a maximum cross-sectional area.

16. Let $x =$ width of the window and $y =$ height of the rectangular part of the window. The perimeter of the window is: $x + 2y + \dfrac{\pi x}{2} = 20$.

Solving for y: $y = \dfrac{40 - 2x - \pi x}{4}$.

The area of the window is:

$$A(x) = x\left(\dfrac{40 - 2x - \pi x}{4}\right) + \dfrac{1}{2}\pi\left(\dfrac{x}{2}\right)^2$$

$$= 10x - \dfrac{x^2}{2} - \dfrac{\pi x^2}{4} + \dfrac{\pi x^2}{8}$$

$$= \left(-\dfrac{1}{2} - \dfrac{\pi}{8}\right)x^2 + 10x.$$

This equation is a parabola opening down; thus, it has a maximum when

$$x = \dfrac{-b}{2a} = \dfrac{-10}{2\left(-\dfrac{1}{2} - \dfrac{\pi}{8}\right)} = \dfrac{10}{\left(1 + \dfrac{\pi}{4}\right)} \approx 5.6 \text{ feet}$$

$$y = \dfrac{40 - 2(5.60) - \pi(5.60)}{4} \approx 2.8 \text{ feet}$$

The width of the window is about 5.6 feet and the height of the rectangular part is approximately 2.8 feet. The radius of the semicircle is roughly 2.8 feet, so the total height is about 5.6 feet.

17. Let $x =$ the width of the rectangle or the diameter of the semicircle and let $y =$ the length of the rectangle.

The perimeter of each semicircle is $\dfrac{\pi x}{2}$.

The perimeter of the track is given by: $\dfrac{\pi x}{2} + \dfrac{\pi x}{2} + y + y = 1500$.

Solving for x:

$$\pi x + 2y = 1500$$

$$\pi x = 1500 - 2y$$

$$x = \dfrac{1500 - 2y}{\pi}$$

The area of the rectangle is:

$$A = xy = \left(\dfrac{1500 - 2y}{\pi}\right)y = \dfrac{-2}{\pi}y^2 + \dfrac{1500}{\pi}y.$$

This equation is a parabola opening down; thus, it has a maximum when

$$y = \dfrac{-b}{2a} = \dfrac{\dfrac{-1500}{\pi}}{2\left(\dfrac{-2}{\pi}\right)} = \dfrac{-1500}{-4} = 375.$$

Thus, $x = \dfrac{1500 - 2(375)}{\pi} = \dfrac{750}{\pi} \approx 238.73$

The dimensions for the rectangle with maximum area are $\dfrac{750}{\pi} \approx 238.73$ meters by 375 meters.

18. Let $x =$ width of the window and $y =$ height of the rectangular part of the window. The perimeter of the window is:

$$3x + 2y = 16$$

$$y = \dfrac{16 - 3x}{2}$$

The area of the window is

$$A(x) = x\left(\dfrac{16 - 3x}{2}\right) + \dfrac{\sqrt{3}}{4}x^2$$

$$= 8x - \dfrac{3}{2}x^2 + \dfrac{\sqrt{3}}{4}x^2$$

$$= \left(-\dfrac{3}{2} + \dfrac{\sqrt{3}}{4}\right)x^2 + 8x$$

This equation is a parabola opening down; thus, it has a maximum when

$$x = \dfrac{-b}{2a} = \dfrac{-8}{2\left(-\dfrac{3}{2} + \dfrac{\sqrt{3}}{4}\right)}$$

$$= \dfrac{-8}{-3 + \dfrac{\sqrt{3}}{2}} = \dfrac{-16}{-6 + \sqrt{3}} \approx 3.75 \text{ ft.}$$

The window is approximately 3.75 feet wide.

$$y = \dfrac{16 - 3\left(\dfrac{-16}{-6 + \sqrt{3}}\right)}{2} = \dfrac{16 + \dfrac{48}{-6 + \sqrt{3}}}{2} = 8 + \dfrac{24}{-6 + \sqrt{3}}$$

The height of the equilateral triangle is

$$\dfrac{\sqrt{3}}{2}\left(\dfrac{-16}{-6 + \sqrt{3}}\right) = \dfrac{-8\sqrt{3}}{-6 + \sqrt{3}} \text{ feet, so the total height is}$$

$$8 + \dfrac{24}{-6 + \sqrt{3}} + \dfrac{-8\sqrt{3}}{-6 + \sqrt{3}} \approx 5.62 \text{ feet.}$$

19. $d = 1.1v + 0.06v^2$

   a. If $v = 45$, then

$$d = 1.1(45) + 0.06(45)^2 = 49.6 + 121.5 = 171$$

A car traveling 45 miles per hour on dry, level concrete will require 171 feet to stop.

   b. If $d = 200$, then

$$200 = 1.1v + 0.06v^2$$

$$0.06v^2 + 1.1v - 200 = 0$$

$$v = \frac{-1.1 \pm \sqrt{(1.1)^2 - 4(0.06)(-200)}}{2(0.06)}$$

$$= \frac{-1.1 \pm \sqrt{49.21}}{0.12}$$

$v \approx -67.62$ or $v \approx 49.29$

Speed cannot be negative, so the maximum speed that you could be traveling and avoid the accident is about 49 miles per hour.

   c. The term $1.1v$ might represent the reaction time distance.

20. $C(x) = 34.87x^2 - 98.1x + 258.3$

   a. The year 2003 corresponds to $x = 4$:

$$C(x) = 34.87(4)^2 - 98.1(4) + 258.3$$

$$= 557.92 - 392.4 + 258.3 = 423.82$$

According to the model, the total cost of claims for the year 2003 was $423.82 million.

   b. Note that $a = 34.87 > 0$, so the quadratic model has a minimum point. The x-coordinate of the minimum point is

$$x = \frac{-b}{2a} = \frac{-(-98.1)}{2(34.87)} \approx 1.41.$$

Now, $1999 + 1.41 = 2000.41$, so according to the model, the catastrophic loss claims were at a minimum during the year 2000.

   c. Answers will vary. One possibility follows: Since the model is based on data only for the years 1999 – 2005, it will most likely not be useful to predict claims so far in the future. Cyclical weather patterns could be the reason for the increase in loss claims.

21. We are given: $V(x) = kx(a - x) = -kx^2 + akx$.

The reaction rate is a maximum when:

$$x = \frac{-b}{2a} = \frac{-ak}{2(-k)} = \frac{ak}{2k} = \frac{a}{2}.$$

22. We have:

$$a(-h)^2 + b(-h) + c = ah^2 - bh + c = y_0$$

$$a(0)^2 + b(0) + c = c = y_1$$

$$a(h)^2 + b(h) + c = ah^2 + bh + c = y_2$$

Equating the two equations for the area, we have:

$$y_0 + 4y_1 + y_2 = ah^2 - bh + c + 4c + ah^2 + bh + c$$

$$= 2ah^2 + 6c.$$

Therefore,

$$\text{Area} = \frac{h}{3}\left(2ah^2 + 6c\right) = \frac{h}{3}\left(y_0 + 4y_1 + y_2\right) \text{ sq. units.}$$

23. $f(x) = -5x^2 + 8, \; h = 1$

$$\text{Area} = \frac{h}{3}\left(2ah^2 + 6c\right) = \frac{1}{3}\left(2(-5)(1)^2 + 6(8)\right)$$

$$= \frac{1}{3}(-10 + 48) = \frac{38}{3} \text{ sq. units}$$

24. $f(x) = 2x^2 + 8, \; h = 2$

$$\text{Area} = \frac{h}{3}(2ah^2 + 6c) = \frac{2}{3}\left(2(2)(2)^2 + 6(8)\right)$$

$$= \frac{2}{3}(16 + 48) = \frac{2}{3}(64) = \frac{128}{3} \text{ sq. units}$$

25. $f(x) = x^2 + 3x + 5, \; h = 4$

$$\text{Area} = \frac{h}{3}\left(2ah^2 + 6c\right) = \frac{4}{3}\left(2(1)(4)^2 + 6(5)\right)$$

$$= \frac{4}{3}(32 + 30) = \frac{248}{3} \text{ sq. units}$$

26. $f(x) = -x^2 + x + 4, \; h = 1$

$$\text{Area} = \frac{h}{3}(2ah^2 + 6c) = \frac{1}{3}\left(2(-1)(1)^2 + 6(4)\right)$$

$$= \frac{1}{3}(-2 + 24) = \frac{1}{3}(22) = \frac{22}{3} \text{ sq. units}$$

27. a.

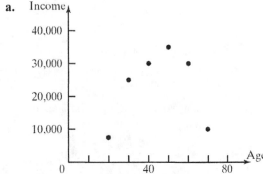

From the graph, the data appear to be quadratic with $a < 0$.

b. $x = \dfrac{-b}{2a} = \dfrac{-3157}{2(-34.3)} \approx 46$

An individual will earn the most income at an age of 46 years.

c. The maximum income will be:

$I(46) = -34.3(46)^2 + 3157(46) - 39,114$
$\approx \$33,529$

d. Using the QUADratic REGression program

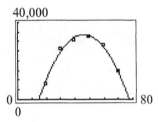

$I(x) = -34.3x^2 + 3157x - 39,114$

e.

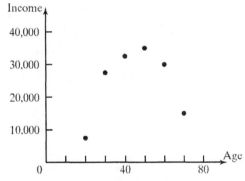

28. a.

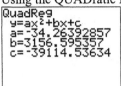

From the graph, the data appear to be quadratic with $a < 0$.

b. $x = \dfrac{-b}{2a} = \dfrac{-3186}{2(-34.5)} \approx 46$

An individual will earn the most income at an age of 46 years.

c. The maximum income will be:

$I(46) = -34.5(46)^2 + 3186(46) - 39,335$
$\approx \$34,219$

d. Using the QUADratic REGression program

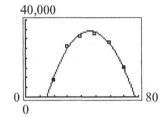

$I(x) = -34.5x^2 + 3186x - 39,335$

e.

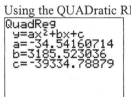

29. a.

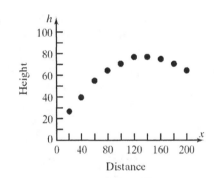

From the graph, the data appear to be quadratic with $a < 0$.

b. $x = \dfrac{-b}{2a} = \dfrac{-1.03}{2(-0.0037)} \approx 139.2$

The ball will travel 139.2 feet before it reaches its maximum height.

c. The maximum height will be:

$h(139.2) = -0.0037(139.2)^2 + 1.03(139.2) + 5.7$
$\approx 77.4 \text{ feet}$

d. Using the QUADratic REGression program

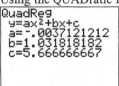

$h(x) = -0.0037x^2 + 1.03x + 5.7$

e.

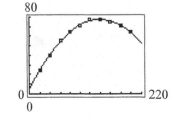

30. a.

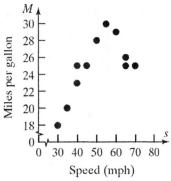

Speed (mph)

From the graph, the data appear to be quadratic with $a < 0$.

b. $x = \dfrac{-b}{2a} = \dfrac{-1.93}{2(-0.017)} \approx 56.8$

The speed that maximizes miles per gallon is 56.8 miles per hour.

c. The miles per gallon for a speed of 56.8 miles per hour is:

$M(63) = -0.017(56.8)^2 + 1.93(56.8) - 25.34$

≈ 29.4 miles per gallon

d. Using the QUADratic REGression program

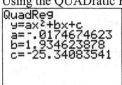

$M(s) = -0.017s^2 + 1.93s - 25.34$

e.

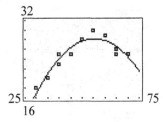

31. Answers will vary. One possibility follows: If the price is $140, no one will buy the calculators, thus making the revenue $0.

Section 4.5

1. $-3x - 2 < 7$

$-3x < 9$

$x > -3$

The solution set is $\{x \mid x > -3\}$ or $(-3, \infty)$.

2. $(-2, 7]$ represents the numbers between -2 and 7, including 7 but not including -2. Using inequality notation, this is written as $-2 < x \le 7$.

3. a. $f(x) > 0$ when the graph of f is above the x-axis. Thus, $\{x \mid x < -2 \text{ or } x > 2\}$ or, using interval notation, $(-\infty, -2) \cup (2, \infty)$.

b. $f(x) \le 0$ when the graph of f is below or intersects the x-axis. Thus, $\{x \mid -2 \le x \le 2\}$ or, using interval notation, $[-2, 2]$.

4. a. $g(x) < 0$ when the graph of g is below the x-axis. Thus, $\{x \mid x < -1 \text{ or } x > 4\}$ or, using interval notation, $(-\infty, -1) \cup (4, \infty)$.

b. $g(x) \ge 0$ when the graph of f is above or intersects the x-axis. Thus, $\{x \mid -1 \le x \le 4\}$ or, using interval notation, $[-1, 4]$.

5. a. $g(x) \ge f(x)$ when the graph of g is above or intersects the graph of f. Thus $\{x \mid -2 \le x \le 1\}$ or, using interval notation, $[-2, 1]$.

b. $f(x) > g(x)$ when the graph of f is above the graph of g. Thus, $\{x \mid x < -2 \text{ or } x > 1\}$ or, using interval notation, $(-\infty, -2) \cup (1, \infty)$.

6. a. $f(x) < g(x)$ when the graph of f is below the graph of g. Thus, $\{x \mid x < -3 \text{ or } x > 1\}$ or, using interval notation, $(-\infty, -3) \cup (1, \infty)$.

b. $f(x) \ge g(x)$ when the graph of f is above or intersects the graph of g. Thus, $\{x \mid -3 \le x \le 1\}$ or, using interval notation, $[-3, 1]$.

7. $x^2 - 3x - 10 < 0$

We graph the function $f(x) = x^2 - 3x - 10$. The intercepts are

y-intercept: $f(0) = -10$

x-intercepts: $x^2 - 3x - 10 = 0$
$$(x - 5)(x + 2) = 0$$
$$x = 5, x = -2$$

The vertex is at $x = \dfrac{-b}{2a} = \dfrac{-(-3)}{2(1)} = \dfrac{3}{2}$. Since

$f\left(\dfrac{3}{2}\right) = -\dfrac{49}{4}$, the vertex is $\left(\dfrac{3}{2}, -\dfrac{49}{4}\right)$.

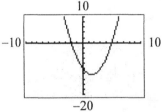

The graph is below the x-axis for $-2 < x < 5$. Since the inequality is strict, the solution set is $\left\{ x \mid -2 < x < 5 \right\}$ or, using interval notation, $(-2, 5)$.

8. $x^2 + 3x - 10 > 0$

We graph the function $f(x) = x^2 + 3x - 10$. The intercepts are

y-intercept: $f(0) = -10$

x-intercepts: $x^2 + 3x - 10 = 0$
$$(x + 5)(x - 2) = 0$$
$$x = -5, x = 2$$

The vertex is at $x = \dfrac{-b}{2a} = \dfrac{-(3)}{2(1)} = -\dfrac{3}{2}$. Since

$f\left(-\dfrac{3}{2}\right) = -\dfrac{49}{4}$, the vertex is $\left(-\dfrac{3}{2}, -\dfrac{49}{4}\right)$.

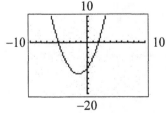

The graph is above the x-axis when $x < -5$ or $x > 2$. Since the inequality is strict, the solution set is $\left\{ x \mid x < -5 \text{ or } x > 2 \right\}$ or, using interval notation, $(-\infty, -5) \cup (2, \infty)$.

9. $x^2 - 4x > 0$

We graph the function $f(x) = x^2 - 4x$. The intercepts are

y-intercept: $f(0) = 0$

x-intercepts: $x^2 - 4x = 0$
$$x(x - 4) = 0$$
$$x = 0, x = 4$$

The vertex is at $x = \dfrac{-b}{2a} = \dfrac{-(-4)}{2(1)} = \dfrac{4}{2} = 2$. Since

$f(2) = -4$, the vertex is $(2, -4)$.

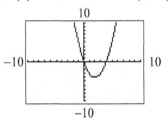

The graph is above the x-axis when $x < 0$ or $x > 4$. Since the inequality is strict, the solution set is $\left\{ x \mid x < 0 \text{ or } x > 4 \right\}$ or, using interval notation, $(-\infty, 0) \cup (4, \infty)$.

10. $x^2 + 8x > 0$

We graph the function $f(x) = x^2 + 8x$. The intercepts are

y-intercept: $f(0) = 0$

x-intercepts: $x^2 + 8x = 0$
$$x(x + 8) = 0$$
$$x = 0, x = -8$$

The vertex is at $x = \dfrac{-b}{2a} = \dfrac{-(8)}{2(1)} = \dfrac{-8}{2} = -4$.

Since $f(-4) = -16$, the vertex is $(-4, -16)$.

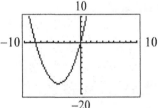

The graph is above the x-axis when $x < -8$ or $x > 0$. Since the inequality is strict, the solution set is $\left\{ x \mid x < -8 \text{ or } x > 0 \right\}$ or, using interval notation, $(-\infty, -8) \cup (0, \infty)$.

11. $x^2 - 9 < 0$

We graph the function $f(x) = x^2 - 9$. The intercepts are

y-intercept: $f(0) = -9$

x-intercepts: $\quad x^2 - 9 = 0$
$$(x+3)(x-3) = 0$$
$$x = -3, \ x = 3$$

The vertex is at $x = \dfrac{-b}{2a} = \dfrac{-(0)}{2(1)} = 0$. Since

$f(0) = -9$, the vertex is $(0, -9)$.

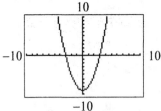

The graph is below the x-axis when $-3 < x < 3$. Since the inequality is strict, the solution set is $\{ x \mid -3 < x < 3 \}$ or, using interval notation, $(-3, 3)$.

12. $x^2 - 1 < 0$

We graph the function $f(x) = x^2 - 1$. The intercepts are

y-intercept: $f(0) = -1$

x-intercepts: $\quad x^2 - 1 = 0$
$$(x+1)(x-1) = 0$$
$$x = -1, \ x = 1$$

The vertex is at $x = \dfrac{-b}{2a} = \dfrac{-(0)}{2(1)} = 0$. Since

$f(0) = -1$, the vertex is $(0, -1)$.

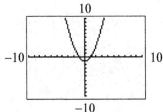

The graph is below the x-axis when $-1 < x < 1$. Since the inequality is strict, the solution set is $\{ x \mid -1 < x < 1 \}$ or, using interval notation, $(-1, 1)$.

13. $\qquad x^2 + x > 12$

$x^2 + x - 12 > 0$

We graph the function $f(x) = x^2 + x - 12$.

y-intercept: $f(0) = -12$

x-intercepts: $\quad x^2 + x - 12 = 0$
$$(x+4)(x-3) = 0$$
$$x = -4, \ x = 3$$

The vertex is at $x = \dfrac{-b}{2a} = \dfrac{-(1)}{2(1)} = -\dfrac{1}{2}$. Since

$f\left(-\dfrac{1}{2}\right) = -\dfrac{49}{4}$, the vertex is $\left(-\dfrac{1}{2}, -\dfrac{49}{4}\right)$.

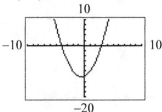

The graph is above the x-axis when $x < -4$ or $x > 3$. Since the inequality is strict, the solution set is $\{ x \mid x < -4 \ \text{or} \ x > 3 \}$ or, using interval notation, $(-\infty, -4) \cup (3, \infty)$.

14. $\qquad x^2 + 7x < -12$

$x^2 + 7x + 12 < 0$

We graph the function $f(x) = x^2 + 7x + 12$.

y-intercept: $f(0) = 12$

x-intercepts: $\quad x^2 + 7x + 12 = 0$
$$(x+4)(x+3) = 0$$
$$x = -4, \ x = -3$$

The vertex is at $x = \dfrac{-b}{2a} = \dfrac{-(7)}{2(1)} = -\dfrac{7}{2}$. Since

$f\left(-\dfrac{7}{2}\right) = -\dfrac{1}{4}$, the vertex is $\left(-\dfrac{1}{2}, -\dfrac{1}{4}\right)$.

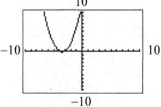

The graph is below the x-axis when $-4 < x < -3$. Since the inequality is strict, the solution set is $\{ x \mid -4 < x < -3 \}$ or, using interval notation, $(-4, -3)$.

15. $2x^2 < 5x + 3$

$2x^2 - 5x - 3 < 0$

We graph the function $f(x) = 2x^2 - 5x - 3$. The intercepts are

y-intercept: $f(0) = -3$

x-intercepts: $2x^2 - 5x - 3 = 0$

$$(2x+1)(x-3) = 0$$

$$x = -\frac{1}{2}, \ x = 3$$

The vertex is at $x = \dfrac{-b}{2a} = \dfrac{-(-5)}{2(2)} = \dfrac{5}{4}$. Since

$f\left(\dfrac{5}{4}\right) = -\dfrac{49}{8}$, the vertex is $\left(\dfrac{5}{4}, -\dfrac{49}{8}\right)$.

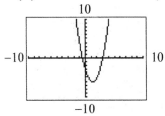

The graph is below the x-axis when $-\dfrac{1}{2} < x < 3$.

Since the inequality is strict, the solution set is

$\left\{ x \middle| -\dfrac{1}{2} < x < 3 \right\}$ or, using interval notation,

$\left(-\dfrac{1}{2}, \ 3\right)$.

16. $6x^2 < 6 + 5x$

$6x^2 - 5x - 6 < 0$

We graph the function $f(x) = 6x^2 - 5x - 6$. The intercepts are

y-intercept: $f(0) = -6$

x-intercepts: $6x^2 - 5x - 6 = 0$

$$(3x+2)(2x-3) = 0$$

$$x = -\frac{2}{3}, \ x = \frac{3}{2}$$

The vertex is at $x = \dfrac{-b}{2a} = \dfrac{-(-5)}{2(6)} = \dfrac{5}{12}$. Since

$f\left(\dfrac{5}{12}\right) = -\dfrac{169}{24}$, the vertex is $\left(\dfrac{5}{12}, -\dfrac{169}{24}\right)$.

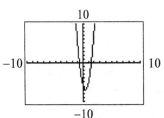

The graph is below the x-axis when $-\dfrac{2}{3} < x < \dfrac{3}{2}$.

Since the inequality is strict, the solution set is

$\left\{ x \middle| -\dfrac{2}{3} < x < \dfrac{3}{2} \right\}$ or, using interval notation,

$\left(-\dfrac{2}{3}, \ \dfrac{3}{2}\right)$.

17. $x(x-7) > 8$

$x^2 - 7x > 8$

$x^2 - 7x - 8 > 0$

We graph the function $f(x) = x^2 - 7x - 8$. The intercepts are

y-intercept: $f(0) = -8$

x-intercepts: $x^2 - 7x - 8 = 0$

$$(x+1)(x-8) = 0$$

$$x = -1, \ x = 8$$

The vertex is at $x = \dfrac{-b}{2a} = \dfrac{-(-7)}{2(1)} = \dfrac{7}{2}$. Since

$f\left(\dfrac{7}{2}\right) = -\dfrac{81}{4}$, the vertex is $\left(\dfrac{7}{2}, -\dfrac{81}{4}\right)$.

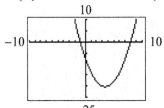

The graph is above the x-axis when $x < -1$ or $x > 8$. Since the inequality is strict, the solution set is $\left\{ x \middle| x < -1 \text{ or } x > 8 \right\}$ or, using interval notation, $(-\infty, -1) \cup (8, \infty)$.

18. $x(x+1) > 20$

$x^2 + x > 20$

$x^2 + x - 20 > 0$

We graph the function $f(x) = x^2 + x - 20$.

y-intercept: $f(0) = -20$

x-intercepts: $x^2 + x - 20 = 0$

$(x+5)(x-4) = 0$

$x = -5,\ x = 4$

The vertex is at $x = \dfrac{-b}{2a} = \dfrac{-(1)}{2(1)} = -\dfrac{1}{2}$. Since

$f\left(-\dfrac{1}{2}\right) = -\dfrac{81}{4}$, the vertex is $\left(-\dfrac{1}{2}, -\dfrac{81}{4}\right)$.

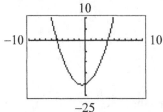

The graph is above the x-axis when $x < -5$ or $x > 4$. Since the inequality is strict, the solution set is $\{x \mid x < -5 \text{ or } x > 4\}$ or, using interval notation, $(-\infty, -5) \cup (4, \infty)$.

19. $4x^2 + 9 < 6x$

$4x^2 - 6x + 9 < 0$

We graph the function $f(x) = 4x^2 - 6x + 9$.

y-intercept: $f(0) = 9$

x-intercepts: $x = \dfrac{-(-6) \pm \sqrt{(-6)^2 - 4(4)(9)}}{2(4)}$

$= \dfrac{6 \pm \sqrt{-108}}{8}$ (not real)

Therefore, f has no x-intercepts.

The vertex is at $x = \dfrac{-b}{2a} = \dfrac{-(-6)}{2(4)} = \dfrac{6}{8} = \dfrac{3}{4}$. Since

$f\left(\dfrac{3}{4}\right) = \dfrac{27}{4}$, the vertex is $\left(\dfrac{3}{4}, \dfrac{27}{4}\right)$.

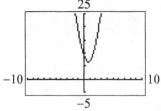

The graph is never below the x-axis. Thus, there is no real solution.

20. $25x^2 + 16 < 40x$

$25x^2 - 40x + 16 < 0$

We graph the function $f(x) = 25x^2 - 40x + 16$.

y-intercept: $f(0) = 16$

x-intercepts: $25x^2 - 40x + 16 = 0$

$(5x-4)^2 = 0$

$5x - 4 = 0$

$x = \dfrac{4}{5}$

The vertex is at $x = \dfrac{-b}{2a} = \dfrac{-(-40)}{2(25)} = \dfrac{40}{50} = \dfrac{4}{5}$.

Since $f\left(\dfrac{4}{5}\right) = 0$, the vertex is $\left(\dfrac{4}{5}, 0\right)$.

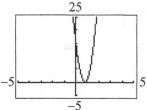

The graph is never below the x-axis. Thus, there is no real solution.

21. $6(x^2 - 1) > 5x$

$6x^2 - 6 > 5x$

$6x^2 - 5x - 6 > 0$

We graph the function $f(x) = 6x^2 - 5x - 6$.

y-intercept: $f(0) = -6$

x-intercepts: $6x^2 - 5x - 6 = 0$

$(3x+2)(2x-3) = 0$

$x = -\dfrac{2}{3},\ x = \dfrac{3}{2}$

The vertex is at $x = \dfrac{-b}{2a} = \dfrac{-(-5)}{2(6)} = \dfrac{5}{12}$. Since

$f\left(\dfrac{5}{12}\right) = -\dfrac{169}{24}$, the vertex is $\left(\dfrac{5}{12}, -\dfrac{169}{24}\right)$.

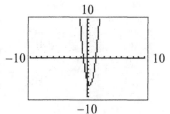

The graph is above the x-axis when $x < -\dfrac{2}{3}$ or

$x > \dfrac{3}{2}$. Since the inequality is strict, solution set

is $\left\{ x \mid x < -\dfrac{2}{3} \text{ or } x > \dfrac{3}{2} \right\}$ or, using interval

notation, $\left(-\infty, -\dfrac{2}{3} \right) \cup \left(\dfrac{3}{2}, \infty \right)$.

22. $2\left(2x^2 - 3x\right) > -9$

$4x^2 - 6x > -9$

$4x^2 - 6x + 9 > 0$

We graph the function $f(x) = 4x^2 - 6x + 9$.

y-intercept: $f(0) = 9$

x-intercepts: $x = \dfrac{-(-6) \pm \sqrt{(-6)^2 - 4(4)(9)}}{2(4)}$

$= \dfrac{6 \pm \sqrt{-108}}{8}$ (not real)

Therefore, f has no x-intercepts.

The vertex is at $x = \dfrac{-b}{2a} = \dfrac{-(-6)}{2(4)} = \dfrac{6}{8} = \dfrac{3}{4}$. Since

$f\left(\dfrac{3}{4}\right) = \dfrac{27}{4}$, the vertex is $\left(\dfrac{3}{4}, \dfrac{27}{4}\right)$.

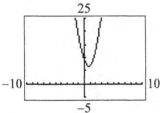

The graph is always above the x-axis. Thus, the solution set is all real numbers or, using interval notation, $(-\infty, \infty)$.

23. The domain of the expression $f(x) = \sqrt{x^2 - 16}$

includes all values for which $x^2 - 16 \geq 0$.

We graph the function $p(x) = x^2 - 16$. The intercepts of p are

y-intercept: $p(0) = -6$

x-intercepts: $x^2 - 16 = 0$

$\qquad (x+4)(x-4) = 0$

$\qquad x = -4, x = 4$

The vertex of p is at $x = \dfrac{-b}{2a} = \dfrac{-(0)}{2(1)} = 0$. Since

$p(0) = -16$, the vertex is $(0, -16)$.

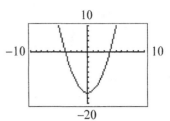

The graph of p is above the x-axis when $x < -4$ or $x > 4$. Since the inequality is not strict, the solution set of $x^2 - 16 \geq 0$ is $\{x \mid x \leq -4 \text{ or } x \geq 4\}$.

Thus, the domain of f is also $\{x \mid x \leq -4 \text{ or } x \geq 4\}$ or, using interval notation, $(-\infty, -4] \cup [4, \infty)$.

24. The domain of the expression $f(x) = \sqrt{x - 3x^2}$

includes all values for which $x - 3x^2 \geq 0$.

We graph the function $p(x) = x - 3x^2$. The intercepts of p are

y-intercept: $p(0) = -6$

x-intercepts: $x - 3x^2 = 0$

$\qquad x(1 - 3x) = 0$

$\qquad x = 0, x = \dfrac{1}{3}$.

The vertex of p is at $x = \dfrac{-b}{2a} = \dfrac{-(1)}{2(-3)} = \dfrac{-1}{-6} = \dfrac{1}{6}$.

Since $p\left(\dfrac{1}{6}\right) = \dfrac{1}{12}$, the vertex is $\left(\dfrac{1}{6}, \dfrac{1}{12}\right)$.

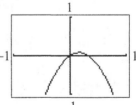

The graph of p is above the x-axis when

$0 < x < \dfrac{1}{3}$. Since the inequality is not strict, the

solution set of $x - 3x^2 \geq 0$ is $\left\{ x \mid 0 \leq x \leq \dfrac{1}{3} \right\}$.

Thus, the domain of f is also $\left\{ x \mid 0 \leq x \leq \dfrac{1}{3} \right\}$ or,

using interval notation, $\left[0, \dfrac{1}{3} \right]$.

367

25. $f(x) = x^2 - 1; \quad g(x) = 3x + 3$

   a. $f(x) = 0$

$$x^2 - 1 = 0$$
$$(x-1)(x+1) = 0$$
$$x = 1; \, x = -1$$

Solution set: $\{-1, 1\}$.

   b. $g(x) = 0$

$$3x + 3 = 0$$
$$3x = -3$$
$$x = -1$$

Solution set: $\{-1\}$.

   c. $f(x) = g(x)$

$$x^2 - 1 = 3x + 3$$
$$x^2 - 3x - 4 = 0$$
$$(x-4)(x+1) = 0$$
$$x = 4; \, x = -1$$

Solution set: $\{-1, 4\}$.

   d. $f(x) > 0$

We graph the function $f(x) = x^2 - 1$.

y-intercept: $f(0) = -1$

x-intercepts: $x^2 - 1 = 0$
$$(x+1)(x-1) = 0$$
$$x = -1, \, x = 1$$

The vertex is at $x = \dfrac{-b}{2a} = \dfrac{-(0)}{2(1)} = 0$. Since

$f(0) = -1$, the vertex is $(0, -1)$.

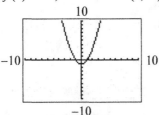

The graph is above the x-axis when $x < -1$ or $x > 1$. Since the inequality is strict, the solution set is $\left\{ x \mid x < -1 \text{ or } x > 1 \right\}$ or, using interval notation, $(-\infty, -1) \cup (1, \infty)$.

   e. $g(x) \leq 0$
$$3x + 3 \leq 0$$
$$3x \leq -3$$
$$x \leq -1$$

The solution set is $\left\{ x \mid x \leq -1 \right\}$ or, using interval notation, $(-\infty, -1]$.

   f. $f(x) > g(x)$
$$x^2 - 1 > 3x + 3$$
$$x^2 - 3x - 4 > 0$$

We graph the function $p(x) = x^2 - 3x - 4$.
The intercepts of p are
y-intercept: $p(0) = -4$

x-intercepts: $x^2 - 3x - 4 = 0$
$$(x-4)(x+1) = 0$$
$$x = 4, \, x = -1$$

The vertex is at $x = \dfrac{-b}{2a} = \dfrac{-(-3)}{2(1)} = \dfrac{3}{2}$. Since

$p\left(\dfrac{3}{2}\right) = -\dfrac{25}{4}$, the vertex is $\left(\dfrac{3}{2}, -\dfrac{25}{4}\right)$.

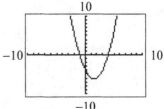

The graph of p is above the x-axis when $x < -1$ or $x > 4$. Since the inequality is strict, the solution set is $\left\{ x \mid x < -1 \text{ or } x > 4 \right\}$ or, using interval notation, $(-\infty, -1) \cup (4, \infty)$.

   g. $f(x) \geq 1$
$$x^2 - 1 \geq 1$$
$$x^2 - 2 \geq 0$$

We graph the function $p(x) = x^2 - 2$. The intercepts of p are
y-intercept: $p(0) = -2$

x-intercepts: $x^2 - 2 = 0$
$$x^2 = 2$$
$$x = \pm\sqrt{2}$$

The vertex is at $x = \dfrac{-b}{2a} = \dfrac{-(0)}{2(1)} = 0$. Since

$p(0) = -2$, the vertex is $(0, -2)$.

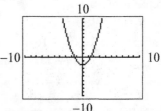

The graph of p is above the x-axis when $x < -\sqrt{2}$ or $x > \sqrt{2}$. Since the inequality is

not strict, the solution set is
$\left\{ x \mid x \le -\sqrt{2} \text{ or } x \ge \sqrt{2} \right\}$ or, using interval
notation, $\left(-\infty, -\sqrt{2} \right] \cup \left[\sqrt{2}, \infty \right)$.

26. $f(x) = -x^2 + 3; \quad g(x) = -3x + 3$

a. $f(x) = 0$
$-x^2 + 3 = 0$
$x^2 = 3$
$x = \pm\sqrt{3}$
Solution set: $\left\{ -\sqrt{3}, \sqrt{3} \right\}$.

b. $g(x) = 0$
$-3x + 3 = 0$
$-3x = -3$
$x = 1$
Solution set: $\{1\}$.

c. $f(x) = g(x)$
$-x^2 + 3 = -3x + 3$
$0 = x^2 - 3x$
$0 = x(x - 3)$
$x = 0; x = 3$
Solution set: $\{0, 3\}$.

d. $f(x) > 0$
We graph the function $f(x) = -x^2 + 3$.
y-intercept: $f(0) = 3$
x-intercepts: $-x^2 + 3 = 0$
$x^2 = 3$
$x = \pm\sqrt{3}$
The vertex is at $x = \dfrac{-b}{2a} = \dfrac{-(0)}{2(-1)} = 0$. Since
$f(0) = 3$, the vertex is $(0, 3)$.

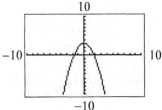

The graph is above the x-axis when
$-\sqrt{3} < x < \sqrt{3}$. Since the inequality is strict,
the solution set is $\left\{ x \mid -\sqrt{3} < x < \sqrt{3} \right\}$ or,
using interval notation, $\left(-\sqrt{3}, \sqrt{3} \right)$.

e. $g(x) \le 0$
$-3x + 3 \le 0$
$-3x \le -3$
$x \ge 1$
The solution set is $\left\{ x \mid x \ge 1 \right\}$ or, using
interval notation, $[1, \infty)$.

f. $f(x) > g(x)$
$-x^2 + 3 > -3x + 3$
$-x^2 + 3x > 0$
We graph the function $p(x) = -x^2 + 3x$.
The intercepts of p are
y-intercept: $p(0) = 0$

x-intercepts: $-x^2 + 3x = 0$
$-x(x - 3) = 0$
$x = 0; x = 3$
The vertex is at $x = \dfrac{-b}{2a} = \dfrac{-(3)}{2(-1)} = \dfrac{-3}{-2} = \dfrac{3}{2}$.
Since $p\left(\dfrac{3}{2}\right) = \dfrac{9}{4}$, the vertex is $\left(\dfrac{3}{2}, \dfrac{9}{4}\right)$.

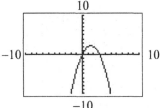

The graph of p is above the x-axis when
$0 < x < 3$. Since the inequality is strict, the
solution set is $\left\{ x \mid 0 < x < 3 \right\}$ or, using
interval notation, $(0, 3)$.

g. $f(x) \ge 1$
$-x^2 + 3 \ge 1$
$-x^2 + 2 \ge 0$
We graph the function $p(x) = -x^2 + 2$. The
intercepts of p are
y-intercept: $p(0) = 2$
x-intercepts: $-x^2 + 2 = 0$
$x^2 = 2$
$x = \pm\sqrt{2}$
The vertex is at $x = \dfrac{-b}{2a} = \dfrac{-(0)}{2(-1)} = 0$. Since
$p(0) = 2$, the vertex is $(0, 2)$.

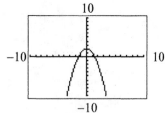

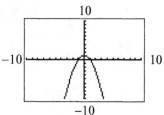

The graph of p is above the x-axis when $-\sqrt{2} < x < \sqrt{2}$. Since the inequality is not strict, the solution set is $\left\{ x \middle| -\sqrt{2} \le x \le \sqrt{2} \right\}$ or, using interval notation, $\left[-\sqrt{2}, \sqrt{2} \right]$.

The graph is above the x-axis when $-1 < x < 1$. Since the inequality is strict, the solution set is $\left\{ x \middle| -1 < x < 1 \right\}$ or, using interval notation, $(-1, 1)$.

27. $f(x) = -x^2 + 1;\quad g(x) = 4x + 1$

a.
$$f(x) = 0$$
$$-x^2 + 1 = 0$$
$$1 - x^2 = 0$$
$$(1-x)(1+x) = 0$$
$$x = 1;\ x = -1$$
Solution set: $\{-1, 1\}$.

b. $g(x) = 0$
$$4x + 1 = 0$$
$$4x = -1$$
$$x = -\frac{1}{4}$$
Solution set: $\left\{ -\frac{1}{4} \right\}$.

c. $f(x) = g(x)$
$$-x^2 + 1 = 4x + 1$$
$$0 = x^2 + 4x$$
$$0 = x(x + 4)$$
$$x = 0;\ x - 4$$
Solution set: $\{-4, 0\}$.

d. $f(x) > 0$

We graph the function $f(x) = -x^2 + 1$.
y-intercept: $f(0) = 1$
x-intercepts:
$$-x^2 + 1 = 0$$
$$x^2 - 1 = 0$$
$$(x+1)(x-1) = 0$$
$$x = -1; x = 1$$

The vertex is at $x = \dfrac{-b}{2a} = \dfrac{-(0)}{2(-1)} = 0$. Since $f(0) = 1$, the vertex is $(0, 1)$.

e. $g(x) \le 0$
$$4x + 1 \le 0$$
$$4x \le -1$$
$$x \le -\frac{1}{4}$$

The solution set is $\left\{ x \middle| x \le -\frac{1}{4} \right\}$ or, using interval notation, $\left(-\infty, -\frac{1}{4} \right]$.

f. $f(x) > g(x)$
$$-x^2 + 1 > 4x + 1$$
$$-x^2 - 4x > 0$$
We graph the function $p(x) = -x^2 - 4x$.
The intercepts of p are
y-intercept: $p(0) = 0$

x-intercepts: $-x^2 - 4x = 0$
$$-x(x + 4) = 0$$
$$x = 0; x = -4$$

The vertex is at $x = \dfrac{-b}{2a} = \dfrac{-(-4)}{2(-1)} = \dfrac{4}{-2} = -2$.

Since $p(-2) = 4$, the vertex is $(-2, 4)$.

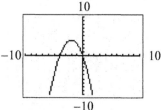

The graph of p is above the x-axis when $-4 < x < 0$. Since the inequality is strict, the solution set is $\left\{ x \middle| -4 < x < 0 \right\}$ or, using interval notation, $(-4, 0)$.

g. $f(x) \geq 1$

$-x^2 + 1 \geq 1$

$-x^2 \geq 0$

We graph the function $p(x) = -x^2$. The

vertex is at $x = \dfrac{-b}{2a} = \dfrac{-(0)}{2(-1)} = 0$. Since

$p(0) = 0$, the vertex is $(0, 0)$. Since

$a = -1 < 0$, the parabola opens downward.

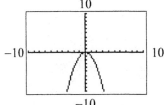

The graph of p is never above the x-axis, but it
does touch the x-axis at $x = 0$. Since the
inequality is not strict, the solution set is $\{0\}$.

28. $f(x) = -x^2 + 4$; $g(x) = -x - 2$

a. $\qquad f(x) = 0$

$-x^2 + 4 = 0$

$x^2 - 4 = 0$

$(x + 2)(x - 2) = 0$

$x = -2; x = 2$

Solution set: $\{-2, 2\}$.

b. $g(x) = 0$

$-x - 2 = 0$

$-2 = x$

Solution set: $\{-2\}$.

c. $\qquad f(x) = g(x)$

$-x^2 + 4 = -x - 2$

$0 = x^2 - x - 6$

$0 = (x - 3)(x + 2)$

$x = 3; x = -2$

Solution set: $\{-2, 3\}$.

d. $\qquad f(x) > 0$

$-x^2 + 4 > 0$

We graph the function $f(x) = -x^2 + 4$.

y-intercept: $f(0) = 4$

x-intercepts: $\qquad -x^2 + 4 = 0$

$x^2 - 4 = 0$

$(x + 2)(x - 2) = 0$

$x = -2; x = 2$

The vertex is at $x = \dfrac{-b}{2a} = \dfrac{-(0)}{2(-1)} = 0$. Since

$f(0) = 4$, the vertex is $(0, 4)$.

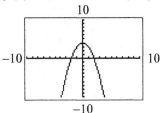

The graph is above the x-axis when
$-2 < x < 2$. Since the inequality is strict,
the solution set is $\{x | -2 < x < 2\}$ or, using
interval notation, $(-2, 2)$.

e. $g(x) \leq 0$

$-x - 2 \leq 0$

$-x \leq 2$

$x \geq -2$

The solution set is $\{x | x \geq -2\}$ or, using

interval notation, $[-2, \infty)$.

f. $\qquad f(x) > g(x)$

$-x^2 + 4 > -x - 2$

$-x^2 + x + 6 > 0$

We graph the function $p(x) = -x^2 + x + 6$.

The intercepts of p are

y-intercept: $p(0) = 6$

x-intercepts: $\quad -x^2 + x + 6 = 0$

$x^2 - x - 6 = 0$

$(x + 2)(x - 3) = 0$

$x = -2; x = 3$

The vertex is at $x = \dfrac{-b}{2a} = \dfrac{-(1)}{2(-1)} = \dfrac{-1}{-2} = \dfrac{1}{2}$.

Since $p\left(\dfrac{1}{2}\right) = \dfrac{25}{4}$, the vertex is $\left(\dfrac{1}{2}, \dfrac{25}{4}\right)$.

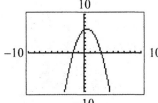

The graph of p is above the x-axis when
$-2 < x < 3$. Since the inequality is strict,
the solution set is $\{x | -2 < x < 3\}$ or, using
interval notation, $(-2, 3)$.

g. $f(x) \geq 1$

$-x^2 + 4 > 1$

$-x^2 + 3 > 0$

We graph the function $p(x) = -x^2 + 3$. The intercepts of p are

y-intercept: $p(0) = 3$

x-intercepts: $-x^2 + 3 = 0$

$$x^2 = 3$$

$$x = \pm\sqrt{3}$$

The vertex is at $x = \dfrac{-b}{2a} = \dfrac{-(0)}{2(-1)} = 0$. Since

$p(0) = 3$, the vertex is $(0, 3)$.

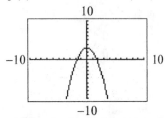

The graph of p is above the x-axis when $-\sqrt{3} < x < \sqrt{3}$. Since the inequality is not strict, the solution set is $\left\{ x \mid -\sqrt{3} \leq x \leq \sqrt{3} \right\}$ or, using interval notation, $\left[-\sqrt{3}, \sqrt{3} \right]$.

29. $f(x) = x^2 - 4; \quad g(x) = -x^2 + 4$

  a. $f(x) = 0$

$$x^2 - 4 = 0$$

$$(x - 2)(x + 2) = 0$$

$$x = 2; x = -2$$

Solution set: $\{-2, 2\}$.

  b. $g(x) = 0$

$$-x^2 + 4 = 0$$

$$x^2 - 4 = 0$$

$$(x + 2)(x - 2) = 0$$

$$x = -2; x = 2$$

Solution set: $\{-2, 2\}$.

  c. $f(x) = g(x)$

$$x^2 - 4 = -x^2 + 4$$

$$2x^2 - 8 = 0$$

$$2(x - 2)(x + 2) = 0$$

$$x = 2; x = -2$$

Solution set: $\{-2, 2\}$.

d. $f(x) > 0$

$x^2 - 4 > 0$

We graph the function $f(x) = x^2 - 4$.

y-intercept: $f(0) = -4$

x-intercepts: $\quad x^2 - 4 = 0$

$$(x + 2)(x - 2) = 0$$

$$x = -2; x = 2$$

The vertex is at $x = \dfrac{-b}{2a} = \dfrac{-(0)}{2(-1)} = 0$. Since

$f(0) = -4$, the vertex is $(0, -4)$.

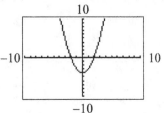

The graph is above the x-axis when $x < -2$ or $x > 2$. Since the inequality is strict, the solution set is $\left\{ x \mid x < -2 \text{ or } x > 2 \right\}$ or, using interval notation, $(-\infty, -2) \cup (2, \infty)$.

e. $g(x) \leq 0$

$-x^2 + 4 \leq 0$

We graph the function $g(x) = -x^2 + 4$.

y-intercept: $g(0) = 4$

x-intercepts: $\quad -x^2 + 4 = 0$

$$x^2 - 4 = 0$$

$$(x + 2)(x - 2) = 0$$

$$x = -2; x = 2$$

The vertex is at $x = \dfrac{-b}{2a} = \dfrac{-(0)}{2(-1)} = 0$. Since

$g(0) = 4$, the vertex is $(0, 4)$.

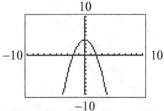

The graph is below the x-axis when $x < -2$ or $x > 2$. Since the inequality is not strict, the solution set is $\left\{ x \mid x \leq -2 \text{ or } x \geq 2 \right\}$ or, using interval notation, $(-\infty, -2] \cup [2, \infty)$.

f. $f(x) > g(x)$

$x^2 - 4 > -x^2 + 4$

$2x^2 - 8 > 0$

We graph the function $p(x) = 2x^2 - 8$.

y-intercept: $p(0) = -8$

x-intercepts: $2x^2 - 8 = 0$

$2(x + 2)(x - 2) = 0$

$x = -2; x = 2$

The vertex is at $x = \dfrac{-b}{2a} = \dfrac{-(0)}{2(2)} = 0$. Since

$p(0) = -8$, the vertex is $(0, -8)$.

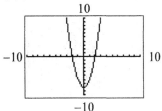

The graph is above the x-axis when $x < -2$ or $x > 2$. Since the inequality is strict, the solution set is $\left\{ x \mid x < -2 \text{ or } x > 2 \right\}$ or, using interval notation, $(-\infty, -2) \cup (2, \infty)$.

g. $f(x) \geq 1$

$x^2 - 4 \geq 1$

$x^2 - 5 \geq 0$

We graph the function $p(x) = x^2 - 5$.

y-intercept: $p(0) = -5$

x-intercepts: $x^2 - 5 = 0$

$x^2 = 5$

$x = \pm\sqrt{5}$

The vertex is at $x = \dfrac{-b}{2a} = \dfrac{-(0)}{2(1)} = 0$. Since

$p(0) = -5$, the vertex is $(0, -5)$.

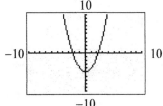

The graph of p is above the x-axis when $x < -\sqrt{5}$ or $x > \sqrt{5}$. Since the inequality is not strict, the solution set is

$\left\{ x \mid x \leq -\sqrt{5} \text{ or } x \geq \sqrt{5} \right\}$ or, using interval

notation, $\left(-\infty, -\sqrt{5}\right] \cup \left[\sqrt{5}, \infty\right)$.

30. $f(x) = x^2 - 2x + 1; \ g(x) = -x^2 + 1$

a. $f(x) = 0$

$x^2 - 2x + 1 = 0$

$(x - 1)^2 = 0$

$x - 1 = 0$

$x = 1$

Solution set: $\{1\}$.

b. $g(x) = 0$

$-x^2 + 1 = 0$

$x^2 - 1 = 0$

$(x + 1)(x - 1) = 0$

$x = -1; x = 1$

Solution set: $\{-1, 1\}$.

c. $f(x) = g(x)$

$x^2 - 2x + 1 = -x^2 + 1$

$2x^2 - 2x = 0$

$2x(x - 1) = 0$

$x = 0, x = 1$

Solution set: $\{0, 1\}$.

d. $f(x) > 0$

$x^2 - 2x + 1 > 0$

We graph the function $f(x) = x^2 - 2x + 1$.

y-intercept: $f(0) = 1$

x-intercepts: $x^2 - 2x + 1 = 0$

$(x - 1)^2 = 0$

$x - 1 = 0$

$x = 1$

The vertex is at $x = \dfrac{-b}{2a} = \dfrac{-(-2)}{2(1)} = \dfrac{2}{2} = 1$.

Since $f(1) = 0$, the vertex is $(1, 0)$.

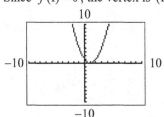

The graph is above the x-axis when $x < 1$ or $x > 1$. Since the inequality is strict, the solution set is $\left\{ x \mid x < 1 \text{ or } x > 1 \right\}$ or, using interval notation, $(-\infty, 1) \cup (1, \infty)$.

e. $g(x) \le 0$

$-x^2 + 1 \le 0$

We graph the function $g(x) = -x^2 + 1$.

y-intercept: $g(0) = 1$

x-intercepts: $-x^2 + 1 = 0$

$x^2 - 1 = 0$

$(x+1)(x-1) = 0$

$x = -1; \ x = 1$

The vertex is at $x = \dfrac{-b}{2a} = \dfrac{-(0)}{2(-1)} = 0$. Since

$g(0) = 1$, the vertex is $(0, 1)$.

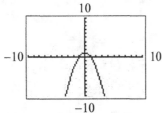

The graph is below the x-axis when $x < -1$ or $x > 1$. Since the inequality is not strict, the solution set is $\{ x \mid x \le -1 \text{ or } x \ge 1 \}$ or, using interval notation, $(-\infty, -1] \cup [1, \infty)$.

f. $f(x) > g(x)$

$x^2 - 2x + 1 > -x^2 + 1$

$2x^2 - 2x > 0$

We graph the function $p(x) = 2x^2 - 2x$.

y-intercept: $p(0) = 0$

x-intercepts: $2x^2 - 2x = 0$

$2x(x-1) = 0$

$x = 0; \ x = 1$

The vertex is at $x = \dfrac{-b}{2a} = \dfrac{-(-2)}{2(2)} = \dfrac{2}{4} = \dfrac{1}{2}$.

Since $p\left(\dfrac{1}{2}\right) = \dfrac{1}{2}$, the vertex is $\left(\dfrac{1}{2}, \dfrac{1}{2}\right)$.

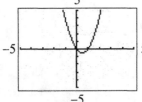

The graph is above the x-axis when $x < 0$ or $x > 1$. Since the inequality is strict, the solution set is $\{ x \mid x < 0 \text{ or } x > 1 \}$ or, using interval notation, $(-\infty, 0) \cup (1, \infty)$.

g. $f(x) \ge 1$

$x^2 - 2x + 1 \ge 1$

$x^2 - 2x \ge 0$

We graph the function $p(x) = x^2 - 2x$.

y-intercept: $p(0) = 0$

x-intercepts: $x^2 - 2x = 0$

$x(x - 2) = 0$

$x = 0; \ x = 2$

The vertex is at $x = \dfrac{-b}{2a} = \dfrac{-(-2)}{2(1)} = \dfrac{2}{2} = 1$.

Since $p(1) = -1$, the vertex is $(1, -1)$.

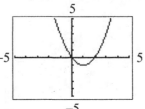

The graph of p is above the x-axis when $x < 0$ or $x > 2$. Since the inequality is not strict, the solution set is $\{ x \mid x \le 0 \text{ or } x \ge 2 \}$ or, using interval notation,

$(-\infty, 0] \cup [2, \infty)$.

31. $f(x) = x^2 - x - 2; \quad g(x) = x^2 + x - 2$

a. $f(x) = 0$

$x^2 - x - 2 = 0$

$(x - 2)(x + 1) = 0$

$x = 2, x = -1$

Solution set: $\{-1, 2\}$.

b. $g(x) = 0$

$x^2 + x - 2 = 0$

$(x + 2)(x - 1) = 0$

$x = -2; \ x = 1$

Solution set: $\{-2, 1\}$.

c. $f(x) = g(x)$

$x^2 - x - 2 = x^2 + x - 2$

$-2x = 0$

$x = 0$

Solution set: $\{0\}$.

d. $f(x) > 0$

$x^2 - x - 2 > 0$

We graph the function $f(x) = x^2 - x - 2$.

y-intercept: $f(0) = -2$

x-intercepts: $x^2 - x - 2 = 0$

$(x - 2)(x + 1) = 0$

$x = 2; x = -1$

The vertex is at $x = \dfrac{-b}{2a} = \dfrac{-(-1)}{2(1)} = \dfrac{1}{2}$. Since

$f\left(\dfrac{1}{2}\right) = -\dfrac{9}{4}$, the vertex is $\left(\dfrac{1}{2}, -\dfrac{9}{4}\right)$.

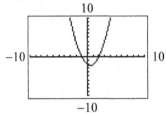

The graph is above the x-axis when $x < -1$ or $x > 2$. Since the inequality is strict, the solution set is $\{x \mid x < -1 \text{ or } x > 2\}$ or, using interval notation, $(-\infty, -1) \cup (2, \infty)$.

e. $g(x) \leq 0$

$x^2 + x - 2 \leq 0$

We graph the function $g(x) = x^2 + x - 2$.

y-intercept: $g(0) = -2$

x-intercepts: $x^2 + x - 2 = 0$

$(x + 2)(x - 1) = 0$

$x = -2; x = 1$

The vertex is at $x = \dfrac{-b}{2a} = \dfrac{-(1)}{2(1)} = -\dfrac{1}{2}$. Since

$f\left(-\dfrac{1}{2}\right) = -\dfrac{7}{4}$, the vertex is $\left(-\dfrac{1}{2}, -\dfrac{7}{4}\right)$.

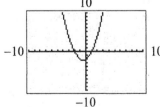

The graph is below the x-axis when $-2 < x < 1$. Since the inequality is not strict, the solution set is $\{x \mid -2 \leq x \leq 1\}$ or, using interval notation, $[-2, 1]$.

f. $f(x) > g(x)$

$x^2 - x - 2 > x^2 + x - 2$

$-2x > 0$

$x < 0$

The solution set is $\{x \mid x < 0\}$ or, using interval notation, $(-\infty, 0)$.

g. $f(x) \geq 1$

$x^2 - x - 2 \geq 1$

$x^2 - x - 3 \geq 0$

We graph the function $p(x) = x^2 - x - 3$.

y-intercept: $p(0) = -3$

x-intercepts: $x^2 - x - 3 = 0$

$x = \dfrac{-(-1) \pm \sqrt{(-1)^2 - 4(1)(-3)}}{2(1)}$

$= \dfrac{1 \pm \sqrt{1 + 12}}{2} = \dfrac{1 \pm \sqrt{13}}{2}$

$x \approx -1.30$ or $x \approx 2.30$

The vertex is at $x = \dfrac{-b}{2a} = \dfrac{-(-1)}{2(1)} = \dfrac{1}{2}$. Since

$p\left(\dfrac{1}{2}\right) = -\dfrac{13}{4}$, the vertex is $\left(\dfrac{1}{2}, -\dfrac{13}{4}\right)$.

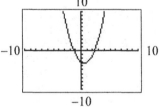

The graph of p is above the x-axis when

$x < \dfrac{1 - \sqrt{13}}{2}$ or $x > \dfrac{1 + \sqrt{13}}{2}$. Since the inequality is not strict, the solution set is

$\left\{x \mid x \leq \dfrac{1 - \sqrt{13}}{2} \text{ or } x \geq \dfrac{1 + \sqrt{13}}{2}\right\}$ or, using interval notation,

$\left(-\infty, \dfrac{1 - \sqrt{13}}{2}\right] \cup \left[\dfrac{1 + \sqrt{13}}{2}, \infty\right)$.

32. $f(x) = -x^2 - x + 1;\quad g(x) = -x^2 + x + 6$

a.
$$f(x) = 0$$
$$-x^2 - x + 1 = 0$$
$$x^2 + x - 1 = 0$$
$$x = \frac{-(1) \pm \sqrt{(1)^2 - 4(1)(-1)}}{2(1)}$$
$$= \frac{-1 \pm \sqrt{1+4}}{2} = \frac{-1 \pm \sqrt{5}}{2}$$

Solution set: $\left\{ \dfrac{-1-\sqrt{5}}{2}, \dfrac{-1+\sqrt{5}}{2} \right\}$.

b.
$$g(x) = 0$$
$$-x^2 + x + 6 = 0$$
$$x^2 - x - 6 = 0$$
$$(x-3)(x+2) = 0$$
$$x = 3; x = -2$$

Solution set: $\{-2, 3\}$.

c.
$$f(x) = g(x)$$
$$-x^2 - x + 1 = -x^2 + x + 6$$
$$-2x - 5 = 0$$
$$-2x = 5$$
$$x = -\frac{5}{2}$$

Solution set: $\left\{ -\dfrac{5}{2} \right\}$.

d.
$$f(x) > 0$$
$$-x^2 - x + 1 > 0$$

We graph the function $f(x) = -x^2 - x + 1$.

y-intercept: $f(0) = -1$

x-intercepts: $-x^2 - x + 2 = 0$
$$x^2 + x - 2 = 0$$
$$x = \frac{-(1) \pm \sqrt{(1)^2 - 4(1)(-1)}}{2(1)}$$
$$= \frac{-1 \pm \sqrt{1+4}}{2} = \frac{-1 \pm \sqrt{5}}{2}$$
$$x \approx -1.62 \text{ or } x \approx 0.62$$

The vertex is at $x = \dfrac{-b}{2a} = \dfrac{-(-1)}{2(-1)} = \dfrac{1}{-2} = -\dfrac{1}{2}$.

Since $f\left(-\dfrac{1}{2}\right) = \dfrac{5}{4}$, the vertex is $\left(-\dfrac{1}{2}, \dfrac{5}{4}\right)$.

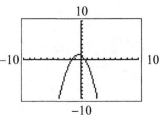

The graph is above the x-axis when
$\dfrac{-1-\sqrt{5}}{2} < x < \dfrac{-1+\sqrt{5}}{2}$. Since the inequality
is strict, the solution set is
$\left\{ x \middle| \dfrac{-1-\sqrt{5}}{2} < x < \dfrac{-1+\sqrt{5}}{2} \right\}$ or, using interval

notation, $\left(\dfrac{-1-\sqrt{5}}{2}, \dfrac{-1+\sqrt{5}}{2} \right)$.

e.
$$g(x) \leq 0$$
$$-x^2 + x + 6 \leq 0$$

We graph the function $g(x) = -x^2 + x + 6$.

y-intercept: $g(0) = 6$

x-intercepts: $\quad -x^2 + x + 6 = 0$
$$x^2 - x - 6 = 0$$
$$(x-3)(x+2) = 0$$
$$x = 3; x = -2$$

The vertex is at $x = \dfrac{-b}{2a} = \dfrac{-(1)}{2(-1)} = \dfrac{-1}{-2} = \dfrac{1}{2}$.

Since $f\left(\dfrac{1}{2}\right) = \dfrac{25}{4}$, the vertex is $\left(\dfrac{1}{2}, \dfrac{25}{4}\right)$.

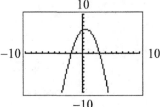

The graph is below the x-axis when $x < -2$
or $x > 3$. Since the inequality is not strict,
the solution set is $\{ x \mid x \leq -2 \text{ or } x \geq 3 \}$ or,
using interval notation, $(-\infty, 2] \cup [3, \infty)$.

f.
$$f(x) > g(x)$$
$$-x^2 - x + 1 > -x^2 + x + 6$$
$$-2x > 5$$
$$x < -\frac{5}{2}$$

The solution set is $\left\{ x \mid x < -\frac{5}{2} \right\}$ or, using

interval notation, $\left(-\infty, -\frac{5}{2}\right)$.

g.

$$f(x) \geq 1$$

$$-x^2 - x + 1 \geq 1$$

$$-x^2 - x \geq 0$$

We graph the function $p(x) = -x^2 - x$.

y-intercept: $p(0) = 0$

x-intercepts: $-x^2 - x = 0$

$$-x(x+1) = 0$$

$$x = 0; x = -1$$

The vertex is at $x = \dfrac{-b}{2a} = \dfrac{-(-1)}{2(-1)} = \dfrac{1}{-2} = -\dfrac{1}{2}$.

Since $p\left(-\dfrac{1}{2}\right) = \dfrac{1}{4}$, the vertex is $\left(-\dfrac{1}{2}, \dfrac{1}{4}\right)$.

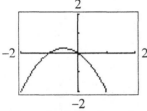

The graph of p is above the x-axis when $-1 < x < 0$. Since the inequality is not strict, the solution set is $\left\{ x \,\middle|\, -1 \leq x \leq 0 \right\}$ or, using interval notation, $[-1, 0]$.

33. a. The ball strikes the ground when $s(t) = 80t - 16t^2 = 0$.

$$80t - 16t^2 = 0$$

$$16t(5 - t) = 0$$

$$t = 0, t = 5$$

The ball strikes the ground after 5 seconds.

b. Find the values of t for which
$$80t - 16t^2 > 96$$

$$-16t^2 + 80t - 96 > 0$$

We graph the function

$f(t) = -16t^2 + 80t - 96$. The intercepts are

y-intercept: $f(0) = -96$

t-intercepts: $-16t^2 + 80t - 96 = 0$

$$-16(t^2 - 5t + 6) = 0$$

$$16(t - 2)(t - 3) = 0$$

$$t = 2, t = 3$$

The vertex is at $t = \dfrac{-b}{2a} = \dfrac{-(80)}{2(-16)} = 2.5$.

Since $f(2.5) = 4$, the vertex is $(2.5, 4)$.

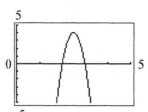

The graph of f is above the t-axis when $2 < t < 3$. Since the inequality is strict, the solution set is $\{t \mid 2 < t < 3\}$ or, using interval notation, $(2, 3)$. The ball is more than 96 feet above the ground for times between 2 and 3 seconds.

34. a. The ball strikes the ground when $s(t) = 96t - 16t^2 = 0$.

$$96t - 16t^2 = 0$$

$$16t(6 - t) = 0$$

$$t = 0, t = 6$$

The ball strikes the ground after 6 seconds.

b. Find the values of t for which
$$96t - 16t^2 > 128$$

$$-16t^2 + 96t - 128 > 0$$

We graph $f(t) = -16t^2 + 96t - 128$. The intercepts are

y-intercept: $f(0) = -128$

t-intercepts: $-16t^2 + 96t - 128 = 0$

$$16(t^2 - 6t + 8) = 0$$

$$-16(t - 4)(t - 2) = 0$$

$$t = 4, t = 2$$

The vertex is at $t = \dfrac{-b}{2a} = \dfrac{-(96)}{2(-16)} = 3$. Since

$f(3) = 16$, the vertex is $(3, 16)$.

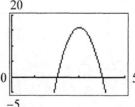

The graph of f is above the t-axis when $2 < t < 4$. Since the inequality is strict, the solution set is $\{t \mid 2 < t < 4\}$ or, using interval notation, $(2, 4)$. The ball is more than 128 feet above the ground for times between 2 and 4 seconds.

35. a. $R(p) = -4p^2 + 4000p = 0$

$-4p(p-1000) = 0$

$p = 0, p = 1000$

Thus, the revenue equals zero when the price is $0 or $1000.

b. Find the values of p for which

$$-4p^2 + 4000p > 800,000$$

$$-4p^2 + 4000p - 800,000 > 0$$

We graph $f(p) = -4p^2 + 4000p - 800,000$.
The intercepts are
y-intercept: $f(0) = -800,000$

p-intercepts:
$-4p^2 + 4000p - 800000 = 0$

$p^2 - 1000p + 200000 = 0$

$$p = \frac{-(-1000) \pm \sqrt{(-1000)^2 - 4(1)(200000)}}{2(1)}$$

$$= \frac{1000 \pm \sqrt{200000}}{2}$$

$$= \frac{1000 \pm 200\sqrt{5}}{2}$$

$$= 500 \pm 100\sqrt{5}$$

$p \approx 276.39; p \approx 723.61$.

The vertex is at $p = \dfrac{-b}{2a} = \dfrac{-(4000)}{2(-4)} = 500$.

Since $f(500) = 200,000$, the vertex is
$(500, 200000)$.

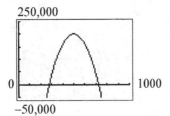

The graph of f is above the p-axis when
$276.39 < p < 723.61$. Since the inequality is strict, the solution set is
$\{p \mid 276.39 < p < 723.61\}$ or, using interval

notation, $(276.39, 723.61)$. The revenue is more than $800,000 for prices between $276.39 and $723.61.

36. a. $R(p) = -\dfrac{1}{2}p^2 + 1900p = 0$

$-\dfrac{1}{2}p(p-3800) = 0$

$p = 0, p = 3800$

Thus, the revenue equals zero when the price is $0 or $3800.

b. Find the values of p for which

$$-\frac{1}{2}p^2 + 1900p > 1200000$$

$$-\frac{1}{2}p^2 + 1900p - 1200000 > 0$$

We graph $f(p) = -\dfrac{1}{2}p^2 + 1900p - 1200000$.

The intercepts are
y-intercept: $f(0) = -1,200,000$

p-intercepts: $-\dfrac{1}{2}p^2 + 1900p - 1200000 = 0$

$$p^2 - 3800p + 2400000 = 0$$

$$(p-800)(p-3000) = 0$$

$$p = 800; p = 3000$$

The vertex is at $p = \dfrac{-b}{2a} = \dfrac{-(-1900)}{2(1/2)} = 1900$.

Since $f(1900) = 605,000$, the vertex is
$(1900, 605000)$.

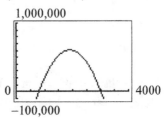

The graph of f is above the p-axis when
$800 < p < 3000$. Since the inequality is strict, the solution set is
$\{p \mid 800 < p < 3000\}$ or, using interval

notation, $(800, 3000)$. The revenue is more than $1,200,000 for prices between $800 and $3000.

37. $y = cx - \left(1 + c^2\right)\left(\dfrac{g}{2}\right)\left(\dfrac{x}{v}\right)^2$

a. Since the round must clear a hill 200 meters high, this mean $y > 200$.

Now $x = 2000$, $v = 897$, and $g = 9.81$.

$$c(2000) - \left(1 + c^2\right)\left(\dfrac{9.81}{2}\right)\left(\dfrac{2000}{897}\right)^2 > 200$$

$$2000c - 24.3845\left(1 + c^2\right) > 200$$

$$2000c - 24.3845 - 24.3845c^2 > 200$$

$$-24.3845c^2 + 2000c - 224.3845 > 0$$

We graph
$$f(c) = -24.3845c^2 + 2000c - 224.3845.$$
The intercepts are

y-intercept: $f(0) = -224.3845$

c-intercepts:

$$-24.3845c^2 + 2000c - 224.3845 = 0$$

$$c = \dfrac{-2000 \pm \sqrt{(2000)^2 - 4(-24.3845)(-224.3845)}}{2(-24.3845)}$$

$$= \dfrac{-2000 \pm \sqrt{3,978,113.985}}{-48.769}$$

$c \approx 0.112$ or $c \approx 81.907$

The vertex is at

$$c = \dfrac{-b}{2a} = \dfrac{-(2000)}{2(-24.3845)} = 41.010 . \text{ Since}$$

$f(41.010) \approx 40,785.273$, the vertex is $(41.010, 40785.273)$.

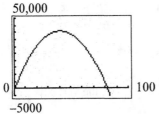

The graph of f is above the c-axis when $0.112 < c < 81.907$. Since the inequality is strict, the solution set is

$\{c \mid 0.112 < c < 81.907\}$ or, using interval notation, $(0.112, 81.907)$.

b. Since the round is to be on the ground $y = 0$. Note, 75 km = 75,000 m. So, $x = 75,000$, $v = 897$, and $g = 9.81$.

$$c(75,000) - \left(1 + c^2\right)\left(\dfrac{9.81}{2}\right)\left(\dfrac{75,000}{897}\right)^2 = 0$$

$$75,000c - 34,290.724\left(1 + c^2\right) = 0$$

$$75,000c - 34,290.724 - 34,290.724c^2 = 0$$

$$-34,290.724c^2 + 75,000c - 34,290.724 = 0$$

We graph
$$f(c) = -34,290.724c^2 + 75,000c - 34,290.724 .$$
The intercepts are

y-intercept: $f(0) = -34,290.724$

c-intercepts:

$$-34,290.724c^2 + 75,000c - 34,290.724 = 0$$

$$c = \dfrac{-(75,000) \pm \sqrt{(75,000)^2 - 4(-34,290.724)(-34,290.724)}}{2(-34,290.724)}$$

$$= \dfrac{-75,000 \pm \sqrt{921,584,990.2}}{-68,581.448}$$

$c \approx 0.651$ or $c \approx 1.536$

It is possible to hit the target 75 kilometers away so long as $c \approx 0.651$ or $c \approx 1.536$.

38. $W = \dfrac{1}{2}kx^2$; $\tilde{W} = \dfrac{w}{2g}v^2$; $x \geq 0$

Note $v = 25$ mph $= \dfrac{110}{3}$ ft/sec. For $k = 9450$,

$w = 4000$, $g = 32.2$, and $v = \dfrac{110}{3}$, we solve

$$W > \tilde{W}$$

$$\dfrac{1}{2}(9450)x^2 > \dfrac{4000}{2(32.2)}\left(\dfrac{110}{3}\right)^2$$

$$4725x^2 > 83,505.866$$

$$x^2 > 17.6732$$

$$x^2 - 17.6732 > 0$$

We graph $f(x) = x^2 - 17.6732$. The intercepts are

y-intercept: $f(0) = -17.6732$

x-intercepts: $x^2 - 17.6732 = 0$

$$x^2 = 17.6732$$

$$x = \pm\sqrt{17.6732}$$

$$x \approx \pm 4.2$$

The vertex is at $x = \dfrac{-b}{2a} = \dfrac{-(0)}{2(1)} = 0$. Since

$f(0) = -17.6732$, the vertex is $(0, -17.6732)$.

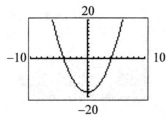

The graph of f is above the x-axis when $x < -4.2$ or $x > 4.2$. Since we are restricted to $x \geq 0$, we disregard $x < -4.2$, so the solution is $x > 4.2$. Therefore, the spring must be able to compress at least 4.3 feet in order to stop the car safely.

39. $(x-4)^2 \leq 0$

We graph the function $f(x) = (x-4)^2$.

y-intercept: $f(0) = 16$

x-intercepts: $(x-4)^2 = 0$

$$x - 4 = 0$$
$$x = 4$$

The vertex is the vertex is $(4, 0)$.

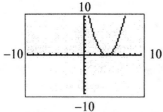

The graph is never below the x-axis. Since the inequality is not strict, the only solution comes from the x-intercept. Therefore, the given inequality has exactly one real solution, namely $x = 4$.

40. $(x-2)^2 > 0$

We graph the function $f(x) = (x-2)^2$.

y-intercept: $f(0) = 4$

x-intercepts: $(x-2)^2 = 0$

$$x - 2 = 0$$
$$x = 2$$

The vertex is the vertex is $(2, 0)$.

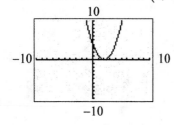

The graph is above the x-axis when $x < 2$ or $x > 2$. Since the inequality is strict, the solution set is $\left\{ x \mid x < 2 \text{ or } x > 2 \right\}$. Therefore, the given inequality has exactly one real number that is not a solution, namely $x \neq 2$.

41. Solving $x^2 + x + 1 > 0$

We graph the function $f(x) = x^2 + x + 1$.

y-intercept: $f(0) = 1$

x-intercepts: $b^2 - 4ac = 1^2 - 4(1)(1) = -3$, so f has no x-intercepts.

The vertex is at $x = \dfrac{-b}{2a} = \dfrac{-(1)}{2(1)} = -\dfrac{1}{2}$. Since $f\left(-\dfrac{1}{2}\right) = \dfrac{3}{4}$, the vertex is $\left(-\dfrac{1}{2}, \dfrac{3}{4}\right)$.

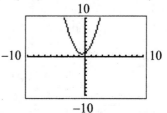

The graph is always above the x-axis. Thus, the solution is the set of all real numbers or, using interval notation, $(-\infty, \infty)$.

42. Solving $x^2 - x + 1 < 0$

We graph the function $f(x) = x^2 - x + 1$.

y-intercept: $f(0) = 1$

x-intercepts: $b^2 - 4ac = (-1)^2 - 4(1)(1) = -3$, so f has no x-intercepts.

The vertex is at $x = \dfrac{-b}{2a} = \dfrac{-(-1)}{2(1)} = \dfrac{1}{2}$. Since $f\left(-\dfrac{1}{2}\right) = \dfrac{3}{4}$, the vertex is $\left(-\dfrac{1}{2}, \dfrac{3}{4}\right)$.

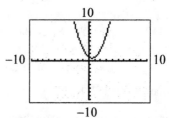

The graph is never below the x-axis. Thus, the inequality has no solution. That is, the solution set is $\{\ \}$ or $\varnothing$.

Chapter 4 Review Exercises

1. $f(x) = 2x - 5$

   a. Slope = 2; y-intercept = -5

   b. Plot the point $(0, -5)$. Use the slope to find an additional point by moving 1 unit to the right and 2 units up.

   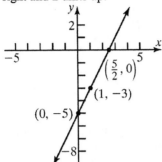

   c. increasing

2. $g(x) = -4x + 7$

   a. Slope = -4; y-intercept = 7

   b. Plot the point $(0, 7)$. Use the slope to find an additional point by moving 1 unit to the right and 4 units down.

   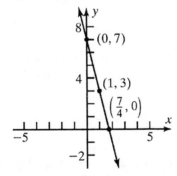

   c. decreasing

3. $h(x) = \dfrac{4}{5}x - 6$

   a. Slope = $\dfrac{4}{5}$; y-intercept = -6

   b. Plot the point $(0, -6)$. Use the slope to find an additional point by moving 5 units to the right and 4 units up.

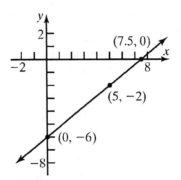

   c. increasing

4. $F(x) = -\dfrac{1}{3}x + 1$

   a. Slope = $-\dfrac{1}{3}$; y-intercept = 1

   b. Plot the point $(0, 1)$. Use the slope to find an additional point by moving 3 units to the right and 1 unit down.

   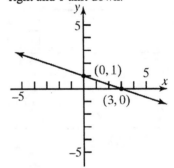

   c. decreasing

5. $G(x) = 4$

   a. Slope = 0; y-intercept = 4

   b. Plot the point $(0, 4)$ and draw a horizontal line through it.

   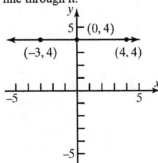

   c. constant

381

6. $H(x) = -3$

   a. Slope $= 0$; y-intercept $= -3$

   b. Plot the point $(0, -3)$ and draw a horizontal line through it.

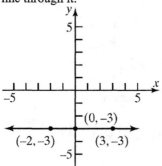

   c. constant

7.

x	$y = f(x)$	Avg. rate of change $= \dfrac{\Delta y}{\Delta x}$
-1	-2	
0	3	$\dfrac{3 - (-2)}{0 - (-1)} = \dfrac{5}{1} = 5$
1	8	$\dfrac{8 - 3}{1 - 0} = \dfrac{5}{1} = 5$
2	13	$\dfrac{13 - 8}{2 - 1} = \dfrac{5}{1} = 5$
3	18	$\dfrac{18 - 13}{3 - 2} = \dfrac{5}{1} = 5$

This is a linear function with slope $= 5$, since the average rate of change is constant at 5.

8.

x	$y = f(x)$	Avg. rate of change $= \dfrac{\Delta y}{\Delta x}$
-1	-3	
0	4	$\dfrac{4 - (-3)}{0 - (-1)} = \dfrac{7}{1} = 7$
1	7	$\dfrac{7 - 4}{1 - 0} = \dfrac{3}{1} = 3$
2	6	
3	1	

This is not a linear function, since the average rate of change is not constant.

9. $f(x) = (x - 2)^2 + 2$

Using the graph of $y = x^2$, shift right 2 units, then shift up 2 units.

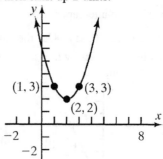

10. $f(x) = (x + 1)^2 - 4$

Using the graph of $y = x^2$, shift left 1 unit, then shift down 4 units.

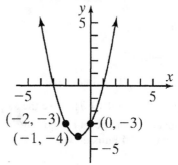

11. $f(x) = -(x - 4)^2$

Using the graph of $y = x^2$, shift the graph 4 units right, then reflect about the x-axis.

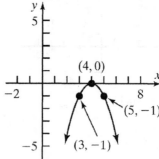

12. $f(x) = (x-1)^2 - 3$

Using the graph of $y = x^2$, shift the graph 1 unit right and shift 3 units down.

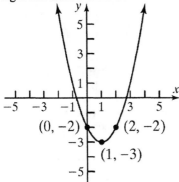

13. $f(x) = 2(x+1)^2 + 4$

Using the graph of $y = x^2$, stretch vertically by a factor of 2, then shift 1 unit left, then shift 4 units up.

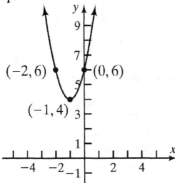

14. $f(x) = -3(x+2)^2 + 1$

Using the graph of $y = x^2$, stretch vertically by a factor of 3, then shift 2 units left, then reflect about the x-axis, then shift 1 unit up.

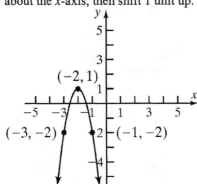

15. a. $f(x) = (x-2)^2 + 2$
$$= x^2 - 4x + 4 + 2$$
$$= x^2 - 4x + 6$$

$a = 1, b = -4, c = 6$. Since $a = 1 > 0$, the graph opens up. The x-coordinate of the vertex is $x = -\dfrac{b}{2a} = -\dfrac{-4}{2(1)} = \dfrac{4}{2} = 2$.

The y-coordinate of the vertex is
$$f\left(-\frac{b}{2a}\right) = f(2) = (2)^2 - 4(2) + 6 = 2.$$

Thus, the vertex is (2, 2).
The axis of symmetry is the line $x = 2$.
The discriminant is:
$b^2 - 4ac = (-4)^2 - 4(1)(6) = -8 < 0$, so the graph has no x-intercepts.
The y-intercept is $f(0) = 6$.

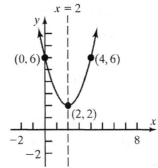

b. The domain is $(-\infty, \infty)$.
The range is $[2, \infty)$.

c. Decreasing on $(-\infty, 2)$.
Increasing on $(2, \infty)$.

16. a. $f(x) = (x+1)^2 - 4$
$$= x^2 + 2x + 1 - 4$$
$$= x^2 + 2x - 3$$

$a = 1, b = 2, c = 2$. Since $a = 1 > 0$, the graph opens up. The x-coordinate of the vertex is $x = -\dfrac{b}{2a} = -\dfrac{2}{2(1)} = -1$.

The y-coordinate of the vertex is
$$f\left(-\frac{b}{2a}\right) = f(-1) = (-1)^2 + 2(-1) - 3 = -4.$$

Thus, the vertex is (-1, -4).
The axis of symmetry is the line $x = -1$.
The discriminant is:
$b^2 - 4ac = (2)^2 - 4(1)(-3) = 16 > 0$, so the graph has two x-intercepts.

The x-intercepts are found by solving:

$$x^2 + 2x - 3 = 0$$

$$(x+3)(x-1) = 0$$

$$x = -3 \text{ or } x = 1$$

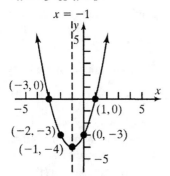

b. The domain is $(-\infty, \infty)$.

The range is $[-4, \infty)$.

c. Decreasing on $(-\infty, -1)$.

Increasing on $(-1, \infty)$.

17. a. $f(x) = \dfrac{1}{4}x^2 - 16$

$a = \dfrac{1}{4}, b = 0, c = -16$. Since $a = \dfrac{1}{4} > 0$, the graph opens up. The x-coordinate of the vertex is $x = -\dfrac{b}{2a} = -\dfrac{-0}{2\left(\frac{1}{4}\right)} = -\dfrac{0}{\frac{1}{2}} = 0$.

The y-coordinate of the vertex is

$$f\left(-\dfrac{b}{2a}\right) = f(0) = \dfrac{1}{4}(0)^2 - 16 = -16.$$

Thus, the vertex is $(0, -16)$.

The axis of symmetry is the line $x = 0$.

The discriminant is:

$$b^2 - 4ac = (0)^2 - 4\left(\dfrac{1}{4}\right)(-16) = 16 > 0, \text{ so}$$

the graph has two x-intercepts.

The x-intercepts are found by solving:

$$\dfrac{1}{4}x^2 - 16 = 0$$

$$x^2 - 64 = 0$$

$$x^2 = 64$$

$$x = 8 \text{ or } x = -8$$

The x-intercepts are -8 and 8.

The y-intercept is $f(0) = -16$.

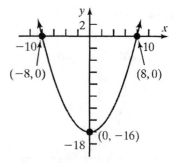

b. The domain is $(-\infty, \infty)$.

The range is $[-16, \infty)$.

c. Decreasing on $(-\infty, 0)$.

Increasing on $(0, \infty)$.

18. a. $f(x) = -\dfrac{1}{2}x^2 + 2$

$a = -\dfrac{1}{2}, b = 0, c = 2$. Since $a = -\dfrac{1}{2} < 0$, the graph opens down. The x-coordinate of the vertex is $x = -\dfrac{b}{2a} = -\dfrac{0}{2\left(-\frac{1}{2}\right)} = -\dfrac{0}{-1} = 0.$

The y-coordinate of the vertex is

$$f\left(-\dfrac{b}{2a}\right) = f(0) = -\dfrac{1}{2}(0)^2 + 2 = 2.$$

The axis of symmetry is the line $x = 0$.

he discriminant is:

$$b^2 - 4ac = (0)^2 - 4\left(-\tfrac{1}{2}\right)(2) = 4 > 0, \text{ so the}$$

graph has two x-intercepts.

The x-intercepts are found by solving:

$$-\dfrac{1}{2}x^2 + 2 = 0$$

$$x^2 - 4 = 0$$

$$x^2 = 4$$

$$x = -2 \text{ or } x = 2$$

The x-intercepts are -2 and 2.

The y-intercept is $f(0) = 2$.

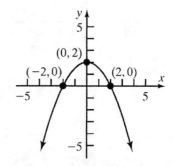

b. The domain is $(-\infty, \infty)$.
The range is $(-\infty, 2]$.

c. Increasing on $(-\infty, 0)$
Decreasing on $(0, \infty)$.

19. a. $f(x) = -4x^2 + 4x$
$a = -4, b = 4, c = 0$. Since $a = -4 < 0$, the graph opens down. The x-coordinate of the vertex is $x = -\dfrac{b}{2a} = -\dfrac{4}{2(-4)} = -\dfrac{4}{-8} = \dfrac{1}{2}$.
The y-coordinate of the vertex is
$$f\left(-\frac{b}{2a}\right) = f\left(\frac{1}{2}\right) = -4\left(\frac{1}{2}\right)^2 + 4\left(\frac{1}{2}\right)$$
$$= -1 + 2 = 1$$
Thus, the vertex is $\left(\dfrac{1}{2}, 1\right)$.

The axis of symmetry is the line $x = \dfrac{1}{2}$.

The discriminant is:
$b^2 - 4ac = 4^2 - 4(-4)(0) = 16 > 0$, so the graph has two x-intercepts.
The x-intercepts are found by solving:
$-4x^2 + 4x = 0$
$-4x(x - 1) = 0$
$x = 0$ or $x = 1$
The x-intercepts are 0 and 1.
The y-intercept is $f(0) = -4(0)^2 + 4(0) = 0$.

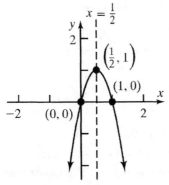

b. The domain is $(-\infty, \infty)$.
The range is $(-\infty, 1]$.

c. Increasing on $\left(-\infty, \dfrac{1}{2}\right)$

Decreasing on $\left(\dfrac{1}{2}, \infty\right)$.

20. a. $f(x) = 9x^2 - 6x + 3$
$a = 9, b = -6, c = 3$. Since $a = 9 > 0$, the graph opens up. The x-coordinate of the vertex is $x = -\dfrac{b}{2a} = -\dfrac{-6}{2(9)} = \dfrac{6}{18} = \dfrac{1}{3}$. The y-coordinate of the vertex is
$$f\left(-\frac{b}{2a}\right) = f\left(\frac{1}{3}\right) = 9\left(\frac{1}{3}\right)^2 - 6\left(\frac{1}{3}\right) + 3$$
$$= 1 - 2 + 3 = 2$$
Thus, the vertex is $\left(\dfrac{1}{3}, 2\right)$.

The axis of symmetry is the line $x = \dfrac{1}{3}$.

The discriminant is:
$b^2 - 4ac = (-6)^2 - 4(9)(3) = -72 < 0$, so the graph has no x-intercepts.
The y-intercept is
$f(0) = 9(0)^2 - 6(0) + 3 = 3$.

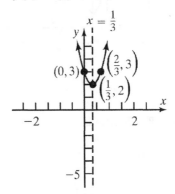

b. The domain is $(-\infty, \infty)$.
The range is $[2, \infty)$.

c. Decreasing on $\left(-\infty, \dfrac{1}{3}\right)$.

Increasing on $\left(\dfrac{1}{3}, \infty\right)$.

21. a. $f(x) = \dfrac{9}{2}x^2 + 3x + 1$

$a = \dfrac{9}{2}, b = 3, c = 1$. Since $a = \dfrac{9}{2} > 0$, the graph opens up. The x-coordinate of the vertex is $x = -\dfrac{b}{2a} = -\dfrac{3}{2\left(\dfrac{9}{2}\right)} = -\dfrac{3}{9} = -\dfrac{1}{3}$.

The y-coordinate of the vertex is

$$f\left(-\frac{b}{2a}\right) = f\left(-\frac{1}{3}\right) = \frac{9}{2}\left(-\frac{1}{3}\right)^2 + 3\left(-\frac{1}{3}\right) + 1$$

$$= \frac{1}{2} - 1 + 1 = \frac{1}{2}$$

Thus, the vertex is $\left(-\frac{1}{3}, \frac{1}{2}\right)$.

The axis of symmetry is the line $x = -\frac{1}{3}$.

The discriminant is:

$$b^2 - 4ac = 3^2 - 4\left(\frac{9}{2}\right)(1) = 9 - 18 = -9 < 0,$$

so the graph has no x-intercepts. The y-intercept is $f(0) = \frac{9}{2}(0)^2 + 3(0) + 1 = 1$.

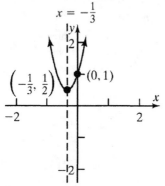

b. The domain is $(-\infty, \infty)$.

The range is $\left[\frac{1}{2}, \infty\right)$.

c. Decreasing on $\left(-\infty, -\frac{1}{3}\right)$.

Increasing on $\left(-\frac{1}{3}, \infty\right)$.

22. a. $f(x) = -x^2 + x + \frac{1}{2}$

$a = -1, b = 1, c = \frac{1}{2}$. Since $a = -1 < 0$, the graph opens down. The x-coordinate of the vertex is $x = -\frac{b}{2a} = -\frac{1}{2(-1)} = -\frac{1}{-2} = \frac{1}{2}$.

The y-coordinate of the vertex is

$$f\left(-\frac{b}{2a}\right) = f\left(\frac{1}{2}\right) = -\left(\frac{1}{2}\right)^2 + \left(\frac{1}{2}\right) + \frac{1}{2}$$

$$= -\frac{1}{4} + 1 = \frac{3}{4}$$

Thus, the vertex is $\left(\frac{1}{2}, \frac{3}{4}\right)$. The axis of symmetry is the line $x = \frac{1}{2}$. The discriminant is: $b^2 - 4ac = 1^2 - 4(-1)\left(\frac{1}{2}\right) = 3 > 0$, so the graph has two x-intercepts. The x-intercepts are found by solving: $-x^2 + x + \frac{1}{2} = 0$.

$$x = \frac{-b \pm \sqrt{b^2 - 4ac}}{2a} = \frac{-1 \pm \sqrt{3}}{2(-1)} = \frac{-1 \pm \sqrt{3}}{-2} = \frac{1 \pm \sqrt{3}}{2}$$

The x-intercepts are $\frac{1 - \sqrt{3}}{2} \approx -0.4$ and $\frac{1 + \sqrt{3}}{2} \approx 1.4$.

The y-intercept is $f(0) = -(0)^2 + (0) + \frac{1}{2} = \frac{1}{2}$.

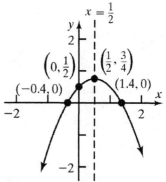

b. The domain is $(-\infty, \infty)$.

The range is $\left(-\infty, \frac{3}{4}\right]$.

c. Increasing on $\left(-\infty, \frac{1}{2}\right)$.

Decreasing on $\left(\frac{1}{2}, \infty\right)$.

23. a. $f(x) = 3x^2 + 4x - 1$

$a = 3, b = 4, c = -1$. Since $a = 3 > 0$, the graph opens up. The x-coordinate of the vertex is $x = -\frac{b}{2a} = -\frac{4}{2(3)} = -\frac{4}{6} = -\frac{2}{3}$.

The y-coordinate of the vertex is

$$f\left(-\frac{b}{2a}\right) = f\left(-\frac{2}{3}\right) = 3\left(-\frac{2}{3}\right)^2 + 4\left(-\frac{2}{3}\right) - 1$$

$$= \frac{4}{3} - \frac{8}{3} - 1 = -\frac{7}{3}$$

Thus, the vertex is $\left(-\dfrac{2}{3}, -\dfrac{7}{3}\right)$.

The axis of symmetry is the line $x = -\dfrac{2}{3}$.

The discriminant is:
$b^2 - 4ac = (4)^2 - 4(3)(-1) = 28 > 0$, so the graph has two x-intercepts.
The x-intercepts are found by solving:
$3x^2 + 4x - 1 = 0$.

$$x = \frac{-b \pm \sqrt{b^2 - 4ac}}{2a} = \frac{-4 \pm \sqrt{28}}{2(3)}$$

$$= \frac{-4 \pm 2\sqrt{7}}{6} = \frac{-2 \pm \sqrt{7}}{3}$$

The x-intercepts are $\dfrac{-2 - \sqrt{7}}{3} \approx -1.55$ and

$\dfrac{-2 + \sqrt{7}}{3} \approx 0.22$.

The y-intercept is $f(0) = 3(0)^2 + 4(0) - 1 = -1$.

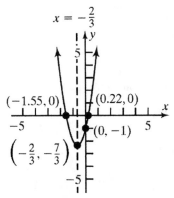

b. The domain is $(-\infty, \infty)$.

The range is $\left[-\dfrac{7}{3}, \infty\right)$.

c. Decreasing on $\left(-\infty, -\dfrac{2}{3}\right)$

Increasing on $\left(-\dfrac{2}{3}, \infty\right)$.

24. a. $f(x) = -2x^2 - x + 4$

$a = -2, b = -1, c = 4$. Since $a = -2 < 0$, the graph opens down. The x-coordinate of the

vertex is $x = -\dfrac{b}{2a} = -\dfrac{-1}{2(-2)} = \dfrac{1}{-4} = -\dfrac{1}{4}$.

The y-coordinate of the vertex is

$$f\left(-\frac{b}{2a}\right) = f\left(-\frac{1}{4}\right) = -2\left(-\frac{1}{4}\right)^2 - \left(-\frac{1}{4}\right) + 4$$

$$= -\frac{1}{8} + \frac{1}{4} + 4 = \frac{33}{8}$$

Thus, the vertex is $\left(-\dfrac{1}{4}, \dfrac{33}{8}\right)$.

The axis of symmetry is the line $x = -\dfrac{1}{4}$.

The discriminant is:
$b^2 - 4ac = (-1)^2 - 4(-2)(4) = 33 > 0$, so the graph has two x-intercepts. The x-intercepts are found by solving: $-2x^2 - x + 4 = 0$.

$$x = \frac{-b \pm \sqrt{b^2 - 4ac}}{2a} = \frac{-(-1) \pm \sqrt{33}}{2(-2)}$$

$$= \frac{1 \pm \sqrt{33}}{-4} = \frac{-1 \pm \sqrt{33}}{4}$$

The x-intercepts are $\dfrac{-1 - \sqrt{33}}{4} \approx -1.7$ and

$\dfrac{-1 + \sqrt{33}}{4} \approx 1.2$.

The y-intercept is $f(0) = -2(0)^2 - 0 + 4 = 4$.

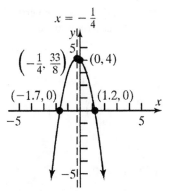

b. The domain is $(-\infty, \infty)$.

The range is $\left(-\infty, \dfrac{33}{8}\right]$.

c. Increasing on $\left(-\infty, -\dfrac{1}{4}\right)$.

Decreasing on $\left(-\dfrac{1}{4}, \infty\right)$.

25. $f(x) = 3x^2 - 6x + 4$

$a = 3, b = -6, c = 4$. Since $a = 3 > 0$, the graph opens up, so the vertex is a minimum point. The minimum occurs at

$$x = -\frac{b}{2a} = -\frac{-6}{2(3)} = \frac{6}{6} = 1.$$

The minimum value is

$$f\left(-\frac{b}{2a}\right) = f(1) = 3(1)^2 - 6(1) + 4$$
$$= 3 - 6 + 4 = 1$$

26. $f(x) = 2x^2 + 8x + 5$

$a = 2, b = 8, c = 5$. Since $a = 2 > 0$, the graph opens up, so the vertex is a minimum point. The minimum occurs at

$$x = -\frac{b}{2a} = -\frac{8}{2(2)} = -\frac{8}{4} = -2.$$

The minimum value is

$$f\left(-\frac{b}{2a}\right) = f(-2) = 2(-2)^2 + 8(-2) + 5$$
$$= 8 - 16 + 5 = -3$$

27. $f(x) = -x^2 + 8x - 4$

$a = -1, b = 8, c = -4$. Since $a = -1 < 0$, the graph opens down, so the vertex is a maximum point. The maximum occurs at

$$x = -\frac{b}{2a} = -\frac{8}{2(-1)} = -\frac{8}{-2} = 4.$$

The maximum value is

$$f\left(-\frac{b}{2a}\right) = f(4) = -(4)^2 + 8(4) - 4$$
$$= -16 + 32 - 4 = 12$$

28. $f(x) = -x^2 - 10x - 3$

$a = -1, b = -10, c = -3$. Since $a = -1 < 0$, the graph opens down, so the vertex is a maximum point. The maximum occurs at

$$x = -\frac{b}{2a} = -\frac{-10}{2(-1)} = \frac{10}{-2} = -5.$$

The maximum value is

$$f\left(-\frac{b}{2a}\right) = f(-5) = -(-5)^2 - 10(-5) - 3$$
$$= -25 + 50 - 3 = 22$$

29. $f(x) = -3x^2 + 12x + 4$

$a = -3, b = 12, c = 4$. Since $a = -3 < 0$, the graph opens down, so the vertex is a maximum point. The maximum occurs at

$$x = -\frac{b}{2a} = -\frac{12}{2(-3)} = -\frac{12}{-6} = 2.$$

The maximum value is

$$f\left(-\frac{b}{2a}\right) = f(2) = -3(2)^2 + 12(2) + 4$$
$$= -12 + 24 + 4 = 16$$

30. $f(x) = -2x^2 + 4$

$a = -2, b = 0, c = 4$. Since $a = -2 < 0$, the graph opens down, so the vertex is a maximum point. The maximum occurs at

$$x = -\frac{b}{2a} = -\frac{0}{2(-2)} = 0.$$

The maximum value is

$$f\left(-\frac{b}{2a}\right) = f(0) = -2(0)^2 + 4 = 4.$$

31. $x^2 + 6x - 16 < 0$

We graph the function $f(x) = x^2 + 6x - 16$. The intercepts are

y-intercept: $f(0) = -16$

x-intercepts: $x^2 + 6x - 16 = 0$

$$(x + 8)(x - 2) = 0$$
$$x = -8, x = 2$$

The vertex is at $x = \frac{-b}{2a} = \frac{-(6)}{2(1)} = -3$. Since

$f(-3) = -25$, the vertex is $(-3, -25)$.

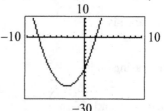

The graph is below the x-axis when $-8 < x < 2$. Since the inequality is strict, the solution set is $\{x \mid -8 < x < 2\}$ or, using interval notation, $(-8, 2)$.

32. $3x^2 - 2x - 1 \geq 0$

We graph the function $f(x) = 3x^2 - 2x - 1$. The intercepts are

y-intercept: $f(0) = -1$

x-intercepts: $3x^2 - 2x - 1 = 0$

$(3x + 1)(x - 1) = 0$

$x = -\dfrac{1}{3}, x = 1$

The vertex is at $x = \dfrac{-b}{2a} = \dfrac{-(-2)}{2(3)} = \dfrac{2}{6} = \dfrac{1}{3}$. Since

$f\left(\dfrac{1}{3}\right) = -\dfrac{4}{3}$, the vertex is $\left(\dfrac{1}{3}, -\dfrac{4}{3}\right)$.

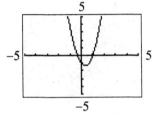

The graph is above the x-axis when $x < -\dfrac{1}{3}$ or $x > 1$. Since the inequality is not strict, the solution set is $\left\{x \mid x \leq -\dfrac{1}{3} \text{ or } x \geq 1\right\}$ or, using interval notation, $\left(-\infty, -\dfrac{1}{3}\right] \cup [1, \infty)$.

33. $3x^2 \geq 14x + 5$

$3x^2 - 14x - 5 \geq 0$

We graph the function $f(x) = 3x^2 - 14x - 5$. The intercepts are

y-intercept: $f(0) = -5$

x-intercepts: $3x^2 - 14x - 5 = 0$

$(3x + 1)(x - 5) = 0$

$x = -\dfrac{1}{3}, x = 5$

The vertex is at $x = \dfrac{-b}{2a} = \dfrac{-(-14)}{2(3)} = \dfrac{14}{6} = \dfrac{7}{3}$.

Since $f\left(\dfrac{7}{3}\right) = -\dfrac{64}{3}$, the vertex is $\left(\dfrac{7}{3}, -\dfrac{64}{3}\right)$.

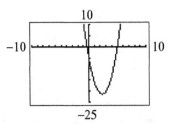

The graph is above the x-axis when $x < -\dfrac{1}{3}$ or $x > 5$. Since the inequality is not strict, the solution set is $\left\{x \mid x \leq -\dfrac{1}{3} \text{ or } x \geq 5\right\}$ or, using interval notation, $\left(-\infty, -\dfrac{1}{3}\right] \cup [5, \infty)$.

34. $4x^2 < 13x - 3$

$4x^2 - 13x + 3 < 0$

We graph the function $f(x) = 4x^2 - 13x + 3$. The intercepts are

y-intercept: $f(0) = 3$

x-intercepts: $4x^2 - 13x + 3 = 0$

$(4x - 1)(x - 3) = 0$

$x = \dfrac{1}{4}, x = 3$

The vertex is at $x = \dfrac{-b}{2a} = \dfrac{-(-13)}{2(4)} = \dfrac{13}{8}$. Since

$f\left(\dfrac{13}{8}\right) = -\dfrac{121}{16}$, the vertex is $\left(\dfrac{13}{8}, -\dfrac{121}{16}\right)$.

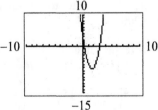

The graph is below the x-axis when $\dfrac{1}{4} < x < 3$. Since the inequality is strict, the solution set is $\left\{x \mid \dfrac{1}{4} < x < 3\right\}$ or, using interval notation, $\left(\dfrac{1}{4}, 3\right)$.

35. a. Company A: $C(x) = 0.06x + 7.00$

Company B: $C(x) = 0.08x$

b. $0.06x + 7.00 = 0.08x$

$7.00 = 0.02x$

$350 = x$

The bill from Company A will equal the bill from Company B if 350 minutes are used.

c. $0.08x < 0.06x + 7.00$

$0.02x < 7.00$

$x < 350$

The bill from Company B will be less than the bill from Company A if fewer than 350 minutes are used. That is, $0 \le x < 350$.

36. a. $S(x) = 0.01x + 15,000$

b. $S(1,000,000) = 0.01(1,000,000) + 15,000$

$= 10,000 + 15,000 = 25,000$

In 2005, Bill's salary was $25,000.

c. $0.01x + 15,000 = 100,000$

$0.01x = 85,000$

$x = 8,500,000$

Bill's sales would have to be $8,500,000 in order to earn $100,000.

d. $0.01x + 15,000 > 150,000$

$0.01x > 135,000$

$x > 13,500,000$

Bill's sales would have to be more than $13,500,000 in order for his salary to exceed $150,000.

37. a. The revenue will equal the quantity x sold times the price p. That is, $R = xp$. Thus,

$$R(x) = x\left(-\frac{1}{10}x + 150\right) = -\frac{1}{10}x^2 + 150x$$

b. $R(100) = -\frac{1}{10}(100)^2 + 150(100) = 14,000$

The revenue is $14,000 if 100 units are sold.

c. $a = -\frac{1}{10}, b = 150, c = 0.$ Since $a = -\frac{1}{10} < 0,$

the graph opens down, so the vertex is a maximum point. The maximum occurs at

$x = \frac{-b}{2a} = \frac{-(150)}{2(-1/10)} = \frac{-150}{-1/5} = 750.$ Thus, the

quantity that maximizes revenue is 750 units.

The maximum revenue is

$$R(750) = -\frac{1}{10}(750)^2 + 150(750)$$

$$= -56,250 + 112,500$$

$$= \$56,250$$

d. From part (c), we know revenue is maximizes when $x = 750$ units are sold. The price that should be charged for this is

$$p = -\frac{1}{10}(750) + 150 = \$75.$$

38. Since there are 200 feet of border, we know that $2x + 2y = 200$. The area is to be maximized, so $A = x \cdot y$. Solving the perimeter formula for y:

$2x + 2y = 200$

$2y = 200 - 2x$

$y = 100 - x$

The area function is:

$A(x) = x(100 - x) = -x^2 + 100x$

The maximum value occurs at the vertex:

$$x = \frac{-b}{2a} = \frac{-(100)}{2(-1)} = \frac{-100}{-2} = 50$$

The pond should be 50 feet by 50 feet for maximum area.

39. Consider the diagram

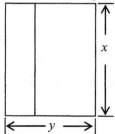

Total amount of fence $= 3x + 2y = 10,000$

$$y = \frac{10,000 - 3x}{2} = 5000 - \frac{3}{2}x$$

Total area enclosed $= (x)(y) = (x)\left(5000 - \frac{3}{2}x\right)$

$$A(x) = 5000x - \frac{3}{2}x^2 = -\frac{3}{2}x^2 + 5000x \text{ is a}$$

quadratic function with $a = -\frac{3}{2} < 0$.

So the vertex corresponds to the maximum value for this function. The vertex occurs when

$$x = -\frac{b}{2a} = -\frac{5000}{2(-3/2)} = \frac{5000}{3}.$$

The maximum area is:

$$A\left(\frac{5000}{3}\right) = -\frac{3}{2}\left(\frac{5000}{3}\right)^2 + 5000\left(\frac{5000}{3}\right)$$

$$= -\frac{3}{2}\left(\frac{25,000,000}{9}\right) + \frac{25,000,000}{3}$$

$$= -\frac{12,500,000}{3} + \frac{25,000,000}{3}$$

$$= \frac{12,500,000}{3}$$

$$\approx 4,166,666.67 \text{ square meters}$$

40. Consider the diagram

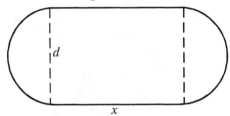

Let d = diameter of the semicircles
= width of the rectangle

Let x = length of the rectangle

100 = outside dimension length

$100 = 2x + 2(\text{circumference of a semicircle})$

$100 = 2x + \text{circumference of a circle}$

$100 = 2x + \pi d$

$100 - \pi d = 2x$

$\dfrac{100 - \pi d}{2} = x$

$50 - \dfrac{1}{2}\pi d = x$

We need an expression for the area of a rectangle in terms of a single variable.

$$A_{\text{rectangle}} = x \cdot d$$

$$= \left(50 - \frac{1}{2}\pi d\right) \cdot d$$

$$= 50d - \frac{1}{2}\pi d^2$$

This is a quadratic function with $a = -\dfrac{1}{2}\pi < 0$.

Therefore, the x-coordinate of the vertex represents the value for d that maximizes the area of the rectangle and the y-coordinate of the vertex is the maximum area of the rectangle. The vertex occurs at

$$d = -\frac{b}{2a} = -\frac{50}{2\left(-\frac{1}{2}\pi\right)} = \frac{-50}{-\pi} = \frac{50}{\pi}$$

This gives us

$$x = 50 - \frac{1}{2}\pi d = 50 - \frac{1}{2}\pi\left(\frac{50}{\pi}\right) = 50 - 25 = 25$$

Therefore, the side of the rectangle with the semicircle should be $\dfrac{50}{\pi}$ feet and the other side should be 25 feet. The maximum area is

$$(25)\left(\frac{50}{\pi}\right) = \frac{1250}{\pi} \approx 397.89 \text{ ft}^2.$$

41. $C(x) = 4.9x^2 - 617.4x + 19,600$;
$a = 4.9$, $b = -617.4$, $c = 19,600$. Since $a = 4.9 > 0$, the graph opens up, so the vertex is a minimum point.

a. The minimum marginal cost occurs at

$$x = -\frac{b}{2a} = -\frac{-617.40}{2(4.9)} = \frac{617.40}{9.8} = 63.$$

Thus, 63 golf clubs should be manufactured in order to minimize the marginal cost.

b. The minimum marginal cost is

$$C(63) = 4.9(63)^2 - (617.40)(63) + 19600$$

$$= \$151.90$$

42. $V(t) = 5.0t^2 - 87.3t + 1761.1$;
$a = 5.0$, $b = -87.3$, $c = 1761.1$
Since $a = 5.0 > 0$, the graph opens up, so the vertex is a minimum point.

a. The minimum occurs at

$$t = \frac{-b}{2a} = \frac{-(-87.3)}{2(5.0)} = \frac{87.3}{10} = 8.73.$$

Now, $1995 + 8.73 = 2003.73$, so fewer violent crimes were committed in about 2004.

b. The minimum number of violent crimes committed was

$$V(8.73) = 5.0(8.73)^2 - 87.3(8.73) + 1761.1$$

$$\approx 1380$$

Thus, approximately 1380 thousand violent crimes were committed in 2003. That is, about 1,380,000 violent crimes.

c. Let $Y1 = 5.0t^2 - 87.3t + 1761.1$.

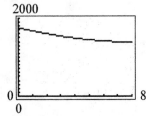

Violent crimes were decreasing from 1995 to 2003.

43. The area function is:

$$A(x) = x(10 - x) = -x^2 + 10x$$

The maximum value occurs at the vertex:

$$x = -\frac{b}{2a} = -\frac{10}{2(-1)} = -\frac{10}{-2} = 5$$

The maximum area is:

$$A(5) = -(5)^2 + 10(5)$$

$$= -25 + 50 = 25 \text{ square units}$$

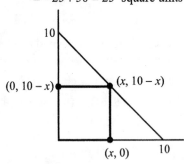

44. Locate the origin at the point directly under the highest point of the arch. Then the equation is in the form: $y = -ax^2 + k$, where $a > 0$. Since the maximum height is 10 feet, when $x = 0$, $y = k = 10$. Since the point $(10, 0)$ is on the parabola, we can find the constant:

$$0 = -a(10)^2 + 10$$

$$a = \frac{10}{10^2} = \frac{1}{10} = 0.10$$

The equation of the parabola is:

$$y = -\frac{1}{10}x^2 + 10$$

At $x = 8$:

$$y = -\frac{1}{10}(8)^2 + 10 = -6.4 + 10 = 3.6 \text{ feet}$$

45. a.

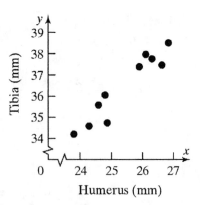

b. Yes, the two variables appear to have a linear relationship.

c. Using the LINear REGression program, the line of best fit is: $y = 1.3902x + 1.1140$

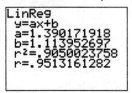

d. $y = 1.39017(26.5) + 1.11395 \approx 37.95$ mm

46. a.

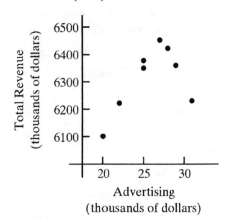

The data appear to be quadratic with $a < 0$.

b. The maximum revenue occurs at

$$A = \frac{-b}{2a} = \frac{-(411.88)}{2(-7.76)}$$

$$= \frac{-411.88}{-15.52} \approx \$26.5 \text{ thousand}$$

c. The maximum revenue is

$$R\left(\frac{-b}{2a}\right) = R(26.53866)$$

$$= -7.76(26.5)^2 + (411.88)(26.5) + 942.72$$

$$\approx \$6408 \text{ thousand}$$

d. Using the QUADratic REGression program, the quadratic function of best fit is:

$y = -7.76x^2 + 411.88x + 942.72$.

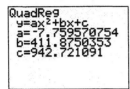

e.

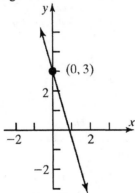

Chapter 4 Test

1. $f(x) = -4x + 3$

  a. Slope $= -4$; y-intercept $= 3$.

  b. The slope is negative, so the graph is decreasing.

  c. Plot the point $(0, 3)$. Use the slope to find an additional point by moving 1 unit to the right and 4 units down.

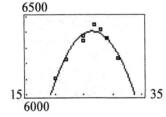

2. $f(x) = 3x^2 - 2x - 8$

y-intercept: $f(0) = -8$

x-intercepts: $\quad 3x^2 - 2x - 8 = 0$

$\qquad\qquad\quad (3x + 4)(x - 2) = 0$

$\qquad\qquad\qquad x = -\dfrac{4}{3}; \ x = 2$

The intercepts are $(0, -8)$, $\left(-\dfrac{4}{3}, 0\right)$, and $(2, 0)$.

3. $G(x) = -2x^2 + 4x + 1$

y-intercept: $G(0) = 1$

x-intercepts: $-2x^2 + 4x + 1 = 0$

$\qquad\qquad\qquad a = -2, b = 4, c = 1$

$$x = \frac{-b \pm \sqrt{b^2 - 4ac}}{2a} = \frac{-4 \pm \sqrt{4^2 - 4(-2)(1)}}{2(-2)}$$

$$= \frac{-4 \pm \sqrt{24}}{-4} = \frac{-4 \pm 2\sqrt{6}}{-4} = \frac{2 \pm \sqrt{6}}{2}$$

The intercepts are $(0, 1)$, $\left(\dfrac{2 - \sqrt{6}}{2}, 0\right)$, and

$\left(\dfrac{2 + \sqrt{6}}{2}, 0\right)$.

4. $\qquad f(x) = g(x)$

$\qquad x^2 + 3x = 5x + 3$

$\qquad x^2 - 2x - 3 = 0$

$\qquad (x + 1)(x - 3) = 0$

$\qquad x + 1 = 0 \quad$ or $\quad x - 3 = 0$

$\qquad\quad x = -1 \ $ or $\qquad x = 3$

The solution set is $\{-1, 3\}$.

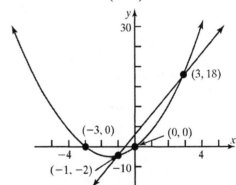

5. $f(x) = (x - 3)^2 - 2$

Using the graph of $y = x^2$, shift right 3 units, then shift down 2 units.

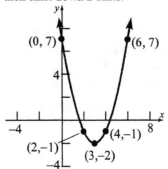

6. a. $f(x) = 3x^2 - 12x + 4$

$a = 3, b = -12, c = 4$. Since $a = 3 > 0$, the graph opens up.

b. The x-coordinate of the vertex is

$$x = -\frac{b}{2a} = -\frac{-12}{2(3)} = -\frac{-12}{6} = 2.$$

The y-coordinate of the vertex is

$$f\left(-\frac{b}{2a}\right) = f(2) = 3(2)^2 - 12(2) + 4$$

$$= 12 - 24 + 4 = -8$$

Thus, the vertex is $(2, -8)$.

c. The axis of symmetry is the line $x = 2$.

d. The discriminant is:

$$b^2 - 4ac = (-12)^2 - 4(3)(4) = 96 > 0,$$ so the graph has two x-intercepts. The x-intercepts are found by solving: $3x^2 - 12x + 4 = 0$.

$$x = \frac{-b \pm \sqrt{b^2 - 4ac}}{2a} = \frac{-(-12) \pm \sqrt{96}}{2(3)}$$

$$= \frac{12 \pm 4\sqrt{6}}{6} = \frac{6 \pm 2\sqrt{6}}{3}$$

The x-intercepts are $\dfrac{6 - 2\sqrt{6}}{3} \approx 0.37$ and

$\dfrac{6 \pm 2\sqrt{6}}{3} \approx 3.63$. The y-intercept is

$f(0) = 3(0)^2 - 12(0) + 4 = 4$.

e.

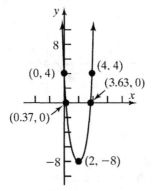

7. $f(x) = -2x^2 + 12x + 3$

$a = -2, b = 12, c = 3$. Since $a = -2 < 0$, the graph opens down, so the vertex is a maximum point. The maximum occurs at

$$x = -\frac{b}{2a} = -\frac{12}{2(-2)} = -\frac{12}{-4} = 3.$$

The maximum value is

$f(3) = -2(3)^2 + 12(3) + 3 = -18 + 36 + 3 = 21$.

8. $x^2 - 10x + 24 \geq 0$

We graph the function $f(x) = x^2 - 10x + 24$.

The intercepts are

y-intercept: $f(0) = 24$

x-intercepts: $x^2 - 10x + 24 = 0$

$$(x - 4)(x - 6) = 0$$

$$x = 4, x = 6$$

The vertex is at $x = \dfrac{-b}{2a} = \dfrac{-(-10)}{2(1)} = \dfrac{10}{2} = 5$.

Since $f(5) = -1$, the vertex is $(5, -1)$.

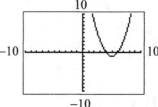

The graph is above the x-axis when $x < 4$ or $x > 6$. Since the inequality is not strict, the solution set is $\{x \mid x \leq 4 \text{ or } x \geq 6\}$ or, using interval notation, $(-\infty, 4] \cup [6, \infty)$.

9. a. $C(m) = 0.15m + 129.50$

b. $C(860) = 0.15(860) + 129.50$

$$= 129 + 129.50 = 258.50$$

If 860 miles are driven, the rental cost is $258.50.

c. $C(m) = 213.80$

$$0.15m + 129.50 = 213.80$$

$$0.15m = 84.30$$

$$m = 562$$

The rental cost is $213.80 if 562 miles were driven.

10. $r(x) = -0.115x^2 + 1.183x + 5.623$;

$a = -0.115, b = 1.183, c = 5.623$

Since $a = -0.115 < 0$, the graph opens down, so the vertex is a maximum point.

a. The maximum interest rate occurs at

$$x = -\frac{b}{2a} = -\frac{-1.183}{2(-0.115)} = \frac{-1.183}{-0.23} \approx 5.14.$$

The maximum interest rate was about

$r(5.14) = -0.115(5.14)^2 + 1.183(5.14) + 5.623$

$$\approx 8.67$$

Thus, the interest rate was highest in 1997, and the highest rate at this time was about 8.67%.

b. The year 2010 corresponds to $x = 18$.

$$r(18) = -0.115(18)^2 + 1.183(18) + 5.623$$
$$\approx -10.34$$

The model estimates the rate in 2010 to be -10.34%. This rate does not make sense since an interest rate cannot be negative.

Chapter 4 Cumulative Review

1. $P = (-1, 3); Q = (4, -2)$

Distance between P and Q:

$$d(P, Q) = \sqrt{(4 - (-1))^2 + (-2 - 3)^2}$$
$$= \sqrt{(5)^2 + (-5)^2}$$
$$= \sqrt{25 + 25} = \sqrt{50} = 5\sqrt{2}$$

Midpoint between P and Q:

$$\left(\frac{-1 + 4}{2}, \frac{3 - 2}{2}\right) = \left(\frac{3}{2}, \frac{1}{2}\right) = (1.5, 0.5)$$

2. $y = x^3 - 3x + 1$

a. $(-2, -1)$: $-1 = (-2)^3 - 3(-2) + 1$
$$-1 = -8 + 6 + 1$$
$$-1 = -1$$
Yes, $(-2, -1)$ is on the graph.

b. $(2, 3)$: $3 = (2)^3 - 3(2) + 1$
$$3 = 8 - 6 + 1$$
$$3 = 3$$
Yes, $(2, 3)$ is on the graph.

c. $(3, 1)$: $1 = (3)^3 - 3(3) + 1$
$$1 = -27 - 9 + 1$$
$$1 \neq -35$$
No, $(3, 1)$ is not on the graph.

3. $5x + 3 \geq 0$
$$5x \geq -3$$
$$x \geq -\frac{3}{5}$$

The solution set is $\left\{x \mid x \geq -\frac{3}{5}\right\}$ or $\left[-\frac{3}{5}, \infty\right)$.

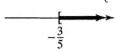

4. $(-1, 4)$ and $(2, -2)$ are points on the line.

$$\text{Slope} = \frac{-2 - 4}{2 - (-1)} = \frac{-6}{3} = -2$$

$$y - y_1 = m(x - x_1)$$
$$y - 4 = -2(x - (-1))$$
$$y - 4 = -2(x + 1)$$
$$y - 4 = -2x - 2$$
$$y = -2x + 2$$

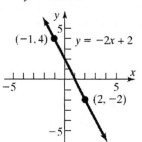

5. Perpendicular to $y = 2x + 1$; Containing $(3, 5)$

$$\text{Slope of perpendicular} = -\frac{1}{2}$$

$$y - y_1 = m(x - x_1)$$
$$y - 5 = -\frac{1}{2}(x - 3)$$
$$y - 5 = -\frac{1}{2}x + \frac{3}{2}$$
$$y = -\frac{1}{2}x + \frac{13}{2}$$

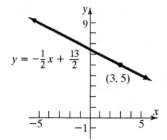

6. $x^2 + y^2 - 4x + 8y - 5 = 0$
$$x^2 - 4x + y^2 + 8y = 5$$
$$(x^2 - 4x + 4) + (y^2 + 8y + 16) = 5 + 4 + 16$$
$$(x - 2)^2 + (y + 4)^2 = 25$$
$$(x - 2)^2 + (y + 4)^2 = 5^2$$

Center: $(2, -4)$ Radius $= 5$

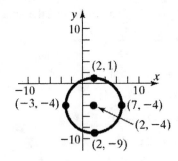

Points on graph: $(2,1)$, $(-3,-4)$, $(7,-4)$, $(2,-4)$, $(2,-9)$

7. Yes, this is a function since each x-value is paired with exactly one y-value.

8. $f(x) = x^2 - 4x + 1$

a. $f(2) = 2^2 - 4(2) + 1 = 4 - 8 + 1 = -3$

b. $f(x) + f(2) = x^2 - 4x + 1 + (-3)$
$$= x^2 - 4x - 2$$

c. $f(-x) = (-x)^2 - 4(-x) + 1 = x^2 + 4x + 1$

d. $-f(x) = -(x^2 - 4x + 1) = -x^2 + 4x - 1$

e. $f(x+2) = (x+2)^2 - 4(x+2) + 1$
$$= x^2 + 4x + 4 - 4x - 8 + 1$$
$$= x^2 - 3$$

f. $\dfrac{f(x+h) - f(x)}{h}$
$$= \frac{(x+h)^2 - 4(x+h) + 1 - (x^2 - 4x + 1)}{h}$$
$$= \frac{x^2 + 2xh + h^2 - 4x - 4h + 1 - x^2 + 4x - 1}{h}$$
$$= \frac{2xh + h^2 - 4h}{h}$$
$$= \frac{h(2x + h - 4)}{h} = 2x + h - 4$$

9. $h(z) = \dfrac{3z - 1}{6z - 7}$

The denominator cannot be zero:
$$6z - 7 \neq 0$$
$$6z \neq 7$$
$$z \neq \frac{7}{6}$$

Domain: $\left\{ z \mid z \neq \dfrac{7}{6} \right\}$

10. Yes, the graph represents a function since it passes the Vertical Line Test.

11. $f(x) = \dfrac{x}{x+4}$

a. $f(1) = \dfrac{1}{1+4} = \dfrac{1}{5} \neq \dfrac{1}{4}$, so $\left(1, \dfrac{1}{4}\right)$ is not on the graph of f.

b. $f(-2) = \dfrac{-2}{-2+4} = \dfrac{-2}{2} = -1$, so $(-2, -1)$ is a point on the graph of f.

c. Solve for x:
$$2 = \frac{x}{x+4}$$
$$2x + 8 = x$$
$$x = -8$$
So, $(-8, 2)$ is a point on the graph of f.

12. $f(x) = \dfrac{x^2}{2x+1}$
$$f(-x) = \frac{(-x)^2}{2(-x)+1} = \frac{x^2}{-2x+1} \neq f(x) \text{ or } -f(x)$$

Therefore, f is neither even nor odd.

13. $f(x) = x^3 - 5x + 4$ on the interval $(-4, 4)$
Use MAXIMUM and MINIMUM on the graph of $y_1 = x^3 - 5x + 4$.

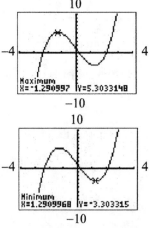

Local maximum is 5.30 and occurs at $x \approx -1.29$;
Local minimum is -3.30 and occurs at $x \approx 1.29$;
f is increasing on $(-4, -1.29)$ or $(1.29, 4)$;
f is decreasing on $(-1.29, 1.29)$.

14. $f(x) = 3x + 5$; $g(x) = 2x + 1$

  a. $f(x) = g(x)$

$3x + 5 = 2x + 1$

$3x + 5 = 2x + 1$

$x = -4$

  b. $f(x) > g(x)$

$3x + 5 > 2x + 1$

$3x + 5 > 2x + 1$

$x > -4$

The solution set is $\{x \mid x > -4\}$ or $(-4, \infty)$.

15. a. Domain: $\{x \mid -4 \le x \le 4\}$ or $[-4, 4]$

Range: $\{y \mid -1 \le y \le 3\}$ or $[-1, 3]$

  b. Intercepts: $(-1, 0)$, $(0, -1)$, $(1, 0)$

x-intercepts: $-1, 1$

y-intercept: -1

  c. The graph is symmetric with respect to the y-axis.

  d. When $x = 2$, the function takes on a value of 1. Therefore, $f(2) = 1$.

  e. The function takes on the value 3 at $x = -4$ and $x = 4$.

  f. $f(x) < 0$ means that the graph lies below the x-axis. This happens for x values between -1 and 1. Thus, the solution set is $\{x \mid -1 < x < 1\}$ or $(-1, 1)$.

  g. The graph of $y = f(x) + 2$ is the graph of $y = f(x)$ but shifted up 2 units.

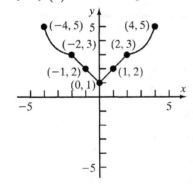

  h. The graph of $y = f(-x)$ is the graph of $y = f(x)$ but reflected about the y-axis.

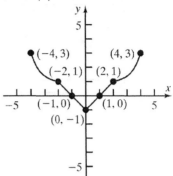

  i. The graph of $y = 2f(x)$ is the graph of $y = f(x)$ but stretched vertically by a factor of 2. That is, the coordinate of each point is multiplied by 2.

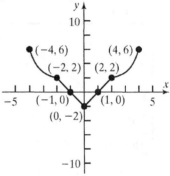

  j. Since the graph is symmetric about the y-axis, the function is even.

  k. The function is increasing on the open interval $(0, 4)$.

Chapter 4 Projects

Project I

Answers will vary depending on the stock selected and the time period.

Project II

a.

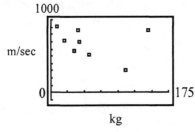

b. The data would be best fit by a quadratic function.

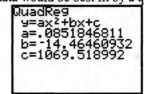

$$y = 0.085x^2 - 14.46x + 1069.52$$

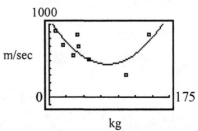

These results seem reasonable since the function fits the data well.

c. $s_0 = 0\text{m}$

Type	Weight kg	Velocity m/sec	Equation in the form: $s(t) = -4.9t^2 + \dfrac{\sqrt{2}}{2}v_0 t + s_0$
MG 17	10.2	905	$s(t) = -4.9t^2 + 639.93t$ Best. (It goes the highest)
MG 131	19.7	710	$s(t) = -4.9t^2 + 502.05t$
MG 151	41.5	850	$s(t) = -4.9t^2 + 601.04t$
MG 151/20	42.3	695	$s(t) = -4.9t^2 + 491.44t$
MG/FF	35.7	575	$s(t) = -4.9t^2 + 406.59t$
MK 103	145	860	$s(t) = -4.9t^2 + 608.11t$
MK 108	58	520	$s(t) = -4.9t^2 + 367.70t$
WGr 21	111	315	$s(t) = -4.9t^2 + 222.74t$

$s_0 = 200\text{m}$

Type	Weight kg	Velocity m/sec	Equation in the form: $s(t) = -4.9t^2 + \dfrac{\sqrt{2}}{2}v_0 t + s_0$
MG 17	10.2	905	$s(t) = -4.9t^2 + 639.93t + 200$ Best. (It goes the highest)
MG 131	19.7	710	$s(t) = -4.9t^2 + 502.05t + 200$
MG 151	41.5	850	$s(t) = -4.9t^2 + 601.04t + 200$
MG 151/20	42.3	695	$s(t) = -4.9t^2 + 491.44t + 200$
MG/FF	35.7	575	$s(t) = -4.9t^2 + 406.59t + 200$
MK 103	145	860	$s(t) = -4.9t^2 + 608.11t + 200$
MK 108	58	520	$s(t) = -4.9t^2 + 367.70t + 200$
WGr 21	111	315	$s(t) = -4.9t^2 + 222.74t + 200$

$s_0 = 30m$

Type	Weight kg	Velocity m/sec	Equation in the form: $s(t) = -4.9t^2 + \dfrac{\sqrt{2}}{2}v_0 t + s_0$
MG 17	10.2	905	$s(t) = -4.9t^2 + 639.93t + 30$ Best. (It goes the highest)
MG 131	19.7	710	$s(t) = -4.9t^2 + 502.05t + 30$
MG 151	41.5	850	$s(t) = -4.9t^2 + 601.04t + 30$
MG 151/20	42.3	695	$s(t) = -4.9t^2 + 491.44t + 30$
MG/FF	35.7	575	$s(t) = -4.9t^2 + 406.59t + 30$
MK 103	145	860	$s(t) = -4.9t^2 + 608.11t + 30$
MK 108	58	520	$s(t) = -4.9t^2 + 367.70t + 30$
WGr 21	111	315	$s(t) = -4.9t^2 + 222.74t + 30$

Notice that the gun is what makes the difference, not how high it is mounted necessarily. The only way to change the true maximum height that the projectile can go is to change the angle at which it fires.

Project III

a.

x	1	2	3	4	5
$y = -2x + 5$	3	1	-1	-3	-5

b.

$$\frac{\Delta y}{\Delta x} = \frac{y_2 - y_1}{x_2 - x_1} = \frac{1 - 3}{1} = -2$$

$$\frac{\Delta y}{\Delta x} = \frac{y_2 - y_1}{x_2 - x_1} = \frac{-1 - 1}{1} = -2$$

$$\frac{\Delta y}{\Delta x} = \frac{y_2 - y_1}{x_2 - x_1} = \frac{-3 - (-1)}{1} = -2$$

$$\frac{\Delta y}{\Delta x} = \frac{y_2 - y_1}{x_2 - x_1} = \frac{-5 - (-3)}{1} = -2$$

All of the values of $\dfrac{\Delta y}{\Delta x}$ are the same.

c.

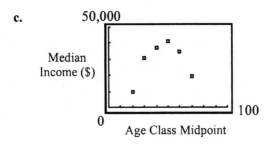

Median Income ($) vs. Age Class Midpoint

d.

$$\frac{\Delta I}{\Delta x} = \frac{30633 - 9548}{10} = 2108.50$$

$$\frac{\Delta I}{\Delta x} = \frac{37088 - 30633}{10} = 645.50$$

$$\frac{\Delta I}{\Delta x} = \frac{41072 - 37088}{10} = 398.40$$

$$\frac{\Delta I}{\Delta x} = \frac{34414 - 41072}{10} = -665.80$$

$$\frac{\Delta I}{\Delta x} = \frac{19167 - 34414}{10} = -1524.70$$

These $\dfrac{\Delta I}{\Delta x}$ values are not all equal. The data are not linearly related.

e.

x	-2	-1	0	1	2	3	4
y	23	9	3	5	15	33	59
$\dfrac{\Delta y}{\Delta x}$		-14	-6	2	10	18	26

As x increases, $\dfrac{\Delta y}{\Delta x}$ increases. This makes sense because the parabola is increasing (going up) steeply as x increases.

f.

x	-2	-1	0	1	2	3	4
y	23	9	3	5	15	33	59
$\dfrac{\Delta^2 y}{\Delta x^2}$			8	8	8	8	8

The second differences are all the same.

399

    g. The paragraph should mention at least two
    observations:

       1. The first differences for a linear function are
         all the same.

       2. The second differences for a quadratic
         function are the same.

Project IV

a. – i. Answers will vary , depending on where the
        CBL is located above the bouncing ball.

j. The ratio of the heights between bounces will
      be the same.

Chapter 5
Polynomial and Rational Functions

Section 5.1

1. $(-2, 0)$, $(2, 0)$, and $(0, 9)$

x-intercepts: let $y = 0$ and solve for x
$$9x^2 + 4(0) = 36$$
$$9x^2 = 36$$
$$x^2 = 4$$
$$x = \pm 2$$

y-intercepts: let $x = 0$ and solve for y
$$9(0)^2 + 4y = 36$$
$$4y = 36$$
$$y = 9$$

2. True; it has the form
$a_n x^n + a_{n-1} x^{n-1} + ... + a_1 x + a_0$ where each a_i is a real number and n is a positive integer.

3. down; 4

4. True; for each x-intercept we have $y = 0$. Therefore, to find the x-intercepts, we solve the equation $y = 0$, or $f(x) = 0$ since $y = f(x)$.

5. smooth; continuous

6. zero

7. touches

8. True

9. False; the x-intercepts of the graph of a polynomial function are also called zeros of the function.

10. False; the graph of f resembles the graph of $y = 3x^4$ for large values of $|x|$.

11. $f(x) = 4x + x^3$ is a polynomial function of degree 3.

12. $f(x) = 5x^2 + 4x^4$ is a polynomial function of degree 4.

13. $g(x) = \dfrac{1 - x^2}{2} = \dfrac{1}{2} - \dfrac{1}{2}x^2$ is a polynomial function of degree 2.

14. $h(x) = 3 - \dfrac{1}{2}x$ is a polynomial function of degree 1.

15. $f(x) = 1 - \dfrac{1}{x} = 1 - x^{-1}$ is not a polynomial function because it contains a negative exponent.

16. $f(x) = x(x-1) = x^2 - x$ is a polynomial function of degree 2.

17. $g(x) = x^{3/2} - x^2 + 2$ is not a polynomial function because it contains a fractional exponent.

18. $h(x) = \sqrt{x}\left(\sqrt{x} - 1\right) = x - x^{1/2}$ is not a polynomial function because it contains fractional exponents.

19. $F(x) = 5x^4 - \pi x^3 + \dfrac{1}{2}$ is a polynomial function of degree 4.

20. $F(x) = \dfrac{x^2 - 5}{x^3} = x^{-1} - 5x^{-3}$ is not a polynomial function because it contains a negative exponent.

21. $G(x) = 2(x-1)^2(x^2 + 1) = 2(x^2 - 2x + 1)(x^2 + 1)$
$$= 2(x^4 + x^2 - 2x^3 - 2x + x^2 + 1)$$
$$= 2(x^4 - 2x^3 + 2x^2 - 2x + 1)$$
$$= 2x^4 - 4x^3 + 4x^2 - 4x + 2$$
is a polynomial function of degree 4.

22. $G(x) = -3x^2(x+2)^3 = -3x^2(x^3 + 6x^2 + 12x + 8)$
$$= -3x^5 - 18x^4 - 36x^3 - 24x^2$$
is a polynomial function of degree 5.

23. $f(x) = (x+1)^4$

Using the graph of $y = x^4$, shift the graph horizontally, 1 unit to the left.

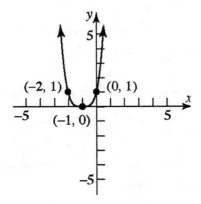

24. $f(x) = (x-2)^5$

Using the graph of $y = x^5$, shift the graph horizontally to the right 2 units.

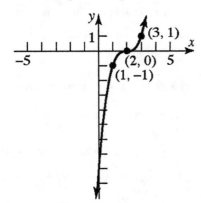

25. $f(x) = x^5 - 3$

Using the graph of $y = x^5$, shift the graph vertically, 3 units down.

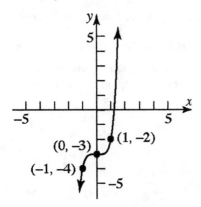

26. $f(x) = x^4 + 2$

Using the graph of $y = x^4$, shift the graph vertically up 2 units.

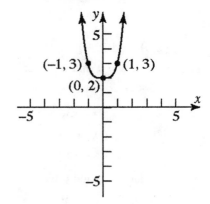

27. $f(x) = \frac{1}{2}x^4$

Using the graph of $y = x^4$, compress the graph vertically by a factor of $\frac{1}{2}$.

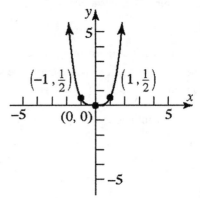

28. $f(x) = 3x^5$

Using the graph of $y = x^5$, stretch the graph vertically by a factor of 3.

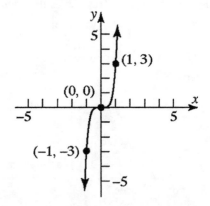

402

29. $f(x) = -x^5$

Using the graph of $y = x^5$, reflect the graph about the *x*-axis.

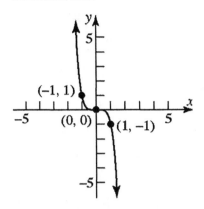

30. $f(x) = -x^4$

Using the graph of $y = x^4$, reflect the graph about the *x*-axis.

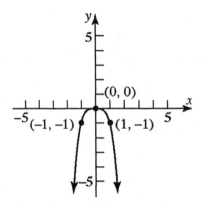

31. $f(x) = (x-1)^5 + 2$

Using the graph of $y = x^5$, shift the graph horizontally, 1 unit to the right, and shift vertically 2 units up.

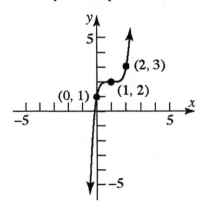

32. $f(x) = (x+2)^4 - 3$

Using the graph of $y = x^4$, shift the graph horizontally left 2 units, and shift vertically down 3 units.

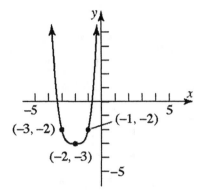

33. $f(x) = 2(x+1)^4 + 1$

Using the graph of $y = x^4$, shift the graph horizontally, 1 unit to the left, stretch vertically by a factor of 2, and shift vertically 1 unit up.

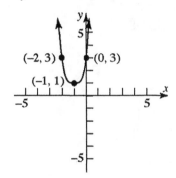

34. $f(x) = \frac{1}{2}(x-1)^5 - 2$

Using the graph of $y = x^5$, shift the graph horizontally 1 unit to the right, compress vertically by a factor of $\frac{1}{2}$, and shift vertically down 2 units.

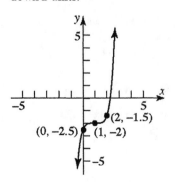

35. $f(x) = 4 - (x-2)^5 = -(x-2)^5 + 4$

Using the graph of $y = x^5$, shift the graph horizontally, 2 units to the right, reflect about the x-axis, and shift vertically 4 units up.

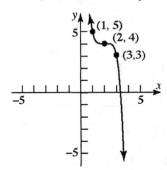

36. $f(x) = 3 - (x+2)^4 = -(x+2)^4 + 3$

Using the graph of $y = x^4$, shift the graph horizontally, 2 units to the left, reflect about the x-axis, and shift vertically 3 units up.

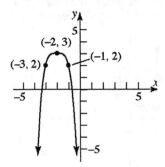

37. $f(x) = a(x - (-1))(x-1)(x-3)$

For $a = 1$:
$$f(x) = (x+1)(x-1)(x-3) = \left(x^2 - 1\right)(x-3)$$
$$= x^3 - 3x^2 - x + 3$$

38. $f(x) = a(x - (-2))(x-2)(x-3)$

For $a = 1$:
$$f(x) = (x+2)(x-2)(x-3) = \left(x^2 - 4\right)(x-3)$$
$$= x^3 - 3x^2 - 4x + 12$$

39. $f(x) = a(x - (-3))(x-0)(x-4)$

For $a = 1$:
$$f(x) = (x+3)(x)(x-4) = \left(x^2 + 3x\right)(x-4)$$
$$= x^3 - 4x^2 + 3x^2 - 12x$$
$$= x^3 - x^2 - 12x$$

40. $f(x) = a(x - (-4))(x-0)(x-2)$

For $a = 1$:
$$f(x) = (x+4)(x)(x-2) = \left(x^2 + 4x\right)(x-2)$$
$$= x^3 - 2x^2 + 4x^2 - 8x$$
$$= x^3 + 2x^2 - 8x$$

41. $f(x) = a(x - (-4))(x - (-1))(x-2)(x-3)$

For $a = 1$:
$$f(x) = (x+4)(x+1)(x-2)(x-3)$$
$$= \left(x^2 + 5x + 4\right)\left(x^2 - 5x + 6\right)$$
$$= x^4 - 5x^3 + 6x^2 + 5x^3 - 25x^2 + 30x + 4x^2 - 20x + 24$$
$$= x^4 - 15x^2 + 10x + 24$$

42. $f(x) = a(x - (-3))(x - (-1))(x-2)(x-5)$

For $a = 1$:
$$f(x) = (x+3)(x+1)(x-2)(x-5)$$
$$= \left(x^2 + 4x + 3\right)\left(x^2 - 7x + 10\right)$$
$$= x^4 - 7x^3 + 10x^2 + 4x^3 - 28x^2$$
$$\quad + 40x + 3x^2 - 21x + 30$$
$$= x^4 - 3x^3 - 15x^2 + 19x + 30$$

43. $f(x) = a(x - (-1))(x-3)^2$

For $a = 1$:
$$f(x) = (x+1)(x-3)^2$$
$$= (x+1)\left(x^2 - 6x + 9\right)$$
$$= x^3 - 6x^2 + 9x + x^2 - 6x + 9$$
$$= x^3 - 5x^2 + 3x + 9$$

44. $f(x) = a(x - (-2))^2 (x-4)$

For $a = 1$:
$$f(x) = (x+2)^2 (x-4)$$
$$= \left(x^2 + 4x + 4\right)(x-4)$$
$$= x^3 - 4x^2 + 4x^2 - 16x + 4x - 16$$
$$= x^3 - 12x - 16$$

45. a. The real zeros of $f(x) = 3(x-7)(x+3)^2$ are: 7, with multiplicity one; and –3, with multiplicity two.

b. The graph crosses the x-axis at 7 (odd multiplicity) and touches it at –3 (even multiplicity).

404

c. Near -3: $f(x) \approx -30(x+3)^2$;

Near 7: $f(x) \approx 300(x-7)$

d. $n-1 = 3-1 = 2$

e. The function resembles $y = 3x^3$ for large values of $|x|$.

46. a. The real zeros of $f(x) = 4(x+4)(x+3)^3$ are: -4, with multiplicity one; and -3, with multiplicity three.

b. The graph crosses the x-axis at -4 and at -3 (odd multiplicities).

c. Near -4: $f(x) \approx -4(x+4)$;

Near -3: $f(x) \approx 4(x+3)^2$

d. $n-1 = 4-1 = 3$

e. The function resembles $y = 4x^4$ for large values of $|x|$.

47. a. The real zeros of $f(x) = 4(x^2+1)(x-2)^3$ is: 2, with multiplicity three.

$x^2 + 1 = 0$ has no real solution.

b. The graph crosses the x-axis at 2 (odd multiplicity).

c. Near 2: $f(x) \approx 20(x-2)^3$

d. $n-1 = 5-1 = 4$

e. The function resembles $y = 4x^5$ for large values of $|x|$.

48. a. The real zeros of $f(x) = 2(x-3)(x+4)^3$ are: 3, with multiplicity one; and -4, with multiplicity three.

b. The graph crosses the x-axis at 3 and at -4 (odd multiplicities).

c. Near -4: $f(x) \approx -14(x+4)^3$;

Near 3: $f(x) \approx 686(x-3)$

d. $n-1 = 4-1 = 3$

e. The function resembles $y = 2x^4$ for large values of $|x|$.

49. a. The real zero of

$$f(x) = -2\left(x+\frac{1}{2}\right)^2 (x^2+4)^2 \text{ is: } -\frac{1}{2}, \text{ with}$$

multiplicity two. $x^2 + 4 = 0$ has no real solution.

b. The graph touches the x-axis at $-\frac{1}{2}$ (even multiplicity).

c. Near $-\frac{1}{2}$: $f(x) \approx -36.125\left(x+\frac{1}{2}\right)^2$

d. $n-1 = 6-1 = 5$

e. The function resembles $y = -2x^6$ for large values of $|x|$.

50. a. The real zeros of $f(x) = \left(x-\frac{1}{3}\right)^2 (x-1)^3$

are: $\frac{1}{3}$, with multiplicity two; and 1, with multiplicity 3.

b. The graph touches the x-axis at $\frac{1}{3}$ (even multiplicity), and crosses the x-axis at 1 (odd multiplicity).

c. Near $\frac{1}{3}$: $f(x) \approx -\frac{8}{27}\left(x-\frac{1}{3}\right)^2$;

Near 1: $f(x) \approx \frac{4}{9}(x-1)^3$

d. $n-1 = 5-1 = 4$

e. The function resembles $y = x^5$ for large values of $|x|$.

51. a. The real zeros of $f(x) = (x-5)^3(x+4)^2$ are: 5, with multiplicity three; and -4, with multiplicity two.

b. The graph crosses the x-axis at 5 (odd multiplicity) and touches it at -4 (even multiplicity).

c. Near -4: $f(x) \approx -729(x+4)^2$;

Near 5: $f(x) \approx 81(x-5)^3$

d. $n-1 = 5-1 = 4$

405

e. The function resembles $y = x^5$ for large values of $|x|$.

52. a. The real zeros of $f(x) = (x + \sqrt{3})^2 (x - 2)^4$ are: $-\sqrt{3}$, with multiplicity two; and 2, with multiplicity four.

b. The graph touches the x-axis at $-\sqrt{3}$ and at 2 (even multiplicities).

c. Near $-\sqrt{3}$: $f(x) \approx 194(x + \sqrt{3})^2$; Near 2: $f(x) \approx 13.93(x - 2)^4$

d. $n - 1 = 6 - 1 = 5$

e. The function resembles $y = x^6$ for large values of $|x|$.

53. a. $f(x) = 3(x^2 + 8)(x^2 + 9)^2$ has no real zeros. $x^2 + 8 = 0$ and $x^2 + 9 = 0$ have no real solutions.

b. The graph neither touches nor crosses the x-axis.

c. No real zeros

d. $n - 1 = 6 - 1 = 5$

e. The function resembles $y = 3x^6$ for large values of $|x|$.

54. a. $f(x) = -2(x^2 + 3)^3$ has no real zeros. $x^2 + 3 = 0$ has no real solutions.

b. The graph neither touches nor crosses the x-axis.

c. No real zeros

d. $n - 1 = 6 - 1 = 5$

e. The function resembles $y = -2x^6$ for large values of $|x|$.

55. a. The real zeros of $f(x) = -2x^2(x^2 - 2)$ are: $-\sqrt{2}$ and $\sqrt{2}$ with multiplicity one; and 0, with multiplicity two.

b. The graph touches the x-axis at 0 (even multiplicity) and crosses the x-axis at $-\sqrt{2}$ and $\sqrt{2}$ (odd multiplicities).

c. Near $-\sqrt{2}$: $f(x) \approx 11.31(x + \sqrt{2})$; Near 0: $f(x) \approx 4x^2$; Near $\sqrt{2}$: $f(x) \approx -11.31(x - \sqrt{2})$

d. $n - 1 = 4 - 1 = 3$

e. The function resembles $y = -2x^4$ for large values of $|x|$.

56. a. The real zeros of $f(x) = 4x(x^2 - 3)$ are: $-\sqrt{3}$, $\sqrt{3}$ and 0, with multiplicity one.

b. The graph crosses the x-axis at $-\sqrt{3}$, $\sqrt{3}$ and 0 (odd multiplicities).

c. Near $-\sqrt{3}$: $f(x) \approx 24(x + \sqrt{3})$; Near 0: $f(x) \approx -12x$; Near $\sqrt{3}$: $f(x) \approx 24(x - \sqrt{3})$

d. $n - 1 = 3 - 1 = 2$

e. The function resembles $y = 4x^3$ for large values of $|x|$.

57. Could be; zeros: $-1, 1, 2$; minimum degree = 3

58. Could be; zeros: $-1, 2$; minimum degree = 4

59. Can't be; not continuous at $x = -1$

60. Can't be; not smooth at $x = 0$

61. c, e, f

62. c, e, f

63. c, e

64. d, f

65. $f(x) = (x - 1)^2$

a. y-intercept: $f(0) = (0 - 1)^2 = 1$ x-intercept: solve $f(x) = 0$ $(x - 1)^2 = 0 \Rightarrow x = 1$

b. The graph touches the x-axis at $x = 1$, since this zero has multiplicity 2.

c. Degree is 2; The function resembles $y = x^2$ for large values of $|x|$.

d. 1

406

e. Near 1: $f(x) \approx (x-1)^2$

f. Graphing:

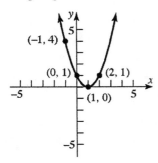

66. $f(x) = (x-2)^3$

a. y-intercept: $f(0) = (0-2)^3 = -8$

x-intercept: solve $f(x) = 0$

$0 = (x-2)^3$

$x = 2$

b. crosses x-axis at $x = 2$

c. Degree is 3. The function resembles $y = x^3$ for large values of $|x|$.

d. 2

e. Near 2: $f(x) \approx (x-2)^3$

f. Graphing by hand

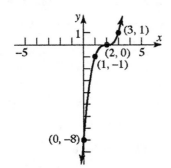

67. $f(x) = x^2(x-3)$

a. y-intercept: $f(0) = 0^2(0-3) = 0$

x-intercepts: solve $f(x) = 0$

$0 = x^2(x-3)$

$x = 0,\ x = 3$

b. touches x-axis at $x = 0$; crosses x-axis at $x = 3$

c. Degree is 3. The function resembles $y = x^3$ for large values of $|x|$.

d. 2

e. Near 0: $f(x) \approx -3x^2$; Near 3: $f(x) \approx 9(x-3)$

f. Graphing by hand:

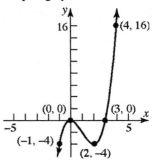

68. $f(x) = x(x+2)^2$

a. y-intercept: $f(0) = 0(0+2)^2 = 0$

x-intercepts: solve $f(x) = 0$

$0 = x(x+2)^2$

$x = 0, -2$

b. touches x-axis at $x = -2$; crosses x-axis at $x = 0$

c. Degree is 3. The function resembles $y = x^3$ for large values of $|x|$.

d. 2

e. Near -2: $f(x) \approx -2(x+2)^2$; Near 0: $f(x) \approx 4x$

f. Graphing by hand:

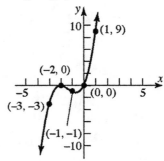

69. $f(x) = 6x^3(x+4)$

   a. x-intercepts: –4, 0; y-intercept: 0

   b. crosses x-axis at x = –4 and x = 0

   c. Degree = 4; The function resembles
      $y = 6x^4$ for large values of $|x|$.

   d. 3

   e. Near -4: $f(x) \approx -384(x+4)$; Near 0:
      $f(x) \approx 24x^3$

   f. graphing by hand

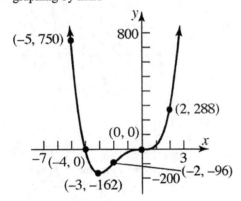

70. $f(x) = 5x(x-1)^3$

   a. x-intercepts: 0, 1; y-intercept: 0

   b. crosses x-axis at x = 0 and x = 1

   c. Degree = 4; The function resembles
      $y = 5x^4$ for large values of $|x|$.

   d. 3

   e. Near 0: $f(x) \approx -5x$; Near 1:
      $f(x) \approx 5(x-1)^3$

   f. graphing by hand

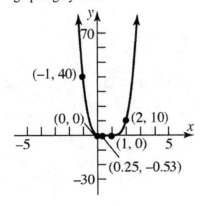

71. $f(x) = -4x^2(x+2)$

   a. x-intercepts: 0, –2 ; y-intercept: 0

   b. crosses x-axis at $x = -2$;
      touches x-axis at $x = 0$

   c. Degree = 3; The function resembles
      $y = -4x^3$ for large values of $|x|$.

   d. 2

   e. Near -2: $f(x) \approx -16(x+2)$; Near 0:
      $f(x) \approx -8x^2$

   f. graphing by hand

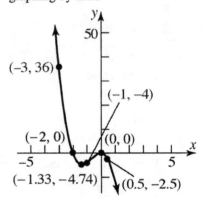

72. $f(x) = -\dfrac{1}{2}x^3(x+4)$

   a. x-intercepts: 0, –4 ; y-intercept: 0

   b. crosses x-axis at $x = 0, x = -4$

   c. Degree = 4; The function resembles
      $y = -\dfrac{1}{2}x^4$ for large values of $|x|$.

   d. 3

   e. Near -4: $f(x) \approx 32(x+4)$; Near 0:
      $f(x) \approx -2x^3$

   f. graphing by hand

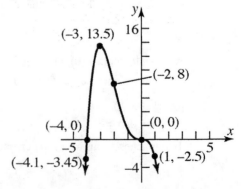

73. $f(x) = (x-1)(x-2)(x+4)$

   a. x-intercepts: $1, 2, -4$; y-intercept: 8

   b. crosses x-axis at $x = 1, 2, -4$

   c. Degree = 3; The function resembles $y = x^3$ for large values of $|x|$.

   d. 2

   e. Near -4: $f(x) \approx 30(x+4)$; Near 1: $f(x) \approx -5(x-1)$; Near 2: $f(x) \approx 6(x-2)$

   f. graphing by hand

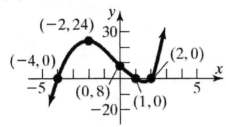

74. $f(x) = (x+1)(x+4)(x-3)$

   a. x-intercepts: $-1, -4, 3$; y-intercept: -12

   b. crosses x-axis at $x = -1, x = -4, x = 3$

   c. Degree = 3; The function resembles $y = x^3$ for large values of $|x|$.

   d. 2

   e. Near -4: $f(x) \approx 21(x+4)$; Near -1: $f(x) \approx -12(x+1)$; Near 3: $f(x) \approx 28(x-3)$

   f. graphing by hand

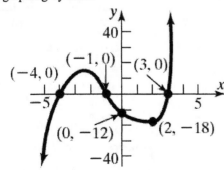

75. $f(x) = 4x - x^3 = x\left(4 - x^2\right)$
$$= x(2+x)(2-x)$$

   a. x-intercepts: $0, -2, 2$; y-intercept: 0

   b. crosses x-axis at $x = 0, x = -2, x = 2$

   c. Degree = 3; The function resembles $y = -x^3$ for large values of $|x|$.

   d. 2

   e. Near -2: $f(x) \approx -8(x+2)$; Near 0: $f(x) \approx 4x$; Near 2: $f(x) \approx -8(x-2)$

   f. graphing by hand

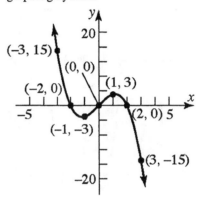

76. $f(x) = x - x^3 = x\left(1 - x^2\right) = x(1+x)(1-x)$

   a. x-intercepts: $0, -1, 1$; y-intercept: 0

   b. crosses x-axis at $x = 0, x = -1, x = 1$

   c. Degree = 3; The function resembles $y = -x^3$ for large values of $|x|$.

   d. 2

   e. Near -1: $f(x) \approx -2(x+1)$; Near 0: $f(x) \approx x$; Near 1: $f(x) \approx -2(x-1)$

   f. graphing by hand

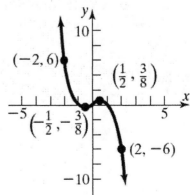

77. $f(x) = x^2(x-2)(x+2)$

   a. *y*-intercept: $f(x) = 0^2(0-2)(0+2) = 0$

     x-intercepts: solve $f(x) = 0$

     $0 = x^2(x-2)(x+2)$

     $x = 0, 2, -2$

   b. crosses *x*-axis at $x = 2, x = -2$; touches *x*-axis at $x = 0$

   c. Degree is 4. The function resembles $y = x^4$ for large values of $|x|$.

   d. 3

   e. Near -2: $f(x) \approx -16(x+2)$; Near 0:

     $f(x) \approx -4x^2$; Near 2: $f(x) \approx 16(x-2)$

   f. graphing by hand

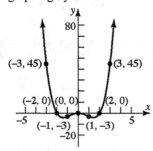

78. $f(x) = x^2(x-3)(x+4)$

   a. *y*-intercept: $f(0) = 0^2(0-3)(0+4) = 0$

     x-intercept: solve $f(x) = 0$

     $x^2(x-3)(x+4) = 0$

     $x = 0$ or $x = 3$ or $x = -4$

   b. The graph touches the *x*-axis at $x = 0$, since this zero has multiplicity 2. The graph crosses the *x*-axis at $x = 3$ and $x = -4$, since these zeros have multiplicity 1.

   c. Degree is 4. The graph of the function resembles $y = x^4$ for large values of $|x|$.

   d. 3

   e. Near -4: $f(x) \approx -112(x+4)$; Near 0:

     $f(x) \approx -12x^2$; Near 3: $f(x) \approx 63(x-3)$

   f. Graphing:

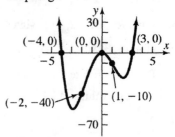

79. $f(x) = (x+2)^2(x-2)^2$

   a. *y*-intercept: 16

     x-intercepts: -2, 2

   b. The graph touches the x-axis at $x = -2$ and $x = 2$ since these zeroes have multiplicity is 2.

   c. Degree is 4. The graph of the function resembles $y = x^4$ for large values of $|x|$.

   d. 3

   e. Near -2: $f(x) \approx 16(x+2)^2$; Near 2:

     $f(x) \approx 16(x-2)^2$

   f. Graphing:

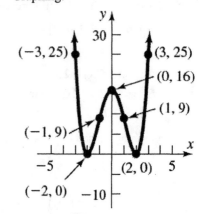

80. $f(x) = (x+1)^3(x-3)$

   a. *y*-intercept: $f(0) = (0+1)^3(0-3) = -3$

     x-intercept: solve $f(x) = 0$

     $(x+1)^3(x-3) = 0 \Rightarrow x = -1$ or $x = 3$

   b. The graph crosses the *x*-axis at $x = -1$, since this zero has multiplicity 3. The graph crosses the *x*-axis at $x = 3$, since this zero has multiplicity 1.

c. Degree is 4. The graph of the function resembles $y = x^4$ for large values of $|x|$.

d. 3

e. Near -1: $f(x) \approx -4(x+1)^3$; Near 3:
$f(x) \approx 64(x-3)$

f. Graphing by hand;

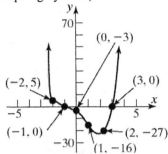

81. $f(x) = (x-1)^2 (x-3)(x+1)$

a. y-intercept:
$$f(0) = (0-1)^2 (0-3)(0+1) = -3$$
x-intercept: solve $f(x) = 0$
$$(x-1)^2 (x-3)(x+1) = 0$$
$$x = 1 \text{ or } x = 3 \text{ or } x = -1$$

b. The graph touches the x-axis at $x = 1$, since this zero has multiplicity 2. The graph crosses the x-axis at $x = 3$ and $x = -1$, since these zeros have multiplicity 1.

c. Degree is 4. The graph of the function resembles $y = x^4$ for large values of $|x|$.

d. 3

e. Near -1: $f(x) \approx -16(x+1)$; Near 1:
$f(x) \approx -4(x-1)^2$; Near 3:
$f(x) \approx 16(x-3)$

f. Graphing:

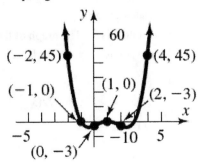

82. $f(x) = (x+1)^2 (x-3)(x-1)$

a. y-intercept: $f(0) = (0+1)^2 (0-3)(0-1) = 3$
x-intercept: solve $f(x) = 0$
$$(x+1)^2 (x-3)(x-1) = 0$$
$$x = -1 \text{ or } x = 3 \text{ or } x = 1$$

b. The graph touches the x-axis at $x = -1$, since this zero has multiplicity 2. The graph crosses the x-axis at $x = 3$ and $x = 1$, since these zeros have multiplicity 1.

c. Degree is 4. The graph of the function resembles $y = x^4$ for large values of $|x|$.

d. 3

e. Near -1: $f(x) \approx 8(x+1)^2$; Near 1:
$f(x) \approx -8(x-1)$; Near 3:
$f(x) \approx 32(x-3)$

f. Graphing:

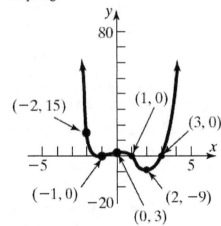

83. $f(x) = (x+2)^2 (x-4)^2$

a. y-intercept: $f(0) = (0+2)^2 (0-4)^2 = 64$
x-intercept: solve $f(x) = 0$
$$(x+2)^2 (x-4)^2 = 0 \Rightarrow x = -2 \text{ or } x = 4$$

b. The graph touches the x-axis at $x = -2$ and $x = 4$ since each zero has multiplicity 2.

c. Degree is 4. The graph of the function resembles $y = x^4$ for large values of $|x|$.

d. 3

411

e. Near -2: $f(x) \approx 36(x+2)^2$; Near 4:

$$f(x) \approx 36(x-4)^2$$

f. Graphing by hand;

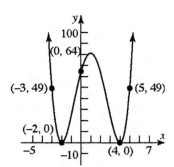

84. $f(x) = (x-2)^2(x+2)(x+4)$

a. *y*-intercept:

$$f(0) = (0-2)^2(0+2)(0+4) = 32$$

x-intercept: solve $f(x) = 0$

$$(x-2)^2(x+2)(x+4) = 0$$

$$x = 2 \text{ or } x = -2 \text{ or } x = -4$$

b. The graph touches the *x*-axis at $x = 2$, since this zero has multiplicity 2. The graph crosses the *x*-axis at $x = -2$ and $x = -4$ since each zero has multiplicity 1.

c. Degree is 4. The graph of the function resembles $y = x^4$ for large values of $|x|$.

d. 3

e. Near -4: $f(x) \approx -72(x+4)$; Near -2:

$$f(x) \approx 32(x+2); \text{ Near 2: } f(x) \approx 24(x-2)^2$$

f. Graphing by hand:

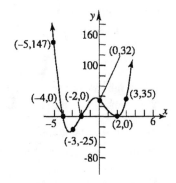

85. $f(x) = x^2(x-2)(x^2+3)$

a. *y*-intercept: $f(0) = 0^2(0-2)(0^2+3) = 0$

x-intercept: solve $f(x) = 0$

$$x^2(x-2)(x^2+3) = 0 \Rightarrow x = 0 \text{ or } x = 2$$

$x^2 + 3 = 0$ has no real solution

b. The graph touches the *x*-axis at $x = 0$, since this zero has multiplicity 2. The graph crosses the *x*-axis at $x = 2$, since this zero has multiplicity 1.

c. Degree is 5. The graph of the function resembles $y = x^5$ for large values of $|x|$.

d. 4

e. Near 0: $f(x) \approx -6x^2$; Near 2:

$$f(x) \approx 28(x-2)$$

f. Graphing by hand:

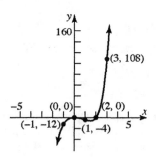

86. $f(x) = x^2(x^2+1)(x+4)$

a. *y*-intercept: $f(0) = 0^2(0^2+1)(0+4) = 0$

x-intercept: solve $f(x) = 0$

$$x^2(x^2+1)(x+4) = 0 \Rightarrow x = 0 \text{ or } x = -4$$

$x^2 + 1 = 0$ has no real solution

b. The graph touches the *x*-axis at $x = 0$, since this zero has multiplicity 2. The graph crosses the *x*-axis at $x = -4$, since this zero has multiplicity 1.

c. Degree is 5. The graph of the function resembles $y = x^5$ for large values of $|x|$.

d. 4

e. Near -4: $f(x) \approx 272(x+4)$; Near 0:

$$f(x) \approx 4x^2$$

f. Graphing by hand:

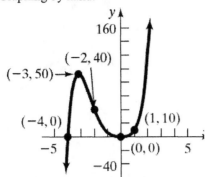

87. $f(x) = -x^2 (x^2 - 1)(x + 1)$

$\qquad = -x^2(x-1)(x+1)(x+1)$

$\qquad = -x^2 (x-1)(x+1)^2$

a. y-intercept: $f(0) = -0^2 (0^2 - 1)(0 + 1) = 0$

x-intercept: solve $f(x) = 0$

$-x^2 (x-1)(x+1)^2 = 0$

$x = 0$ or $x = 1$ or $x = -1$

b. The graph touches the x-axis at $x = 0$ and $x = -1$, since each zero has multiplicity 2. The graph crosses the x-axis at $x = 1$, since this zero has multiplicity 1.

c. Degree is 5. The graph of the function resembles $y = -x^5$ for large values of $|x|$.

d. 4

e. Near -1: $f(x) \approx 2(x+1)^2$; Near 0: $f(x) \approx x^2$; Near 1: $f(x) \approx -4(x-1)$

f. Graphing by hand:

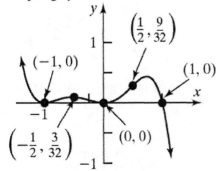

88. $f(x) = -x^2 (x^2 - 4)(x - 5)$

$\qquad = -x^2 (x+2)(x-2)(x-5)$

a. y-intercept: $f(0) = -0^2(0^2 - 4)(0 - 5) = 0$

x-intercept: solve $f(x) = 0$

$-x^2 (x+2)(x-2)(x-5) = 0$

$x = 0$ or $x = -2$ or $x = 2$ or $x = 5$

b. The graph touches the x-axis at $x = 0$, since this zero has multiplicity 2. The graph crosses the x-axis at $x = -2, x = 2$, and $x = 5$, since each zero has multiplicity 1.

c. Degree is 5. The graph of the function resembles $y = -x^5$ for large values of $|x|$.

d. 4

e. Near -2: $f(x) \approx -112(x+2)$; Near 0: $f(x) \approx -20x^2$; Near 2: $f(x) \approx 48(x-2)$;

Near 5: $f(x) \approx -525(x-5)$

f. Graphing:

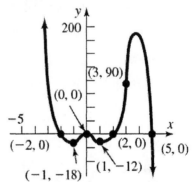

89. $f(x) = x^3 + 0.2x^2 - 1.5876x - 0.31752$

a. Degree = 3; The graph of the function resembles $y = x^3$ for large values of $|x|$.

b. Graphing utility

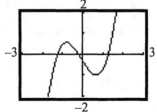

c. x-intercepts: $-1.26, -0.2, 1.26$; y-intercept: -0.31752

413

d. Above on $(-1.26, -0.20)$ and $(1.26, \infty)$;

Below on $(-\infty, -1.26)$ and $(-0.20, 1.26)$.

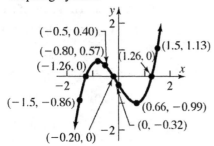

e. 2 turning points;
local maximum: $(-0.80, 0.57)$;
local minimum: $(0.66, -0.99)$

f. Graphing by hand

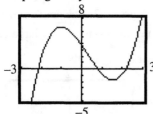

g. Domain: $\{x \mid x \text{ is any real number}\}$;
Range: $\{y \mid y \text{ is any real number}\}$.

h. f is increasing on $(-\infty, -0.80)$ and $(0.66, \infty)$; f is decreasing on $(-0.80, 0.66)$

90. $f(x) = x^3 - 0.8x^2 - 4.6656x + 3.73248$

a. Degree = 3; The graph of the function resembles $y = x^3$ for large values of $|x|$.

b. Graphing utility

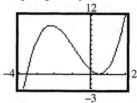

c. x-intercepts: $-2.16, 0.8, 2.16$;
y-intercept: 3.73248

d. Above on $(-2.16, 0.80)$ and $(2.16, \infty)$;

Below on $(-\infty, -2.16)$ and $(0.80, 2.16)$.

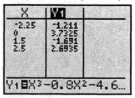

e. 2 turning points;
local maximum: $(-1.01, 6.60)$;
local minimum: $(1.54, -1.70)$

f. Graphing by hand

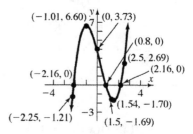

g. Domain: $\{x \mid x \text{ is any real number}\}$;
Range : $\{y \mid y \text{ is any real number}\}$.

h. f is increasing on $(-\infty, -1.01)$ and $(1.54, \infty)$; f is decreasing on $(-1.01, 1.54)$

91. $f(x) = x^3 + 2.56x^2 - 3.31x + 0.89$

a. Degree = 3; The graph of the function resembles $y = x^3$ for large values of $|x|$.

b. Graphing utility

c. x-intercepts: $-3.56, 0.50$; y-intercept: 0.89

d. Above on $(-3.56, 0.5)$ and $(0.5, \infty)$;

below on $(-\infty, -3.56)$.

414

e. 2 turning points;
local maximum: (−2.21, 9.91);
local minimum: (0.50, 0)

f. Graphing by hand

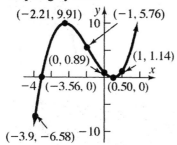

g. Domain: $\{x \mid x \text{ is any real number}\}$;
Range: $\{y \mid y \text{ is any real number}\}$.

h. f is increasing on $(−\infty, −2.21)$ and
$(0.50, \infty)$; f is decreasing on
$(−2.21, 0.50)$

92. $f(x) = x^3 - 2.91x^2 - 7.668x - 3.8151$

a. Degree = 3; The graph of the function
resembles $y = x^3$ for large values of $|x|$.

b. Graphing utility

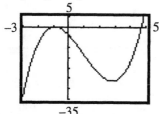

c. x-intercepts: −0.90, 4.71;
y-intercept: −3.8151

d. Above on $(4.71, \infty)$; below on $(−\infty, −0.9)$
and $(−0.9, 4.71)$.

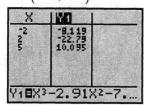

e. 2 turning points; local maximum: (−0.90, 0);
local minimum: (2.84, −26.16)

f. Graphing by hand

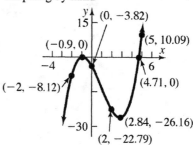

g. Domain: $\{x \mid x \text{ is any real number}\}$;
Range: $\{y \mid y \text{ is any real number}\}$.

h. f is increasing on $(−\infty, −0.90)$ and
$(2.84, \infty)$; f is decreasing on $(−0.90, 2.84)$

93. $f(x) = x^4 - 2.5x^2 + 0.5625$

a. Degree = 4; The graph of the function r
resembles $y = x^4$ for large values of $|x|$.

b. Graphing utility

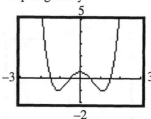

c. x-intercepts: −1.50, −0.50, 0.50, 1.50;
y-intercept: 0.5625

d. Above on $(−\infty, −1.5)$, $(−0.5, 0.5)$, and
$(1.5, \infty)$; below on $(−1.5, −0.5)$ and
$(0.5, 1.5)$.

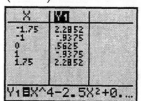

e. 3 turning points:
local maximum: (0, 0.5625);
local minima: (−1.12, −1), (1.12, −1)

415

f. Graphing by hand

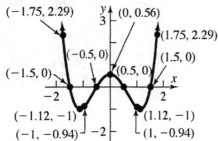

g. Domain: $\{x | x \text{ is any real number}\}$;
Range: $\{y | y \geq -1\}$.

h. f is increasing on $(-1.12, 0)$ and $(1.12, \infty)$; f is decreasing on $(-\infty, -1.12)$ and $(0, 1.12)$

94. $f(x) = x^4 - 18.5x^2 + 50.2619$

a. Degree = 4; The graph of the function resembles $y = x^4$ for large values of $|x|$.

b. graphing utility

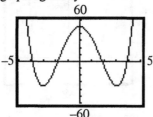

c. x-intercepts: $-3.90, -1.82, 1.82, 3.90$; y-intercept: 50.2619

d. Above on $(-\infty, -3.90)$, $(-1.82, 1.82)$, and $(3.90, \infty)$; below on $(-3.90, -1.82)$ and $(1.82, 3.90)$.

X	Y1
-4	10.262
-2.5	-26.3
0	50.262
2.5	-26.3
4.25	42.36

Y1◻X^4-18.5X²+5...

e. 3 turning points:
local maximum: (0, 50.26);
local minima: (-3.04, -35.30), (3.04, -35.30)

f. Graphing by hand

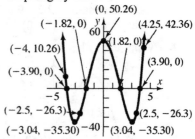

g. Domain: $\{x | x \text{ is any real number}\}$;
Range: $\{y | y \geq -35.30\}$.

h. f is increasing on $(-3.04, 0)$ and on $(3.04, \infty)$; f is decreasing on $(-\infty, -3.04)$ and $(0, 3.04)$

95. $f(x) = 2x^4 - \pi x^3 + \sqrt{5}x - 4$

a. Degree = 4; The graph of the function resembles $y = 2x^4$ for large values of $|x|$.

b. Graphing utility:

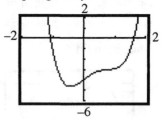

c. x-intercepts: $-1.07, 1.62$; y-intercept: -4

d. Above on $(-\infty, -1.07)$ and $(1.62, \infty)$; below on $(-1.07, 1.62)$.

X	Y1
-1.25	4.2237
0	-4
1.75	1.834

Y1◻2X^4-πX³+√(5...

e. 1 turning point;
local minimum: (-0.42, -4.64)

f. Graphing by hand

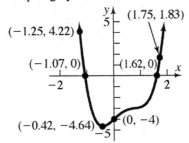

g. Domain: $\{x \mid x \text{ is any real number}\}$;

Range: $\{y \mid y \geq -4.64\}$.

h. f is increasing on $(-0.42, \infty)$; f is decreasing on $(-\infty, -0.42)$

96. $f(x) = -1.2x^4 + 0.5x^2 - \sqrt{3}x + 2$

a. Degree = 4; The graph of the function resembles $y = -1.2x^4$ for large values of $|x|$.

b. Graphing utility

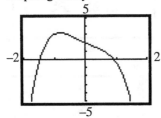

c. x-intercepts: $-1.47, 0.91$; y-intercept: 2

d. Above on $(-1.47, 0.91)$; below on $(-\infty, -1.47)$ and $(0.91, \infty)$.

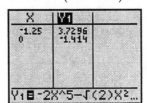

e. 1 turning point:
local maximum: $(-0.81, 3.21)$

f. Graphing by hand

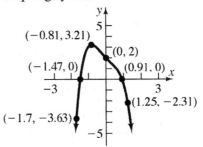

g. Domain: $\{x \mid x \text{ is any real number}\}$;

Range: $\{y \mid y \leq 3.21\}$.

h. f is increasing on $(-\infty, -0.81)$; f is decreasing on $(-0.81, \infty)$

97. $f(x) = -2x^5 - \sqrt{2}x^2 - x - \sqrt{2}$

a. Degree = 5; The graph of the function resembles $y = -2x^5$ for large values of $|x|$.

b. Graphing utility

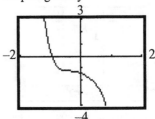

c. x-intercept: -0.98; y-intercept: $-\sqrt{2} \approx -1.41$

d. Above on $(-\infty, -0.98)$; below on $(-0.98, \infty)$

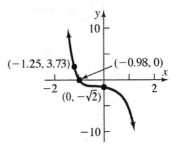

e. No turning points; No local extrema

f. Graphing by hand

g. Domain: $\{x \mid x \text{ is any real number}\}$;

Range: $\{y \mid y \text{ is any real number}\}$.

h. f is decreasing on $(-\infty, \infty)$

98. $f(x) = \pi x^5 + \pi x^4 + \sqrt{3}x + 1$

   a. Degree = 5; The graph of the function resembles $y = \pi x^5$ for large values of $|x|$.

   b. graphing utility

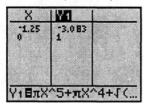

   c. x-intercept: –0.71; y-intercept: 1

   d. Above on $(-0.71, \infty)$; below on $(-\infty, -0.71)$.

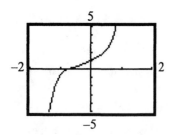

   e. No turning points; No local extrema

   f. graphing by hand

   g. Domain: $\{x \mid x \text{ is any real number}\}$;

      Range: $\{y \mid y \text{ is any real number}\}$.

   h. f is increasing on $(-\infty, \infty)$

99. a. Graphing, we see that the graph may be a cubic relation.

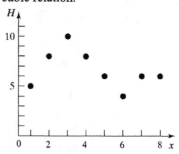

   b. For the decade 1961-1970, we have $x = 5$.

$$H(5) = 0.16(5)^3 - 2.32(5)^2 + 9.33(5) - 2.21$$
$$= 6.44$$

The model predicts that 6 or 7 major hurricanes struck the United States between 1961 and 1970.

   c. The graphing utility agrees to two decimal places.

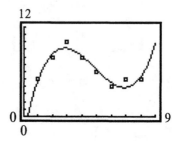

   d.

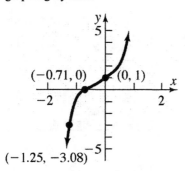

   e. For the decade 2001 to 2010 we have $x = 9$.

$$H(9) = 0.16(9)^3 - 2.32(9)^2 + 9.33(9) - 2.21$$
$$= 10.48$$

The model predicts that the increase in the number of major hurricanes will continue during this decade. This agrees with the scientists.

   f. This tends to support the prediction. The model predicted about 10 major hurricanes. 2005 is halfway through the decade and half the predicted number of major hurricanes have already occurred.

100. a. Graphing, we see that the graph may be a cubic relation.

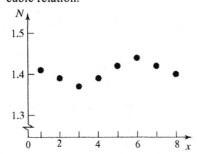

b. For the year 2002, we have $x = 5$.

$$N(5) = -0.00146(5)^3 + 0.0198(5)^2$$
$$- 0.0742(5) + 1.4671$$
$$= 1.4086$$

The model predicts that about 1,408,600 were on active duty in 2002.

c. The graphing utility agrees with the given function.

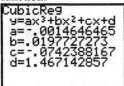

d.

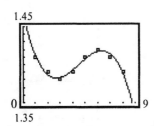

e. Answers will vary. 2010 is too far from the given data so it is not likely that the model will be useful. Note that the model indicates the number of active duty personnel will continue to decrease every year after 2006. This does not seem realistic.

101. a. Graphing, we see that the graph may be a cubic relation.

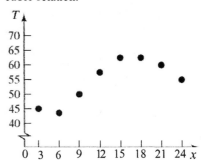

b. $\dfrac{\Delta T}{\Delta x} = \dfrac{T(12) - T(9)}{12 - 9} = \dfrac{57.9 - 51.1}{12 - 9}$

$$= \dfrac{6.8}{3} \approx 2.27$$

The average rate of change in temperature from 9am to noon was about 2.27°F per hour.

c. $\dfrac{\Delta T}{\Delta x} = \dfrac{T(18) - T(15)}{18 - 15} = \dfrac{63.0 - 63.0}{18 - 15} = 0$

The average rate of change in temperature from 9am to noon was 0°F per hour.

d. At 5pm we have $x = 17$.

$$T(17) = -0.0103(17)^3 + 0.32(17)^2$$
$$-1.37(17) + 45.39$$
$$= 63.9761$$

The predicted temperature at 5pm is $\approx 64°F$.

e. The graphing utility agrees with the given model.

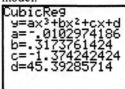

f.

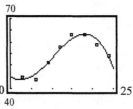

g. The y-intercept is 45.4°F. The model predicts that the midnight temperature was 45.4°F.

419

102. The graph of a polynomial function will always have a *y*-intercept since the domain of every polynomial function is the set of real numbers. Therefore $f(0)$ will always produce a *y*-coordinate on the graph. A polynomial function might have no *x*-intercepts. For example, $f(x) = x^2 + 1$ has no *x*-intercepts since the equation $x^2 + 1 = 0$ has no real solutions.

103. Answers will vary.

104. Answers will vary, one such polynomial is
$$f(x) = x^2(x+1)(4-x)(x-2)^2$$

105. Answers will vary, $f(x) = (x+2)(x-1)^2$ and $g(x) = (x+2)^3(x-1)^2$ are two such polynomials.

106. $f(x) = \dfrac{1}{x}$ is smooth but not continuous;

$g(x) = |x|$ is continuous but not smooth.

107. $f(x) = x^3 + bx^2 + cx + d$

  a. True since every polynomial function has exactly one *y*-intercept, in this case (0, *d*).

  b. True, a third degree polynomial will have at most 3 *x*-intercepts since the equation $x^3 + bx^2 + cx + d = 0$ will have at most 3 real solutions.

  c. True, a third degree polynomial will have at least 1 *x*-intercept since the equation $x^3 + bx^2 + cx + d = 0$ will have at least 1 real solution.

  d. True, since f has degree 3 and the leading coefficient 1.

  e. False, since
$$f(-x) = (-x)^3 + b(-x)^2 + c(-x) + d$$
$$= -x^3 + bx^2 - cx + d$$
$$\neq -f(x). \text{ (unless } b = d = 0)$$

  f. True only if *d* = 0, otherwise the statement is false.

108. a. The degree will be even because the ends of the graph go in the same direction.

  b. The leading coefficient is positive because both ends go up.

  c. The function appears to be symmetric about the y-axis. Therefore, it is an even function.

  d. The graph touches the x-axis at $x = 0$. Therefore, x^n must be a factor, where *n* is even and $n \geq 2$.

  e. There are 6 zeros with odd multiplicity and 1 with even multiplicity. Therefore, the minimum degree is $6(1) + 1(2) = 8$.

  f. Answers will vary.

109. Answers will vary. One possibility:
$$f(x) = -5(x-1)^3(x-2)\left(x-\frac{1}{2}\right)\left(x+\frac{3}{5}\right)$$

Section 5.2

1. True

2. Quotient: $3x + 3$; Remainder: $2x^2 - 3x - 3$

$$
\begin{array}{r}
3x + 3 \\
x^3 - x^2 + 1 \overline{)3x^4 + 0x^3 - x^2 + 0x + 0} \\
-\left(3x^4 - 3x^3 \qquad + 3x\right) \\
\hline
3x^3 - x^2 - 3x \\
-\left(3x^3 - 3x^2 \quad + 3\right) \\
\hline
2x^2 - 3x - 3
\end{array}
$$

3. $y = \dfrac{1}{x}$

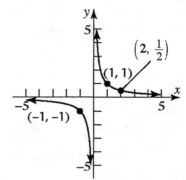

4. Using the graph of $y = x^2$, stretch vertically by a factor of 2, then shift left 1 unit, then shift down 3 units.

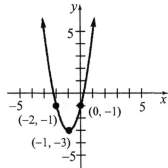

5. $y = 1$

6. $x = -1$

7. proper

8. False

9. True

10. True

11. In $R(x) = \dfrac{4x}{x-3}$, the denominator, $q(x) = x - 3$, has a zero at 3. Thus, the domain of $R(x)$ is all real numbers except 3. $\{x \mid x \neq 3\}$

12. In $R(x) = \dfrac{5x^2}{3+x}$, the denominator, $q(x) = 3 + x$, has a zero at –3. Thus, the domain of $R(x)$ is all real numbers except –3. $\{x \mid x \neq -3\}$

13. In $H(x) = \dfrac{-4x^2}{(x-2)(x+4)}$, the denominator, $q(x) = (x-2)(x+4)$, has zeros at 2 and –4. Thus, the domain of $H(x)$ is all real numbers except 2 and –4. $\{x \mid x \neq 2, -4\}$

14. In $G(x) = \dfrac{6}{(x+3)(4-x)}$, the denominator, $q(x) = (x+3)(4-x)$, has zeros at –3 and 4. Thus, the domain of $G(x)$ is all real numbers except –3 and 4. $\{x \mid x \neq -3, 4\}$

15. In $F(x) = \dfrac{3x(x-1)}{2x^2 - 5x - 3}$, the denominator, $q(x) = 2x^2 - 5x - 3 = (2x+1)(x-3)$, has zeros at $-\dfrac{1}{2}$ and 3. Thus, the domain of $F(x)$ is all real numbers except $-\dfrac{1}{2}$ and 3. $\left\{ x \mid x \neq -\dfrac{1}{2}, 3 \right\}$

16. In $Q(x) = \dfrac{-x(1-x)}{3x^2 + 5x - 2}$, the denominator, $q(x) = 3x^2 + 5x - 2 = (3x-1)(x+2)$, has zeros at $\dfrac{1}{3}$ and –2. Thus, the domain of $Q(x)$ is all real numbers except $\dfrac{1}{3}$ and –2. $\left\{ x \mid x \neq \dfrac{1}{3}, -2 \right\}$

17. In $R(x) = \dfrac{x}{x^3 - 8}$, the denominator, $q(x) = x^3 - 8 = (x-2)(x^2 + 2x + 4)$, has a zero at 2 ($x^2 + 2x + 4$ has no real zeros). Thus, the domain of $R(x)$ is all real numbers except 2. $\{x \mid x \neq 2\}$

18. In $R(x) = \dfrac{x}{x^4 - 1}$, the denominator, $q(x) = x^4 - 1 = (x-1)(x+1)(x^2 + 1)$, has zeros at –1 and 1 ($x^2 + 1$ has no real zeros). Thus, the domain of $R(x)$ is all real numbers except –1 and 1. $\{x \mid x \neq -1, 1\}$

19. In $H(x) = \dfrac{3x^2 + x}{x^2 + 4}$, the denominator, $q(x) = x^2 + 4$, has no real zeros. Thus, the domain of $H(x)$ is all real numbers.

20. In $G(x) = \dfrac{x-3}{x^4 + 1}$, the denominator, $q(x) = x^4 + 1$, has no real zeros. Thus, the domain of $G(x)$ is all real numbers.

21. In $R(x) = \dfrac{3(x^2 - x - 6)}{4(x^2 - 9)}$, the denominator, $q(x) = 4(x^2 - 9) = 4(x-3)(x+3)$, has zeros at 3 and –3. Thus, the domain of $R(x)$ is all real numbers except 3 and –3. $\{x \mid x \neq 3, -3\}$

421

22. In $F(x) = \dfrac{-2(x^2 - 4)}{3(x^2 + 4x + 4)}$, the denominator,

$q(x) = 3(x^2 + 4x + 4) = 3(x + 2)^2$, has a zero at

-2. Thus, the domain of $F(x)$ is all real

numbers except -2. $\{x \mid x \neq -2\}$

23. a. Domain: $\{x \mid x \neq 2\}$; Range: $\{y \mid y \neq 1\}$

    b. Intercept: $(0, 0)$

    c. Horizontal Asymptote: $y = 1$

    d. Vertical Asymptote: $x = 2$

    e. Oblique Asymptote: none

24. a. Domain: $\{x \mid x \neq -1\}$; Range: $\{y \mid y > 0\}$

    b. Intercept: $(0, 2)$

    c. Horizontal Asymptote: $y = 0$

    d. Vertical Asymptote: $x = -1$

    e. Oblique Asymptote: none

25. a. Domain: $\{x \mid x \neq 0\}$;

    Range: all real numbers

    b. Intercepts: $(-1, 0)$ and $(1, 0)$

    c. Horizontal Asymptote: none

    d. Vertical Asymptote: $x = 0$

    e. Oblique Asymptote: $y = 2x$

26. a. Domain: $\{x \mid x \neq 0\}$;

    Range: $\{y \mid y \geq 2 \text{ or } y \leq -2\}$

    b. Intercepts: none

    c. Horizontal Asymptote: none

    d. Vertical Asymptote: $x = 0$

    e. Oblique Asymptote: $y = -x$

27. a. Domain: $\{x \mid x \neq -2, x \neq 2\}$;

    Range: $\{y \mid y \leq 0 \text{ or } y > 1\}$

    b. Intercept: $(0, 0)$

    c. Horizontal Asymptote: $y = 1$

    d. Vertical Asymptotes: $x = -2, x = 2$

    e. Oblique Asymptote: none

28. a. Domain: $\{x \mid x \neq -1, x \neq 1\}$;

    Range: all real numbers

    b. Intercept: $(0, 0)$

    c. Horizontal Asymptote: $y = 0$

    d. Vertical Asymptotes: $x = -1, x = 1$

    e. Oblique Asymptote: none

29. $F(x) = 2 + \dfrac{1}{x}$; Using the function, $y = \dfrac{1}{x}$, shift

the graph vertically 2 units up.

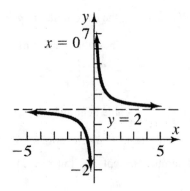

30. $Q(x) = 3 + \dfrac{1}{x^2}$; Using the function $y = \dfrac{1}{x^2}$, shift

the graph vertically 3 units up.

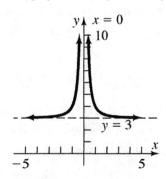

31. $R(x) = \dfrac{1}{(x-1)^2}$; Using the function, $y = \dfrac{1}{x^2}$, shift the graph horizontally 1 unit to the right.

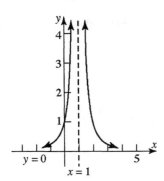

32. $Q(x) = \dfrac{3}{x} = 3\left(\dfrac{1}{x}\right)$; Using the function $y = \dfrac{1}{x}$, stretch the graph vertically by a factor of 3.

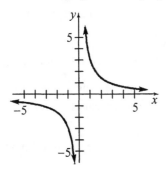

33. $H(x) = \dfrac{-2}{x+1} = -2\left(\dfrac{1}{x+1}\right)$; Using the function $y = \dfrac{1}{x}$, shift the graph horizontally 1 unit to the left, reflect about the x-axis, and stretch vertically by a factor of 2.

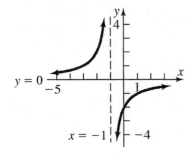

34. $G(x) = \dfrac{2}{(x+2)^2} = 2\left(\dfrac{1}{(x+2)^2}\right)$; Using the function $y = \dfrac{1}{x^2}$, shift the graph horizontally 2 units to the left, and stretch vertically by a factor of 2.

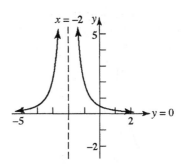

35. $R(x) = \dfrac{-1}{x^2 + 4x + 4} = -\dfrac{1}{(x+2)^2}$; Using the function $y = \dfrac{1}{x^2}$, shift the graph horizontally 2 units to the left, and reflect about the x-axis.

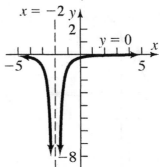

36. $R(x) = \dfrac{1}{x-1} + 1$; Using the function $y = \dfrac{1}{x}$, shift the graph horizontally 1 unit to the right, and shift vertically 1 unit up.

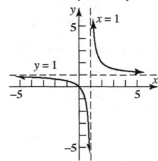

37. $G(x) = 1 + \dfrac{2}{(x-3)^2} = \dfrac{2}{(x-3)^2} + 1$;

$$= 2\left(\dfrac{1}{(x-3)^2}\right) + 1$$

Using the function $y = \dfrac{1}{x^2}$, shift the graph right 3 units, stretch vertically by a factor of 2, and shift vertically 1 unit up.

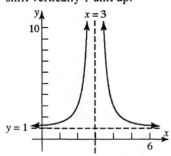

38. $F(x) = 2 - \dfrac{1}{x+1} = -\left(\dfrac{1}{x+1}\right) + 2$; Using the function $y = \dfrac{1}{x}$, shift the graph left 1 unit, reflect about the x-axis, and shift vertically up 2 units.

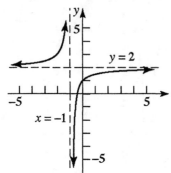

39. $R(x) = \dfrac{x^2 - 4}{x^2} = 1 - \dfrac{4}{x^2} = -4\left(\dfrac{1}{x^2}\right) + 1$; Using the function $y = \dfrac{1}{x^2}$, reflect about the x-axis, stretch vertically by a factor of 4, and shift vertically 1 unit up.

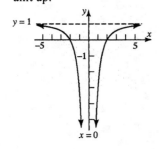

40. $R(x) = \dfrac{x-4}{x} = 1 - \dfrac{4}{x} = -4\left(\dfrac{1}{x}\right) + 1$; Using the function $y = \dfrac{1}{x}$, reflect about the x-axis, stretch vertically by a factor of 4, and shift vertically 1 unit up.

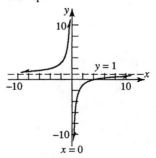

41. $R(x) = \dfrac{3x}{x+4}$; The degree of the numerator, $p(x) = 3x$, is $n = 1$. The degree of the denominator, $q(x) = x + 4$, is $m = 1$. Since $n = m$, the line $y = \dfrac{3}{1} = 3$ is a horizontal asymptote. The denominator is zero at $x = -4$, so $x = -4$ is a vertical asymptote.

42. $R(x) = \dfrac{3x+5}{x-6}$; The degree of the numerator, $p(x) = 3x + 5$, is $n = 1$. The degree of the denominator, $q(x) = x - 6$, is $m = 1$. Since $n = m$, the line $y = \dfrac{3}{1} = 3$ is a horizontal asymptote. The denominator is zero at $x = 6$, so $x = 6$ is a vertical asymptote.

43. $H(x) = \dfrac{x^3 - 8}{x^2 - 5x + 6} = \dfrac{(x-2)(x^2 + 2x + 4)}{(x-2)(x-3)}$

$= \dfrac{x^2 + 2x + 4}{x - 3}$, where $x \neq 2, 3$

The degree of the numerator in lowest terms is $n = 2$. The degree of the denominator in lowest terms is $m = 1$. Since $n = m + 1$, there is an oblique asymptote.
Dividing:

$$x - 3 \overline{)\begin{array}{l} x + 5 \\ x^2 + 2x + 4 \end{array}}$$

$$\begin{array}{r} -(x^2 - 3x) \\ \hline 5x + 4 \\ -(5x - 15) \\ \hline 19 \end{array}$$

$H(x) = x + 5 + \dfrac{19}{x - 3}$, $x \neq 2, 3$

Thus, the oblique asymptote is $y = x + 5$.
The denominator in lowest terms is zero at $x = 3$ so $x = 3$ is a vertical asymptote.

44. $G(x) = \dfrac{-x^2 + 1}{x^2 - 5x + 6} = \dfrac{-(x-1)(x+1)}{(x-2)(x-3)}$

The degree of the numerator,
$p(x) = -x^2 + 1$, is $n = 2$. The degree of the denominator, $q(x) = x^2 - 5x + 6$, is $m = 2$.
Since $n = m$, there is a horizontal asymptote.

The line $y = \dfrac{-1}{1} = -1$ is the horizontal

asymptote.
The denominator is zero at $x = 2, 3$, so
$x = 2$ and $x = 3$ are vertical asymptotes.

45. $T(x) = \dfrac{x^3}{x^4 - 1}$; The degree of the numerator,

$p(x) = x^3$, is $n = 3$. The degree of the denominator, $q(x) = x^4 - 1$ is $m = 4$. Since
$n < m$, the line $y = 0$ is a horizontal asymptote.
The denominator is zero at $x = -1$ and $x = 1$, so
$x = -1$ and $x = 1$ are vertical asymptotes.

46. $P(x) = \dfrac{4x^5}{x^3 - 1}$; The degree of the numerator,

$p(x) = 4x^5$, is $n = 5$. The degree of the denominator, $q(x) = x^3 - 1$ is $m = 3$. Since
$n > m + 1$, there is no horizontal asymptote or oblique asymptote. The denominator is zero at
$x = 1$, so $x = 1$ is a vertical asymptote.

47. $Q(x) = \dfrac{5 - x^2}{3x^4}$; The degree of the numerator,

$p(x) = 5 - x^2$, is $n = 2$. The degree of the denominator, $q(x) = 3x^4$ is $m = 4$. Since
$n < m$, the line $y = 0$ is a horizontal asymptote.
The denominator is zero at $x = 0$, so $x = 0$ is a
vertical asymptote.

48. $F(x) = \dfrac{-2x^2 + 1}{2x^3 + 4x^2} = \dfrac{-2x^2 + 1}{2x^2(x + 2)}$; The degree of

the numerator, $p(x) = -2x^2 + 1$, is $n = 2$. The degree of the denominator,
$q(x) = 2x^3 + 4x^2$ is $m = 3$. Since $n < m$, the line $y = 0$ is a horizontal asymptote. The
denominator is zero at $x = 0$ and $x = -2$, so
$x = 0$ and $x = -2$ are vertical asymptotes.

49. $R(x) = \dfrac{3x^4 + 4}{x^3 + 3x}$; The degree of the numerator,

$p(x) = 3x^4 + 4$, is $n = 4$. The degree of the denominator, $q(x) = x^3 + 3x$ is $m = 3$. Since
$n = m + 1$, there is an oblique asymptote.
Dividing:

$$x^3 + 3x \overline{)\begin{array}{l} 3x \\ 3x^4 \qquad\qquad + 4 \end{array}}$$

$$\begin{array}{r} 3x^4 \quad + 9x^2 \\ \hline -9x^2 \quad + 4 \end{array}$$

$R(x) = 3x + \dfrac{-9x^2 + 4}{x^3 + 3x}$

Thus, the oblique asymptote is $y = 3x$.
The denominator is zero at $x = 0$, so $x = 0$ is a
vertical asymptote.

50. $R(x) = \dfrac{6x^2 + x + 12}{3x^2 - 5x - 2} = \dfrac{6x^2 + x + 12}{(3x+1)(x-2)}$; The

degree of the numerator,

$p(x) = 6x^2 + x + 12$, is $n = 2$. The degree of the

denominator, $q(x) = 3x^2 - 5x - 2$ is $m = 2$.

Since $n = m$, the line $y = \dfrac{6}{3} = 2$ is a horizontal

asymptote. The denominator is zero at

$x = -\dfrac{1}{3}$ and $x = 2$, so $x = -\dfrac{1}{3}$ and $x = 2$ are

vertical asymptotes.

51. $G(x) = \dfrac{x^3 - 1}{x - x^2}$; The degree of the numerator,

$p(x) = x^3 - 1$, is $n = 3$. The degree of the

denominator, $q(x) = x - x^2$ is $m = 2$. Since

$n = m + 1$, there is an oblique asymptote.
Dividing:

$$\begin{array}{r} -x - 1 \\ -x^2 + x \overline{)\,x^3 \qquad\qquad -1} \\ x^3 - x^2 \\ \hline x^2 \\ x^2 - x \\ \hline x - 1 \end{array}$$

$G(x) = -x - 1 + \dfrac{x-1}{x - x^2} = -x - 1 - \dfrac{1}{x}, \; x \neq 1$

Thus, the oblique asymptote is $y = -x - 1$.

$G(x)$ must be in lowest terms to find the vertical
asymptote:

$G(x) = \dfrac{x^3 - 1}{x - x^2} = \dfrac{(x-1)(x^2 + x + 1)}{-x(x-1)} = \dfrac{x^2 + x + 1}{-x}$

The denominator is zero at $x = 0$, so $x = 0$ is a
vertical asymptote.

52. $F(x) = \dfrac{x-1}{x - x^3} = \dfrac{x-1}{-x(x^2 - 1)}$

$= \dfrac{x-1}{-x(x-1)(x+1)} = \dfrac{1}{-x(x+1)}$

The degree of the numerator,

$p(x) = x - 1$, is $n = 1$. The degree of the

denominator, $q(x) = x - x^3$ is $m = 3$. Since

$n < m$, the line $y = 0$ is a horizontal asymptote.

The denominator is zero at $x = 0$, and $x = -1$, so

$x = 0$ and $x = -1$ are vertical asymptotes.

53. $g(h) = \dfrac{3.99 \times 10^{14}}{\left(6.374 \times 10^6 + h\right)^2}$

a. $g(0) = \dfrac{3.99 \times 10^{14}}{\left(6.374 \times 10^6 + 0\right)^2} \approx 9.8208 \text{ m/s}^2$

b. $g(443) = \dfrac{3.99 \times 10^{14}}{\left(6.374 \times 10^6 + 443\right)^2}$

$\approx 9.8195 \text{ m/s}^2$

c. $g(8848) = \dfrac{3.99 \times 10^{14}}{\left(6.374 \times 10^6 + 8848\right)^2}$

$\approx 9.7936 \text{ m/s}^2$

d. $g(h) = \dfrac{3.99 \times 10^{14}}{\left(6.374 \times 10^6 + h\right)^2}$

$\approx \dfrac{3.99 \times 10^{14}}{h^2} \to 0$ as $h \to \infty$

Thus, the h-axis is the horizontal asymptote.

e. $g(h) = \dfrac{3.99 \times 10^{14}}{\left(6.374 \times 10^6 + h\right)^2} = 0$, to solve this

equation would require that $3.99 \times 10^{14} = 0$,
which is impossible. Therefore, there is no
height above sea level at which $g = 0$. In
other words, there is no point in the entire
universe that is unaffected by the Earth's
gravity!

54. $P(t) = \dfrac{50(1 + 0.5t)}{2 + 0.01t}$

a. $P(0) = \dfrac{50(1 + 0)}{2 + 0} = \dfrac{50}{2} = 25$ insects

b. 5 years = 60 months;

$P(60) = \dfrac{50(1 + 0.5(60))}{2 + 0.01(60)} = \dfrac{1550}{2.6}$

≈ 596 insects

c. $P(t) = \dfrac{50(1 + 0.5t)}{2 + 0.01t} \approx \dfrac{50(0.5t)}{0.01t} = 2500$

as $t \to \infty$

Thus, $y = 2500$ is the horizontal asymptote.
The area can sustain a maximum population
of 2500 insects.

55. a. $R_{tot} = \dfrac{10R_2}{10 + R_2}$

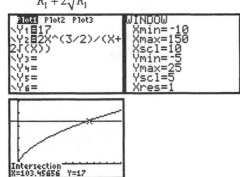

b. Horizontal asymptote: $y = R_{tot} = 10$

As the value of R_2 increases without bound, the total resistance approaches 10 ohms, the resistance of R_1.

c. $R_{tot} = \dfrac{R_1 R_2}{R_1 + R_2}$

$$17 = \frac{R_1 \cdot 2\sqrt{R_1}}{R_1 + 2\sqrt{R_1}}$$

```
Plot1 Plot2 Plot3     WINDOW
\Y1=17                Xmin=-10
\Y2=2X^(3/2)/(X+      Xmax=150
2√(X))                Xscl=10
\Y3=                  Ymin=-5
\Y4=                  Ymax=25
\Y5=                  Yscl=5
\Y6=                  Xres=1
```

```
Intersection
X=103.45656  Y=17
```

We would need $R_1 \approx 103.5$ ohms.

56. a. $p(-3) = (-3)^3 - 7(-3) - 40 = -46$

$p(5) = (5)^3 - 7(5) - 40 = 50$

b. Since $p(x)$ is continuous and

$p(-3) < 0 < p(5)$, there must be at least

one zero in the interval $(-3, 5)$

[Intermediate Value Theorem].

c. From the problem statement, we find the derivative to be $p'(x) = 3x^2 - 7$.

From the Intermediate Value Theorem, we know there is at least one real zero in the interval $(-3, 5)$.

$p(-3) = (-3)^3 - 7(-3) - 40 = -34$

Since $p(3) < 0 < p(5)$, we start with $x_0 = 4$.

$$x_1 = 4 - \frac{p(4)}{p'(4)} \approx 4.097560976$$

$$x_2 = 4.097560976 - \frac{p(4.097560976)}{p'(4.097560976)}$$

$$\approx 4.094906$$

$$x_3 = 4.094906 - \frac{p(4.094906)}{p'(4.094906)} \approx 4.094904$$

The zero is approximately $x = 4.0949$.

d. $p(x) = x^3 - 7x - 40$

```
        50




-5 ┤─────────────┤ 5




       -50
```

From the graph we can see that there is exactly one real zero in the interval $(-3, 5)$.

e. $p(4.0949) = (4.0949)^3 - 7(4.0949) - 40$

$$\approx -0.00017$$

This result is close to 0. Since 4.0949 is rounded, we expect some error when evaluating the function.

57. Answers will vary. If $x = 4$ is a vertical asymptote, then $x = 4$ is a zero of the denominator. If $x = 4$ is a zero of a polynomial, then $(x - 4)$ is a factor of the polynomial. Therefore, if $x = 4$ is a vertical asymptote of a rational function, then $(x - 4)$ must be a factor of the denominator.

58. Answers will vary. With rational functions, the only way to get a non-zero horizontal asymptote is if the degree of the numerator equals the degree of the denominator. In such cases, the horizontal asymptote is the ratio of the leading coefficients.

427

59. A rational function cannot have both a horizontal and oblique asymptote. To have an oblique asymptote, the degree of the numerator must be exactly one larger than the degree of the denominator. However, if the numerator has a higher degree, there is no horizontal asymptote.

60. Answers will vary. We want a rational function such that $r(x) = 2x + 1 + \dfrac{n(x)}{d(x)}$ where n and d are polynomial functions and the degree of $n(x)$ is less than the degree of $d(x)$. We could let $n(x) = 1$ and $d(x) = x + 1$. Then our function is

$r(x) = 2x + 1 + \dfrac{1}{x+1}$. Getting a common denominator yields

$r(x) = \dfrac{(2x+1)(x+1)}{x+1} + \dfrac{1}{x+1}$

$= \dfrac{2x^2 + x + 2x + 1 + 1}{x+1}$

$= \dfrac{2x^2 + 3x + 2}{x+1}$

Therefore, one possibility is $r(x) = \dfrac{2x^2 + 3x + 2}{x+1}$.

Section 5.3

1. x-intercepts:
Set the numerator equal to 0 and solve for x.
$x - 1 = 0$
$\quad x = 1$

y-intercept:
Set x equal to 0 and solve for y.
$y = \dfrac{0 - 1}{0^2 - 4} = \dfrac{-1}{-4} = \dfrac{1}{4}$

The intercepts are $(1, 0)$ and $\left(0, \dfrac{1}{4}\right)$.

2. in lowest terms

3. False; polynomials are always continuous.

4. False; the graph of a rational function may cross horizontal asymptotes.

5. False; the graph of a rational function never crosses a vertical asymptote.

6. True

In problems 7–44, we will use the terminology: $R(x) = \dfrac{p(x)}{q(x)}$, *where the degree of* $p(x) = n$ *and the degree of*

$q(x) = m$.

7. $R(x) = \dfrac{x+1}{x(x+4)}$ $\quad p(x) = x+1;\ q(x) = x(x+4) = x^2 + 4x;\ n = 1;\ m = 2$

Step 1:   Domain: $\{x \mid x \neq -4, x \neq 0\}$

Since 0 is not in the domain, there is no y-intercept.

Step 2:   The function is in lowest terms. The x-intercept is the zero of $p(x)$: $x = -1$

The x-intercept is -1. Near -1, $R(x) \approx -\dfrac{1}{3}(x+1)$. Plot the point $(-1, 0)$ and show a line with negative slope there.

Step 3: $R(x) = \dfrac{x+1}{x(x+4)}$ is in lowest terms.

The vertical asymptotes are the zeros of $q(x)$: $x = -4$ and $x = 0$. Plot these lines using dashes.

Step 4: Since $n < m$, the line $y = 0$ is the horizontal asymptote. Solve $R(x) = 0$ to find intersection points:

$$\frac{x+1}{x(x+4)} = 0$$

$$x + 1 = 0$$

$$x = -1$$

$R(x)$ intersects $y = 0$ at $(-1, 0)$. Plot the point $(-1, 0)$ and the line $y = 0$ using dashes.

Step 5:

	-4	-1	0	
Interval	$(-\infty, -4)$	$(-4, -1)$	$(-1, 0)$	$(0, \infty)$
Number Chosen	-5	-2	$-\frac{1}{2}$	1
Value of R	$R(-5) = -\frac{4}{5}$	$R(-2) = \frac{1}{4}$	$R\left(-\frac{1}{2}\right) = -\frac{2}{7}$	$R(1) = \frac{2}{5}$
Location of Graph	Below x-axis	Above x-axis	Below x-axis	Above x-axis
Point on Graph	$\left(-5, -\frac{4}{5}\right)$	$\left(-2, \frac{1}{4}\right)$	$\left(-\frac{1}{2}, -\frac{2}{7}\right)$	$\left(1, \frac{2}{5}\right)$

Steps 6 & 7: Graphing

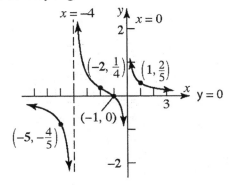

8. $R(x) = \dfrac{x}{(x-1)(x+2)}$ $p(x) = x;$ $q(x) = (x-1)(x+2) = x^2 + x - 2;$ $n = 1;$ $m = 2$

Step 1: Domain: $\{x \mid x \neq -2, x \neq 1\}$

The y-intercept; $R(0) = 0$

Step 2: The function is in lowest terms. The x-intercept is the zero of $p(x)$. 0

Near 0, $R(x) \approx -\dfrac{1}{2}x$. Plot the point $(0, 0)$ and show a line with negative slope there.

Step 3: $R(x) = \dfrac{x}{(x-1)(x+2)}$ is in lowest terms.

The vertical asymptotes are the zeros of $q(x)$: $x = -2$ and $x = 1$. Graph these asymptotes using dashed lines.

Step 4: Since $n < m$, the line $y = 0$ is the horizontal asymptote. Solve to find intersection points:

$$\frac{x}{(x-1)(x+2)} = 0$$

$$x = 0$$

$R(x)$ intersects $y = 0$ at $(0, 0)$. Plot the point $(0, 0)$ and the line $y = 0$ using dashes.

429

Step 5:

Interval	$(-\infty, -2)$	$(-2, 0)$	$(0, 1)$	$(1, \infty)$
Number Chosen	-3	-1	$\frac{1}{2}$	2
Value of R	$R(-3) = -\frac{3}{4}$	$R(-1) = \frac{1}{2}$	$R\left(\frac{1}{2}\right) = -\frac{2}{5}$	$R(2) = \frac{1}{2}$
Location of Graph	Below x-axis	Above x-axis	Below x-axis	Above x-axis
Point on Graph	$\left(-3, -\frac{3}{4}\right)$	$\left(-1, \frac{1}{2}\right)$	$\left(\frac{1}{2}, -\frac{2}{5}\right)$	$\left(2, \frac{1}{2}\right)$

Steps 6 & 7: Graphing:

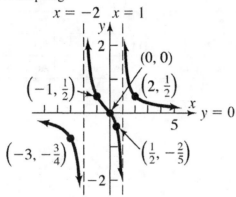

9. $R(x) = \dfrac{3x+3}{2x+4}$ $p(x) = 3x+3;\ q(x) = 2x+4;\ n=1;\ m=1$

Step 1: Domain: $\left\{x \mid x \neq -2\right\}$

The y-intercept is $R(0) = \dfrac{3(0)+3}{2(0)+4} = \dfrac{3}{4}$. Plot the point $\left(0, \dfrac{3}{4}\right)$.

Step 2: $R(x) = \dfrac{3x+3}{2x+4} = \dfrac{3(x+1)}{2(x+2)}$ is in lowest terms. The x-intercept is the zero of $p(x)$, $x = -1$.

Near -1, $R(x) \approx \dfrac{3}{2}(x+1)$. Plot the point $(-1, 0)$ and show a line with positive slope there.

Step 3: $R(x) = \dfrac{3x+3}{2x+4} = \dfrac{3(x+1)}{2(x+2)}$ is in lowest terms.

The vertical asymptote is the zero of $q(x)$: $x = -2$. Graph this asymptote using a dashed line.

Step 4: Since $n = m$, the line $y = \dfrac{3}{2}$ is the horizontal asymptote.

Solve to find intersection points:
$$\frac{3x+3}{2x+4} = \frac{3}{2}$$
$$2(3x+3) = 3(2x+4)$$
$$6x+6 = 6x+4$$
$$0 \neq 2$$

$R(x)$ does not intersect $y = \dfrac{3}{2}$. Plot the line $y = \dfrac{3}{2}$ with dashes.

430

Step 5:

Interval	$(-\infty, -2)$	$(-2, -1)$	$(-1, \infty)$
Number Chosen	-3	$-\frac{3}{2}$	0
Value of R	$R(-3) = 3$	$R\left(-\frac{3}{2}\right) = -\frac{3}{2}$	$R(0) = \frac{3}{4}$
Location of Graph	Above x-axis	Below x-axis	Above x-axis
Point on Graph	$(-3, 3)$	$\left(-\frac{3}{2}, -\frac{3}{2}\right)$	$\left(0, \frac{3}{4}\right)$

Steps 6 & 7: Graphing:

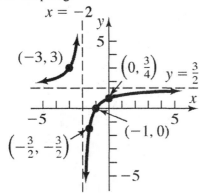

10. $R(x) = \dfrac{2x+4}{x-1} = \dfrac{2(x+2)}{x-1}$ $p(x) = 2x+4;\ q(x) = x-1;\ n = 1;\ m = 1$

Step 1:   Domain: $\{x \mid x \neq 1\}$

The y-intercept is $R(0) = \dfrac{2(0)+4}{0-1} = \dfrac{4}{-1} = -4$. Plot the point $(0, -4)$.

Step 2: R is in lowest terms. The x-intercept is the zero of $p(x)$: $x = -2$

Near -2, $R(x) \approx -\dfrac{2}{3}(x+2)$. Plot the point $(-2, 0)$ and show a line with negative slope there.

Step 3: $R(x) = \dfrac{2x+4}{x-1} = \dfrac{2(x+2)}{x-1}$ is in lowest terms.

The vertical asymptote is the zero of $q(x)$: $x = 1$. Graph this asymptote using a dashed line.

Step 4:   Since $n = m$, the line $y = 2$ is the horizontal asymptote. Solve to find intersection points:
$$\frac{2x+4}{x-1} = 2$$
$$2x+4 = 2(x-1)$$
$$2x+4 = 2x-1$$
$$0 \neq -5$$
$R(x)$ does not intersect $y = 2$. Plot the line $y = 2$ with dashes.

431

Step 5:

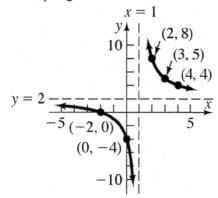

Interval	$(-\infty, -2)$	$(-2, 1)$	$(1, \infty)$
Number Chosen	-3	0	2
Value of R	$R(-3) = \frac{1}{2}$	$R(0) = -4$	$R(2) = 8$
Location of Graph	Above x-axis	Below x-axis	Above x-axis
Point on Graph	$\left(-3, \frac{1}{2}\right)$	$(0, -4)$	$(2, 8)$

Steps 6 & 7: Graphing:

11. $R(x) = \dfrac{3}{x^2 - 4} = \dfrac{3}{(x-2)(x+2)}$ $p(x) = 3;\ q(x) = x^2 - 4;\ n = 0;\ m = 2$

Step 1:   Domain: $\left\{x \mid x \neq -2, x \neq 2\right\}$

The y-intercept is $R(0) = \dfrac{3}{0^2 - 4} = \dfrac{3}{-4} = -\dfrac{3}{4}$. Plot the point $\left(0, -\dfrac{3}{4}\right)$.

Step 2: R is in lowest terms. The x-intercepts are the zeros of $p(x)$. Since $p(x)$ is a constant, there are no x-intercepts.

Step 3: $R(x) = \dfrac{3}{x^2 - 4}$ is in lowest terms. The vertical asymptotes are the zeros of $q(x)$: $x = -2$ and $x = 2$. Graph each of these asymptotes using dashed lines.

Step 4:   Since $n < m$, the line $y = 0$ is the horizontal asymptote. Solve to find intersection points:

$$\dfrac{3}{x^2 - 4} = 0$$

$$3 = 0\left(x^2 - 4\right)$$

$$3 \neq 0$$

$R(x)$ does not intersect $y = 0$. Plot the line $y = 0$ with dashes.

Step 5:

Interval	$(-\infty, -2)$	$(-2, 2)$	$(2, \infty)$
Number Chosen	-3	0	3
Value of R	$R(-3) = \frac{3}{5}$	$R(0) = -\frac{3}{4}$	$R(3) = \frac{3}{5}$
Location of Graph	Above x-axis	Below x-axis	Above x-axis
Point on Graph	$\left(-3, \frac{3}{5}\right)$	$\left(0, -\frac{3}{4}\right)$	$\left(3, \frac{3}{5}\right)$

Steps 6 & 7: Graphing:

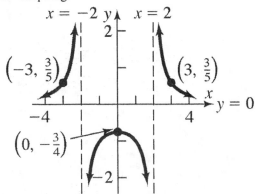

12. $R(x) = \dfrac{6}{x^2 - x - 6} = \dfrac{6}{(x-3)(x+2)}$ $p(x) = 6;\ q(x) = x^2 - x - 6;\ n = 0;\ m = 2$

Step 1:   Domain: $\left\{x \mid x \neq -2, x \neq 3\right\}$

The y-intercept is $R(0) = \dfrac{6}{0^2 - 0 - 6} = \dfrac{6}{-6} = -1$. Plot the point $(0, -1)$.

Step 2: R is in lowest terms. The x-intercepts are the zeros of $p(x)$. Since $p(x)$ is a constant, there are no x-intercepts.

Step 3: $R(x) = \dfrac{6}{x^2 - x - 6}$ is in lowest terms. The vertical asymptotes are the zeros of $q(x)$: $x = -2$ and $x = 3$.
Graph each of these asymptotes using dashed lines.

Step 4:   Since $n < m$, the line $y = 0$ is the horizontal asymptote. Solve to find intersection points:

$$\frac{6}{x^2 - x - 6} = 0$$

$$6 = 0\left(x^2 - x - 6\right)$$

$$6 \neq 0$$

$R(x)$ does not intersect $y = 0$.

Step 5:

	$(-\infty, -2)$	$(-2, 3)$	$(3, \infty)$
Interval	$(-\infty, -2)$	$(-2, 3)$	$(3, \infty)$
Number Chosen	-3	0	4
Value of R	$R(-3) = 1$	$R(0) = -1$	$R(4) = 1$
Location of Graph	Above x-axis	Below x-axis	Above x-axis
Point on Graph	$(-3, 1)$	$(0, -1)$	$(4, 1)$

Steps 6 & 7: Graphing:

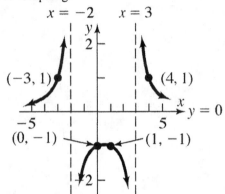

13. $P(x) = \dfrac{x^4 + x^2 + 1}{x^2 - 1}$ $p(x) = x^4 + x^2 + 1$; $q(x) = x^2 - 1$; $n = 4$; $m = 2$

Step 1: Domain: $\left\{ x \mid x \neq -1, x \neq 1 \right\}$

The y-intercept is $P(0) = \dfrac{0^4 + 0^2 + 1}{0^2 - 1} = \dfrac{1}{-1} = -1$. Plot the point $(0, -1)$.

Step 2: $P(x) = \dfrac{x^4 + x^2 + 1}{x^2 - 1}$ is in lowest terms. The x-intercept is the zero of $p(x)$. Since $p(x)$ is never 0, there are no x-intercepts.

Step 3: $P(x) = \dfrac{x^4 + x^2 + 1}{x^2 - 1}$ is in lowest terms. The vertical asymptotes are the zeros of $q(x)$: $x = -1$ and $x = 1$. Graph each of these asymptotes using dashed lines.

Step 4: Since $n > m + 1$, there is no horizontal or oblique asymptote.

434

Step 5:

Interval	$(-\infty, -1)$	$(-1, 1)$	$(1, \infty)$
Number Chosen	-2	0	2
Value of P	$P(-2) = 7$	$P(0) = -1$	$P(2) = 7$
Location of Graph	Above x-axis	Below x-axis	Above x-axis
Point on Graph	$(-2, 7)$	$(0, -1)$	$(2, 7)$

Steps 6 & 7: Graphing:

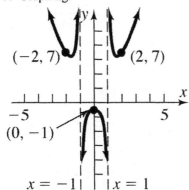

14. $Q(x) = \dfrac{x^4 - 1}{x^2 - 4} = \dfrac{(x^2 + 1)(x + 1)(x - 1)}{(x + 2)(x - 2)}$ $p(x) = x^4 - 1;\ q(x) = x^2 - 4;\ n = 4;\ m = 2$

Step 1: Domain: $\left\{ x \mid x \neq -2, x \neq 2 \right\}$

The y-intercept is $Q(0) = \dfrac{0^4 - 1}{0^2 - 4} = \dfrac{-1}{-4} = \dfrac{1}{4}$. Plot the point $\left(0, \dfrac{1}{4} \right)$.

Step 2: $Q(x) = \dfrac{x^4 - 1}{x^2 - 4} = \dfrac{(x^2 + 1)(x + 1)(x - 1)}{(x + 2)(x - 2)}$ is in lowest terms. The x-intercepts are the zeros of $p(x)$: -1
and 1.

Near -1, $Q(x) \approx \dfrac{4}{3}(x + 1)$; Near 1, $Q(x) \approx -\dfrac{4}{3}(x - 1)$.

Plot the point $(-1, 0)$ and indicate a line with positive slope there.

Plot the point $(1, 0)$ and indicate a line with negative slope there.

Step 3: $Q(x) = \dfrac{x^4 - 1}{x^2 - 4} = \dfrac{(x^2 + 1)(x + 1)(x - 1)}{(x + 2)(x - 2)}$ is in lowest terms.

The vertical asymptotes are the zeros of $q(x)$: $x = -2$ and $x = 2$. Graph each of these asymptotes using dashed lines.

Step 4: Since $n > m + 1$, there is no horizontal asymptote and no oblique asymptote.

435

Step 5:

Interval	$(-\infty, -2)$	$(-2, -1)$	$(-1, 1)$	$(1, 2)$	$(2, \infty)$
Number Chosen	-3	$-\frac{3}{2}$	0	$\frac{3}{2}$	3
Value of Q	$Q(-3) = 16$	$Q\left(-\frac{3}{2}\right) \approx -2.3$	$Q(0) = \frac{1}{4}$	$Q\left(\frac{3}{2}\right) \approx -2.3$	$Q(3) = 16$
Location of Graph	Above x-axis	Below x-axis	Above x-axis	Below x-axis	Above x-axis
Point on Graph	$(-3, 16)$	$\left(-\frac{3}{2}, -2.3\right)$	$\left(0, \frac{1}{4}\right)$	$\left(\frac{3}{2}, -2.3\right)$	$(3, 16)$

Steps 6 & 7: Graphing:

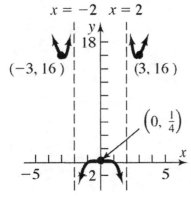

15. $H(x) = \dfrac{x^3 - 1}{x^2 - 9} = \dfrac{(x-1)(x^2 + x + 1)}{(x+3)(x-3)}$ $p(x) = x^3 - 1; \ q(x) = x^2 - 9; \ n = 3; \ m = 2$

Step 1: Domain: $\{x \mid x \neq -3, x \neq 3\}$

The y-intercept is $H(0) = \dfrac{0^3 - 1}{0^2 - 9} = \dfrac{-1}{-9} = \dfrac{1}{9}$. Plot the point $\left(0, \dfrac{1}{9}\right)$.

Step 2: $H(x)$ is in lowest terms. The x-intercept is the zero of $p(x)$: 1.

Near 1, $H(x) \approx -\dfrac{3}{8}(x - 1)$. Plot the point $(1, 0)$ and indicate a line with negative slope there.

Step 3: $H(x)$ is in lowest terms. The vertical asymptotes are the zeros of $q(x)$: $x = -3$ and $x = 3$. Graph each of these asymptotes using dashed lines.

Step 4: Since $n = m + 1$, there is an oblique asymptote. Dividing:

$$\begin{array}{r} x \phantom{{}+0x^2+0x-1} \\ x^2 - 9 \overline{)\, x^3 + 0x^2 + 0x - 1} \\ \underline{x^3 \phantom{{}+0x^2} - 9x} \\ 9x - 1 \end{array} \qquad H(x) = x + \dfrac{9x - 1}{x^2 - 9}$$

The oblique asymptote is $y = x$. Graph this asymptote with a dashed line. Solve to find intersection points:

$$\frac{x^3 - 1}{x^2 - 9} = x$$

$$x^3 - 1 = x^3 - 9x$$

$$-1 = -9x$$

$$x = \frac{1}{9}$$

The oblique asymptote intersects $H(x)$ at $\left(\frac{1}{9}, \frac{1}{9}\right)$.

Step 5:

Interval	$(-\infty, -3)$	$(-3, 1)$	$(1, 3)$	$(3, \infty)$
Number Chosen	-4	0	2	4
Value of H	$H(-4) \approx -9.3$	$H(0) = \frac{1}{9}$	$H(2) = -1.4$	$H(4) = 9$
Location of Graph	Below x-axis	Above x-axis	Below x-axis	Above x-axis
Point on Graph	$(-4, -9.3)$	$\left(0, \frac{1}{9}\right)$	$(2, -1.4)$	$(4, 9)$

Steps 6 & 7: Graphing:

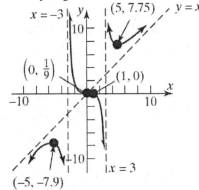

16. $G(x) = \dfrac{x^3 + 1}{x^2 + 2x} = \dfrac{(x+1)(x^2 - x + 1)}{x(x+2)}$ $p(x) = x^3 + 1;\ q(x) = x^2 + 2x;\ n = 3;\ m = 2$

Step 1: Domain: $\{x \mid x \neq -2, x \neq 0\}$

There is no y-intercept since $G(0) = \dfrac{0^3 + 1}{0^2 + 2(0)} = \dfrac{1}{0}$.

Step 2: $G(x) = \dfrac{x^3 + 1}{x^2 + 2x}$ is in lowest terms. The x-intercept is the zero of $p(x)$: -1.

Near -1, $G(x) \approx -3(x + 1)$. Plot the point $(-1, 0)$ and indicate a line with negative slope there.

Step 3: $G(x) = \dfrac{x^3 + 1}{x^2 + 2x}$ is in lowest terms. The vertical asymptotes are the zeros of $q(x)$: $x = -2$ and $x = 0$.

Graph each of these asymptotes using dashed lines.

437

Step 4:   Since $n = m+1$, there is an oblique asymptote. Dividing:

$$\begin{array}{r} x-2 \\ x^2+2x\overline{\smash{\big)}\,x^3+0x^2+0x+1} \\ \underline{x^3+2x^2} \\ -2x^2\qquad+1 \\ \underline{-2x^2-4x} \\ 4x+1 \end{array} \qquad G(x) = x-2+\dfrac{4x+1}{x^2+2x}$$

The oblique asymptote is $y = x-2$. Graph this asymptote with a dashed line. Solve to find intersection points:

$$\frac{x^3+1}{x^2+2x} = x-2$$
$$x^3+1 = x^3-4x$$
$$1 = -4x$$
$$x = -\frac{1}{4}$$

The oblique asymptote intersects $G(x)$ at $\left(-\dfrac{1}{4}, -\dfrac{9}{4}\right)$.

Step 5:

Interval	$(-\infty, -2)$	$(-2, -1)$	$(-1, 0)$	$(0, \infty)$
Number Chosen	-4	-1.5	-0.25	1
Value of G	$G(-4) = -7.875$	$G(-1.5) \approx 3.2$	$G(-0.25) = -2.25$	$G(1) = \frac{2}{3}$
Location of Graph	Below x-axis	Above x-axis	Below x-axis	Above x-axis
Point on Graph	$(-4, -7.875)$	$(-1.5, 3.17)$	$(-0.25, -2.25)$	$(1, \frac{2}{3})$

Steps 6 & 7: Graphing:

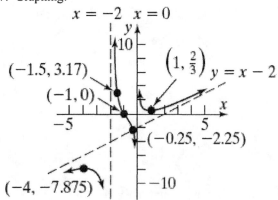

17. $R(x) = \dfrac{x^2}{x^2 + x - 6} = \dfrac{x^2}{(x+3)(x-2)}$ $p(x) = x^2; \; q(x) = x^2 + x - 6; \; n = 2; \; m = 2$

Step 1:   Domain: $\{x \mid x \neq -3, \, x \neq 2\}$

The y-intercept is $R(0) = \dfrac{0^2}{0^2 + 0 - 6} = \dfrac{0}{-6} = 0$. Plot the point $(0, 0)$.

Step 2: $R(x) = \dfrac{x^2}{x^2 + x - 6}$ is in lowest terms. The x-intercept is the zero of $p(x)$: 0

Near 0, $R(x) \approx -\dfrac{1}{6}x^2$. Plot the point $(0, 0)$ and indicate a parabola opening down there.

Step 3: $R(x) = \dfrac{x^2}{x^2 + x - 6}$ is in lowest terms. The vertical asymptotes are the zeros of $q(x)$:

$x = -3$ and $x = 2$. Graph each of these asymptotes using dashed lines.

Step 4:   Since $n = m$, the line $y = 1$ is the horizontal asymptote. Graph this asymptote with a dashed line.
Solve to find intersection points:

$$\frac{x^2}{x^2 + x - 6} = 1$$
$$x^2 = x^2 + x - 6$$
$$0 = x - 6$$
$$x = 6$$

$R(x)$ intersects $y = 1$ at $(6, 1)$.

Step 5:

Interval	$(-\infty, -3)$	$(-3, 0)$	$(0, 2)$	$(2, \infty)$
Number Chosen	-6	-1	1	3
Value of R	$R(-6) = 1.5$	$R(-1) = -\frac{1}{6}$	$R(1) = -0.25$	$R(3) = 1.5$
Location of Graph	Above x-axis	Below x-axis	Below x-axis	Above x-axis
Point on Graph	$(-6, 1.5)$	$\left(-1, -\frac{1}{6}\right)$	$(1, -0.25)$	$(3, 1.5)$

Steps 6 & 7:   Graphing:

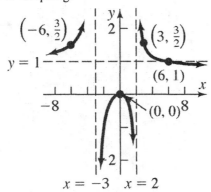

18. $R(x) = \dfrac{x^2 + x - 12}{x^2 - 4} = \dfrac{(x+4)(x-3)}{(x+2)(x-2)}$ $p(x) = x^2 + x - 12$; $q(x) = x^2 - 4$; $n = 2$; $m = 2$

Step 1: Domain: $\{x \mid x \neq -2, x \neq 2\}$

The y-intercept is $R(0) = \dfrac{0^2 + 0 - 12}{0^2 - 4} = \dfrac{-12}{-4} = 3$. Plot the point $(0, 3)$.

Step 2: $R(x) = \dfrac{x^2 + x - 12}{x^2 - 4} = \dfrac{(x+4)(x-3)}{(x+2)(x-2)}$ is in lowest terms.

The x-intercepts are the zeros of $p(x)$: -4 and 3

Near -4, $R(x) \approx -\dfrac{7}{12}(x+4)$; Near 3, $R(x) \approx \dfrac{7}{5}(x-3)$.

Plot the point $(-4, 0)$ and indicate a line with negative slope there.

Plot the point $(3, 0)$ and indicate a line with positive slope there.

Step 3: $R(x) = \dfrac{x^2 + x - 12}{x^2 - 4}$ is in lowest terms.

The vertical asymptotes are the zeros of $q(x)$: $x = -2$ and $x = 2$. Graph each of these asymptotes using a dashed line.

Step 4: Since $n = m$, the line $y = 1$ is the horizontal asymptote. Graph this asymptote using a dashed line.
Solve to find intersection points:

$$\frac{x^2 + x - 12}{x^2 - 4} = 1$$

$$x^2 + x - 12 = x^2 - 4$$

$$x = 8$$

$R(x)$ intersects $y = 1$ at $(8, 1)$.

Step 5:

Interval	$(-\infty, -4)$	$(-4, -2)$	$(-2, 2)$	$(2, 3)$	$(3, \infty)$
Number Chosen	-7	-3	0	2.5	8
Value of R	$R(-7) = \frac{2}{3}$	$R(-3) = -1.2$	$R(0) = 3$	$R(2.5) \approx -1.44$	$R(8) = 1$
Location of Graph	Above x-axis	Below x-axis	Above x-axis	Below x-axis	Above x-axis
Point on Graph	$\left(-7, \frac{2}{3}\right)$	$(-3, -1.2)$	$(0, 3)$	$(2.5, -1.44)$	$(8, 1)$

Steps 6 & 7: Graphing:

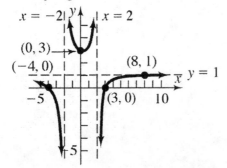

440

19. $G(x) = \dfrac{x}{x^2 - 4} = \dfrac{x}{(x+2)(x-2)}$ $p(x) = x;\ q(x) = x^2 - 4;\ n = 1;\ m = 2$

Step 1:   Domain: $\{x \mid x \neq -2,\ x \neq 2\}$

The y-intercept is $G(0) = \dfrac{0}{0^2 - 4} = \dfrac{0}{-4} = 0$. Plot the point $(0,0)$.

Step 2: $G(x) = \dfrac{x}{x^2 - 4}$ is in lowest terms. The x-intercept is the zero of $p(x)$: 0

Near 0, $G(x) \approx -\dfrac{1}{4}x$. Plot the point $(0,0)$ and indicate a line with negative slope there.

Step 3: $G(x) = \dfrac{x}{x^2 - 4}$ is in lowest terms. The vertical asymptotes are the zeros of $q(x)$: $x = -2$ and $x = 2$.

Graph each of these asymptotes using a dashed line.

Step 4:   Since $n < m$, the line $y = 0$ is the horizontal asymptote. Graph this asymptote using a dashed line.
Solve to find intersection points:

$$\frac{x}{x^2 - 4} = 0$$
$$x = 0$$

$G(x)$ intersects $y = 0$ at $(0, 0)$.

Step 5:

Interval	$(-\infty, -2)$	$(-2, 0)$	$(0, 2)$	$(2, \infty)$
Number Chosen	-3	-1	1	3
Value of G	$G(-3) = -\frac{3}{5}$	$G(-1) = \frac{1}{3}$	$G(1) = -\frac{1}{3}$	$G(3) = \frac{3}{5}$
Location of Graph	Below x-axis	Above x-axis	Below x-axis	Above x-axis
Point on Graph	$\left(-3, -\frac{3}{5}\right)$	$\left(-1, \frac{1}{3}\right)$	$\left(1, -\frac{1}{3}\right)$	$\left(3, \frac{3}{5}\right)$

Steps 6 & 7: Graphing:

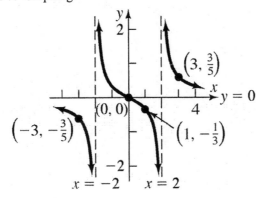

441

20. $G(x) = \dfrac{3x}{x^2 - 1} = \dfrac{3x}{(x+1)(x-1)}$ $\quad p(x) = 3x; \;\; q(x) = x^2 - 1; \;\; n = 1; \;\; m = 2$

Step 1: Domain: $\{x \mid x \neq -1, \; x \neq 1\}$

The y-intercept is $G(0) = \dfrac{3(0)}{0^2 - 1} = \dfrac{0}{-1} = 0$. Plot the point $(0,0)$.

Step 2: $G(x) = \dfrac{3x}{x^2 - 1}$ is in lowest terms. The x-intercept is the zero of $p(x)$: $\;0$

Near 0, $G(x) \approx -3x$. Plot the point $(0,0)$ and indicate a line with negative slope there.

Step 3: $G(x) = \dfrac{3x}{x^2 - 1}$ is in lowest terms. The vertical asymptotes are the zeros of $q(x)$: $\;x = -1$ and $x = 1$

Graph each of these asymptotes using a dashed line.

Step 4: Since $n < m$, the line $y = 0$ is the horizontal asymptote. Graph this asymptote using a dashed line.

Solve to find intersection points:

$$\frac{3x}{x^2 - 1} = 0$$
$$3x = 0$$
$$x = 0$$

$G(x)$ intersects $y = 0$ at $(0, 0)$.

Step 5:

Interval	$(-\infty, -1)$	$(-1, 0)$	$(0, 1)$	$(1, \infty)$
Number Chosen	-2	$-\frac{1}{2}$	$\frac{1}{2}$	2
Value of G	$G(-2) = -2$	$G\left(-\frac{1}{2}\right) = 2$	$G\left(\frac{1}{2}\right) = -2$	$G(2) = 2$
Location of Graph	Below x-axis	Above x-axis	Below x-axis	Above x-axis
Point on Graph	$(-2, -2)$	$\left(-\frac{1}{2}, 2\right)$	$\left(\frac{1}{2}, -2\right)$	$(2, 2)$

Steps 6 & 7: Graphing:

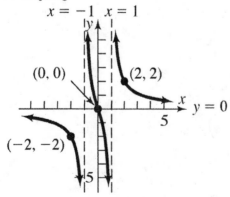

21. $R(x) = \dfrac{3}{(x-1)(x^2-4)} = \dfrac{3}{(x-1)(x+2)(x-2)}$ $p(x) = 3;\ q(x) = (x-1)(x^2-4);\ n = 0;\ m = 3$

Step 1: Domain: $\{x \mid x \neq -2,\ x \neq 1,\ x \neq 2\}$

The y-intercept is $R(0) = \dfrac{3}{(0-1)(0^2-4)} = \dfrac{3}{4}$. Plot the point $\left(0, \dfrac{3}{4}\right)$.

Step 2: $R(x) = \dfrac{3}{(x-1)(x^2-4)}$ is in lowest terms. There is no x-intercept.

Step 3: $R(x) = \dfrac{3}{(x-1)(x^2-4)}$ is in lowest terms.

The vertical asymptotes are the zeros of $q(x)$: $x = -2,\ x = 1,$ and $x = 2$.
Graph each of these asymptotes using a dashed line.

Step 4: Since $n < m$, the line $y = 0$ is the horizontal asymptote. Graph this asymptote with a dashed line.
Solve to find intersection points:

$$\frac{3}{(x-1)(x^2-4)} = 0$$

$$3 \neq 0$$

$R(x)$ does not intersect $y = 0$.

Step 5:

Interval	$(-\infty, -2)$	$(-2, 1)$	$(1, 2)$	$(2, \infty)$
Number Chosen	-3	0	$\frac{3}{2}$	3
Value of R	$R(-3) = -\frac{3}{20}$	$R(0) = \left(\frac{3}{4}\right)$	$R(\frac{3}{2}) = -\frac{24}{7}$	$R(3) = \frac{3}{10}$
Location of Graph	Below x-axis	Above x-axis	Below x-axis	Above x-axis
Point on Graph	$\left(-3, -\frac{3}{20}\right)$	$\left(0, \frac{3}{4}\right)$	$\left(\frac{3}{2}, -\frac{24}{7}\right)$	$\left(3, \frac{3}{10}\right)$

Steps 6 & 7: Graphing:

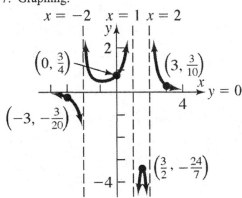

443

22. $R(x) = \dfrac{-4}{(x+1)(x^2-9)} = \dfrac{-4}{(x+1)(x+3)(x-3)}$ $p(x) = -4;$ $q(x) = (x+1)(x^2-9);$ $n = 0;$ $m = 3$

Step 1: Domain: $\{x \mid x \neq -3,\, x \neq -1,\, x \neq 3\}$

The y-intercept is $R(0) = \dfrac{-4}{(0+1)(0^2-9)} = \dfrac{-4}{-9} = \dfrac{4}{9}$. Plot the point $\left(0, \dfrac{4}{9}\right)$.

Step 2: $R(x) = \dfrac{-4}{(x+1)(x^2-9)}$ is in lowest terms. There is no x-intercept.

Step 3: $R(x) = \dfrac{-4}{(x+1)(x^2-9)}$ is in lowest terms.

The vertical asymptotes are the zeros of $q(x)$: $x = -3$, $x = -1$, and $x = 3$

Graph each of these asymptotes using a dashed line.

Step 4: Since $n < m$, the line $y = 0$ is the horizontal asymptote. Graph this asymptote with a dashed line.

Solve to find intersection points:

$$\dfrac{-4}{(x+1)(x^2-9)} = 0$$

$$-4 \neq 0$$

$R(x)$ does not intersect $y = 0$.

Step 5:

	-3		-1		3

Interval	$(-\infty, -3)$	$(-3, -1)$	$(-1, 3)$	$(3, \infty)$
Number Chosen	-4	-2	0	4
Value of R	$R(-4) \approx 0.19$	$R(-2) = -0.8$	$R(0) = \frac{4}{9}$	$R(4) \approx -0.11$
Location of Graph	Above x-axis	Below x-axis	Above x-axis	Below x-axis
Point on Graph	$(-4, 0.19)$	$(-2, -0.8)$	$\left(0, \frac{4}{9}\right)$	$(4, -0.11)$

Steps 6 & 7: Graphing:

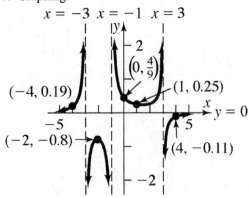

23. $H(x) = \dfrac{x^2 - 1}{x^4 - 16} = \dfrac{(x-1)(x+1)}{(x^2+4)(x+2)(x-2)}$ $\quad p(x) = x^2 - 1; \quad q(x) = x^4 - 16; \quad n = 2; \ m = 4$

Step 1:   Domain: $\{x \mid x \neq -2, x \neq 2\}$

The y-intercept is $H(0) = \dfrac{0^2 - 1}{0^4 - 16} = \dfrac{-1}{-16} = \dfrac{1}{16}$. Plot the point $\left(0, \dfrac{1}{16}\right)$.

Step 2: $H(x) = \dfrac{x^2 - 1}{x^4 - 16}$ is in lowest terms. The x-intercepts are the zeros of $p(x)$: -1 and 1

Near -1, $H(x) \approx \dfrac{2}{15}(x+1)$; Near 1, $H(x) \approx -\dfrac{2}{15}(x-1)$

Plot $(-1, 0)$ and indicate a line with positive slope there.

Plot $(1, 0)$ and indicate a line with negative slope there.

Step 3: $H(x) = \dfrac{x^2 - 1}{x^4 - 16}$ is in lowest terms. The vertical asymptotes are the zeros of $q(x)$: $x = -2$ and $x = 2$
Graph each of these asymptotes using a dashed line.

Step 4:   Since $n < m$, the line $y = 0$ is the horizontal asymptote. Graph this asymptote using a dashed line.
Solve to find intersection points:

$$\frac{x^2 - 1}{x^4 - 16} = 0$$
$$x^2 - 1 = 0$$
$$x = \pm 1$$

$H(x)$ intersects $y = 0$ at $(-1, 0)$ and $(1, 0)$.

Step 5:

Interval	$(-\infty, -2)$	$(-2, -1)$	$(-1, 1)$	$(1, 2)$	$(2, \infty)$
Number Chosen	-3	-1.5	0	1.5	3
Value of H	$H(-3) \approx 0.12$	$H(-1.5) \approx -0.11$	$H(0) = \frac{1}{16}$	$H(1.5) \approx -0.11$	$H(3) \approx 0.12$
Location of Graph	Above x-axis	Below x-axis	Above x-axis	Below x-axis	Above x-axis
Point on Graph	$(-3, 0.12)$	$(-1.5, -0.11)$	$\left(0, \frac{1}{16}\right)$	$(1.5, -0.11)$	$(3, 0.12)$

Steps 6 & 7: Graphing:

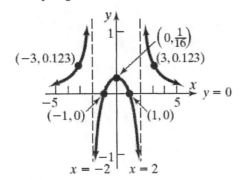

445

24. $H(x) = \dfrac{x^2+4}{x^4-1} = \dfrac{x^2+4}{(x^2+1)(x+1)(x-1)}$ $\quad p(x) = x^2+4;\; q(x) = x^4-1;\quad n=2;\; m=4$

Step 1: Domain: $\{x \mid x \neq -1,\, x \neq 1\}$

The y-intercept is $H(0) = \dfrac{0^2+4}{0^4-1} = \dfrac{4}{-1} = -4$. Plot the point $(0,-4)$.

Step 2: $H(x) = \dfrac{x^2+4}{x^4-1}$ is in lowest terms. There are no x-intercepts.

Step 3: $H(x) = \dfrac{x^2+4}{x^4-1}$ is in lowest terms. The vertical asymptotes are the zeros of $q(x)$: $x = -1$ and $x = 1$.
Graph each of these asymptotes using a dashed line.

Step 4: Since $n < m$, the line $y = 0$ is the horizontal asymptote. Graph this asymptote using a dashed line.
Solve to find intersection points:

$$\frac{x^2+4}{x^4-1} = 0$$

$$x^2 + 4 = 0$$

$\quad$ no real solution

$H(x)$ does not intersect $y = 0$.

Step 5:

Interval	$(-\infty, -1)$	$(-1, 1)$	$(1, \infty)$
Number Chosen	-2	0	2
Value of H	$H(-2) = \frac{8}{15}$	$H(0) = -4$	$H(2) = \frac{8}{15}$
Location of Graph	Above x-axis	Below x-axis	Above x-axis
Point on Graph	$\left(-2, \frac{8}{15}\right)$	$(0, -4)$	$\left(2, \frac{8}{15}\right)$

Steps 6 & 7: Graphing:

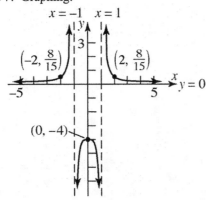

25. $F(x) = \dfrac{x^2 - 3x - 4}{x + 2} = \dfrac{(x+1)(x-4)}{x+2}$ $p(x) = x^2 - 3x - 4;$ $q(x) = x + 2;$ $n = 2;$ $m = 1$

Step 1: Domain: $\{x \mid x \neq -2\}$

The y-intercept is $F(0) = \dfrac{0^2 - 3(0) - 4}{0 + 2} = \dfrac{-4}{2} = -2$. Plot the point $(0, -2)$.

Step 2: $F(x) = \dfrac{x^2 - 3x - 4}{x + 2}$ is in lowest terms. The x-intercepts are the zeros of $p(x)$: -1 and 4.

Near -1, $F(x) \approx -5(x+1)$; Near 4, $F(x) \approx \dfrac{5}{6}(x-4)$.

Plot $(-1, 0)$ and indicate a line with negative slope there.

Plot $(4, 0)$ and indicate a line with positive slope there.

Step 3: $F(x) = \dfrac{x^2 - 3x - 4}{x + 2}$ is in lowest terms. The vertical asymptote is the zero of $q(x)$: $x = -2$

Graph this asymptote using a dashed line.

Step 4: Since $n = m + 1$, there is an oblique asymptote. Dividing:

$$\begin{array}{r} x - 5 \\ x + 2 \overline{\smash{\big)}\, x^2 - 3x - 4} \\ \underline{x^2 + 2x} \\ -5x - 4 \\ \underline{-5x - 10} \\ 6 \end{array} \qquad F(x) = x - 5 + \dfrac{6}{x + 2}$$

The oblique asymptote is $y = x - 5$. Graph this asymptote using a dashed line. Solve to find intersection points:

$$\dfrac{x^2 - 3x - 4}{x + 2} = x - 5$$

$$x^2 - 3x - 4 = x^2 - 3x - 10$$

$$-4 \neq -10$$

The oblique asymptote does not intersect $F(x)$.

Step 5:

Interval	$(-\infty, -2)$	$(-2, -1)$	$(-1, 4)$	$(4, \infty)$
Number Chosen	-3	-1.5	0	5
Value of F	$F(-3) = -14$	$F(-1.5) = 5.5$	$F(0) = -2$	$F(5) \approx 0.86$
Location of Graph	Below x-axis	Above x-axis	Below x-axis	Above x-axis
Point on Graph	$(-3, -14)$	$(-1.5, 5.5)$	$(0, -2)$	$(5, 0.86)$

447

Steps 6 & 7: Graphing:

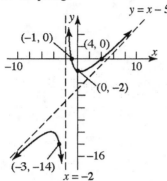

26. $F(x) = \dfrac{x^2 + 3x + 2}{x - 1} = \dfrac{(x+2)(x+1)}{x-1}$ $p(x) = x^2 + 3x + 2;$ $q(x) = x - 1;$ $n = 2;$ $m = 1$

Step 1: Domain: $\{x \mid x \neq 1\}$

The y-intercept is $F(0) = \dfrac{0^2 + 3(0) + 2}{0 - 1} = \dfrac{2}{-1} = -2$. Plot the point $(0, -2)$.

Step 2: $F(x) = \dfrac{x^2 + 3x + 2}{x - 1}$ is in lowest terms. The x-intercepts are the zeros of $p(x)$: -2 and -1.

Near -2, $F(x) \approx \dfrac{1}{3}(x+2)$; Near -1, $F(x) \approx -\dfrac{1}{2}(x+1)$.

Plot $(-2, 0)$ and indicate a line with positive slope there.

Plot $(-1, 0)$ and indicate a line with negative slope there.

Step 3: $F(x) = \dfrac{x^2 + 3x + 2}{x - 1}$ is in lowest terms. The vertical asymptote is the zero of $q(x)$: $x = 1$

Graph this asymptote using a dashed line.

Step 4: Since $n = m + 1$, there is an oblique asymptote. Dividing:

$$x - 1 \overline{)\,x^2 + 3x + 2\,} \quad F(x) = x + 4 + \dfrac{6}{x - 1}$$

$$\begin{array}{r} x + 4 \\ x-1 \overline{)\,x^2 + 3x + 2\,} \\ \underline{x^2 - x} \\ 4x + 2 \\ \underline{4x - 4} \\ 6 \end{array}$$

The oblique asymptote is $y = x + 4$. Graph this asymptote using a dashed line. Solve to find intersection points:

$$\dfrac{x^2 + 3x + 2}{x - 1} = x + 4$$

$$x^2 + 3x + 2 = x^2 + 3x - 4$$

$$2 \neq -4$$

The oblique asymptote does not intersect $F(x)$.

Step 5:

Interval	$(-\infty, -2)$	$(-2, -1)$	$(-1, 1)$	$(1, \infty)$
Number Chosen	-3	-1.5	0	2
Value of F	$F(-3) = -0.5$	$F(-1.5) = 0.1$	$F(0) = -2$	$F(2) = 12$
Location of Graph	Below x-axis	Above x-axis	Below x-axis	Above x-axis
Point on Graph	$(-3, -0.5)$	$(-1.5, 0.1)$	$(0, -2)$	$(2, 12)$

Steps 6 & 7: Graphing:

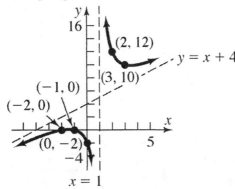

27. $R(x) = \dfrac{x^2 + x - 12}{x - 4} = \dfrac{(x+4)(x-3)}{x-4}$ $p(x) = x^2 + x - 12;\ q(x) = x - 4;\ n = 2;\ m = 1$

Step 1: Domain: $\{x \mid x \neq 4\}$

The y-intercept is $R(0) = \dfrac{0^2 + 0 - 12}{0 - 4} = \dfrac{-12}{-4} = 3$. Plot the point $(0, 3)$.

Step 2: $R(x) = \dfrac{x^2 + x - 12}{x - 4}$ is in lowest terms. The x-intercepts are the zeros of $p(x)$: -4 and 3.

Near -4, $R(x) \approx \dfrac{7}{8}(x + 4)$; Near 3, $R(x) \approx -7(x - 3)$.

Plot $(-4, 0)$ and indicate a line with positive slope there.

Plot $(3, 0)$ and indicate a line with negative slope there.

Step 3: $R(x) = \dfrac{x^2 + x - 12}{x - 4}$ is in lowest terms. The vertical asymptote is the zero of $q(x)$: $x = 4$

Graph this asymptote using a dashed line.

449

Step 4:   Since $n = m+1$, there is an oblique asymptote. Dividing:

$$x-4 \overline{)\begin{array}{r} x+5 \\ x^2 + x - 12 \end{array}} \qquad R(x) = x+5+\dfrac{8}{x-4}$$

$$\underline{x^2 - 4x}$$
$$5x - 12$$
$$\underline{5x - 20}$$
$$8$$

The oblique asymptote is $y = x+5$. Graph this asymptote using a dashed line. Solve to find intersection points:

$$\dfrac{x^2 + x - 12}{x-4} = x+5$$
$$x^2 + x - 12 = x^2 + x - 20$$
$$-12 \neq -20$$

The oblique asymptote does not intersect $R(x)$.

Step 5:

Interval	$(-\infty, -4)$	$(-4, 3)$	$(3, 4)$	$(4, \infty)$
Number Chosen	-5	0	3.5	5
Value of R	$R(-5) = -\frac{8}{9}$	$R(0) = 3$	$R(3.5) = -7.5$	$R(5) = 18$
Location of Graph	Below x-axis	Above x-axis	Below x-axis	Above x-axis
Point on Graph	$\left(-5, -\frac{8}{9}\right)$	$(0, 3)$	$(3.5, -7.5)$	$(5, 18)$

The number line markers: -4, 3, 4

Steps 6 & 7:   Graphing:

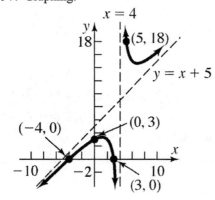

28. $R(x) = \dfrac{x^2 - x - 12}{x + 5} = \dfrac{(x-4)(x+3)}{x+5}$ $p(x) = x^2 - x - 12$; $q(x) = x + 5$; $n = 2$; $m = 1$

Step 1: Domain: $\{x \mid x \neq -5\}$

The y-intercept is $R(0) = \dfrac{0^2 - 0 - 12}{0 + 5} = -\dfrac{12}{5}$. Plot the point $\left(0, -\dfrac{12}{5}\right)$.

Step 2: $R(x) = \dfrac{x^2 - x - 12}{x + 5}$ is in lowest terms. The x-intercepts are the zeros of $p(x)$: -3 and 4.

Near -3, $R(x) \approx -\dfrac{7}{2}(x + 3)$; Near 4, $R(x) \approx \dfrac{7}{9}(x - 4)$.

Plot $(-3, 0)$ and indicate a line with negative slope there.

Plot $(4, 0)$ and indicate a line with positive slope there.

Step 3: $R(x) = \dfrac{x^2 - x - 12}{x + 5}$ is in lowest terms. The vertical asymptote is the zero of $q(x)$: $x = -5$.
Graph this asymptote using a dashed line.

Step 4: Since $n = m + 1$, there is an oblique asymptote. Dividing:

$$\begin{array}{r} x - 6 \\ x+5 \overline{)\ x^2 -\ \ x - 12} \\ \underline{x^2 + 5x} \\ -6x - 12 \\ \underline{-6x - 30} \\ 18 \end{array}$$ $R(x) = x - 6 + \dfrac{18}{x + 5}$

The oblique asymptote is $y = x - 6$. Graph this asymptote using a dashed line. Solve to find intersection points:

$\dfrac{x^2 - x - 12}{x + 5} = x - 6$

$x^2 - x - 12 = x^2 - x - 30$

$-12 \neq -30$

The oblique asymptote does not intersect $R(x)$.

Step 5:

Interval	$(-\infty, -5)$	$(-5, -3)$	$(-3, 4)$	$(4, \infty)$
Number Chosen	-7	-4	0	5
Value of R	$R(-7) = -22$	$R(-4) = 8$	$R(0) = -2.4$	$R(5) = 0.8$
Location of Graph	Below x-axis	Above x-axis	Below x-axis	Above x-axis
Point on Graph	$(-7, -22)$	$(-4, 8)$	$(0, -2.4)$	$(5, 0.8)$

451

Steps 6 & 7: Graphing:

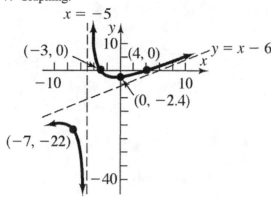

29. $F(x) = \dfrac{x^2 + x - 12}{x + 2} = \dfrac{(x+4)(x-3)}{x+2}$ $p(x) = x^2 + x - 12$; $q(x) = x + 2$; $n = 2$; $m = 1$

Step 1:   Domain: $\{x \mid x \neq -2\}$

The y-intercept is $F(0) = \dfrac{0^2 + 0 - 12}{0 + 2} = \dfrac{-12}{2} = -6$. Plot the point $(0, -6)$.

Step 2: $F(x) = \dfrac{x^2 + x - 12}{x + 2}$ is in lowest terms. The x-intercepts are the zeros of $p(x)$: -4 and 3.

Near -4, $F(x) \approx \dfrac{7}{2}(x+4)$; Near 3, $F(x) \approx \dfrac{7}{5}(x-3)$.

Plot $(-4, 0)$ and indicate a line with positive slope there.

Plot $(3, 0)$ and indicate a line with positive slope there.

Step 3: $F(x) = \dfrac{x^2 + x - 12}{x + 2}$ is in lowest terms. The vertical asymptote is the zero of $q(x)$: $x = -2$

Graph this asymptote using a dashed line.

Step 4:   Since $n = m + 1$, there is an oblique asymptote. Dividing:

$$\begin{array}{r} x - 1 \\ x+2\overline{)x^2 + \ \ x - 12} \\ \underline{x^2 + 2x} \\ -x - 12 \\ \underline{-x - 2} \\ -10 \end{array}$$

$F(x) = x - 1 + \dfrac{-10}{x + 2}$

The oblique asymptote is $y = x - 1$. Graph this asymptote using a dashed line. Solve to find intersection points:

$$\dfrac{x^2 + x - 12}{x + 2} = x - 1$$

$$x^2 + x - 12 = x^2 + x - 2$$

$$-12 \neq -2$$

The oblique asymptote does not intersect $F(x)$.

452

Step 5:

	-4	-2	3	
Interval	$(-\infty, -4)$	$(-4, -2)$	$(-2, 3)$	$(3, \infty)$
Number Chosen	-5	-3	0	4
Value of F	$F(-5) = -\frac{8}{3}$	$F(-3) = 6$	$F(0) = -6$	$F(4) = \frac{4}{3}$
Location of Graph	Below x-axis	Above x-axis	Below x-axis	Above x-axis
Point on Graph	$\left(-5, -\frac{8}{3}\right)$	$(-3, 6)$	$(0, -6)$	$\left(4, \frac{4}{3}\right)$

Steps 6 & 7: Graphing:

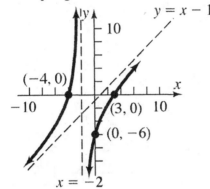

30. $G(x) = \dfrac{x^2 - x - 12}{x+1} = \dfrac{(x+3)(x-4)}{x+1}$ $p(x) = x^2 - x - 12;\ q(x) = x+1;\ n = 2;\ m = 1$

Step 1:   Domain: $\{x \mid x \neq -1\}$

The y-intercept is $F(0) = \dfrac{0^2 - 0 - 12}{0+1} = \dfrac{-12}{1} = -12$. Plot the point $(0, -12)$.

Step 2: $G(x) = \dfrac{x^2 - x - 12}{x+1}$ is in lowest terms. The x-intercepts are the zeros of $p(x)$: -3 and 4.

Near -3, $G(x) \approx \dfrac{7}{2}(x+3)$; Near 4, $G(x) \approx \dfrac{7}{5}(x-4)$.

Plot $(-3, 0)$ and indicate a line with positive slope there.

Plot $(4, 0)$ and indicate a line with positive slope there.

Step 3: $G(x) = \dfrac{x^2 - x - 12}{x+1}$ is in lowest terms. The vertical asymptote is the zero of $q(x)$: $x = -1$

Graph this asymptote using a dashed line.

453

Step 4: Since $n = m + 1$, there is an oblique asymptote. Dividing:

$$
\begin{array}{r}
x - 2 \\
x + 1 \overline{) x^2 - x - 12} \\
\underline{x^2 + x} \\
-2x - 12 \\
\underline{-2x - 2} \\
-10
\end{array}
\qquad G(x) = x - 2 + \dfrac{-10}{x + 1}
$$

The oblique asymptote is $y = x - 2$. Graph this asymptote using a dashed line. Solve to find intersection points:

$$\frac{x^2 - x - 12}{x + 1} = x - 2$$

$$x^2 - x - 12 = x^2 - x - 2$$

$$-12 \neq -2$$

The oblique asymptote does not intersect $G(x)$.

Step 5:

Interval	$(-\infty, -3)$	$(-3, -1)$	$(-1, 4)$	$(4, \infty)$
Number Chosen	-4	-2	0	5
Value of G	$G(-4) = -\frac{8}{3}$	$G(-2) = 6$	$G(0) = -12$	$G(5) = \frac{4}{3}$
Location of Graph	Below x-axis	Above x-axis	Below x-axis	Above x-axis
Point on Graph	$\left(-4, -\frac{8}{3}\right)$	$(-2, 6)$	$(0, -12)$	$\left(5, \frac{4}{3}\right)$

Steps 6 & 7: Graphing:

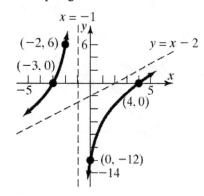

31. $R(x) = \dfrac{x(x-1)^2}{(x+3)^3}$ $\quad p(x) = x(x-1)^2;\ q(x) = (x+3)^3;\ n = 3;\ m = 3$

Step 1: Domain: $\left\{ x \mid x \neq -3 \right\}$

The y-intercept is $R(0) = \dfrac{0(0-1)^2}{(0+3)^3} = \dfrac{0}{27} = 0$. Plot the point $(0,0)$.

Step 2: $R(x) = \dfrac{x(x-1)^2}{(x+3)^3}$ is in lowest terms. The x-intercepts are the zeros of $p(x)$: 0 and 1

Near 0, $R(x) \approx \dfrac{1}{27}x$; Near 1, $R(x) \approx \dfrac{1}{64}(x-1)^2$.

Plot $(0,0)$ and indicate a line with positive slope there.

Plot $(1,0)$ and indicate a parabola that opens up there.

Step 3: $R(x) = \dfrac{x(x-1)^2}{(x+3)^3}$ is in lowest terms. The vertical asymptote is the zero of $q(x)$: $x = -3$

Graph this asymptote with a dashed line.

Step 4: Since $n = m$, the line $y = 1$ is the horizontal asymptote. Graph this asymptote with a dashed line.
Solve to find intersection points:

$$\frac{x(x-1)^2}{(x+3)^3} = 1$$

$$x^3 - 2x^2 + x = x^3 + 9x^2 + 27x + 27$$

$$0 = 11x^2 + 26x + 27$$

$$b^2 - 4ac = 26^2 - 4(11)(27) = -512$$

no real solution

$R(x)$ does not intersect $y = 1$.

Step 5:

Interval	$(-\infty, -3)$	$(-3, 0)$	$(0, 1)$	$(1, \infty)$
Number Chosen	-4	-1	$\frac{1}{2}$	2
Value of R	$R(-4) = 100$	$R(-1) = -0.5$	$R\left(\frac{1}{2}\right) \approx 0.003$	$R(2) = 0.016$
Location of Graph	Above x-axis	Below x-axis	Above x-axis	Above x-axis
Point on Graph	$(-4, 100)$	$(-1, -0.5)$	$\left(\frac{1}{2}, 0.003\right)$	$(2, 0.016)$

Steps 6 & 7: Graphing:

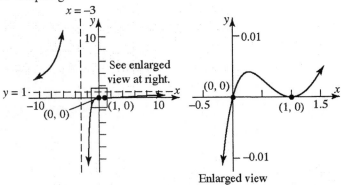

32. $R(x) = \dfrac{(x-1)(x+2)(x-3)}{x(x-4)^2}$ $p(x) = (x-1)(x+2)(x-3);$ $q(x) = x(x-4)^2;$ $n = 3;$ $m = 3$

Step 1:   Domain: $\{x \mid x \neq 0,\, x \neq 4\}$

There is no y-intercept since $R(0) = \dfrac{(0-1)(0+2)(0-3)}{0(0-4)^2} = \dfrac{6}{0}$.

Step 2: $R(x) = \dfrac{(x-1)(x+2)(x-3)}{x(x-4)^2}$ is in lowest terms. The x-intercepts are the zeros of $p(x)$: -2, 1, and 3

Near -2, $R(x) \approx -\dfrac{5}{24}(x+2)$; Near 1, $R(x) \approx -\dfrac{2}{3}(x-1)$; Near 3, $R(x) \approx \dfrac{10}{3}(x-3)$.

Plot $(-2, 0)$ and indicate a line with negative slope there. Plot $(1, 0)$ and indicate a line with negative slope there. Plot $(3, 0)$ and indicate a line with positive slope there.

Step 3: $R(x) = \dfrac{(x-1)(x+2)(x-3)}{x(x-4)^2}$ is in lowest terms.

The vertical asymptotes are the zeros of $q(x)$: $x = 0$ and $x = 4$
Graph each of these asymptotes with a dashed line.

Step 4:   Since $n = m$, the line $y = 1$ is the horizontal asymptote. Graph this asymptote with a dashed line.
Solve to find intersection points:

$$\dfrac{(x-1)(x+2)(x-3)}{x(x-4)^2} = 1$$

$$(x^2 + x - 2)(x-3) = x(x^2 - 8x + 16)$$

$$x^3 - 2x^2 - 5x + 6 = x^3 - 8x^2 + 16x$$

$$6x^2 - 21x + 6 = 0$$

$$2x^2 - 7x + 2 = 0$$

$$x = \dfrac{7 \pm \sqrt{49 - 4(2)(2)}}{2(2)} = \dfrac{7 \pm \sqrt{33}}{4}$$

$R(x)$ intersects $y = 1$ at $\left(\dfrac{7 - \sqrt{33}}{4}, 1\right)$ and $\left(\dfrac{7 + \sqrt{33}}{4}, 1\right)$.

Step 5:

Interval	$(-\infty, -2)$	$(-2, 0)$	$(0, 1)$	$(1, 3)$	$(3, 4)$	$(4, \infty)$
Number Chosen	-3	-1	$\frac{1}{2}$	2	3.186	6
Value of R	$R(-3) \approx 0.16$	$R(-1) = -0.32$	$R\left(\frac{1}{2}\right) \approx 0.51$	$R(2) = -0.5$	$R(3.186) \approx 1$	$R(6) = 5$
Location of Graph	Above x-axis	Below x-axis	Above x-axis	Below x-axis	Above x-axis	Above x-axis
Point on Graph	$(-3, 0.16)$	$(-1, -0.32)$	$\left(\frac{1}{2}, 0.51\right)$	$(2, -0.5)$	$(3.186, 1)$	$(6, 5)$

456

Steps 6 & 7: Graphing:

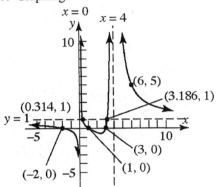

33. $R(x) = \dfrac{x^2 + x - 12}{x^2 - x - 6} = \dfrac{(x+4)(x-3)}{(x-3)(x+2)} = \dfrac{x+4}{x+2}$ $p(x) = x^2 + x - 12$; $q(x) = x^2 - x - 6$; $n = 2$; $m = 2$

Step 1: Domain: $\left\{ x \mid x \neq -2, \, x \neq 3 \right\}$

The y-intercept is $R(0) = \dfrac{0^2 + 0 - 12}{0^2 - 0 - 6} = \dfrac{-12}{-6} = 2$. Plot the point $(0,2)$.

Step 2: In lowest terms, $R(x) = \dfrac{x+4}{x+2}$, $x \neq 3$. Note: $R(x)$ is still undefined at both 3 and -2.

The x-intercept is the zero of $y = x + 4$: -4

Near -4, $R(x) \approx -\dfrac{1}{2}(x+4)$. Plot $(-4,0)$ and indicate a line with negative slope there.

Step 3: In lowest terms, $R(x) = \dfrac{x+4}{x+2}$, $x \neq 3$. The vertical asymptote is the zero of $f(x) = x + 2$: $x = -2$;

Graph this asymptote using a dashed line. Note: $x = 3$ is not a vertical asymptote because the reduced

form must be used to find the asymptotes. The graph has a hole at $\left(3, \dfrac{7}{5} \right)$.

Step 4: Since $n = m$, the line $y = 1$ is the horizontal asymptote. Graph this asymptote using a dashed line.
Solve to find intersection points:

$\dfrac{x^2 + x - 12}{x^2 - x - 6} = 1$

$x^2 + x - 12 = x^2 - x - 6$

$2x = 6$

$x = 3$

$R(x)$ does not intersect $y = 1$ because $R(x)$ is not defined at $x = 3$.

Step 5:

	-4	-2	3

Interval	$(-\infty, -4)$	$(-4, -2)$	$(-2, 3)$	$(3, \infty)$
Number Chosen	-5	-3	0	4
Value of R	$R(-5) = \frac{1}{3}$	$R(-3) = -1$	$R(0) = 2$	$R(4) = \frac{4}{3}$
Location of Graph	Above x-axis	Below x-axis	Above x-axis	Above x-axis
Point on Graph	$\left(-5, \frac{1}{3}\right)$	$(-3, -1)$	$(0, 2)$	$\left(4, \frac{4}{3}\right)$

Steps 6 & 7: Graphing:

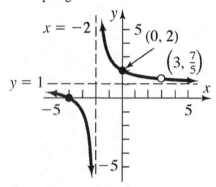

34. $R(x) = \dfrac{x^2 + 3x - 10}{x^2 + 8x + 15} = \dfrac{(x+5)(x-2)}{(x+5)(x+3)} = \dfrac{x-2}{x+3}$ $\quad p(x) = x^2 + 3x - 10; \quad q(x) = x^2 + 8x + 15; \quad n = 2; \; m = 2$

Step 1: Domain: $\left\{ x \mid x \neq -5, x \neq -3 \right\}$

The y-intercept is $R(0) = \dfrac{0^2 + 3(0) - 10}{0^2 + 8(0) + 15} = \dfrac{-10}{15} = -\dfrac{2}{3}$. Plot the point $\left(0, -\dfrac{2}{3}\right)$.

Step 2: In lowest terms, $R(x) = \dfrac{x-2}{x+3}$, $x \neq -5$. The x-intercept is the zero of $y = x - 2$: 2;

Note: -5 is not a zero because reduced form must be used to find the zeros.

Near 2, $R(x) \approx \dfrac{1}{5}(x-2)$. Plot the point $(2, 0)$ and indicate a line with positive slope there.

Step 3: In lowest terms, $R(x) = \dfrac{x-2}{x+3}$, $x \neq -5$. The vertical asymptote is the zero of $f(x) = x + 3$: $x = -3$;

Graph this asymptote using a dashed line.

Note: $x = -5$ is not a vertical asymptote because reduced form must be used to find the asymptotes.

The graph has a hole at $(-5, 3.5)$.

Step 4:   Since $n = m$, the line $y = 1$ is the horizontal asymptote. Graph this asymptote using a dashed line. Solve to find intersection points:

$$\frac{x^2 + 3x - 10}{x^2 + 8x + 15} = 1$$

$$x^2 + 3x - 10 = x^2 + 8x + 15$$

$$-5x = 25$$

$$x = -5$$

$R(x)$ does not intersect $y = 1$ because $R(x)$ is not defined at $x = -5$.

Step 5:

| | -5 | -3 | 2 |

Interval	$(-\infty, -5)$	$(-5, -3)$	$(-3, 2)$	$(2, \infty)$
Number Chosen	-6	-4	0	3
Value of R	$R(-6) = \frac{8}{3}$	$R(-4) = 6$	$R(0) = -\frac{2}{3}$	$R(3) = \frac{1}{6}$
Location of Graph	Above x-axis	Above x-axis	Below x-axis	Above x-axis
Point on Graph	$\left(-6, \frac{8}{3}\right)$	$(-4, 6)$	$\left(0, -\frac{2}{3}\right)$	$\left(3, \frac{1}{6}\right)$

Steps 6 & 7: Graphing:

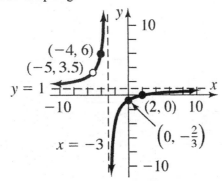

35. $R(x) = \dfrac{6x^2 - 7x - 3}{2x^2 - 7x + 6} = \dfrac{(3x+1)(2x-3)}{(2x-3)(x-2)} = \dfrac{3x+1}{x-2}$ $p(x) = 6x^2 - 7x - 3;$ $q(x) = 2x^2 - 7x + 6;$ $n = 2;$ $m = 2$

Step 1:   Domain: $\left\{ x \,\middle|\, x \neq \dfrac{3}{2},\ x \neq 2 \right\}$

The y-intercept is $R(0) = \dfrac{6(0)^2 - 7(0) - 3}{2(0)^2 - 7(0) + 6} = \dfrac{-3}{6} = -\dfrac{1}{2}$. Plot the point $\left(0, -\dfrac{1}{2}\right)$.

Step 2:   In lowest terms, $R(x) = \dfrac{3x+1}{x-2},\ x \neq \dfrac{3}{2}$. The x-intercept is the zero of $y = 3x + 1$: $-\dfrac{1}{3}$;

Note: $x = \dfrac{3}{2}$ is not a zero because reduced form must be used to find the zeros.

Near $-\dfrac{1}{3}$, $R(x) \approx -\dfrac{3}{7}(3x+1)$. Plot the point $\left(-\dfrac{1}{3}, 0\right)$ and indicate a line with negative slope there.

459

Step 3: In lowest terms, $R(x) = \dfrac{3x+1}{x-2}$, $x \neq \dfrac{3}{2}$. The vertical asymptote is the zero of $f(x) = x - 2$: $x = 2$; Graph this asymptote using a dashed line.

Note: $x = \dfrac{3}{2}$ is not a vertical asymptote because reduced form must be used to find the asymptotes.

The graph has a hole at $\left(\dfrac{3}{2}, -11\right)$.

Step 4: Since $n = m$, the line $y = 3$ is the horizontal asymptote. Graph this asymptote using a dashed line. Solve to find intersection points:

$$\frac{6x^2 - 7x - 3}{2x^2 - 7x + 6} = 3$$
$$6x^2 - 7x - 3 = 6x^2 - 21x + 18$$
$$14x = 21$$
$$x = \frac{3}{2}$$

$R(x)$ does not intersect $y = 3$ because $R(x)$ is not defined at $x = \dfrac{3}{2}$.

Step 5:

Interval	$\left(-\infty, -\frac{1}{3}\right)$	$\left(-\frac{1}{3}, \frac{3}{2}\right)$	$\left(\frac{3}{2}, 2\right)$	$(2, \infty)$
Number Chosen	-1	0	1.7	6
Value of R	$R(-1) = \frac{2}{3}$	$R(0) = -\frac{1}{2}$	$R(1.7) \approx -20.3$	$R(6) = 4.75$
Location of Graph	Above x-axis	Below x-axis	Below x-axis	Above x-axis
Point on Graph	$\left(-1, \frac{2}{3}\right)$	$\left(0, -\frac{1}{2}\right)$	$(1.7, -20.3)$	$(6, 4.75)$

Steps 6 & 7: Graphing:

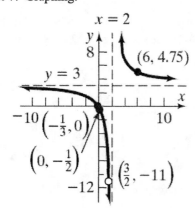

36. $R(x) = \dfrac{8x^2 + 26x + 15}{2x^2 - x - 15} = \dfrac{(4x+3)(2x+5)}{(2x+5)(x-3)} = \dfrac{4x+3}{x-3}$ $\quad p(x) = 8x^2 + 26x + 15; \quad q(x) = 2x^2 - x - 15; \quad n = 2; \quad m = 2$

Step 1: Domain: $\left\{ x \,\middle|\, x \ne -\dfrac{5}{2}, x \ne 3 \right\}$

The y-intercept is $R(0) = \dfrac{8(0)^2 + 26(0) + 15}{2(0)^2 - 0 - 15} = \dfrac{15}{-15} = -1$. Plot the point $(0, -1)$.

Step 2: In lowest terms, $R(x) = \dfrac{4x+3}{x-3}$, $x \ne -\dfrac{5}{2}$. The x-intercept is the zero of $y = 4x + 3$: $-\dfrac{3}{4}$;

Note: $-\dfrac{5}{2}$ is not a zero because reduced form must be used to find the zeros.

Near $-\dfrac{3}{4}$, $R(x) \approx -\dfrac{4}{15}(4x+3)$. Plot the point $\left(-\dfrac{3}{4}, 0\right)$ and indicate a line with negative slope there.

Step 3: In lowest terms, $R(x) = \dfrac{4x+3}{x-3}$, $x \ne -\dfrac{5}{2}$. The vertical asymptote is the zero of $f(x) = x - 3 : x = 3$;
Graph this asymptote using a dashed line.

Note: $x = -\dfrac{5}{2}$ is not a vertical asymptote because reduced form must be used to find the asymptotes.

The graph has a hole at $\left(-\dfrac{5}{2}, \dfrac{14}{11}\right)$.

Step 4: Since $n = m$, the line $y = 4$ is the horizontal asymptote. Graph this asymptote using a dashed line.
Solve to find intersection points:

$$\frac{8x^2 + 26x + 15}{2x^2 - x - 15} = 4$$
$$8x^2 + 26x + 15 = 8x^2 - 4x - 60$$
$$30x = -75$$
$$x = -\frac{5}{2}$$

$R(x)$ does not intersect $y = 4$ because $R(x)$ is not defined at $x = -\dfrac{5}{2}$.

Step 5:

Interval	$(-\infty, -2.5)$	$\left(-2.5, -\frac{3}{4}\right)$	$\left(-\frac{3}{4}, 3\right)$	$(3, \infty)$
Number Chosen	-3	-1	0	6
Value of R	$R(-3) = \frac{3}{2}$	$R(-1) = \frac{1}{4}$	$R(0) = -1$	$R(6) = 9$
Location of Graph	Above x-axis	Above x-axis	Below x-axis	Above x-axis
Point on Graph	$\left(-3, \frac{3}{2}\right)$	$\left(-1, \frac{1}{4}\right)$	$(0, -1)$	$(6, 9)$

Steps 6 & 7: Graphing:

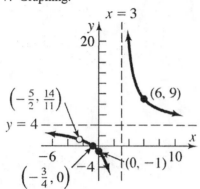

37. $R(x) = \dfrac{x^2 + 5x + 6}{x+3} = \dfrac{(x+2)(x+3)}{x+3} = x+2$ $p(x) = x^2 + 5x + 6; \quad q(x) = x+3; \quad n = 2; \quad m = 1$

Step 1: Domain: $\{x \mid x \neq -3\}$

The y-intercept is $R(0) = \dfrac{0^2 + 5(0) + 6}{0+3} = \dfrac{6}{3} = 2$. Plot the point $(0,2)$.

Step 2: In lowest terms, $R(x) = x+2, \; x \neq -3$. The x-intercept is the zero of $y = x+2$: -2;
Note: -3 is not a zero because reduced form must be used to find the zeros.
Near -2, $R(x) = x+2$. Plot the point $(0,-2)$ and indicate the line $y = x+2$ there.

Step 3: In lowest terms, $R(x) = x+2, \; x \neq -3$. There are no vertical asymptotes. Note: $x = -3$ is not a vertical asymptote because reduced form must be used to find the asymptotes. The graph has a hole at $(-3,-1)$.

Step 4: Since $n = m+1$ there is an oblique asymptote. The line $y = x+2$ is the oblique asymptote. Solve to find intersection points:

$$\dfrac{x^2 + 5x + 6}{x+3} = x+2$$

$$x^2 + 5x + 6 = (x+2)(x+3)$$

$$x^2 + 5x + 6 = x^2 + 5x + 6$$

$$0 = 0$$

The oblique asymptote intersects $R(x)$ at every point of the form $(x, x+2)$ except $(-3, -1)$.

Step 5:

Interval	$(-\infty, -3)$	$(-3, -2)$	$(-2, \infty)$
Number Chosen	-4	-2.5	0
Value of R	$R(-4) = -2$	$R(-2.5) = -\frac{1}{2}$	$R(0) = 2$
Location of Graph	Below x-axis	Below x-axis	Above x-axis
Point on Graph	$(-4, -2)$	$\left(-2.5, -\frac{1}{2}\right)$	$(0, 2)$

462

Steps 6 & 7: Graphing:

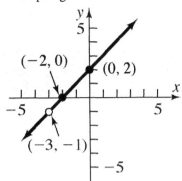

38. $R(x) = \dfrac{x^2 + x - 30}{x+6} = \dfrac{(x+6)(x-5)}{x+6} = x - 5$ $p(x) = x^2 + x - 30;$ $q(x) = x + 6;$ $n = 2;$ $m = 1$

Step 1:   Domain: $\{x \mid x \neq -6\}$

   The y-intercept is $R(0) = \dfrac{0^2 + (0) - 30}{0+6} = \dfrac{-30}{6} = -5$. Plot the point $(0, -5)$.

Step 2:   In lowest terms, $R(x) = x - 5$, $x \neq -6$. The x-intercept is the zero of $y = x - 5 : 5$;
   Note: -6 is not a zero because reduced form must be used to find the zeros.
   Near 5, $R(x) = x - 5$. Plot the point $(5, 0)$ and indicate the line $y = x - 5$ there.

Step 3:   In lowest terms, $R(x) = x - 5$, $x \neq -6$. There are no vertical asymptotes. Note: $x = -6$ is not a vertical
   asymptote because reduced form must be used to find the asymptotes. The graph has a hole at
   $(-6, -11)$.

Step 4:   Since $n = m + 1$ there is an oblique asymptote. The line $y = x - 5$ is the oblique asymptote.
   Solve to find intersection points:
   $$\dfrac{x^2 + x - 30}{x+6} = x - 5$$
   $$x^2 + x - 30 = (x+6)(x-5)$$
   $$x^2 + x - 30 = x^2 + x - 30$$
   $$0 = 0$$
   The oblique asymptote intersects $R(x)$ at every point of the form $(x, x-5)$ except $(-6, -11)$.

Step 5:

Interval	$(-\infty, -6)$	$(-6, 5)$	$(5, \infty)$
Number Chosen	-7	0	6
Value of R	$R(-7) = -12$	$R(0) = -5$	$R(6) = 1$
Location of Graph	Below x-axis	Below x-axis	Above x-axis
Point on Graph	$(-7, -12)$	$(0, -5)$	$(6, 1)$

463

Steps 6 & 7: Graphing:

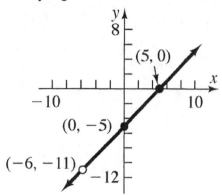

39. $f(x) = x + \dfrac{1}{x} = \dfrac{x^2 + 1}{x}$ $p(x) = x^2 + 1$; $q(x) = x$; $n = 2$; $m = 1$

Step 1:   Domain: $\{x \mid x \neq 0\}$

There is no y-intercept because 0 is not in the domain.

Step 2: $f(x) = \dfrac{x^2 + 1}{x}$ is in lowest terms. There are no x-intercepts since $x^2 + 1 = 0$ has no real solutions.

Step 3: $f(x) = \dfrac{x^2 + 1}{x}$ is in lowest terms. The vertical asymptote is the zero of $q(x)$: $x = 0$ Graph this asymptote using a dashed line.

Step 4:   Since $n = m + 1$, there is an oblique asymptote.

Dividing: $x \overline{\smash{\big)}\, x^2 + 1}$ with quotient x $f(x) = x + \dfrac{1}{x}$

$\dfrac{x^2}{}$

1

The oblique asymptote is $y = x$.

Graph this asymptote using a dashed line. Solve to find intersection points:

$$\frac{x^2 + 1}{x} = x$$
$$x^2 + 1 = x^2$$
$$1 \neq 0$$

The oblique asymptote does not intersect $f(x)$.

Step 5:

$$0$$

Interval	$(-\infty, 0)$	$(0, \infty)$
Number Chosen	-1	1
Value of f	$f(-1) = -2$	$f(1) = 2$
Location of Graph	Below x-axis	Above x-axis
Point on Graph	$(-1, -2)$	$(1, 2)$

Steps 6 & 7: Graphing :

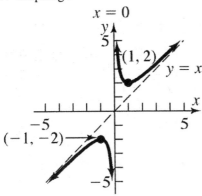

40. $f(x) = 2x + \dfrac{9}{x} = \dfrac{2x^2 + 9}{x}$ $p(x) = 2x^2 + 9$; $q(x) = x$; $n = 2$; $m = 1$

Step 1: Domain: $\left\{ x \mid x \neq 0 \right\}$

There is no y-intercept because 0 is not in the domain.

Step 2: $f(x) = \dfrac{2x^2 + 9}{x}$ is in lowest terms. There are no x-intercepts since $2x^2 + 9 = 0$ has no real solutions.

Step 3: $f(x) = \dfrac{2x^2 + 9}{x}$ is in lowest terms. The vertical asymptote is the zero of $q(x)$: $x = 0$

Graph this asymptote using a dashed line.

Step 4: Since $n = m + 1$, there is an oblique asymptote. Dividing:

$$x \overline{\smash{\big)}\, 2x^2 + 9} \quad \begin{array}{c} 2x \\ \end{array}$$
$$\underline{2x^2}$$
$$9$$

$f(x) = 2x + \dfrac{9}{x}$

The oblique asymptote is $y = 2x$. Graph this asymptote using a dashed line. Solve to find intersection points:

$$\dfrac{2x^2 + 9}{x} = 2x$$
$$2x^2 + 9 = 2x^2$$
$$9 \neq 0$$

The oblique asymptote does not intersect $f(x)$.

Step 5:

Interval	$(-\infty, 0)$	$(0, \infty)$
Number Chosen	-1	1
Value of f	$f(-1) = -11$	$f(1) = 11$
Location of Graph	Below x-axis	Above x-axis
Point on Graph	$(-1, -11)$	$(1, 11)$

Steps 6 & 7: Graphing:

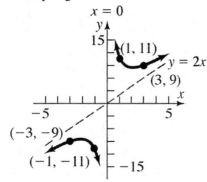

41. $f(x) = x^2 + \dfrac{1}{x} = \dfrac{x^3 + 1}{x} = \dfrac{(x+1)(x^2 - x + 1)}{x}$ $p(x) = x^3 + 1;\ q(x) = x;\ n = 3;\ m = 1.$

Step 1: Domain: $\{x \mid x \neq 0\}$

There is no y-intercept because 0 is not in the domain.

Step 2: $f(x) = \dfrac{x^3 + 1}{x}$ is in lowest terms. The x-intercept is the zero of $p(x)$: -1

Near -1, $f(x) \approx -3(x + 1)$. Plot the point $(-1, 0)$ and indicate a line with negative slope there.

Step 3: $f(x) = \dfrac{x^3 + 1}{x}$ is in lowest terms. The vertical asymptote is the zero of $q(x)$: $x = 0$

Graph this asymptote using a dashed line.

Step 4: Since $n > m + 1$, there is no horizontal or oblique asymptote.

Step 5:

Interval	$(-\infty, -1)$	$(-1, 0)$	$(0, \infty)$
Number Chosen	-2	$-\frac{1}{2}$	1
Value of f	$f(-2) = 3.5$	$f\left(-\frac{1}{2}\right) = -1.75$	$f(1) = 2$
Location of Graph	Above x-axis	Below x-axis	Above x-axis
Point on Graph	$(-2, 3.5)$	$\left(-\frac{1}{2}, -1.75\right)$	$(1, 2)$

466

Steps 6 & 7: Graphing:

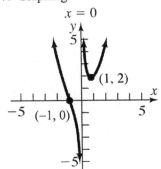

$x = 0$

(1, 2)

-5 (−1, 0)

42. $f(x) = 2x^2 + \dfrac{16}{x} = \dfrac{2x^3 + 16}{x} = \dfrac{2(x^3 + 8)}{x} = \dfrac{2(x+2)(x^2 - 2x + 4)}{x}$ $\quad p(x) = 2x^3 + 16; \ q(x) = x; \ n = 3; \ m = 1$

Step 1: Domain: $\{x \mid x \ne 0\}$

There is no y-intercept because 0 is not in the domain.

Step 2: $f(x) = \dfrac{2x^3 + 16}{x}$ is in lowest terms. The x-intercept is the zero of $p(x)$: -2

Near -2, $f(x) \approx -12(x+2)$. Plot $(-2, 0)$ and indicate a line with negative slope there.

Step 3: $f(x) = \dfrac{2x^3 + 16}{x}$ is in lowest terms. The vertical asymptote is the zero of $q(x)$: $x = 0$

Graph this asymptote using a dashed line.

Step 4: Since $n > m + 1$, there is no horizontal or oblique asymptote.

Step 5:

$-2 \qquad 0$

Interval	$(-\infty, -2)$	$(-2, 0)$	$(0, \infty)$
Number Chosen	-3	-1	1
Value of f	$f(-3) = \dfrac{38}{3}$	$f(-1) = -14$	$f(1) = 18$
Location of Graph	Above x-axis	Below x-axis	Above x-axis
Point on Graph	$\left(-3, \dfrac{38}{3}\right)$	$(-1, -14)$	$(1, 18)$

Steps 6 & 7: Graphing:

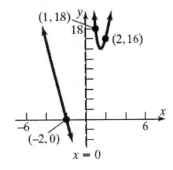

(1, 18)

18

(2, 16)

-6

6

(−2, 0)

$x = 0$

467

43. $f(x) = x + \dfrac{1}{x^3} = \dfrac{x^4 + 1}{x^3}$ $p(x) = x^4 + 1;$ $q(x) = x^3;$ $n = 4;$ $m = 3$

Step 1:   Domain: $\{x \mid x \neq 0\}$

There is no y-intercept because 0 is not in the domain.

Step 2: $f(x) = \dfrac{x^4 + 1}{x^3}$ is in lowest terms. There are no x-intercepts since $x^4 + 1 = 0$ has no real solutions.

Step 3: $f(x) = \dfrac{x^4 + 1}{x^3}$ is in lowest terms. The vertical asymptote is the zero of $q(x)$: $x = 0$

Graph this asymptote using a dashed line.

Step 4:   Since $n = m + 1$, there is an oblique asymptote. Dividing:

$$\begin{array}{r} x \\ x^3 \overline{)\, x^4 + 1} \\ \underline{x^4} \\ 1 \end{array}$$

$$f(x) = x + \dfrac{1}{x^3}$$

The oblique asymptote is $y = x$. Graph this asymptote using a dashed line. Solve to find intersection points:

$$\dfrac{x^4 + 1}{x^3} = x$$
$$x^4 + 1 = x^4$$
$$1 \neq 0$$

The oblique asymptote does not intersect $f(x)$.

Step 5:

	0	

Interval	$(-\infty, 0)$	$(0, \infty)$
Number Chosen	-1	1
Value of f	$f(-1) = -2$	$f(1) = 2$
Location of Graph	Below x-axis	Above x-axis
Point on Graph	$(-1, -2)$	$(1, 2)$

Steps 6 & 7: Graphing:

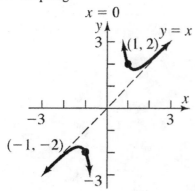

468

44. $f(x) = 2x + \dfrac{9}{x^3} = \dfrac{2x^4 + 9}{x^3}$ $p(x) = 2x^4 + 9;$ $q(x) = x^3;$ $n = 4;$ $m = 3$

Step 1: Domain: $\{x \mid x \neq 0\}$

There is no *y*-intercept because 0 is not in the domain.

Step 2: $f(x) = \dfrac{2x^4 + 9}{x^3}$ is in lowest terms. There are no *x*-intercepts since $2x^4 + 9 = 0$ has no real solutions.

Step 3: $f(x) = \dfrac{2x^4 + 9}{x^3}$ is in lowest terms. The vertical asymptote is the zero of $q(x)$: $x = 0$

Graph this asymptote using a dashed line.

Step 4: Since $n = m + 1$, there is an oblique asymptote. Dividing:

$$\begin{array}{r} 2x \\ x^3 \overline{\smash{\big)}\, 2x^4 + 9} \\ \underline{2x^4} \\ 9 \end{array} \qquad\qquad f(x) = 2x + \dfrac{9}{x^3}$$

The oblique asymptote is $y = 2x$. Graph this asymptote using a dashed line. Solve to find intersection points:

$$\dfrac{2x^4 + 9}{x^3} = 2x$$

$$2x^4 + 9 = 2x^4$$

$$9 \neq 0$$

The oblique asymptote does not intersect $f(x)$.

Step 5:

Interval	$(-\infty, 0)$	$(0, \infty)$
Number Chosen	-2	2
Value of f	$f(-2) = -5.125$	$f(2) = 5.125$
Location of Graph	Below *x*-axis	Above *x*-axis
Point on Graph	(-2, -5.125)	(2, 5.125)

Steps 6 & 7: Graphing:

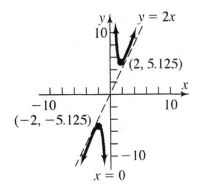

469

45. One possibility: $R(x) = \dfrac{x^2}{x^2 - 4}$

46. One possibility: $R(x) = \dfrac{-x}{x^2 - 1}$

47. One possibility: $R(x) = \dfrac{(x-1)(x-3)(x^2+a)}{(x+1)^2(x-2)^2}$

(Using the point $(0,1)$ leads to $a = 4/3$.)

48. One possibility: $R(x) = \dfrac{3(x+2)(x-1)^2}{(x+3)(x-4)^2}$

49. a. The degree of the numerator is 1 and the degree of the denominator is 2.
Thus, the horizontal asymptote is $y = 0$.
The concentration of the drug decreases to 0 as time increases.

b. Graphing:

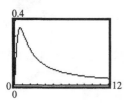

c. Using MAXIMUM, the concentration is highest when $t \approx 0.71$ hours.

50. a. The degree of the numerator is 1 and the degree of the denominator is 2. Thus, the horizontal asymptote is $y = 0$. The concentration of the drug decreases to 0 as time increases.

b. Graphing:

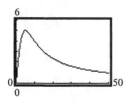

c. Using MAXIMUM, the concentration is highest when $t = 5$ minutes.

51. a. The cost of the project is the sum of the cost for the parallel side, the two other sides, and the posts.

$A = xy$

$1000 = xy$

$y = \dfrac{1000}{x}$

If the length of a perpendicular side is x feet, the length of the parallel side is $y = \dfrac{1000}{x}$ feet. Thus,

$$C(x) = 2 \cdot 8 \cdot x + 5 \cdot \dfrac{1000}{x} + 4(25)$$

$$= 16x + \dfrac{5000}{x} + 100$$

b. The domain is $x > 0$. Note that x is a length so it cannot be negative. In addition, if $x = 0$, there is no rectangle (that is, the area is 0 square feet).

c. $C(x) = 16x + \dfrac{5000}{x} + 100$

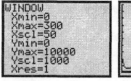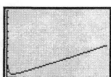

d. Using MINIMUM, the dimensions of cheapest cost are about 17.7 feet by 56.6 feet (longer side parallel to river).

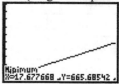

Note: $x = 17\dfrac{2}{3} = \dfrac{53}{3}$ feet and

$y = \dfrac{1000}{53/3} = \dfrac{3000}{53}$ feet.

52. a. $f'(v_s) = 600\left(\dfrac{772.4 - 45}{772.4 - v_s}\right) = 600\left(\dfrac{727.4}{772.4 - v_s}\right)$

$= \dfrac{436,440}{772.4 - v_s}$

b. $620 = \dfrac{436,440}{772.4 - v_s}$

$620(772.4 - v_s) = 436,440$

$772.4 - v_s = \dfrac{436,440}{620}$

$v_s = 772.4 - \dfrac{436,440}{620} \approx 68.5$

If $f' = 620$ Hz, the speed of the ambulance is roughly 68.5 miles per hour.

c. $y = \dfrac{436,440}{772.4 - x}$

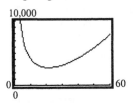

d. Let $Y_1 = \dfrac{436,440}{772.4 - x}$ and $Y_2 = 620$, then find the intersection point.

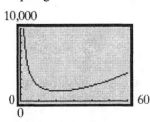

The graph agrees with our direct calculation.

53. a. The surface area is the sum of the areas of the six sides.

$S = xy + xy + xy + xy + x^2 + x^2 = 4xy + 2x^2$

The volume is

$x \cdot x \cdot y = x^2 y = 10,000 \quad \Rightarrow \quad y = \dfrac{10,000}{x^2}$

Thus, $S(x) = 4x\left(\dfrac{10,000}{x^2}\right) + 2x^2$

$= 2x^2 + \dfrac{40,000}{x}$

$= \dfrac{2x^3 + 40,000}{x}$

b. Graphing:

c. Using MINIMUM, the minimum surface area (amount of cardboard) is about 2785 square inches.

d. The surface area is a minimum when $x \approx 21.54$ inches.

$y = \dfrac{10,000}{(21.544)^2} \approx 21.54$ inches

The dimensions of the box are: 21.54 in. by 21.54 in. by 21.54 in.

e. Answers will vary. One possibility is to save costs or reduce weight by minimizing the material needed to construct the box.

54. a. The surface area is the sum of the areas of the five sides.

$S = xy + xy + xy + xy + x^2 = 4xy + x^2$

The volume is

$x \cdot x \cdot y = x^2 y = 5000 \quad \Rightarrow \quad y = \dfrac{5000}{x^2}$

Thus, $S(x) = 4x\left(\dfrac{5000}{x^2}\right) + x^2$

$= x^2 + \dfrac{20,000}{x} = \dfrac{x^3 + 20,000}{x}$

b. Graphing:

c. Using MINIMUM, the minimum surface area (amount of cardboard) is about 1392.48 square inches.

d. The surface area is a minimum when $x = 21.54$.

$y = \dfrac{5000}{(21.54)^2} \approx 10.78$

The dimensions of the box are: 21.54 in. by 21.54 in. by 10.78 in.

e. Answers will vary. One possibility is to save costs or reduce weight by minimizing the material needed to construct the box.

55. a. $500 = \pi r^2 h \Rightarrow h = \dfrac{500}{\pi r^2}$

$C(r) = 6(2\pi r^2) + 4(2\pi rh)$

$= 12\pi r^2 + 8\pi r\left(\dfrac{500}{\pi r^2}\right)$

$= 12\pi r^2 + \dfrac{4000}{r}$

b. Graphing:

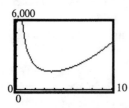

Using MINIMUM, the cost is least for $r \approx 3.76$ cm.

56. a. $100 = \pi r^2 h \Rightarrow h = \dfrac{100}{\pi r^2}$

$A(r) = 2\pi r^2 + 2\pi rh$

$= 2\pi r^2 + 2\pi r\left(\dfrac{100}{\pi r^2}\right)$

$= 2\pi r^2 + \dfrac{200}{r}$

b. $A(3) = 2\pi \cdot 3^2 + \dfrac{200}{3}$

$= 18\pi + \dfrac{200}{3} \approx 123.22$ square feet

c. $A(4) = 2\pi \cdot 4^2 + \dfrac{200}{4}$

$= 32\pi + 50 \approx 150.53$ square feet

d. $A(5) = 2\pi \cdot 5^2 + \dfrac{200}{5}$

$= 50\pi + 40 \approx 197.08$ square feet

e. Graphing:

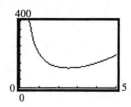

Using MINIMUM, the area is smallest when $r \approx 2.52$ feet.

57. $y = \dfrac{x^2 - 1}{x - 1}$

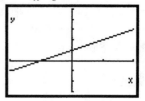

$y = \dfrac{x^3 - 1}{x - 1}$

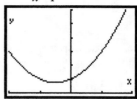

$y = \dfrac{x^4 - 1}{x - 1}$

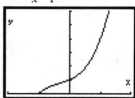

$y = \dfrac{x^5 - 1}{x - 1}$

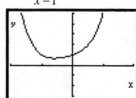

$x = 1$ is not a vertical asymptote because of the following behavior:
When $x \neq 1$:

$y = \dfrac{x^2 - 1}{x - 1} = \dfrac{(x+1)(x-1)}{x - 1} = x + 1$

$$y = \frac{x^3 - 1}{x - 1} = \frac{(x-1)(x^2 + x + 1)}{x - 1} = x^2 + x + 1$$

$$y = \frac{x^4 - 1}{x - 1} = \frac{(x^2 + 1)(x^2 - 1)}{x - 1}$$

$$= \frac{(x^2 + 1)(x - 1)(x + 1)}{x - 1}$$

$$= x^3 + x^2 + x + 1$$

$$y = \frac{x^5 - 1}{x - 1} = \frac{(x^4 + x^3 + x^2 + x + 1)(x - 1)}{x - 1}$$

$$= x^4 + x^3 + x^2 + x + 1$$

In general, the graph of

$$y = \frac{x^n - 1}{x - 1}, \ n \geq 1, \text{ an integer, will have a}$$

"hole" with coordinates $(1, n)$.

58. $y = \dfrac{x^2}{x - 1}$

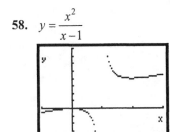

$y = \dfrac{x^4}{x - 1}$

$y = \dfrac{x^6}{x - 1}$

$y = \dfrac{x^8}{x - 1}$

All four graphs have a vertical asymptote at

$x = 1$. $y = \dfrac{x^2}{x - 1}$ has an oblique asymptote at

$y = x + 1$.

59. Answers will vary.

60. Answers will vary, one example is

$$R(x) = \frac{3(x - 2)(x + 1)^2}{(x + 5)(x - 6)^2}.$$

61. Answers will vary, one example is

$$R(x) = \frac{2(x - 3)(x + 2)^2}{(x - 1)^3}.$$

62. Answers will vary.

Section 5.4

1. $3 - 4x > 5$

$-4x > 2$

$x < -\dfrac{1}{2}$

$\{x \mid x < -\dfrac{1}{2}\}$

2. False; the first step would be to add 4 to both sides of the inequality yielding $x^2 + 4x + 4 \geq 0$.

473

3. $(x-5)^2(x+2) < 0$

$f(x) = (x-5)^2(x+2)$

$x = 5, x = -2$ are the zeros of f.

Interval	$(-\infty, -2)$	$(-2, 5)$	$(5, \infty)$
Number Chosen	-3	0	6
Value of f	-64	50	8
Conclusion	Negative	Positive	Positive

The solution set is $\{x \mid x < -2\}$, or, using interval notation, $(-\infty, -2)$.

4. $(x-5)(x+2)^2 > 0$

$f(x) = (x-5)(x+2)^2$

$x = 5, x = -2$ are the zeros of f.

Interval	$(-\infty, -2)$	$(-2, 5)$	$(5, \infty)$
Number Chosen	-3	0	6
Value of f	-8	-20	64
Conclusion	Negative	Negative	Positive

The solution set is $\{x \mid x > 5\}$, or, using interval notation, $(5, \infty)$.

5. $x^3 - 4x^2 > 0$

$x^2(x-4) > 0$

$f(x) = x^3 - 4x^2 = x^2(x-4)$

$x = 0, x = 4$ are the zeros of f.

Interval	$(-\infty, 0)$	$(0, 4)$	$(4, \infty)$
Number Chosen	-1	1	5
Value of f	-5	-3	25
Conclusion	Negative	Negative	Positive

The solution set is $\{x \mid x > 4\}$, or, using interval notation, $(4, \infty)$.

6. $x^3 + 8x^2 < 0$

$x^2(x+8) < 0$

$f(x) = x^3 + 8x^2 = x^2(x+8)$

$x = -8, x = 0$ are the zeros of f.

Interval	$(-\infty, -8)$	$(-8, 0)$	$(0, \infty)$
Number Chosen	-9	-1	1
Value of f	-81	7	9
Conclusion	Negative	Positive	Positive

The solution set is $\{x \mid x < -8\}$, or, using interval notation, $(-\infty, -8)$.

7. $x^3 - 9x \le 0$

$x(x-3)(x+3) \le 0$

$f(x) = x^3 - 9x$

$x = -3, x = 0, x = 3$ are the zeros of f.

Interval	$(-\infty, -3)$	$(-3, 0)$	$(0, 3)$	$(3, \infty)$
Number Chosen	-4	-1	1	4
Value of f	-28	8	-8	28
Conclusion	Negative	Positive	Negative	Positive

The solution set is $\{x \mid x \le -3 \text{ or } 0 \le x \le 3\}$, or, using interval notation, $(-\infty, -3]$ or $[0, 3]$.

8. $x^3 - x \ge 0$

$x(x-1)(x+1) \ge 0$

$f(x) = x^3 - x$

$x = -1, x = 0, x = 1$ are the zeros of f.

Interval	$(-\infty, -1)$	$(-1, 0)$	$(0, 1)$	$(1, \infty)$
Number Chosen	-2	$-\dfrac{1}{2}$	$\dfrac{1}{2}$	2
Value of f	-6	0.375	-0.375	6
Conclusion	Negative	Positive	Negative	Positive

The solution set is $\{x \mid -1 \le x \le 0 \text{ or } x \ge 1\}$, or, using interval notation, $[-1, 0]$ or $[1, \infty)$.

9.
$$2x^3 > -8x^2$$
$$2x^3 + 8x^2 > 0$$
$$2x^2(x+4) > 0$$
$$f(x) = 2x^3 + 8x^2$$
$x = 0, x = -4$ are the zeros of f.

Interval	$(-\infty, -4)$	$(-4, 0)$	$(0, \infty)$
Number Chosen	-5	-1	1
Value of f	-50	6	10
Conclusion	Negative	Positive	Positive

The solution set is $\{x \mid -4 < x < 0 \text{ or } x > 0\}$, or, using interval notation, $(-4, 0)$ or $(0, \infty)$.

10.
$$3x^3 < -15x^2$$
$$3x^3 + 15x^2 < 0$$
$$3x^2(x+5) < 0$$
$$f(x) = 3x^3 + 15x^2$$
$x = 0, x = -5$ are the zeros of f.

Interval	$(-\infty, -5)$	$(-5, 0)$	$(0, \infty)$
Number Chosen	-6	-1	1
Value of f	-108	12	18
Conclusion	Negative	Positive	Positive

The solution set is $\{x \mid x < -5\}$, or, using interval notation, $(-\infty, -5)$.

11. $(x-1)\left(x^2 + x + 4\right) \geq 0$
$$f(x) = (x-1)\left(x^2 + x + 4\right)$$
$x = 1$ is the zero of f. $x^2 + x + 4 = 0$ has no real solution.

Interval	$(-\infty, 1)$	$(1, \infty)$
Number Chosen	0	2
Value of f	-4	10
Conclusion	Negative	Positive

The solution set is $\{x \mid x \geq 1\}$, or, using interval notation, $[1, \infty)$.

12. $(x+2)\left(x^2 - x + 1\right) \geq 0$
$$f(x) = (x+2)\left(x^2 - x + 1\right)$$
$x = -2$ is the zero of f; $x^2 - x + 1 = 0$ has no real solution.

Interval	$(-\infty, -2)$	$(-2, \infty)$
Number Chosen	-3	0
Value of f	-13	2
Conclusion	Negative	Positive

The solution set is $\{x \mid x \geq -2\}$, or, using interval notation, $[-2, \infty)$.

13. $(x-1)(x-2)(x-3) \leq 0$
$$f(x) = (x-1)(x-2)(x-3)$$
$x = 1, x = 2, x = 3$ are the zeros of f.

Interval	$(-\infty, 1)$	$(1, 2)$	$(2, 3)$	$(3, \infty)$
Number Chosen	0	1.5	2.5	4
Value of f	-6	0.375	-0.375	6
Conclusion	Negative	Positive	Negative	Positive

The solution set is $\{x \mid x \leq 1 \text{ or } 2 \leq x \leq 3\}$, or, using interval notation, $(-\infty, 1]$ or $[2, 3]$.

14. $(x+1)(x+2)(x+3) \leq 0$
$$f(x) = (x+1)(x+2)(x+3)$$
$x = -1, x = -2, x = -3$ are the zeros of f.

Interval	$(-\infty, -3)$	$(-3, -2)$	$(-2, -1)$	$(-1, \infty)$
Number Chosen	-4	-2.5	-1.5	0
Value of f	-6	0.375	-0.375	6
Conclusion	Negative	Positive	Negative	Positive

The solution set is $\{x \mid x \leq -3 \text{ or } -2 \leq x \leq -1\}$, or, using interval notation, $(-\infty, -3]$ or $[-2, -1]$.

15. $x^3 - 2x^2 - 3x > 0$

$x(x^2 - 2x - 3) > 0$

$x(x+1)(x-3) > 0$

$f(x) = x^3 - 2x^2 - 3x$

$x = -1, x = 0, x = 3$ are the zeros of f.

Interval	$(-\infty, -1)$	$(-1, 0)$	$(0, 3)$	$(3, \infty)$
Number Chosen	-2	-0.5	1	4
Value of f	-10	0.875	-4	20
Conclusion	Negative	Positive	Negative	Positive

The solution set is $\{x \mid -1 < x < 0 \text{ or } x > 3\}$, or, using interval notation, $(-1, 0)$ or $(3, \infty)$.

16. $x^3 + 2x^2 - 3x > 0$

$x(x^2 + 2x - 3) > 0$

$x(x+3)(x-1) > 0$

$f(x) = x(x+3)(x-1)$

$x = 0, x = -3, x = 1$ are the zeros of f

Interval	$(-\infty, -3)$	$(-3, 0)$	$(0, 1)$	$(1, \infty)$
Number Chosen	-4	-1	0.5	2
Value of f	-20	4	-0.875	10
Conclusion	Negative	Positive	Negative	Positive

The solution set is $\{x \mid -3 < x < 0 \text{ or } x > 1\}$, or, using interval notation, $(-3, 0)$ or $(1, \infty)$.

17. $x^4 > x^2$

$x^4 - x^2 > 0$

$x^2(x^2 - 1) > 0$

$x^2(x-1)(x+1) > 0$

$f(x) = x^2(x-1)(x+1)$

$x = -1, x = 0, x = 1$ are the zeros of f

Interval	$(-\infty, -1)$	$(-1, 0)$	$(0, 1)$	$(1, \infty)$
Number Chosen	-2	-0.5	0.5	2
Value of f	12	-0.1875	-0.1875	12
Conclusion	Positive	Negative	Negative	Positive

The solution set is $\{x \mid x < -1 \text{ or } x > 1\}$, or, using interval notation, $(-\infty, -1)$ or $(1, \infty)$.

18. $x^4 < 9x^2$

$x^4 - 9x^2 < 0$

$x^2(x^2 - 9) < 0$

$x^2(x-3)(x+3) < 0$

$f(x) = x^2(x-3)(x+3)$

$x = 0, x = 3, x = -3$ are the zeros of f

Interval	$(-\infty, -3)$	$(-3, 0)$	$(0, 3)$	$(3, \infty)$
Number Chosen	-4	-1	1	4
Value of f	112	-8	-8	112
Conclusion	Positive	Negative	Negative	Positive

The solution set is $\{x \mid -3 < x < 0 \text{ or } 0 < x < 3\}$ or, using interval notation, $(-3, 0)$ or $(0, 3)$.

19. $x^4 > 1$

$x^4 - 1 > 0$

$(x^2 - 1)(x^2 + 1) > 0$

$(x-1)(x+1)(x^2 + 1) > 0$

$f(x) = (x-1)(x+1)(x^2 + 1)$

$x = 1, x = -1$ are the zeros of f; $x^2 + 1$ has no real solution

Interval	$(-\infty, -1)$	$(-1, 1)$	$(1, \infty)$
Number Chosen	-2	0	2
Value of f	15	-1	15
Conclusion	Positive	Negative	Positive

The solution set is $\{x \mid x < -1 \text{ or } x > 1\}$, or, using interval notation, $(-\infty, -1)$ or $(1, \infty)$.

20.
$$x^3 > 1$$
$$x^3 - 1 > 0$$
$$(x-1)(x^2+x+1) > 0$$
$$f(x) = (x-1)(x^2+x+1)$$

$x = 1$ is the zero of f ; $x^2 + x + 1$ has no real solution

Interval	$(-\infty, 1)$	$(1, \infty)$
Number Chosen	0	2
Value of f	-1	7
Conclusion	Negative	Positive

The solution set is $\left\{ x \mid x > 1 \right\}$, or, using interval notation, $(1, \infty)$.

21. $\dfrac{x+1}{x-1} > 0$

$$f(x) = \dfrac{x+1}{x-1}$$

The zeros and values where f is undefined are $x = -1$ and $x = 1$.

Interval	$(-\infty, -1)$	$(-1, 1)$	$(1, \infty)$
Number Chosen	-2	0	2
Value of f	$\dfrac{1}{3}$	-1	3
Conclusion	Positive	Negative	Positive

The solution set is $\left\{ x \mid x < -1 \text{ or } x > 1 \right\}$, or, using interval notation, $(-\infty, -1)$ or $(1, \infty)$.

22. $\dfrac{x-3}{x+1} > 0$

$$f(x) = \dfrac{x-3}{x+1}$$

The zeros and values where f is undefined are $x = -1$ and $x = 3$.

Interval	$(-\infty, -1)$	$(-1, 3)$	$(3, \infty)$
Number Chosen	-2	0	4
Value of f	5	-3	0.2
Conclusion	Positive	Negative	Positive

The solution set is $\left\{ x \mid x < -1 \text{ or } x > 3 \right\}$, or, using interval notation, $(-\infty, -1)$ or $(3, \infty)$.

23. $\dfrac{(x-1)(x+1)}{x} \le 0$

$$f(x) = \dfrac{(x-1)(x+1)}{x}$$

The zeros and values where f is undefined are $x = -1$, $x = 0$ and $x = 1$.

Interval	$(-\infty, -1)$	$(-1, 0)$	$(0, 1)$	$(1, \infty)$
Number Chosen	-2	-0.5	0.5	2
Value of f	-1.5	1.5	-1.5	1.5
Conclusion	Negative	Positive	Negative	Positive

The solution set is $\left\{ x \mid x \le -1 \text{ or } 0 < x \le 1 \right\}$, or, using interval notation, $(-\infty, -1]$ or $(0, 1]$.

24. $\dfrac{(x-3)(x+2)}{x-1} \le 0$

$$f(x) = \dfrac{(x-3)(x+2)}{x-1}$$

The zeros and values where f is undefined are $x = -2$, $x = 1$ and $x = 3$.

Interval	$(-\infty, -2)$	$(-2, 1)$	$(1, 3)$	$(3, \infty)$
Number Chosen	-3	0	2	4
Value of f	-1.5	6	-4	2
Conclusion	Negative	Positive	Negative	Positive

The solution set is $\left\{ x \mid x \le -2 \text{ or } 1 < x \le 3 \right\}$, or, using interval notation, $(-\infty, -2]$ or $(1, 3]$.

25.

$$\frac{(x-2)^2}{x^2-1} \ge 0$$

$$\frac{(x-2)^2}{(x+1)(x-1)} \ge 0$$

$$f(x) = \frac{(x-2)^2}{x^2-1}$$

The zeros and values where f is undefined are $x = -1$, $x = 1$ and $x = 2$.

Interval	$(-\infty, -1)$	$(-1, 1)$	$(1, 2)$	$(2, \infty)$
Number Chosen	-2	0	1.5	3
Value of f	$\dfrac{16}{3}$	-4	0.2	0.125
Conclusion	Positive	Negative	Positive	Positive

The solution set is $\{x \mid x < -1 \text{ or } x > 1\}$, or, using interval notation, $(-\infty, -1)$ or $(1, \infty)$.

26.

$$\frac{(x+5)^2}{x^2-4} \ge 0$$

$$\frac{(x+5)^2}{(x+2)(x-2)} \ge 0$$

$$f(x) = \frac{(x+5)^2}{x^2-4}$$

The zeros and values where f is undefined are $x = -5$, $x = -2$ and $x = 2$.

Interval	$(-\infty, -5)$	$(-5, -2)$	$(-2, 2)$	$(2, \infty)$
Number Chosen	-6	-3	0	3
Value of f	0.03125	0.8	-6.25	12.8
Conclusion	Positive	Positive	Negative	Positive

The solution set is $\{x \mid x < -2 \text{ or } x > 2\}$, or, using interval notation, $(-\infty, -2)$ or $(2, \infty)$.

27.

$$6x - 5 < \frac{6}{x}$$

$$6x - 5 - \frac{6}{x} < 0$$

$$\frac{6x^2 - 5x - 6}{x} < 0$$

$$\frac{(2x-3)(3x+2)}{x} < 0$$

$$f(x) = \frac{(2x-3)(3x+2)}{x}$$

The zeros and values where f is undefined are $x = -\dfrac{2}{3}$, $x = 0$ and $x = \dfrac{3}{2}$.

Interval	$\left(-\infty, -\dfrac{2}{3}\right)$	$\left(-\dfrac{2}{3}, 0\right)$	$\left(0, \dfrac{3}{2}\right)$	$\left(\dfrac{3}{2}, \infty\right)$
Number Chosen	-1	-0.5	1	2
Value of f	-5	4	-5	4
Conclusion	Negative	Positive	Negative	Positive

The solution set is $\left\{x \mid x < -\dfrac{2}{3} \text{ or } 0 < x < \dfrac{3}{2}\right\}$, or, using interval notation, $\left(-\infty, -\dfrac{2}{3}\right)$ or $\left(0, \dfrac{3}{2}\right)$.

28.

$$x + \frac{12}{x} < 7$$

$$x + \frac{12}{x} - 7 < 0$$

$$\frac{x^2 - 7x + 12}{x} < 0$$

$$\frac{(x-3)(x-4)}{x} < 0$$

$$f(x) = \frac{(x-3)(x-4)}{x}$$; The zeros and values where f is undefined are $x = 0$, $x = 3$ and $x = 4$.

Interval	$(-\infty, 0)$	$(0, 3)$	$(3, 4)$	$(4, \infty)$
Number Chosen	-1	1	3.5	5
Value of f	-20	6	$-\dfrac{1}{14}$	0.4
Conclusion	Negative	Positive	Negative	Positive

The solution set is $\{x \mid x < 0 \text{ or } 3 < x < 4\}$, or, using interval notation, $(-\infty, 0)$ or $(3, 4)$.

29.
$$\frac{x+4}{x-2} \le 1$$
$$\frac{x+4}{x-2} - 1 \le 0$$
$$\frac{x+4-(x-2)}{x-2} \le 0$$
$$\frac{6}{x-2} \le 0$$
$$f(x) = \frac{6}{x-2}$$

The value where f is undefined is $x = 2$.

Interval	$(-\infty, 2)$	$(2, \infty)$
Number Chosen	0	3
Value of f	-3	6
Conclusion	Negative	Positive

The solution set is $\{ x \mid x < 2 \}$, or, using interval notation, $(-\infty, 2)$.

30.
$$\frac{x+2}{x-4} \ge 1$$
$$\frac{x+2}{x-4} - 1 \ge 0$$
$$\frac{x+2-(x-4)}{x-4} \ge 0$$
$$\frac{6}{x-4} \ge 0$$
$$f(x) = \frac{6}{x-4}$$

The value where f is undefined is $x = 4$.

Interval	$(-\infty, 4)$	$(4, \infty)$
Number Chosen	0	5
Value of f	-1.5	6
Conclusion	Negative	Positive

The solution set is $\{ x \mid x > 4 \}$, or, using interval notation, $(4, \infty)$.

31.
$$\frac{3x-5}{x+2} \le 2$$
$$\frac{3x-5}{x+2} - 2 \le 0$$
$$\frac{3x-5-2(x+2)}{x+2} \le 0$$
$$\frac{x-9}{x+2} \le 0$$
$$f(x) = \frac{x-9}{x+2}$$

The zeros and values where f is undefined are $x = -2$ and $x = 9$.

Interval	$(-\infty, -2)$	$(-2, 9)$	$(9, \infty)$
Number Chosen	-3	0	10
Value of f	12	-4.5	$\frac{1}{12}$
Conclusion	Positive	Negative	Positive

The solution set is $\{ x \mid -2 < x \le 9 \}$, or, using interval notation, $(-2, 9]$.

32.
$$\frac{x-4}{2x+4} \ge 1$$
$$\frac{x-4}{2x+4} - 1 \ge 0$$
$$\frac{x-4-2x-4}{2x+4} \ge 0$$
$$\frac{x+8}{2(x+2)} \le 0$$
$$f(x) = \frac{x+8}{2(x+2)}$$

The zeros and values where f is undefined are $x = -8$ and $x = -2$.

Interval	$(-\infty, -8)$	$(-8, -2)$	$(-2, \infty)$
Number Chosen	-9	-3	0
Value of f	$\frac{1}{14}$	-2.5	2
Conclusion	Positive	Negative	Positive

The solution set is $\{ x \mid -8 \le x < -2 \}$, or, using interval notation, $[-8, -2)$.

33.
$$\frac{1}{x-2} < \frac{2}{3x-9}$$

$$\frac{1}{x-2} - \frac{2}{3x-9} < 0$$

$$\frac{3x-9-2(x-2)}{(x-2)(3x-9)} < 0$$

$$\frac{x-5}{(x-2)(3x-9)} < 0$$

$$f(x) = \frac{x-5}{(x-2)(3x-9)}$$

The zeros and values where f is undefined are $x = 2$, $x = 3$, and $x = 5$.

Interval	$(-\infty, 2)$	$(2, 3)$	$(3, 5)$	$(5, \infty)$
Number Chosen	0	2.5	4	6
Value of f	$-\dfrac{5}{18}$	$\dfrac{10}{3}$	$-\dfrac{1}{6}$	$\dfrac{1}{36}$
Conclusion	Negative	Positive	Negative	Positive

The solution set is $\left\{ x \mid x < 2 \text{ or } 3 < x < 5 \right\}$, or, using interval notation, $(-\infty, 2)$ or $(3, 5)$.

34.
$$\frac{5}{x-3} > \frac{3}{x+1}$$

$$\frac{5}{x-3} - \frac{3}{x+1} > 0$$

$$\frac{5x+5-3x+9}{(x-3)(x+1)} > 0$$

$$\frac{2(x+7)}{(x-3)(x+1)} > 0$$

$$f(x) = \frac{2(x+7)}{(x-3)(x+1)}$$

The zeros and values where f is undefined are $x = -7$, $x = -1$, and $x = 3$.

Interval	$(-\infty, -7)$	$(-7, -1)$	$(-1, 3)$	$(3, \infty)$
Number Chosen	-8	-2	0	4
Value of f	$-\dfrac{2}{77}$	2	$-\dfrac{14}{3}$	$\dfrac{22}{5}$
Conclusion	Negative	Positive	Negative	Positive

The solution set is $\left\{ x \mid -7 < x < -1 \text{ or } x > 3 \right\}$, or, using interval notation, $(-7, -1)$ or $(3, \infty)$.

35.
$$\frac{2x+5}{x+1} > \frac{x+1}{x-1}$$

$$\frac{2x+5}{x+1} - \frac{x+1}{x-1} > 0$$

$$\frac{(2x+5)(x-1)-(x+1)(x+1)}{(x+1)(x-1)} > 0$$

$$\frac{2x^2+3x-5-\left(x^2+2x+1\right)}{(x+1)(x-1)} > 0$$

$$\frac{x^2+x-6}{(x+1)(x-1)} > 0$$

$$\frac{(x+3)(x-2)}{(x+1)(x-1)} > 0$$

$$f(x) = \frac{(x+3)(x-2)}{(x+1)(x-1)}$$

The zeros and values where f is undefined are $x = -3$, $x = -1$, $x = 1$ and $x = 2$.

Interval	Number Chosen	Value of f	Conclusion
$(-\infty, -3)$	-4	0.4	Positive
$(-3, -1)$	-2	$-\dfrac{4}{3}$	Negative
$(-1, 1)$	0	6	Positive
$(1, 2)$	1.5	-1.8	Negative
$(2, \infty)$	3	0.75	Positive

The solution set is $\left\{ x \mid x < -3 \text{ or } -1 < x < 1 \text{ or } x > 2 \right\}$, or, using interval notation, $(-\infty, -3)$ or $(-1, 1)$ or $(2, \infty)$.

36.
$$\frac{1}{x+2} > \frac{3}{x+1}$$

$$\frac{1}{x+2} - \frac{3}{x+1} > 0$$

$$\frac{x+1-3(x+2)}{(x+2)(x+1)} > 0$$

$$\frac{x+1-3x-6}{(x+2)(x+1)} > 0$$

$$\frac{2x+5}{(x+2)(x+1)} < 0$$

$$f(x) = \frac{2x+5}{(x+2)(x+1)}$$

The zeros and values where f is undefined are

$x = -\dfrac{5}{2}$, $x = -2$ and $x = -1$.

Interval	Number Chosen	Value of f	Conclusion
$\left(-\infty, -\dfrac{5}{2}\right)$	-3	-0.5	Negative
$\left(-\dfrac{5}{2}, -2\right)$	-2.25	1.6	Positive
$(-2, -1)$	-1.5	-8	Negative
$(-1, \infty)$	0	2.5	Positive

The solution set is

$\left\{ x \,\middle|\, x < -\dfrac{5}{2} \text{ or } -2 < x < -1 \right\}$, or, using interval

notation, $\left(-\infty, -\dfrac{5}{2}\right)$ or $(-2, -1)$.

37. $\dfrac{x^2(3+x)(x+4)}{(x+5)(x-1)} \geq 0$

$f(x) = \dfrac{x^2(3+x)(x+4)}{(x+5)(x-1)}$

The zeros and values where f is undefined are

$x = -5$, $x = -4$, $x = -3$, $x = 0$ and $x = 1$.

Interval	Number Chosen	Value of f	Conclusion
$(-\infty, -5)$	-6	$\dfrac{216}{7}$	Positive
$(-5, -4)$	-4.5	$-\dfrac{243}{44}$	Negative
$(-4, -3)$	-3.5	$\dfrac{49}{108}$	Positive
$(-3, 0)$	-1	-0.75	Negative
$(0, 1)$	0.5	$-\dfrac{63}{44}$	Negative
$(1, \infty)$	2	$\dfrac{120}{7}$	Positive

The solution set is

$\left\{ x \,\middle|\, x < -5 \text{ or } -4 \leq x \leq -3 \text{ or } x = 0 \text{ or } x > 1 \right\}$,

or, using interval notation,

$(-\infty, -5)$ or $[-4, -3]$ or 0 or $(1, \infty)$.

38. $\dfrac{x(x^2+1)(x-2)}{(x-1)(x+1)} \geq 0$

$f(x) = \dfrac{x(x^2+1)(x-2)}{(x-1)(x+1)}$

The zeros and values where f is undefined are

$x = -1$, $x = 0$, $x = 1$ and $x = 2$.

Interval	$(-\infty, -1)$	$(-1, 0)$	$(0, 1)$	$(1, 2)$	$(2, \infty)$
Number Chosen	-2	-0.5	0.5	1.5	3
Value of f	$\dfrac{40}{3}$	$-\dfrac{25}{12}$	1.25	-1.95	3.75
Conclusion	Positive	Negative	Positive	Negative	Positive

The solution set is

$\left\{ x \,\middle|\, x < -1 \text{ or } 0 \leq x < 1 \text{ or } x \geq 2 \right\}$, or, using

interval notation, $(-\infty, -1)$ or $[0, 1)$ or $[2, \infty)$.

39. $\dfrac{(3-x)^3(2x+1)}{x^3 - 1} < 0$

$\dfrac{(3-x)^3(2x+1)}{(x-1)(x^2+x+1)} < 0$

$f(x) = \dfrac{(3-x)^3(2x+1)}{(x-1)(x^2+x+1)}$

The zeros and values where f is undefined are

$x = 3$, $x = -\dfrac{1}{2}$, and $x = 1$.

Interval	Number Chosen	Value of f	Conclusion
$\left(-\infty, -\dfrac{1}{2}\right)$	-1	32	Positive
$\left(-\dfrac{1}{2}, 1\right)$	0	-27	Negative
$(1, 3)$	2	$5/7$	Positive
$(3, \infty)$	4	$-1/7$	Negative

The solution set is $\left\{ x \,\middle|\, -\dfrac{1}{2} < x < 1 \text{ or } x > 3 \right\}$, or,

using interval notation, $\left(-\dfrac{1}{2}, 1\right)$ or $(3, \infty)$.

40. $\dfrac{(2-x)^3(3x-2)}{x^3+1}<0$

$\dfrac{(2-x)^3(3x-2)}{(x+1)(x^2-x+1)}<0$

$f(x)=\dfrac{(2-x)^3(3x-2)}{(x+1)(x^2-x+1)}$

The zeros and values where f is undefined are

$x=2, x=\dfrac{2}{3}$, and $x=-1$.

Interval	Number Chosen	Value of f	Conclusion
$(-\infty,-1)$	-2	$512/7$	Positive
$\left(-1,\dfrac{2}{3}\right)$	0	-16	Negative
$\left(\dfrac{2}{3},2\right)$	1	$1/2$	Positive
$(2,\infty)$	3	$-1/4$	Negative

The solution set is $\left\{x\left|-1<x<\dfrac{2}{3}\text{ or }x>2\right.\right\}$, or,

using interval notation, $\left(-1,\dfrac{2}{3}\right)$ or $(2,\infty)$.

41. Let x be the positive number. Then

$x^3>4x^2$

$x^3-4x^2>0$

$x^2(x-4)>0$

$f(x)=x^2(x-4)$

$x=0$ and $x=4$ are the zeros of f.

Interval	$(-\infty,0)$	$(0,4)$	$(4,\infty)$
Number Chosen	-1	1	5
Value of f	-5	-3	25
Conclusion	Negative	Negative	Positive

Since x must be positive, all real numbers greater than 4 satisfy the condition. The solution set is $\{x\,|\,x>4\}$, or, using interval notation,

$(4,\infty)$.

42. Let x be the positive number. Then

$x^3<x$

$x^3-x<0$

$x(x-1)(x+1)<0$

$f(x)=x(x-1)(x+1)$

$x=-1, x=0$, and $x=1$ are the zeros of f.

Interval	$(-\infty,-1)$	$(-1,0)$	$(0,1)$	$(1,\infty)$
Number Chosen	-2	$-1/2$	$1/2$	2
Value of f	-6	0.375	-0.375	6
Conclusion	Negative	Positive	Negative	Positive

Since x must be positive, all real numbers between (but not including) 0 and 1 satisfy the condition. The solution set is $\{x\,|\,0<x<1\}$, or, using interval notation, $(0,1)$.

43. The domain of the expression consists of all real numbers x for which

$x^4-16\ge 0$

$(x^2+4)(x^2-4)\ge 0$

$\left(x^2+4\right)(x-2)(x+2)\ge 0$

$p(x)=\left(x^2+4\right)(x-2)(x+2)$

$x=-2$ and $x=2$ are the zeros of p.

Interval	$(-\infty,-2)$	$(-2,2)$	$(2,\infty)$
Number Chosen	-3	0	3
Value of p	65	-16	65
Conclusion	Positive	Negative	Positive

The domain of f is $\{x\,|\,x\le-2\text{ or }x\ge 2\}$, or, using interval notation, $(-\infty,-2]$ or $[2,\infty)$.

44. The domain of the expression consists of all real numbers x for which

$$x^3 - 3x^2 \geq 0$$

$$x^2(x-3) \geq 0$$

$$p(x) = x^2(x-3)$$

$x = 0$ and $x = 3$ are the zeros of p.

Interval	$(-\infty, 0)$	$(0,3)$	$(3, \infty)$
Number Chosen	-1	1	4
Value of p	-4	-2	16
Conclusion	Negative	Negative	Positive

The domain of f is $\{x \mid x = 0$ or $x \geq 3\}$, or, using interval notation, 0 or $[3, \infty)$.

45. The domain of the expression includes all values for which

$$\frac{x-2}{x+4} \geq 0$$

$$f(x) = \frac{x-2}{x+4}$$

The zeros and values where the expression is undefined are $x = -4$ and $x = 2$.

Interval	$(-\infty, -4)$	$(-4, 2)$	$(2, \infty)$
Number Chosen	-5	0	3
Value of f	7	$-\dfrac{1}{2}$	$\dfrac{1}{7}$
Conclusion	Positive	Negative	Positive

The solution or domain is $\{x \mid x < -4$ or $x \geq 2\}$, or, using interval notation, $(-\infty, -4)$ or $[2, \infty)$.

46. The domain of the expression includes all values for which

$$\frac{x-1}{x+4} \geq 0$$

$$f(x) = \frac{x-1}{x+4}$$

The zeros and values where the expression is undefined are $x = -4$ and $x = 1$.

Interval	$(-\infty, -4)$	$(-4, 1)$	$(1, \infty)$
Number Chosen	-5	0	2
Value of f	6	$-\dfrac{1}{4}$	$\dfrac{1}{6}$
Conclusion	Positive	Negative	Positive

The solution or domain is $\{x \mid x < -4$ or $x \geq 1\}$, or, using interval notation, $(-\infty, -4)$ or $[1, \infty)$.

47.
$$f(x) \leq g(x)$$
$$x^4 - 1 \leq -2x^2 + 2$$
$$x^4 + 2x^2 - 3 \leq 0$$
$$(x^2 + 3)(x^2 - 1) \leq 0$$
$$(x^2 + 3)(x-1)(x+1) \leq 0$$
$$h(x) = (x^2 + 3)(x-1)(x+1)$$

$x = -1$ and $x = 1$ are the zeros of h.

Interval	$(-\infty, -1)$	$(-1, 1)$	$(1, \infty)$
Number Chosen	-2	0	2
Value of h	21	-3	21
Conclusion	Positive	Negative	Positive

$f(x) \leq g(x)$ if $-1 \leq x \leq 1$. That is, on the interval $[-1, 1]$.

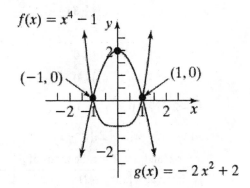

$f(x) = x^4 - 1$

$g(x) = -2x^2 + 2$

48.

$$f(x) \le g(x)$$
$$x^4 - 1 \le x - 1$$
$$x^4 - x \le 0$$
$$x(x^3 - 1) \le 0$$
$$x(x-1)(x^2 + x + 1) \le 0$$
$$h(x) = x(x-1)(x^2 + x + 1)$$

$x = 0$ and $x = 1$ are the zeros of h.

Interval	$(-\infty, 0)$	$(0,1)$	$(1, \infty)$
Number Chosen	-1	$1/2$	2
Value of h	2	$-7/16$	14
Conclusion	Positive	Negative	Positive

$f(x) \le g(x)$ if $0 \le x \le 1$. That is, on the interval $[0,1]$.

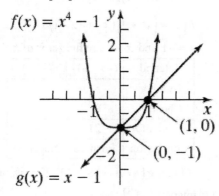

49.

$$f(x) \le g(x)$$
$$x^4 - 4 \le 3x^2$$
$$x^4 - 3x^2 - 4 \le 0$$
$$(x^2 - 4)(x^2 + 1) \le 0$$
$$(x-2)(x+2)(x^2 + 1) \le 0$$
$$h(x) = (x-2)(x+2)(x^2 + 1)$$

$x = -2$ and $x = 2$ are the zeros of h.

Interval	$(-\infty, -2)$	$(-2,2)$	$(2, \infty)$
Number Chosen	-3	0	3
Value of h	50	-4	50
Conclusion	Positive	Negative	Positive

$f(x) \le g(x)$ if $-2 \le x \le 2$. That is, on the interval $[-2,2]$.

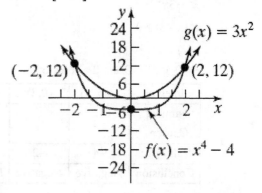

50.

$$f(x) \le g(x)$$
$$x^4 \le 2 - x^2$$
$$x^4 + x^2 - 2 \le 0$$
$$(x^2 + 2)(x^2 - 1) \le 0$$
$$(x^2 + 2)(x-1)(x+1) \le 0$$
$$h(x) = (x^2 + 2)(x-1)(x+1)$$

$x = -1$ and $x = 1$ are the zeros of h.

Interval	$(-\infty, -1)$	$(-1,1)$	$(1, \infty)$
Number Chosen	-2	0	2
Value of h	18	-2	18
Conclusion	Positive	Negative	Positive

$f(x) \le g(x)$ if $-1 \le x \le 1$. That is, on the interval $[-1,1]$.

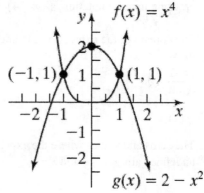

51. We need to solve $\overline{C}(x) \le 100$.

$$\frac{80x + 5000}{x} \le 100$$

$$\frac{80x + 5000}{x} - \frac{100x}{x} \le 0$$

$$\frac{5000 - 20x}{x} \le 0$$

$$\frac{20(250 - x)}{x} \le 0$$

$$f(x) = \frac{20(250 - x)}{x}$$

The zeros and values where the expression is undefined are $x = 0$ and $x = 250$.

Interval	$(-\infty, 0)$	$(0, 250)$	$(250, \infty)$
Number Chosen	-1	1	260
Value of f	-5020	4980	$-10/13$
Conclusion	Negative	Positive	Negative

The number of bicycles produced cannot be negative, so the solution is $\{x \mid x \ge 250\}$, or, using interval notation, $[250, \infty)$. The company must produce at least 250 bicycles each day to keep average costs to no more than $100.

52. We need to solve $\overline{C}(x) \le 100$.

$$\frac{80x + 6000}{x} \le 100$$

$$\frac{80x + 6000}{x} - \frac{100x}{x} \le 0$$

$$\frac{6000 - 20x}{x} \le 0$$

$$\frac{20(300 - x)}{x} \le 0$$

$$f(x) = \frac{20(300 - x)}{x}$$

The zeros and values where the expression is undefined are $x = 0$ and $x = 300$.

Interval	$(-\infty, 0)$	$(0, 300)$	$(300, \infty)$
Number Chosen	-1	1	310
Value of f	-6020	5980	$-20/31$
Conclusion	Negative	Positive	Negative

The number of bicycles produced cannot be negative, so the solution is $\{x \mid x \ge 300\}$, or,

using interval notation, $[300, \infty)$. The company must produce at least 300 bicycles each day to keep average costs to no more than $100.

53. a.
$$K \ge 16$$

$$\frac{2(150)(S + 42)}{S^2} \ge 16$$

$$\frac{300S + 12,600}{S^2} \ge 16$$

$$\frac{300S + 12,600}{S^2} - 16 \ge 0$$

$$\frac{300S + 12,600 - 16S^2}{S^2} \ge 0$$

Solve $-16S^2 + 300S + 12,600 = 0$ and $S^2 = 0$. The zeros and values where the left-hand side is undefined are $S = 0$, $S \approx 39$, $S \approx -20$. Since the stretch cannot be negative, we only consider cases where $S \ge 0$.

Interval	$(0, 39)$	$(39, \infty)$
Number Chosen	1	40
Value of left side	12884	-0.625
Conclusion	Positive	Negative

The cord will stretch less than 39 feet.

b. The safe height is determined by the minimum clearance (3 feet), the free length of the cord (42 feet), and the stretch in the cord (39 feet). Therefore, the platform must be at least $3 + 42 + 39 = 84$ feet above the ground.

54. Let r = the distance between Earth and the object in kilometers. Then $384,400 - r$ = the distance between the object and the moon. We want

$$G\frac{m_{moon}m_{obj}}{\left(384,400-r\right)^2} > G\frac{m_{earth}m_{obj}}{r^2}$$

$$\frac{m_{moon}}{\left(384,400-r\right)^2} > \frac{m_{earth}}{r^2}$$

$$\frac{m_{moon}}{\left(384,400-r\right)^2} - \frac{m_{earth}}{r^2} > 0$$

$$\frac{r^2 m_{moon} - \left(384,400-r\right)^2 m_{earth}}{r^2\left(384,400-r\right)^2} > 0$$

The zeros and values where the left-hand side is undefined are $r = 0$, $r \approx 432,353$, $r \approx 346,022$, and $r = 384,400$. Since the distance from Earth to the object will be greater than 0 but less than the distance to the moon, we can exclude some of these values.

Interval	$(0, 346022)$	$(346022, 384400)$
Number Chosen	$100,000$	$350,000$
Value of left side	-6×10^{14}	1.3×10^{13}
Conclusion	Negative	Positive

The force on the object due to the moon will be greater than the force due to the Earth when the object is more than 346,022 kilometers from Earth.

55. Answers will vary, for example, $x^2 < 0$ has no real solution and $x^2 \leq 0$ has exactly one real solution.

56. $x^4 + 1 < -5$ has no solution because the quantity $x^4 + 1$ is never negative. ($x^4 + 1 \geq 1$)

57. No, the student is not correct. For example, $x = -5$ is in the solution set, but does not satisfy the original inequality.

$$\frac{-5+4}{-5-3} = \frac{-1}{-8} = \frac{1}{8} \nleq 0$$

When multiplying both sides of an inequality by a negative, we must switch the direction of the inequality. Since we do not know the sign of $x+3$, we cannot multiply both sides of the inequality by this quantity.

58. Answers will vary. One example:

$$\frac{x-5}{x+3} \leq 0$$

Section 5.5

1. $f(-1) = 2(-1)^2 - (-1) = 2 + 1 = 3$

2. $6x^2 + x - 2 = (3x+2)(2x-1)$

3. Using synthetic division:

$$3\overline{)\begin{array}{ccccc} 3 & -5 & 0 & 7 & -4 \\ & 9 & 12 & 36 & 129 \\ \hline 3 & 4 & 12 & 43 & 125 \end{array}}$$

Quotient: $3x^3 + 4x^2 + 12x + 43$
Remainder: 125

4. $x^2 + x - 3 = 0$

$$x = \frac{-1 \pm \sqrt{1^2 - 4(1)(-3)}}{2(1)}$$

$$= \frac{-1 \pm \sqrt{1+12}}{2} = \frac{-1 \pm \sqrt{13}}{2}$$

The solution set is $\left\{ \dfrac{-1-\sqrt{13}}{2}, \dfrac{-1+\sqrt{13}}{2} \right\}$.

5. Remainder, Dividend

6. $f(c)$

7. -4

8. False; every polynomial function of degree 3 with real coefficients has at most three real zeros.

9. False; the potential rational zeros are $\pm\dfrac{1}{2}$ and ± 1.

10. True

11. $f(x) = 4x^3 - 3x^2 - 8x + 4; \quad c = 2$

$$f(2) = 4(2)^3 - 3(2)^2 - 8(2) + 4$$
$$= 32 - 12 - 16 + 4 = 8 \neq 0$$

Thus, 2 is not a zero of f and $x - 2$ is not a factor of f.

12. $f(x) = -4x^3 + 5x^2 + 8; \quad c = -3$

$f(-3) = -4(-3)^3 + 5(-3)^2 + 8$

$\qquad = 108 + 45 + 8 = 161 \neq 0$

Thus, -3 is not a zero of f and $x + 3$ is not a factor of f.

13. $f(x) = 3x^4 - 6x^3 - 5x + 10; \quad c = 2$

$f(2) = 3(2)^4 - 6(2)^3 - 5(2) + 10$

$\qquad = 48 - 48 - 10 + 10 = 0$

Thus, 2 is a zero of f and $x - 2$ is a factor of f.

14. $f(x) = 4x^4 - 15x^2 - 4; \quad c = 2$

$f(2) = 4(2)^4 - 15(2)^2 - 4 = 64 - 60 - 4 = 0$

Thus, 2 is a zero of f and $x - 2$ is a factor of f.

15. $f(x) = 3x^6 + 82x^3 + 27; \quad c = -3$

$f(-3) = 3(-3)^6 + 82(-3)^3 + 27$

$\qquad = 2187 - 2214 + 27 = 0$

Thus, -3 is a zero of f and $x + 3$ is a factor of f.

16. $f(x) = 2x^6 - 18x^4 + x^2 - 9; \quad c = -3$

$f(-3) = 2(-3)^6 - 18(-3)^4 + (-3)^2 - 9$

$\qquad = 1458 - 1458 + 9 - 9 = 0$

Thus, -3 is a zero of f and $x + 3$ is a factor of f.

17. $f(x) = 4x^6 - 64x^4 + x^2 - 15; \quad c = -4$

$f(-4) = 4(-4)^6 - 64(-4)^4 + (-4)^2 - 15$

$\qquad = 16{,}384 - 16{,}384 + 16 - 15 = 1 \neq 0$

Thus, -4 is not a zero of f and $x + 4$ is not a factor of f.

18. $f(x) = x^6 - 16x^4 + x^2 - 16; \quad c = -4$

$f(-4) = (-4)^6 - 16(-4)^4 + (-4)^2 - 16$

$\qquad = 4096 - 4096 + 16 - 16 = 0$

Thus, -4 is a zero of f and $x + 4$ is a factor of f.

19. $f(x) = 2x^4 - x^3 + 2x - 1; \quad c = \dfrac{1}{2}$

$f\left(\dfrac{1}{2}\right) = 2\left(\dfrac{1}{2}\right)^4 - \left(\dfrac{1}{2}\right)^3 + 2\left(\dfrac{1}{2}\right) - 1$

$\qquad = \dfrac{1}{8} - \dfrac{1}{8} + 1 - 1 = 0$

Thus, $\dfrac{1}{2}$ is a zero of f and $x - \dfrac{1}{2}$ is a factor of f.

20. $f(x) = 3x^4 + x^3 - 3x + 1; \quad c = -\dfrac{1}{3}$

$f\left(-\dfrac{1}{3}\right) = 3\left(-\dfrac{1}{3}\right)^4 + \left(-\dfrac{1}{3}\right)^3 - 3\left(-\dfrac{1}{3}\right) + 1$

$\qquad = \dfrac{1}{27} - \dfrac{1}{27} + 1 + 1 = 2 \neq 0$

Thus, $-\dfrac{1}{3}$ is not a zero of f and $x + \dfrac{1}{3}$ is not a factor of f.

21. $f(x) = -4x^7 + x^3 - x^2 + 2$

The maximum number of zeros is the degree of the polynomial, which is 7.

Examining $f(x) = -4x^7 + x^3 - x^2 + 2$, there are three variations in sign; thus, there are three positive real zeros or there is one positive real zero.

Examining

$f(-x) = -4(-x)^7 + (-x)^3 - (-x)^2 + 2$,

$\qquad = 4x^7 - x^3 - x^2 + 2$

there are two variations in sign; thus, there are two negative real zeros or no negative real zeros.

22. $f(x) = 5x^4 + 2x^2 - 6x - 5$

The maximum number of zeros is the degree of the polynomial, which, is 4.

Examining $f(x) = 5x^4 + 2x^2 - 6x - 5$, there is one variation in sign; thus, there is one positive real zero.

Examining

$f(-x) = 5(-x)^4 + 2(-x)^2 - 6(-x) - 5$,

$\qquad = 5x^4 + 2x^2 + 6x - 5$

there is one variation in sign; thus, there is one negative real zero.

23. $f(x) = 2x^6 - 3x^2 - x + 1$

The maximum number of zeros is the degree of the polynomial, which is 6.

Examining $f(x) = 2x^6 - 3x^2 - x + 1$, there are two variations in sign; thus, there are two positive real zeros or no positive real zeros. Examining

$$f(-x) = 2(-x)^6 - 3(-x)^2 - (-x) + 1,$$
$$= 2x^6 - 3x^2 + x + 1$$

there are two variations in sign; thus, there are two negative real zeros or no negative real zeros.

24. $f(x) = -3x^5 + 4x^4 + 2$

The maximum number of zeros is the degree of the polynomial, which is 5.

Examining $f(x) = -3x^5 + 4x^4 + 2$, there is one variation in sign; thus, there is one positive real zero.

Examining

$$f(-x) = -3(-x)^5 + 4(-x)^4 + 2,$$
$$= 3x^5 + 4x^4 + 2$$

there is no variation in sign; thus, there are no negative real zeros.

25. $f(x) = 3x^3 - 2x^2 + x + 2$

The maximum number of zeros is the degree of the polynomial, which is 3.

Examining $f(x) = 3x^3 - 2x^2 + x + 2$, there are two variations in sign; thus, there are two positive real zeros or no positive real zeros. Examining

$$f(-x) = 3(-x)^3 - 2(-x)^2 + (-x) + 2,$$
$$= -3x^3 - 2x^2 - x + 2$$

there is one variation in sign; thus, there is one negative real zero.

26. $f(x) = -x^3 - x^2 + x + 1$

The maximum number of zeros is the degree of the polynomial, which is 3.

Examining $f(x) = -x^3 - x^2 + x + 1$, there is one variation in sign; thus, there is one positive real zero.

Examining

$$f(-x) = -(-x)^3 - (-x)^2 + (-x) + 1,$$
$$= x^3 - x^2 - x + 1$$

there are two variations in sign; thus, there are two negative real zeros or no negative real zeros.

27. $f(x) = -x^4 + x^2 - 1$

The maximum number of zeros is the degree of the polynomial, which is 4.

Examining $f(x) = -x^4 + x^2 - 1$, there are two variations in sign; thus, there are two positive real zeros or no positive real zeros.

Examining $f(-x) = -(-x)^4 + (-x)^2 - 1$

$= -x^4 + x^2 - 1$, there are two variations in sign; thus, there are two negative real zeros or no negative real zeros.

28. $f(x) = x^4 + 5x^3 - 2$

The maximum number of zeros is the degree of the polynomial, which is 4.

Examining $f(x) = x^4 + 5x^3 - 2$, there is one variation in sign; thus, there is one positive real zero.

Examining

$$f(-x) = (-x)^4 + 5(-x)^3 - 2 = x^4 - 5x^3 - 2,$$

there is one variation in sign; thus, there is one negative real zero.

29. $f(x) = x^5 + x^4 + x^2 + x + 1$

The maximum number of zeros is the degree of the polynomial, which is 5.

Examining $f(x) = x^5 + x^4 + x^2 + x + 1$, there are no variations in sign; thus, there are no positive real zeros.

Examining

$$f(-x) = (-x)^5 + (-x)^4 + (-x)^2 + (-x) + 1,$$
$$= -x^5 + x^4 + x^2 - x + 1$$

there are three variations in sign; thus, there are three negative real zeros or there is one negative real zero.

30. $f(x) = x^5 - x^4 + x^3 - x^2 + x - 1$

The maximum number of zeros is the degree of the polynomial, which is 5.

Examining $f(x) = x^5 - x^4 + x^3 - x^2 + x - 1$,

there are five variations in sign; thus, there are five positive real zeros or three positive real zeros or there is one positive real zero.

Examining

$$f(-x) = (-x)^5 - (-x)^4 + (-x)^3 - (-x)^2 + (-x) - 1$$
$$= -x^5 - x^4 - x^3 - x^2 - x - 1$$

there is no variation in sign; thus, there are no negative real zeros.

31. $f(x) = x^6 - 1$

The maximum number of zeros is the degree of the polynomial, which is 6.

Examining $f(x) = x^6 - 1$, there is one variation in sign; thus, there is one positive real zero.

Examining $f(-x) = (-x)^6 - 1 = x^6 - 1$, there is one variation in sign; thus, there is one negative real zero.

32. $f(x) = x^6 + 1$

The maximum number of zeros is the degree of the polynomial, which is 6.

Examining $f(x) = x^6 + 1$, there is no variation in sign; thus, there are no positive real zeros.

Examining $f(-x) = (-x)^6 + 1 = x^6 + 1$, there is no variation in sign; thus, there are no negative real zeros.

33. $f(x) = 3x^4 - 3x^3 + x^2 - x + 1$

p must be a factor of 1: $p = \pm 1$

q must be a factor of 3: $q = \pm 1, \pm 3$

The possible rational zeros are: $\dfrac{p}{q} = \pm 1, \pm \dfrac{1}{3}$

34. $f(x) = x^5 - x^4 + 2x^2 + 3$

p must be a factor of 3: $p = \pm 1, \pm 3$

q must be a factor of 1: $q = \pm 1$

The possible rational zeros are: $\dfrac{p}{q} = \pm 1, \pm 3$

35. $f(x) = x^5 - 6x^2 + 9x - 3$

p must be a factor of -3: $p = \pm 1, \pm 3$

q must be a factor of 1: $q = \pm 1$

The possible rational zeros are: $\dfrac{p}{q} = \pm 1, \pm 3$

36. $f(x) = 2x^5 - x^4 - x^2 + 1$

p must be a factor of 1: $p = \pm 1$

q must be a factor of 2: $q = \pm 1, \pm 2$

The possible rational zeros are: $\dfrac{p}{q} = \pm 1, \pm \dfrac{1}{2}$

37. $f(x) = -4x^3 - x^2 + x + 2$

p must be a factor of 2: $p = \pm 1, \pm 2$

q must be a factor of -4: $q = \pm 1, \pm 2, \pm 4$

The possible rational zeros are:

$\dfrac{p}{q} = \pm 1, \pm 2, \pm \dfrac{1}{2}, \pm \dfrac{1}{4}$

38. $f(x) = 6x^4 - x^2 + 2$

p must be a factor of 2: $p = \pm 1, \pm 2$

q must be a factor of 6: $q = \pm 1, \pm 2, \pm 3, \pm 6$

The possible rational zeros are:

$\dfrac{p}{q} = \pm 1, \pm 2, \pm \dfrac{1}{2}, \pm \dfrac{1}{3}, \pm \dfrac{2}{3}, \pm \dfrac{1}{6}$

39. $f(x) = 6x^4 - x^2 + 9$

p must be a factor of 9: $p = \pm 1, \pm 3, \pm 9$

q must be a factor of 6: $q = \pm 1, \pm 2, \pm 3, \pm 6$

The possible rational zeros are:

$\dfrac{p}{q} = \pm 1, \pm \dfrac{1}{2}, \pm \dfrac{1}{3}, \pm \dfrac{1}{6}, \pm 3, \pm \dfrac{3}{2}, \pm 9, \pm \dfrac{9}{2}$

40. $f(x) = -4x^3 + x^2 + x + 6$

p must be a factor of 6: $p = \pm 1, \pm 2, \pm 3, \pm 6$

q must be a factor of -4: $q = \pm 1, \pm 2, \pm 4$

The possible rational zeros are:

$\dfrac{p}{q} = \pm 1, \pm 2, \pm \dfrac{1}{2}, \pm \dfrac{1}{4}, \pm 3, \pm \dfrac{3}{2}, \pm \dfrac{3}{4}, \pm 6$

41. $f(x) = 2x^5 - x^3 + 2x^2 + 12$

p must be a factor of 12:

$p = \pm 1, \pm 2, \pm 3, \pm 4, \pm 6, \pm 12$

q must be a factor of 2: $q = \pm 1, \pm 2$

The possible rational zeros are:

$\dfrac{p}{q} = \pm 1, \pm 2, \pm 4, \pm \dfrac{1}{2}, \pm 3, \pm \dfrac{3}{2}, \pm 6, \pm 12$

42. $f(x) = 3x^5 - x^2 + 2x + 18$

p must be a factor of 18:

$p = \pm 1, \pm 2, \pm 3, \pm 6, \pm 9, \pm 18$

q must be a factor of 3: $q = \pm 1, \pm 3$

The possible rational zeros are:

$\dfrac{p}{q} = \pm 1, \pm \dfrac{1}{3}, \pm 2, \pm \dfrac{2}{3}, \pm 3, \pm 6, \pm 9 \pm 18$

43. $f(x) = 6x^4 + 2x^3 - x^2 + 20$

p must be a factor of 20:
$p = \pm1, \pm2, \pm4, \pm5, \pm10, \pm20$

q must be a factor of 6: $q = \pm1, \pm2, \pm3, \pm6$

The possible rational zeros are:

$\dfrac{p}{q} = \pm1, \pm2, \pm\dfrac{1}{2}, \pm\dfrac{1}{3}, \pm\dfrac{2}{3}, \pm\dfrac{1}{6}, \pm4, \pm\dfrac{4}{3}, \pm5, \pm\dfrac{5}{2},$

$\pm\dfrac{5}{3}, \pm\dfrac{5}{6}, \pm10, \pm\dfrac{10}{3}, \pm20, \pm\dfrac{20}{3}$

44. $f(x) = -6x^3 - x^2 + x + 10$

p must be a factor of 10: $p = \pm1, \pm2, \pm5, \pm10$

q must be a factor of -6: $q = \pm1, \pm2, \pm3, \pm6$

The possible rational zeros are:

$\dfrac{p}{q} = \pm1, \pm\dfrac{1}{2}, \pm\dfrac{1}{3}, \pm\dfrac{1}{6}, \pm2, \pm\dfrac{2}{3}, \pm5, \pm\dfrac{5}{2},$

$\pm\dfrac{5}{3}, \pm\dfrac{5}{6}, \pm10, \pm\dfrac{10}{3}$

45. $f(x) = x^3 + 2x^2 - 5x - 6$

Step 1: $f(x)$ has at most 3 real zeros.

Step 2: By Descartes' Rule of Signs, there is one positive real zero.

$f(-x) = (-x)^3 + 2(-x)^2 - 5(-x) - 6$

$\quad = -x^3 + 2x^2 + 5x - 6$

thus, there are two negative real zeros or no negative real zeros.

Step 3: Possible rational zeros:
$p = \pm1, \pm2, \pm3, \pm6; \quad q = \pm1;$

$\dfrac{p}{q} = \pm1, \pm2, \pm3, \pm6$

Step 4: Using synthetic division:
We try $x + 3$:

$$
\begin{array}{r|rrrr}
-3) & 1 & 2 & -5 & -6 \\
    &   & -3 & 3 & 6 \\
\hline
    & 1 & -1 & -2 & 0
\end{array}
$$

Since the remainder is 0, $x - (-3) = x + 3$ is a factor. The other factor is the quotient:
$x^2 - x - 2$.
Thus, $f(x) = (x + 3)(x^2 - x - 2)$

$\quad = (x + 3)(x + 1)(x - 2)$

The real zeros are -3, -1, and 2, each of multiplicity 1.

46. $f(x) = x^3 + 8x^2 + 11x - 20$

Step 1: $f(x)$ has at most 3 real zeros.

Step 2: By Descartes' Rule of Signs, there is one positive real zero.

$f(-x) = (-x)^3 + 8(-x)^2 + 11(-x) - 20$,

$\quad = -x^3 + 8x^2 - 11x - 20$

thus, there are two negative real zeros or no negative real zeros.

Step 3: Possible rational zeros:
$p = \pm1, \pm2, \pm4, \pm5, \pm10, \pm20$

$q = \pm1$

$\dfrac{p}{q} = \pm1, \pm2, \pm4, \pm5, \pm10, \pm20$

Step 4: Using synthetic division:
We try $x + 5$:

$$
\begin{array}{r|rrrr}
-5) & 1 & 8 & 11 & -20 \\
    &   & -5 & -15 & 20 \\
\hline
    & 1 & 3 & -4 & 0
\end{array}
$$

Since the remainder is 0, $x - (-5) = x + 5$ is a factor. The other factor is the quotient:
$x^2 + 3x - 4$.
Thus,

$f(x) = (x + 5)(x^2 + 3x - 4)$

$\quad = (x + 5)(x + 4)(x - 1)$

The real zeros are -5, -4, and 1, each of multiplicity 1.

47. $f(x) = 2x^3 - x^2 + 2x - 1$

Step 1: $f(x)$ has at most 3 real zeros.

Step 2: By Descartes' Rule of Signs, there are three positive real zeros or there is one positive real zero.

$f(-x) = 2(-x)^3 - (-x)^2 + 2(-x) - 1$

$\quad = -2x^3 - x^2 - 2x - 1$

thus, there are no negative real zeros.

Step 3: Possible rational zeros:
$p = \pm1 \quad q = \pm1, \pm2$

$\dfrac{p}{q} = \pm1, \pm\dfrac{1}{2}$

Step 4: Using synthetic division:

We try $x - 1$:

$$1\overline{)2 \quad -1 \quad 2 \quad -1}$$
$$ \quad 2 \quad 1 \quad 3$$
$$\overline{2 \quad 1 \quad 3 \quad 2}$$

$x - 1$ is **not** a factor

We try $x - \dfrac{1}{2}$:

$$\tfrac{1}{2}\overline{)2 \quad -1 \quad 2 \quad -1}$$
$$\phantom{\tfrac{1}{2})2} \quad 1 \quad 0 \quad 1$$
$$\overline{\phantom{\tfrac{1}{2}}2 \quad 0 \quad 2 \quad 0}$$

$x - \dfrac{1}{2}$ is a factor and the quotient is $2x^2 + 2$.

Thus,

$$f(x) = 2x^3 - x^2 + 2x - 1 = \left(x - \frac{1}{2}\right)\left(2x^2 + 2\right)$$

$$= 2\left(x - \frac{1}{2}\right)\left(x^2 + 1\right)$$

Since $x^2 + 1 = 0$ has no real solutions, the only real zero is $x = \dfrac{1}{2}$, of multiplicity 1.

48. $f(x) = 2x^3 + x^2 + 2x + 1$

Step 1: $f(x)$ has at most 3 real zeros.

Step 2: By Descartes' Rule of Signs, there are no positive real zeros.

$$f(-x) = 2(-x)^3 + (-x)^2 + 2(-x) + 1$$
$$= -2x^3 + x^2 - 2x + 1$$

thus, there are three negative real zeros or there is one negative real zero.

Step 3: Possible rational zeros:

$p = \pm 1; \quad q = \pm 1, \pm 2;$

$$\frac{p}{q} = \pm 1, \pm \frac{1}{2}$$

Step 4: Using synthetic division:

We try $x + 1$:

$$-1\overline{)2 \quad 1 \quad 2 \quad 1}$$
$$ \quad -2 \quad 1 \quad -3$$
$$\overline{2 \quad -1 \quad 3 \quad -2}$$

$x + 1$ is **not** a factor

We try $x + \dfrac{1}{2}$:

$$-\tfrac{1}{2}\overline{)2 \quad 1 \quad 2 \quad 1}$$
$$\phantom{-\tfrac{1}{2})2} \quad -1 \quad 0 \quad -1$$
$$\overline{\phantom{-\tfrac{1}{2}}2 \quad 0 \quad 2 \quad 0}$$

$x + \dfrac{1}{2}$ is a factor and the quotient is $2x^2 + 2$

$$f(x) = 2x^3 + x^2 + 2x + 1 = \left(x + \frac{1}{2}\right)\left(2x^2 + 2\right)$$

$$= 2\left(x + \frac{1}{2}\right)\left(x^2 + 1\right)$$

Since $x^2 + 1 = 0$ has no real solutions, the only real zero is $x = -\dfrac{1}{2}$, of multiplicity 1.

49. $f(x) = 2x^3 - 4x^2 - 10x + 20$

$$= 2\left(x^3 - 2x^2 - 5x + 10\right)$$

Step 1: $f(x)$ has at most 3 real zeros.

Step 2: By Descartes' Rule of Signs, there are two positive real zeros or no positive real zeros.

$$f(-x) = 2(-x)^3 - 4(-x)^2 - 10(-x) + 20,$$
$$= -2x^3 - 4x^2 + 10x + 20$$

thus, there is one negative real zeros.

Step 3: Possible rational zeros:

$p = \pm 1, \pm 2, \pm 5, \pm 10; \quad q = \pm 1;$

$$\frac{p}{q} = \pm 1, \pm 2, \pm 5, \pm 10$$

Step 4: Using synthetic division:

We try $x - 2$:

$$2\overline{)1 \quad -2 \quad -5 \quad 10}$$
$$ \quad 2 \quad 0 \quad -10$$
$$\overline{1 \quad 0 \quad -5 \quad 0}$$

Since the remainder is 0, $x - 2$ is a factor. The other factor is the quotient: $x^2 - 5$.

We can find the remaining real zeros by solving $x^2 - 5 = 0$

$$x^2 = 5$$
$$x = \pm\sqrt{5}$$

Thus, $f(x) = 2(x - 2)\left(x - \sqrt{5}\right)\left(x + \sqrt{5}\right)$. The real zeros are 2, $\sqrt{5}$, and $-\sqrt{5}$, each of multiplicity 1.

50. $f(x) = 3x^3 + 6x^2 - 15x - 30$

$\qquad = 3\left(x^3 + 2x^2 - 5x - 10\right)$

Step 1: $f(x)$ has at most 3 real zeros.

Step 2: By Descartes' Rule of Signs, there is one positive real zero.

$f(-x) = 3(-x)^3 + 6(-x)^2 - 15(-x) - 30$,

$\qquad = -3x^3 + 6x^2 + 15x - 30$

thus, there are two negative real zeros or no negative real zeros.

Step 3: Possible rational zeros:
$p = \pm 1, \pm 2, \pm 5, \pm 10; \quad q = \pm 1;$

$\dfrac{p}{q} = \pm 1, \pm 2, \pm 5, \pm 10$

Step 4: Using synthetic division:
We try $x + 2$:

$$
\begin{array}{r|rrr}
-2 & 1 & 2 & -5 & -10 \\
   &   & -2 & 0 & 10 \\
\hline
   & 1 & 0 & -5 & 0
\end{array}
$$

Since the remainder is 0, $x + 2$ is a factor. The other factor is the quotient: $x^2 - 5$.
We can find the remaining real zeros by solving

$x^2 - 5 = 0$

$\qquad x^2 = 5$

$\qquad x = \pm\sqrt{5}$

Thus, $f(x) = 3(x + 2)\left(x - \sqrt{5}\right)\left(x + \sqrt{5}\right)$. The real zeros are -2, $\sqrt{5}$, and $-\sqrt{5}$, each of multiplicity 1.

51. $f(x) = 2x^4 + x^3 - 7x^2 - 3x + 3$

Step 1: $f(x)$ has at most 4 real zeros.

Step 2: By Descartes' Rule of Signs, there are two positive real zeros or no positive real zeros.

$f(-x) = 2(-x)^4 + (-x)^3 - 7(-x)^2 - 3(-x) + 3$

$\qquad = 2x^4 - x^3 - 7x^2 + 3x + 3$

thus, there are two negative real zeros or no negative real zeros.

Step 3: Possible rational zeros:
$p = \pm 1, \pm 3; \quad q = \pm 1, \pm 2;$

$\dfrac{p}{q} = \pm\dfrac{1}{2}, \pm 1, \pm\dfrac{3}{2}, \pm 3$

Step 4: Using synthetic division:
We try $x + 1$:

$$
\begin{array}{r|rrrr}
-1 & 2 & 1 & -7 & -3 & 3 \\
   &   & -2 & 1 & 6 & -3 \\
\hline
   & 2 & -1 & -6 & 3 & 0
\end{array}
$$

$x + 1$ is a factor and the quotient is
$2x^3 - x^2 - 6x + 3$.
Factoring by grouping gives
$2x^3 - x^2 - 6x + 3 = x^2(2x - 1) - 3(2x - 1)$

$\qquad\qquad = (2x - 1)\left(x^2 - 3\right)$

Set each of these factors equal to 0 and solve:

$$
\begin{array}{ll}
2x - 1 = 0 & \qquad x^2 - 3 = 0 \\
2x = 1 & \qquad\qquad x^2 = 3 \\
x = \dfrac{1}{2} & \qquad\qquad x = \pm\sqrt{3}
\end{array}
$$

Thus,

$f(x) = (2x - 1)(x + 1)\left(x - \sqrt{3}\right)\left(x + \sqrt{3}\right)$

$\qquad = 2\left(x - \dfrac{1}{2}\right)(x + 1)\left(x - \sqrt{3}\right)\left(x + \sqrt{3}\right)$

The real zeros are $\dfrac{1}{2}$, -1, $\sqrt{3}$, and $-\sqrt{3}$, each of multiplicity 1.

52. $f(x) = 2x^4 - x^3 - 5x^2 + 2x + 2$

Step 1: $f(x)$ has at most 4 real zeros.

Step 2: By Descartes' Rule of Signs, there are two positive real zeros or no positive real zeros.

$f(-x) = 2(-x)^4 - (-x)^3 - 5(-x)^2 + 2(-x) + 2$

$\qquad = 2x^4 - x^3 - 5x^2 - 2x + 2$

thus, there are two negative real zeros or no negative real zeros.

Step 3: Possible rational zeros:
$p = \pm 1, \pm 2; \quad q = \pm 1, \pm 2;$

$\dfrac{p}{q} = \pm\dfrac{1}{2}, \pm 1, \pm 2, \pm 3$

Step 4: Using synthetic division:
We try $x - 1$:

$$
\begin{array}{r|rrrr}
1 & 2 & -1 & -5 & 2 & 2 \\
  &   & 2 & 1 & -4 & -2 \\
\hline
  & 2 & 1 & -4 & -2 & 0
\end{array}
$$

$x - 1$ is a factor and the quotient is
$2x^3 + x^2 - 4x - 2$.

Factoring by grouping gives
$$2x^3 + x^2 - 4x - 2 = x^2(2x+1) - 2(2x+1)$$
$$= (2x+1)(x^2 - 2)$$

Set each of these factors equal to 0 and solve:

$2x + 1 = 0$ $x^2 - 2 = 0$

$\quad 2x = -1$ $\quad x^2 = 2$

$\quad\quad x = -\dfrac{1}{2}$ $\quad\quad x = \pm\sqrt{2}$

Thus,
$$f(x) = (2x+1)(x-1)(x-\sqrt{2})(x+\sqrt{2})$$
$$= 2\left(x+\dfrac{1}{2}\right)(x-1)(x-\sqrt{2})(x+\sqrt{2})$$

The real zeros are $-\dfrac{1}{2}$, 1, $\sqrt{2}$, and $-\sqrt{2}$, each of multiplicity 1.

53. $f(x) = x^4 + x^3 - 3x^2 - x + 2$

Step 1: $f(x)$ has at most 4 real zeros.

Step 2: By Descartes' Rule of Signs, there are two positive real zeros or no positive real zeros.
$$f(-x) = (-x)^4 + (-x)^3 - 3(-x)^2 - (-x) + 2 \text{ thus,}$$
$$= x^4 - x^3 - 3x^2 + x + 2$$
there are two negative real zeros or no negative real zeros.

Step 3: Possible rational zeros:
$p = \pm 1, \pm 2; \quad q = \pm 1;$

$\dfrac{p}{q} = \pm 1, \pm 2$

Step 4: Using synthetic division:
We try $x + 2$:

$$\begin{array}{r|rrrr} -2 & 1 & 1 & -3 & -1 & 2 \\ & & -2 & 2 & 2 & -2 \\ \hline & 1 & -1 & -1 & 1 & 0 \end{array}$$

$x + 2$ is a factor and the quotient is $x^3 - x^2 - x + 1$.

We try $x + 1$ on $x^3 - x^2 - x + 1$

$$\begin{array}{r|rrrr} -1 & 1 & -1 & -1 & 1 \\ & & -1 & 2 & -1 \\ \hline & 1 & -2 & 1 & 0 \end{array}$$

$x + 1$ is a factor and the quotient is $x^2 - 2x + 1$.
Thus,

$$f(x) = (x+2)(x+1)(x^2 - 2x + 1)$$
$$= (x+2)(x+1)(x-1)^2$$

The real zeros are -2, -1, each of multiplicity 1, and 1, of multiplicity 2.

54. $f(x) = x^4 - x^3 - 6x^2 + 4x + 8$

Step 1: $f(x)$ has at most 4 real zeros.

Step 2: By Descartes' Rule of Signs, there are two positive real zeros or no positive real zeros.
$$f(-x) = (-x)^4 - (-x)^3 - 6(-x)^2 + 4(-x) + 8$$
$$= x^4 + x^3 - 6x^2 - 4x + 8$$
thus, there are two negative real zeros or no negative real zeros.

Step 3: Possible rational zeros:
$p = \pm 1, \pm 2, \pm 4, \pm 8; \quad q = \pm 1;$

$\dfrac{p}{q} = \pm 1, \pm 2, \pm 4, \pm 8$

Step 4: Using synthetic division:
We try $x + 2$:

$$\begin{array}{r|rrrr} -2 & 1 & -1 & -6 & 4 & 8 \\ & & -2 & 6 & 0 & -8 \\ \hline & 1 & -3 & 0 & 4 & 0 \end{array}$$

$x + 2$ is a factor and the quotient is $x^3 - 3x^2 + 4$.

We try $x + 1$ on $x^3 - 3x^2 + 4$

$$\begin{array}{r|rrrr} -1 & 1 & -3 & 0 & 4 \\ & & -1 & 4 & -4 \\ \hline & 1 & -4 & 4 & 0 \end{array}$$

$x + 1$ is a factor and the quotient is $x^2 - 4x + 4$.
Thus,
$$f(x) = (x+2)(x+1)(x^2 - 4x + 4)$$
$$= (x+2)(x+1)(x-2)^2$$

The real zeros are -2, -1, each of multiplicity 1, and 2, of multiplicity 2.

493

55. $f(x) = 4x^4 + 5x^3 + 9x^2 + 10x + 2$

Step 1: $f(x)$ has at most 4 real zeros.

Step 2: By Descartes' Rule of Signs, there are no positive real zeros.
$$f(-x) = 4(-x)^4 + 5(-x)^3 + 9(-x)^2 + 10(-x) + 2$$
$$= 4x^4 - 5x^3 + 9x^2 - 10x + 2$$
thus, there are four negative real zeros or two negative real zeros or no negative real zeros.

Step 3: Possible rational zeros:
$p = \pm 1, \pm 2; \quad q = \pm 1, \pm 2, \pm 4;$
$$\frac{p}{q} = \pm \frac{1}{4}, \pm \frac{1}{2}, \pm 1, \pm 2$$

Step 4: Using synthetic division:
We try $x + 1$:

$$
\begin{array}{r|rrrrr}
-1 & 4 & 5 & 9 & 10 & 2 \\
   &   & -4 & -1 & -8 & -2 \\
\hline
   & 4 & 1 & 8 & 2 & 0 \\
\end{array}
$$

$x + 1$ is a factor and the quotient is
$4x^3 + x^2 + 8x + 2$.
Factoring by grouping gives
$$4x^3 + x^2 + 8x + 2 = x^2(4x + 1) + 2(4x + 1)$$
$$= (4x + 1)(x^2 + 2)$$

Set each of these factors equal to 0 and solve:

$4x + 1 = 0 \qquad\qquad x^2 + 2 = 0$
$\quad 4x = -1 \qquad\qquad\quad x^2 = -2$
$\quad\; x = -\dfrac{1}{4} \qquad\qquad x = \pm\sqrt{-2}$
$\qquad\qquad\qquad\qquad\quad$ no real sol.

Thus,
$$f(x) = (4x + 1)(x + 1)(x^2 + 2)$$
$$= 4\left(x + \frac{1}{4}\right)(x + 1)(x^2 + 2)$$

The real zeros are $-\dfrac{1}{4}$ and -1, each of multiplicity 1.

56. $f(x) = 3x^4 + 4x^3 + 7x^2 + 8x + 2$

Step 1: $f(x)$ has at most 4 real zeros.

Step 2: By Descartes' Rule of Signs, there are no positive real zeros.
$$f(-x) = 3(-x)^4 + 4(-x)^3 + 7(-x)^2 + 8(-x) + 2$$
$$= 3x^4 - 4x^3 + 7x^2 - 8x + 2$$
thus, there are four negative real zeros or two negative real zeros or no negative real zeros.

Step 3: Possible rational zeros:
$p = \pm 1, \pm 2; \quad q = \pm 1, \pm 3;$
$$\frac{p}{q} = \pm \frac{1}{3}, \pm \frac{2}{3}, \pm 1, \pm 2$$

Step 4: Using synthetic division:
We try $x + 1$:

$$
\begin{array}{r|rrrrr}
-1 & 3 & 4 & 7 & 8 & 2 \\
   &   & -3 & -1 & -6 & -2 \\
\hline
   & 3 & 1 & 6 & 2 & 0 \\
\end{array}
$$

$x + 1$ is a factor and the quotient is
$3x^3 + x^2 + 6x + 2$.
Factoring by grouping gives
$$3x^3 + x^2 + 6x + 2 = x^2(3x + 1) + 2(3x + 1)$$
$$= (3x + 1)(x^2 + 2)$$

Set each of these factors equal to 0 and solve:

$3x + 1 = 0 \qquad\qquad x^2 + 2 = 0$
$\quad 3x = -1 \qquad\qquad\quad x^2 = -2$
$\quad\; x = -\dfrac{1}{3} \qquad\qquad x = \pm\sqrt{-2}$
$\qquad\qquad\qquad\qquad\quad$ no real sol.

Thus,
$$f(x) = (3x + 1)(x + 1)(x^2 + 2)$$
$$= 3\left(x + \frac{1}{3}\right)(x + 1)(x^2 + 2)$$

The real zeros are $-\dfrac{1}{3}$ and -1, each of multiplicity 1.

57. $x^4 - x^3 + 2x^2 - 4x - 8 = 0$

The solutions of the equation are the zeros
of $f(x) = x^4 - x^3 + 2x^2 - 4x - 8$.

Step 1: $f(x)$ has at most 4 real zeros.

Step 2: By Descartes' Rule of Signs, there are
three positive real zeros or there is one positive
real zero.
$f(-x) = (-x)^4 - (-x)^3 + 2(-x)^2 - 4(-x) - 8$
$\quad = x^4 + x^3 + 2x^2 + 4x - 8$
thus, there is one negative real zero.

Step 3: Possible rational zeros:
$p = \pm 1, \pm 2, \pm 4, \pm 8; \quad q = \pm 1;$

$\dfrac{p}{q} = \pm 1, \pm 2, \pm 4, \pm 8$

Step 4: Using synthetic division:
We try $x + 1$:

$$
\begin{array}{r|rrrrr}
-1) & 1 & -1 & 2 & -4 & -8 \\
   &   & -1 & 2 & -4 & 8 \\
\hline
   & 1 & -2 & 4 & -8 & 0
\end{array}
$$

$x + 1$ is a factor and the quotient is
$x^3 - 2x^2 + 4x - 8$.

We try $x - 2$ on $x^3 - 2x^2 + 4x - 8$

$$
\begin{array}{r|rrrr}
2) & 1 & -2 & 4 & -8 \\
   &   & 2 & 0 & 8 \\
\hline
   & 1 & 0 & 4 & 0
\end{array}
$$

$x - 2$ is a factor and the quotient is $x^2 + 4$.
Thus, $f(x) = (x+1)(x-2)(x^2+4)$.

Since $x^2 + 4 = 0$ has no real solutions, the
solution set is $\{-1,\ 2\}$.

58. $2x^3 + 3x^2 + 2x + 3 = 0$
Solve by factoring:
$x^2(2x+3) + (2x+3) = 0$
$\quad (2x+3)(x^2+1) = 0$

$$x = -\frac{3}{2}$$

Since $x^2 + 1 = 0$ has no real solutions, the
solution set is $\left\{-\dfrac{3}{2}\right\}$.

59. $3x^3 + 4x^2 - 7x + 2 = 0$
The solutions of the equation are the zeros of
$f(x) = 3x^3 + 4x^2 - 7x + 2$.

Step 1: $f(x)$ has at most 3 real zeros.

Step 2: By Descartes' Rule of Signs, there are
two positive real zeros or no positive real zeros.
$f(-x) = 3(-x)^3 + 4(-x)^2 - 7(-x) + 2$
$\quad = -3x^3 + 4x^2 + 7x + 2$
thus, there is one negative real zero.

Step 3: Possible rational zeros:
$p = \pm 1, \pm 2; \quad q = \pm 1, \pm 3$

$\dfrac{p}{q} = \pm 1, \pm 2, \pm \dfrac{1}{3}, \pm \dfrac{2}{3}$

Step 4: Using synthetic division:
We try $x - \dfrac{2}{3}$:

$$
\begin{array}{r|rrrr}
\frac{2}{3}) & 3 & 4 & -7 & 2 \\
   &   & 2 & 4 & -2 \\
\hline
   & 3 & 6 & -3 & 0
\end{array}
$$

$x - \dfrac{2}{3}$ is a factor. The other factor is the quotient
$3x^2 + 6x - 3$. Thus,
$$f(x) = \left(x - \frac{2}{3}\right)(3x^2 + 6x - 3)$$
$$= 3\left(x - \frac{2}{3}\right)(x^2 + 2x - 1)$$

Using the quadratic formula to solve
$x^2 + 2x - 1 = 0$:
$$x = \frac{-2 \pm \sqrt{4 - 4(1)(-1)}}{2(1)}$$
$$= \frac{-2 \pm \sqrt{8}}{2}$$
$$= \frac{-2 \pm 2\sqrt{2}}{2} = -1 \pm \sqrt{2}$$

The solution set is $\left\{-1 - \sqrt{2},\ -1 + \sqrt{2},\ \dfrac{2}{3}\right\}$.

60. $2x^3 - 3x^2 - 3x - 5 = 0$

The solutions of the equation are the zeros

of $f(x) = 2x^3 - 3x^2 - 3x - 5$.

Step 1: $f(x)$ has at most 3 real zeros.

Step 2: By Descartes' Rule of Signs, there is
one positive real zero.

$f(-x) = 2(-x)^3 - 3(-x)^2 - 3(-x) - 5$

$\qquad = -2x^3 - 3x^2 + 3x - 5$

thus, there are two negative real zeros or no
negative real zeros.

Step 3: Possible rational zeros:
$p = \pm 1, \pm 5; \quad q = \pm 1, \pm 2$

$\dfrac{p}{q} = \pm 1, \pm 5, \pm \dfrac{1}{2}, \pm \dfrac{5}{2}$

Step 4: Using synthetic division:

We try $x - \dfrac{5}{2}$:

$$\dfrac{5}{2}\overline{)\begin{array}{rrrr} 2 & -3 & -3 & -5 \\ & 5 & 5 & 5 \\ \hline 2 & 2 & 2 & 0 \end{array}}$$

$x - \dfrac{5}{2}$ is a factor. The other factor is the

quotient: $2x^2 + 2x + 2$. Thus,

$f(x) = \left(x - \dfrac{5}{2}\right)\left(2x^2 + 2x + 2\right)$

$\qquad = 2\left(x - \dfrac{5}{2}\right)\left(x^2 + x + 1\right)$

Since $x^2 + x + 1 = 0$ has no real solutions, the

solution set is $\left\{\dfrac{5}{2}\right\}$.

61. $3x^3 - x^2 - 15x + 5 = 0$
Solving by factoring:

$x^2(3x - 1) - 5(3x - 1) = 0$

$(3x - 1)(x^2 - 5) = 0$

$(3x - 1)(x - \sqrt{5})(x + \sqrt{5}) = 0$

The solution set is $\left\{-\sqrt{5}, \sqrt{5}, \dfrac{1}{3}\right\}$.

62. $2x^3 - 11x^2 + 10x + 8 = 0$

The solutions of the equation are the zeros

of $f(x) = 2x^3 - 11x^2 + 10x + 8$.

Step 1: $f(x)$ has at most 3 real zeros.

Step 2: By Descartes' Rule of Signs, there are
two positive real zeros or no positive real zeros.

$f(-x) = 2(-x)^3 - 11(-x)^2 + 10(-x) + 8$

$\qquad = -2x^3 - 11x^2 - 10x + 8$

thus, there is one negative real zero.

Step 3: Possible rational zeros:
$p = \pm 1, \pm 2, \pm 4, \pm 8; \quad q = \pm 1, \pm 2$

$\dfrac{p}{q} = \pm 1, \pm 2, \pm 4, \pm 8, \pm \dfrac{1}{2}$

Step 4: Using synthetic division:
We try $x - 4$:

$$4\overline{)\begin{array}{rrrr} 2 & -11 & 10 & 8 \\ & 8 & -12 & -8 \\ \hline 2 & -3 & -2 & 0 \end{array}}$$

$x - 4$ is a factor. The other factor is the

quotient: $2x^2 - 3x - 2$. Thus,

$f(x) = (x - 4)(2x^2 - 3x - 2)$

$\qquad = (x - 4)(2x + 1)(x - 2)$

The solution set is $\left\{-\dfrac{1}{2}, 2, 4\right\}$.

63. $x^4 + 4x^3 + 2x^2 - x + 6 = 0$
The solutions of the equation are the zeros

of $f(x) = x^4 + 4x^3 + 2x^2 - x + 6$.

Step 1: $f(x)$ has at most 4 real zeros.

Step 2: By Descartes' Rule of Signs, there are
two positive real zeros or no positive real zeros.

$f(-x) = (-x)^4 + 4(-x)^3 + 2(-x)^2 - (-x) + 6$

$\qquad = x^4 - 4x^3 + 2x^2 + x + 6$

thus, there are two negative real zeros or no
negative real zeros.

Step 3: Possible rational zeros:
$p = \pm 1, \pm 2, \pm 3, \pm 6; \quad q = \pm 1;$

$\dfrac{p}{q} = \pm 1, \pm 2, \pm 3, \pm 6$

Step 4: Using synthetic division:
We try $x + 3$:

496

$$-3 \overline{)\begin{array}{rrrr} 1 & 4 & 2 & -1 & 6 \\ & -3 & -3 & 3 & -6 \\ \hline 1 & 1 & -1 & 2 & 0 \end{array}}$$

$x+3$ is a factor and the quotient is
$x^3 + x^2 - x + 2$.

We try $x+2$ on $x^3 + x^2 - x + 2$
$$-2 \overline{)\begin{array}{rrrr} 1 & 1 & -1 & 2 \\ & -2 & 2 & -2 \\ \hline 1 & -1 & 1 & 0 \end{array}}$$

$x+2$ is a factor and the quotient is $x^2 - x + 1$.
Thus, $f(x) = (x+3)(x+2)(x^2 - x + 1)$.

Since $x^2 - x + 1 = 0$ has no real solutions, the
solution set is $\{-3, -2\}$.

64. $x^4 - 2x^3 + 10x^2 - 18x + 9 = 0$
The solutions of the equation are the zeros
of $f(x) = x^4 - 2x^3 + 10x^2 - 18x + 9$

Step 1: $f(x)$ has at most 4 real zeros.

Step 2: By Descartes' Rule of Signs, there are
four positive real zeros or two positive real zeros
or no positive real zeros.
$f(-x) = (-x)^4 - 2(-x)^3 + 10(-x)^2 - 18(-x) + 9$
$\qquad = x^4 + 2x^3 + 10x^2 + 18x + 9$
Thus, there are no negative real zeros.

Step 3: Possible rational zeros:
$p = \pm1, \pm3, \pm9; \quad q = \pm1$

$\dfrac{p}{q} = \pm1, \pm3, \pm9$

Step 4: Using synthetic division:
We try $x-1$:
$$1 \overline{)\begin{array}{rrrr} 1 & -2 & 10 & -18 & 9 \\ & 1 & -1 & 9 & -9 \\ \hline 1 & -1 & 9 & -9 & 0 \end{array}}$$
$x-1$ is a factor and the quotient is
$x^3 - x^2 + 9x - 9$.

We try $x-1$ on $x^3 - x^2 + 9x - 9$
$$1 \overline{)\begin{array}{rrr} 1 & -1 & 9 & -9 \\ & 1 & 0 & 9 \\ \hline 1 & 0 & 9 & 0 \end{array}}$$

$x-1$ is a factor and the quotient is $x^2 + 9$. Thus,
$f(x) = (x-1)^2(x^2 + 9)$.

Since $x^2 + 9 = 0$ has no real solutions, the
solution set is $\{1\}$.

65. $x^3 - \dfrac{2}{3}x^2 + \dfrac{8}{3}x + 1 = 0 \Rightarrow 3x^3 - 2x^2 + 8x + 3 = 0$

The solutions of the equation are the zeros of
$f(x) = 3x^3 - 2x^2 + 8x + 3$.

Step 1: $f(x)$ has at most 3 real zeros.

Step 2: By Descartes' Rule of Signs, there are
two positive real zeros or no positive real zeros.
$f(-x) = 3(-x)^3 - 2(-x)^2 + 8(-x) + 3$,
$\qquad = -3x^3 - 2x^2 - 8x + 3$
thus, there is one negative real zero.

Step 3: To find the possible rational zeros:
$p = \pm1, \pm3; \quad q = \pm1, \pm3$

$\dfrac{p}{q} = \pm1, \pm3, \pm\dfrac{1}{3}$

Step 4: Using synthetic division:
We try $x + \dfrac{1}{3}$:

$$-\dfrac{1}{3} \overline{)\begin{array}{rrr} 3 & -2 & 8 & 3 \\ & -1 & 1 & -3 \\ \hline 3 & -3 & 9 & 0 \end{array}}$$

$x + \dfrac{1}{3}$ is a factor. The other factor is the

quotient: $3x^2 - 3x + 9$.
Thus,
$$f(x) = \left(x + \dfrac{1}{3}\right)(3x^2 - 3x + 9)$$

$$= \left(x + \dfrac{1}{3}\right)(3)(x^2 - x + 3)$$

$$= (3x + 1)(x^2 - x + 3)$$

Since $x^2 - x + 3 = 0$ has no real solutions, the

solution set is $\left\{-\dfrac{1}{3}\right\}$.

66. $x^3 + \dfrac{3}{2}x^2 + 3x - 2 = 0 \Rightarrow 2x^3 + 3x^2 + 6x - 4 = 0$

The solutions of the equation are the zeros of
$f(x) = 2x^3 + 3x^2 + 6x - 4$.

Step 1: $f(x)$ has at most 3 real zeros.

Step 2: By Descartes' Rule of Signs, there is one positive real zero.

$f(-x) = 2(-x)^3 + 3(-x)^2 + 6(-x) - 4$

$ = -2x^3 + 3x^2 - 6x - 4$

thus, there are two negative real zeros or no negative real zeros.

Step 3: To find the possible rational zeros:
$p = \pm1, \pm 2, \pm 4; \quad q = \pm1, \pm 2$

$\dfrac{p}{q} = \pm1, \pm\dfrac{1}{2}, \pm 2, \pm 4$

Step 4: Using synthetic division:
We try $x - 1$:

$$\begin{array}{r|rrr}
1 & 2 & 3 & 6 & -4 \\
  &   & 2 & 5 & 11 \\
\hline
  & 2 & 5 & 11 & 7
\end{array}$$

$x - 1$ **is not** a factor

We try $x - \frac{1}{2}$

$$\begin{array}{r|rrr}
\frac{1}{2} & 2 & 3 & 6 & -4 \\
  &   & 1 & 2 & 4 \\
\hline
  & 2 & 4 & 8 & 0
\end{array}$$

$x - \frac{1}{2}$ **is** a factor Thus,

$f(x) = \left(x - \dfrac{1}{2} \right)\left(2x^2 + 4x + 8 \right)$

$ = 2\left(x - \dfrac{1}{2} \right)\left(x^2 + 2x + 4 \right)$

Since $x^2 + 2x + 4 = 0$ has no real solutions, the solution set is $\left\{ \dfrac{1}{2} \right\}$.

67. $2x^4 - 19x^3 + 57x^2 - 64x + 20 = 0$
The solutions of the equation are the zeros of
$f(x) = 2x^4 - 19x^3 + 57x^2 - 64x + 20$.

Step 1: $f(x)$ has at most 4 real zeros.

Step 2: By Descartes' Rule of Signs, there are four positive real zeros or two positive real zeros or no positive real zeros.

$f(-x) = 2(-x)^4 - 19(-x)^3 + 57(-x)^2 - 64(-x) + 20$

$ = 2x^4 + 19x^3 + 57x^2 + 64x + 20$

Thus, there are no negative real zeros.

Step 3: To find the possible rational zeros:
$p = \pm1, \pm 2, \pm4, \pm5, \pm10, \pm20; \quad q = \pm1, \pm 2;$

$\dfrac{p}{q} = \pm1, \pm\dfrac{1}{2}, \pm2, \pm4, \pm5, \pm\dfrac{5}{2}, \pm10, \pm20$

Step 4: Using synthetic division:
We try $x - 1$:

$$\begin{array}{r|rrrr}
1 & 2 & -19 & 57 & -64 & 20 \\
  &   & 2 & -17 & 40 & -24 \\
\hline
  & 2 & -17 & 40 & -24 & -4
\end{array}$$

$x - 1$ **is not** a factor

We try $x - \dfrac{1}{2}$:

$$\begin{array}{r|rrrr}
\frac{1}{2} & 2 & -19 & 57 & -64 & 20 \\
  &   & 1 & -9 & 24 & -20 \\
\hline
  & 2 & -18 & 48 & -40 & 0
\end{array}$$

$x - \dfrac{1}{2}$ is a factor and the quotient is

$2x^3 - 18x^2 + 48x - 40$. Thus,

$f(x) = \left(x - \dfrac{1}{2} \right)\left(2x^3 - 18x^2 + 48x - 40 \right)$

$ = 2\left(x - \dfrac{1}{2} \right)\left(x^3 - 9x^2 + 24x - 20 \right)$

Now try $x - 2$ as a factor of $x^3 - 9x^2 + 24x - 20$.

$$\begin{array}{r|rrr}
2 & 1 & -9 & 24 & -20 \\
  &   & 2 & -14 & 20 \\
\hline
  & 1 & -7 & 10 & 0
\end{array}$$

$x - 2$ is a factor, and the other factor is the quotient $x^2 - 7x + 10$. Thus,

$x^3 - 9x^2 + 24x - 20 = (x - 2)(x^2 - 7x + 10)$

$ = (x - 2)(x - 2)(x - 5)$

$f(x) = 2\left(x - \dfrac{1}{2} \right)(x - 2)^2(x - 5)$

The solution set is $\left\{ \dfrac{1}{2}, 2, 5 \right\}$.

68. $2x^4 + x^3 - 24x^2 + 20x + 16 = 0$

The solutions of the equation are the zeros of

$f(x) = 2x^4 + x^3 - 24x^2 + 20x + 16$.

Step 1: $f(x)$ has at most 4 real zeros.

Step 2: By Descartes' Rule of Signs, there are two positive real zeros or no positive real zeros.

$f(-x) = 2(-x)^4 + (-x)^3 - 24(-x)^2 + 20(-x) + 16$

$\quad = 2x^4 - x^3 - 24x^2 - 20x + 16$

thus, there are two negative real zeros or no negative real zeros.

Step 3: To find the possible rational zeros:

$p = \pm 1, \pm 2, \pm 4, \pm 8, \pm 16; \quad q = \pm 1, \pm 2;$

$\dfrac{p}{q} = \pm 1, \pm \dfrac{1}{2}, \pm 2, \pm 4, \pm 8, \pm 16$

Step 4: Using synthetic division:

We try $x - 2$:

$$
\begin{array}{r|rrrrr}
2) & 2 & 1 & -24 & 20 & 16 \\
   &   & 4 & 10 & -28 & -16 \\
\hline
   & 2 & 5 & -14 & -8 & 0
\end{array}
$$

$x - 2$ is a factor, and the other factor is the quotient $2x^3 + 5x^2 - 14x - 8$.

Thus, $f(x) = (x-2)\left(2x^3 + 5x^2 - 14x - 8\right)$.

Now try $x + 4$ as a factor of $2x^3 + 5x^2 - 14x - 8$.

$$
\begin{array}{r|rrrr}
-4) & 2 & 5 & -14 & -8 \\
    &   & -8 & 12 & 8 \\
\hline
    & 2 & -3 & -2 & 0
\end{array}
$$

$x + 4$ is a factor, and the other factor is the quotient $2x^2 - 3x - 2$. Thus,

$2x^3 + 5x^2 - 14x - 8 = (x+4)\left(2x^2 - 3x - 2\right)$

$\qquad\qquad\qquad\quad = (x+4)(2x+1)(x-2)$

$f(x) = (x-2)(x+4)(2x+1)(x-2)$

$\qquad = (x-2)^2 (x+4)(2x+1)$

The solution set is $\left\{-4, -\dfrac{1}{2}, 2\right\}$.

69. $f(x) = x^3 + 2x^2 - 5x - 6 = (x+3)(x+1)(x-2)$

    x-intercepts: $-3, -1, 2$;

    Near -3: $f(x) \approx (x+3)(-3+1)(-3-2) = 10(x+3)$

    Near -1: $f(x) \approx (-1+3)(x+1)(-1-2) = -6(x+1)$

    Near 2: $f(x) \approx (2+3)(2+1)(x-2) = 15(x-2)$

    Plot the point $(-3, 0)$ and show a line with positive slope there.

    Plot the point $(-1, 0)$ and show a line with negative slope there.

    Plot the point $(2, 0)$ and show a line with positive slope there.

    y-intercept: $f(0) = 0^3 + 2(0)^2 - 5(0) - 6 = -6$;

    The graph of f crosses the x-axis at $x = -3, -1$ and 2 since each zero has multiplicity 1.

Interval	$(-\infty, -3)$	$(-3, -1)$	$(-1, 2)$	$(2, \infty)$
Number Chosen	-4	-2	0	3
Value of f	-18	4	-6	24
Location of Graph	Below x-axis	Above x-axis	Below x-axis	Above x-axis
Point on Graph	$(-4, -18)$	$(-2, 4)$	$(0, -6)$	$(3, 24)$

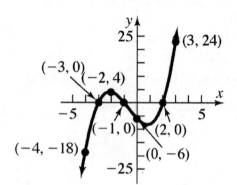

70. $f(x) = x^3 + 8x^2 + 11x - 20 = (x+5)(x+4)(x-1)$

    x-intercepts: $-5, -4, 1$;

    Near -5: $f(x) \approx (x+5)(-5+4)(-5-1) = 6(x+5)$

    Near -4: $f(x) \approx (-4+5)(x+4)(-4-1) = -5(x+4)$

    Near 1: $f(x) \approx (1+5)(1+4)(x-1) = 30(x-1)$

    Plot the point $(-5, 0)$ and show a line with positive slope there.

    Plot the point $(-4, 0)$ and show a line with negative slope there.

    Plot the point $(1, 0)$ and show a line with positive slope there.

y-intercept: $f(0) = 0^3 + 8(0)^2 + 11(0) - 20 = -20$

The graph of f crosses the *x*-axis at $x = -5, -4$ and 1 since each zero has multiplicity 1.

Interval	$(-\infty, -5)$	$(-5, -4)$	$(-4, 1)$	$(1, \infty)$
Number Chosen	-6	-4.5	0	2
Value of f	-14	1.375	-20	42
Location of Graph	Below *x*-axis	Above *x*-axis	Below *x*-axis	Above *x*-axis
Point on Graph	$(-6, -14)$	$(-4.5, 1.375)$	$(0, -20)$	$(2, 42)$

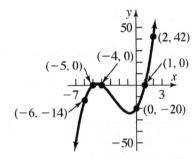

71. $f(x) = 2x^3 - x^2 + 2x - 1 = \left(x - \dfrac{1}{2}\right)\left(2x^2 + 2\right)$

x-intercept: $\dfrac{1}{2}$; Near $\dfrac{1}{2}$: $f(x) \approx \left(x - \dfrac{1}{2}\right)\left(2\left(\dfrac{1}{2}\right)^2 + 2\right) = \dfrac{5}{2}\left(x - \dfrac{1}{2}\right)$

Plot the point $\left(\dfrac{1}{2}, 0\right)$ and show a line with positive slope there.

y-intercept: $f(0) = 2(0)^3 - 0^2 + 2(0) - 1 = -1$

The graph of f crosses the *x*-axis at $x = \dfrac{1}{2}$ since the zero has multiplicity 1.

Interval	$\left(-\infty, \dfrac{1}{2}\right)$	$\left(\dfrac{1}{2}, \infty\right)$
Number Chosen	0	1
Value of f	-1	2
Location of Graph	Below *x*-axis	Above *x*-axis
Point on Graph	$(0, -1)$	$(1, 2)$

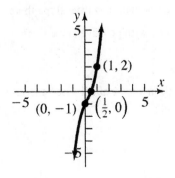

501

72. $f(x) = 2x^3 + x^2 + 2x + 1 = \left(x + \dfrac{1}{2}\right)\left(2x^2 + 2\right)$

x-intercept: $-\dfrac{1}{2}$

Near $-\dfrac{1}{2}$: $f(x) \approx \left(x + \dfrac{1}{2}\right)\left(2\left(-\dfrac{1}{2}\right)^2 + 2\right) = \dfrac{5}{2}\left(x + \dfrac{1}{2}\right)$

Plot the point $\left(-\dfrac{1}{2}, 0\right)$ and show a line with positive slope there.

y-intercept: $f(0) = 2(0)^3 + 0^2 + 2(0) + 1 = 1$

The graph of f crosses the x-axis at $x = -\dfrac{1}{2}$ since the zero has multiplicity 1.

Interval	$\left(-\infty, -\dfrac{1}{2}\right)$	$\left(-\dfrac{1}{2}, \infty\right)$
Number Chosen	-1	0
Value of f	-2	1
Location of Graph	Below x-axis	Above x-axis
Point on Graph	$(-1, -2)$	$(0, 1)$

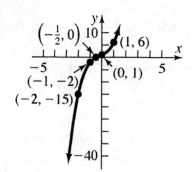

73. $f(x) = x^4 + x^2 - 2 = (x+1)(x-1)(x^2+2)$

x-intercepts: -1, 1

Near -1: $f(x) \approx (x+1)(-1-1)\left((-1)^2 + 2\right) = -6(x+1)$

Near 1: $f(x) \approx (1+1)(x-1)\left(1^2 + 2\right) = 6(x-1)$

Plot the point $(-1, 0)$ and show a line with negative slope there.

Plot the point $(1, 0)$ and show a line with positive slope there.

y-intercept: $f(0) = 0^4 + 0^2 - 2 = -2$

The graph of f crosses the x-axis at $x = -1$ and 1 since each zero has multiplicity 1.

Interval	$(-\infty,-1)$	$(-1,1)$	$(1,\infty)$
Number Chosen	-2	0	2
Value of f	18	-2	18
Location of Graph	Above x-axis	Below x-axis	Above x-axis
Point on Graph	$(-2,18)$	$(0,-2)$	$(2,18)$

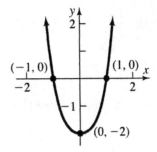

74. $f(x) = x^4 - 3x^2 - 4 = (x+2)(x-2)(x^2+1)$

x-intercepts: $-2, 2$

Near -2: $f(x) \approx (x+2)(-2-2)\left((-2)^2+1\right) = -20(x+2)$

Near 2: $f(x) \approx (2+2)(x-2)\left(2^2+1\right) = 20(x-2)$

Plot the point $(-2,0)$ and show a line with negative slope there.

Plot the point $(2,0)$ and show a line with positive slope there.

y-intercept: $f(0) = 0^4 - 3(0)^2 - 4 = -4$

The graph of f crosses the x-axis at $x = -2$ and 2 since each zero has multiplicity 1.

Interval	$(-\infty,-2)$	$(-2,2)$	$(2,\infty)$
Number Chosen	-3	0	3
Value of f	50	-4	50
Location of Graph	Above x-axis	Below x-axis	Above x-axis
Point on Graph	$(-3,50)$	$(0,-4)$	$(3,50)$

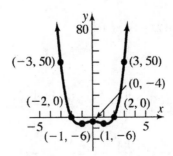

75. $f(x) = 4x^4 + 7x^2 - 2 = (2x+1)(2x-1)(x^2+2)$

x-intercepts: $-\dfrac{1}{2}, \dfrac{1}{2}$

Near $-\dfrac{1}{2}$: $f(x) \approx (2x+1)\left(2\left(-\dfrac{1}{2}\right)-1\right)\left(\left(-\dfrac{1}{2}\right)^2+2\right) = -\dfrac{9}{2}(2x+1)$

Near $\dfrac{1}{2}$: $f(x) \approx \left(2\left(\dfrac{1}{2}\right)+1\right)(2x-1)\left(\left(\dfrac{1}{2}\right)^2+2\right) = \dfrac{9}{2}(2x-1)$

Plot the point $\left(-\dfrac{1}{2}, 0\right)$ and show a line with negative slope there.

Plot the point $\left(\dfrac{1}{2}, 0\right)$ and show a line with positive slope there.

y-intercept: $f(0) = 4(0)^4 + 7(0)^2 - 2 = -2$

The graph of f crosses the x-axis at $x = -\dfrac{1}{2}$ and $\dfrac{1}{2}$ since each zero has multiplicity 1.

Interval	$\left(-\infty, -\dfrac{1}{2}\right)$	$\left(-\dfrac{1}{2}, \dfrac{1}{2}\right)$	$\left(\dfrac{1}{2}, \infty\right)$
Number Chosen	-1	0	1
Value of f	9	-2	9
Location of Graph	Above x-axis	Below x-axis	Above x-axis
Point on Graph	$(-1, 9)$	$(0, -2)$	$(1, 9)$

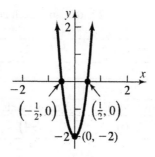

76. $f(x) = 4x^4 + 15x^2 - 4 = (2x+1)(2x-1)(x^2+4)$

x-intercepts: $-\dfrac{1}{2}, \dfrac{1}{2}$

Near $-\dfrac{1}{2}$: $f(x) \approx (2x+1)\left(2\left(-\dfrac{1}{2}\right)-1\right)\left(\left(-\dfrac{1}{2}\right)^2+4\right) = -\dfrac{17}{2}(2x+1)$

Near $\dfrac{1}{2}$: $f(x) \approx \left(2\left(\dfrac{1}{2}\right)+1\right)(2x-1)\left(\left(\dfrac{1}{2}\right)^2+4\right) = \dfrac{17}{2}(2x-1)$

Plot the point $\left(-\dfrac{1}{2},0\right)$ and show a line with negative slope there.

Plot the point $\left(\dfrac{1}{2},0\right)$ and show a line with positive slope there.

y-intercept: $f(0)=4(0)^4+15(0)^2-4=-4$

The graph of f crosses the *x*-axis at $x=-\dfrac{1}{2}$ and $\dfrac{1}{2}$ since each zero has multiplicity 1.

Interval	$\left(-\infty,-\dfrac{1}{2}\right)$	$\left(-\dfrac{1}{2},\dfrac{1}{2}\right)$	$\left(\dfrac{1}{2},\infty\right)$
Number Chosen	-1	0	1
Value of f	15	-4	15
Location of Graph	Above *x*-axis	Below *x*-axis	Above *x*-axis
Point on Graph	$(-1,15)$	$(0,-4)$	$(1,15)$

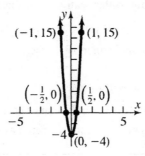

77. $f(x)=x^4+x^3-3x^2-x+2=(x+2)(x+1)(x-1)^2$

x-intercepts: $-2, -1, 1$

Near -2: $f(x)\approx(x+2)(-2+1)(-2-1)^2=-9(x+2)$

Near -1: $f(x)\approx(-1+2)(x+1)(-1-1)^2=4(x+1)$

Near 1: $f(x)\approx(1+2)(1+1)(x-1)^2=6(x-1)^2$

Plot the point $(-2,0)$ and show a line with negative slope there.

Plot the point $(-1,0)$ and show a line with positive slope there.

Plot the point $(1,0)$ and show a parabola opening up there.

y-intercept: $f(0)=0^4+0^3-3(0)^2-0+2=2$

The graph of f crosses the *x*-axis at $x=-2$ and -1 since each zero has multiplicity 1.

The graph of f touches the *x*-axis at $x=1$ since the zero has multiplicity 2.

Interval	$(-\infty,-2)$	$(-2,-1)$	$(-1,1)$	$(1,\infty)$
Number Chosen	-3	-1.5	0	2
Value of f	32	-1.5625	2	12
Location of Graph	Above *x*-axis	Below *x*-axis	Above *x*-axis	Above *x*-axis
Point on Graph	$(-3,32)$	$(-1.5,-1.5625)$	$(0,2)$	$(2,12)$

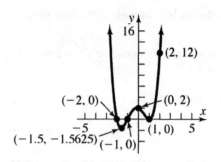

78. $f(x) = x^4 - x^3 - 6x^2 + 4x + 8 = (x+2)(x+1)(x-2)^2$

x-intercepts: $-2, -1, 2$

Near -2: $f(x) \approx (x+2)(-2+1)(-2-2)^2 = -16(x+2)$

Near -1: $f(x) \approx (-1+2)(x+1)(-1-2)^2 = 9(x+1)$

Near 2: $f(x) \approx (2+2)(2+1)(x-2)^2 = 12(x-2)^2$

Plot the point $(-2, 0)$ and show a line with negative slope there.

Plot the point $(-1, 0)$ and show a line with positive slope there.

Plot the point $(2, 0)$ and show a parabola opening up there.

y-intercept: $f(0) = 0^4 - 0^3 - 6(0)^2 + 4(0) + 8 = 8$

The graph of f crosses the x-axis at $x = -2$ and -1 since each zero has multiplicity 1.

The graph of f touches the x-axis at $x = 2$ since the zero has multiplicity 2.

Interval	$(-\infty, -2)$	$(-2, -1)$	$(-1, 2)$	$(2, \infty)$
Number Chosen	-3	-1.5	0	3
Value of f	50	-3.0625	8	20
Location of Graph	Above x-axis	Below x-axis	Above x-axis	Above x-axis
Point on Graph	$(-3, 50)$	$(-1.5, -3.0625)$	$(0, 8)$	$(3, 20)$

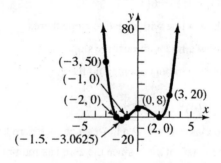

79. $f(x) = 4x^5 - 8x^4 - x + 2 = (x-2)(\sqrt{2}x - 1)(\sqrt{2}x + 1)(2x^2 + 1)$

x-intercepts: $-\dfrac{\sqrt{2}}{2}, \dfrac{\sqrt{2}}{2}, 2$

Near $-\dfrac{\sqrt{2}}{2}$: $f(x) \approx \left(-\dfrac{\sqrt{2}}{2} - 2\right)\left(\sqrt{2}\left(-\dfrac{\sqrt{2}}{2}\right) - 1\right)(\sqrt{2}x + 1)\left(2\left(\dfrac{\sqrt{2}}{2}\right)^2 + 1\right) = 2(\sqrt{2} + 4)(\sqrt{2}x + 1)$

Near $\dfrac{\sqrt{2}}{2}$: $f(x) \approx \left(\dfrac{\sqrt{2}}{2} - 2\right)(\sqrt{2}x - 1)\left(\sqrt{2}\left(\dfrac{\sqrt{2}}{2}\right) + 1\right)\left(2\left(\dfrac{\sqrt{2}}{2}\right)^2 + 1\right) = 2(\sqrt{2} - 4)(\sqrt{2}x - 1)$

Near 2: $f(x) \approx (x-2)(\sqrt{2}(2) - 1)(\sqrt{2}(2) + 1)(2(2)^2 + 1) = 63(x - 2)$

Plot the point $\left(-\dfrac{\sqrt{2}}{2}, 0\right)$ and show a line with positive slope there.

Plot the point $\left(\dfrac{\sqrt{2}}{2}, 0\right)$ and show a line with negative slope there.

Plot the point $(2, 0)$ and show a line with positive slope there.

y-intercept: $f(0) = 4(0)^5 - 8(0)^4 - 0 + 2 = 2$

The graph of f crosses the x-axis at $x = -\dfrac{\sqrt{2}}{2}$, $x = \dfrac{\sqrt{2}}{2}$ and $x = 2$ since each zero has multiplicity 1.

Interval	$\left(-\infty, -\dfrac{\sqrt{2}}{2}\right)$	$\left(-\dfrac{\sqrt{2}}{2}, \dfrac{\sqrt{2}}{2}\right)$	$\left(\dfrac{\sqrt{2}}{2}, 2\right)$	$(2, \infty)$
Number Chosen	-1	0	1	3
Value of f	-9	2	-3	323
Location of Graph	Below x-axis	Above x-axis	Below x-axis	Above x-axis
Point on Graph	$(-1, -9)$	$(0, 2)$	$(1, -3)$	$(3, 323)$

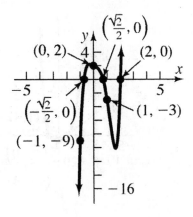

80. $f(x) = 4x^5 + 12x^4 - x - 3 = (x+3)\left(\sqrt{2}x - 1\right)\left(\sqrt{2}x + 1\right)\left(2x^2 + 1\right)$

x-intercepts: $-3, -\dfrac{\sqrt{2}}{2}, \dfrac{\sqrt{2}}{2}$

Near -3: $f(x) \approx (x+3)\left(\sqrt{2}(-3) - 1\right)\left(\sqrt{2}(-3) + 1\right)\left(2(-3)^2 + 1\right) = 323(x+3)$

Near $-\dfrac{\sqrt{2}}{2}$: $f(x) \approx \left(-\dfrac{\sqrt{2}}{2} + 3\right)\left(\sqrt{2}\left(-\dfrac{\sqrt{2}}{2}\right) - 1\right)\left(\sqrt{2}x + 1\right)\left(2\left(-\dfrac{\sqrt{2}}{2}\right)^2 + 1\right) = 2\left(\sqrt{2} - 6\right)\left(\sqrt{2}x + 1\right)$

Near $\dfrac{\sqrt{2}}{2}$: $f(x) = \left(\dfrac{\sqrt{2}}{2} + 3\right)\left(\sqrt{2}x - 1\right)\left(\sqrt{2}\left(\dfrac{\sqrt{2}}{2}\right) + 1\right)\left(2\left(\dfrac{\sqrt{2}}{2}\right)^2 + 1\right) = 2\left(\sqrt{2} + 6\right)\left(\sqrt{2}x - 1\right)$

Plot the point $(-3, 0)$ and show a line with positive slope there.

Plot the point $\left(-\dfrac{\sqrt{2}}{2}, 0\right)$ and show a line with negative slope there.

Plot the point $\left(\dfrac{\sqrt{2}}{2}, 0\right)$ and show a line with positive slope there.

y-intercept: $f(0) = 4(0)^5 + 12(0)^4 - 0 - 3 = -3$

The graph of f crosses the x-axis at $x = -\dfrac{\sqrt{2}}{2}$, $x = \dfrac{\sqrt{2}}{2}$ and $x = -3$ since each zero has multiplicity 1.

Interval	$(-\infty, -3)$	$\left(-3, -\dfrac{\sqrt{2}}{2}\right)$	$\left(-\dfrac{\sqrt{2}}{2}, \dfrac{\sqrt{2}}{2}\right)$	$\left(\dfrac{\sqrt{2}}{2}, \infty\right)$
Number Chosen	-4	-2	0	1
Value of f	-1023	63	-3	12
Location of Graph	Below x-axis	Above x-axis	Below x-axis	Above x-axis
Point on Graph	$(-4, -1023)$	$(-2, 63)$	$(0, -3)$	$(1, 12)$

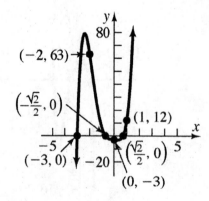

81. $f(x) = x^4 - 3x^2 - 4$

$a_3 = 0, a_2 = -3, a_1 = 0, a_0 = -4$

$$\text{Max}\{1, |-4| + |0| + |-3| + |0|\}$$
$$= \text{Max}\{1, 4 + 0 + 3 + 0\}$$
$$= \text{Max}\{1, 7\} = 7$$

$$1 + \text{Max}\{|-4|, |0|, |-3|, |0|\}$$
$$= 1 + \text{Max}\{4, 0, 3, 0\}$$
$$= 1 + 4 = 5$$

The smaller of the two numbers is 5. Thus, every zero of f lies between -5 and 5.

82. $f(x) = x^4 - 5x^2 - 36$

$a_3 = 0, a_2 = -5, a_1 = 0, a_0 = -36$

$$\text{Max}\{1, |-36| + |0| + |-5| + |0|\}$$
$$= \text{Max}\{1, 36 + 0 + 5 + 0\}$$
$$= \text{Max}\{1, 41\} = 41$$

$$1 + \text{Max}\{|-36|, |0|, |-5|, |0|\}$$
$$= 1 + \text{Max}\{36, 0, 5, 0\}$$
$$= 1 + 36 = 37$$

The smaller of the two numbers is 37. Thus, every zero of f lies between -37 and 37.

83. $f(x) = x^4 + x^3 - x - 1$

$a_3 = 1, a_2 = 0, a_1 = -1, a_0 = -1$

$$\text{Max}\{1, |-1| + |-1| + |0| + |1|\}$$
$$= \text{Max}\{1, 1 + 1 + 0 + 1\}$$
$$= \text{Max}\{1, 3\} = 3$$

$$1 + \text{Max}\{|-1|, |-1|, |0|, |1|\}$$
$$= 1 + \text{Max}\{1, 1, 0, 1\}$$
$$= 1 + 1 = 2$$

The smaller of the two numbers is 2. Thus, every zero of f lies between -2 and 2.

84. $f(x) = x^4 - x^3 + x - 1$

$a_3 = -1, a_2 = 0, a_1 = 1, a_0 = -1$

$$\text{Max}\{1, |-1| + |1| + |0| + |-1|\}$$
$$= \text{Max}\{1, 1 + 1 + 0 + 1\}$$
$$= \text{Max}\{1, 3\} = 3$$

$$1 + \text{Max}\{|-1|, |1|, |0|, |-1|\}$$
$$= 1 + \text{Max}\{1, 1, 0, 1\}$$
$$= 1 + 1 = 2$$

The smaller of the two numbers is 2. Thus, every zero of f lies between -2 and 2.

85. $f(x) = 3x^4 + 3x^3 - x^2 - 12x - 12 = 3\left(x^4 + x^3 - \frac{1}{3}x^2 - 4x - 4\right)$

Note: The leading coefficient must be 1.

$a_3 = 1, a_2 = -\dfrac{1}{3}, a_1 = -4, a_0 = -4$

$$\text{Max}\left\{1, |-4| + |-4| + \left|-\frac{1}{3}\right| + |1|\right\}$$
$$= \text{Max}\left\{1, 4 + 4 + \frac{1}{3} + 1\right\}$$
$$= \text{Max}\left\{1, \frac{28}{3}\right\} = \frac{28}{3}$$

$$1 + \text{Max}\left\{|-4|, |-4|, \left|-\frac{1}{3}\right|, |1|\right\}$$
$$= 1 + \text{Max}\left\{4, 4, \frac{1}{3}, 1\right\}$$
$$= 1 + 4 = 5$$

The smaller of the two numbers is 5. Thus, every zero of f lies between -5 and 5.

509

86. $f(x) = 3x^4 - 3x^3 - 5x^2 + 27x - 36 = 3\left(x^4 - x^3 - \dfrac{5}{3}x^2 + 9x - 12\right)$

Note: The leading coefficient must be 1.

$a_3 = -1, a_2 = -\dfrac{5}{3}, a_1 = 9, a_0 = -12$

$\text{Max}\left\{1, |-12| + |9| + \left|-\dfrac{5}{3}\right| + |-1|\right\}$

$\qquad = \text{Max}\left\{1, 12 + 9 + \dfrac{5}{3} + 1\right\}$

$\qquad = \text{Max}\left\{1, \dfrac{71}{3}\right\} = \dfrac{71}{3}$

$1 + \text{Max}\left\{|-12|, |9|, \left|-\dfrac{5}{3}\right|, |-1|\right\}$

$\qquad = 1 + \text{Max}\left\{12, 9, \dfrac{5}{3}, 1\right\}$

$\qquad = 1 + 12 = 13$

The smaller of the two numbers is 13. Thus, every zero of f lies between -13 and 13.

87. $f(x) = 4x^5 - x^4 + 2x^3 - 2x^2 + x - 1 = 4\left(x^5 - \dfrac{1}{4}x^4 + \dfrac{1}{2}x^3 - \dfrac{1}{2}x^2 + \dfrac{1}{4}x - \dfrac{1}{4}\right)$

Note: The leading coefficient must be 1.

$a_4 = -\dfrac{1}{4}, a_3 = \dfrac{1}{2}, a_2 = -\dfrac{1}{2}, a_1 = \dfrac{1}{4}, a_0 = -\dfrac{1}{4}$

$\text{Max}\left\{1, \left|-\dfrac{1}{4}\right| + \left|\dfrac{1}{4}\right| + \left|-\dfrac{1}{2}\right| + \left|\dfrac{1}{2}\right| + \left|-\dfrac{1}{4}\right|\right\}$

$\qquad = \text{Max}\left\{1, \dfrac{1}{4} + \dfrac{1}{4} + \dfrac{1}{2} + \dfrac{1}{2} + \dfrac{1}{4}\right\}$

$\qquad = \text{Max}\left\{1, \dfrac{7}{4}\right\} = \dfrac{7}{4}$

$1 + \text{Max}\left\{\left|-\dfrac{1}{4}\right|, \left|\dfrac{1}{4}\right|, \left|-\dfrac{1}{2}\right|, \left|\dfrac{1}{2}\right|, \left|-\dfrac{1}{4}\right|\right\}$

$\qquad = 1 + \text{Max}\left\{\dfrac{1}{4}, \dfrac{1}{4}, \dfrac{1}{2}, \dfrac{1}{2}, \dfrac{1}{4}\right\}$

$\qquad = 1 + \dfrac{1}{2} = \dfrac{3}{2}$

The smaller of the two numbers is $\dfrac{3}{2}$. Thus, every zero of f lies between $-\dfrac{3}{2}$ and $\dfrac{3}{2}$.

88. $f(x) = 4x^5 + x^4 + x^3 + x^2 - 2x - 2 = 4\left(x^5 + \dfrac{1}{4}x^4 + \dfrac{1}{4}x^3 + \dfrac{1}{4}x^2 - \dfrac{1}{2}x - \dfrac{1}{2}\right)$

Note: The leading coefficient must be 1.

$a_4 = \dfrac{1}{4}, a_3 = \dfrac{1}{4}, a_2 = \dfrac{1}{4}, a_1 = -\dfrac{1}{2}, a_0 = -\dfrac{1}{2}$

$\text{Max}\left\{1, \left|-\dfrac{1}{2}\right| + \left|-\dfrac{1}{2}\right| + \left|\dfrac{1}{4}\right| + \left|\dfrac{1}{4}\right| + \left|\dfrac{1}{4}\right|\right\}$

$\qquad = \text{Max}\left\{1, \dfrac{1}{2} + \dfrac{1}{2} + \dfrac{1}{4} + \dfrac{1}{4} + \dfrac{1}{4}\right\}$

$\qquad = \text{Max}\left\{1, \dfrac{7}{4}\right\} = \dfrac{7}{4}$

$1 + \text{Max}\left\{\left|-\dfrac{1}{2}\right|, \left|-\dfrac{1}{2}\right|, \left|\dfrac{1}{4}\right|, \left|\dfrac{1}{4}\right|, \left|\dfrac{1}{4}\right|\right\}$

$\qquad = 1 + \text{Max}\left\{\dfrac{1}{2}, \dfrac{1}{2}, \dfrac{1}{4}, \dfrac{1}{4}, \dfrac{1}{4}\right\}$

$\qquad = 1 + \dfrac{1}{2} = \dfrac{3}{2}$

The smaller of the two numbers is $\dfrac{3}{2}$. Thus, every zero of f lies between $-\dfrac{3}{2}$ and $\dfrac{3}{2}$.

89. $f(x) = 8x^4 - 2x^2 + 5x - 1;$ $[0, 1]$

$f(0) = -1 < 0$ and $f(1) = 10 > 0$

The value of the function is positive at one endpoint and negative at the other. Since the function is continuous, the Intermediate Value Theorem guarantees at least one zero in the given interval.

90. $f(x) = x^4 + 8x^3 - x^2 + 2;$ $[-1, 0]$

$f(-1) = -6 < 0$ and $f(0) = 2 > 0$

The value of the function is positive at one endpoint and negative at the other. Since the function is continuous, the Intermediate Value Theorem guarantees at least one zero in the given interval.

91. $f(x) = 2x^3 + 6x^2 - 8x + 2;$ $[-5, -4]$

$f(-5) = -58 < 0$ and $f(-4) = 2 > 0$

The value of the function is positive at one endpoint and negative at the other. Since the function is continuous, the Intermediate Value Theorem guarantees at least one zero in the given interval.

92. $f(x) = 3x^3 - 10x + 9;$ $[-3, -2]$

$f(-3) = -42 < 0$ and $f(-2) = 5 > 0$

The value of the function is positive at one endpoint and negative at the other. Since the function is continuous, the Intermediate Value Theorem guarantees at least one zero in the given interval.

93. $f(x) = x^5 - x^4 + 7x^3 - 7x^2 - 18x + 18;$ $[1.4, 1.5]$

$f(1.4) = -0.1754 < 0$ and $f(1.5) = 1.4063 > 0$

The value of the function is positive at one endpoint and negative at the other. Since the function is continuous, the Intermediate Value Theorem guarantees at least one zero in the given interval.

94. $f(x) = x^5 - 3x^4 - 2x^3 + 6x^2 + x + 2;$ $[1.7, 1.8]$

$f(1.7) = 0.35627 > 0$ and $f(1.8) = -1.021 < 0$

The value of the function is positive at one endpoint and negative at the other. Since the function is continuous, the Intermediate Value Theorem guarantees at least one zero in the given interval.

95. $8x^4 - 2x^2 + 5x - 1 = 0;$ $0 \le r \le 1$

Consider the function $f(x) = 8x^4 - 2x^2 + 5x - 1$

Subdivide the interval $[0, 1]$ into 10 equal subintervals:
$[0, 0.1]; [0.1, 0.2]; [0.2, 0.3]; [0.3, 0.4]; [0.4, 0.5];$
$[0.5, 0.6]; [0.6, 0.7]; [0.7, 0.8]; [0.8, 0.9]; [0.9, 1]$

$f(0) = -1; f(0.1) = -0.5192$

$f(0.1) = -0.5192; f(0.2) = -0.0672$

$f(0.2) = -0.0672; f(0.3) = 0.3848$

So f has a real zero on the interval $[0.2, 0.3]$.

Subdivide the interval $[0.2, 0.3]$ into 10 equal subintervals:
$[0.2, 0.21]; [0.21, 0.22]; [0.22, 0.23]; [0.23, 0.24];$
$[0.24, 0.25]; [0.25, 0.26]; [0.26, 0.27]; [0.27, 0.28];$
$[0.28, 0.29]; [0.29, 0.3]$

$f(0.2) = -0.0672; f(0.21) \approx -0.02264$

$f(0.21) \approx -0.02264; f(0.22) \approx 0.0219$

So f has a real zero on the interval $[0.21, 0.22]$, therefore $r = 0.21$, correct to two decimal places.

96. $x^4 + 8x^3 - x^2 + 2 = 0;$ $-1 \le r \le 0$

Consider the function $f(x) = x^4 + 8x^3 - x^2 + 2$

Subdivide the interval $[-1, 0]$ into 10 equal subintervals:
$[-1, -0.9]; [-0.9, -0.8]; [-0.8, -0.7]; [-0.7, -0.6];$
$[-0.6, -0.5]; [-0.5, -0.4]; [-0.4, -0.3];$
$[-0.3, -0.2]; [-0.2, -0.1]; [-0.1, 0]$

$f(-1) = -6; f(-0.9) = -3.9859$

$f(-0.9) = -3.9859; f(-0.8) = -2.3264$

$f(-0.8) = -2.3264; f(-0.7) = -0.9939$

$f(-0.7) = -0.9939; f(-0.6) = 0.0416$

So f has a real zero on the interval $[-0.7, -0.6]$.

Subdivide the interval $[-0.7, -0.6]$ into 10 equal subintervals:
$[-0.7, -0.69]; [-0.69, -0.68]; [-0.68, -0.67];$
$[-0.67, -0.66]; [-0.66, -0.65]; [-0.65, -0.64];$
$[-0.64, -0.63]; [-0.63, -0.62]; [-0.62, -0.61];$
$[-0.61, -0.6]$

$f(-0.7) = -0.9939; f(-0.69) \approx -0.8775$

$f(-0.69) \approx -0.8775; f(-0.68) \approx -0.7640$

$f(-0.68) \approx -0.7640; f(-0.67) \approx -0.6535$

$f(-0.67) \approx -0.6535; f(-0.66) \approx -0.5458$

$f(-0.66) \approx -0.5458; f(-0.65) \approx -0.4410$

511

$f(-0.65) \approx -0.4410; f(-0.64) \approx -0.3390$

$f(-0.64) \approx -0.3390; f(-0.63) \approx -0.2397$

$f(-0.63) \approx -0.2397; f(-0.62) \approx -0.1433$

$f(-0.62) \approx -0.1433; f(-0.61) \approx -0.0495$

$f(-0.61) \approx -0.0495; f(-0.60) \approx 0.0416$

So f has a real zero on the interval
$[-0.61, -0.6]$, therefore $r = -0.60$, correct to two decimal places.

97. $2x^3 + 6x^2 - 8x + 2 = 0$; $-5 \le r \le -4$

Consider the function $f(x) = 2x^3 + 6x^2 - 8x + 2$

Subdivide the interval $[-5, -4]$ into 10 equal subintervals:
$[-5, -4.9]; [-4.9, -4.8]; [-4.8, -4.7]; [-4.7, -4.6];$
$[-4.6, -4.5]; [-4.5, -4.4]; [-4.4, -4.3];$
$[-4.3, -4.2]; [-4.2, -4.1]; [-4.1, -4]$

$f(-5) = -58; f(-4.9) = -50.038$

$f(-4.9) = -50.038; f(-4.8) = -42.544$

$f(-4.8) = -42.544; f(-4.7) = -35.506$

$f(-4.7) = -35.506; f(-4.6) = -28.912$

$f(-4.6) = -28.912; f(-4.5) = -22.75$

$f(-4.5) = -22.75; f(-4.4) = -17.008$

$f(-4.4) = -17.008; f(-4.3) = -11.674$

$f(-4.3) = -11.674; f(-4.2) = -6.736$

$f(-4.2) = -6.736; f(-4.1) = -2.182$

$f(-4.1) = -2.182; f(-4) = 2$

So f has a real zero on the interval $[-4.1, -4]$.

Subdivide the interval $[-4.1, -4]$ into 10 equal subintervals:
$[-4.1, -4.09]; [-4.09, -4.08]; [-4.08, -4.07];$
$[-4.07, -4.06]; [-4.06, -4.05]; [-4.05, -4.04];$
$[-4.04, -4.03]; [-4.03, -4.02]; [-4.02, -4.01];$
$[-4.01, -4]$

$f(-4.1) = -2.182; f(-4.09) \approx -1.7473$

$f(-4.09) \approx -1.7473; f(-4.08) \approx -1.3162$

$f(-4.08) \approx -1.3162; f(-4.07) \approx -0.8889$

$f(-4.07) \approx -0.8889; f(-4.06) \approx -0.4652$

$f(-4.06) \approx -0.4652; f(-4.05) \approx -0.0453$

$f(-4.05) \approx -0.4653; f(-4.04) \approx 0.3711$

So f has a real zero on the interval
$[-4.05, -4.04]$, therefore $r = -4.04$, correct to two decimal places.

98. $3x^3 - 10x + 9 = 0$; $-3 \le r \le -2$

Consider the function $f(x) = 3x^3 - 10x + 9$

Subdivide the interval $[-3, -2]$ into 10 equal subintervals:
$[-3, -2.9]; [-2.9, -2.8]; [-2.8, -2.7]; [-2.7, -2.6];$
$[-2.6, -2.5]; [-2.5, -2.4]; [-2.4, -2.3];$
$[-2.3, -2.2]; [-2.2, -2.1]; [-2.1, -2]$

$f(-3) = -42; f(-2.9) = -35.167$

$f(-2.9) = -35.167; f(-2.8) = -28.856$

$f(-2.8) = -28.856; f(-2.7) = -23.049$

$f(-2.7) = -23.049; f(-2.6) = -17.728$

$f(-2.6) = -17.728; f(-2.5) = -12.875$

$f(-2.5) = -12.875; f(-2.4) = -8.472$

$f(-2.4) = -8.472; f(-2.3) = -4.501$

$f(-2.3) = -4.501; f(-2.2) = -0.944$

$f(-2.2) = -0.944; f(-2.1) = 2.217$

So f has a real zero on the interval $[-2.2, -2.1]$.

Subdivide the interval $[-2.2, -2.1]$ into 10 equal subintervals:
$[-2.2, -2.19]; [-2.19, -2.18]; [-2.18, -2.17];$
$[-2.17, -2.16]; [-2.16, -2.15]; [-2.15, -2.14];$
$[-2.14, -2.13]; [-2.13, -2.12]; [-2.12, -2.11];$
$[-2.11, -2.1]$

$f(-2.2) = -0.944; f(-2.19) \approx -0.6104$

$f(-2.19) \approx -0.6104; f(-2.18) \approx -0.2807$

$f(-2.18) \approx -0.2807; f(-2.17) \approx 0.0451$

So f has a real zero on the interval
$[-2.18, -2.17]$, therefore $r = -2.17$, correct to two decimal places.

99. $f(x) = x^3 + x^2 + x - 4$

$f(1) = -1; f(2) = 10$

So f has a real zero on the interval $[1,2]$.

Subdivide the interval $[1,2]$ into 10 equal subintervals:
$[1,1.1]; [1.1,1.2]; [1.2,1.3]; [1.3,1.4]; [1.4,1.5];$
$[1.5,1.6]; [1.6,1.7]; [1.7,1.8]; [1.8,1.9]; [1.9,2]$

$f(1) = -1; f(1.1) = -0.359$

$f(1.1) = -0.359; f(1.2) = 0.368$

So f has a real zero on the interval $[1.1,1.2]$.

Subdivide the interval $[1.1,1.2]$ into 10 equal subintervals:
$[1.1,1.11]; [1.11,1.12]; [1.12,1.13]; [1.13,1.14];$

[1.14,1.15]; [1.15,1.16];[1.16,1.17]; [1.17,1.18];
[1.18,1.19]; [1.19,1.2]

$f(1.1) = -0.359; f(1.11) \approx -0.2903$

$f(1.11) \approx -0.2903; f(1.12) \approx -0.2207$

$f(1.12) \approx -0.2207; f(1.13) \approx -0.1502$

$f(1.13) \approx -0.1502; f(1.14) \approx -0.0789$

$f(1.14) \approx -0.0789; f(1.15) \approx -0.0066$

$f(1.15) \approx -0.0066; f(1.16) \approx 0.0665$

So f has a real zero on the interval [1.15,1.16], therefore $r = 1.15$, correct to two decimal places.

100. $f(x) = 2x^4 + x^2 - 1$

$f(0) = -1; f(1) = 2$

So f has a real zero on the interval [0,1].
Subdivide the interval [0,1] into 10 equal subintervals:
[0,0.1]; [0.1,0.2]; [0.2,0.3]; [0.3,0.4]; [0.4,0.5];
[0.5,0.6]; [0.6,0.7]; [0.7,0.8]; [0.8,0.9]; [0.9,1]

$f(0) = -1; f(0.1) = -0.9898$

$f(0.1) = -0.9898; f(0.2) = -0.9568$

$f(0.2) = -0.9568; f(0.3) = -0.8938$

$f(0.3) = -0.8938; f(0.4) = -0.7888$

$f(0.4) = -0.7888; f(0.5) = -0.625$

$f(0.5) = -0.625; f(0.6) = -0.3808$

$f(0.6) = -0.3808; f(0.7) = -0.0298$

$f(0.7) = -0.0298; f(0.8) = 0.4592$

So f has a real zero on the interval [0.7,0.8].

Subdivide the interval [0.7,0.8] into 10 equal subintervals:
[0.7,0.71]; [0.71,0.72]; [0.72,0.73]; [0.73,0.74];
[0.74,0.75]; [0.75,0.76];[0.76,0.77]; [0.77,0.78];
[0.78,0.79]; [0.79,0.8]

$f(0.7) = -0.298; f(0.71) \approx 0.0123$

So f has a real zero on the interval [0.7,0.71], therefore $r = 0.70$, correct to two decimal places.

101. $f(x) = 2x^4 - 3x^3 - 4x^2 - 8$

$f(2) = -16; f(3) = 37$

So f has a real zero on the interval [2,3].
Subdivide the interval [2,3] into 10 equal subintervals:

[2,2.1]; [2.1,2.2]; [2.2,2.3]; [2.3,2.4]; [2.4,2.5];
[2.5,2.6]; [2.6,2.7]; [2.7,2.8]; [2.8,2.9]; [2.9,3]

$f(2) = -16; f(2.1) = -14.5268$

$f(2.1) = -14.5268; f(2.2) = -12.4528$

$f(2.2) = -12.4528; f(2.3) = -9.6928$

$f(2.3) = -9.6928; f(2.4) = -6.1568$

$f(2.4) = -6.1568; f(2.5) = -1.75$

$f(2.5) = -1.75; f(2.6) = 3.6272$

So f has a real zero on the interval [2.5,2.6].

Subdivide the interval [2.5,2.6] into 10 equal subintervals:
[2.5,2.51]; [2.51,2.52]; [2.52,2.53]; [2.53,2.54];
[2.54,2.55]; [2.55,2.56];[2.56,2.57]; [2.57,2.58];
[2.58,2.59]; [2.59,2.6]

$f(2.5) = -1.75; f(2.51) \approx -1.2576$

$f(2.51) \approx -1.2576; f(2.52) \approx -0.7555$

$f(2.52) \approx -0.7555; f(2.53) \approx -0.2434$

$f(2.53) \approx -0.2434; f(2.54) \approx 0.2787$

So f has a real zero on the interval [2.53,2.54], therefore $r = 2.53$, correct to two decimal places.

102. $f(x) = 3x^3 - 2x^2 - 20$

$f(2) = -4; f(3) = 43$

So f has a real zero on the interval [2,3].
Subdivide the interval [2,3] into 10 equal subintervals:
[2,2.1]; [2.1,2.2]; [2.2,2.3]; [2.3,2.4]; [2.4,2.5];
[2.5,2.6]; [2.6,2.7]; [2.7,2.8]; [2.9,3]

$f(2) = -4; f(2.1) = -1.037$

$f(2.1) = -1.037; f(2.2) = 2.264$

So f has a real zero on the interval [2.1,2.2].

Subdivide the interval [2.1,2.2] into 10 equal subintervals:
[2.1,2.11]; [2.11,2.12]; [2.12,2.13]; [2.13,2.14];
[2.14,2.15]; [2.15,2.16];[2.16,2.17]; [2.17,2.18];
[2.18,2.19]; [2.19,2.2]

$f(2.1) = -1.037; f(2.11) \approx -0.7224$

$f(2.11) \approx -0.7224; f(2.12) \approx -0.4044$

$f(2.12) \approx -0.4044; f(2.13) \approx -0.0830$

$f(2.13) \approx -0.0830; f(2.14) \approx 0.2418$

So f has a real zero on the interval [2.13,2.14], therefore $r = 2.13$, correct to two decimal places.

103. From the Remainder and Factor Theorems,
$x - 2$ is a factor of f if $f(2) = 0$.
$$(2)^3 - k(2)^2 + k(2) + 2 = 0$$
$$8 - 4k + 2k + 2 = 0$$
$$-2k + 10 = 0$$
$$-2k = -10$$
$$k = 5$$

104. From the Remainder and Factor Theorems,
$x + 2$ is a factor of f if $f(-2) = 0$.
$$(-2)^4 - k(-2)^3 + k(-2)^2 + 1 = 0$$
$$16 + 8k + 4k + 1 = 0$$
$$12k + 17 = 0$$
$$12k = -17$$
$$k = -\frac{17}{12}$$

105. From the Remainder Theorem, we know that the remainder is
$$f(1) = 2(1)^{20} - 8(1)^{10} + 1 - 2 = 2 - 8 + 1 - 2 = -7$$
The remainder is -7.

106. From the Remainder Theorem, we know that the remainder is
$$f(-1) = -3(-1)^{17} + (-1)^9 - (-1)^5 + 2(-1) = 1$$
The remainder is 1.

107. We want to prove that $x - c$ is a factor of $x^n - c^n$, for any positive integer n. By the Factor Theorem, $x - c$ will be a factor of $f(x)$ provided $f(c) = 0$. Here, $f(x) = x^n - c^n$, so that $f(c) = c^n - c^n = 0$. Therefore, $x - c$ is a factor of $x^n - c^n$.

108. We want to prove that $x + c$ is a factor of $x^n + c^n$, if $n \geq 1$ is an odd integer. By the Factor Theorem, $x + c$ will be a factor of $f(x)$ provided $f(-c) = 0$. Here, $f(x) = x^n + c^n$, so that $f(-c) = (-c)^n + c^n = -c^n + c^n = 0$ if $n \geq 1$ is an odd integer. Therefore, $x + c$ is a factor of $x^n + c^n$ if $n \geq 1$ is an odd integer.

109. $x^3 - 8x^2 + 16x - 3 = 0$ has solution $x = 3$, so $x - 3$ is a factor of $f(x) = x^3 - 8x^2 + 16x - 3$.
Using synthetic division
$$3\overline{)1 \quad -8 \quad 16 \quad -3}$$
$$\underline{\quad\quad 3 \quad -15 \quad 3\quad}$$
$$1 \quad -5 \quad 1 \quad 0$$
Thus,
$$f(x) = x^3 - 8x^2 + 16x - 3 = (x - 3)(x^2 - 5x + 1).$$
Solving $x^2 - 5x + 1 = 0$
$$x = \frac{5 \pm \sqrt{25 - 4}}{2} = \frac{5 \pm \sqrt{21}}{2}$$
The sum of these two roots is
$$\frac{5 + \sqrt{21}}{2} + \frac{5 - \sqrt{21}}{2} = \frac{10}{2} = 5.$$

110. $x^3 + 5x^2 + 5x - 2 = 0$ has solution $x = -2$, so $x + 2$ is a factor of $f(x) = x^3 + 5x^2 + 5x - 2$.
Using synthetic division
$$-2\overline{)1 \quad 5 \quad 5 \quad -2}$$
$$\underline{\quad\quad -2 \quad -6 \quad 2\quad}$$
$$1 \quad 3 \quad -1 \quad 0$$
Thus,
$$f(x) = x^3 + 5x^2 + 5x - 2 = (x + 2)(x^2 + 3x - 1).$$
Solving $x^2 + 3x - 1 = 0$,
$$x = \frac{-3 \pm \sqrt{9 + 4}}{2} = \frac{-3 \pm \sqrt{13}}{2}.$$
The sum of these two roots is
$$\frac{-3 + \sqrt{13}}{2} + \frac{-3 - \sqrt{13}}{2} = \frac{-6}{2} = -3.$$

111. Let x be the length of a side of the original cube. After removing the 1-inch slice, one dimension will be $x - 1$. The volume of the new solid will be: $(x - 1) \cdot x \cdot x$.
Solve the volume equation:
$$(x - 1) \cdot x \cdot x = 294$$
$$x^3 - x^2 = 294$$
$$x^3 - x^2 - 294 = 0$$
The solutions to this equation are the same as the real zeros of $f(x) = x^3 - x^2 - 294$.
By Descartes' Rule of Signs, we know that there is one positive real zero.
$$p = \pm 1, \pm 2, \pm 3, \pm 6, \pm 7, \pm 14, \pm 21, \pm 42, \pm 49, \pm 98,$$
$$\pm 147, \pm 294$$

$q = \pm 1$

The possible rational zeros are the same as the values for p.

$\dfrac{p}{q} = \pm 1, \pm 2, \pm 3, \pm 6, \pm 7, \pm 14, \pm 21, \pm 42, \pm 49, \pm 98,$

$\qquad \pm 147, \pm 294$

Using synthetic division:

$$7 \overline{)\begin{array}{cccc} 1 & -1 & 0 & -294 \\ & 7 & 42 & 294 \\ \hline 1 & 6 & 42 & 0 \end{array}}$$

7 is a zero, so the length of the edge of the original cube was 7 inches.

112. Let x be the length of a side of the original cube. The volume is x^3. The dimensions are changed to $x+6$, $x+12$, and $x-4$. The volume of the new solid will be $(x+6)(x+12)(x-4)$. Solve the volume equation:

$(x+6)(x+12)(x-4) = 2x^3$

$\left(x^2 + 18x + 72\right)(x-4) = 2x^3$

$\qquad x^3 + 14x^2 - 288 = 2x^3$

$\qquad x^3 - 14x^2 + 288 = 0$

The solutions to this equation are the same as the real zeros of $f(x) = x^3 - 14x^2 + 288$.

By Descartes' Rule of Signs, we know that there are two positive real zeros or no positive real zeros.

$p = \pm 1, \pm 2, \pm 3, \pm 4, \pm 6, \pm 8, \pm 9, \pm 12, \pm 16, \pm 18, \pm 24,$

$\qquad \pm 32, \pm 36, \pm 48, \pm 72, \pm 96, \pm 144, \pm 288$

$q = \pm 1$

The possible rational zeros are the same as the values for p:

$\dfrac{p}{q} = \pm 1, \pm 2, \pm 3, \pm 4, \pm 6, \pm 8, \pm 9, \pm 12, \pm 16, \pm 18, \pm 24,$

$\qquad \pm 32, \pm 36, \pm 48, \pm 72, \pm 96, \pm 144, \pm 288$

Using synthetic division:

$$6 \overline{)\begin{array}{cccc} 1 & -14 & 0 & 288 \\ & 6 & -48 & -288 \\ \hline 1 & -8 & -48 & 0 \end{array}}$$

Therefore, 6 is a zero; the other factor is $x^2 - 8x - 48 = (x-12)(x+4)$. The other zeros are 12 and –4. The length of the edge of the original cube was 6 inches or 12 inches.

113. $f(x) = x^n + a_{n-1}x^{n-1} + a_{n-2}x^{n-2} + \ldots + a_1 x + a_0$; where $a_{n-1}, a_{n-2}, \ldots a_1, a_0$ are integers. If r is a real zero of f, then r is either rational or irrational. We know that the rational roots of f must be of the form $\dfrac{p}{q}$ where p is a divisor of a_0 and q is a divisor of 1. This means that $q = \pm 1$. So if r is rational, then $r = \dfrac{p}{q} = \pm p$.

Therefore, r is an integer or r is irrational.

114. Let $\dfrac{p}{q}$ be a root of the polynomial $f(x) = a_n x^n + a_{n-1}x^{n-1} + a_{n-2}x^{n-2} + \ldots + a_1 x + a_0$ where

$a_n, a_{n-1}, a_{n-2}, \ldots a_1, a_0$ are integers. Suppose also that p and q have no common factors other than 1 and -1. Then

$$f\left(\dfrac{p}{q}\right) = a_n \left(\dfrac{p}{q}\right)^n + a_{n-1}\left(\dfrac{p}{q}\right)^{n-1} + a_{n-2}\left(\dfrac{p}{q}\right)^{n-2} + \ldots + a_1 \left(\dfrac{p}{q}\right) + a_0 = 0$$

$$\Rightarrow \dfrac{1}{q^n}\left(a_n p^n + a_{n-1}p^{n-1}q + a_{n-2}p^{n-2}q^2 + \ldots + a_1 pq^{n-1} + a_0 q^n\right) = 0$$

$$\Rightarrow a_n p^n + a_{n-1}p^{n-1}q + a_{n-2}p^{n-2}q^2 + \ldots + a_1 pq^{n-1} + a_0 q^n = 0$$

$$\Rightarrow a_n p^n + a_{n-1}p^{n-1}q + a_{n-2}p^{n-2}q^2 + \ldots + a_1 pq^{n-1} = -a_0 q^n$$

Because p is a factor of the left side of this equation, p must also be a factor of $a_0 q^n$. Since p is not a factor of q, p must be a factor of a_0. Similarly, q must be a factor of a_n.

515

115. (a) $f(x) = 8x^4 - 2x^2 + 5x - 1 \quad 0 \le r \le 1$

We begin with the interval [0,1].

$f(0) = -1; \quad f(1) = 10$

Let m_i = the midpoint of the interval being considered.

So $m_1 = 0.5$

n	m_n	$f(m_n)$	New interval
1	0.5	$f(0.5) = 1.5 > 0$	[0,0.5]
2	0.25	$f(0.25) = 0.15625 > 0$	[0,0.25]
3	0.125	$f(0.125) \approx -0.4043 < 0$	[0.125,0.25]
4	0.1875	$f(0.1875) \approx -0.1229 < 0$	[0.1875,0.25]
5	0.21875	$f(0.21875) \approx 0.0164 > 0$	[0.1875,0.21875]
6	0.203125	$f(0.203125) \approx -0.0533 < 0$	[0.203125,0.21875]
7	0.2109375	$f(0.2109375) \approx -0.0185 < 0$	[0.2109375,0.21875]

Since the endpoints of the new interval at Step 7 agree to two decimal places, $r = 0.21$, correct to two decimal places.

(b) $f(x) = x^4 + 8x^3 - x^2 + 2; \quad -1 \le r \le 0$

We begin with the interval [−1,0].

$f(-1) = -6; \quad f(0) = 2$

Let m_i = the midpoint of the interval being considered.

So $m_1 = -0.5$

n	m_n	$f(m_n)$	New interval
1	−0.5	$f(-0.5) = 0.8125 > 0$	[−1, −0.5]
2	−0.75	$f(-0.75) \approx -1.6211 < 0$	[−0.75, −0.5]
3	−0.625	$f(-0.625) \approx -0.1912 < 0$	[−0.625, −0.5]
4	−0.5625	$f(-0.5625) \approx 0.3599 > 0$	[−0.625, −0.5625]
5	−0.59375	$f(-0.59375) \approx 0.0972 > 0$	[−0.625, −0.59375]
6	−0.609375	$f(-0.609375) \approx -0.0437 < 0$	[−0.609375, −0.59375]
7	−0.6015625	$f(-0.6015625) \approx 0.0275 > 0$	[−0.609375, −0.6015625]

Since the endpoints of the new interval at Step 7 agree to two decimal places, $r = -0.60$, correct to two decimal places.

(c) $f(x) = 2x^3 + 6x^2 - 8x + 2;$ $-5 \le r \le -4$

We begin with the interval $[-5, -4]$.

$f(-5) = -58;$ $f(-4) = 2$

Let m_i = the midpoint of the interval being considered.

So $m_1 = -4.5$

n	m_n	$f(m_n)$	New interval
1	-4.5	$f(-4.5) = -22.75 < 0$	$[-4.5, -4]$
2	-4.25	$f(-4.25) \approx -9.156 < 0$	$[-4.25, -4]$
3	-4.125	$f(-4.125) \approx -3.2852 < 0$	$[-4.125, -4]$
4	-4.0625	$f(-4.0625) \approx -0.5708 < 0$	$[-4.0625, -4]$
5	-4.03125	$f(-4.03125) \approx 0.7324 > 0$	$[-4.0625, -4.03125]$
6	-4.046875	$f(-4.046875) \approx 0.0852 > 0$	$[-4.0625, -4.046875]$
7	-4.0546875	$f(-4.0546875) \approx -0.2417 < 0$	$[-4.0546875, -4.046875]$
8	-4.05078125	$f(-4.05078125) \approx -0.0779 < 0$	$[-4.05078125, -4.046875]$
9	-4.048828125	$f(-4.048828125) \approx 0.0037 > 0$	$[-4.05078125, -4.048828125]$
10	-4.0498046875	$f(-4.0498045875) \approx -0.0371 < 0$	$[-4.0498046875, -4.048828125]$

Since the endpoints of the new interval at Step 10 agree to two decimal places,
$r = -4.05$, correct to two decimal places.

(d) $f(x) = 3x^3 - 10x + 9;$ $-3 \le r \le -2$

We begin with the interval $[-3, -2]$.

$f(-3) = -42;$ $f(-2) = 5$

Let m_i = the midpoint of the interval being considered.

So $m_1 = -2.5$

n	m_n	$f(m_n)$	New interval
1	-2.5	$f(-2.5) = -12.875 < 0$	$[-2.5, -2]$
2	-2.25	$f(-2.25) \approx -2.6719 < 0$	$[-2.25, -2]$
3	-2.125	$f(-2.125) \approx 1.4629 > 0$	$[-2.25, -2.125]$
4	-2.1875	$f(-2.1875) \approx -0.5276 < 0$	$[-2.1875, -2.125]$
5	-2.15625	$f(-2.15625) \approx 0.4866 > 0$	$[-2.1875, -2.15625]$
6	-2.171875	$f(-2.171875) \approx -0.0157 < 0$	$[-2.171875, -2.15625]$
7	-2.1640625	$f(-2.1640625) \approx 0.2366 > 0$	$[-2.171875, -2.1640625]$
8	-2.16796875	$f(-2.16796875) \approx 0.1108 > 0$	$[-2.171875, -2.16796875]$
9	-2.169921875	$f(-2.169921875) \approx 0.0476 > 0$	$[-2.171875, -2.169921875]$
10	-2.1708984375	$f(-2.1708984375) \approx 0.0160 > 0$	$[-2.171875, -2.1708984375]$

Since the endpoints of the new interval at Step 10 agree to two decimal places,
$r = -2.17$, correct to two decimal places.

(e) $f(x) = x^3 + x^2 + x - 4$; $\quad 1 \le r \le 2$

We begin with the interval [1,2].

$f(1) = -1$; $\quad f(2) = 10$

Let m_i = the midpoint of the interval being considered.

So $m_1 = 1.5$

n	m_n	$f(m_n)$	New interval
1	1.5	$f(1.5) = 3.125 > 0$	[1,1.5]
2	1.25	$f(1.25) \approx 0.7656 > 0$	[1,1.25]
3	1.125	$f(1.125) \approx -0.1855 < 0$	[1.125,1.25]
4	1.1875	$f(1.1875) \approx 0.2722 > 0$	[1.125,1.1875]
5	1.15625	$f(1.15625) \approx 0.0390 > 0$	[1.125,1.15625]
6	1.140625	$f(1.140625) \approx -0.0744 < 0$	[1.140625,1.15625]
7	1.1484375	$f(1.1484375) \approx -0.0180 < 0$	[1.1484375,1.15625]
8	1.15234375	$f(1.15234375) \approx 0.0140 > 0$	[1.1484375,1.15234375]
9	1.150390625	$f(1.150390625) \approx -0.0038 < 0$	[1.150390625,1.15234375]

Since the endpoints of the new interval at Step 9 agree to two decimal places, $r = 1.15$, correct to two decimal places.

(f) $f(x) = 2x^4 + x^2 - 1$; $\quad 0 \le r \le 1$

We begin with the interval [0,1].

$f(0) = -1$; $\quad f(1) = 2$

Let m_i = the midpoint of the interval being considered.

So $m_1 = 0.5$

n	m_n	$f(m_n)$	New interval
1	0.5	$f(0.5) = -0.625 < 0$	[0.5,1]
2	0.75	$f(0.75) \approx 0.1953 > 0$	[0.5,0.75]
3	0.625	$f(0.625) \approx -0.3042 < 0$	[0.625,0.75]
4	0.6875	$f(0.6875) \approx -0.0805 < 0$	[0.6875,0.75]
5	0.71875	$f(0.71875) \approx 0.0504 > 0$	[0.6875,0.71875]
6	0.703125	$f(0.703125) \approx -0.0168 < 0$	[0.703125,0.71875]
7	0.7109375	$f(0.7109375) \approx 0.0164 > 0$	[0.703125, 0.7109375]
8	0.70703125	$f(0.70703125) \approx -0.0003 < 0$	[0.70703125, 0.7109375]
9	0.708984375	$f(0.708984375) \approx 0.0080 > 0$	[0.70703125, 0.708984375]

Since the endpoints of the new interval at Step 9 agree to two decimal places, $r = 0.70$, correct to two decimal places.

(g) $f(x) = 2x^4 - 3x^3 - 4x^2 - 8; \quad 2 \le r \le 3$

We begin with the interval [2,3]

$f(2) = -16; \quad f(3) = 37$

Let m_i = the midpoint of the interval being considered.

So $m_1 = 2.5$

n	m_n	$f(m_n)$	New interval
1	2.5	$f(2.5) = -1.75 < 0$	[2.5,3]
2	2.75	$f(2.75) \approx 13.7422 > 0$	[2.5,2.75]
3	2.625	$f(2.625) \approx 5.1353 > 0$	[2.5,2.625]
4	2.5625	$f(2.5625) \approx 1.4905 > 0$	[2.5,2.5625]
5	2.53125	$f(2.53125) \approx -0.1787 < 0$	[2.53125,2.5625]
6	2.546875	$f(2.546875) \approx 0.6435 > 0$	[2.53125, 2.546875]
7	2.5390625	$f(2.5390625) \approx 0.2293 > 0$	[2.53125, 2.5390625]

Since the endpoints of the new interval at Step 7 agree to two decimal places,
$r = 2.53$, correct to two decimal places.

(h) $f(x) = 3x^3 - 2x^2 - 20; \quad 2 \le r \le 3$

We begin with the interval [2,3].

$f(2) = -4; \quad f(3) = 43$

Let m_i = the midpoint of the interval being considered.

So $m_1 = 2.5$

n	m_n	$f(m_n)$	New interval
1	2.5	$f(2.5) = 14.375 > 0$	[2,2.5]
2	2.25	$f(2.25) \approx 4.0469 > 0$	[2,2.25]
3	2.125	$f(2.125) \approx -0.2441 < 0$	[2.125,2.25]
4	2.1875	$f(2.1875) \approx 1.8323 > 0$	[2.125,2.1875]
5	2.15625	$f(2.15625) \approx 0.7771 > 0$	[2.125,2.15625]
6	2.140625	$f(2.140625) \approx 0.2622 > 0$	[2.125, 2.140625]
7	2.1328125	$f(2.1328125) \approx 0.0080 > 0$	[2.125, 2.1328125]
8	2.12890625	$f(2.12890625) \approx -0.1183 < 0$	[2.12890625, 2.1328125]
9	2.130859375	$f(2.130859375) \approx -0.0552 < 0$	[2.130859375, 2.1328125]

Since the endpoints of the new interval at Step 7 agree to two decimal places,
$r = 2.13$, correct to two decimal places.

519

116. $f(x) = 2x^3 + 3x^2 - 6x + 7$

By the Rational Zero Theorem, the only possible rational zeros are: $\dfrac{p}{q} = \pm 1, \pm 7, \pm \dfrac{1}{2}, \pm \dfrac{7}{2}$.

Since $\dfrac{1}{3}$ is not in the list of possible rational zeros, it is not a zero of f.

117. $f(x) = 4x^3 - 5x^2 - 3x + 1$

By the Rational Zero Theorem, the only possible rational zeros are: $\dfrac{p}{q} = \pm 1, \pm \dfrac{1}{2}, \pm \dfrac{1}{4}$.

Since $\dfrac{1}{3}$ is not in the list of possible rational zeros, it is not a zero of f.

118. $f(x) = 2x^6 - 5x^4 + x^3 - x + 1$

By the Rational Zero Theorem, the only possible rational zeros are: $\dfrac{p}{q} = \pm 1, \pm \dfrac{1}{2}$.

Since $\dfrac{3}{5}$ is not in the list of possible rational zeros, it is not a zero of $f(x)$.

119. $f(x) = x^7 + 6x^5 - x^4 + x + 2$

By the Rational Zero Theorem, the only possible rational zeros are: $\dfrac{p}{q} = \pm 1, \pm 2$.

Since $\dfrac{2}{3}$ is not in the list of possible rational zeros, it is not a zero of f.

Section 5.6

1. $(3 - 2i) + (-3 + 5i) = 3 - 3 - 2i + 5i$
$$= 3i$$
$$(3 - 2i)(-3 + 5i) = -9 + 15i + 6i - 10i^2$$
$$= -9 + 21i - 10(-1)$$
$$= 1 + 21i$$

2. The zeros of $f(x)$ are the solutions to the equation $x^2 + 2x + 2 = 0$.
$$x^2 + 2x + 2 = 0$$
$$a = 1, b = 2, c = 2$$
$$x = \frac{-2 \pm \sqrt{2^2 - 4(1)(2)}}{2(1)} = \frac{-2 \pm \sqrt{-4}}{2} = \frac{-2 \pm 2i}{2} = -1 \pm i$$
The solution set is $\{-1 - i, -1 + i\}$.

3. one

4. $3 - 4i$

5. True

6. False

7. Since complex zeros appear in conjugate pairs, $4 + i$, the conjugate of $4 - i$, is the remaining zero of f.

8. Since complex zeros appear in conjugate pairs, $3 - i$, the conjugate of $3 + i$, is the remaining zero of f.

9. Since complex zeros appear in conjugate pairs, $-i$, the conjugate of i, and $1 - i$, the conjugate of $1 + i$, are the remaining zeros of f.

10. Since complex zeros appear in conjugate pairs, $2 - i$, the conjugate of $2 + i$, is the remaining zero of f.

11. Since complex zeros appear in conjugate pairs, $-i$, the conjugate of i, and $-2i$, the conjugate of $2i$, are the remaining zeros of f.

12. Since complex zeros appear in conjugate pairs, $-i$, the conjugate of i, is the remaining zero.

13. Since complex zeros appear in conjugate pairs, $-i$, the conjugate of i, is the remaining zero.

14. Since complex zeros appear in conjugate pairs, $2 + i$, the conjugate of $2 - i$, and i, the conjugate of $-i$, are the remaining zeros of f.

15. Since complex zeros appear in conjugate pairs, $2 - i$, the conjugate of $2 + i$, and $-3 + i$, the conjugate of $-3 - i$, are the remaining zeros.

16. Since complex zeros appear in conjugate pairs, $-i$, the conjugate of i, $3 + 2i$, the conjugate of $3 - 2i$, and $-2 - i$, the conjugate of $-2 + i$, are the remaining zeros of f.

For 17–22, we will use $a_n = 1$ as the lead coefficient of the polynomial. Also note that

$$(x - (a + bi))(x - (a - bi)) = ((x - a) - bi)((x - a) + bi)$$
$$= (x - a)^2 - (bi)^2$$

17. Since $3 + 2i$ is a zero, its conjugate $3 - 2i$ is also a zero of f.

$$f(x) = (x - 4)(x - 4)(x - (3 + 2i))(x - (3 - 2i))$$
$$= (x^2 - 8x + 16)((x - 3) - 2i)((x - 3) + 2i)$$
$$= (x^2 - 8x + 16)(x^2 - 6x + 9 - 4i^2)$$
$$= (x^2 - 8x + 16)(x^2 - 6x + 13)$$
$$= x^4 - 6x^3 + 13x^2 - 8x^3 + 48x^2$$
$$\quad - 104x + 16x^2 - 96x + 208$$
$$= x^4 - 14x^3 + 77x^2 - 200x + 208$$

18. Since $1 + 2i$ and i are zeros, their conjugates $1 - 2i$ and $-i$ are also zeros of f.

$$f(x) = (x - i)(x - (-i))(x - (1 + 2i))(x - (1 - 2i))$$
$$= (x - i)(x + i)((x - 1) - 2i)((x - 1) + 2i)$$
$$= (x^2 - i^2)(x^2 - 2x + 1 - 4i^2)$$
$$= (x^2 + 1)(x^2 - 2x + 5)$$
$$= x^4 - 2x^3 + 5x^2 + 1x^2 - 2x + 5$$
$$= x^4 - 2x^3 + 6x^2 - 2x + 5$$

19. Since $-i$ is a zero, its conjugate i is also a zero, and since $1 + i$ is a zero, its conjugate $1 - i$ is also a zero of f.

$$f(x) = (x - 2)(x + i)(x - i)(x - (1 + i))(x - (1 - i))$$
$$= (x - 2)(x^2 - i^2)((x - 1) - i)((x - 1) + i)$$
$$= (x - 2)(x^2 + 1)(x^2 - 2x + 1 - i^2)$$
$$= (x^3 - 2x^2 + x - 2)(x^2 - 2x + 2)$$
$$= x^5 - 2x^4 + 2x^3 - 2x^4 + 4x^3 - 4x^2$$
$$\quad + x^3 - 2x^2 + 2x - 2x^2 + 4x - 4$$
$$= x^5 - 4x^4 + 7x^3 - 8x^2 + 6x - 4$$

20. Since i is a zero, its conjugate $-i$ is also a zero; since $4 - i$ is a zero, its conjugate $4 + i$ is also a zero; and since $2 + i$ is a zero, its conjugate $2 - i$ is also a zero of f.

$$f(x) = (x + i)(x - i)(x - (4 + i))(x - (4 - i))(x - (2 + i))(x - (2 - i))$$
$$= (x^2 - i^2)((x - 4) - i)((x - 4) + i)((x - 2) - i)((x - 2) + i)$$
$$= (x^2 + 1)(x^2 - 8x + 16 - i^2)(x^2 - 4x + 4 - i^2)$$
$$= (x^2 + 1)(x^2 - 8x + 17)(x^2 - 4x + 5)$$
$$= (x^4 - 8x^3 + 17x^2 + x^2 - 8x + 17)(x^2 - 4x + 5)$$
$$= (x^4 - 8x^3 + 18x^2 - 8x + 17)(x^2 - 4x + 5)$$
$$= x^6 - 4x^5 + 5x^4 - 8x^5 + 32x^4 - 40x^3 + 18x^4 - 72x^3 + 90x^2 - 8x^3 + 32x^2 - 40x + 17x^2 - 68x + 85$$
$$= x^6 - 12x^5 + 55x^4 - 120x^3 + 139x^2 - 108x + 85$$

21. Since $-i$ is a zero, its conjugate i is also a zero.

$$f(x) = (x - 3)(x - 3)(x + i)(x - i)$$
$$= (x^2 - 6x + 9)(x^2 - i^2)$$
$$= (x^2 - 6x + 9)(x^2 + 1)$$
$$= x^4 + x^2 - 6x^3 - 6x + 9x^2 + 9$$
$$= x^4 - 6x^3 + 10x^2 - 6x + 9$$

521

22. Since $1+i$ is a zero, its conjugate $1-i$ is also a zero of f.

$$\begin{aligned}
f(x) &= (x-1)^3\left(x-(1+i)\right)\left(x-(1-i)\right)\\
&= \left(x^3-3x^2+3x-1\right)\left((x-1)-i\right)\left((x-1)+i\right)\\
&= \left(x^3-3x^2+3x-1\right)\left(x^2-2x+1-i^2\right)\\
&= \left(x^3-3x^2+3x-1\right)\left(x^2-2x+2\right)\\
&= x^5-2x^4+2x^3-3x^4+6x^3-6x^2\\
&\quad +3x^3-6x^2+6x-x^2+2x-2\\
&= x^5-5x^4+11x^3-13x^2+8x-2
\end{aligned}$$

23. Since $2i$ is a zero, its conjugate $-2i$ is also a zero of f. $x-2i$ and $x+2i$ are factors of f.

Thus, $(x-2i)(x+2i)=x^2+4$ is a factor of f. Using division to find the other factor:

$$\begin{array}{r}
x-4 \\
x^2+4\overline{)x^3-4x^2+4x-16} \\
\underline{x^3\qquad\;\;+4x} \\
-4x^2\qquad-16 \\
\underline{-4x^2\qquad-16} \\
\end{array}$$

$x-4$ is a factor, so the remaining zero is 4.
The zeros of f are $4, 2i, -2i$.

24. Since $-5i$ is a zero, its conjugate $5i$ is also a zero of g. $x+5i$ and $x-5i$ are factors of g.

Thus, $(x+5i)(x-5i)=x^2+25$ is a factor of g. Using division to find the other factor:

$$\begin{array}{r}
x+3 \\
x^2+25\overline{)x^3+3x^2+25x+75} \\
\underline{x^3\qquad\;\;+25x} \\
3x^2\qquad+75 \\
\underline{3x^2\qquad+75} \\
\end{array}$$

$x+3$ is a factor, so the remaining zero is -3.
The zeros of g are $-3, 5i, -5i$.

25. Since $-2i$ is a zero, its conjugate $2i$ is also a zero of f. $x-2i$ and $x+2i$ are factors of f.

Thus, $(x-2i)(x+2i)=x^2+4$ is a factor of f. Using division to find the other factor:

$$\begin{array}{r}
2x^2+5x-3 \\
x^2+4\overline{)2x^4+5x^3+5x^2+20x-12} \\
\underline{2x^4\qquad\;\;+8x^2} \\
5x^3-3x^2+20x \\
\underline{5x^3\qquad+20x} \\
-3x^2\qquad-12 \\
\underline{-3x^2\qquad-12} \\
\end{array}$$

$2x^2+5x-3=(2x-1)(x+3)$

The remaining zeros are $\dfrac{1}{2}$ and -3.

The zeros of f are $2i, -2i, -3, \dfrac{1}{2}$.

26. Since $3i$ is a zero, its conjugate $-3i$ is also a zero of h. $x-3i$ and $x+3i$ are factors of h.

Thus, $(x-3i)(x+3i)=x^2+9$ is a factor of h. Using division to find the other factor:

$$\begin{array}{r}
3x^2+5x-2 \\
x^2+9\overline{)3x^4+5x^3+25x^2+45x-18} \\
\underline{3x^4\qquad\;\;+27x^2} \\
5x^3-2x^2+45x \\
\underline{5x^3\qquad+45x} \\
-2x^2\qquad-18 \\
\underline{-2x^2\qquad-18} \\
\end{array}$$

$3x^2+5x-2=(3x-1)(x+2)$

The remaining zeros are $\dfrac{1}{3}$ and -2.

The zeros of h are $3i, -3i, -2, \dfrac{1}{3}$.

27. Since $3-2i$ is a zero, its conjugate $3+2i$ is also a zero of h. $x-(3-2i)$ and $x-(3+2i)$ are factors of h.

Thus,

$$(x-(3-2i))(x-(3+2i)) = ((x-3)+2i)((x-3)-2i)$$
$$= x^2 - 6x + 9 - 4i^2$$
$$= x^2 - 6x + 13$$

is a factor of h.

Using division to find the other factor:

$$
\begin{array}{r}
x^2 - 3x - 10 \\
x^2 - 6x + 13 \overline{\smash{\big)}\, x^4 - 9x^3 + 21x^2 + 21x - 130} \\
\underline{x^4 - 6x^3 + 13x^2} \\
-3x^3 + 8x^2 + 21x \\
\underline{-3x^3 + 18x^2 - 39x} \\
-10x^2 + 60x - 130 \\
\underline{-10x^2 + 60x - 130}
\end{array}
$$

$x^2 - 3x - 10 = (x+2)(x-5)$

The remaining zeros are -2 and 5.

The zeros of h are $3-2i, 3+2i, -2, 5$.

28. Since $1+3i$ is a zero, its conjugate $1-3i$ is also a zero of f. $x-(1+3i)$ and $x-(1-3i)$ are factors of f. Thus,

$(x-(1+3i))(x-(1-3i)) = ((x-1)-3i)((x-1)+3i)$ is a factor of f.

$$((x-1)-3i)((x-1)+3i) = x^2 - 2x + 1 - 9i^2$$
$$= x^2 - 2x + 10$$

Using division to find the other factor:

$$
\begin{array}{r}
x^2 - 5x - 6 \\
x^2 - 2x + 10 \overline{\smash{\big)}\, x^4 - 7x^3 + 14x^2 - 38x - 60} \\
\underline{x^4 - 2x^3 + 10x^2} \\
-5x^3 + 4x^2 - 38x \\
\underline{-5x^3 + 10x^2 - 50x} \\
-6x^2 + 12x - 60 \\
\underline{-6x^2 + 12x - 60}
\end{array}
$$

$x^2 - 5x - 6 = (x+1)(x-6)$

The remaining zeros are -1 and 6.

The zeros of f are $1+3i, 1-3i, -1, 6$.

29. Since $-4i$ is a zero, its conjugate $4i$ is also a zero of h. $x-4i$ and $x+4i$ are factors of h.

Thus, $(x-4i)(x+4i) = x^2 + 16$ is a factor of h.

Using division to find the other factor:

$$
\begin{array}{r}
3x^3 + 2x^2 - 33x - 22 \\
x^2 + 16 \overline{\smash{\big)}\, 3x^5 + 2x^4 + 15x^3 + 10x^2 - 528x - 352} \\
\underline{3x^5 \qquad + 48x^3} \\
2x^4 - 33x^3 + 10x^2 \\
\underline{2x^4 \qquad + 32x^2} \\
-33x^3 - 22x^2 - 528x \\
\underline{-33x^3 \qquad - 528x} \\
-22x^2 \qquad - 352 \\
\underline{-22x^2 \qquad - 352}
\end{array}
$$

$3x^3 + 2x^2 - 33x - 22 = x^2(3x+2) - 11(3x+2)$
$$= (3x+2)(x^2 - 11)$$
$$= (3x+2)\left(x - \sqrt{11}\right)\left(x + \sqrt{11}\right)$$

The remaining zeros are $-\dfrac{2}{3}, \sqrt{11}$, and $-\sqrt{11}$.

The zeros of h are $4i, -4i, -\sqrt{11}, \sqrt{11}, -\dfrac{2}{3}$.

30. Since $3i$ is a zero, its conjugate $-3i$ is also a zero of g. $x-3i$ and $x+3i$ are factors of g.

Thus, $(x-3i)(x+3i) = x^2 + 9$ is a factor of g.

Using division to find the other factor:

$$
\begin{array}{r}
2x^3 - 3x^2 - 23x + 12 \\
x^2 + 9 \overline{\smash{\big)}\, 2x^5 - 3x^4 - 5x^3 - 15x^2 - 207x + 108} \\
\underline{2x^5 \qquad + 18x^3} \\
-3x^4 - 23x^3 - 15x^2 \\
\underline{-3x^4 \qquad - 27x^2} \\
-23x^3 + 12x^2 - 207x \\
\underline{-23x^3 \qquad - 207x} \\
12x^2 \qquad + 108 \\
\underline{12x^2 \qquad + 108} \\
0
\end{array}
$$

Using the Rational Root theorem, we see that -3 is a potential rational zero.

$$-3 \overline{)\begin{array}{cccc} 2 & -3 & -23 & 12 \\ & -6 & 27 & -12 \\ \hline 2 & -9 & 4 & 0 \end{array}}$$

$x+3$ is a factor. The remaining factor is $2x^2 - 9x + 4 = (2x-1)(x-4)$.

The zeros of g are $3i, -3i, -3, \dfrac{1}{2}, 4$.

31. $f(x) = x^3 - 1 = (x-1)(x^2 + x + 1)$ The solutions of $x^2 + x + 1 = 0$ are:

$$x = \frac{-1 \pm \sqrt{1^2 - 4(1)(1)}}{2(1)} = \frac{-1 \pm \sqrt{-3}}{2}$$

$$= -\frac{1}{2} + \frac{\sqrt{3}}{2}i \text{ and } -\frac{1}{2} - \frac{\sqrt{3}}{2}i$$

The zeros are: $1, -\dfrac{1}{2} + \dfrac{\sqrt{3}}{2}i, -\dfrac{1}{2} - \dfrac{\sqrt{3}}{2}i$.

$$f(x) = (x-1)\left(x + \frac{1}{2} - \frac{\sqrt{3}}{2}i\right)\left(x + \frac{1}{2} + \frac{\sqrt{3}}{2}i\right)$$

32. $f(x) = x^4 - 1 = (x^2 - 1)(x^2 + 1)$

$$= (x-1)(x+1)(x^2 + 1)$$

The solutions of $x^2 + 1 = 0$ are $x = \pm i$.
The zeros are: $-1, 1, -i, i$.

$$f(x) = (x+1)(x-1)(x+i)(x-i)$$

33. $f(x) = x^3 - 8x^2 + 25x - 26$

Step 1: $f(x)$ has 3 complex zeros.

Step 2: By Descartes Rule of Signs, there are three positive real zeros or there is one positive real zero.

$f(-x) = (-x)^3 - 8(-x)^2 + 25(-x) - 26$, thus,

$$= -x^3 - 8x^2 - 25x - 26$$

there are no negative real zeros.

Step 3: Possible rational zeros:

$p = \pm 1, \pm 2, \pm 13, \pm 26; \quad q = \pm 1;$

$\dfrac{p}{q} = \pm 1, \pm 2, \pm 13, \pm 26$

Step 4: Using synthetic division:

We try $x - 2$:

$$2 \overline{)\begin{array}{cccc} 1 & -8 & 25 & -26 \\ & 2 & -12 & 26 \\ \hline 1 & -6 & 13 & 0 \end{array}}$$

$x - 2$ is a factor. The other factor is the quotient: $x^2 - 6x + 13$.

The solutions of $x^2 - 6x + 13 = 0$ are:

$$x = \frac{-(-6) \pm \sqrt{(-6)^2 - 4(1)(13)}}{2(1)}.$$

$$= \frac{6 \pm \sqrt{-16}}{2} = \frac{6 \pm 4i}{2} = 3 \pm 2i$$

The zeros are $2, 3-2i, 3+2i$.

$$f(x) = (x-2)(x-3+2i)(x-3-2i)$$

34. $f(x) = x^3 + 13x^2 + 57x + 85$

Step 1: $f(x)$ has 3 complex zeros.

Step 2: By Descartes Rule of Signs, there are no positive real zeros.

$f(-x) = (-x)^3 + 13(-x)^2 + 57(-x) + 85$, thus,

$$= -x^3 + 13x^2 - 57x + 85$$

there are three negative real zeros or there is one negative real zero.

Step 3: Possible rational zeros:

$p = \pm 1, \pm 5, \pm 17, \pm 85; \quad q = \pm 1;$

$\dfrac{p}{q} = \pm 1, \pm 5, \pm 17, \pm 85$

Step 4: Using synthetic division:

We try $x + 5$:

$$-5 \overline{)\begin{array}{cccc} 1 & 13 & 57 & 85 \\ & -5 & -40 & -85 \\ \hline 1 & 8 & 17 & 0 \end{array}}$$

$x + 5$ is a factor. The other factor is the quotient: $x^2 + 8x + 17$.

The solutions of $x^2 + 8x + 17 = 0$ are:

$$x = \frac{-8 \pm \sqrt{8^2 - 4(1)(17)}}{2(1)} = \frac{-8 \pm \sqrt{-4}}{2}$$

$$= \frac{-8 \pm 2i}{2} = -4 \pm i$$

The zeros are -5, $-4 - i$, $-4 + i$.

$$f(x) = (x + 5)(x + 4 + i)(x + 4 - i)$$

35. $f(x) = x^4 + 5x^2 + 4 = \left(x^2 + 4\right)\left(x^2 + 1\right)$

$$= (x + 2i)(x - 2i)(x + i)(x - i)$$

The zeros are: $-2i$, $-i$, i, $2i$.

36. $f(x) = x^4 + 13x^2 + 36 = \left(x^2 + 4\right)\left(x^2 + 9\right)$

$$= (x + 2i)(x - 2i)(x + 3i)(x - 3i)$$

The zeros are: $-3i$, $-2i$, $2i$, $3i$.

$$f(x) = (x + 3i)(x + 2i)(x - 2i)(x - 3i)$$

37. $f(x) = x^4 + 2x^3 + 22x^2 + 50x - 75$

Step 1: $f(x)$ has 4 complex zeros.

Step 2: By Descartes Rule of Signs, there is 1 positive real zero.

$$f(-x) = (-x)^4 + 2(-x)^3 + 22(-x)^2 + 50(-x) - 75$$
$$= x^4 - 2x^3 + 22x^2 - 50x - 75$$

Thus, there are three negative real zeros or there is one negative real zero.

Step 3: Possible rational zeros:

$p = \pm 1, \pm 3, \pm 5, \pm 15, \pm 25, \pm 75; \quad q = \pm 1;$

$\dfrac{p}{q} = \pm 1, \pm 3, \pm 5, \pm 15, \pm 25, \pm 75$

Step 4: Using synthetic division:

We try $x + 3$:

```
-3)1   2   22    50   -75
      -3    3   -75    75
    1  -1   25   -25    0
```

$x + 3$ is a factor. The other factor is the quotient: $x^3 - x^2 + 25x - 25$.

$$x^3 - x^2 + 25x - 25 = x^2(x - 1) + 25(x - 1)$$
$$= (x - 1)\left(x^2 + 25\right)$$
$$= (x - 1)(x + 5i)(x - 5i)$$

The zeros are -3, 1, $-5i$, $5i$.

$$f(x) = (x + 3)(x - 1)(x + 5i)(x - 5i)$$

38. $f(x) = x^4 + 3x^3 - 19x^2 + 27x - 252$

Step 1: $f(x)$ has 4 complex zeros.

Step 2: By Descartes Rule of Signs, there are three positive real zeros or there is one positive real zero.

$$f(-x) = (-x)^4 + 3(-x)^3 - 19(-x)^2 + 27(-x) - 252$$
$$= x^4 - 3x^3 - 19x^2 - 27x - 252$$

Thus, there is 1 negative real zero.

Step 3: Possible rational zeros:

$p = \pm 1, \pm 2, \pm 3, \pm 4, \pm 6, \pm 7, \pm 9,$
$\quad \pm 12, \pm 14, \pm 18, \pm 21, \pm 28, \pm 36,$
$\quad \pm 42, \pm 63, \pm 84, \pm 126, \pm 252;$
$q = \pm 1;$

The possible rational zeros are the same as the values of p.

Step 4: Using synthetic division:

We try $x + 7$:

```
-7)1    3   -19    27   -252
      -7    28   -63    252
    1  -4     9   -36      0
```

$x + 7$ is a factor. The other factor is the quotient:

$$x^3 - 4x^2 + 9x - 36 = x^2(x - 4) + 9(x - 4)$$
$$= (x - 4)\left(x^2 + 9\right)$$
$$= (x - 4)(x + 3i)(x - 3i)$$

The zeros are -7, 4, $-3i$, $3i$.

$$f(x) = (x + 7)(x - 4)(x + 3i)(x - 3i)$$

39. $f(x) = 3x^4 - x^3 - 9x^2 + 159x - 52$

Step 1: $f(x)$ has 4 complex zeros.

Step 2: By Descartes Rule of Signs, there are three positive real zeros or there is one positive real zero.

$f(-x) = 3(-x)^4 - (-x)^3 - 9(-x)^2 + 159(-x) - 52$
$= 3x^4 + x^3 - 9x^2 - 159x - 52$

Thus, there is 1 negative real zero.

Step 3: Possible rational zeros:

$p = \pm 1, \pm 2, \pm 4, \pm 13, \pm 26, \pm 52;$
$q = \pm 1, \pm 3;$

$\dfrac{p}{q} = \pm 1, \pm 2, \pm 4, \pm 13, \pm 26, \pm 52,$

$\pm \dfrac{1}{3}, \pm \dfrac{2}{3}, \pm \dfrac{4}{3}, \pm \dfrac{13}{3}, \pm \dfrac{26}{3}, \pm \dfrac{52}{3}$

Step 4: Using synthetic division:

We try $x + 4$:

$$\begin{array}{r|rrrrr} -4 & 3 & -1 & -9 & 159 & -52 \\ & & -12 & 52 & -172 & 52 \\ \hline & 3 & -13 & 43 & -13 & 0 \end{array}$$

$x + 4$ is a factor and the quotient is $3x^3 - 13x^2 + 43x - 13$.

We try $x - \dfrac{1}{3}$ on $3x^3 - 13x^2 + 43x - 13$:

$$\begin{array}{r|rrrr} \frac{1}{3} & 3 & -13 & 43 & -13 \\ & & 1 & -4 & 13 \\ \hline & 3 & -12 & 39 & 0 \end{array}$$

$x - \dfrac{1}{3}$ is a factor and the quotient is $3x^2 - 12x + 39$.

$3x^2 - 12x + 39 = 3(x^2 - 4x + 13)$

The solutions of $x^2 - 4x + 13 = 0$ are:

$x = \dfrac{-(-4) \pm \sqrt{(-4)^2 - 4(1)(13)}}{2(1)}.$

$= \dfrac{4 \pm \sqrt{-36}}{2} = \dfrac{4 \pm 6i}{2} = 2 \pm 3i$

The zeros are -4, $\dfrac{1}{3}$, $2 - 3i$, $2 + 3i$.

$f(x) = 3(x+4)\left(x - \dfrac{1}{3}\right)(x - 2 + 3i)(x - 2 - 3i)$

40. $f(x) = 2x^4 + x^3 - 35x^2 - 113x + 65$

Step 1: $f(x)$ has 4 complex zeros.

Step 2: By Descartes Rule of Signs, there are two positive real zeros or no positive real zeros.

$f(-x) = 2(-x)^4 + (-x)^3 - 35(-x)^2 - 113(-x) + 65$
$= 2x^4 - x^3 - 35x^2 + 113x + 65$

Thus, there are two negative real zeros or no negative real zeros.

Step 3: Possible rational zeros:

$p = \pm 1, \pm 5, \pm 13, \pm 65; \quad q = \pm 1, \pm 2;$
$\dfrac{p}{q} = \pm 1, \pm 5, \pm 13, \pm 65, \pm \dfrac{1}{2}, \pm \dfrac{5}{2}, \pm \dfrac{13}{2}, \pm \dfrac{65}{2}$

Step 4: Using synthetic division:

We try $x - 5$:

$$\begin{array}{r|rrrrr} 5 & 2 & 1 & -35 & -113 & 65 \\ & & 10 & 55 & 100 & -65 \\ \hline & 2 & 11 & 20 & -13 & 0 \end{array}$$

$x - 5$ is a factor and the quotient is $2x^3 + 11x^2 + 20x - 13$

We try $x - \dfrac{1}{2}$ on $2x^3 + 11x^2 + 20x - 13$:

$$\begin{array}{r|rrrr} \frac{1}{2} & 2 & 11 & 20 & -13 \\ & & 1 & 6 & 13 \\ \hline & 2 & 12 & 26 & 0 \end{array}$$

$x - \dfrac{1}{2}$ is a factor and the quotient is

$2x^2 + 12x + 26$.

$2x^2 + 12x + 26 = 2\left(x^2 + 6x + 13\right)$

The solutions of $x^2 + 6x + 13 = 0$ are:

$x = \dfrac{-6 \pm \sqrt{6^2 - 4(1)(13)}}{2(1)}$.

$= \dfrac{-6 \pm \sqrt{-16}}{2} = \dfrac{-6 \pm 4i}{2}$

$= -3 \pm 2i$

The zeros are 5, $\dfrac{1}{2}$, $-3 - 2i$, $-3 + 2i$.

$f(x) = 2(x - 5)\left(x - \dfrac{1}{2}\right)(x + 3 + 2i)(x + 3 - 2i)$

41. If the coefficients are real numbers and $2 + i$ is a zero, then $2 - i$ would also be a zero. This would then require a polynomial of degree 4.

42. Three zeros are given. If the coefficients are real numbers, then the complex zeros would also have their conjugates as zeros. This would mean that there are 5 zeros, which would require a polynomial of degree 5.

43. If the coefficients are real numbers, then complex zeros must appear in conjugate pairs. We have a conjugate pair and one real zero. Thus, there is only one remaining zero, and it must be real because a complex zero would require a pair of complex conjugates.

44. One of the remaining zeros must be $4 + i$, the conjugate of $4 - i$. The third zero is a real number. Thus, the fourth zero must also be a real number in order to have a degree 4 polynomial.

Chapter 5 Review Exercises

1. $f(x) = 4x^5 - 3x^2 + 5x - 2$ is a polynomial of degree 5.

2. $f(x) = \dfrac{3x^5}{2x + 1}$ is not a polynomial because there are variables in the denominator.

3. $f(x) = 3x^2 + 5x^{1/2} - 1$ is not a polynomial because the variable x is raised to the $\dfrac{1}{2}$ power, which is not a nonnegative integer.

4. $f(x) = 3$ is a polynomial of degree 0.

5. $f(x) = (x + 2)^3$

Using the graph of $y = x^3$, shift left 2 units.

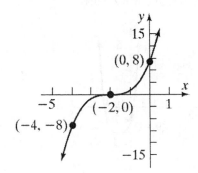

6. $f(x) = -x^3 + 3$

Using the graph of $y = x^3$, reflect about the x-axis, then shift up 3 units.

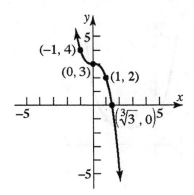

7. $f(x) = -(x-1)^4$

Using the graph of $y = x^4$, shift right 1 unit, then reflect about the *x*-axis.

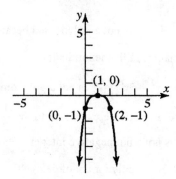

8. $f(x) = (x-1)^4 - 2$

Using the graph of $y = x^4$, shift right 1 unit, then shift down 2 units.

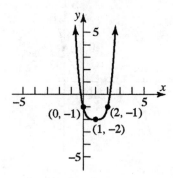

9. $f(x) = (x-1)^4 + 2$

Using the graph of $y = x^4$, shift right 1 unit, then shift up 2 units.

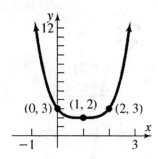

10. $f(x) = (1-x)^3 = -(x-1)^3$

Using the graph of $y = x^3$, shift right 1 unit, then reflect about the *x*-axis.

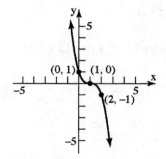

11. $f(x) = x(x+2)(x+4)$

(a) *y*-intercept: $f(0) = (0)(0+2)(0+4) = 0$

   x-intercepts: solve $f(x) = 0$:

   $x(x+2)(x+4) = 0$

   $x = 0$ or $x = -2$ or $x = -4$

(b) The graph crosses the *x*-axis at $x = -4$, $x = -2$ and $x = 0$ since each zero has multiplicity 1.

(c) The function resembles $y = x^3$ for large values of $|x|$.

(d) The polynomial is of degree 3 so the graph has at most $3 - 1 = 2$ turning points.

(e) Near -4:

   $f(x) \approx -4(-4+2)(x+4) = 8(x+4)$

   (a line with slope 8)

   Near -2:

   $f(x) \approx -2(x+2)(-2+4) = -4(x+2)$

   (a line with slope -4)

   Near 0: $f(x) \approx x(0+2)(0+4) = 8x$

   (a line with slope 8)

(f) Graphing:

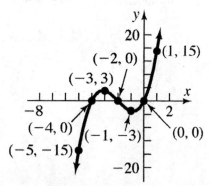

12. $f(x) = x(x-2)(x-4)$

(a) *y*-intercept: $f(0) = (0)(0-2)(0-4) = 0$

x-intercepts: solve $f(x) = 0$:

$x(x-2)(x-4) = 0$

$x = 0$ or $x = 2$ or $x = 4$

(b) The graph crosses the *x*-axis at $x = 0$, $x = 2$ and $x = 4$ since each zero has multiplicity 1.

(c) The function resembles $y = x^3$ for large values of $|x|$.

(d) The polynomial is of degree 3 so the graph has at most $3-1 = 2$ turning points.

(e) Near 0: $f(x) \approx x(0-2)(0-4) = 8x$
(a line with slope 8)

Near 2: $f(x) \approx 2(x-2)(2-4) = -4(x-2)$
(a line with slope -4)

Near 4: $f(x) \approx 4(4-2)(x-4) = 8(x-4)$
(a line with slope 8)

(f) Graphing:

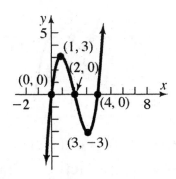

13. $f(x) = (x-2)^2 (x+4)$

(a) *y*-intercept: $f(0) = (0-2)^2 (0+4) = 16$

x-intercepts: solve $f(x) = 0$:

$(x-2)^2 (x+4) = 0 \Rightarrow x = 2$ or $x = -4$

(b) The graph crosses the *x*-axis at $x = -4$ since this zero has multiplicity 1. The graph touches the *x*-axis at $x = 2$ since this zero has multiplicity 2.

(c) The function resembles $y = x^3$ for large values of $|x|$.

(d) The polynomial is of degree 3 so the graph has at most $3-1 = 2$ turning points.

(e) Near -4:
$$f(x) \approx (-4-2)^2 (x+4) = 36(x+4)$$
(a line with slope 36)

Near 2: $f(x) \approx (x-2)^2 (2+4) = 6(x-2)^2$
(a parabola opening upward)

(f) Graphing:

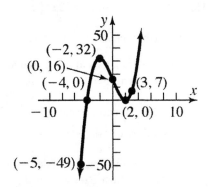

14. $f(x) = (x-2)(x+4)^2$

(a) *y*-intercept: $f(0) = (0-2)(0+4)^2 = -32$

x-intercepts: solve $f(x) = 0$:

$(x-2)(x+4)^2 = 0 \Rightarrow x = 2$ or $x = -4$

(b) The graph crosses the *x*-axis at $x = 2$ since this zero has multiplicity 1. The graph touches the *x*-axis at $x = -4$ since this zero has multiplicity 2.

(c) The function resembles $y = x^3$ for large values of $|x|$.

(d) The polynomial is of degree 3 so the graph has at most $3-1 = 2$ turning points.

(e) Near -4:
$$f(x) \approx (-4-2)(x+4)^2 = -6(x+4)^2$$
(a parabola opening downward)

Near 2: $f(x) \approx (x-2)(2+4)^2 = 36(x-2)$
(a line with slope 36)

(f) Graphing:

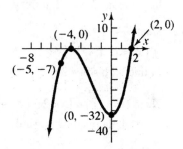

15. $f(x) = -2x^3 + 4x^2 = -2x^2(x-2)$

(a) *x*-intercepts: 0, 2; *y*-intercept: 0

(b) crosses x axis at $x = 2$ and touches the x axis at $x = 0$

(c) The function resembles $y = -2x^3$ for large values of $|x|$

(d) The polynomial is of degree 3 so the graph has at most $3-1=2$ turning points.

(e) Near 0: $f(x) \approx -2x^2(0-2) = 4x^2$
(a parabola opening upward)

Near 2: $f(x) \approx -2(2)^2(x-2) = -8(x-2)$
(a line with slope -8)

(f) Graphing by hand

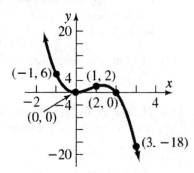

16. $f(x) = -4x^3 + 4x = -4x(x-1)(x+1)$

(a) *y*-intercept: $f(0) = -4(0)^3 + 4(0) = 0$
x-intercepts: solve $f(x) = 0$:
$-4x(x-1)(x+1) = 0$
$x = 0$, $x = 1$, or $x = -1$

(b) The graph crosses the *x*-axis at $x = 0$, $x = -1$, and $x = 1$ since each zero has multiplicity 1.

(c) The function resembles $y = -4x^3$ for large values of $|x|$.

(d) The polynomial is of degree 3 so the graph has at most $3-1=2$ turning points.

(e) Near -1:
$f(x) \approx -4(-1)(-1-1)(x+1) = -8(x+1)$
(a line with slope -8)

Near 0: $f(x) \approx -4x(0-1)(0+1) = 4x$
(a line with slope 4)

Near 1:
$f(x) \approx -4(1)(x-1)(1+1) = -8(x-1)$
(a line with slope -8)

(f) Graphing:

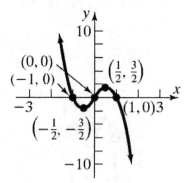

17. $f(x) = (x-1)^2(x+3)(x+1)$

(a) *y*-intercept: $f(0) = (0-1)^2(0+3)(0+1)$
$= 3$
x-intercepts: solve $f(x) = 0$:
$(x-1)^2(x+3)(x+1) = 0$
$x = 1$ or $x = -3$ or $x = -1$

(b) The graph crosses the *x*-axis at $x = -3$ and $x = -1$ since each zero has multiplicity 1. The graph touches the *x*-axis at $x = 1$ since this zero has multiplicity 2.

(c) The function resembles $y = x^4$ for large values of $|x|$.

(d) The polynomial is of degree 4 so the graph has at most $4-1=3$ turning points.

(e) Near -3:

$$f(x) \approx (-3-1)^2(x+3)(-3+1) = -32(x+3)$$

(a line with slope -32)

Near -1:

$$f(x) \approx (-1-1)^2(-1+3)(x+1) = 8(x+1)$$

(a line with slope 8)

Near 1:

$$f(x) \approx (x-1)^2(1+3)(1+1) = 8(x-1)^2$$

(a parabola opening upward)

(f) Graphing:

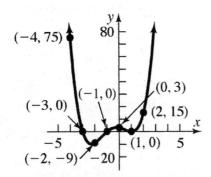

18. $f(x) = (x-4)(x+2)^2(x-2)$

(a) y-intercept: $f(0) = (0-4)(0+2)^2(0-2)$
$$= 32$$

x-intercepts: solve $f(x) = 0$:

$$(x-4)(x+2)^2(x-2) = 0$$
$$x = 4 \text{ or } x = -2 \text{ or } x = 2$$

(b) The graph crosses the x-axis at $x = 2$ and $x = 4$ since each zero has multiplicity 1. The graph touches the x-axis at $x = -2$ since this zero has multiplicity 2.

(c) The function resembles $y = x^4$ for large values of $|x|$.

(d) The polynomial is of degree 4 so the graph has at most $4-1=3$ turning points.

(e) Near -2:

$$f(x) \approx (-2-4)(x+2)^2(-2-2) = 24(x+2)^2$$

(a parabola opening upward)

Near 2:

$$f(x) \approx (2-4)(2+2)^2(x-2) = -32(x-2)$$

(a line with slope -32)

Near 4:

$$f(x) \approx (x-4)(4+2)^2(4-2) = 72(x-4)$$

(a line with slope 72)

(f) Graphing:

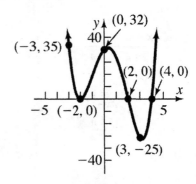

19. $R(x) = \dfrac{x+2}{x^2-9} = \dfrac{x+2}{(x+3)(x-3)}$ is in lowest terms.

The denominator has zeros at -3 and 3. Thus, the domain is $\{x \mid x \neq -3, x \neq 3\}$. The degree of the numerator, $p(x) = x+2$, is $n = 1$. The degree of the denominator, $q(x) = x^2 - 9$, is $m = 2$. Since $n < m$, the line $y = 0$ is a horizontal asymptote. Since the denominator is zero at -3 and 3, $x = -3$ and $x = 3$ are vertical asymptotes.

531

20. $R(x) = \dfrac{x^2 + 4}{x - 2}$ is in lowest terms. The

denominator has a zero at 2. Thus, the domain is $\{x \mid x \neq 2\}$. The degree of the numerator,

$p(x) = x^2 + 4$, is $n = 2$. The degree of the denominator, $q(x) = x - 2$, is $m = 1$. Since $n = m + 1$, there is an oblique asymptote.

Dividing:

$$
\begin{array}{r}
x + 2 \\
x - 2 \overline{\smash{\big)}\ x^2 + 4} \\
\underline{x^2 - 2x } \\
2x + 4 \\
\underline{2x - 4} \\
8
\end{array}
$$

$R(x) = x + 2 + \dfrac{8}{x - 2}$

Thus, the oblique asymptote is $y = x + 2$. Since the denominator is zero at 2, $x = 2$ is a vertical asymptote.

21. $R(x) = \dfrac{x^2 + 3x + 2}{(x + 2)^2} = \dfrac{(x + 2)(x + 1)}{(x + 2)^2} = \dfrac{x + 1}{x + 2}$ is in

lowest terms. The denominator has a zero at -2. Thus, the domain is $\{x \mid x \neq -2\}$. The degree of the numerator, $p(x) = x^2 + 3x + 2$, is $n = 2$. The degree of the denominator,

$q(x) = (x + 2)^2 = x^2 + 4x + 4$, is $m = 2$. Since

$n = m$, the line $y = \dfrac{1}{1} = 1$ is a horizontal

asymptote. Since the denominator of $y = \dfrac{x + 1}{x + 2}$

is zero at -2, $x = -2$ is a vertical asymptote.

22. $R(x) = \dfrac{x^3}{x^3 - 1}$ is in lowest terms. The

denominator has a zero at 1. Thus, the domain is $\{x \mid x \neq 1\}$. The degree of the numerator,

$p(x) = x^3$, is $n = 3$. The degree of the denominator, $q(x) = x^3 - 1$, is $m = 3$. Since

$n = m$, the line $y = \dfrac{1}{1} = 1$ is a horizontal

asymptote. Since the denominator is zero at 1, $x = 1$ is a vertical asymptote.

23. $R(x) = \dfrac{2x - 6}{x}$ $p(x) = 2x - 6$; $q(x) = x$; $n = 1$; $m = 1$

Step 1:   Domain: $\{x \mid x \neq 0\}$
There is no y-intercept because 0 is not in the domain.

Step 2: $R(x) = \dfrac{2x - 6}{x} = \dfrac{2(x - 3)}{x}$ is in lowest terms. The x-intercept is the zero of $p(x)$: 3

Near 3: $R(x) \approx \dfrac{2}{3}(x - 3)$. Plot the point $(3, 0)$ and show a line with positive slope there.

Step 3: $R(x) = \dfrac{2x - 6}{x} = \dfrac{2(x - 3)}{x}$ is in lowest terms. The vertical asymptote is the zero of $q(x)$: $x = 0$.
Graph this asymptote using a dashed line.

Step 4: Since $n = m$, the line $y = \dfrac{2}{1} = 2$ is the horizontal asymptote. Solve to find intersection points:

$$\dfrac{2x - 6}{x} = 2$$
$$2x - 6 = 2x$$
$$-6 \neq 0$$

$R(x)$ does not intersect $y = 2$. Plot the line $y = 2$ with dashes.

Step 5:

	$(-\infty, 0)$	$(0, 3)$	$(3, \infty)$
Interval	$(-\infty, 0)$	$(0, 3)$	$(3, \infty)$
Number Chosen	-2	1	4
Value of R	$R(-2) = 5$	$R(1) = -4$	$R(4) = \frac{1}{2}$
Location of Graph	Above x-axis	Below x-axis	Above x-axis
Point on Graph	$(-2, 5)$	$(1, -4)$	$\left(4, \frac{1}{2}\right)$

Steps 6 & 7: Graphing:

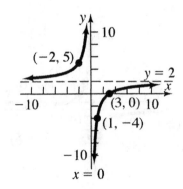

24. $R(x) = \dfrac{4 - x}{x}$ $p(x) = 4 - x$; $q(x) = x$; $n = 1$; $m = 1$

Step 1: Domain: $\{x \mid x \neq 0\}$

There is no y-intercept because 0 is not in the domain.

Step 2: $R(x) = \dfrac{4 - x}{x}$ is in lowest terms. The x-intercept is the zero of $p(x)$: 4

Near 4: $R(x) \approx \dfrac{4 - x}{4} = -\dfrac{1}{4}x + 1$. Plot the point $(4, 0)$ and show a line with negative slope there.

Step 3: $R(x) = \dfrac{4 - x}{x}$ is in lowest terms. The vertical asymptote is the zero of $q(x)$: $x = 0$.

Graph this asymptote using a dashed line.

Step 4:   Since $n = m$, the line $y = \dfrac{-1}{1} = -1$ is the horizontal asymptote. Solve to find intersection points:

$$\frac{4-x}{x} = -1$$
$$4 - x = -x$$
$$4 \neq 0$$

$R(x)$ does not intersect $y = -1$. Plot the line $y = -1$ using dashes.

Step 5:

Interval	$(-\infty, 0)$	$(0, 4)$	$(4, \infty)$
Number Chosen	-1	1	5
Value of R	$R(-1) = -5$	$R(1) = 3$	$R(5) = -0.2$
Location of Graph	Below x-axis	Above x-axis	Below x-axis
Point on Graph	$(-1, -5)$	$(1, 3)$	$(5, -0.2)$

Steps 6 & 7:   Graphing:

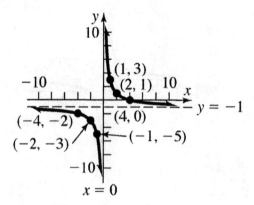

25. $H(x) = \dfrac{x+2}{x(x-2)}$ $p(x) = x + 2$; $q(x) = x(x - 2) = x^2 - 2x$; $n = 1$; $m = 2$

Step 1:   Domain: $\{x \mid x \neq 0, \, x \neq 2\}$.

There is no y-intercept because 0 is not in the domain.

Step 2: $H(x) = \dfrac{x+2}{x(x-2)}$ is in lowest terms. The x-intercept is the zero of $p(x)$: -2

Near -2: $H(x) \approx \dfrac{1}{8}(x+2)$. Plot the point $(-2, 0)$ and show a line with positive slope there.

Step 3: $H(x) = \dfrac{x+2}{x(x-2)}$ is in lowest terms. The vertical asymptotes are the zeros of $q(x)$: $x = 0$ and $x = 2$.

Graph these asymptotes using dashed lines.

Step 4: Since $n < m$, the line $y = 0$ is the horizontal asymptote. Solve to find intersection points:

$$\frac{x+2}{x(x-2)} = 0$$
$$x + 2 = 0$$
$$x = -2$$

$H(x)$ intersects $y = 0$ at $(-2, 0)$. Plot the line $y = 0$ using dashes.

Step 5:

Interval	$(-\infty, -2)$	$(-2, 0)$	$(0, 2)$	$(2, \infty)$
Number Chosen	-3	-1	1	3
Value of H	$H(-3) = -\frac{1}{15}$	$H(-1) = \frac{1}{3}$	$H(1) = -3$	$H(3) = \frac{5}{3}$
Location of Graph	Below x-axis	Above x-axis	Below x-axis	Above x-axis
Point on Graph	$\left(-3, -\frac{1}{15}\right)$	$\left(-1, \frac{1}{3}\right)$	$(1, -3)$	$\left(3, \frac{5}{3}\right)$

Steps 6 & 7: Graphing:

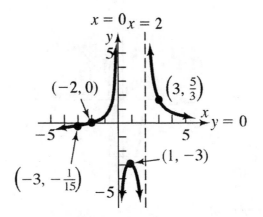

26. $H(x) = \dfrac{x}{x^2 - 1} = \dfrac{x}{(x-1)(x+1)}$ $p(x) = x;\ q(x) = x^2 - 1;\ n = 1;\ m = 2$

Step 1: Domain: $\{x \mid x \neq -1, x \neq 1\}$.

The y-intercept is $H(0) = \dfrac{0}{0^2 - 1} = 0$. Plot the point $(0, 0)$.

Step 2: $H(x) = \dfrac{x}{x^2 - 1} = \dfrac{x}{(x-1)(x+1)}$ is in lowest terms. The x-intercept is the zero of $p(x)$: 0

Near 0: $H(x) \approx -x$. Plot the point $(0, 0)$ and show a line with negative slope there.

Step 3: $H(x) = \dfrac{x}{x^2 - 1} = \dfrac{x}{(x-1)(x+1)}$ is in lowest terms. The vertical asymptotes are the zeros of $q(x)$:

$x = -1$ and $x = 1$. Graph these asymptotes using dashed lines.

Step 4: Since $n < m$, the line $y = 0$ is the horizontal asymptote. Solve to find intersection points:

$$\frac{x}{x^2 - 1} = 0$$
$$x = 0$$

$H(x)$ intersects $y = 0$ at (0, 0). Plot the line $y = 0$ using dashes.

Step 5:

Interval	$(-\infty, -1)$	$(-1, 0)$	$(0, 1)$	$(1, \infty)$
Number Chosen	-2	$-\frac{1}{2}$	$\frac{1}{2}$	2
Value of H	$H(-2) = -\frac{2}{3}$	$H\left(-\frac{1}{2}\right) = \frac{2}{3}$	$H\left(\frac{1}{2}\right) = -\frac{2}{3}$	$H(2) = \frac{2}{3}$
Location of Graph	Below x-axis	Above x-axis	Below x-axis	Above x-axis
Point on Graph	$\left(-2, -\frac{2}{3}\right)$	$\left(-\frac{1}{2}, \frac{2}{3}\right)$	$\left(\frac{1}{2}, -\frac{2}{3}\right)$	$\left(2, \frac{2}{3}\right)$

Steps 6 & 7: Graphing:

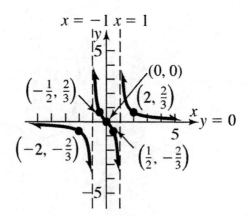

27. $R(x) = \dfrac{x^2 + x - 6}{x^2 - x - 6} = \dfrac{(x+3)(x-2)}{(x-3)(x+2)}$ $p(x) = x^2 + x - 6;\ q(x) = x^2 - x - 6;$

Step 1: Domain: $\{x \mid x \neq -2, x \neq 3\}$.

The y-intercept is $R(0) = \dfrac{0^2 + 0 - 6}{0^2 - 0 - 6} = \dfrac{-6}{-6} = 1$. Plot the point $(0, 1)$.

Step 2: $R(x) = \dfrac{x^2 + x - 6}{x^2 - x - 6}$ is in lowest terms. The x-intercepts are the zeros of $p(x)$: -3 and 2.

Near -3: $R(x) \approx -\dfrac{5}{6}(x + 3)$. Plot the point $(-3, 0)$ and show a line with negative slope there.

Near 2: $R(x) \approx -\dfrac{5}{4}(x - 2)$. Plot the point $(2, 0)$ and show a line with negative slope there.

Step 3: $R(x) = \dfrac{x^2 + x - 6}{x^2 - x - 6}$ is in lowest terms. The vertical asymptotes are the zeros of $q(x)$:

$x = -2$ and $x = 3$. Graph these asymptotes with dashed lines.

536

Step 4: Since $n = m$, the line $y = \dfrac{1}{1} = 1$ is the horizontal asymptote. Solve to find intersection points:

$$\frac{x^2 + x - 6}{x^2 - x - 6} = 1$$

$$x^2 + x - 6 = x^2 - x - 6$$

$$2x = 0$$

$$x = 0$$

$R(x)$ intersects $y = 1$ at $(0, 1)$. Plot the line $y = 1$ using dashes.

Step 5:

Interval	$(-\infty, -3)$	$(-3, -2)$	$(-2, 2)$	$(2, 3)$	$(3, \infty)$
Number Chosen	-4	-2.5	0	2.5	4
Value of R	$R(-4) \approx 0.43$	$R(-2.5) \approx -0.82$	$R(0) = 1$	$R(2.5) \approx -1.22$	$R(4) = \frac{7}{3}$
Location of Graph	Above x-axis	Below x-axis	Above x-axis	Below x-axis	Above x-axis
Point on Graph	$(-4, 0.43)$	$(-2.5, -0.82)$	$(0, 1)$	$(2.5, -1.22)$	$\left(4, \frac{7}{3}\right)$

Steps 6 & 7: Graphing:

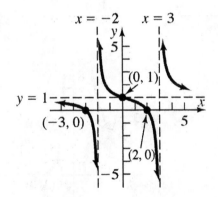

28. $R(x) = \dfrac{x^2 - 6x + 9}{x^2} = \dfrac{(x-3)^2}{x^2}$ $\quad p(x) = x^2 - 6x + 9; \ q(x) = x^2; \ n = 2; \ m = 2$

Step 1: Domain: $\{x \mid x \neq 0\}$.

There is no y-intercept because 0 is not in the domain.

Step 2: $R(x) = \dfrac{x^2 - 6x + 9}{x^2}$ is in lowest terms. The x-intercept is the zero of $p(x)$: 3.

Near 3: $R(x) \approx \dfrac{1}{9}(x - 3)^2$. Plot the point $(3, 0)$ and show a parabola open upward there.

Step 3: $R(x) = \dfrac{x^2 - 6x + 9}{x^2}$ is in lowest terms. The vertical asymptote is the zero of $q(x)$: $x = 0$.

Graph this asymptote using a dashed line.

Step 4:   Since $n = m$, the line $y = \dfrac{1}{1} = 1$ is the horizontal asymptote. Solve to find intersection points:

$$\frac{x^2 - 6x + 9}{x^2} = 1$$
$$x^2 = x^2 - 6x + 9$$
$$6x = 9$$
$$x = \frac{3}{2}$$

R(x) intersects $y = 1$ at $\left(\dfrac{3}{2}, 1\right)$. Plot the line $y = 1$ using dashes.

Step 5:

Interval	$(-\infty, 0)$	$(0, 3)$	$(3, \infty)$
Number Chosen	-3	1	4
Value of R	$R(-3) = 4$	$R(1) = 4$	$R(4) = \frac{1}{16}$
Location of Graph	Above x-axis	Above x-axis	Above x-axis
Point on Graph	$(-3, 4)$	$(1, 4)$	$\left(4, \frac{1}{16}\right)$

Steps 6 & 7: Graphing:

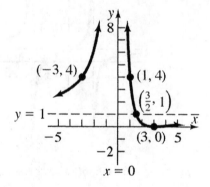

29. $F(x) = \dfrac{x^3}{x^2 - 4} = \dfrac{x^3}{(x+2)(x-2)}$ $p(x) = x^3;\ q(x) = x^2 - 4;\ n = 3;\ m = 2$

Step 1:   Domain: $\{x \mid x \neq -2, x \neq 2\}$.

The y-intercept is $F(0) = \dfrac{0^3}{0^2 - 4} = \dfrac{0}{-4} = 0$. Plot the point $(0, 0)$.

Step 2: $F(x) = \dfrac{x^3}{x^2 - 4}$ is in lowest terms. The x-intercept is the zero of $p(x)$: 0.

Near 0: $F(x) \approx -\dfrac{1}{4}x^3$. Plot the point $(0, 0)$ and indicate a cubic function there (left tail up and right tail down).

Step 3: $F(x) = \dfrac{x^3}{x^2 - 4}$ is in lowest terms. The vertical asymptotes are the zeros of $q(x)$: $x = -2$ and $x = 2$.

Graph these asymptotes using dashed lines.

Step 4:   Since $n = m + 1$, there is an oblique asymptote. Dividing:

$$x^2 - 4 \overline{\smash{\big)}\,x^3} \qquad \qquad \dfrac{x^3}{x^2 - 4} = x + \dfrac{4x}{x^2 - 4}$$
$$\underline{x^3 \qquad -4x}$$
$$\qquad\qquad 4x$$

The oblique asymptote is $y = x$. Solve to find intersection points:

$$\dfrac{x^3}{x^2 - 4} = x$$
$$x^3 = x^3 - 4x$$
$$4x = 0$$
$$x = 0$$

$F(x)$ intersects $y = x$ at $(0, 0)$. Plot the line $y = x$ using dashed lines.

Step 5:

Interval	$(-\infty, -2)$	$(-2, 0)$	$(0, 2)$	$(2, \infty)$
Number Chosen	-3	-1	1	3
Value of F	$F(-3) = -\frac{27}{5}$	$F(-1) = \frac{1}{3}$	$F(1) = -\frac{1}{3}$	$F(3) = \frac{27}{5}$
Location of Graph	Below x-axis	Above x-axis	Below x-axis	Above x-axis
Point on Graph	$\left(-3, -\frac{27}{5}\right)$	$\left(-1, \frac{1}{3}\right)$	$\left(1, -\frac{1}{3}\right)$	$\left(3, \frac{27}{5}\right)$

Steps 6 & 7: Graphing:

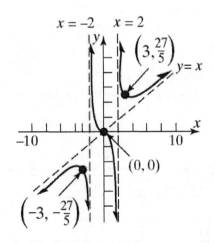

539

30. $F(x) = \dfrac{3x^3}{(x-1)^2}$ $p(x) = 3x^3$; $q(x) = (x-1)^2$; $n = 3$; $m = 2$

Step 1:   Domain: $\{x \mid x \neq 1\}$.

The y-intercept is $F(0) = \dfrac{3 \cdot 0^3}{(0-1)^2} = \dfrac{0}{1} = 0$. Plot the point $(0,0)$.

Step 2: $F(x) = \dfrac{3x^3}{(x-1)^2}$ is in lowest terms. The x-intercept is the zero of $p(x)$: 0.

Near 0: $F(x) \approx 3x^3$. Plot the point $(0,0)$ and show a cubic function there (left tail up and right tail down)

Step 3: $F(x) = \dfrac{3x^3}{(x-1)^2}$ is in lowest terms. The vertical asymptote is the zero of $q(x)$: $x = 1$.

Graph this asymptote using a dashed line.

Step 4:   Since $n = m + 1$, there is an oblique asymptote. Dividing:

$$
\begin{array}{r}
3x+6 \\
x^2-2x+1 \overline{\smash{\big)}\, 3x^3 } \\
\underline{3x^3 - 6x^2 + 3x} \\
6x^2 - 3x \\
\underline{6x^2 - 12x + 6} \\
9x - 6
\end{array}
\qquad
\dfrac{3x^3}{(x-1)^2} = 3x + 6 + \dfrac{9x-6}{(x-1)^2}
$$

The oblique asymptote is $y = 3x + 6$. Solve to find intersection points:

$$\dfrac{3x^3}{x^2 - 2x + 1} = 3x + 6$$

$$3x^3 = 3x^3 - 9x + 6$$

$$9x = 6$$

$$x = \dfrac{2}{3}$$

$F(x)$ intersects $y = 3x + 6$ at $\left(\dfrac{2}{3}, 8\right)$. Plot the line $y = 3x + 6$ using dashes.

Step 5:

Interval	$(-\infty, 0)$	$(0, 1)$	$(1, \infty)$
Number Chosen	-1	$\frac{1}{2}$	2
Value of F	$F(-1) = -\frac{3}{4}$	$F\left(\frac{1}{2}\right) = 1.5$	$F(2) = 24$
Location of Graph	Below x-axis	Above x-axis	Above x-axis
Point on Graph	$\left(-1, -\frac{3}{4}\right)$	$\left(\frac{1}{2}, 1.5\right)$	$(2, 24)$

Steps 6 & 7: Graphing:

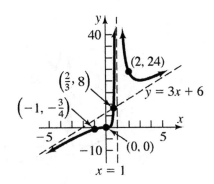

31. $R(x) = \dfrac{2x^4}{(x-1)^2}$ $p(x) = 2x^4$; $q(x) = (x-1)^2$; $n = 4$; $m = 2$

Step 1:   Domain: $\{x \mid x \neq 1\}$.

The y-intercept is $R(0) = \dfrac{2(0)^4}{(0-1)^2} = \dfrac{0}{1} = 0$. Plot the point $(0,0)$.

Step 2: $R(x) = \dfrac{2x^4}{(x-1)^2}$ is in lowest terms. The x-intercept is the zero of $p(x)$: 0.

Near 0: $R(x) \approx 2x^4$. Plot the point $(0,0)$ and show the graph of a quartic opening up there.

Step 3: $R(x) = \dfrac{2x^4}{(x-1)^2}$ is in lowest terms. The vertical asymptote is the zero of $q(x)$: $x = 1$.

Graph this asymptote using a dashed line.

Step 4:   Since $n > m+1$, there is no horizontal asymptote and no oblique asymptote.

Step 5:

Interval	$(-\infty, 0)$	$(0, 1)$	$(1, \infty)$
Number Chosen	-2	$\frac{1}{2}$	2
Value of R	$R(-2) \approx \frac{32}{9}$	$R\left(\frac{1}{2}\right) = \frac{1}{2}$	$R(2) = 32$
Location of Graph	Above x-axis	Above x-axis	Above x-axis
Point on Graph	$\left(-2, \frac{32}{9}\right)$	$\left(\frac{1}{2}, \frac{1}{2}\right)$	$(2, 32)$

541

Steps 6 & 7: Graphing:

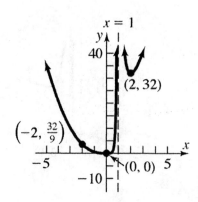

32. $R(x) = \dfrac{x^4}{x^2 - 9} = \dfrac{x^4}{(x+3)(x-3)}$ $p(x) = x^4$; $q(x) = x^2 - 9$; $n = 4$; $m = 2$

Step 1:   Domain: $\{x \mid x \neq -3,\, x \neq 3\}$.

The y-intercept is $R(0) = \dfrac{(0)^4}{0^2 - 9} = \dfrac{0}{-9} = 0$. Plot the point $(0,0)$.

Step 2: $R(x) = \dfrac{x^4}{x^2 - 9}$ is in lowest terms. The x-intercept is the zero of $p(x)$: 0.

Near 0: $R(x) \approx -\dfrac{1}{9}x^4$. Plot the point $(0,0)$ and show the graph of a quartic opening down there.

Step 3: $R(x) = \dfrac{x^4}{x^2 - 9}$ is in lowest terms. The vertical asymptotes are the zeros of $q(x)$: $x = -3$ and $x = 3$.
Graph these asymptotes using dashed lines.

Step 4:   Since $n > m + 1$, there is no horizontal asymptote and no oblique asymptote.

Step 5:

Interval	$(-\infty, -3)$	$(-3, 0)$	$(0, 3)$	$(3, \infty)$
Number Chosen	-4	-1	1	4
Value of R	$R(-4) \approx 37$	$R(-1) = -\frac{1}{8}$	$R(1) = -\frac{1}{8}$	$R(4) \approx 37$
Location of Graph	Above x-axis	Below x-axis	Below x-axis	Above x-axis
Point on Graph	$(-4, 37)$	$\left(-1, -\frac{1}{8}\right)$	$\left(1, -\frac{1}{8}\right)$	$(4, 37)$

Steps 6 & 7: Graphing:

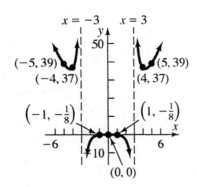

33. $G(x) = \dfrac{x^2 - 4}{x^2 - x - 2} = \dfrac{(x+2)(x-2)}{(x-2)(x+1)} = \dfrac{x+2}{x+1}$ $p(x) = x^2 - 4;$ $q(x) = x^2 - x - 2;$

Step 1: Domain: $\{x \mid x \neq -1,\ x \neq 2\}$.

The y-intercept is $G(0) = \dfrac{0^2 - 4}{0^2 - 0 - 2} = \dfrac{-4}{-2} = 2$. Plot the point $(0, 2)$.

Step 2: In lowest terms, $G(x) = \dfrac{x+2}{x+1}$, $x \neq 2$. The x-intercept is the zero of $y = x + 2$: -2; Note: 2 is not a zero because reduced form must be used to find the zeros.

Near -2: $G(x) \approx -x - 2$. Plot the point $(-2, 0)$ and show a line with negative slope there.

Step 3: In lowest terms, $G(x) = \dfrac{x+2}{x+1}$, $x \neq 2$. The vertical asymptote is the zero of $f(x) = x + 1$: $x = -1$; Graph this asymptote using a dashed line. Note: $x = 2$ is not a vertical asymptote because reduced form must be used to find the asymptotes. The graph has a hole at $\left(2, \dfrac{4}{3}\right)$.

Step 4: Since $n = m$, the line $y = \dfrac{1}{1} = 1$ is the horizontal asymptote. Solve to find intersection points:

$$\frac{x^2 - 4}{x^2 - x - 2} = 1$$
$$x^2 - 4 = x^2 - x - 2$$
$$x = 2$$

$G(x)$ does not intersect $y = 1$ because $G(x)$ is not defined at $x = 2$. Plot the line $y = 1$ using dashes.

Step 5:

Interval	$(-\infty, -2)$	$(-2, -1)$	$(-1, 2)$	$(2, \infty)$
Number Chosen	-3	-1.5	0	3
Value of G	$G(-3) = \frac{1}{2}$	$G(-1.5) = -1$	$G(0) = 2$	$G(3) = 1.25$
Location of Graph	Above x-axis	Below x-axis	Above x-axis	Above x-axis
Point on Graph	$\left(-3, \frac{1}{2}\right)$	$(-1.5, -1)$	$(0, 2)$	$(3, 1.25)$

Steps 6 & 7: Graphing:

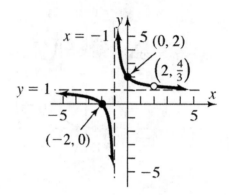

34. $F(x) = \dfrac{(x-1)^2}{x^2-1} = \dfrac{(x-1)(x-1)}{(x+1)(x-1)} = \dfrac{x-1}{x+1}$; $\quad p(x) = (x-1)^2$; $\quad q(x) = x^2 - 1$; $\quad n = 2$; $m = 2$

Step 1:   Domain: $\{x \mid x \neq -1, x \neq 1\}$.

         The y-intercept is $F(0) = \dfrac{(0-1)^2}{0^2 - 1} = \dfrac{1}{-1} = -1$. Plot the point $(0, -1)$.

Step 2:   In lowest terms, $F(x) = \dfrac{x-1}{x+1}$, $x \neq 1$. There is no x-intercept since 1 is not in the domain.

Step 3:   In lowest terms, $F(x) = \dfrac{x-1}{x+1}$, $x \neq 1$. The vertical asymptote is the zero of $g(x) = x+1$: $x = -1$;

         Graph this asymptote using a dashed line. Note: $x = 1$ is not a vertical asymptote because reduced form must be used to find the asymptotes. The graph has a hole at $(1, 0)$.

Step 4:   Since $n = m$, the line $y = \frac{1}{1} = 1$ is the horizontal asymptote. Solve to find intersection points:

$$\frac{x^2 - 2x + 1}{x^2 - 1} = 1$$
$$x^2 - 2x + 1 = x^2 - 1$$
$$-2x = -2$$
$$x = 1$$

         $F(x)$ does not intersect $y = 1$ because $F(x)$ is not defined at $x = 1$. Plot the line $y = 1$ using dashes.

Step 5:

Interval	$(-\infty, -1)$	$(-1, 1)$	$(1, \infty)$
Number Chosen	-2	0	3
Value of F	$F(-2) = 3$	$F(0) = -1$	$F(3) = \frac{1}{2}$
Location of Graph	Above x-axis	Below x-axis	Above x-axis
Point on Graph	$(-2, 3)$	$\left(0, -1\right)$	$\left(3, \frac{1}{2}\right)$

Steps 6 & 7: Graphing:

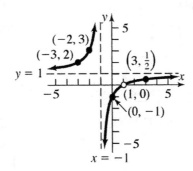

35.
$$x^3 + x^2 < 4x + 4$$
$$x^3 + x^2 - 4x - 4 < 0$$
$$x^2(x+1) - 4(x+1) < 0$$
$$(x^2 - 4)(x+1) < 0$$
$$(x-2)(x+2)(x+1) < 0$$
$$f(x) = (x-2)(x+2)(x+1)$$
$x = -2$, $x = -1$, and $x = 2$ are the zeros of f.

Interval	$(-\infty, -2)$	$(-2, -1)$	$(-1, 2)$	$(2, \infty)$
Number Chosen	-3	$-3/2$	0	3
Value of f	-10	0.875	-4	20
Conclusion	Negative	Positive	Negative	Positive

The solution set is $\{x \mid x < -2 \text{ or } -1 < x < 2\}$, or, using interval notation, $(-\infty, -2) \cup (-1, 2)$.

36.
$$x^3 + 4x^2 \ge x + 4$$
$$x^3 + 4x^2 - x - 4 \ge 0$$
$$x^2(x+4) - 1(x+4) \ge 0$$
$$(x^2 - 1)(x+4) \ge 0$$
$$(x-1)(x+1)(x+4) \ge 0$$
$$f(x) = (x-1)(x+1)(x+4)$$
$x = -4$, $x = -1$, and $x = 1$ are the zeros of f.

Interval	$(-\infty, -4)$	$(-4, -1)$	$(-1, 1)$	$(1, \infty)$
Number Chosen	-5	-2	0	2
Value of f	-24	6	-4	18
Conclusion	Negative	Positive	Negative	Positive

The solution set is $\{x \mid -4 \le x \le -1 \text{ or } x \ge 1\}$, or, using interval notation, $[-4, -1] \cup [1, \infty)$.

37.
$$\frac{6}{x+3} \ge 1$$
$$\frac{6}{x+3} - 1 \ge 0 \Rightarrow \frac{6 - 1(x+3)}{x+3} \ge 0 \Rightarrow \frac{-x+3}{x+3} \ge 0$$
$$f(x) = \frac{-(x-3)}{x+3}$$
The zeros and values where the expression is undefined are $x = 3$ and $x = -3$.

Interval	$(-\infty, -3)$	$(-3, 3)$	$(3, \infty)$
Number Chosen	-4	0	4
Value of f	-7	1	$-\frac{1}{7}$
Conclusion	Negative	Positive	Negative

The solution set is $\{x \mid -3 < x \le 3\}$, or, using interval notation, $(-3, 3]$.

38.
$$\frac{-2}{1 - 3x} < 1$$
$$\frac{-2}{1 - 3x} - 1 < 0 \Rightarrow \frac{-2 - 1 + 3x}{1 - 3x} < 0 \Rightarrow \frac{3x - 3}{1 - 3x} < 0$$
$$f(x) = \frac{3(x-1)}{1 - 3x}$$
The zeros and values where the expression is undefined are $x = \frac{1}{3}$ and $x = 1$.

Interval	$\left(-\infty, \frac{1}{3}\right)$	$\left(\frac{1}{3}, 1\right)$	$(1, \infty)$
Number Chosen	0	0.5	2
Value of f	-3	3	$-\frac{3}{5}$
Conclusion	Negative	Positive	Negative

The solution set is $\left\{x \mid x < \frac{1}{3} \text{ or } x > 1\right\}$, or, using interval notation, $\left(-\infty, \frac{1}{3}\right) \cup (1, \infty)$.

39. $\dfrac{2x-6}{1-x} < 2$

$$\dfrac{2x-6}{1-x} - 2 < 0$$

$$\dfrac{2x-6-2(1-x)}{1-x} < 0$$

$$\dfrac{4x-8}{1-x} < 0$$

$$f(x) = \dfrac{4(x-2)}{1-x}$$

The zeros and values where the expression is undefined are $x = 1$, and $x = 2$.

Interval	$(-\infty, 1)$	$(1, 2)$	$(2, \infty)$
Number Chosen	0	1.5	3
Value of f	-8	4	-2
Conclusion	Negative	Positive	Negative

The solution set is $\{x \mid x < 1 \text{ or } x > 2\}$, or, using interval notation, $(-\infty, 1) \cup (2, \infty)$.

40. $\dfrac{3-2x}{2x+5} \geq 2$

$$f(x) = \dfrac{3-2x}{2x+5} - 2$$

$$\dfrac{3-2x}{2x+5} - 2 \geq 0$$

$$\dfrac{3-2x-4x-10}{2x+5} \geq 0$$

$$\dfrac{-6x-7}{2x+5} \geq 0$$

The zeros and values where the expression is undefined are $x = -\dfrac{7}{6}$ and $x = -\dfrac{5}{2}$.

Interval	$\left(-\infty, -\frac{5}{2}\right)$	$\left(-\frac{5}{2}, -\frac{7}{6}\right)$	$\left(-\frac{7}{6}, \infty\right)$
Number Chosen	-3	-2	0
Value of f	-11	5	$-\frac{7}{5}$
Conclusion	Negative	Positive	Negative

The solution set is $\left\{x \mid -\dfrac{5}{2} < x \leq -\dfrac{7}{6}\right\}$, or, using interval notation, $\left[-\dfrac{5}{2}, -\dfrac{7}{6}\right]$.

41. $\dfrac{(x-2)(x-1)}{x-3} \geq 0$

$$f(x) = \dfrac{(x-2)(x-1)}{x-3}$$

The zeros and values where the expression is undefined are $x = 1$, $x = 2$, and $x = 3$.

Interval	$(-\infty, 1)$	$(1, 2)$	$(2, 3)$	$(3, \infty)$
Number Chosen	0	1.5	2.5	4
Value of f	$-\frac{2}{3}$	$\frac{1}{6}$	$-\frac{3}{2}$	6
Conclusion	Negative	Positive	Negative	Positive

The solution set is $\{x \mid 1 \leq x \leq 2 \text{ or } x > 3\}$, or, using interval notation, $[1, 2] \cup (3, \infty)$.

42. $\dfrac{x+1}{x(x-5)} \leq 0$

$$f(x) = \dfrac{x+1}{x(x-5)}$$

The zeros and values where the expression is undefined are $x = -1$, $x = 0$, and $x = 5$.

Interval	$(-\infty, -1)$	$(-1, 0)$	$(0, 5)$	$(5, \infty)$
Number Chosen	-2	-0.5	1	6
Value of f	$-\dfrac{1}{14}$	$\dfrac{2}{11}$	$-\dfrac{1}{2}$	$\dfrac{7}{6}$
Conclusion	Negative	Positive	Negative	Positive

The solution set is $\{x \mid x \le -1 \text{ or } 0 < x < 5\}$, or, using interval notation, $(-\infty, -1] \cup (0, 5)$.

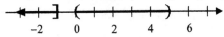

43. $\dfrac{x^2 - 8x + 12}{x^2 - 16} > 0$

$f(x) = \dfrac{x^2 - 8x + 12}{x^2 - 16}$

$\dfrac{(x-2)(x-6)}{(x+4)(x-4)} > 0$

The zeros and values where the expression is undefined are $x = -4$, $x = 2$, $x = 4$, and $x = 6$.

Interval	Number Chosen	Value of f	Conclusion
$(-\infty, -4)$	-5	$\dfrac{77}{9}$	Positive
$(-4, 2)$	0	$-\dfrac{3}{4}$	Negative
$(2, 4)$	3	$\dfrac{3}{7}$	Positive
$(4, 6)$	5	$-\dfrac{1}{3}$	Negative
$(6, \infty)$	7	$\dfrac{5}{33}$	Positive

The solution set is $\{x \mid x < -4 \text{ or } 2 < x < 4 \text{ or } x > 6\}$, or, using interval notation, $(-\infty, -4) \cup (2, 4) \cup (6, \infty)$.

44. $\dfrac{x\left(x^2 + x - 2\right)}{x^2 + 9x + 20} \le 0$

$f(x) = \dfrac{x\left(x^2 + x - 2\right)}{x^2 + 9x + 20}$

$\dfrac{x(x+2)(x-1)}{(x+5)(x+4)} \le 0$

The zeros and values where the expression is

undefined are $x = -5$, $x = -4$, $x = -2$, $x = 0$, and $x = 1$.

Interval	Number Chosen	Value of f	Conclusion
$(-\infty, -5)$	-6	-84	Negative
$(-5, -4)$	-4.5	247.5	Positive
$(-4, -2)$	-3	-6	Negative
$(-2, 0)$	-1	$\dfrac{1}{6}$	Positive
$(0, 1)$	0.5	-0.025	Negative
$(1, \infty)$	2	0.19	Positive

The solution set is $\{x \mid x < -5 \text{ or } -4 < x \le -2 \text{ or } 0 \le x \le 1\}$, or, using interval notation,
$(-\infty, -5) \cup (-4, -2] \cup [0, 1]$.

45. $f(x) = 8x^3 - 3x^2 + x + 4$

Since $g(x) = x - 1$ then $c = 1$. From the Remainder Theorem, the remainder R when $f(x)$ is divided by $g(x)$ is $f(c)$:

$f(1) = 8(1)^3 - 3(1)^2 + 1 + 4$
$= 8 - 3 + 1 + 4$
$= 10$

So $R = 10$ and g is not a factor of f.

46. $f(x) = 2x^3 + 8x^2 - 5x + 5$

Since $g(x) = x - 2$ then $c = 2$. From the Remainder Theorem, the remainder R when $f(x)$ is divided by $g(x)$ is $f(c)$:

$f(2) = 2(2)^3 + 8(2)^2 - 5(2) + 5$
$= 2(8) + 8(4) - 10 + 5$
$= 43$

So $R = 43$ and g is not a factor of f.

47. $f(x) = x^4 - 2x^3 + 15x - 2$

Since $g(x) = x + 2$ then $c = -2$. From the Remainder Theorem, the remainder R when $f(x)$ is divided by $g(x)$ is $f(c)$:

$f(-2) = (-2)^4 - 2(-2)^3 + 15(-2) - 2$
$= 16 - 2(-8) - 30 - 2$
$= 0$

So $R = 0$ and g is a factor of f.

48. $f(x) = x^4 - x^2 + 2x + 2$

Since $g(x) = x + 1$ then $c = -1$. From the Remainder Theorem, the remainder R when $f(x)$ is divided by $g(x)$ is $f(c)$:

$$f(-1) = (-1)^4 - (-1)^2 + 2(-1) + 2$$
$$= 1 - 1 - 2 + 2$$
$$= 0$$

So $R = 0$ and g is a factor of f.

49.

$$4\overline{)\begin{array}{ccccccc} 12 & 0 & -8 & 0 & 0 & 0 & 1 \end{array}}$$

| | 48 | 192 | 736 | 2944 | 11,776 | 47,104 |

| 12 | 48 | 184 | 736 | 2944 | 11,776 | 47,105 |

$f(4) = 47,105$

50.

$$-2\overline{)\begin{array}{cccc} -16 & 18 & -1 & 2 \end{array}}$$

| | 32 | -100 | 202 |

| -16 | 50 | -101 | 204 |

$f(-2) = 204$

51. $f(x) = 12x^8 - x^7 + 8x^4 - 2x^3 + x + 3$

There are 4 sign changes in $f(x)$, so there are 4 positive real zeros, 2 positive real zeros, or no positive real zeros.

$$f(-x) = 12(-x)^8 - (-x)^7 + 8(-x)^4 - 2(-x)^3 + (-x) + 3$$
$$= 12x^8 + x^7 + 8x^4 + 2x^3 - x + 3$$

There are 2 sign changes in $f(-x)$, so there are 2 negative real zeros or no negative real zeros.

52. $f(x) = -6x^5 + x^4 + 5x^3 + x + 1$

There is 1 sign change in $f(x)$ so there is exactly one positive real zero.

$$f(-x) = -6(-x)^5 + (-x)^4 + 5(-x)^3 + (-x) + 1$$
$$= 6x^5 + x^4 - 5x^3 - x + 1$$

There are 2 sign changes in $f(-x)$, so there are 2 negative real zeros or no negative real zeros.

53. $a_0 = -3$, $a_8 = 12$

$p = \pm 1, \pm 3$

$q = \pm 1, \pm 2, \pm 3, \pm 4, \pm 6, \pm 12$

$$\frac{p}{q} = \pm 1, \pm 3, \pm \frac{1}{2}, \pm \frac{3}{2}, \pm \frac{1}{3}, \pm \frac{1}{4}, \pm \frac{3}{4}, \pm \frac{1}{6}, \pm \frac{1}{12}$$

54. $a_0 = 1$, $a_5 = -6$

$p = \pm 1$

$q = \pm 1, \pm 2, \pm 3, \pm 6$

$$\frac{p}{q} = \pm 1, \pm \frac{1}{2}, \pm \frac{1}{3}, \pm \frac{1}{6}$$

55. $f(x) = x^3 - 3x^2 - 6x + 8$

By Descartes' Rule of Signs, there are two positive real zeros or no positive real zeros.

$f(-x) = (-x)^3 - 3(-x)^2 - 6(-x) + 8$, there is one

$$= -x^3 - 3x^2 + 6x + 8$$

negative real zero.

Possible rational zeros:

$p = \pm 1, \pm 2, \pm 4, \pm 8; \quad q = \pm 1;$

$$\frac{p}{q} = \pm 1, \pm 2, \pm 4, \pm 8$$

Using synthetic division:
We try $x + 2$:

$$-2\overline{)\begin{array}{cccc} 1 & -3 & -6 & 8 \end{array}}$$

| | -2 | 10 | -8 |

| 1 | -5 | 4 | 0 |

$x + 2$ is a factor. The other factor is the quotient: $x^2 - 5x + 4$.

Thus, $f(x) = (x + 2)(x^2 - 5x + 4)$.

$$= (x + 2)(x - 1)(x - 4)$$

The zeros are –2, 1, and 4, each of multiplicity 1.

56. $f(x) = x^3 - x^2 - 10x - 8$

By Descartes' Rule of Signs, there is one positive real zero.

$f(-x) = (-x)^3 - (-x)^2 - 10(-x) - 8$,

$$= -x^3 - x^2 + 10x - 8$$

there are two negative real zeros or no negative real zeros.

Possible rational zeros:

$p = \pm 1, \pm 2, \pm 4, \pm 8; \quad q = \pm 1;$

$$\frac{p}{q} = \pm 1, \pm 2, \pm 4, \pm 8$$

Using synthetic division:
We try $x + 2$:

$$-2\overline{)\begin{array}{cccc} 1 & -1 & -10 & -8 \end{array}}$$

| | -2 | 6 | 8 |

| 1 | -3 | -4 | 0 |

548

$x + 2$ is a factor. The other factor is the quotient:
$x^2 - 3x - 4$.
Thus, $f(x) = (x+2)(x^2 - 3x - 4)$.
$$= (x+2)(x+1)(x-4)$$
The zeros are $-2, -1$, and 4, each with multiplicity 1.

57. $f(x) = 4x^3 + 4x^2 - 7x + 2$

By Descartes' Rule of Signs, there are two positive real zeros or no positive real zeros.
$f(-x) = 4(-x)^3 + 4(-x)^2 - 7(-x) + 2$;
$$= -4x^3 + 4x^2 + 7x + 2$$
thus, there is one negative real zero.

Possible rational zeros:
$p = \pm 1, \pm 2; \quad q = \pm 1, \pm 2, \pm 4;$
$\dfrac{p}{q} = \pm 1, \pm 2, \pm \dfrac{1}{2}, \pm \dfrac{1}{4}$

Using synthetic division:
We try $x + 2$:

```
-2)4    4   -7    2
        -8    8   -2
    4   -4    1    0
```

$x + 2$ is a factor. The other factor is the quotient:
$4x^2 - 4x + 1$.
Thus, $f(x) = (x+2)(4x^2 - 4x + 1)$.
$$= (x+2)(2x-1)(2x-1)$$

The zeros are -2, of multiplicity 1 and $\dfrac{1}{2}$, of multiplicity 2.

58. $f(x) = 4x^3 - 4x^2 - 7x - 2$

By Descartes' Rule of Signs, there is one positive real zero.
$f(-x) = 4(-x)^3 - 4(-x)^2 - 7(-x) - 2$;
$$= -4x^3 - 4x^2 + 7x - 2$$
thus, there are two negative real zeros or no negative real zeros.

Possible rational zeros:
$p = \pm 1, \pm 2; \quad q = \pm 1, \pm 2, \pm 4;$
$\dfrac{p}{q} = \pm 1, \pm 2, \pm \dfrac{1}{2}, \pm \dfrac{1}{4}$

Using synthetic division: We try $x - 2$:

```
2)4   -4   -7   -2
       8    8    2
   4    4    1    0
```

$x - 2$ is a factor. The other factor is the quotient: $4x^2 + 4x + 1$.
Thus, $f(x) = (x-2)(4x^2 + 4x + 1)$
$$= (x-2)(2x+1)(2x+1)$$

The zeros are 2, of multiplicity 1 and $-\dfrac{1}{2}$, of multiplicity 2.

59. $f(x) = x^4 - 4x^3 + 9x^2 - 20x + 20$

By Descartes' Rule of Signs, there are four positive real zeros or two positive real zeros or no positive real zeros.
$f(-x) = (-x)^4 - 4(-x)^3 + 9(-x)^2 - 20(-x) + 20$
$$= x^4 + 4x^3 + 9x^2 + 20x + 20;$$
Thus, there are no negative real zeros.

Possible rational zeros:
$p = \pm 1, \pm 2, \pm 4, \pm 5, \pm 10, \pm 20; \quad q = \pm 1;$
$\dfrac{p}{q} = \pm 1, \pm 2, \pm 4, \pm 5, \pm 10, \pm 20$

Using synthetic division:
We try $x - 2$:

```
2)1   -4    9   -20    20
       2   -4    10   -20
   1   -2    5   -10     0
```

$x - 2$ is a factor and the quotient is
$x^3 - 2x^2 + 5x - 10 = x^2(x-2) + 5(x-2)$
$$= (x-2)(x^2 + 5)$$
Thus, $f(x) = (x-2)(x-2)(x^2 + 5)$
$$= (x-2)^2(x^2 + 5)$$

Since $x^2 + 5 = 0$ has no real solutions, the only zero is 2, of multiplicity 2.

60. $f(x) = x^4 + 6x^3 + 11x^2 + 12x + 18$

By Descartes' Rule of Signs, there are no positive real zeros.
$f(-x) = (-x)^4 + 6(-x)^3 + 11(-x)^2 + 12(-x) + 18$
$$= x^4 - 6x^3 + 11x^2 - 12x + 18;$$
Thus, there are four negative real zeros or two negative real zeros or no negative real zeros.

549

Possible rational zeros:

$p = \pm 1, \pm 2, \pm 3, \pm 6, \pm 9, \pm 18; \quad q = \pm 1;$

$\dfrac{p}{q} = \pm 1, \pm 2, \pm 3, \pm 6, \pm 9, \pm 18$

Using synthetic division:
We try $x + 3$:

$$-3\overline{)\begin{array}{ccccc} 1 & 6 & 11 & 12 & 18 \\ & -3 & -9 & -6 & -18 \\ \hline 1 & 3 & 2 & 6 & 0 \end{array}}$$

$x + 3$ is a factor and the quotient is

$x^3 + 3x^2 + 2x + 6 = x^2(x+3) + 2(x+3)$.

$\qquad = (x+3)(x^2+2)$

Thus, $f(x) = (x+3)(x+3)(x^2+2)$

$\qquad = (x+3)^2(x^2+2)$

Since $x^2 + 2 = 0$ has no real solutions, the only zero is -3, of multiplicity 2.

61. $2x^4 + 2x^3 - 11x^2 + x - 6 = 0$

The solutions of the equation are the zeros of

$f(x) = 2x^4 + 2x^3 - 11x^2 + x - 6$.

By Descartes' Rule of Signs, there are three positive real zeros or there is one positive real zero.

$f(-x) = 2(-x)^4 + 2(-x)^3 - 11(-x)^2 + (-x) - 6$

$\qquad = 2x^4 - 2x^3 - 11x^2 - x - 6$

Thus, there is one negative real zero.

Possible rational zeros:

$p = \pm 1, \pm 2, \pm 3, \pm 6; \quad q = \pm 1, \pm 2;$

$\dfrac{p}{q} = \pm 1, \pm 2, \pm 3, \pm 6, \pm \dfrac{1}{2}, \pm \dfrac{3}{2}$

Using synthetic division:
We try $x + 3$:

$$-3\overline{)\begin{array}{ccccc} 2 & 2 & -11 & 1 & -6 \\ & -6 & 12 & -3 & 6 \\ \hline 2 & -4 & 1 & -2 & 0 \end{array}}$$

$x + 3$ is a factor and the quotient is

$2x^3 - 4x^2 + x - 2 = 2x^2(x-2) + 1(x-2)$

$\qquad = (x-2)(2x^2+1)$

Thus, $f(x) = (x+3)(x-2)(2x^2+1)$.

Since $2x^2 + 1 = 0$ has no real solutions, the solution set is $\{-3, 2\}$.

62. $3x^4 + 3x^3 - 17x^2 + x - 6 = 0$

The solutions of the equation are the zeros of

$f(x) = 3x^4 + 3x^3 - 17x^2 + x - 6$.

By Descartes' Rule of Signs, there are three positive real zeros or there is one positive real zero.

$f(-x) = 3(-x)^4 + 3(-x)^3 - 17(-x)^2 + (-x) - 6$

$\qquad = 3x^4 - 3x^3 - 17x^2 - x - 6$

Thus, there is one negative real zero.

Possible rational zeros:

$p = \pm 1, \pm 2, \pm 3, \pm 6; \quad q = \pm 1, \pm 3;$

$\dfrac{p}{q} = \pm 1, \pm 2, \pm 3, \pm 6, \pm \dfrac{1}{3}, \pm \dfrac{2}{3}$

Using synthetic division:
We try $x + 3$:

$$-3\overline{)\begin{array}{ccccc} 3 & 3 & -17 & 1 & -6 \\ & -9 & 18 & -3 & 6 \\ \hline 3 & -6 & 1 & -2 & 0 \end{array}}$$

$x + 3$ is a factor and the quotient is

$3x^3 - 6x^2 + x - 2 = 3x^2(x-2) + 1(x-2)$.

$\qquad = (x-2)(3x^2+1)$

Thus, $f(x) = (x+3)(x-2)(3x^2+1)$.

Since $3x^2 + 1 = 0$ has no real solutions, the solution set is $\{-3, 2\}$.

63. $2x^4 + 7x^3 + x^2 - 7x - 3 = 0$

The solutions of the equation are the zeros of

$f(x) = 2x^4 + 7x^3 + x^2 - 7x - 3$.

By Descartes' Rule of Signs, there is one positive real zero.

$f(-x) = 2(-x)^4 + 7(-x)^3 + (-x)^2 - 7(-x) - 3$

$\qquad = 2x^4 - 7x^3 + x^2 + 7x - 3$

Thus, there are three negative real zeros or there is one negative real zero.

Possible rational zeros:

$p = \pm 1, \pm 3; \quad q = \pm 1, \pm 2;$

$\dfrac{p}{q} = \pm 1, \pm 3, \pm \dfrac{1}{2}, \pm \dfrac{3}{2}$

Using synthetic division:
We try $x + 3$:

$$-3\overline{)\begin{array}{ccccc} 2 & 7 & 1 & -7 & -3 \\ & -6 & -3 & 6 & 3 \\ \hline 2 & 1 & -2 & -1 & 0 \end{array}}$$

$x+3$ is a factor and the quotient is

$2x^3 + x^2 - 2x - 1 = x^2(2x+1) - 1(2x+1)$.

$$= (2x+1)(x^2-1)$$

Thus, $\quad f(x) = (x+3)(2x+1)(x^2-1)$

$$= (x+3)(2x+1)(x-1)(x+1)$$

The solution set is $\left\{-3, \ -1, \ -\dfrac{1}{2}, \ 1\right\}$.

64. $2x^4 + 7x^3 - 5x^2 - 28x - 12 = 0$

The solutions of the equation are the zeros of

$f(x) = 2x^4 + 7x^3 - 5x^2 - 28x - 12$.

By Descartes' Rule of Signs, there is one positive real zero.

$f(-x) = 2(-x)^4 + 7(-x)^3 - 5(-x)^2 - 28(-x) - 12$

$$= 2x^4 - 7x^3 - 5x^2 + 28x - 12;$$

Thus, there are three negative real zeros or there is one negative real zero.

Possible rational zeros:

$p = \pm1, \pm2, \pm3, \pm4, \pm6, \pm12; \quad q = \pm1, \pm2;$

$\dfrac{p}{q} = \pm1, \pm2, \pm3, \pm4, \pm6, \pm12, \pm\dfrac{1}{2}, \pm\dfrac{3}{2}$

Using synthetic division:

We try $x+3$:

$$
\begin{array}{r|rrrr}
-3 & 2 & 7 & -5 & -28 & -12 \\
   &   & -6 & -3 & 24 & 12 \\
\hline
   & 2 & 1 & -8 & -4 & 0
\end{array}
$$

$x+3$ is a factor and the quotient is

$2x^3 + x^2 - 8x - 4 = x^2(2x+1) - 4(2x+1)$

$$= (2x+1)(x^2-4)$$

Thus, $f(x) = (x+3)(2x+1)(x^2-4)$

$$= (x+3)(2x+1)(x-2)(x+2)$$

The solution set is $\left\{-3, \ -2, \ -\dfrac{1}{2}, \ 2\right\}$.

65. $f(x) = x^3 - x^2 - 4x + 2$

$a_2 = -1, \quad a_1 = -4, \quad a_0 = 2$

Max $\left\{1, |2| + |-4| + |-1|\right\} = $ Max $\{1, 7\} = 7$

$1 + $ Max $\left\{|2|, |-4|, |-1|\right\} = 1 + 4 = 5$

The smaller of the two numbers is 5, so every real zero of f lies between -5 and 5.

66. $f(x) = x^3 + x^2 - 10x - 5$

$a_2 = 1, \quad a_1 = -10, \quad a_0 = -5$

Max $\left\{1, |-5| + |-10| + |1|\right\} = $ Max $\{1, 16\} = 16$

$1 + $ Max $\left\{|-5|, |-10|, |1|\right\} = 1 + 10 = 11$

The smaller of the two numbers is 11, so every real zero of f lies between -11 and 11.

67. $f(x) = 2x^3 - 7x^2 - 10x + 35$

$$= 2\left(x^3 - \frac{7}{2}x^2 - 5x + \frac{35}{2}\right)$$

$a_2 = -\dfrac{7}{2}, \quad a_1 = -5, \quad a_0 = \dfrac{35}{2}$

Max $\left\{1, \left|\dfrac{35}{2}\right| + |-5| + \left|-\dfrac{7}{2}\right|\right\} = $ Max $\{1, 26\}$

$$= 26$$

$1 + $ Max $\left\{\left|\dfrac{35}{2}\right|, |-5|, \left|-\dfrac{7}{2}\right|\right\} = 1 + \dfrac{35}{2}$

$$= \dfrac{37}{2} = 18.5$$

The smaller of the two numbers is 18.5, so every real zero of f lies between -18.5 and 18.5.

68. $f(x) = 3x^3 - 7x^2 - 6x + 14$

$$= 3\left(x^3 - \frac{7}{3}x^2 - 2x + \frac{14}{3}\right)$$

$a_2 = -\dfrac{7}{3}, \quad a_1 = -2, \quad a_0 = \dfrac{14}{3}$

Max $\left\{1, \left|\dfrac{14}{3}\right| + |-2| + \left|-\dfrac{7}{3}\right|\right\} = $ Max $\{1, 9\}$

$$= 9$$

$1 + $ Max $\left\{\left|\dfrac{14}{3}\right|, |-2|, \left|-\dfrac{7}{3}\right|\right\} = 1 + \dfrac{14}{3}$

$$= \dfrac{17}{3} = 5.\overline{66}$$

The smaller of the two numbers is $5.\overline{66}$, so every real zero of f lies between $-5.\overline{66}$ and $5.\overline{66}$.

69. $f(x) = 3x^3 - x - 1;$ $[0, 1]$

$f(0) = -1 < 0$ and $f(1) = 1 > 0$

The value of the function is positive at one endpoint and negative at the other. Since the function is continuous, the Intermediate Value Theorem guarantees at least one zero in the given interval.

70. $f(x) = 2x^3 - x^2 - 3;$ $[1, 2]$

$f(1) = -2 < 0$ and $f(2) = 9 > 0$

The value of the function is positive at one endpoint and negative at the other. Since the function is continuous, the Intermediate Value Theorem guarantees at least one zero in the given interval.

71. $f(x) = 8x^4 - 4x^3 - 2x - 1;$ $[0, 1]$

$f(0) = -1 < 0$ and $f(1) = 1 > 0$

The value of the function is positive at one endpoint and negative at the other. Since the function is continuous, the Intermediate Value Theorem guarantees at least one zero in the given interval.

72. $f(x) = 3x^4 + 4x^3 - 8x - 2;$ $[1, 2]$

$f(1) = -3 < 0$ and $f(2) = 62 > 0$

The value of the function is positive at one endpoint and negative at the other. Since the function is continuous, the Intermediate Value Theorem guarantees at least one zero in the given interval.

73. $f(x) = x^3 - x - 2$

$f(1) = -2;$ $f(2) = 4$

So by the Intermediate Value Theorem, f has a zero on the interval $[1, 2]$.
Subdivide the interval $[1, 2]$ into 10 equal subintervals:
$[1, 1.1]; [1.1, 1.2]; [1.2, 1.3]; [1.3, 1.4]; [1.4, 1.5]; [1.5, 1.6]; [1.6, 1.7]; [1.7, 1.8]; [1.8, 1.9]; [1.9, 2]$

$f(1) = -2; f(1.1) = -1.769$

$f(1.1) = -1.769; f(1.2) = -1.472$

$f(1.2) = -1.472; f(1.3) = -1.103$

$f(1.3) = -1.103; f(1.4) = -0.656$

$f(1.4) = -0.656; f(1.5) = -0.125$

$f(1.5) = -0.125; f(1.6) = 0.496$

So f has a real zero on the interval $[1.5, 1.6]$.

Subdivide the interval $[1.5, 1.6]$ into 10 equal subintervals:
$[1.5, 1.51]; [1.51, 1.52]; [1.52, 1.53]; [1.53, 1.54]; [1.54, 1.55]; [1.55, 1.56]; [1.56, 1.57]; [1.57, 1.58]; [1.58, 1.59]; [1.59, 1.6]$

$f(1.5) = -0.125; f(1.51) \approx -0.0670$

$f(1.51) \approx -0.0670; f(1.52) \approx -0.0082$

$f(1.52) \approx -0.0082; f(1.53) \approx 0.0516$

So f has a real zero on the interval $[1.52, 1.53]$, therefore the zero is 1.52, correct to two decimal places.

74. $f(x) = 2x^3 - x^2 - 3$

$f(1) = -2;$ $f(2) = 9$

So by the Intermediate Value Theorem, f has a zero on the interval $[1, 2]$.
Subdivide the interval $[1, 2]$ into 10 equal subintervals:
$[1, 1.1]; [1.1, 1.2]; [1.2, 1.3]; [1.3, 1.4]; [1.4, 1.5]; [1.5, 1.6]; [1.6, 1.7]; [1.7, 1.8]; [1.8, 1.9]; [1.9, 2]$

$f(1) = -2; f(1.1) = -1.548$

$f(1.1) = -1.548; f(1.2) = -0.984$

$f(1.2) = -0.984; f(1.3) = -0.296$

$f(1.3) = -0.296; f(1.4) = 0.528$

So f has a real zero on the interval $[1.3, 1.4]$.

Subdivide the interval $[1.3, 1.4]$ into 10 equal subintervals:
$[1.3, 1.31]; [1.31, 1.32]; [1.32, 1.33]; [1.33, 1.34]; [1.34, 1.35]; [1.35, 1.36]; [1.36, 1.37]; [1.37, 1.38]; [1.38, 1.39]; [1.39, 1.4]$

$f(1.3) = -0.296; f(1.31) \approx -0.2200$

$f(1.31) \approx -0.2200; f(1.32) \approx -0.1425$

$f(1.32) \approx -0.1425; f(1.33) \approx -0.0636$

$f(1.33) \approx -0.0636; f(1.34) \approx 0.0166$

So f has a real zero on the interval $[1.33, 01.34]$, therefore the zero is 1.33, correct to two decimal places.

75. $f(x) = 8x^4 - 4x^3 - 2x - 1$

$f(0) = -1;\ f(1) = 1$,

So by the Intermediate Value Theorem, f has a zero on the interval $[0,1]$.

Subdivide the interval $[0,1]$ into 10 equal subintervals:

$[0,0.1];\ [0.1,0.2];\ [0.2,0.3];\ [0.3,0.4];\ [0.4,0.5];$
$[0.5,0.6];\ [0.6,0.7];\ [0.7,0.8];\ [0.8,0.9];\ [0.9,1]$

$f(0) = -1;\ f(0.1) = -1.2032$

$f(0.1) = -1.2032;\ f(0.2) = -1.4192$

$f(0.2) = -1.4192;\ f(0.3) = -1.6432$

$f(0.3) = -1.6432;\ f(0.4) = -1.8512$

$f(0.4) = -1.8512;\ f(0.5) = -2$

$f(0.5) = -2;\ f(0.6) = -2.0272$

$f(0.6) = -2.0272;\ f(0.7) = -1.8512$

$f(0.7) = -1.8512;\ f(0.8) = -1.3712$

$f(0.8) = -1.3712;\ f(0.9) = -0.4672$

$f(0.9) = -0.4672;\ f(1) = 1$

So f has a real zero on the interval $[0.9,1]$.

Subdivide the interval $[0.9,1]$ into 10 equal subintervals:

$[0.9,0.91];\ [0.91,0.92];\ [0.92,0.93];\ [0.93,0.94];$
$[0.94,0.95];\ [0.95,0.96];[0.96,0.97];\ [0.97,0.98];$
$[0.98,0.99];\ [0.99,1]$

$f(0.9) = -0.4672;\ f(0.91) \approx -0.3483$

$f(0.91) \approx -0.3483;\ f(0.92) \approx -0.2236$

$f(0.92) \approx -0.2236;\ f(0.93) \approx -0.0930$

$f(0.93) \approx -0.0930;\ f(0.94) \approx 0.0437$

So f has a real zero on the interval $[0.93,0.94]$, therefore the zero is 0.93, correct to two decimal places.

76. $f(x) = 3x^4 + 4x^3 - 8x - 2$

$f(1) = -3;\ f(2) = 62$

So by the Intermediate Value Theorem, f has a zero on the interval $[1,2]$.

Subdivide the interval $[1,2]$ into 10 equal subintervals:

$[1,1.1];\ [1.1,1.2];\ [1.2,1.3];\ [1.3,1.4];\ [1.4,1.5];$
$[1.5,1.6];\ [1.6,1.7];\ [1.7,1.8];\ [1.8,1.9];\ [1.9,2]$

$f(1) = -3;\ f(1.1) = -1.0837$

$f(1.1) = -1.0837;\ f(1.2) = 1.5328$

So f has a real zero on the interval $[1.1,1.2]$.

Subdivide the interval $[1.1,1.2]$ into 10 equal subintervals:

$[1.1,1.11];\ [1.11,1.12];\ [1.12,1.13];\ [1.13,1.14];$
$[1.14,1.15];\ [1.15,1.16];[1.16,1.17];\ [1.17,1.18];$
$[1.18,1.19];\ [1.19,1.2]$

$f(1.1) = -1.0837;\ f(1.11) \approx -0.8553$

$f(1.11) \approx -0.8553;\ f(1.12) \approx -0.6197$

$f(1.12) \approx -0.6197;\ f(1.13) \approx -0.3770$

$f(1.13) \approx -0.3770;\ f(1.14) \approx -0.1269$

$f(1.14) \approx -0.1269;\ f(1.15) \approx 0.1305$

So f has a real zero on the interval $[1.14,1.15]$, therefore the zero is 1.14, correct to two decimal places.

77. Since complex zeros appear in conjugate pairs, $4 - i$, the conjugate of $4 + i$, is the remaining zero of f.

$f(x) = (x-6)(x-4-i)(x-4+i)$
$\quad = x^3 - 14x^2 + 65x - 102$

78. Since complex zeros appear in conjugate pairs, $3 - 4i$, the conjugate of $3 + 4i$, is the remaining zero of f.

$f(x) = (x-5)(x-3-4i)(x-3+4i)$
$\quad = x^3 - 11x^2 + 55x - 125$

79. Since complex zeros appear in conjugate pairs, $-i$, the conjugate of i, and $1 - i$, the conjugate of $1 + i$, are the remaining zeros of f.

$f(x) = (x-i)(x+i)(x-1-i)(x-1+i)$
$\quad = x^4 - 2x^3 + 3x^2 - 2x + 2$

80. Since complex zeros appear in conjugate pairs, $1-i$, the conjugate of $1+i$, is the remaining zero of f.

$$f(x) = (x-1)(x-2)(x-1-i)(x-1+i)$$
$$= x^4 - 5x^3 + 10x^2 - 10x + 4$$

81. $f(x) = x^3 - 3x^2 - 6x + 8$.

By Descartes' Rule of Signs, there are two positive real zeros or no positive real zeros.

$$f(-x) = (-x)^3 - 3(-x)^2 - 6(-x) + 8$$
$$= -x^3 - 3x^2 + 6x + 8$$

thus, there is one negative real zero.

Possible rational zeros:
$$p = \pm 1, \pm 2, \pm 4, \pm 8; \quad q = \pm 1;$$

$$\frac{p}{q} = \pm 1, \pm 2, \pm 4, \pm 8$$

Using synthetic division:
We try $x - 1$:

$$\begin{array}{r|rrrr} 1 & 1 & -3 & -6 & 8 \\ & & 1 & -2 & -8 \\ \hline & 1 & -2 & -8 & 0 \end{array}$$

$x - 1$ is a factor and the quotient is $x^2 - 2x - 8$
Thus,

$$f(x) = (x-1)(x^2 - 2x - 8) = (x-1)(x-4)(x+2).$$

The complex zeros are 1, 4, and –2, each of multiplicity 1.

82. $f(x) = x^3 - x^2 - 10x - 8$.

By Descartes' Rule of Signs, there is one positive real zero.

$$f(-x) = (-x)^3 - (-x)^2 - 10(-x) - 8$$
$$= -x^3 + x^2 + 10x - 8$$

Thus, there are two negative real zeros or no negative real zeros.

Possible rational zeros:
$$p = \pm 1, \pm 2, \pm 4, \pm 8; \quad q = \pm 1;$$

$$\frac{p}{q} = \pm 1, \pm 2, \pm 4, \pm 8$$

Using synthetic division:
We try $x + 1$:

$$\begin{array}{r|rrrr} -1 & 1 & -1 & -10 & -8 \\ & & -1 & 2 & 8 \\ \hline & 1 & -2 & -8 & 0 \end{array}$$

$x + 1$ is a factor and the quotient is $x^2 - 2x - 8$.
Thus,

$$f(x) = (x+1)(x^2 - 2x - 8)$$
$$= (x+1)(x-4)(x+2)$$

The complex zeros are –1, 4, and –2, each of multiplicity 1.

83. $f(x) = 4x^3 + 4x^2 - 7x + 2$.

By Descartes' Rule of Signs, there are two positive real zeros or no positive real zeros.

$$f(-x) = 4(-x)^3 + 4(-x)^2 - 7(-x) + 2$$
$$= -4x^3 + 4x^2 + 7x + 2$$

Thus, there is one negative real zero.

Possible rational zeros:
$$p = \pm 1, \pm 2; \quad q = \pm 1, \pm 2, \pm 4;$$

$$\frac{p}{q} = \pm 1, \pm\frac{1}{2}, \pm\frac{1}{4}, \pm 2$$

Using synthetic division:
We try $x + 2$:

$$\begin{array}{r|rrrr} -2 & 4 & 4 & -7 & 2 \\ & & -8 & 8 & -2 \\ \hline & 4 & -4 & 1 & 0 \end{array}$$

$x + 2$ is a factor and the quotient is $4x^2 - 4x + 1$.
Thus,

$$f(x) = (x+2)(4x^2 - 4x + 1)$$
$$= (x+2)(2x-1)(2x-1)$$
$$= (x+2)(2x-1)^2 = 4(x+2)\left(x+\frac{1}{2}\right)^2$$

The complex zeros are –2, of multiplicity 1, and $\frac{1}{2}$, of multiplicity 2.

84. $f(x) = 4x^3 - 4x^2 - 7x - 2$.

By Descartes' Rule of Signs, there is one positive real zero.

$$f(-x) = 4(-x)^3 - 4(-x)^2 - 7(-x) - 2$$
$$= -4x^3 - 4x^2 + 7x - 2$$

thus, there are two negative real zeros or no negative real zeros.

Possible rational zeros:
$$p = \pm 1, \pm 2; \quad q = \pm 1, \pm 2, \pm 4;$$

$$\frac{p}{q} = \pm 1, \pm\frac{1}{2}, \pm\frac{1}{4}, \pm 2$$

Using synthetic division:
We try $x - 2$:

$$2\overline{)\begin{array}{rrrr} 4 & -4 & -7 & -2 \\ & 8 & 8 & 2 \\ \hline 4 & 4 & 1 & 0 \end{array}}$$

$x - 2$ is a factor and the quotient is $4x^2 + 4x + 1$.
Thus,

$$f(x) = (x-2)\left(4x^2 + 4x + 1\right)$$
$$= (x-2)(2x+1)(2x+1)$$
$$= (x-2)(2x+1)^2 = 4(x-2)\left(x+\tfrac{1}{2}\right)^2$$

The complex zeros are 2, of multiplicity 1, and
$-\dfrac{1}{2}$, of multiplicity 2.

85. $f(x) = x^4 - 4x^3 + 9x^2 - 20x + 20$.

By Descartes' Rule of Signs, there are four positive real zeros or two positive real zeros or no positive real zeros.

$$f(-x) = (-x)^4 - 4(-x)^3 + 9(-x)^2 - 20(-x) + 20$$
$$= x^4 + 4x^3 + 9x^2 + 20x + 20$$

thus, there are no negative real zeros.

Possible rational zeros:
$p = \pm 1, \pm 2, \pm 4, \pm 5, \pm 10, \pm 20; \quad q = \pm 1;$

$$\frac{p}{q} = \pm 1, \pm 2, \pm 4, \pm 5, \pm 10, \pm 20$$

Using synthetic division:
We try $x - 2$:

$$2\overline{)\begin{array}{rrrrr} 1 & -4 & 9 & -20 & 20 \\ & 2 & -4 & 10 & -20 \\ \hline 1 & -2 & 5 & -10 & 0 \end{array}}$$

$x - 2$ is a factor and the quotient is
$x^3 - 2x^2 + 5x - 10$.

Thus, $f(x) = (x-2)\left(x^3 - 2x^2 + 5x - 10\right)$.

We can factor $x^3 - 2x^2 + 5x - 10$ by grouping.
$$x^3 - 2x^2 + 5x - 10 = x^2(x-2) + 5(x-2)$$
$$= (x-2)\left(x^2 + 5\right)$$
$$= (x-2)\left(x + \sqrt{5}i\right)\left(x - \sqrt{5}i\right)$$
$$f(x) = (x-2)^2\left(x + \sqrt{5}i\right)\left(x - \sqrt{5}i\right)$$

The complex zeros are 2, of multiplicity 2, and
$\sqrt{5}i$ and $-\sqrt{5}i$, each of multiplicity 1.

86. $f(x) = x^4 + 6x^3 + 11x^2 + 12x + 18$.

By Descartes' Rule of Signs, there are no positive real zeros.

$$f(-x) = (-x)^4 + 6(-x)^3 + 11(-x)^2 + 12(-x) + 18$$
$$= x^4 - 6x^3 + 11x^2 - 12x + 18;$$

Thus, there are four negative real zeros or two negative real zeros or no negative real zeros.

Possible rational zeros:
$p = \pm 1, \pm 2, \pm 3, \pm 6, \pm 9, \pm 18; \quad q = \pm 1;$

$$\frac{p}{q} = \pm 1, \pm 2, \pm 3, \pm 6, \pm 9, \pm 18$$

Using synthetic division: We try $x + 3$:

$$-3\overline{)\begin{array}{rrrrr} 1 & 6 & 11 & 12 & 18 \\ & -3 & -9 & -6 & -18 \\ \hline 1 & 3 & 2 & 6 & 0 \end{array}}$$

$x + 3$ is a factor and the quotient is
$x^3 + 3x^2 + 2x + 6$.

Thus, $f(x) = (x+3)\left(x^3 + 3x^2 + 2x + 6\right)$.

We can factor $x^3 + 3x^2 + 2x + 6$ by grouping.
$$x^3 + 3x^2 + 2x + 6 = x^2(x+3) + 2(x+3)$$
$$= (x+3)\left(x^2 + 2\right)$$
$$= (x+3)\left(x + \sqrt{2}i\right)\left(x - \sqrt{2}i\right)$$
$$f(x) = (x+3)^2\left(x + \sqrt{2}i\right)\left(x - \sqrt{2}i\right)$$

The complex zeros are -3, of multiplicity 2, and
$\sqrt{2}i$ and $-\sqrt{2}i$, each of multiplicity 1.

87. $f(x) = 2x^4 + 2x^3 - 11x^2 + x - 6$.

By Descartes' Rule of Signs, there are 3 positive real zeros or there is one positive real zero.

$$f(-x) = 2(-x)^4 + 2(-x)^3 - 11(-x)^2 + (-x) - 6$$
$$= 2x^4 - 2x^3 - 11x^2 - x - 6$$

thus, there is one negative real zero.

Possible rational zeros:
$p = \pm 1, \pm 2, \pm 3, \pm 6; \quad q = \pm 1, \pm 2;$

$$\frac{p}{q} = \pm 1, \pm\frac{1}{2}, \pm 2, \pm 3, \pm\frac{3}{2}, \pm 6$$

Using synthetic division:
We try $x - 2$:

$$2\overline{)\begin{array}{rrrrr} 2 & 2 & -11 & 1 & -6 \\ & 4 & 12 & 2 & 6 \\ \hline 2 & 6 & 1 & 3 & 0 \end{array}}$$

$x-2$ is a factor and the quotient is
$2x^3 + 6x^2 + x + 3$.

Thus, $f(x) = (x-2)(2x^3 + 6x^2 + x + 3)$.

We can factor $2x^3 + 6x^2 + x + 3$ by grouping.
$2x^3 + 6x^2 + x + 3 = 2x^2(x+3) + (x+3)$
$$= (x+3)(2x^2 + 1)$$
$$= (x+3)(\sqrt{2}x + i)(\sqrt{2}x - i)$$
$$f(x) = (x-2)(x+3)(\sqrt{2}x + i)(\sqrt{2}x - i)$$
$$= 2(x-2)(x+3)\left(x + \tfrac{\sqrt{2}}{2}i\right)\left(x - \tfrac{\sqrt{2}}{2}i\right)$$

The complex zeros are 2, -3, $-\dfrac{\sqrt{2}}{2}i$, and $\dfrac{\sqrt{2}}{2}i$,
each of multiplicity 1.

88. $f(x) = 3x^4 + 3x^3 - 17x^2 + x - 6$.

By Descartes' Rule of Signs, there are 3 positive real zeros or there is one positive real zero.
$$f(-x) = 3(-x)^4 + 3(-x)^3 - 17(-x)^2 + (-x) - 6$$
$$= 3x^4 - 3x^3 - 17x^2 - x - 6$$
thus, there is one negative real zero.

Possible rational zeros:
$p = \pm 1, \pm 2, \pm 3, \pm 6;\quad q = \pm 1, \pm 3;$

$\dfrac{p}{q} = \pm 1, \pm \dfrac{1}{3}, \pm 2, \pm \dfrac{2}{3}, \pm 3, \pm 6$

Using synthetic division:
We try $x-2$:

$$
\begin{array}{r|rrrr}
2 & 3 & 3 & -17 & 1 & -6 \\
  &   & 6 & 18 & 2 & 6 \\
\hline
  & 3 & 9 & 1 & 3 & 0
\end{array}
$$

$x-2$ is a factor and the quotient is
$3x^3 + 9x^2 + x + 3$.

Thus, $f(x) = (x-2)(3x^3 + 9x^2 + x + 3)$.

We can factor $3x^3 + 9x^2 + x + 3$ by grouping.
$3x^3 + 9x^2 + x + 3 = 3x^2(x+3) + (x+3)$
$$= (x+3)(3x^2 + 1)$$
$$= (x+3)(\sqrt{3}x + i)(\sqrt{3}x - i)$$
$$f(x) = 3(x-2)(x+3)\left(x + \tfrac{\sqrt{3}}{3}i\right)\left(x - \tfrac{\sqrt{3}}{3}i\right)$$

The complex zeros are 2, -3, $-\dfrac{\sqrt{3}}{3}i$, and $\dfrac{\sqrt{3}}{3}i$,
each of multiplicity 1.

89. **a.** $250 = \pi r^2 h \;\Rightarrow\; h = \dfrac{250}{\pi r^2};$

$$A(r) = 2\pi r^2 + 2\pi r h = 2\pi r^2 + 2\pi r\left(\frac{250}{\pi r^2}\right)$$
$$= 2\pi r^2 + \frac{500}{r}$$

b. $A(3) = 2\pi \cdot 3^2 + \dfrac{500}{3}$

$$= 18\pi + \frac{500}{3} \approx 223.22 \text{ square cm}$$

c. $A(5) = 2\pi \cdot 5^2 + \dfrac{500}{5}$

$$= 50\pi + 100 \approx 257.08 \text{ square cm}$$

d. Use MINIMUM on the graph of
$$y_1 = 2\pi x^2 + \frac{500}{x}$$

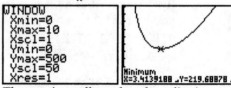

The area is smallest when the radius is approximately 3.41 cm.

Chapter 5 Test

1. $f(x) = (x-3)^4 - 2$

   Using the graph of $y = x^4$, shift right 3 units, then shift down 2 units.

   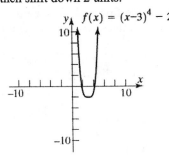

2. **a.** The maximum number of real zeros is the degree, $n = 3$.

   b. First we write the polynomial so that the leading coefficient is 1.
   $$g(x) = 2\left(x^3 + \frac{5}{2}x^2 - 14x - \frac{15}{2}\right)$$
   For the expression in parentheses, we have
   $a_2 = \frac{5}{2}$, $a_1 = -14$, and $a_0 = -\frac{15}{2}$.
   $$\max\left\{1, |a_0| + |a_1| + |a_2|\right\}$$
   $$= \max\left\{1, \left|-\frac{15}{2}\right| + |-14| + \left|\frac{5}{2}\right|\right\}$$
   $$= \max\{1, 24\} = 24$$
   $$1 + \max\left\{|a_0|, |a_1|, |a_2|\right\}$$
   $$= 1 + \max\left\{\left|-\frac{15}{2}\right|, |-14|, \left|\frac{5}{2}\right|\right\}$$
   $$= 1 + 14 = 15$$
   The smaller of the two numbers, 15, is the bound. Therefore, every zero of g lies between -15 and 15.

   c. $g(x) = 2x^3 + 5x^2 - 28x - 15$

   We list all integers p that are factors of $a_0 = -15$ and all the integers q that are factors of $a_3 = 2$.
   $p: \pm 1, \pm 3, \pm 5, \pm 15$
   $q: \pm 1, \pm 2$

   Now we form all possible ratios $\frac{p}{q}$:
   $$\frac{p}{q}: \pm\frac{1}{2}, \pm 1, \pm\frac{3}{2}, \pm\frac{5}{2}, \pm 3, \pm 5, \pm\frac{15}{2}, \pm 15$$
   If g has a rational zero, it must be one of the 16 possibilities listed.

   d. We can find the rational zeros by using the fact that if r is a zero of g, then $g(r) = 0$.

   That is, we evaluate the function for different values from our list of rational zeros. If we get $g(r) = 0$, we have a zero. Then we use long division to reduce the polynomial and start again on the reduced polynomial.

   We will start with the positive integers:
   $$g(1) = 2(1)^3 + 5(1)^2 - 28(1) - 15,$$
   $$= 2 + 5 - 28 - 15$$
   $$= -36$$
   $$g(3) = 2(3)^3 + 5(3)^2 - 28(3) - 15$$
   $$= 54 + 45 - 84 - 15$$
   $$= 0$$
   So, we know that 3 is a zero. This means that $(x-3)$ must be a factor of g. Using long division we get

   $$\begin{array}{r} 2x^2 + 11x + 5 \\ x-3 \overline{)2x^3 + 5x^2 - 28x - 15} \\ -(2x^3 - 6x^2) \\ \hline 11x^2 - 28x \\ -(11x^2 - 33x) \\ \hline 5x - 15 \\ -(5x - 15) \\ \hline 0 \end{array}$$

   Thus, we can now write
   $$g(x) = (x-3)(2x^2 + 11x + 5)$$
   The quadratic factor can be factored so we get:
   $$g(x) = (x-3)(2x+1)(x+5)$$
   To find the remaining zeros of g, we set the last two factors equal to 0 and solve.
   $2x + 1 = 0 \qquad x + 5 = 0$
   $2x = -1 \qquad x = -5$
   $x = -\frac{1}{2}$

   Therefore, the zeros are -5, $-\frac{1}{2}$, and 3.

   Notice how these rational zeros were all in the list of potential rational zeros.

e. The x-intercepts of a graph are the same as the zeros of the function. In the previous part, we found the zeros to be -5, $-\dfrac{1}{2}$, and 3. Therefore, the x-intercepts are -5, $-\dfrac{1}{2}$, and 3.

To find the y-intercept, we simply find $g(0)$.

$$g(0) = 2(0)^3 + 5(0)^2 - 28(0) - 15 = -15$$

So, the y-intercept is -15.

f. Whether the graph crosses or touches at an x-intercept is determined by the multiplicity. Each factor of the polynomial occurs once, so the multiplicity of each zero is 1. For odd multiplicity, the graph will cross the x-axis at the zero. Thus, the graph crosses the x-axis at each of the three x-intercepts.

g. The power function that the graph of g resembles for large values of $|x|$ is given by the term with the highest power of x. In this case, the power function is $y = 2x^3$. So, the graph of g will resemble the graph of $y = 2x^3$ for large values of $|x|$.

h. The three intercepts are -5, $-\dfrac{1}{2}$, and 3.

Near -5:
$$g(x) = (x-3)(2x+1)(x+5)$$
$$\approx -8(-9)(x+5) = 72(x+5)$$
(a line with slope 72)

Near $-\dfrac{1}{2}$:
$$g(x) = (x-3)(2x+1)(x+5)$$
$$\approx \left(-\frac{7}{2}\right)(2x+1)\left(\frac{9}{2}\right)$$
$$= -\frac{63}{4}(2x+1) = -\frac{63}{2}x - \frac{63}{4}$$
(a line with slope $-\dfrac{63}{2}$ or -31.5)

Near 3:
$$g(x) = (x-3)(2x+1)(x+5)$$
$$= (x-3)(7)(8) = 56(x-3)$$
(a line with slope 56)

i. We could first evaluate the function at several values for x to help determine the scale.
Putting all this information together, we obtain the following graph:

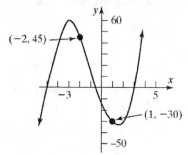

$(-2, 45)$ $(1, -30)$

3. $x^3 - 4x^2 + 25x - 100 = 0$
$$x^2(x-4) + 25(x-4) = 0$$
$$(x-4)(x^2+25) = 0$$
$$x - 4 = 0 \quad \text{or} \quad x^2 + 25 = 0$$
$$x = 4 \qquad\qquad x^2 = -25$$
$$x = \pm\sqrt{-25}$$
$$x = \pm 5i$$
The solution set is $\{4, -5i, 5i\}$.

4. $\qquad 3x^3 + 2x - 1 = 8x^2 - 4$
$$3x^3 - 8x^2 + 2x + 3 = 0$$
If we let the left side of the equation be $f(x)$, then we are simply finding the zeros of f.
We list all integers p that are factors of $a_0 = 3$ and all the integers q that are factors of $a_3 = 3$.
$$p : \pm 1, \pm 3; \quad q : \pm 1, \pm 3$$
Now we form all possible ratios $\dfrac{p}{q}$:
$$\frac{p}{q} : \pm\frac{1}{3}, \pm 1, \pm 3$$

Plot1	Plot2	Plot3

$\backslash Y_1 \boxminus 3X^3 - 8X^2 + 2X + 3$
$\backslash Y_2 =$
$\backslash Y_3 =$
$\backslash Y_4 =$
$\backslash Y_5 =$
$\backslash Y_6 =$

It appears that there is a zero near $x = 1$.

$$f(1) = 3(1)^3 - 8(1)^2 + 2(1) + 3 = 0$$

Therefore, x=1 is a zero and $(x-1)$ is a factor of $f(x)$. We can reduce the polynomial expression by using synthetic division.

$$\begin{array}{r|rrrr}
1 & 3 & -8 & 2 & 3 \\
 & & 3 & -5 & -3 \\
\hline
 & 3 & -5 & -3 & 0
\end{array}$$

Thus, $f(x) = (x-1)(3x^2 - 5x - 3)$. We can find the remaining zeros by using the quadratic formula.

$$3x^2 - 5x - 3 = 0$$
$$a = 3, b = -5, c = -3$$
$$x = \frac{-(-5) \pm \sqrt{(-5)^2 - 4(3)(-3)}}{2(3)}$$
$$= \frac{5 \pm \sqrt{25 + 36}}{6} = \frac{5 \pm \sqrt{61}}{6}$$

Thus, the solution set is
$$\left\{ 1, \frac{5 - \sqrt{61}}{6} \approx -0.468, \frac{5 + \sqrt{61}}{6} \approx 2.135 \right\}.$$

5. We start by factoring the numerator and denominator.
$$g(x) = \frac{2x^2 - 14x + 24}{x^2 + 6x - 40} = \frac{2(x-3)(x-4)}{(x+10)(x-4)}$$
The domain of f is $\{x \mid x \neq -10, x \neq 4\}$.

In lowest terms, $g(x) = \frac{2(x-3)}{x+10}$ with $x \neq 4$.

The graph has one vertical asymptote, $x = -10$, since $x + 10$ is the only factor of the denominator of g in lowest terms. The graph is still undefined at $x = 4$, but there is a hole in the graph there instead of an asymptote.

Since the degree of the numerator is the same as the degree of the denominator, the graph has a horizontal asymptote equal to the quotient of the leading coefficients. The leading coefficient in the numerator is 2 and the leading coefficient in the denominator is 1. Therefore, the graph has the horizontal asymptote $y = \frac{2}{1} = 2$.

6. $r(x) = \frac{x^2 + 2x - 3}{x + 1}$

Start by factoring the numerator.
$$r(x) = \frac{(x+3)(x-1)}{x+1}$$
The domain of the function is $\{x \mid x \neq -1\}$.

Asymptotes:
Since the function is in lowest terms, the graph has one vertical asymptote, $x = -1$.
The degree of the numerator is one more than the degree of the denominator so the graph will have an oblique asymptote. To find it, we need to use long division (note: we could also use synthetic division in this case because the dividend is linear).

$$\begin{array}{r}
x+1 \\
x+1 \overline{\smash{)}\, x^2 + 2x - 3} \\
\underline{-(x^2 + x)} \\
x - 3 \\
\underline{-(x+1)} \\
-4
\end{array}$$

The oblique asymptote is $y = x + 1$.

7. From problem 6 we know that the domain is $\{x \mid x \neq -1\}$ and that the graph has one vertical asymptote, $x = -1$, and one oblique asymptote, $y = x + 1$.

x-intercepts:
To find the x-intercepts, we need to set the numerator equal to 0 and solve the resulting equation.
$$(x+3)(x-1) = 0$$
$$x + 3 = 0 \quad \text{or} \quad x - 1 = 0$$
$$x = -3 \qquad x = 1$$
The x-intercepts are -3 and 1.
The points $(-3, 0)$ and $(1, 0)$ are on the graph.

y-intercept:
$$r(0) = \frac{0^2 + 2(0) - 3}{0 + 1} = -3$$
The y-intercept is -3. The point $(0, -3)$ is on the graph.

Test for symmetry:

$$r(-x) = \frac{(-x)^2 + 2(-x) - 3}{(-x) + 1} = \frac{x^2 - 2x - 3}{-x + 1}$$

Since $r(-x) \neq r(x)$, the graph is not symmetric with respect to the y-axis.
Since $r(-x) \neq -r(x)$, the graph is not symmetric with respect to the origin.

Behavior near the asymptotes:
To determine if the graph crosses the oblique asymptote, we solve the equation

$$r(x) = x + 1$$

$$\frac{x^2 + 2x - 3}{x + 1} = x + 1, \quad x \neq -1$$

$$x^2 + 2x - 3 = x^2 + 2x + 1$$

$$-3 = 1 \text{ false}$$

The result is a contradiction so the graph does not cross the oblique asymptote.

The zeros of the numerator and denominator, -3, -1, and 1, divide the x-axis into four subintervals.

$$(-\infty, -3), (-3, -1), (-1, 1), (1, \infty)$$

We can check a point in each subinterval to determine if the graph is above or below the x-axis.

Interval	$(-\infty, -3)$	$(-3, -1)$	$(-1, 1)$	$(1, \infty)$
Number	-5	-2	0	3
Value of r	-3	3	-3	3
Location	below	above	below	above
Point	$(-5, -3)$	$(-2, 3)$	$(0, -3)$	$(3, 3)$

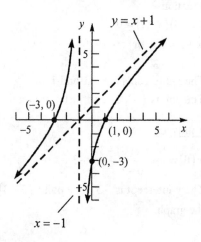

8. Since the polynomial has real coefficients, we can apply the Conjugate Pairs Theorem to find the remaining zero. If $3 + i$ is a zero, then its conjugate, $3 - i$, must also be a zero. Thus, the four zeros are -2, 0, $3 - i$, and $3 + i$. The Factor Theorem says that if $f(c) = 0$, then $(x - c)$ is a factor of the polynomial. This allows us to write the following function:

$$f(x) = a(x - (-2))(x - 0)(x - (3 - i))(x - (3 + i))$$

where a is any real number. If we let $a = 1$, we get

$$f(x) = (x + 2)(x)(x - 3 + i)(x - 3 - i)$$
$$= (x^2 + 2x)(x - 3 + i)(x - 3 - i)$$
$$= (x^2 + 2x)(x^2 - 6x + 10)$$
$$= x^4 - 6x^3 + 10x^2 + 2x^3 - 12x^2 + 20x$$
$$= x^4 - 4x^3 - 2x^2 + 20x$$

9. Since the domain excludes 4 and 9, the denominator must contain the factors $(x - 4)$ and $(x - 9)$. However, because there is only one vertical asymptote, $x = 4$, the numerator must also contain the factor $(x - 9)$.

The horizontal asymptote, $y = 2$, indicates that the degree of the numerator must be the same as the degree of the denominator and that the ratio of the leading coefficients needs to be 2. We can accomplish this by including another factor in the numerator, $(x - a)$, where $a \neq 4$, along with a factor of 2.

Therefore, we have $r(x) = \dfrac{2(x - 9)(x - a)}{(x - 4)(x - 9)}$.

If we let $a = 1$, we get

$$r(x) = \frac{2(x - 9)(x - 1)}{(x - 4)(x - 9)} = \frac{2x^2 - 20x + 18}{x^2 - 13x + 36}.$$

10. Since we have a polynomial function and polynomials are continuous, we simply need to show that $f(a)$ and $f(b)$ have opposite signs (where a and b are the endpoints of the interval).

$$f(0) = -2(0)^2 - 3(0) + 8 = 8$$

$$f(4) = -2(4)^2 - 3(4) + 8 = -36$$

Since $f(0) = 8 > 0$ and $f(4) = -36 < 0$, the Intermediate Value Theorem guarantees that there is at least one real zero between 0 and 4.

11. $\dfrac{x+2}{x-3} < 2$

We note that the domain of the variable consists of all real numbers except 3.

Rearrange the terms so that the right side is 0.

$$\frac{x+2}{x-3} - 2 < 0$$

For $f(x) = \dfrac{x+2}{x-3} - 2$, we find the zeros of f and the values of x at which f is undefined. To do this, we need to write f as a single rational expression.

$$f(x) = \frac{x+2}{x-3} - 2$$

$$= \frac{x+2}{x-3} - 2 \cdot \frac{x-3}{x-3}$$

$$= \frac{x+2-2x+6}{x-3}$$

$$= \frac{-x+8}{x-3}$$

The zero of f is $x = 8$ and f is undefined at $x = 3$. We use these two values to divide the real number line into three subintervals.

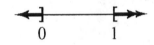

Interval	$(-\infty, 3)$	$(3, 8)$	$(8, \infty)$
Num. chosen	0	4	9
Value of f	$-\dfrac{8}{3}$	4	$-\dfrac{1}{6}$
Conclusion	negative	positive	negative

Since we want to know where $f(x)$ is negative, we conclude that values of x for which $x < 3$ or $x > 8$ are solutions. The inequality is strict so the solution set is $\{x \mid x < 3 \text{ or } x > 8\}$. In interval notation we write $(-\infty, 3)$ or $(8, \infty)$.

Chapter 5 Cumulative Review

1. $P = (1, 3)$, $Q = (-4, 2)$

$$d_{P,Q} = \sqrt{(-4-1)^2 + (2-3)^2}$$

$$= \sqrt{(-5)^2 + (-1)^2} = \sqrt{25+1}$$

$$= \sqrt{26}$$

2. $\quad x^2 \geq x$

$$x^2 - x \geq 0$$

$$x(x-1) \geq 0$$

$$f(x) = x^2 - x$$

$x = 0$, $x = 1$ are the zeros of f.

Interval	$(-\infty, 0)$	$(0, 1)$	$(1, \infty)$
Number Chosen	-1	0.5	2
Value of f	2	-0.25	2
Conclusion	Positive	Negative	Positive

The solution set is $\{x \mid x \leq 0 \text{ or } x \geq 1\}$ or $(-\infty, 0]$ or $[1, \infty)$ in interval notation.

3. $\quad x^2 - 3x < 4$

$$x^2 - 3x - 4 < 0$$

$$(x-4)(x+1) < 0$$

$$f(x) = x^2 - 3x - 4$$

$x = -1$, $x = 4$ are the zeros of f.

Interval	$(-\infty, -1)$	$(-1, 4)$	$(4, \infty)$
Number Chosen	-2	0	5
Value of f	6	-4	6
Conclusion	Positive	Negative	Positive

The solution set is $\{x \mid -1 < x < 4\}$ or $(-1, 4)$ in interval notation.

4. Slope −3, Containing the point (−1, 4)

Using the point-slope formula yields:
$$y - y_1 = m(x - x_1)$$
$$y - 4 = -3(x - (-1))$$
$$y - 4 = -3x - 3$$
$$y = -3x + 1$$
Thus, $f(x) = -3x + 1$.

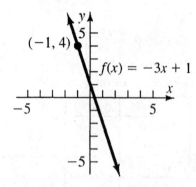

5. Parallel to $y = 2x + 1$; Slope 2, Containing the point (3, 5)

Using the point-slope formula yields:
$$y - y_1 = m(x - x_1)$$
$$y - 5 = 2(x - 3)$$
$$y - 5 = 2x - 6$$
$$y = 2x - 1$$

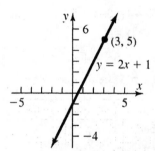

6. $y = x^3$

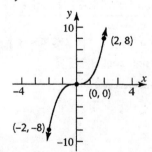

7. This relation is not a function because the ordered pairs (3, 6) and (3, 8) have the same first element, but different second elements.

8.
$$x^3 - 6x^2 + 8x = 0$$
$$x(x^2 - 6x + 8) = 0$$
$$x(x - 4)(x - 2) = 0$$
$$x = 0 \text{ or } x = 4 \text{ or } x = 2$$

The solution set is $\{0, 2, 4\}$.

9. $3x + 2 \le 5x - 1$
$$3 \le 2x$$
$$\frac{3}{2} \le x$$
$$x \ge \frac{3}{2}$$

The solution set is $\left\{x \mid x \ge \frac{3}{2}\right\}$ or $\left[\frac{3}{2}, \infty\right)$ in interval notation.

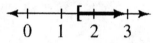

10.
$$x^2 + 4x + y^2 - 2y - 4 = 0$$
$$(x^2 + 4x + 4) + (y^2 - 2y + 1) = 4 + 4 + 1$$
$$(x + 2)^2 + (y - 1)^2 = 9$$
$$(x + 2)^2 + (y - 1)^2 = 3^2$$
Center: (−2, 1)
Radius 3

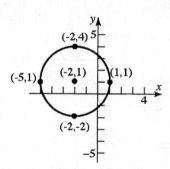

11. $y = x^3 - 9x$

x-intercepts: $0 = x^3 - 9x$

$$0 = x(x^2 - 9)$$
$$0 = x(x+3)(x-3)$$
$$x = 0, -3, \text{ and } 3$$
$$(0,0), \ (-3,0), \ (3,0)$$

y-intercepts: $y = 0^3 - 9(0) = 0 \Rightarrow (0,0)$

Test for symmetry:

x-axis: Replace y by $-y$: $-y = x^3 - 9x$, which is not equivalent to $y = x^3 - 9x$.

y-axis: Replace x by $-x$: $y = (-x)^3 - 9(-x)$
$$= -x^3 + 9x$$

which is not equivalent to $y = x^3 - 9x$.

Origin: Replace x by $-x$ and y by $-y$:
$$-y = (-x)^3 - 9(-x)$$
$$y = -x^3 + 9x$$

which is equivalent to $y = x^3 - 9x$. Therefore, the graph is symmetric with respect to origin.

12. $3x - 2y = 7$
$$-2y = -3x + 7$$
$$y = \frac{3}{2}x - \frac{7}{2}$$

The given line has slope $\frac{3}{2}$. Every line that is perpendicular to the given line will have slope $-\frac{2}{3}$. Using the point $(1,5)$ and the point-slope formula yields:
$$y - y_1 = m(x - x_1)$$
$$y - 5 = -\frac{2}{3}(x - 1)$$
$$y - 5 = -\frac{2}{3}x + \frac{2}{3}$$
$$y = -\frac{2}{3}x + \frac{17}{3}$$

13. Not a function, since the graph fails the Vertical Line Test, for example, when $x = 0$.

14. $f(x) = x^2 + 5x - 2$

a. $f(3) = 3^2 + 5(3) - 2 = 9 + 15 - 2 = 22$

b. $f(-x) = (-x)^2 + 5(-x) - 2 = x^2 - 5x - 2$

c. $-f(x) = -(x^2 + 5x - 2) = -x^2 - 5x + 2$

d. $f(3x) = (3x)^2 + 5(3x) - 2 = 9x^2 + 15x - 2$

e. $\dfrac{f(x+h) - f(x)}{h}$

$$= \frac{(x+h)^2 + 5(x+h) - 2 - (x^2 + 5x - 2)}{h}$$

$$= \frac{x^2 + 2xh + h^2 + 5x + 5h - 2 - x^2 - 5x + 2}{h}$$

$$= \frac{2xh + h^2 + 5h}{h}$$

$$= 2x + h + 5$$

15. $f(x) = \dfrac{x+5}{x-1}$

a. Domain $\{x \mid x \neq 1\}$.

b. $f(2) = \dfrac{2+5}{2-1} = \dfrac{7}{1} = 7 \neq 6$;

$(2,6)$ is not on the graph of f.

The point $(2,7)$ is on the graph.

c. $f(3) = \dfrac{3+5}{3-1} = \dfrac{8}{2} = 4$;

$(3,4)$ is on the graph of f.

d. Solve for x
$$\frac{x+5}{x-1} = 9$$
$$x + 5 = 9(x-1)$$
$$x + 5 = 9x - 9$$
$$14 = 8x$$
$$x = \frac{14}{8} = \frac{7}{4}$$

Therefore, $\left(\dfrac{7}{4}, 9\right)$ is on the graph of f.

16. $f(x) = -3x + 7$

The graph is a line with slope -3 and y-intercept $(0, 7)$.

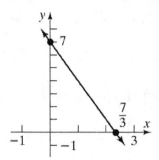

17. $f(x) = 2x^2 - 4x + 1$

$a = 2$, $b = -4$, $c = 1$. Since $a = 2 > 0$, the graph opens up.

The x-coordinate of the vertex is

$$x = -\frac{b}{2a} = -\frac{-4}{2(2)} = 1.$$

The y-coordinate of the vertex is

$$f\left(-\frac{b}{2a}\right) = f(1) = 2(1)^2 - 4(1) + 1 = -1.$$

Thus, the vertex is $(1, -1)$.
The axis of symmetry is the line $x = 1$.

The discriminant is:
$b^2 - 4ac = (-4)^2 - 4(2)(1) = 8 > 0$, so the graph has two x-intercepts.

The x-intercepts are found by solving:
$2x^2 - 4x + 1 = 0$

$$x = \frac{-(-4) \pm \sqrt{8}}{2(2)}$$

$$= \frac{4 \pm 2\sqrt{2}}{4} = \frac{2 \pm \sqrt{2}}{2}$$

The x-intercepts are $\dfrac{2 - \sqrt{2}}{2}$ and $\dfrac{2 + \sqrt{2}}{2}$.

The y-intercept is $f(0) = 1$.

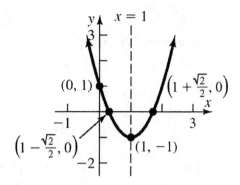

18. $f(x) = x^2 + 3x + 1$

average rate of change of f from 1 to 2:

$$\frac{f(2) - f(1)}{2 - 1} = \frac{11 - 5}{1} = 6 = m_{\sec}$$

$f(2) = 11$ so the point $(2, 11)$ is on the graph. Using this point and the slope $m = 6$, we can obtain the equation of the secant line:

$$y - y_1 = m(x - x_1)$$
$$y - 11 = 6(x - 2)$$
$$y - 11 = 6x - 12$$
$$y = 6x - 1$$

19. a. x-intercepts: $(-5, 0); (-1, 0); (5, 0)$; y-intercept: $(0, -3)$

b. The graph is not symmetric with respect to the origin, x-axis or y-axis.

c. The function is neither even nor odd.

d. f is increasing on $(-\infty, -3)$ and $(2, \infty)$; f is decreasing on $(-3, 2)$;

e. f has a local maximum at $x = -3$, and the local maximum is $f(-3) = 5$.

f. f has a local minimum at $x = 2$, and the local minimum is $f(2) = -6$.

20. $f(x) = \dfrac{5x}{x^2 - 9}$

$$f(-x) = \frac{5(-x)}{(-x)^2 - 9} = \frac{-5x}{x^2 - 9} = -f(x), \text{ therefore}$$

f is an odd function.

21. $f(x) = \begin{cases} 2x+1 & \text{if } -3 < x < 2 \\ -3x+4 & \text{if } x \geq 2 \end{cases}$

   a. Domain: $\{x \mid x > -3\}$ or $(-3, \infty)$

   b. x-intercept: $\left(-\dfrac{1}{2}, 0\right)$

      y-intercept: $(0, 1)$

   c.

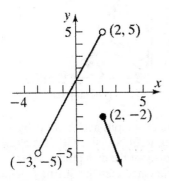

   d. Range: $\{y \mid y < 5\}$ or $(-\infty, 5)$

22. $f(x) = -3(x+1)^2 + 5$

Using the graph of $y = x^2$, shift left 1 unit, vertically stretch by a factor of 3, reflect about the x-axis, then shift up 5 units.

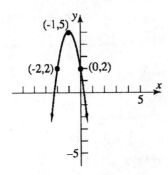

23. $f(x) = x^2 - 5x + 1 \qquad g(x) = -4x - 7$

   a. $(f+g)(x) = x^2 - 5x + 1 + (-4x - 7)$

              $= x^2 - 9x - 6$

     The domain is: $\{x \mid x \text{ is a real number}\}$.

   b. $\left(\dfrac{f}{g}\right)(x) = \dfrac{f(x)}{g(x)} = \dfrac{x^2 - 5x + 1}{-4x - 7}$

     The domain is: $\left\{x \mid x \neq -\dfrac{7}{4}\right\}$.

24. a. $R(x) = x \cdot p$

           $= x\left(-\dfrac{1}{10}x + 150\right)$

           $= -\dfrac{1}{10}x^2 + 150x$

   b. $R(100) = -\dfrac{1}{10}(100)^2 + 150(100)$

               $= -1000 + 15{,}000$

               $= \$14{,}000$

   c. Since $R(x) = -\dfrac{1}{10}x^2 + 150x$ is a quadratic

     function with $a = -\dfrac{1}{10} < 0$, the vertex will

     be a maximum point. The vertex occurs

     when $x = -\dfrac{b}{2a} = -\dfrac{150}{2(-1/10)} = 750$.

     Thus, the revenue is maximized when $x = 750$ units sold.

     The maximum revenue is given by

     $R(750) = -\dfrac{1}{10}(750)^2 + 150(750)$.

             $= -56{,}250 + 112{,}500$

             $= \$56{,}250$

   d. $p = -\dfrac{1}{10}(750) + 150 = -75 + 150 = \$75$ is

     the selling price that maximizes the revenue.

Chapter 5 Projects

Project I

1.

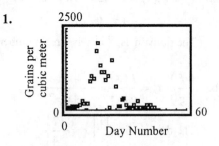

2. Sketching a hand-drawn curve, you could obtain a second, third, or fourth degree curve. The answers for the questions will depend upon your sketch.

3.

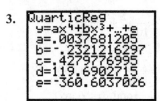

$$y = 0.00377x^4 - 0.23212x^3 + 0.42798x^2$$
$$+119.69x - 360.60$$

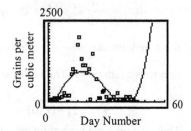

4.

CubicReg
y=ax³+bx²+cx+d
a=.1221781462
b=-10.34489887
c=234.6017164
d=-655.1199095

$$y = 0.12218x^3 - 10.345x^2 + 234.60x - 655.12$$

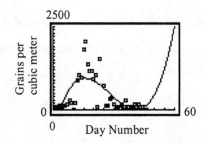

5.

QuadReg
y=ax²+bx+c
a=-1.734476806
b=71.06835919
c=19.41639837

$$y = -1.7345x^2 + 71.068x + 19.416$$

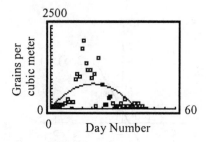

6. From the graphs above, the cubic function seems to fit best since it is the closest to a majority of the data points and is less complicated than the quartic function.

7. Answers will vary.

Project II

a. $x^2 + 8x - 9 = 0$

$(x+9)(x-1) = 0$

sum $= -9 + 1 = -8$, product $= (-9)(1) = -9$

$x = -9$ or $x = 1$

b. $x^2 + bx + c = 0$

$(x - r_1)(x - r_2) = 0$

$x^2 - r_1 x - r_2 x + r_1 r_2 = 0$

$x^2 - (r_1 + r_2)x + r_1 r_2 = 0$

$b = -(r_1 + r_2)$

$c = r_1 r_2$

c. $f(x) = x^3 - x^2 - 10x - 8$

$f(x) = (x+2)(x^2 - 3x - 4)$

$f(x) = (x+2)(x-4)(x+1)$

zeros: -2. 4. -1

sum $= -2 + 4 - 1 = 1$, product $= (-2)(4)(-1) = 8$

sum of double products

$= -2(4) + (-2)(-1) + 4(-1) = -8 + 2 - 4 = -10$

The coefficient of x^2 is the negative sum. The coefficient of x is the sum of the double products. The constant term is the negative product.

d. $f(x) = x^3 + bx^2 + cx + d$

$f(x) = (x - r_1)(x - r_2)(x - r_3)$

$f(x) = (x^2 - (r_1 + r_2)x + r_1 r_2)(x - r_3)$

$f(x) = x^3 - (r_1 + r_2 + r_3)x^2$
$\qquad + (r_1 r_2 + r_1 r_3 + r_2 r_3)x - r_1 r_2 r_3$

$b = -(r_1 + r_2 + r_3)$

$c = r_1 r_2 + r_1 r_3 + r_2 r_3$

$d = -r_1 r_2 r_3$

e. $f(x) = x^4 + bx^3 + cx^2 + dx + e$

$f(x) = (x - r_1)(x - r_2)(x - r_3)(x - r_4)$

$f(x) = (x^3 - (r_1 + r_2 + r_3)x^2$
$\qquad + (r_1 r_2 + r_1 r_3 + r_2 r_3)x - r_1 r_2 r_3)(x - r_3)$

$f(x) = x^4 - (r_1 + r_2 + r_3 + r_4)x^3$
$\qquad + \left(r_1 r_2 + r_1 r_3 + r_2 r_3 + r_1 r_4 + r_2 r_4 + r_3 r_4\right)x^2$
$\qquad - (r_1 r_2 r_4 + r_1 r_3 r_4 + r_2 r_3 r_4 + r_1 r_2 r_3)x + r_1 r_2 r_3 r_4$

$b = -(r_1 + r_2 + r_3 + r_4)$

$c = r_1 r_2 + r_1 r_3 + r_2 r_3 + r_1 r_4 + r_2 r_4 + r_3 r_4$

$d = -(r_1 r_2 r_4 + r_1 r_3 r_4 + r_2 r_3 r_4 + r_1 r_2 r_3)$

$e = r_1 r_2 r_3 r_4$

f. The coefficients are sums, products, or sums of products of the zeros.

If $f(x) = x^n + a_{n-1}x^{n-1} + a_{n-2}x^{n-2} + \ldots + a_1 x + a_0$,
then:

a_{n-1} will be the negative of the sum of the zeros.

a_{n-2} will be the sum of the double products.

a_1 will be the negative (if n is even) or positive (if n is odd) of the sum of (n-1) products.

a_0 will be the negative (if n is odd) or positive (if n is even) product of the zeros.

These will always hold. These would be useful if you needed to multiply a number of binomials in $x - c$ form together and you did not want to have to do the multiplication out. These formulas would help same time.

Chapter 6

Exponential and Logarithmic Functions

Section 6.1

1. $f(3) = -4(3)^2 + 5(3)$
   $= -4(9) + 15$
   $= -36 + 15$
   $= -21$

2. $f(3x) = 4 - 2(3x)^2$
   $= 4 - 2(9x^2)$
   $= 4 - 18x^2$

3. $f(x) = \dfrac{x^2 - 1}{x^2 - 25}$
   $x^2 - 25 \neq 0$
   $(x+5)(x-5) \neq 0$
   $x \neq -5, \quad x \neq 5$
   Domain: $\{x \mid x \neq -5, \ x \neq 5\}$

4. $(g \circ f)(x)$ or $g(f(x))$

5. False

6. False. The domain of $(f \circ g)(x)$ is a subset of the domain of $g(x)$.

7.
   a. $(f \circ g)(1) = f(g(1)) = f(0) = -1$
   b. $(f \circ g)(-1) = f(g(-1)) = f(0) = -1$
   c. $(g \circ f)(-1) = g(f(-1)) = g(-3) = 8$
   d. $(g \circ f)(0) = g(f(0)) = g(-1) = 0$
   e. $(g \circ g)(-2) = g(g(-2)) = g(3) = 8$
   f. $(f \circ f)(-1) = f(f(-1)) = f(-3) = -7$

8.
   a. $(f \circ g)(1) = f(g(1)) = f(0) = 5$
   b. $(f \circ g)(2) = f(g(2)) = f(-3) = 11$
   c. $(g \circ f)(2) = g(f(2)) = g(1) = 0$
   d. $(g \circ f)(3) = g(f(3)) = g(-1) = 0$
   e. $(g \circ g)(1) = g(g(1)) = g(0) = 1$
   f. $(f \circ f)(3) = f(f(3)) = f(-1) = 7$

9.
   a. $g(f(-1)) = g(1) = 4$
   b. $g(f(0)) = g(0) = 5$
   c. $f(g(-1)) = f(3) = -1$
   d. $f(g(4)) = f(2) = -2$

10.
   a. $g(f(1)) = g(-1) = 3$
   b. $g(f(5)) = g(1) = 4$
   c. $f(g(0)) = f(5) = 1$
   d. $f(g(2)) = f(2) = -2$

11. $f(x) = 2x \qquad g(x) = 3x^2 + 1$
   a. $(f \circ g)(4) = f(g(4))$
      $= f(3(4)^2 + 1)$
      $= f(49)$
      $= 2(49)$
      $= 98$
   b. $(g \circ f)(2) = g(f(2))$
      $= g(2 \cdot 2)$
      $= g(4)$
      $= 3(4)^2 + 1$
      $= 48 + 1$
      $= 49$
   c. $(f \circ f)(1) = f(f(1))$
      $= f(2(1))$
      $= f(2)$
      $= 2(2)$
      $= 4$
   d. $(g \circ g)(0) = g(g(0))$
      $= g(3(0)^2 + 1)$
      $= g(1)$
      $= 3(1)^2 + 1$
      $= 4$

568

12. $f(x) = 3x + 2 \qquad g(x) = 2x^2 - 1$

  a. $(f \circ g)(4) = f(g(4))$
$$= f\left(2(4)^2 - 1\right)$$
$$= f(31)$$
$$= 3(31) + 2$$
$$= 95$$

  b. $(g \circ f)(2) = g(f(2))$
$$= g(3(2) + 2)$$
$$= g(8)$$
$$= 2(8)^2 - 1$$
$$= 128 - 1$$
$$= 127$$

  c. $(f \circ f)(1) = f(f(1))$
$$= f\left(3(1) + 2\right)$$
$$= f(5)$$
$$= 3(5) + 2$$
$$= 17$$

  d. $(g \circ g)(0) = g(g(0))$
$$= g\left(2(0)^2 - 1\right)$$
$$= g(-1)$$
$$= 2(-1)^2 - 1$$
$$= 1$$

13. $f(x) = 4x^2 - 3 \qquad g(x) = 3 - \frac{1}{2}x^2$

  a. $(f \circ g)(4) = f(g(4))$
$$= f\left(3 - \frac{1}{2}(4)^2\right)$$
$$= f(-5)$$
$$= 4(-5)^2 - 3$$
$$= 97$$

  b. $(g \circ f)(2) = g(f(2))$
$$= g(4(2)^2 - 3)$$
$$= g(13)$$
$$= 3 - \frac{1}{2}(13)^2$$
$$= 3 - \frac{169}{2}$$
$$= -\frac{163}{2}$$

  c. $(f \circ f)(1) = f(f(1))$
$$= f(4(1)^2 - 3)$$
$$= f(1)$$
$$= 4(1)^2 - 3$$
$$= 1$$

  d. $(g \circ g)(0) = g(g(0))$
$$= g\left(3 - \frac{1}{2}(0)^2\right)$$
$$= g(3)$$
$$= 3 - \frac{1}{2}(3)^2$$
$$= 3 - \frac{9}{2}$$
$$= -\frac{3}{2}$$

14. $f(x) = 2x^2 \qquad g(x) = 1 - 3x^2$

  a. $(f \circ g)(4) = f(g(4))$
$$= f\left(1 - 3(4)^2\right)$$
$$= f(-47)$$
$$= 2(-47)^2$$
$$= 4418$$

  b. $(g \circ f)(2) = g(f(2))$
$$= g(2(2)^2)$$
$$= g(8)$$
$$= 1 - 3(8)^2$$
$$= 1 - 192$$
$$= -191$$

  c. $(f \circ f)(1) = f(f(1))$
$$= f\left(2(1)^2\right)$$
$$= f(2)$$
$$= 2(2)^2$$
$$= 8$$

  d. $(g \circ g)(0) = g(g(0))$
$$= g\left(1 - 3(0)^2\right)$$
$$= g(1)$$
$$= 1 - 3(1)^2$$
$$= 1 - 3$$
$$= -2$$

15. $f(x) = \sqrt{x}$ $\quad$ $g(x) = 2x$

a. $(f \circ g)(4) = f(g(4))$
$$= f(2(4))$$
$$= f(8)$$
$$= \sqrt{8}$$
$$= 2\sqrt{2}$$

b. $(g \circ f)(2) = g(f(2))$
$$= g\left(\sqrt{2}\right)$$
$$= 2\sqrt{2}$$

c. $(f \circ f)(1) = f(f(1))$
$$= f\left(\sqrt{1}\right)$$
$$= f(1)$$
$$= \sqrt{1}$$
$$= 1$$

d. $(g \circ g)(0) = g(g(0))$
$$= g(2(0))$$
$$= g(0)$$
$$= 2(0)$$
$$= 0$$

16. $f(x) = \sqrt{x+1}$ $\quad$ $g(x) = 3x$

a. $(f \circ g)(4) = f(g(4))$
$$= f(3(4))$$
$$= f(12)$$
$$= \sqrt{12+1}$$
$$= \sqrt{13}$$

b. $(g \circ f)(2) = g(f(2))$
$$= g\left(\sqrt{2+1}\right)$$
$$= g\left(\sqrt{3}\right)$$
$$= 3\sqrt{3}$$

c. $(f \circ f)(1) = f(f(1))$
$$= f\left(\sqrt{1+1}\right)$$
$$= f\left(\sqrt{2}\right)$$
$$= \sqrt{\sqrt{2}+1}$$

d. $(g \circ g)(0) = g(g(0))$
$$= g(3(0))$$
$$= g(0)$$
$$= 3(0)$$
$$= 0$$

17. $f(x) = |x|$ $\quad$ $g(x) = \dfrac{1}{x^2+1}$

a. $(f \circ g)(4) = f(g(4))$
$$= f\left(\frac{1}{4^2+1}\right)$$
$$= f\left(\frac{1}{17}\right)$$
$$= \left|\frac{1}{17}\right|$$
$$= \frac{1}{17}$$

b. $(g \circ f)(2) = g(f(2))$
$$= g(|2|)$$
$$= g(2)$$
$$= \frac{1}{2^2+1}$$
$$= \frac{1}{5}$$

c. $(f \circ f)(1) = f(f(1))$
$$= f(|1|)$$
$$= f(1)$$
$$= |1|$$
$$= 1$$

d. $(g \circ g)(0) = g(g(0))$
$$= g\left(\frac{1}{0^2+1}\right)$$
$$= g(1)$$
$$= \frac{1}{1^2+1}$$
$$= \frac{1}{2}$$

18. $f(x) = |x-2|$ $\quad g(x) = \dfrac{3}{x^2+2}$

a. $(f \circ g)(4) = f(g(4))$

$$= f\left(\dfrac{3}{4^2+2}\right)$$

$$= f\left(\dfrac{3}{18}\right)$$

$$= f\left(\dfrac{1}{6}\right)$$

$$= \left|\dfrac{1}{6}-2\right|$$

$$= \left|-\dfrac{11}{6}\right|$$

$$= \dfrac{11}{6}$$

b. $(g \circ f)(2) = g(f(2))$

$$= g\left(|2-2|\right)$$

$$= g(0)$$

$$= \dfrac{3}{0^2+2}$$

$$= \dfrac{3}{2}$$

c. $(f \circ f)(1) = f(f(1))$

$$= f\left(|1-2|\right)$$

$$= f(1)$$

$$= |1-2|$$

$$= 1$$

d. $(g \circ g)(0) = g(g(0))$

$$= g\left(\dfrac{3}{0^2+2}\right)$$

$$= g\left(\dfrac{3}{2}\right)$$

$$= \dfrac{3}{\left(\dfrac{3}{2}\right)^2+2}$$

$$= \dfrac{3}{\dfrac{17}{4}}$$

$$= \dfrac{12}{17}$$

19. $f(x) = \dfrac{3}{x+1}$ $\quad g(x) = \sqrt[3]{x}$

a. $(f \circ g)(4) = f(g(4))$

$$= f\left(\sqrt[3]{4}\right)$$

$$= \dfrac{3}{\sqrt[3]{4}+1}$$

b. $(g \circ f)(2) = g(f(2))$

$$= g\left(\dfrac{3}{2+1}\right)$$

$$= g\left(\dfrac{3}{3}\right)$$

$$= g(1)$$

$$= \sqrt[3]{1}$$

$$= 1$$

c. $(f \circ f)(1) = f(f(1))$

$$= f\left(\dfrac{3}{1+1}\right)$$

$$= f\left(\dfrac{3}{2}\right)$$

$$= \dfrac{3}{\dfrac{3}{2}+1}$$

$$= \dfrac{3}{\dfrac{5}{2}}$$

$$= \dfrac{6}{5}$$

d. $(g \circ g)(0) = g(g(0))$

$$= g\left(\sqrt[3]{0}\right)$$

$$= g(0)$$

$$= \sqrt[3]{0}$$

$$= 0$$

20. $f(x) = x^{3/2}$ $g(x) = \dfrac{2}{x+1}$

   a. $(f \circ g)(4) = f(g(4))$

$$= f\left(\frac{2}{4+1}\right)$$

$$= f\left(\frac{2}{5}\right)$$

$$= \left(\frac{2}{5}\right)^{3/2}$$

$$= \sqrt{\left(\frac{2}{5}\right)^3}$$

$$= \sqrt{\frac{8}{125}}$$

$$= \frac{2\sqrt{2}}{5\sqrt{5}} \cdot \frac{\sqrt{5}}{\sqrt{5}}$$

$$= \frac{2\sqrt{10}}{25}$$

   b. $(g \circ f)(2) = g(f(2))$

$$= g\left(2^{3/2}\right)$$

$$= g\left(\sqrt{2^3}\right)$$

$$= g\left(2\sqrt{2}\right)$$

$$= \frac{2}{2\sqrt{2}+1} \text{ or } \frac{4\sqrt{2}-2}{7}$$

   c. $(f \circ f)(1) = f(f(1))$

$$= f\left(1^{3/2}\right)$$

$$= f(1)$$

$$= 1^{3/2}$$

$$= 1$$

   d. $(g \circ g)(0) = g(g(0))$

$$= g\left(\frac{2}{0+1}\right)$$

$$= g(2)$$

$$= \frac{2}{2+1}$$

$$= \frac{2}{3}$$

21. The domain of g is $\{x \mid x \neq 0\}$. The domain of f is $\{x \mid x \neq 1\}$. Thus, $g(x) \neq 1$, so we solve:

$$g(x) = 1$$
$$\frac{2}{x} = 1$$
$$x = 2$$

Thus, $x \neq 2$; so the domain of $f \circ g$ is $\{x \mid x \neq 0, x \neq 2\}$.

22. The domain of g is $\{x \mid x \neq 0\}$. The domain of f is $\{x \mid x \neq -3\}$. Thus, $g(x) \neq -3$, so we solve:

$$g(x) = -3$$
$$-\frac{2}{x} = -3$$
$$x = \frac{2}{3}$$

Thus, $x \neq \frac{2}{3}$; so the domain of $f \circ g$ is $\left\{x \mid x \neq 0, x \neq \frac{2}{3}\right\}$.

23. The domain of g is $\{x \mid x \neq 0\}$. The domain of f is $\{x \mid x \neq 1\}$. Thus, $g(x) \neq 1$, so we solve:

$$g(x) = 1$$
$$-\frac{4}{x} = 1$$
$$x = -4$$

Thus, $x \neq -4$; so the domain of $f \circ g$ is $\{x \mid x \neq -4, x \neq 0\}$.

24. The domain of g is $\{x \mid x \neq 0\}$. The domain of f is $\{x \mid x \neq -3\}$. Thus, $g(x) \neq -3$, so we solve:

$$g(x) = -3$$
$$\frac{2}{x} = -3$$
$$x = -\frac{2}{3}$$

Thus, $x \neq -\frac{2}{3}$; so the domain of $f \circ g$ is $\left\{x \mid x \neq -\frac{2}{3}, x \neq 0\right\}$.

25. The domain of g is $\{x \mid x \text{ is any real number}\}$.

The domain of f is $\{x \mid x \geq 0\}$. Thus, $g(x) \geq 0$, so we solve:
$$2x + 3 \geq 0$$
$$x \geq -\frac{3}{2}$$

Thus, the domain of $f \circ g$ is $\left\{x \mid x \geq -\frac{3}{2}\right\}$.

26. The domain of g is $\{x \mid x \leq 1\}$. The domain of f is $\{x \mid x \text{ is any real number}\}$. Thus, the domain of $f \circ g$ is $\{x \mid x \leq 1\}$.

27. The domain of g is $\{x \mid x \geq 1\}$. The domain of f is $\{x \mid x \text{ is any real number}\}$. Thus, the domain of $f \circ g$ is $\{x \mid x \geq 1\}$.

28. The domain of g is $\{x \mid x \geq 2\}$. The domain of f is $\{x \mid x \text{ is any real number}\}$. Thus, the domain of $f \circ g$ is $\{x \mid x \geq 2\}$.

29. $f(x) = 2x + 3 \qquad g(x) = 3x$

The domain of f is $\{x \mid x \text{ is any real number}\}$.

The domain of g is $\{x \mid x \text{ is any real number}\}$.

   a. $(f \circ g)(x) = f(g(x))$
$$= f(3x)$$
$$= 2(3x) + 3$$
$$= 6x + 3$$

    Domain: $\{x \mid x \text{ is any real number}\}$.

   b. $(g \circ f)(x) = g(f(x))$
$$= g(2x + 3)$$
$$= 3(2x + 3)$$
$$= 6x + 9$$

    Domain: $\{x \mid x \text{ is any real number}\}$.

   c. $(f \circ f)(x) = f(f(x))$
$$= f(2x + 3)$$
$$= 2(2x + 3) + 3$$
$$= 4x + 6 + 3$$
$$= 4x + 9$$

    Domain: $\{x \mid x \text{ is any real number}\}$.

   d. $(g \circ g)(x) = g(g(x))$
$$= g(3x)$$
$$= 3(3x)$$
$$= 9x$$

    Domain: $\{x \mid x \text{ is any real number}\}$.

30. $f(x) = -x \qquad g(x) = 2x - 4$

The domain of f is $\{x \mid x \text{ is any real number}\}$.

The domain of g is $\{x \mid x \text{ is any real number}\}$.

   a. $(f \circ g)(x) = f(g(x))$
$$= f(2x - 4)$$
$$= -(2x - 4)$$
$$= -2x + 4$$

    Domain: $\{x \mid x \text{ is any real number}\}$.

   b. $(g \circ f)(x) = g(f(x))$
$$= g(-x)$$
$$= 2(-x) - 4$$
$$= -2x - 4$$

    Domain: $\{x \mid x \text{ is any real number}\}$.

   c. $(f \circ f)(x) = f(f(x))$
$$= f(-x)$$
$$= -(-x)$$
$$= x$$

    Domain: $\{x \mid x \text{ is any real number}\}$.

   d. $(g \circ g)(x) = g(g(x))$
$$= g(2x - 4)$$
$$= 2(2x - 4) - 4$$
$$= 4x - 8 - 4$$
$$= 4x - 12$$

    Domain: $\{x \mid x \text{ is any real number}\}$.

31. $f(x) = 3x + 1$ $\quad$ $g(x) = x^2$

The domain of f is $\{x \mid x \text{ is any real number}\}$.

The domain of g is $\{x \mid x \text{ is any real number}\}$.

a. $(f \circ g)(x) = f(g(x))$
$$= f\left(x^2\right)$$
$$= 3x^2 + 1$$
Domain: $\{x \mid x \text{ is any real number}\}$.

b. $(g \circ f)(x) = g(f(x))$
$$= g(3x + 1)$$
$$= (3x + 1)^2$$
$$= 9x^2 + 6x + 1$$
Domain: $\{x \mid x \text{ is any real number}\}$.

c. $(f \circ f)(x) = f(f(x))$
$$= f(3x + 1)$$
$$= 3(3x + 1) + 1$$
$$= 9x + 3 + 1$$
$$= 9x + 4$$
Domain: $\{x \mid x \text{ is any real number}\}$.

d. $(g \circ g)(x) = g(g(x))$
$$= g\left(x^2\right)$$
$$= \left(x^2\right)^2$$
$$= x^4$$
Domain: $\{x \mid x \text{ is any real number}\}$.

32. $f(x) = x + 1$ $\quad$ $g(x) = x^2 + 4$

The domain of f is $\{x \mid x \text{ is any real number}\}$.

The domain of g is $\{x \mid x \text{ is any real number}\}$.

a. $(f \circ g)(x) = f(g(x))$
$$= f\left(x^2 + 4\right)$$
$$= x^2 + 4 + 1$$
$$= x^2 + 5$$
Domain: $\{x \mid x \text{ is any real number}\}$.

b. $(g \circ f)(x) = g(f(x))$
$$= g(x + 1)$$
$$= (x + 1)^2 + 4$$
$$= x^2 + 2x + 1 + 4$$
$$= x^2 + 2x + 5$$
Domain: $\{x \mid x \text{ is any real number}\}$.

c. $(f \circ f)(x) = f(f(x))$
$$= f(x + 1)$$
$$= (x + 1) + 1$$
$$= x + 2$$
Domain: $\{x \mid x \text{ is any real number}\}$.

d. $(g \circ g)(x) = g(g(x))$
$$= g\left(x^2 + 4\right)$$
$$= \left(x^2 + 4\right)^2 + 4$$
$$= x^4 + 8x^2 + 16 + 4$$
$$= x^4 + 8x^2 + 20$$
Domain: $\{x \mid x \text{ is any real number}\}$.

33. $f(x) = x^2$ $\quad$ $g(x) = x^2 + 4$

The domain of f is $\{x \mid x \text{ is any real number}\}$.

The domain of g is $\{x \mid x \text{ is any real number}\}$.

a. $(f \circ g)(x) = f(g(x))$
$$= f\left(x^2 + 4\right)$$
$$= \left(x^2 + 4\right)^2$$
$$= x^4 + 8x^2 + 16$$
Domain: $\{x \mid x \text{ is any real number}\}$.

b. $(g \circ f)(x) = g(f(x))$
$$= g\left(x^2\right)$$
$$= \left(x^2\right)^2 + 4$$
$$= x^4 + 4$$
Domain: $\{x \mid x \text{ is any real number}\}$.

c. $(f \circ f)(x) = f(f(x))$
$$= f\left(x^2\right)$$
$$= \left(x^2\right)^2$$
$$= x^4$$
Domain: $\{x \mid x \text{ is any real number}\}$.

d. $(g \circ g)(x) = g(g(x))$
$$= g\left(x^2 + 4\right)$$
$$= \left(x^2 + 4\right)^2 + 4$$
$$= x^4 + 8x^2 + 16 + 4$$
$$= x^4 + 8x^2 + 20$$
Domain: $\{x \mid x \text{ is any real number}\}$.

34. $f(x) = x^2 + 1 \qquad g(x) = 2x^2 + 3$

The domain of f is $\{x \mid x \text{ is any real number}\}$.

The domain of g is $\{x \mid x \text{ is any real number}\}$.

a. $(f \circ g)(x) = f(g(x))$

$\qquad = f\left(2x^2 + 3\right)$

$\qquad = \left(2x^2 + 3\right)^2 + 1$

$\qquad = 4x^4 + 12x^2 + 9 + 1$

$\qquad = 4x^4 + 12x^2 + 10$

Domain: $\{x \mid x \text{ is any real number}\}$.

b. $(g \circ f)(x) = g(f(x))$

$\qquad = g\left(x^2 + 1\right)$

$\qquad = 2\left(x^2 + 1\right)^2 + 3$

$\qquad = 2\left(x^4 + 2x^2 + 1\right) + 3$

$\qquad = 2x^4 + 4x^2 + 2 + 3$

$\qquad = 2x^4 + 4x^2 + 5$

Domain: $\{x \mid x \text{ is any real number}\}$.

c. $(f \circ f)(x) = f(f(x))$

$\qquad = f\left(x^2 + 1\right)$

$\qquad = \left(x^2 + 1\right)^2 + 1$

$\qquad = x^4 + 2x^2 + 1 + 1$

$\qquad = x^4 + 2x^2 + 2$

Domain: $\{x \mid x \text{ is any real number}\}$.

d. $(g \circ g)(x) = g(g(x))$

$\qquad = g\left(2x^2 + 3\right)$

$\qquad = 2\left(2x^2 + 3\right)^2 + 3$

$\qquad = 2\left(4x^4 + 12x^2 + 9\right) + 3$

$\qquad = 8x^4 + 24x^2 + 18 + 3$

$\qquad = 8x^4 + 24x^2 + 21$

Domain: $\{x \mid x \text{ is any real number}\}$.

35. $f(x) = \dfrac{3}{x-1} \qquad g(x) = \dfrac{2}{x}$

The domain of f is $\{x \mid x \neq 1\}$. The domain of g is $\{x \mid x \neq 0\}$.

a. $(f \circ g)(x) = f(g(x))$

$\qquad = f\left(\dfrac{2}{x}\right)$

$\qquad = \dfrac{3}{\dfrac{2}{x} - 1}$

$\qquad = \dfrac{3}{\dfrac{2-x}{x}}$

$\qquad = \dfrac{3x}{2-x}$

Domain $\{x \mid x \neq 0, \ x \neq 2\}$.

b. $(g \circ f)(x) = g(f(x))$

$\qquad = g\left(\dfrac{3}{x-1}\right)$

$\qquad = \dfrac{2}{\dfrac{3}{x-1}}$

$\qquad = \dfrac{2(x-1)}{3}$

Domain $\{x \mid x \neq 1\}$

c. $(f \circ f)(x) = f(f(x))$

$\qquad = f\left(\dfrac{3}{x-1}\right)$

$\qquad = \dfrac{3}{\dfrac{3}{x-1} - 1} = \dfrac{3}{\dfrac{3-(x-1)}{x-1}}$

$\qquad = \dfrac{3(x-1)}{4-x}$

Domain $\{x \mid x \neq 1, \ x \neq 4\}$.

d. $(g \circ g)(x) = g(g(x)) = g\left(\dfrac{2}{x}\right) = \dfrac{2}{\dfrac{2}{x}} = \dfrac{2x}{2} = x$

Domain $\{x \mid x \neq 0\}$.

36. $f(x) = \dfrac{1}{x+3}$ $\qquad g(x) = -\dfrac{2}{x}$

The domain of f is $\{x \mid x \neq -3\}$. The domain of g is $\{x \mid x \neq 0\}$.

a. $(f \circ g)(x) = f(g(x))$

$$= f\left(-\dfrac{2}{x}\right)$$

$$= \dfrac{1}{-\dfrac{2}{x}+3} = \dfrac{1}{\dfrac{-2+3x}{x}}$$

$$= \dfrac{x}{-2+3x} \quad \text{or} \quad \dfrac{x}{3x-2}$$

Domain $\left\{x \mid x \neq 0, \ x \neq \dfrac{2}{3}\right\}$.

b. $(g \circ f)(x) = g(f(x))$

$$= g\left(\dfrac{1}{x+3}\right)$$

$$= -\dfrac{2}{\dfrac{1}{x+3}} = \dfrac{-2(x+3)}{1}$$

$$= -2(x+3)$$

Domain $\{x \mid x \neq -3\}$.

c. $(f \circ f)(x) = f(f(x))$

$$= f\left(\dfrac{1}{x+3}\right)$$

$$= \dfrac{1}{\dfrac{1}{x+3}+3} = \dfrac{1}{\dfrac{1+3x+9}{x+3}}$$

$$= \dfrac{x+3}{3x+10}$$

Domain $\left\{x \mid x \neq -\dfrac{10}{3}, \ x \neq -3\right\}$.

d. $(g \circ g)(x) = g(g(x))$

$$= g\left(-\dfrac{2}{x}\right)$$

$$= -\dfrac{2}{-\dfrac{2}{x}} = -\dfrac{2x}{-2}$$

$$= x$$

Domain $\{x \mid x \neq 0\}$.

37. $f(x) = \dfrac{x}{x-1}$ $\qquad g(x) = -\dfrac{4}{x}$

The domain of f is $\{x \mid x \neq 1\}$. The domain of g is $\{x \mid x \neq 0\}$.

a. $(f \circ g)(x) = f(g(x))$

$$= f\left(-\dfrac{4}{x}\right)$$

$$= \dfrac{-\dfrac{4}{x}}{-\dfrac{4}{x}-1} = \dfrac{-\dfrac{4}{x}}{\dfrac{-4-x}{x}} = \dfrac{-4}{-4-x}$$

$$= \dfrac{4}{4+x}$$

Domain $\{x \mid x \neq -4, \ x \neq 0\}$.

b. $(g \circ f)(x) = g(f(x))$

$$= g\left(\dfrac{x}{x-1}\right)$$

$$= -\dfrac{4}{\dfrac{x}{x-1}}$$

$$= \dfrac{-4(x-1)}{x}$$

Domain $\{x \mid x \neq 0, \ x \neq 1\}$.

c. $(f \circ f)(x) = f(f(x))$

$$= f\left(\dfrac{x}{x-1}\right)$$

$$= \dfrac{\dfrac{x}{x-1}}{\dfrac{x}{x-1}-1} = \dfrac{\dfrac{x}{x-1}}{\dfrac{x-(x-1)}{x-1}} = \dfrac{\dfrac{x}{x-1}}{\dfrac{1}{x-1}}$$

$$= x$$

Domain $\{x \mid x \neq 1\}$.

d. $(g \circ g)(x) = g(g(x))$

$$= g\left(\dfrac{-4}{x}\right)$$

$$= -\dfrac{4}{-\dfrac{4}{x}} = \dfrac{-4x}{-4}$$

$$= x$$

Domain $\{x \mid x \neq 0\}$.

38. $f(x) = \dfrac{x}{x+3} \qquad g(x) = \dfrac{2}{x}$

The domain of f is $\{x \mid x \neq -3\}$. The domain of g is $\{x \mid x \neq 0\}$.

a. $(f \circ g)(x) = f(g(x))$

$$= f\left(\dfrac{2}{x}\right)$$

$$= \dfrac{\dfrac{2}{x}}{\dfrac{2}{x}+3} = \dfrac{\dfrac{2}{x}}{\dfrac{2+3x}{x}}$$

$$= \dfrac{2}{2+3x}$$

Domain $\left\{x \mid x \neq -\dfrac{2}{3},\ x \neq 0\right\}$.

b. $(g \circ f)(x) = g(f(x))$

$$= g\left(\dfrac{x}{x+3}\right)$$

$$= \dfrac{2}{\dfrac{x}{x+3}}$$

$$= \dfrac{2(x+3)}{x}$$

Domain $\{x \mid x \neq -3,\ x \neq 0\}$.

c. $(f \circ f)(x) = f(f(x))$

$$= f\left(\dfrac{x}{x+3}\right)$$

$$= \dfrac{\dfrac{x}{x+3}}{\dfrac{x}{x+3}+3} = \dfrac{\dfrac{x}{x+3}}{\dfrac{4x+9}{x+3}}$$

$$= \dfrac{x}{4x+9}$$

Domain $\left\{x \mid x \neq -3,\ x \neq -\dfrac{9}{4}\right\}$.

d. $(g \circ g)(x) = g(g(x)) = g\left(\dfrac{2}{x}\right) = \dfrac{2}{\dfrac{2}{x}} = \dfrac{2x}{2} = x$

Domain $\{x \mid x \neq 0\}$.

39. $f(x) = \sqrt{x} \qquad g(x) = 2x+3$

The domain of f is $\{x \mid x \geq 0\}$. The domain of g is $\{x \mid x \text{ is any real number}\}$.

a. $(f \circ g)(x) = f(g(x)) = f(2x+3) = \sqrt{2x+3}$

Domain $\left\{x \mid x \geq -\dfrac{3}{2}\right\}$.

b. $(g \circ f)(x) = g(f(x)) = g\left(\sqrt{x}\right) = 2\sqrt{x}+3$

Domain $\{x \mid x \geq 0\}$.

c. $(f \circ f)(x) = f(f(x))$

$$= f\left(\sqrt{x}\right)$$

$$= \sqrt{\sqrt{x}}$$

$$= \left(x^{1/2}\right)^{1/2}$$

$$= x^{1/4}$$

$$= \sqrt[4]{x}$$

Domain $\{x \mid x \geq 0\}$.

d. $(g \circ g)(x) = g(g(x))$

$$= g(2x+3)$$

$$= 2(2x+3)+3$$

$$= 4x+6+3$$

$$= 4x+9$$

Domain $\{x \mid x \text{ is any real number}\}$.

40. $f(x) = \sqrt{x-2} \qquad g(x) = 1-2x$

The domain of f is $\{x \mid x \geq 2\}$. The domain of g is $\{x \mid x \text{ is any real number}\}$.

a. $(f \circ g)(x) = f(g(x))$

$$= f(1-2x)$$

$$= \sqrt{1-2x-2}$$

$$= \sqrt{-2x-1}$$

Domain $\left\{x \mid x \leq -\dfrac{1}{2}\right\}$.

b. $(g \circ f)(x) = g(f(x))$

$$= g\left(\sqrt{x-2}\right)$$

$$= 1-2\sqrt{x-2}$$

Domain $\{x \mid x \geq 2\}$.

c. $(f \circ f)(x) = f(f(x))$

$$= f\left(\sqrt{x-2}\right)$$

$$= \sqrt{\sqrt{x-2}-2}$$

Now, $\sqrt{x-2}-2 \geq 0$

$$\sqrt{x-2} \geq 2$$

$$x-2 \geq 4$$

$$x \geq 6$$

Domain $\left\{x \mid x \geq 6\right\}$.

d. $(g \circ g)(x) = g(g(x))$

$$= g(1-2x)$$

$$= 1-2(1-2x)$$

$$= 1-2+4x$$

$$= 4x-1$$

Domain $\left\{x \mid x \text{ is any real number}\right\}$.

41. $f(x) = x^2 + 1 \qquad g(x) = \sqrt{x-1}$

The domain of f is $\left\{x \mid x \text{ is any real number}\right\}$.

The domain of g is $\left\{x \mid x \geq 1\right\}$.

a. $(f \circ g)(x) = f(g(x))$

$$= f\left(\sqrt{x-1}\right)$$

$$= \left(\sqrt{x-1}\right)^2 + 1$$

$$= x-1+1$$

$$= x$$

Domain $\left\{x \mid x \geq 1\right\}$.

b. $(g \circ f)(x) = g(f(x))$

$$= g\left(x^2 + 1\right)$$

$$= \sqrt{x^2 + 1 - 1}$$

$$= \sqrt{x^2}$$

$$= |x|$$

Domain $\left\{x \mid x \text{ is any real number}\right\}$.

c. $(f \circ f)(x) = f(f(x))$

$$= f\left(x^2 + 1\right)$$

$$= \left(x^2 + 1\right)^2 + 1$$

$$= x^4 + 2x^2 + 1 + 1$$

$$= x^4 + 2x^2 + 2$$

Domain $\left\{x \mid x \text{ is any real number}\right\}$.

d. $(g \circ g)(x) = g(g(x))$

$$= g\left(\sqrt{x-1}\right) = \sqrt{\sqrt{x-1}-1}$$

Now, $\sqrt{x-1}-1 \geq 0$

$$\sqrt{x-1} \geq 1$$

$$x-1 \geq 1$$

$$x \geq 2$$

Domain $\left\{x \mid x \geq 2\right\}$.

42. $f(x) = x^2 + 4 \qquad g(x) = \sqrt{x-2}$

The domain of f is $\left\{x \mid x \text{ is any real number}\right\}$.

The domain of g is $\left\{x \mid x \geq 2\right\}$.

a. $(f \circ g)(x) = f(g(x))$

$$= f\left(\sqrt{x-2}\right)$$

$$= \left(\sqrt{x-2}\right)^2 + 4$$

$$= x-2+4$$

$$= x+2$$

Domain $\left\{x \mid x \geq 2\right\}$.

b. $(g \circ f)(x) = g(f(x))$

$$= g\left(x^2 + 4\right)$$

$$= \sqrt{x^2 + 4 - 2}$$

$$= \sqrt{x^2 + 2}$$

Domain $\left\{x \mid x \text{ is any real number}\right\}$.

c. $(f \circ f)(x) = f(f(x))$

$$= f\left(x^2 + 4\right)$$

$$= \left(x^2 + 4\right)^2 + 4$$

$$= x^4 + 8x^2 + 16 + 4$$

$$= x^4 + 8x^2 + 20$$

Domain $\left\{x \mid x \text{ is any real number}\right\}$.

d. $(g \circ g)(x) = g(g(x))$

$$= g\left(\sqrt{x-2}\right) = \sqrt{\sqrt{x-2}-2}$$

Now, $\sqrt{x-2}-2 \geq 0$

$$\sqrt{x-2} \geq 2$$

$$x-2 \geq 4$$

$$x \geq 6$$

Domain $\left\{x \mid x \geq 6\right\}$.

43. $f(x) = \dfrac{x-5}{x+1}$ $\qquad$ $g(x) = \dfrac{x+2}{x-3}$

The domain of f is $\{x \mid x \neq -1\}$. The domain of g is $\{x \mid x \neq 3\}$.

a. $(f \circ g)(x) = f(g(x)) = f\left(\dfrac{x+2}{x-3}\right)$

$$= \dfrac{\dfrac{x+2}{x-3}-5}{\dfrac{x+2}{x-3}+1} = \dfrac{\left(\dfrac{x+2}{x-3}-5\right)(x-3)}{\left(\dfrac{x+2}{x-3}+1\right)(x-3)}$$

$$= \dfrac{x+2-5(x-3)}{x+2+1(x-3)} = \dfrac{x+2-5x+15}{x+2+x-3}$$

$$= \dfrac{-4x+17}{2x-1} \quad \text{or} \quad -\dfrac{4x-17}{2x-1}$$

Now, $2x-1 \neq 0$, so $x \neq \dfrac{1}{2}$. Also, from the domain of g, we know $x \neq 3$.

Domain of $f \circ g$: $\left\{x \mid x \neq \dfrac{1}{2}, x \neq 3\right\}$.

b. $(g \circ f)(x) = g(f(x)) = g\left(\dfrac{x-5}{x+1}\right)$

$$= \dfrac{\dfrac{x-5}{x+1}+2}{\dfrac{x-5}{x+1}-3} = \dfrac{\left(\dfrac{x-5}{x+1}+2\right)(x+1)}{\left(\dfrac{x-5}{x+1}-3\right)(x+1)}$$

$$= \dfrac{x-5+2(x+1)}{x-5-3(x+1)} = \dfrac{x-5+2x+2}{x-5-3x-3}$$

$$= \dfrac{3x-3}{-2x-8} \quad \text{or} \quad -\dfrac{3x-3}{2x+8}$$

Now, $-2x-8 \neq 0$, so $x \neq -4$. Also, from the domain of f, we know $x \neq -1$.

Domain of $g \circ f$: $\{x \mid x \neq -4, x \neq -1\}$.

c. $(f \circ f)(x) = f(f(x)) = f\left(\dfrac{x-5}{x+1}\right)$

$$= \dfrac{\dfrac{x-5}{x+1}-5}{\dfrac{x-5}{x+1}+1} = \dfrac{\left(\dfrac{x-5}{x+1}-5\right)(x+1)}{\left(\dfrac{x-5}{x+1}+1\right)(x+1)}$$

$$= \dfrac{x-5-5(x+1)}{x-5+1(x+1)} = \dfrac{x-5-5x-5}{x-5+x+1}$$

$$= \dfrac{-4x-10}{2x-4} = \dfrac{-2(2x+5)}{2(x-2)} = -\dfrac{2x+5}{x-2}$$

Now, $x-2 \neq 0$, so $x \neq 2$. Also, from the domain of f, we know $x \neq -1$.

Domain of $f \circ f$: $\{x \mid x \neq -1, x \neq 2\}$.

d. $(g \circ g)(x) = g(g(x)) = g\left(\dfrac{x+2}{x-3}\right)$

$$= \dfrac{\dfrac{x+2}{x-3}+2}{\dfrac{x+2}{x-3}-3} = \dfrac{\left(\dfrac{x+2}{x-3}+2\right)(x-3)}{\left(\dfrac{x+2}{x-3}-3\right)(x-3)}$$

$$= \dfrac{x+2+2(x-3)}{x+2-3(x-3)} = \dfrac{x+2+2x-6}{x+2-3x+9}$$

$$= \dfrac{3x-4}{-2x+11} \quad \text{or} \quad -\dfrac{3x-4}{2x-11}$$

Now, $-2x+11 \neq 0$, so $x \neq \dfrac{11}{2}$. Also, from the domain of g, we know $x \neq 3$.

Domain of $g \circ g$: $\left\{x \mid x \neq \dfrac{11}{2}, x \neq 3\right\}$.

44. $f(x) = \dfrac{2x-1}{x-2}$ $\qquad$ $g(x) = \dfrac{x+4}{2x-5}$

The domain of f is $\{x \mid x \neq 2\}$. The domain of g is $\left\{x \mid x \neq \dfrac{5}{2}\right\}$.

a. $(f \circ g)(x) = f(g(x)) = f\left(\dfrac{x+4}{2x-5}\right)$

$$= \dfrac{2\left(\dfrac{x+4}{2x-5}\right)-1}{\dfrac{x+4}{2x-5}-2}$$

$$= \dfrac{\left(2\left(\dfrac{x+4}{2x-5}\right)-1\right)(2x-5)}{\left(\dfrac{x+4}{2x-5}-2\right)(2x-5)}$$

$$= \dfrac{2(x+4)-1(2x-5)}{x+4-2(2x-5)}$$

$$= \dfrac{2x+8-2x+5}{x+4-4x+10}$$

$$= \dfrac{13}{-3x+14} \quad \text{or} \quad -\dfrac{13}{3x-14}$$

Now, $-3x+14 \neq 0$, so $x \neq \dfrac{14}{3}$. Also, from the domain of g, we know $x \neq \dfrac{5}{2}$.

Domain of $f \circ g$: $\left\{x \mid x \neq \dfrac{5}{2}, x \neq \dfrac{14}{3}\right\}$.

579

b. $(g \circ f)(x) = g(f(x)) = g\left(\dfrac{2x-1}{x-2}\right)$

$$= \dfrac{\dfrac{2x-1}{x-2}+4}{2\left(\dfrac{2x-1}{x-2}\right)-5}$$

$$= \dfrac{\left(\dfrac{2x-1}{x-2}+4\right)(x-2)}{\left(2\left(\dfrac{2x-1}{x-2}\right)-5\right)(x-2)}$$

$$= \dfrac{2x-1+4(x-2)}{2(2x-1)-5(x-2)}$$

$$= \dfrac{2x-1+4x-8}{4x-2-5x+10}$$

$$= \dfrac{6x-9}{-x+8} \quad \text{or} \quad -\dfrac{6x-9}{x-8}$$

Now, $-x+8 \neq 0$, so $x \neq 8$. Also, from the domain of f, we know $x \neq 2$.
Domain of $f \circ g$: $\{x \mid x \neq 2, x \neq 8\}$.

c. $(f \circ f)(x) = f(f(x)) = f\left(\dfrac{2x-1}{x-2}\right)$

$$= \dfrac{2\left(\dfrac{2x-1}{x-2}\right)-1}{\dfrac{2x-1}{x-2}-2}$$

$$= \dfrac{\left(2\left(\dfrac{2x-1}{x-2}\right)-1\right)(x-2)}{\left(\dfrac{2x-1}{x-2}-2\right)(x-2)}$$

$$= \dfrac{2(2x-1)-1(x-2)}{2x-1-2(x-2)}$$

$$= \dfrac{4x-2-x+2}{2x-1-2x+4} = \dfrac{3x}{3} = x$$

From the domain of f, we know $x \neq 2$.
Domain of $f \circ f$: $\{x \mid x \neq 2\}$.

d. $(g \circ g)(x) = g(g(x)) = g\left(\dfrac{x+4}{2x-5}\right)$

$$= \dfrac{\dfrac{x+4}{2x-5}+4}{2\left(\dfrac{x+4}{2x-5}\right)-5}$$

$$= \dfrac{\left(\dfrac{x+4}{2x-5}+4\right)(2x-5)}{\left(2\left(\dfrac{x+4}{2x-5}\right)-5\right)(2x-5)}$$

$$= \dfrac{x+4+4(2x-5)}{2(x+4)-5(2x-5)}$$

$$= \dfrac{x+4+8x-20}{2x+8-10x+25}$$

$$= \dfrac{9x-16}{-8x+33} \quad \text{or} \quad -\dfrac{9x-16}{8x-33}$$

Now, $8x-33 \neq 0$, so $x \neq \dfrac{33}{8}$. Also, from the domain of g, we know $x \neq \dfrac{5}{2}$.

Domain of $f \circ g$: $\left\{x \mid x \neq \dfrac{5}{2}, x \neq \dfrac{33}{8}\right\}$.

45. $(f \circ g)(x) = f(g(x)) = f\left(\dfrac{1}{2}x\right) = 2\left(\dfrac{1}{2}x\right) = x$

$(g \circ f)(x) = g(f(x)) = g(2x) = \dfrac{1}{2}(2x) = x$

46. $(f \circ g)(x) = f(g(x)) = f\left(\dfrac{1}{4}x\right) = 4\left(\dfrac{1}{4}x\right) = x$

$(g \circ f)(x) = g(f(x)) = g(4x) = \dfrac{1}{4}(4x) = x$

47. $(f \circ g)(x) = f(g(x)) = f\left(\sqrt[3]{x}\right) = \left(\sqrt[3]{x}\right)^3 = x$

$(g \circ f)(x) = g(f(x)) = g\left(x^3\right) = \sqrt[3]{x^3} = x$

48. $(f \circ g)(x) = f(g(x)) = f(x-5) = x-5+5 = x$

$(g \circ f)(x) = g(f(x)) = g(x+5) = x+5-5 = x$

49. $(f \circ g)(x) = f(g(x))$

$\qquad = f\left(\dfrac{1}{2}(x+6)\right)$

$\qquad = 2\left(\dfrac{1}{2}(x+6)\right) - 6$

$\qquad = x + 6 - 6$

$\qquad = x$

$(g \circ f)(x) = g(f(x))$

$\qquad = g(2x - 6)$

$\qquad = \dfrac{1}{2}((2x - 6) + 6)$

$\qquad = \dfrac{1}{2}(2x)$

$\qquad = x$

50. $(f \circ g)(x) = f(g(x))$

$\qquad = f\left(\dfrac{1}{3}(4 - x)\right)$

$\qquad = 4 - 3\left(\dfrac{1}{3}(4 - x)\right)$

$\qquad = 4 - 4 + x$

$\qquad = x$

$(g \circ f)(x) = g(f(x))$

$\qquad = g(4 - 3x)$

$\qquad = \dfrac{1}{3}(4 - (4 - 3x))$

$\qquad = \dfrac{1}{3}(3x)$

$\qquad = x$

51. $(f \circ g)(x) = f(g(x))$

$\qquad = f\left(\dfrac{1}{a}(x - b)\right)$

$\qquad = a\left(\dfrac{1}{a}(x - b)\right) + b$

$\qquad = x - b + b$

$\qquad = x$

$(g \circ f)(x) = g(f(x))$

$\qquad = g(ax + b)$

$\qquad = \dfrac{1}{a}((ax + b) - b)$

$\qquad = \dfrac{1}{a}(ax)$

$\qquad = x$

52. $(f \circ g)(x) = f(g(x)) = f\left(\dfrac{1}{x}\right) = \dfrac{1}{\dfrac{1}{x}} = 1 \cdot \dfrac{x}{1} = x$

$(g \circ f)(x) = g(f(x)) = g\left(\dfrac{1}{x}\right) = \dfrac{1}{\dfrac{1}{x}} = 1 \cdot \dfrac{x}{1} = x$

53. $H(x) = (2x + 3)^4$

Answers may vary. One possibility is
$f(x) = x^4, \quad g(x) = 2x + 3$

54. $H(x) = \left(1 + x^2\right)^3$

Answers may vary. One possibility is
$f(x) = x^3, \quad g(x) = 1 + x^2$

55. $H(x) = \sqrt{x^2 + 1}$

Answers may vary. One possibility is
$f(x) = \sqrt{x}, \quad g(x) = x^2 + 1$

56. $H(x) = \sqrt{1 - x^2}$

Answers may vary. One possibility is
$f(x) = \sqrt{x}, \quad g(x) = 1 - x^2$

57. $H(x) = |2x + 1|$

Answers may vary. One possibility is
$f(x) = |x|, \quad g(x) = 2x + 1$

58. $H(x) = |2x^2 + 3|$

Answer may vary. One possibility is
$f(x) = |x|, \quad g(x) = 2x^2 + 3$

59. $f(x) = 2x^3 - 3x^2 + 4x - 1 \qquad g(x) = 2$

$(f \circ g)(x) = f(g(x))$

$\qquad = f(2)$

$\qquad = 2(2)^3 - 3(2)^2 + 4(2) - 1$

$\qquad = 16 - 12 + 8 - 1$

$\qquad = 11$

$(g \circ f)(x) = g(f(x)) = g\left(2x^3 - 3x^2 + 4x - 1\right) = 2$

60. $f(x) = \dfrac{x+1}{x-1}, \ x \neq 1$

$(f \circ f)(x) = f(f(x))$

$= f\left(\dfrac{x+1}{x-1}\right)$

$= \dfrac{\dfrac{x+1}{x-1}+1}{\dfrac{x+1}{x-1}-1}$

$= \dfrac{\dfrac{x+1+x-1}{x-1}}{\dfrac{x+1-(x-1)}{x-1}}$

$= \dfrac{\dfrac{2x}{x-1}}{\dfrac{2}{x-1}}$

$= \dfrac{2x}{x-1} \cdot \dfrac{x-1}{2}$

$= x, \quad x \neq 1$

61. $f(x) = 2x^2 + 5 \qquad g(x) = 3x + a$

$(f \circ g)(x) = f(g(x)) = f(3x+a) = 2(3x+a)^2 + 5$

When $x = 0$, $(f \circ g)(0) = 23$.

Solving: $2(3 \cdot 0 + a)^2 + 5 = 23$

$2a^2 + 5 = 23$

$2a^2 - 18 = 0$

$2(a+3)(a-3) = 0$

$a = -3 \ \text{ or } \ a = 3$

62. $f(x) = 3x^2 - 7 \qquad g(x) = 2x + a$

$(f \circ g)(x) = f(g(x)) = f(2x+a) = 3(2x+a)^2 - 7$

When $x = 0$, $(f \circ g)(0) = 68$.

Solving: $3(2 \cdot 0 + a)^2 - 7 = 68$

$3a^2 - 7 = 68$

$3a^2 - 75 = 0$

$3(a+5)(a-5) = 0$

$a = -5 \text{ or } a = 5$

63. a. $(f \circ g)(x) = f(g(x))$

$= f(cx+d)$

$= a(cx+d) + b$

$= acx + ad + b$

b. $(g \circ f)(x) = g(f(x))$

$= g(ax+b)$

$= c(ax+b) + d$

$= acx + bc + d$

c. Since the domain of f is the set of all real numbers and the domain of g is the set of all real numbers, the domains of both $f \circ g$ and $g \circ f$ are all real numbers.

d. $(f \circ g)(x) = (g \circ f)(x)$

$acx + ad + b = acx + bc + d$

$ad + b = bc + d$

Thus, $f \circ g = g \circ f$ when $ad + b = bc + d$.

64. a. $(f \circ g)(x) = f(g(x))$

$= f(mx)$

$= \dfrac{a(mx)+b}{c(mx)+d}$

$= \dfrac{amx+b}{cmx+d}$

b. $(g \circ f)(x) = g(f(x))$

$= g\left(\dfrac{ax+b}{cx+d}\right)$

$= m\left(\dfrac{ax+b}{cx+d}\right)$

$= \dfrac{m(ax+b)}{cx+d}$

c. To find the domain of $f \circ g$, we first recognize that the domain of g is the set of all real numbers. This means that the only restrictions are those that cause zero in the denominator of the final result in part (a).

$cmx + d \neq 0$

$cmx \neq -d$

$x \neq -\dfrac{d}{cm}$

Thus the domain of $f \circ g$ is $\left\{ x \,\middle|\, x \neq -\dfrac{d}{cm} \right\}$.

To find the domain of $g \circ f$, we first recognize that the domain of f is $\left\{ x \,\middle|\, x \neq -\dfrac{d}{c} \right\}$ and the domain of g is the set of all real numbers. Thus, the domain of $g \circ f$ is also $\left\{ x \,\middle|\, x \neq -\dfrac{d}{c} \right\}$.

d.
$$(f \circ g)(x) = (g \circ f)(x)$$
$$\frac{amx+b}{cmx+d} = \frac{m(ax+b)}{cx+d}$$
$$\frac{amx+b}{cmx+d} = \frac{amx+bm}{cx+d}$$
$$(amx+bm)(cmx+d) = (amx+b)(cx+d)$$
Now, this equation will only be true if
$m = 1$. Thus, $f \circ g = g \circ f$ when $m = 1$.

65. $S(r) = 4\pi r^2 \qquad r(t) = \frac{2}{3}t^3, \ t \geq 0$

$$S(r(t)) = S\left(\frac{2}{3}t^3\right)$$
$$= 4\pi\left(\frac{2}{3}t^3\right)^2$$
$$= 4\pi\left(\frac{4}{9}t^6\right)$$
$$= \frac{16}{9}\pi t^6$$

Thus, $S(t) = \frac{16}{9}\pi t^6$.

66. $V(r) = \frac{4}{3}\pi r^3 \qquad r(t) = \frac{2}{3}t^3, \ t \geq 0$

$$V(r(t)) = V\left(\frac{2}{3}t^3\right)$$
$$= \frac{4}{3}\pi\left(\frac{2}{3}t^3\right)^3$$
$$= \frac{4}{3}\pi\left(\frac{8}{27}t^9\right)$$
$$= \frac{32}{81}\pi t^9$$

Thus, $V(t) = \frac{32}{81}\pi t^9$.

67. $N(t) = 100t - 5t^2, \ 0 \leq t \leq 10$
$C(N) = 15,000 + 8000N$

$$C(N(t)) = C\left(100t - 5t^2\right)$$
$$= 15,000 + 8000\left(100t - 5t^2\right)$$
$$= 15,000 + 800,000t - 40,000t^2$$

Thus, $C(t) = 15,000 + 800,000t - 40,000t^2$.

68. $A(r) = \pi r^2 \qquad r(t) = 200\sqrt{t}$

$$A(r(t)) = A\left(200\sqrt{t}\right) = \pi\left(200\sqrt{t}\right)^2 = 40,000\pi t$$

Thus, $A(t) = 40,000\pi t$.

69. $p = -\frac{1}{4}x + 100, \quad 0 \leq x \leq 400$

$$\frac{1}{4}x = 100 - p$$
$$x = 4(100 - p)$$

$$C = \frac{\sqrt{x}}{25} + 600$$
$$= \frac{\sqrt{4(100-p)}}{25} + 600$$
$$= \frac{2\sqrt{100-p}}{25} + 600, \quad 0 \leq p \leq 100$$

Thus, $C(p) = \frac{2\sqrt{100-p}}{25} + 600, \quad 0 \leq p \leq 100$.

70. $p = -\frac{1}{5}x + 200, \quad 0 \leq x \leq 1000$

$$\frac{1}{5}x = 200 - p$$
$$x = 5(200 - p)$$

$$C = \frac{\sqrt{x}}{10} + 400$$
$$= \frac{\sqrt{5(200-p)}}{10} + 400$$
$$= \frac{\sqrt{1000-5p}}{10} + 400, \quad 0 \leq p \leq 200$$

Thus, $C(p) = \frac{\sqrt{1000-5p}}{10} + 400, \quad 0 \leq p \leq 200$.

71. $V = \pi r^2 h \qquad h = 2r$
$$V(r) = \pi r^2(2r) = 2\pi r^3$$

72. $V = \frac{1}{3}\pi r^2 h \quad h = 2r$
$$V(r) = \frac{1}{3}\pi r^2(2r) = \frac{2}{3}\pi r^3$$

73. $f(x)$ = the number of Euros bought for x dollars;
$g(x)$ = the number of yen bought for x Euros

a. $f(x) = 0.8382x$

b. $g(x) = 140.9687x$

c. $(g \circ f)(x) = g(f(x))$
$$= g(0.8382x)$$
$$= 140.9687(0.8382x)$$
$$= 118.15996x$$

d. $(g \circ f)(1000) = 118.15996(1000)$
$$= 118{,}159.96 \text{ yen}$$

74. a. Given $C(F) = \dfrac{5}{9}(F - 32)$ and

$K(C) = C + 273$, we need to find
$K(C(F))$.

$$K(C(F)) = \left[\frac{5}{9}(F - 32)\right] + 273$$

$$= \frac{5}{9}(F - 32) + 273$$

$$= \frac{5}{9}F - \frac{160}{9} + 273$$

$$= \frac{5}{9}F + \frac{2297}{9} \quad \text{or} \quad \frac{5F + 2297}{9}$$

b. $K(C(80)) = \dfrac{5(80) + 2297}{9} \approx 299.7 \text{ kelvins}$

75. Given that f and g are odd functions, we know that $f(-x) = -f(x)$ and $g(-x) = -g(x)$ for all x in the domain of f and g, respectively. The composite function $(f \circ g)(x) = f(g(x))$ has the following property:
$$(f \circ g)(-x) = f(g(-x))$$
$$= f(-g(x)) \quad \text{since } g \text{ is odd}$$
$$= -f(g(x)) \quad \text{since } f \text{ is odd}$$
$$= -(f \circ g)(x)$$
Thus, $f \circ g$ is an odd function.

76. Given that f is odd and g is even, we know that $f(-x) = -f(x)$ and $g(-x) = g(x)$ for all x in the domain of f and g, respectively. The composite function $(f \circ g)(x) = f(g(x))$ has the following property:

$$(f \circ g)(-x) = f(g(-x))$$
$$= f(g(x)) \quad \text{since } g \text{ is even}$$
$$= (f \circ g)(x)$$
Thus, $f \circ g$ is an even function.

The composite function $(g \circ f)(x) = g(f(x))$ has the following property:
$$(g \circ f)(-x) = g(f(-x))$$
$$= g(-f(x)) \quad \text{since } f \text{ is odd}$$
$$= g(f(x)) \quad \text{since } g \text{ is even}$$
$$= (g \circ f)(x)$$
Thus, $g \circ f$ is an even function.

Section 6.2

1. The set of ordered pairs is a function because there are no ordered pairs with the same first element and different second elements.

2. The function $f(x) = x^2$ is increasing on the interval $(0, \infty)$. It is decreasing on the interval $(-\infty, 0)$.

3. The function is not defined when $x^2 + 3x - 18 = 0$.
Solve: $x^2 + 3x - 18 = 0$
$$(x + 6)(x - 3) = 0$$
$x = -6$ or $x = 3$
The domain is $\{x \mid x \neq -6,\ x \neq 3\}$.

4. one-to-one

5. $y = x$

6. $[4, \infty)$

7. False. If f and g are inverse functions, then the range of f is the domain of g and the domain of f is the range of g.

8. True

9. The function is one-to-one because there are no two distinct inputs that correspond to the same output.

10. The function is one-to-one because there are no two distinct inputs that correspond to the same output.

11. The function is not one-to-one because there are two different inputs, 20 Hours and 50 Hours, that correspond to the same output, $200.

12. The function is not one-to-one because there are two different inputs, John and Chuck, that correspond to the same output, Marcia.

13. The function is not one-to-one because there are two distinct inputs, 2 and -3, that correspond to the same output.

14. The function is one-to-one because there are no two distinct inputs that correspond to the same output.

15. The function is one-to-one because there are no two distinct inputs that correspond to the same output.

16. The function is one-to-one because there are no two distinct inputs that correspond to the same output.

17. The function f is one-to-one because every horizontal line intersects the graph at exactly one point.

18. The function f is one-to-one because every horizontal line intersects the graph at exactly one point.

19. The function f is not one-to-one because there are horizontal lines (for example, $y = 1$) that intersect the graph at more than one point.

20. The function f is not one-to-one because there are horizontal lines (for example, $y = 1$) that intersect the graph at more than one point.

21. The function f is one-to-one because every horizontal line intersects the graph at exactly one point.

22. The function f is not one-to-one because the horizontal line $y = 2$ intersects the graph at more than one point.

23. To find the inverse, interchange the elements in the domain with the elements in the range:

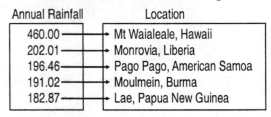

Domain: {460.00, 202.01, 196.46, 191.02, 182.87}

Range: {Mt Waialeale, Monrovia, Pago Pago, Moulmein, Lea}

24. To find the inverse, interchange the elements in the domain with the elements in the range:

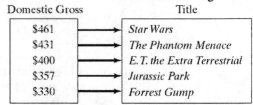

Domain: {461, 431, 400, 357, 330} (in millions)

Range: {*Star Wars, The Phantom Menace, E.T. the Extra Terrestrial, Jurassic Park, Forrest Gump*}

25. To find the inverse, interchange the elements in the domain with the elements in the range:

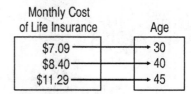

Domain: {$7.09, $8.40, $11.29}

Range: {30, 40, 45}

26. To find the inverse, interchange the elements in the domain with the elements in the range:

Unemployment Rate | State
11% → Virginia
5.5% → Nevada
5.1% → Tennessee
6.3% → Texas

Domain: {11%, 5.5%, 5.1%, 6.3%}

Range: {Virginia, Nevada, Tennessee, Texas}

27. Interchange the entries in each ordered pair:
$\{(5,-3),\ (9,-2),\ (2,-1),\ (11,0),\ (-5,1)\}$

Domain: $\{5,\ 9,\ 2,\ 11,-5\}$

Range: $\{-3,-2,-1,\ 0,\ 1\}$

28. Interchange the entries in each ordered pair:
$\{(2,-2),\ (6,-1),\ (8,0),\ (-3,1),\ (9,2)\}$

Domain: $\{2,\ 6,\ 8,-3,\ 9\}$

Range: $\{-2,-1,\ 0,\ 1,\ 2\}$

29. Interchange the entries in each ordered pair:
$\{(1,-2),\ (2,-3),\ (0,-10),\ (9,1),\ (4,2)\}$

Domain: $\{1,\ 2,\ 0,\ 9,\ 4\}$

Range: $\{-2,-3,-10,\ 1,\ 2\}$

30. Interchange the entries in each ordered pair:
$\{(-8,-2),\ (-1,-1),\ (0,0),\ (1,1),\ (8,2)\}$

Domain: $\{-8,-1,\ 0,\ 1,\ 8\}$

Range: $\{-2,-1,\ 0,\ 1,\ 2\}$

31. $f(x) = 3x+4; \qquad g(x) = \dfrac{1}{3}(x-4)$

$$f\big(g(x)\big) = f\left(\frac{1}{3}(x-4)\right)$$
$$= 3\left(\frac{1}{3}(x-4)\right)+4$$
$$= (x-4)+4$$
$$= x$$

$$g\big(f(x)\big) = g(3x+4)$$
$$= \frac{1}{3}\big((3x+4)-4\big)$$
$$= \frac{1}{3}(3x)$$
$$= x$$

Thus, f and g are inverses of each other.

32. $f(x) = 3-2x; \qquad g(x) = -\dfrac{1}{2}(x-3)$

$$f\big(g(x)\big) = f\left(-\frac{1}{2}(x-3)\right)$$
$$= 3-2\left(-\frac{1}{2}(x-3)\right)$$
$$= 3+(x-3)$$
$$= x$$

$$g\big(f(x)\big) = g(3-2x)$$
$$= -\frac{1}{2}\big((3-2x)-3\big)$$
$$= -\frac{1}{2}(-2x)$$
$$= x$$

Thus, f and g are inverses of each other.

33. $f(x) = 4x-8; \qquad g(x) = \dfrac{x}{4}+2$

$$f\big(g(x)\big) = f\left(\frac{x}{4}+2\right)$$
$$= 4\left(\frac{x}{4}+2\right)-8$$
$$= x+8-8$$
$$= x$$

$$g\big(f(x)\big) = g(4x-8)$$
$$= \frac{4x-8}{4}+2$$
$$= x-2+2$$
$$= x$$

Thus, f and g are inverses of each other.

34. $f(x) = 2x+6; \qquad g(x) = \dfrac{1}{2}x-3$

$$f\big(g(x)\big) = f\left(\frac{1}{2}x-3\right)$$
$$= 2\left(\frac{1}{2}x-3\right)+6 = x-6+6$$
$$= x$$

$$g\big(f(x)\big) = g(2x+6)$$
$$= \frac{1}{2}(2x+6)-3 = x+3-3$$
$$= x$$

Thus, f and g are inverses of each other.

35. $f(x) = x^3 - 8;$ $g(x) = \sqrt[3]{x+8}$

$$f(g(x)) = f\left(\sqrt[3]{x+8}\right)$$
$$= \left(\sqrt[3]{x+8}\right)^3 - 8$$
$$= x + 8 - 8$$
$$= x$$

$$g(f(x)) = g(x^3 - 8)$$
$$= \sqrt[3]{(x^3 - 8) + 8}$$
$$= \sqrt[3]{x^3}$$
$$= x$$

Thus, f and g are inverses of each other.

36. $f(x) = (x-2)^2, x \geq 2;$ $g(x) = \sqrt{x} + 2$

$$f(g(x)) = f\left(\sqrt{x} + 2\right)$$
$$= \left(\sqrt{x} + 2 - 2\right)^2$$
$$= \left(\sqrt{x}\right)^2$$
$$= x$$

$$g(f(x)) = g\left((x-2)^2\right)$$
$$= \sqrt{(x-2)^2} + 2$$
$$= x - 2 + 2$$
$$= x$$

Thus, f and g are inverses of each other.

37. $f(x) = \dfrac{1}{x};$ $g(x) = \dfrac{1}{x}$

$$f(g(x)) = f\left(\frac{1}{x}\right) = \frac{1}{\frac{1}{x}} = 1 \cdot \frac{x}{1} = x$$

$$g(f(x)) = g\left(\frac{1}{x}\right) = \frac{1}{\frac{1}{x}} = 1 \cdot \frac{x}{1} = x$$

Thus, f and g are inverses of each other.

38. $f(x) = x;$ $g(x) = x$

$$f(g(x)) = f(x) = x$$

$$g(f(x)) = g(x) = x$$

Thus, f and g are inverses of each other.

39. $f(x) = \dfrac{2x+3}{x+4};$ $g(x) = \dfrac{4x-3}{2-x}$

$$f(g(x)) = f\left(\frac{4x-3}{2-x}\right)$$
$$= \frac{2\left(\dfrac{4x-3}{2-x}\right) + 3}{\dfrac{4x-3}{2-x} + 4}$$
$$= \frac{\left(2\left(\dfrac{4x-3}{2-x}\right) + 3\right)(2-x)}{\left(\dfrac{4x-3}{2-x} + 4\right)(2-x)}$$
$$= \frac{2(4x-3) + 3(2-x)}{4x-3 + 4(2-x)}$$
$$= \frac{8x - 6 + 6 - 3x}{4x - 3 + 8 - 4x}$$
$$= \frac{5x}{5}$$
$$= x$$

$$g(f(x)) = g\left(\frac{2x+3}{x+4}\right)$$
$$= \frac{4\left(\dfrac{2x+3}{x+4}\right) - 3}{2 - \dfrac{2x+3}{x+4}}$$
$$= \frac{\left(4\left(\dfrac{2x+3}{x+4}\right) - 3\right)(x+4)}{\left(2 - \dfrac{2x+3}{x+4}\right)(x+4)}$$
$$= \frac{4(2x+3) - 3(x+4)}{2(x+4) - (2x+3)}$$
$$= \frac{8x + 12 - 3x - 12}{2x + 8 - 2x - 3}$$
$$= \frac{5x}{5}$$
$$= x$$

Thus, f and g are inverses of each other.

40. $f(x) = \dfrac{x-5}{2x+3}$; $g(x) = \dfrac{3x+5}{1-2x}$

$$f\big(g(x)\big) = f\left(\dfrac{3x+5}{1-2x}\right)$$

$$= \dfrac{\dfrac{3x+5}{1-2x} - 5}{2\left(\dfrac{3x+5}{1-2x}\right) + 3}$$

$$= \dfrac{\left(\dfrac{3x+5}{1-2x} - 5\right)(1-2x)}{\left(2\left(\dfrac{3x+5}{1-2x}\right) + 3\right)(1-2x)}$$

$$= \dfrac{3x+5-5(1-2x)}{2(3x+5)+3(1-2x)}$$

$$= \dfrac{3x+5-5+10x}{6x+10+3-6x}$$

$$= \dfrac{13x}{13}$$

$$= x$$

$$g\big(f(x)\big) = g\left(\dfrac{x-5}{2x+3}\right)$$

$$= \dfrac{3\left(\dfrac{x-5}{2x+3}\right) + 5}{1 - 2\left(\dfrac{x-5}{2x+3}\right)}$$

$$= \dfrac{\left(3\left(\dfrac{x-5}{2x+3}\right) + 5\right)(2x+3)}{\left(1 - 2\left(\dfrac{x-5}{2x+3}\right)\right)(2x+3)}$$

$$= \dfrac{3(x-5)+5(2x+3)}{1(2x+3)-2(x-5)}$$

$$= \dfrac{3x-15+10x+15}{2x+3-2x+10}$$

$$= \dfrac{13x}{13}$$

$$= x$$

Thus, f and g are inverses of each other.

41. Graphing the inverse:

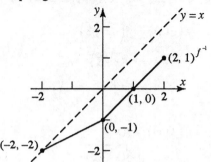

42. Graphing the inverse:

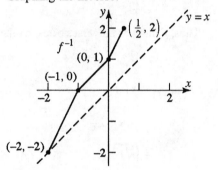

43. Graphing the inverse:

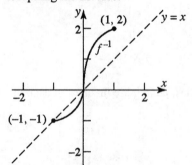

44. Graphing the inverse:

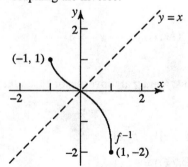

45. Graphing the inverse:

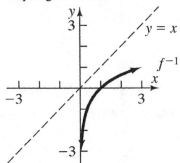

46. Graphing the inverse:

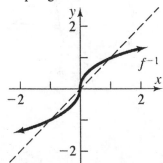

47. $f(x) = 3x$

$y = 3x$

$x = 3y$ Inverse

$y = \dfrac{x}{3}$

$f^{-1}(x) = \dfrac{1}{3}x$

Verifying: $f\left(f^{-1}(x)\right) = f\left(\dfrac{1}{3}x\right) = 3\left(\dfrac{1}{3}x\right) = x$

$f^{-1}\left(f(x)\right) = f^{-1}(3x) = \dfrac{1}{3}(3x) = x$

Domain of f = Range of f^{-1} = All real numbers

Range of f = Domain of f^{-1} = All real numbers

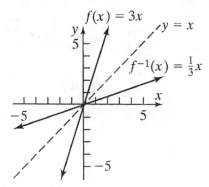

48. $f(x) = -4x$

$y = -4x$

$x = -4y$ Inverse

$y = \dfrac{x}{-4}$

$f^{-1}(x) = -\dfrac{1}{4}x$

Verifying:

$f\left(f^{-1}(x)\right) = f\left(-\dfrac{1}{4}x\right) = -4\left(-\dfrac{1}{4}x\right) = x$

$f^{-1}\left(f(x)\right) = f^{-1}(-4x) = -\dfrac{1}{4}(-4x) = x$

Domain of f = Range of f^{-1} = All real numbers

Range of f = Domain of f^{-1} = All real numbers

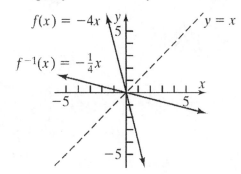

49. $f(x) = 4x + 2$

$y = 4x + 2$

$x = 4y + 2$ Inverse

$4y = x - 2$

$y = \dfrac{x - 2}{4}$

$y = \dfrac{x}{4} - \dfrac{1}{2}$

$f^{-1}(x) = \dfrac{x}{4} - \dfrac{1}{2}$

Verifying:

$f\left(f^{-1}(x)\right) = f\left(\dfrac{x}{4} - \dfrac{1}{2}\right) = 4\left(\dfrac{x}{4} - \dfrac{1}{2}\right) + 2$

$= x - 2 + 2 = x$

$f^{-1}\left(f(x)\right) = f^{-1}\left(4x + 2\right) = \dfrac{4x + 2}{4} - \dfrac{1}{2}$

$= x + \dfrac{1}{2} - \dfrac{1}{2} = x$

Domain of f = Range of f^{-1} = All real numbers

Range of f = Domain of f^{-1} = All real numbers

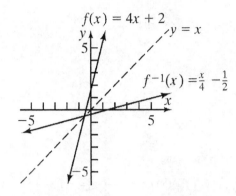

$$f(x) = 4x + 2$$

$$f^{-1}(x) = \frac{x}{4} - \frac{1}{2}$$

50. $f(x) = 1 - 3x$

$y = 1 - 3x$

$x = 1 - 3y$ Inverse

$3y = 1 - x$

$y = \dfrac{1-x}{3}$

$f^{-1}(x) = \dfrac{1-x}{3}$

Verifying:

$$f\left(f^{-1}(x)\right) = f\left(\frac{1-x}{3}\right) = 1 - 3\left(\frac{1-x}{3}\right)$$

$$= 1 - (1-x) = x$$

$$f^{-1}\left(f(x)\right) = f^{-1}(1-3x) = \frac{1-(1-3x)}{3} = \frac{3x}{3} = x$$

Domain of f = Range of f^{-1} = All real numbers

Range of f = Domain of f^{-1} = All real numbers

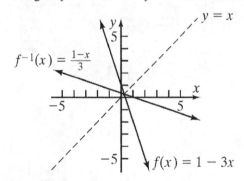

$$f^{-1}(x) = \frac{1-x}{3}$$

$$f(x) = 1 - 3x$$

51. $f(x) = x^3 - 1$

$y = x^3 - 1$

$x = y^3 - 1$ Inverse

$y^3 = x + 1$

$y = \sqrt[3]{x+1}$

$f^{-1}(x) = \sqrt[3]{x+1}$

Verifying:

$$f\left(f^{-1}(x)\right) = f\left(\sqrt[3]{x+1}\right) = \left(\sqrt[3]{x+1}\right)^3 - 1$$

$$= x + 1 - 1 = x$$

$$f^{-1}\left(f(x)\right) = f^{-1}\left(x^3 - 1\right) = \sqrt[3]{\left(x^3 - 1\right) + 1}$$

$$= \sqrt[3]{x^3} = x$$

Domain of f = Range of f^{-1} = All real numbers

Range of f = Domain of f^{-1} = All real numbers

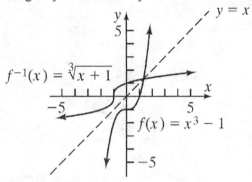

$$f^{-1}(x) = \sqrt[3]{x+1}$$

$$f(x) = x^3 - 1$$

52. $f(x) = x^3 + 1$

$y = x^3 + 1$

$x = y^3 + 1$ Inverse

$y^3 = x - 1$

$y = \sqrt[3]{x-1}$

$f^{-1}(x) = \sqrt[3]{x-1}$

Verifying:

$$f\left(f^{-1}(x)\right) = f\left(\sqrt[3]{x-1}\right) = \left(\sqrt[3]{x-1}\right)^3 + 1$$

$$= x - 1 + 1 = x$$

$$f^{-1}\left(f(x)\right) = f^{-1}\left(x^3 + 1\right) = \sqrt[3]{\left(x^3 + 1\right) - 1}$$

$$= \sqrt[3]{x^3} = x$$

Domain of f = Range of f^{-1} = All real numbers

Range of f = Domain of f^{-1} = All real numbers

$$f(x) = x^3 + 1$$

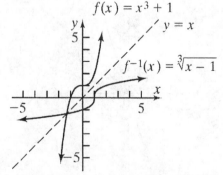

$$f^{-1}(x) = \sqrt[3]{x-1}$$

53. $f(x) = x^2 + 4, \ x \geq 0$

$\quad y = x^2 + 4, \ x \geq 0$

$\quad x = y^2 + 4, \ y \geq 0$ Inverse

$\quad y^2 = x - 4, \ x \geq 4$

$\quad y = \sqrt{x-4}, \ x \geq 4$

$\quad f^{-1}(x) = \sqrt{x-4}, \ x \geq 4$

Verifying: $f\left(f^{-1}(x)\right) = f\left(\sqrt{x-4}\right)$

$\qquad\qquad = \left(\sqrt{x-4}\right)^2 + 4$

$\qquad\qquad = x - 4 + 4 = x$

$\qquad f^{-1}\left(f(x)\right) = f^{-1}\left(x^2 + 4\right)$

$\qquad\qquad = \sqrt{\left(x^2 + 4\right) - 4}$

$\qquad\qquad = \sqrt{x^2} = |x|$

$\qquad\qquad = x, \ x \geq 0$

Domain of f = Range of f^{-1} = $\{x \mid x \geq 0\}$ or $[0, \infty)$

Range of f = Domain of f^{-1} = $\{x \mid x \geq 4\}$ or $[4, \infty)$

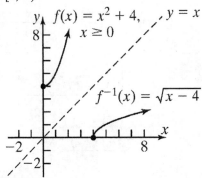

54. $f(x) = x^2 + 9, \ x \geq 0$

$\quad y = x^2 + 9, \ x \geq 0$

$\quad x = y^2 + 9, \ y \geq 0$ Inverse

$\quad y^2 = x - 9, \ x \geq 9$

$\quad y = \sqrt{x-9}, \ x \geq 9$

$\quad f^{-1}(x) = \sqrt{x-9}, \ x \geq 9$

Verifying: $f\left(f^{-1}(x)\right) = f\left(\sqrt{x-9}\right)$

$\qquad\qquad = \left(\sqrt{x-9}\right)^2 + 9$

$\qquad\qquad = x - 9 + 9$

$\qquad\qquad = x$

$f^{-1}\left(f(x)\right) = f^{-1}\left(x^2 + 9\right)$

$\qquad\qquad = \sqrt{\left(x^2 + 9\right) - 9}$

$\qquad\qquad = \sqrt{x^2}$

$\qquad\qquad = |x|$

$\qquad\qquad = x, \ x \geq 0$

Domain of f = Range of f^{-1} = $\{x \mid x \geq 0\}$ or $[0, \infty)$

Range of f = Domain of f^{-1} = $\{x \mid x \geq 9\}$ or $[9, \infty)$

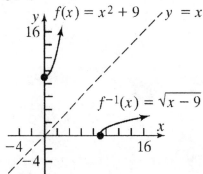

55. $f(x) = \dfrac{4}{x}$

$\quad y = \dfrac{4}{x}$

$\quad x = \dfrac{4}{y}$ Inverse

$\quad xy = 4$

$\quad y = \dfrac{4}{x}$

$\quad f^{-1}(x) = \dfrac{4}{x}$

Verifying:

$f\left(f^{-1}(x)\right) = f\left(\dfrac{4}{x}\right) = \dfrac{4}{\dfrac{4}{x}} = 4 \cdot \left(\dfrac{x}{4}\right) = x$

$f^{-1}\left(f(x)\right) = f^{-1}\left(\dfrac{4}{x}\right) = \dfrac{4}{\dfrac{4}{x}} = 4 \cdot \left(\dfrac{x}{4}\right) = x$

Domain of f = Range of f^{-1}

$\qquad$ = All real numbers except 0.

Range of f = Domain of f^{-1}

$\qquad$ = All real numbers except 0.

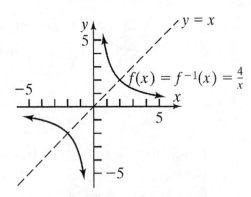

56. $f(x) = -\dfrac{3}{x}$

$y = -\dfrac{3}{x}$

$x = -\dfrac{3}{y}$ Inverse

$xy = -3$

$y = -\dfrac{3}{x}$

$f^{-1}(x) = -\dfrac{3}{x}$

Verifying:

$f\left(f^{-1}(x)\right) = f\left(-\dfrac{3}{x}\right) = -\dfrac{3}{-\dfrac{3}{x}} = -3\cdot\left(-\dfrac{x}{3}\right) = x$

$f^{-1}\left(f(x)\right) = f^{-1}\left(-\dfrac{3}{x}\right) = -\dfrac{3}{-\dfrac{3}{x}} = -3\cdot\left(-\dfrac{x}{3}\right) = x$

Domain of f = Range of f^{-1}

    = All real numbers except 0.

Range of f = Domain of f^{-1}

    = All real numbers except 0.

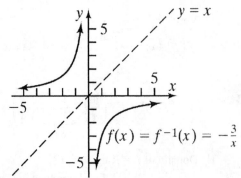

57. $f(x) = \dfrac{1}{x-2}$

$y = \dfrac{1}{x-2}$

$x = \dfrac{1}{y-2}$ Inverse

$xy - 2x = 1$

$xy = 2x + 1$

$y = \dfrac{2x+1}{x}$

$f^{-1}(x) = \dfrac{2x+1}{x}$

Verifying:

$f\left(f^{-1}(x)\right) = f\left(\dfrac{2x+1}{x}\right) = \dfrac{1}{\dfrac{2x+1}{x}-2}$

$= \dfrac{1\cdot x}{\left(\dfrac{2x+1}{x}-2\right)x} = \dfrac{x}{2x+1-2x}$

$= \dfrac{x}{1} = x$

$f^{-1}\left(f(x)\right) = f^{-1}\left(\dfrac{1}{x-2}\right) = \dfrac{2\left(\dfrac{1}{x-2}\right)+1}{\dfrac{1}{x-2}}$

$= \dfrac{\left(2\left(\dfrac{1}{x-2}\right)+1\right)(x-2)}{\left(\dfrac{1}{x-2}\right)(x-2)}$

$= \dfrac{2+(x-2)}{1} = \dfrac{x}{1} = x$

Domain of f = Range of f^{-1}

    = All real numbers except 2.

Range of f = Domain of f^{-1}

    = All real numbers except 0.

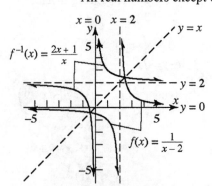

58. $f(x) = \dfrac{4}{x+2}$

$$y = \dfrac{4}{x+2}$$

$$x = \dfrac{4}{y+2} \quad \text{Inverse}$$

$$x(y+2) = 4$$

$$xy + 2x = 4$$

$$xy = 4 - 2x$$

$$y = \dfrac{4-2x}{x}$$

$$f^{-1}(x) = \dfrac{4-2x}{x}$$

Verifying:

$$f\left(f^{-1}(x)\right) = f\left(\dfrac{4-2x}{x}\right) = \dfrac{4}{\dfrac{4-2x}{x}+2}$$

$$= \dfrac{4 \cdot x}{\left(\dfrac{4-2x}{x}+2\right)x} = \dfrac{4x}{4-2x+2x} = \dfrac{4x}{4} = x$$

$$f^{-1}\left(f(x)\right) = f^{-1}\left(\dfrac{4}{x+2}\right) = \dfrac{4-2\left(\dfrac{4}{x+2}\right)}{\dfrac{4}{x+2}}$$

$$= \dfrac{\left(4-2\left(\dfrac{4}{x+2}\right)\right)(x+2)}{\left(\dfrac{4}{x+2}\right)(x+2)} = \dfrac{4(x+2)-2(4)}{4}$$

$$= \dfrac{4x+8-8}{4} = \dfrac{4x}{4} = x$$

Domain of f = Range of f^{-1}

= All real numbers except -2.

Range of f = Domain of f^{-1}

= All real numbers except 0.

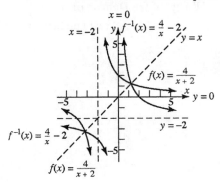

59. $f(x) = \dfrac{2}{3+x}$

$$y = \dfrac{2}{3+x}$$

$$x = \dfrac{2}{3+y} \quad \text{Inverse}$$

$$x(3+y) = 2$$

$$3x + xy = 2$$

$$xy = 2 - 3x$$

$$y = \dfrac{2-3x}{x}$$

$$f^{-1}(x) = \dfrac{2-3x}{x}$$

Verifying:

$$f\left(f^{-1}(x)\right) = f\left(\dfrac{2-3x}{x}\right) = \dfrac{2}{3+\dfrac{2-3x}{x}}$$

$$= \dfrac{2 \cdot x}{\left(3+\dfrac{2-3x}{x}\right)x} = \dfrac{2x}{3x+2-3x}$$

$$= \dfrac{2x}{2} = x$$

$$f^{-1}\left(f(x)\right) = f^{-1}\left(\dfrac{2}{3+x}\right) = \dfrac{2-3\left(\dfrac{2}{3+x}\right)}{\dfrac{2}{3+x}}$$

$$= \dfrac{\left(2-3\left(\dfrac{2}{3+x}\right)\right)(3+x)}{\left(\dfrac{2}{3+x}\right)(3+x)}$$

$$= \dfrac{2(3+x)-3(2)}{2} = \dfrac{6+2x-6}{2}$$

$$= \dfrac{2x}{2} = x$$

Domain of f = Range of f^{-1}

= All real numbers except -3.

Range of f = Domain of f^{-1}

= All real numbers except 0.

60.

$$f(x) = \frac{4}{2-x}$$

$$y = \frac{4}{2-x}$$

$$x = \frac{4}{2-y} \quad \text{Inverse}$$

$$x(2-y) = 4$$

$$2x - xy = 4$$

$$xy = 2x - 4$$

$$y = \frac{2x-4}{x}$$

$$y = 2 - \frac{4}{x}$$

$$f^{-1}(x) = 2 - \frac{4}{x}$$

Verifying:

$$f\left(f^{-1}(x)\right) = f\left(2 - \frac{4}{x}\right) = \frac{4}{2 - \left(2 - \frac{4}{x}\right)}$$

$$= \frac{4}{2 - 2 + \frac{4}{x}} = \frac{4}{\frac{4}{x}} = 4 \cdot \frac{x}{4} = x$$

$$f^{-1}\left(f(x)\right) = f^{-1}\left(\frac{4}{2-x}\right) = 2 - \frac{4}{\left(\frac{4}{2-x}\right)}$$

$$= 2 - 4\left(\frac{2-x}{4}\right) = 2 - (2-x)$$

$$= 2 - 2 + x = x$$

Domain of f = Range of f^{-1}
  = All real numbers except 2.
Range of f = Domain of f^{-1}
  = All real numbers except 0.

61.

$$f(x) = \frac{3x}{x+2}$$

$$y = \frac{3x}{x+2}$$

$$x = \frac{3y}{y+2} \quad \text{Inverse}$$

$$x(y+2) = 3y$$

$$xy + 2x = 3y$$

$$xy - 3y = -2x$$

$$y(x-3) = -2x$$

$$y = \frac{-2x}{x-3}$$

$$f^{-1}(x) = \frac{-2x}{x-3}$$

Verifying:

$$f\left(f^{-1}(x)\right) = f\left(\frac{-2x}{x-3}\right)$$

$$= \frac{3\left(\frac{-2x}{x-3}\right)}{\frac{-2x}{x-3} + 2} = \frac{\left(3\left(\frac{-2x}{x-3}\right)\right)(x-3)}{\left(\frac{-2x}{x-3} + 2\right)(x-3)}$$

$$= \frac{-6x}{-2x + 2x - 6} = \frac{-6x}{-6} = x$$

$$f^{-1}\left(f(x)\right) = f^{-1}\left(\frac{3x}{x+2}\right)$$

$$= \frac{-2\left(\frac{3x}{x+2}\right)}{\frac{3x}{x+2} - 3} = \frac{\left(-2\left(\frac{3x}{x+2}\right)\right)(x+2)}{\left(\frac{3x}{x+2} - 3\right)(x+2)}$$

$$= \frac{-6x}{3x - 3x - 6} = \frac{-6x}{-6} = x$$

Domain of f = Range of f^{-1}
  = All real numbers except -2.
Range of f = Domain of f^{-1}
  = All real numbers except 3.

62. $f(x) = -\dfrac{2x}{x-1}$

$y = -\dfrac{2x}{x-1}$

$x = -\dfrac{2y}{y-1}$ Inverse

$x(y-1) = -2y$

$xy + -x = -2y$

$xy + 2y = x$

$y(x+2) = x$

$y = \dfrac{x}{x+2}$

$f^{-1}(x) = \dfrac{x}{x+2}$

Verifying:

$f\left(f^{-1}(x)\right) = f\left(\dfrac{x}{x+2}\right) = -\dfrac{2\left(\dfrac{x}{x+2}\right)}{\dfrac{x}{x+2}-1}$

$= -\dfrac{\left(2\left(\dfrac{x}{x+2}\right)\right)(x+2)}{\left(\dfrac{x}{x+2}-1\right)(x+2)}$

$= \dfrac{-2x}{x-(x+2)}$

$= \dfrac{-2x}{-2}$

$= x$

$f^{-1}\left(f(x)\right) = f^{-1}\left(\dfrac{-2x}{x-1}\right) = \dfrac{-\dfrac{2x}{x-1}}{-\dfrac{2x}{x-1}+2}$

$= \dfrac{\left(-\dfrac{2x}{x-1}\right)(x-1)}{\left(-\dfrac{2x}{x-1}+2\right)(x-1)}$

$= \dfrac{-2x}{-2x+2x-2}$

$= \dfrac{-2x}{-2}$

$= x$

Domain of f = Range of f^{-1}

= All real numbers except 1.

Range of f = Domain of f^{-1}

= All real numbers except -2.

63. $f(x) = \dfrac{2x}{3x-1}$

$y = \dfrac{2x}{3x-1}$

$x = \dfrac{2y}{3y-1}$ Inverse

$3xy - x = 2y$

$3xy - 2y = x$

$y(3x-2) = x$

$y = \dfrac{x}{3x-2}$

$f^{-1}(x) = \dfrac{x}{3x-2}$

Verifying:

$f\left(f^{-1}(x)\right) = f\left(\dfrac{x}{3x-2}\right) = \dfrac{2\left(\dfrac{x}{3x-2}\right)}{3\left(\dfrac{x}{3x-2}\right)-1}$

$= \dfrac{\left(2\left(\dfrac{x}{3x-2}\right)\right)(3x-2)}{\left(3\left(\dfrac{x}{3x-2}\right)-1\right)(3x-2)}$

$= \dfrac{2x}{3x-(3x-2)} = \dfrac{2x}{2} = x$

$f^{-1}\left(f(x)\right) = f\left(\dfrac{2x}{3x-1}\right) = \dfrac{\dfrac{2x}{3x-1}}{3\left(\dfrac{2x}{3x-1}\right)-2}$

$= \dfrac{\left(\dfrac{2x}{3x-1}\right)(3x-1)}{\left(3\left(\dfrac{2x}{3x-1}\right)-2\right)(3x-1)}$

$= \dfrac{2x}{3(2x)-2(3x-1)}$

$= \dfrac{2x}{6x-6x+2} = \dfrac{2x}{2} = x$

Domain of f = Range of f^{-1}

= All real numbers except $\dfrac{1}{3}$.

Range of f = Domain of f^{-1}

= All real numbers except $\dfrac{2}{3}$.

64. $f(x) = -\dfrac{3x+1}{x}$

$y = -\dfrac{3x+1}{x}$

$x = -\dfrac{3y+1}{y}$ Inverse

$xy = -(3y+1)$

$xy = -3y-1$

$xy + 3y = -1$

$y(x+3) = -1$

$y = \dfrac{-1}{x+3}$

$f^{-1}(x) = \dfrac{-1}{x+3}$

Verifying:

$f\left(f^{-1}(x)\right) = f\left(\dfrac{x}{x+2}\right)$

$= \dfrac{3\left(-\dfrac{1}{x+3}\right)+1}{-\left(-\dfrac{1}{x+3}\right)} = \dfrac{\dfrac{-3}{x+3}+1}{\dfrac{1}{x+3}}$

$= \left(\dfrac{-3}{x+3}+1\right) \cdot \dfrac{x+3}{1}$

$= -3 + (x+3)$

$= x$

$f^{-1}\left(f(x)\right) = f^{-1}\left(\dfrac{3x+1}{-x}\right)$

$= \dfrac{1}{-\left(\dfrac{3x+1}{-x}\right)-3} = \dfrac{1}{\dfrac{3x+1}{x}-3}$

$= \dfrac{1 \cdot x}{\left(\dfrac{3x+1}{x}-3\right)x} = \dfrac{x}{3x+1-3x}$

$= \dfrac{x}{1} = x$

Domain of f = Range of f^{-1}
    = All real numbers except 0.
Range of f = Domain of f^{-1}
    = All real numbers except -3.

65. $f(x) = \dfrac{3x+4}{2x-3}$

$y = \dfrac{3x+4}{2x-3}$

$x = \dfrac{3y+4}{2y-3}$ Inverse

$x(2y-3) = 3y+4$

$2xy - 3x = 3y+4$

$2xy - 3y = 3x+4$

$y(2x-3) = 3x+4$

$y = \dfrac{3x+4}{2x-3}$

$f^{-1}(x) = \dfrac{3x+4}{2x-3}$

Verifying:

$f\left(f^{-1}(x)\right) = f\left(\dfrac{x}{x+2}\right) = \dfrac{3\left(\dfrac{3x+4}{2x-3}\right)+4}{2\left(\dfrac{3x+4}{2x-3}\right)-3}$

$= \dfrac{\left(3\left(\dfrac{3x+4}{2x-3}\right)+4\right)(2x-3)}{\left(2\left(\dfrac{3x+4}{2x-3}\right)-3\right)(2x-3)}$

$= \dfrac{3(3x+4)+4(2x-3)}{2(3x+4)-3(2x-3)}$

$= \dfrac{9x+12+8x-12}{6x+8-6x+9} = \dfrac{17x}{17} = x$

$f^{-1}\left(f(x)\right) = f^{-1}\left(\dfrac{3x+4}{2x-3}\right) = \dfrac{3\left(\dfrac{3x+4}{2x-3}\right)+4}{2\left(\dfrac{3x+4}{2x-3}\right)-3}$

$= \dfrac{\left(3\left(\dfrac{3x+4}{2x-3}\right)+4\right)(2x-3)}{\left(2\left(\dfrac{3x+4}{2x-3}\right)-3\right)(2x-3)}$

$= \dfrac{3(3x+4)+4(2x-3)}{2(3x+4)-3(2x-3)}$

$= \dfrac{9x+12+8x-12}{6x+8-6x+9} = \dfrac{17x}{17} = x$

Domain of f = Range of f^{-1}

    = All real numbers except $\dfrac{3}{2}$.

Range of f = Domain of f^{-1}

    = All real numbers except $\dfrac{3}{2}$.

66. $f(x) = \dfrac{2x-3}{x+4}$

$y = \dfrac{2x-3}{x+4}$

$x = \dfrac{2y-3}{y+4}$ Inverse

$x(y+4) = 2y-3$

$xy + 4x = 2y - 3$

$xy - 2y = -4x - 3$

$y(x-2) = -(4x+3)$

$y = \dfrac{-(4x+3)}{x-2} = \dfrac{4x+3}{2-x}$

$f^{-1}(x) = \dfrac{4x+3}{2-x}$

Verifying:

$f\left(f^{-1}(x)\right) = f\left(\dfrac{4x+3}{2-x}\right) = \dfrac{2\left(\dfrac{4x+3}{2-x}\right)-3}{\dfrac{4x+3}{2-x}+4}$

$= \dfrac{2(4x+3)-3(2-x)}{4x+3+4(2-x)}$

$= \dfrac{8x+6-6+3x}{4x+3+8-4x}$

$= \dfrac{11x}{11}$

$= x$

$f^{-1}\left(f(x)\right) = f^{-1}\left(\dfrac{2x-3}{x+4}\right)$

$= \dfrac{-4\left(\dfrac{2x-3}{x+4}\right)-3}{\dfrac{2x-3}{x+4}-2}$

$= \dfrac{-4(2x-3)-3(x+4)}{2x-3-2(x+4)}$

$= \dfrac{-8x+12-3x-12}{2x-3-2x-8}$

$= \dfrac{-11x}{-11}$

$= x$

Domain of f = Range of f^{-1}
   = All real numbers except -4.

Range of f = Domain of f^{-1}
   = All real numbers except 2.

67. $f(x) = \dfrac{2x+3}{x+2}$

$y = \dfrac{2x+3}{x+2}$

$x = \dfrac{2y+3}{y+2}$ Inverse

$xy + 2x = 2y + 3$

$xy - 2y = -2x + 3$

$y(x-2) = -2x + 3$

$y = \dfrac{-2x+3}{x-2}$

$f^{-1}(x) = \dfrac{-2x+3}{x-2}$

Verifying:

$f\left(f^{-1}(x)\right) = f\left(\dfrac{-2x+3}{x-2}\right) = \dfrac{2\left(\dfrac{-2x+3}{x-2}\right)+3}{\dfrac{-2x+3}{x-2}+2}$

$= \dfrac{\left(2\left(\dfrac{-2x+3}{x-2}\right)+3\right)(x-2)}{\left(\dfrac{-2x+3}{x-2}+2\right)(x-2)}$

$= \dfrac{2(-2x+3)+3(x-2)}{-2x+3+2(x-2)}$

$= \dfrac{-4x+6+3x-6}{-2x+3+2x-4} = \dfrac{-x}{-1} = x$

$f^{-1}\left(f(x)\right) = f^{-1}\left(\dfrac{2x+3}{x+2}\right) = \dfrac{-2\left(\dfrac{2x+3}{x+2}\right)+3}{\dfrac{2x+3}{x+2}-2}$

$= \dfrac{\left(-2\left(\dfrac{2x+3}{x+2}\right)+3\right)(x+2)}{\left(\dfrac{2x+3}{x+2}-2\right)(x+2)}$

$= \dfrac{-2(2x+3)+3(x+2)}{2x+3-2(x+2)}$

$= \dfrac{-4x-6+3x+6}{2x+3-2x-4} = \dfrac{-x}{-1} = x$

Domain of f = Range of f^{-1}
   = All real numbers except -2.

Range of f = Domain of f^{-1}
   = All real numbers except 2.

68. $f(x) = \dfrac{-3x-4}{x-2}$

$y = \dfrac{-3x-4}{x-2}$

$x = \dfrac{-3y-4}{y-2}$ Inverse

$x(y-2) = -3y-4$

$xy - 2x = -3y - 4$

$xy + 3y = 2x - 4$

$y(x+3) = 2x - 4$

$y = \dfrac{2x-4}{x+3}$

$f^{-1}(x) = \dfrac{2x-4}{x+3}$

Verifying:

$f\left(f^{-1}(x)\right) = f\left(\dfrac{2x-4}{x+3}\right)$

$= \dfrac{-3\left(\dfrac{2x-4}{x+3}\right)-4}{\dfrac{2x-4}{x+3}-2}$

$= \dfrac{-3(2x-4)-4(x+3)}{2x-4-2(x+3)}$

$= \dfrac{-6x+12-4x-12}{2x-4-2x-6}$

$= \dfrac{-10x}{-10}$

$= x$

$f^{-1}\left(f(x)\right) = f^{-1}\left(\dfrac{-3x-4}{x-2}\right)$

$= \dfrac{2\left(\dfrac{-3x-4}{x-2}\right)-4}{\dfrac{-3x-4}{x-2}+3}$

$= \dfrac{2(-3x-4)-4(x-2)}{-3x-4+3(x-2)}$

$= \dfrac{-6x-8-4x+8}{-3x-4+3x-6}$

$= \dfrac{-10x}{-10}$

$= x$

Domain of f = Range of f^{-1}

     = All real numbers except 2.

Range of f = Domain of f^{-1}

     = All real numbers except -3.

69. $f(x) = \dfrac{x^2-4}{2x^2}, \ x > 0$

$y = \dfrac{x^2-4}{2x^2}, \ \ x > 0$

$x = \dfrac{y^2-4}{2y^2}, \ \ y > 0$ Inverse

$2xy^2 = y^2 - 4, \ \ x < \dfrac{1}{2}$

$2xy^2 - y^2 = -4, \ \ \ \ x < \dfrac{1}{2}$

$y^2(2x-1) = -4, \ \ \ \ x < \dfrac{1}{2}$

$y^2(1-2x) = 4, \ \ \ \ \ x < \dfrac{1}{2}$

$y^2 = \dfrac{4}{1-2x}, \ \ \ \ \ x < \dfrac{1}{2}$

$y = \sqrt{\dfrac{4}{1-2x}}, \ \ \ x < \dfrac{1}{2}$

$y = \dfrac{2}{\sqrt{1-2x}}, \ \ \ x < \dfrac{1}{2}$

$f^{-1}(x) = \dfrac{2}{\sqrt{1-2x}}, \ \ \ x < \dfrac{1}{2}$

Verifying:

$f\left(f^{-1}(x)\right) = f\left(\dfrac{2}{\sqrt{1-2x}}\right) = \dfrac{\left(\dfrac{2}{\sqrt{1-2x}}\right)^2 - 4}{2\left(\dfrac{2}{\sqrt{1-2x}}\right)^2}$

$= \dfrac{\dfrac{4}{1-2x}-4}{2\left(\dfrac{4}{1-2x}\right)} = \dfrac{\left(\dfrac{4}{1-2x}-4\right)(1-2x)}{\left(2\left(\dfrac{4}{1-2x}\right)\right)(1-2x)}$

$= \dfrac{4-4(1-2x)}{2(4)} = \dfrac{4-4+8x}{8} = \dfrac{8x}{8} = x$

$f^{-1}\left(f(x)\right) = f^{-1}\left(\dfrac{x^2-4}{2x^2}\right) = \dfrac{2}{\sqrt{1-2\left(\dfrac{x^2-4}{2x^2}\right)}}$

$= \dfrac{2}{\sqrt{1-\dfrac{x^2-4}{x^2}}} = \dfrac{2}{\sqrt{1-1+\dfrac{4}{x^2}}}$

$= \dfrac{2}{\sqrt{\dfrac{4}{x^2}}} = \dfrac{2}{\dfrac{2}{|x|}} = 2 \cdot \dfrac{|x|}{2}$

$= |x| = x, \ \ x > 0$

598

Domain of f = Range of f^{-1}
$$= \{x \mid x > 0\} \text{ or } (0, \infty)$$

Range of f = Domain of f^{-1}
$$= \left\{ x \,\middle|\, x < \frac{1}{2} \right\} \text{ or } \left(-\infty, \frac{1}{2}\right)$$

70. $f(x) = \dfrac{x^2 + 3}{3x^2}, \quad x > 0$

$y = \dfrac{x^2 + 3}{3x^2}, \quad x > 0$

$x = \dfrac{y^2 + 3}{3y^2}, \quad y > 0 \quad$ Inverse

$3xy^2 = y^2 + 3, \quad x > \dfrac{1}{3}$

$3xy^2 - y^2 = 3, \quad x > \dfrac{1}{3}$

$y^2(3x - 1) = 3, \quad x > \dfrac{1}{3}$

$y^2 = \dfrac{3}{3x - 1}, \quad x > \dfrac{1}{3}$

$y = \sqrt{\dfrac{3}{3x - 1}}, \quad x > \dfrac{1}{3}$

$f^{-1}(x) = \sqrt{\dfrac{3}{3x - 1}}, \quad x > \dfrac{1}{3}$

Verifying:

$$f\left(f^{-1}(x)\right) = f\left(\sqrt{\dfrac{3}{3x - 1}}\right) = \dfrac{\left(\sqrt{\dfrac{3}{3x-1}}\right)^2 + 3}{3\left(\sqrt{\dfrac{3}{3x-1}}\right)^2}$$

$$= \dfrac{\dfrac{3}{3x-1} + 3}{3\left(\dfrac{3}{3x-1}\right)} = \dfrac{\left(\dfrac{3}{3x-1} + 3\right)(3x-1)}{\left(3\left(\dfrac{3}{3x-1}\right)\right)(3x-1)}$$

$$= \dfrac{3 + 3(3x - 1)}{3(3)}$$

$$= \dfrac{3 + 9x - 3}{9}$$

$$= \dfrac{9x}{9}$$

$$= x$$

$$f^{-1}(f(x)) = f^{-1}\left(\frac{x^2+3}{3x^2}\right) = \sqrt{\dfrac{3}{3\left(\dfrac{x^2+3}{3x^2}\right) - 1}}$$

$$= \sqrt{\dfrac{3}{\dfrac{x^2+3}{x^2} - 1}} = \sqrt{\dfrac{3}{1 + \dfrac{3}{x^2} - 1}}$$

$$= \sqrt{\dfrac{3}{\dfrac{3}{x^2}}} = \sqrt{(3)\left(\dfrac{x^2}{3}\right)} = \sqrt{x^2}$$

$$= |x| = x, \quad x > 0$$

Domain of f = Range of f^{-1}
$$= \{x \mid x > 0\} \text{ or } (0, \infty)$$

Range of f = Domain of f^{-1}
$$= \left\{ x \,\middle|\, x > \frac{1}{3} \right\} \text{ or } \left(\frac{1}{3}, \infty\right)$$

71. a. Because the ordered pair $(-1, 0)$ is on the graph, $f(-1) = 0$.

b. Because the ordered pair $(1, 2)$ is on the graph, $f(1) = 2$.

c. Because the ordered pair $(0, 1)$ is on the graph, $f^{-1}(1) = 0$.

d. Because the ordered pair $(1, 2)$ is on the graph, $f^{-1}(2) = 1$.

72. a. Because the ordered pair $\left(2, \dfrac{1}{2}\right)$ is on the graph, $f(2) = \dfrac{1}{2}$.

b. Because the ordered pair $(1, 0)$ is on the graph, $f(1) = 0$.

c. Because the ordered pair $(1, 0)$ is on the graph, $f^{-1}(0) = 1$.

d. Because the ordered pair $(0, -1)$ is on the graph, $f^{-1}(-1) = 0$.

73. Since $f(7) = 13$, we have $f^{-1}(13) = 7$; the input of the function is the output of the inverse when the output of the function is the input of the inverse.

74. Since $g(-5) = 3$, we have $g^{-1}(3) = -5$; the input of the function is the output of the inverse when the output of the function is the input of the inverse.

75. Since the domain of a function is the range of the inverse, and the range of the function is the domain of the inverse, we get the following for f^{-1}:

Domain: $[-2, \infty)$ Range: $[5, \infty)$

76. Since the domain of a function is the range of the inverse, and the range of the function is the domain of the inverse, we get the following for f^{-1}:

Domain: $[5, \infty)$ Range: $[0, \infty)$

77. Since the domain of a function is the range of the inverse, and the range of the function is the domain of the inverse, we get the following for g^{-1}:

Domain: $[0, \infty)$ Range: all real numbers

78. Since the domain of a function is the range of the inverse, and the range of the function is the domain of the inverse, we get the following for g^{-1}:

Domain: $(0, 8)$ Range: $[0, 15]$

79. Since $f(x)$ is increasing on the interval $(0, 5)$, it is one-to-one on the interval and has an inverse, $f^{-1}(x)$. In addition, we can say that $f^{-1}(x)$ is increasing on the interval $(f(0), f(5))$.

80. Since $f(x)$ is decreasing on the interval $(0, 5)$, it is one-to-one on the interval and has an inverse, $f^{-1}(x)$. In addition, we can say that $f^{-1}(x)$ is decreasing on the interval $(f(5), f(0))$.

81.
$$f(x) = mx + b, \quad m \neq 0$$
$$y = mx + b$$
$$x = my + b \quad \text{Inverse}$$
$$x - b = my$$
$$y = \frac{1}{m}(x - b)$$
$$f^{-1}(x) = \frac{1}{m}(x - b), \quad m \neq 0$$

82.
$$f(x) = \sqrt{r^2 - x^2}, \quad 0 \leq x \leq r$$
$$y = \sqrt{r^2 - x^2}$$
$$x = \sqrt{r^2 - y^2} \quad \text{Inverse}$$
$$x^2 = r^2 - y^2$$
$$y^2 = r^2 - x^2$$
$$y = \sqrt{r^2 - x^2}$$
$$f^{-1}(x) = \sqrt{r^2 - x^2}, \quad 0 \leq x \leq r$$

83. If (a, b) is on the graph of f, then (b, a) is on the graph of f^{-1}. Since the graph of f^{-1} lies in quadrant I, both coordinates of (a, b) are positive, which means that both coordinates of (b, a) are positive. Thus, the graph of f^{-1} must lie in quadrant I.

84. If (a, b) is on the graph of f, then (b, a) is on the graph of f^{-1}. Since the graph of f lies in quadrant II, a must be negative and b must be positive. Thus, (b, a) must be a point in quadrant IV, which means the graph of f^{-1} lies in quadrant IV.

85. Answers may vary. One possibility follows:
$f(x) = |x|, x \geq 0$ is one-to-one.
Thus, $f(x) = x, x \geq 0$
$$y = x, x \geq 0$$
$$f^{-1}(x) = x, x \geq 0$$

86. Answers may vary. One possibility follows:
$f(x) = x^4, x \geq 0$ is one-to-one.
Thus, $f(x) = x^4, \quad x \geq 0$
$$y = x^4, \quad x \geq 0$$
$$x = y^4 \quad \text{Inverse}$$
$$y = \sqrt[4]{x}, \quad x \geq 0$$
$$f^{-1}(x) = \sqrt[4]{x}, \quad x \geq 0$$

87. a.
$$d = 6.97r - 90.39$$
$$d + 90.39 = 6.97r$$
$$\frac{d + 90.39}{6.97} = r$$
Therefore, we would write
$$r(d) = \frac{d + 90.39}{6.97}$$

b. $r(d(r)) = \dfrac{(6.97r - 90.39) + 90.39}{6.97}$
$$= \frac{6.97r + 90.39 - 90.39}{6.97} = \frac{6.97r}{6.97}$$
$$= r$$

$$d(r(d)) = 6.97\left(\frac{d + 90.39}{6.97}\right) - 90.39$$
$$= d + 90.39 - 90.39$$
$$= d$$

c. $r(300) = \dfrac{300 + 90.39}{6.97} \approx 56.01$

If the distance required to stop was 300 feet, the speed of the car was roughly 56 miles per hour.

88. a.
$$H(C) = 2.15C - 10.53$$
$$H = 2.15C - 10.53$$
$$H + 10.53 = 2.15C$$
$$\frac{H + 10.53}{2.15} = C$$
$$C(H) = \frac{H + 10.53}{2.15}$$

b. $H(C(H)) = 2.15\left(\dfrac{H + 10.53}{2.15}\right) - 10.53$
$$= H + 10.53 - 10.53$$
$$= H$$

$$C(H(C)) = \frac{(2.15C - 10.53) + 10.53}{2.15}$$
$$= \frac{2.15C - 10.53 + 10.53}{2.15}$$
$$= \frac{2.15C}{2.15} = C$$

c. $C(26) = \dfrac{26 + 10.53}{2.15} \approx 16.99$

The head circumference of a child who is 26 inches tall is about 17 inches.

89. a. 6 feet = 72 inches
$$W(72) = 50 + 2.3(72 - 60)$$
$$= 50 + 2.3(12) = 50 + 27.6 = 77.6$$
The ideal weight of a 6-foot male is 77.6 kilograms.

b.
$$W = 50 + 2.3(h - 60)$$
$$W - 50 = 2.3h - 138$$
$$W + 88 = 2.3h$$
$$\frac{W + 88}{2.3} = h$$
Therefore, we would write
$$h(W) = \frac{W + 88}{2.3}$$

c. $h(W(h)) = \dfrac{(50 + 2.3(h - 60)) + 88}{2.3}$
$$= \frac{50 + 2.3h - 138 + 88}{2.3} = \frac{2.3h}{2.3} = h$$

$$W(h(W)) = 50 + 2.3\left(\frac{W + 88}{2.3} - 60\right)$$
$$= 50 + W + 88 - 138 = W$$

d. $h(80) = \dfrac{80 + 88}{2.3} = \dfrac{168}{2.3} \approx 73.04$

The height of a male who is at his ideal weight of 80 kg is roughly 73 inches.

90. a.
$$F = \frac{9}{5}C + 32$$
$$F - 32 = \frac{9}{5}C$$
$$\frac{5}{9}(F - 32) = C$$
Therefore, we would write
$$C(F) = \frac{5}{9}(F - 32)$$

b. $C(F(C)) = \dfrac{5}{9}\left(\left(\dfrac{9}{5}C + 32\right) - 32\right)$
$$= \frac{5}{9} \cdot \frac{9}{5}C = C$$

$$F(C(F)) = \frac{9}{5}\left(\frac{5}{9}(F - 32)\right) + 32$$
$$= F - 32 + 32 = F$$

c. $C(70) = \dfrac{5}{9}(70 - 32) = \dfrac{5}{9}(38) \approx 21.1°C$

601

91. a. From the restriction given in the problem statement, the domain is
$$\{g \mid 30,650 \le g \le 74,200\} \text{ or } [30650, 74200].$$

b. $T(15,100) = 4220 + 0.25(30,650 - 30,650)$
$$= 4220$$
$$T(74,200) = 4220 + 0.25(74,200 - 30,650)$$
$$= 15,107.5$$
Since T is linear and increasing, we have that the range is $\{T \mid 4220 \le T \le 15,107.5\}$ or $[4220, 15107.5]$.

c. $$T = 4220 + 0.25(g - 30,650)$$
$$T - 4220 = 0.25(g - 30,650)$$
$$\frac{T - 4220}{0.25} = g - 30,650$$
$$\frac{T - 4220}{0.25} + 30,650 = g$$
Therefore, we would write
$$g(T) = \frac{T - 4220}{0.25} + 30,650$$
Domain: $\{T \mid 4220 \le T \le 15,107.5\}$
Range: $\{g \mid 30,650 \le g \le 74,200\}$

92. a. From the restriction given in the problem statement, the domain is
$$\{g \mid 15,100 \le g \le 61,300\} \text{ or } [15100, 61300].$$

b. $T(15,100) = 1510 + 0.15(15,100 - 15,100)$
$$= 1510$$
$$T(61,300) = 1510 + 0.15(61,300 - 15,100)$$
$$= 8440$$
Since T is linear and increasing, we have that the range is $\{T \mid 1510 \le T \le 8440\}$ or $[1510, 8440]$.

c. $$T = 1510 + 0.15(g - 15,100)$$
$$T - 1510 = 0.15(g - 15,100)$$
$$\frac{T - 1510}{0.15} = g - 15,100$$
$$\frac{T - 1510}{0.15} + 15,100 = g$$
We would write $g(T) = \dfrac{T - 1510}{0.15} + 15,100$.
Domain: $\{T \mid 1510 \le T \le 8440\}$
Range: $\{g \mid 15,100 \le g \le 61,300\}$

93. a. The graph of H is symmetric about the y-axis. Since t represents the number of seconds *after* the rock begins to fall, we know that $t \ge 0$. The graph is strictly decreasing over its domain, so it is one-to-one.

b. $$H = 100 - 4.9t^2$$
$$H + 4.9t^2 = 100$$
$$4.9t^2 = 100 - H$$
$$t^2 = \frac{100 - H}{4.9}$$
$$t = \sqrt{\frac{100 - H}{4.9}}$$
Therefore, we would write $t(H) = \sqrt{\dfrac{100 - H}{4.9}}$.
(Note: we only need the principal square root since we know $t \ge 0$)
$$H(t(H)) = 100 - 4.9\left(\sqrt{\frac{100 - H}{4.9}}\right)^2$$
$$= 100 - 4.9\left(\frac{100 - H}{4.9}\right)$$
$$= 100 - 100 + H$$
$$= H$$
$$t(H(t)) = \sqrt{\frac{100 - (100 - 4.9t^2)}{4.9}}$$
$$= \sqrt{\frac{4.9t^2}{4.9}} = \sqrt{t^2} = t \quad (\text{since } t \ge 0)$$

c. $t(80) = \sqrt{\dfrac{100 - 80}{4.9}} \approx 2.02$
It will take the rock about 2.02 seconds to fall 80 meters.

94. a. $T(l) = 2\pi\sqrt{\dfrac{l}{32.2}}$
$$T = 2\pi\sqrt{\frac{l}{32.2}}$$
$$\frac{T}{2\pi} = \sqrt{\frac{l}{32.2}}$$
$$\frac{T^2}{4\pi^2} = \frac{l}{32.2}$$
$$l = \frac{32.2T^2}{4\pi^2}$$
$$l(T) = \frac{8.05T^2}{\pi^2} = 8.05\left(\frac{T}{\pi}\right)^2, \quad T > 0$$

b. $l(3) = 8.05 \left(\dfrac{3}{\pi}\right)^2 \approx 7.34$

A pendulum whose period is 3 seconds will be about 7.34 feet long.

95. $f(x) = \dfrac{ax+b}{cx+d}$

$y = \dfrac{ax+b}{cx+d}$

$x = \dfrac{ay+b}{cy+d} \quad$ Inverse

$x(cy+d) = ay+b$

$cxy + dx = ay + b$

$cxy - ay = b - dx$

$y(cx - a) = b - dx$

$y = \dfrac{b - dx}{cx - a}$

$f^{-1}(x) = \dfrac{-dx + b}{cx - a}$

Now, $f = f^{-1}$ provided that $\dfrac{ax+b}{cx+d} = \dfrac{-dx+b}{cx-a}$.

This is only true if $a = -d$.

96. Yes. In order for a one-to-one function and its inverse to be equal, its graph must be symmetric about the line $y = x$. One such example is the function $f(x) = \dfrac{1}{x}$.

97. Answers will vary.

98. Answers will vary. One example is

$f(x) = \begin{cases} \dfrac{1}{x}, & \text{if } x < 0 \\ x, & \text{if } x \ge 0 \end{cases}$

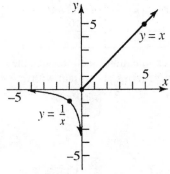

This function is one-to-one since the graph passes the Horizontal Line Test. However, the function is neither increasing nor decreasing on its domain.

99. No, not every odd function is one-to-one. For example, $f(x) = x^3 - x$ is an odd function, but it is not one-to-one.

100. $C^{-1}(800,000)$ represents the number of cars manufactured for $800,000.

Section 6.3

1. $4^3 = 64$; $8^{2/3} = \left(\sqrt[3]{8}\right)^2 = 2^2 = 4$; $3^{-2} = \dfrac{1}{3^2} = \dfrac{1}{9}$

2. $5x - 2 = 3$

$5x = 5$

$x = 1$

The solution set is $\{1\}$.

3. False. To obtain the graph of $y = (x-2)^3$, we would shift the graph of $y = x^3$ to the *right* 2 units.

4. $\dfrac{f(4) - f(0)}{4 - 0} = \dfrac{[3(4) - 5] - [3(0) - 5]}{4}$

$= \dfrac{(12 - 5) - (0 - 5)}{4}$

$= \dfrac{7 - (-5)}{4}$

$= \dfrac{12}{4}$

$= 3$

5. True

6. $\left(-1, \dfrac{1}{a}\right)$, $(0, 1)$, $(1, a)$

7. 1

8. 4

9. False

10. False. The range will be $\{x \mid x > 0\}$ or $(0, \infty)$.

11. a. $3^{2.2} \approx 11.212$

b. $3^{2.23} \approx 11.587$

c. $3^{2.236} \approx 11.664$

d. $3^{\sqrt{5}} \approx 11.665$

603

12. **a.** $5^{1.7} \approx 15.426$

    b. $5^{1.73} \approx 16.189$

    c. $5^{1.732} \approx 16.241$

    d. $5^{\sqrt{3}} \approx 16.242$

13. **a.** $2^{3.14} \approx 8.815$

    b. $2^{3.141} \approx 8.821$

    c. $2^{3.1415} \approx 8.824$

    d. $2^{\pi} \approx 8.825$

14. **a.** $2^{2.7} \approx 6.498$

    b. $2^{2.71} \approx 6.543$

    c. $2^{2.718} \approx 6.580$

    d. $2^{e} \approx 6.581$

15. **a.** $3.1^{2.7} \approx 21.217$

    b. $3.14^{2.71} \approx 22.217$

    c. $3.141^{2.718} \approx 22.440$

    d. $\pi^{e} \approx 22.459$

16. **a.** $2.7^{3.1} \approx 21.738$

    b. $2.71^{3.14} \approx 22.884$

    c. $2.718^{3.141} \approx 23.119$

    d. $e^{\pi} \approx 23.141$

17. $e^{1.2} \approx 3.320$

18. $e^{-1.3} \approx 0.273$

19. $e^{-0.85} \approx 0.427$

20. $e^{2.1} \approx 8.166$

21.

x	$y = f(x)$	$\dfrac{f(x+1)}{f(x)}$
-1	3	$\dfrac{6}{3} = 2$
0	6	$\dfrac{12}{6} = 2$
1	12	$\dfrac{18}{12} = \dfrac{3}{2}$
2	18	
3	30	

Not an exponential function since the ratio of consecutive terms is not constant.

22.

x	$y = g(x)$	$\dfrac{g(x+1)}{g(x)}$
-1	2	$\dfrac{5}{2}$
0	5	$\dfrac{8}{5}$
1	8	
2	11	
3	14	

Not an exponential function since the ratio of consecutive terms is not constant.

23.

x	$y = H(x)$	$\dfrac{H(x+1)}{H(x)}$
-1	$\dfrac{1}{4}$	$\dfrac{1}{(1/4)} = 4$
0	1	$\dfrac{4}{1} = 4$
1	4	$\dfrac{16}{4} = 4$
2	16	$\dfrac{64}{16} = 4$
3	64	

Yes, an exponential function since the ratio of consecutive terms is constant with $a = 4$. So the base is 4.

24.

x	$y = F(x)$	$\dfrac{F(x+1)}{F(x)}$
-1	$\dfrac{2}{3}$	$\dfrac{1}{(2/3)} = 1 \cdot \dfrac{3}{2} = \dfrac{3}{2}$
0	1	$\dfrac{(3/2)}{1} = \dfrac{3}{2}$
1	$\dfrac{3}{2}$	$\dfrac{(9/4)}{(3/2)} = \dfrac{9}{4} \cdot \dfrac{2}{3} = \dfrac{3}{2}$
2	$\dfrac{9}{4}$	$\dfrac{(27/8)}{(9/4)} = \dfrac{27}{8} \cdot \dfrac{4}{9} = \dfrac{3}{2}$
3	$\dfrac{27}{8}$	

Yes, an exponential function since the ratio of consecutive terms is constant with $a = \dfrac{3}{2}$. So the base is $\dfrac{3}{2}$.

25.

x	$y = f(x)$	$\dfrac{f(x+1)}{f(x)}$
-1	$\dfrac{3}{2}$	$\dfrac{3}{(3/2)} = 3 \cdot \dfrac{2}{3} = 2$
0	3	$\dfrac{6}{3} = 2$
1	6	$\dfrac{12}{6} = 2$
2	12	$\dfrac{24}{12} = 2$
3	24	

Yes, an exponential function since the ratio of consecutive terms is constant with $a = 2$. So the base is 2.

26.

x	$y = g(x)$	$\dfrac{g(x+1)}{g(x)}$
-1	6	$\dfrac{1}{6}$
0	1	$\dfrac{0}{1} = 0$
1	0	
2	3	
3	10	

Not an exponential function since the ratio of consecutive terms is not constant.

27.

x	$y = H(x)$	$\dfrac{H(x+1)}{H(x)}$
-1	2	$\dfrac{4}{2} = 2$
0	4	$\dfrac{6}{4} = \dfrac{3}{2}$
1	6	
2	8	
3	10	

Not an exponential function since the ratio of consecutive terms is not constant.

28.

x	$y = f(x)$	$\dfrac{f(x+1)}{f(x)}$
-1	$\dfrac{1}{2}$	$\dfrac{(1/4)}{(1/2)} = \dfrac{1}{4} \cdot \dfrac{2}{1} = \dfrac{1}{2}$
0	$\dfrac{1}{4}$	$\dfrac{(1/8)}{(1/4)} = \dfrac{1}{8} \cdot \dfrac{4}{1} = \dfrac{1}{2}$
1	$\dfrac{1}{8}$	$\dfrac{(1/16)}{(1/8)} = \dfrac{1}{16} \cdot \dfrac{8}{1} = \dfrac{1}{2}$
2	$\dfrac{1}{16}$	$\dfrac{(1/32)}{(1/16)} = \dfrac{1}{32} \cdot \dfrac{16}{1} = \dfrac{1}{2}$
3	$\dfrac{1}{32}$	

Yes, an exponential function since the ratio of consecutive terms is constant with $a = \dfrac{1}{2}$. So The base is $\dfrac{1}{2}$.

29. *B*

30. *F*

31. *D*

32. *H*

33. *A*

34. *C*

35. *E*

36. *G*

37. $f(x) = 2^x + 1$

Using the graph of $y = 2^x$, shift the graph up 1 unit.

Domain: All real numbers

Range: $\{y \mid y > 0\}$ or $(1, \infty)$

Horizontal Asymptote: $y = 1$

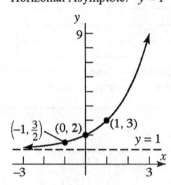

38. $f(x) = 3^x - 2$

Using the graph of $y = 3^x$, shift the graph down 2 units.

Domain: All real numbers

Range: $\{y \mid y > -2\}$ or $(-2, \infty)$

Horizontal Asymptote: $y = -2$

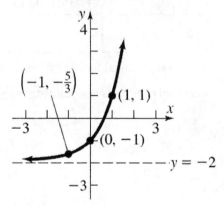

39. $f(x) = 3^{x-1}$

Using the graph of $y = 3^x$, shift the graph right 1 unit.

Domain: All real numbers

Range: $\{y \mid y > 0\}$ or $(0, \infty)$

Horizontal Asymptote: $y = 0$

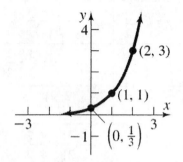

40. $f(x) = 2^{x+2}$

Using the graph of $y = 2^x$, shift the graph left 2 units.

Domain: All real numbers

Range: $\{y \mid y > 0\}$ or $(0, \infty)$

Horizontal Asymptote: $y = 0$

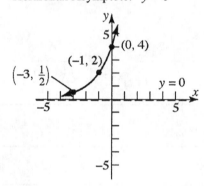

41. $f(x) = 3 \cdot \left(\dfrac{1}{2}\right)^x$

Using the graph of $y = \left(\dfrac{1}{2}\right)^x$, vertically stretch the graph by a factor of 3. That is, for each point on the graph, multiply the y-coordinate by 3.

Domain: All real numbers

Range: $\{y \mid y > 0\}$ or $(0, \infty)$

Horizontal Asymptote: $y = 0$

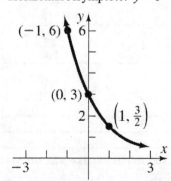

42. $f(x) = 4 \cdot \left(\dfrac{1}{3}\right)^x$

Using the graph of $y = \left(\dfrac{1}{3}\right)^x$, vertically stretch the
graph by a factor of 4. That is, for each point on the
graph, multiply the y-coordinate by 4.
Domain: All real numbers
Range: $\{y \mid y > 0\}$ or $(0, \infty)$
Horizontal Asymptote: $y = 0$

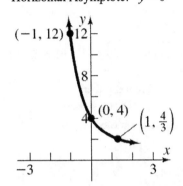

43. $f(x) = 3^{-x} - 2$

Using the graph of $y = 3^x$, reflect the graph about
the y-axis, and shift down 2 units.
Domain: All real numbers
Range: $\{y \mid y > -2\}$ or $(-2, \infty)$
Horizontal Asymptote: $y = -2$

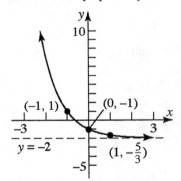

44. $f(x) = -3^x + 1$

Using the graph of $y = 3^x$, reflect the graph about
the x-axis, and shift up 1 unit.
Domain: All real numbers
Range: $\{y \mid y < 1\}$ or $(-\infty, 1)$
Horizontal Asymptote: $y = 1$

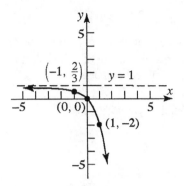

45. $f(x) = 2 + 4^{x-1}$

Using the graph of $y = 4^x$, shift the graph to the
right one unit and up 2 units.
Domain: All real numbers
Range: $\{y \mid y > 2\}$ or $(2, \infty)$
Horizontal Asymptote: $y = 2$

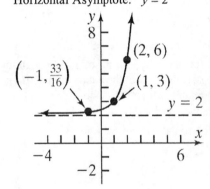

46. $f(x) = 1 - 2^{x+3}$

Using the graph of $y = 2^x$, shift the graph to the
left 3 units, reflect about the x-axis, and shift up 1
unit.
Domain: All real numbers
Range: $\{y \mid y < 1\}$ or $(-\infty, 1)$
Horizontal Asymptote: $y = 1$

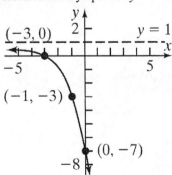

47. $f(x) = 2 + 3^{x/2}$

Using the graph of $y = 3^x$, stretch the graph horizontally by a factor of 2, and shift up 2 units.
Domain: All real numbers
Range: $\{y \mid y > 2\}$ or $(2, \infty)$
Horizontal Asymptote: $y = 2$

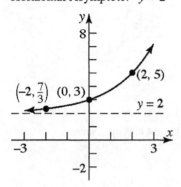

48. $f(x) = 1 - 2^{-x/3}$

Using the graph of $y = 2^x$, stretch the graph horizontally by a factor of 3, reflect about the y-axis, reflect about the x-axis, and shift up 1 unit.
Domain: All real numbers
Range: $\{y \mid y < 1\}$ or $(-\infty, 1)$
Horizontal Asymptote: $y = 1$

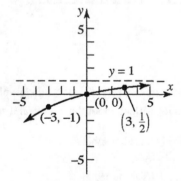

49. $f(x) = e^{-x}$

Using the graph of $y = e^x$, reflect the graph about the y-axis.
Domain: All real numbers
Range: $\{y \mid y > 0\}$ or $(0, \infty)$
Horizontal Asymptote: $y = 0$

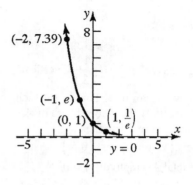

50. $f(x) = -e^x$

Using the graph of $y = e^x$, reflect the graph about the x-axis.
Domain: All real numbers
Range: $\{y \mid y < 0\}$ or $(-\infty, 0)$
Horizontal Asymptote: $y = 0$

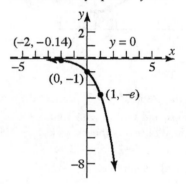

51. $f(x) = e^{x+2}$

Using the graph of $y = e^x$, shift the graph 2 units to the left.
Domain: All real numbers
Range: $\{y \mid y > 0\}$ or $(0, \infty)$
Horizontal Asymptote: $y = 0$

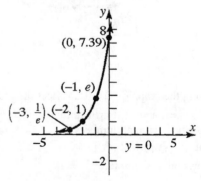

52. $f(x) = e^x - 1$

Using the graph of $y = e^x$, shift the graph down 1 unit.
Domain: All real numbers
Range: $\{y \mid y > -1\}$ or $(-1, \infty)$
Horizontal Asymptote: $y = -1$

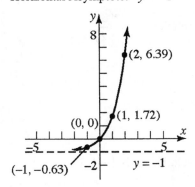

53. $f(x) = 5 - e^{-x}$

Using the graph of $y = e^x$, reflect the graph about the y-axis, reflect about the x-axis, and shift up 5 units.
Domain: All real numbers
Range: $\{y \mid y < 5\}$ or $(-\infty, 5)$
Horizontal Asymptote: $y = 5$

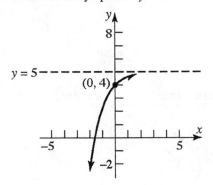

54. $f(x) = 9 - 3e^{-x}$

Using the graph of $y = e^x$, reflect the graph about the y-axis, stretch vertically by a factor of 3, reflect about the x-axis, and shift up 9 units.
Domain: All real numbers
Range: $\{y \mid y < 9\}$ or $(-\infty, 9)$
Horizontal Asymptote: $y = 9$

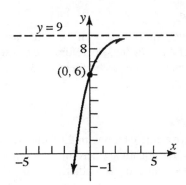

55. $f(x) = 2 - e^{-x/2}$

Using the graph of $y = e^x$, reflect the graph about the y-axis, stretch horizontally by a factor of 2, reflect about the x-axis, and shift up 2 units.
Domain: All real numbers
Range: $\{y \mid y < 2\}$ or $(-\infty, 2)$
Horizontal Asymptote: $y = 2$

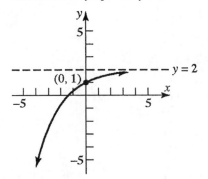

56. $f(x) = 7 - 3e^{-2x}$

Using the graph of $y = e^x$, reflect the graph about the y-axis, shrink horizontally by a factor of $\frac{1}{2}$, stretch vertically by a factor of 3, reflect about the x-axis, and shift up 7 units.
Domain: All real numbers
Range: $\{y \mid y < 7\}$ or $(-\infty, 7)$
Horizontal Asymptote: $y = 7$

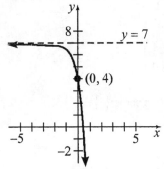

609

57. $7^x = 7^3$

We have a single term with the same base on both sides of the equation. Therefore, we can set the exponents equal to each other: $x = 3$.

The solution set is $\{3\}$.

58. $5^x = 5^{-6}$

We have a single term with the same base on both sides of the equation. Therefore, we can set the exponents equal to each other: $x = -6$.

The solution set is $\{-6\}$.

59. $2^{-x} = 16$

$2^{-x} = 2^4$

$-x = 4$

$x = -4$

The solution set is $\{-4\}$.

60. $3^{-x} = 81$

$3^{-x} = 3^4$

$-x = 4$

$x = -4$

The solution set is $\{-4\}$.

61. $\left(\frac{1}{5}\right)^x = \frac{1}{25}$

$\left(\frac{1}{5}\right)^x = \frac{1}{5^2}$

$\left(\frac{1}{5}\right)^x = \left(\frac{1}{5}\right)^2$

$x = 2$

The solution set is $\{2\}$.

62. $\left(\frac{1}{4}\right)^x = \frac{1}{64}$

$\left(\frac{1}{4}\right)^x = \frac{1}{4^3}$

$\left(\frac{1}{4}\right)^x = \left(\frac{1}{4}\right)^3$

$x = 3$

The solution set is $\{3\}$.

63. $2^{2x-1} = 4$

$2^{2x-1} = 2^2$

$2x - 1 = 2$

$2x = 3$

$x = \frac{3}{2}$

The solution set is $\left\{\frac{3}{2}\right\}$.

64. $5^{x+3} = \frac{1}{5}$

$5^{x+3} = 5^{-1}$

$x + 3 = -1$

$x = -4$

The solution set is $\{-4\}$.

65. $3^{x^3} = 9^x$

$3^{x^3} = \left(3^2\right)^x$

$3^{x^3} = 3^{2x}$

$x^3 = 2x$

$x^3 - 2x = 0$

$x\left(x^2 - 2\right) = 0$

$x = 0$ or $x^2 - 2 = 0$

$x^2 = 2$

$x = \pm\sqrt{2}$

The solution set is $\left\{-\sqrt{2}, 0, \sqrt{2}\right\}$.

66. $4^{x^2} = 2^x$

$\left(2^2\right)^{x^2} = 2^x$

$2^{2x^2} = 2^x$

$2x^2 = x$

$2x^2 - x = 0$

$x(2x - 1) = 0$

$x = 0$ or $2x - 1 = 0$

$2x = 1$

$x = \frac{1}{2}$

The solution set is $\left\{0, \frac{1}{2}\right\}$.

67.
$$8^{-x+14} = 16^x$$
$$\left(2^3\right)^{-x+14} = \left(2^4\right)^x$$
$$2^{-3x+42} = 2^{4x}$$
$$-3x + 42 = 4x$$
$$42 = 7x$$
$$6 = x$$
The solution set is $\{6\}$.

68.
$$9^{-x+15} = 27^x$$
$$\left(3^2\right)^{-x+15} = \left(3^3\right)^x$$
$$3^{-2x+30} = 3^{3x}$$
$$-2x + 30 = 3x$$
$$30 = 5x$$
$$6 = x$$
The solution set is $\{6\}$.

69.
$$3^{x^2-7} = 27^{2x}$$
$$3^{x^2-7} = \left(3^3\right)^{2x}$$
$$3^{x^2-7} = 3^{6x}$$
$$x^2 - 7 = 6x$$
$$x^2 - 6x - 7 = 0$$
$$(x-7)(x+1) = 0$$
$$x - 7 = 0 \quad \text{or} \quad x + 1 = 0$$
$$x = 7 \qquad\qquad x = -1$$
The solution set is $\{-1, 7\}$.

70.
$$5^{x^2+8} = 125^{2x}$$
$$5^{x^2+8} = \left(5^3\right)^{2x}$$
$$5^{x^2+8} = 5^{6x}$$
$$x^2 + 8 = 6x$$
$$x^2 - 6x + 8 = 0$$
$$(x-4)(x-2) = 0$$
$$x - 4 = 0 \quad \text{or} \quad x - 2 = 0$$
$$x = 4 \qquad\qquad x = 2$$
The solution set is $\{2, 4\}$.

71.
$$4^x \cdot 2^{x^2} = 16^2$$
$$\left(2^2\right)^x \cdot 2^{x^2} = \left(2^4\right)^2$$
$$2^{2x} \cdot 2^{x^2} = 2^8$$
$$2^{2x+x^2} = 2^8$$
$$x^2 + 2x = 8$$
$$x^2 + 2x - 8 = 0$$
$$(x+4)(x-2) = 0$$
$$x + 4 = 0 \quad \text{or} \quad x - 2 = 0$$
$$x = -4 \qquad\qquad x = 2$$
The solution set is $\{-4, 2\}$.

72.
$$9^{2x} \cdot 27^{x^2} = 3^{-1}$$
$$\left(3^2\right)^{2x} \cdot \left(3^3\right)^{x^2} = 3^{-1}$$
$$3^{4x} \cdot 3^{3x^2} = 3^{-1}$$
$$3^{4x+3x^2} = 3^{-1}$$
$$3x^2 + 4x = -1$$
$$3x^2 + 4x + 1 = 0$$
$$(3x+1)(x+1) = 0$$
$$3x + 1 = 0 \quad \text{or} \quad x + 1 = 0$$
$$3x = -1 \qquad\qquad x = -1$$
$$x = -\frac{1}{3}$$
The solution set is $\left\{-1, -\frac{1}{3}\right\}$.

73.
$$e^x = e^{3x+8}$$
$$x = 3x + 8$$
$$-2x = 8$$
$$x = -4$$
The solution set is $\{-4\}$.

74.
$$e^{3x} = e^{2-x}$$
$$3x = 2 - x$$
$$4x = 2$$
$$x = \frac{1}{2}$$
The solution set is $\left\{\frac{1}{2}\right\}$.

75.
$$e^{x^2} = e^{3x} \cdot \frac{1}{e^2}$$
$$e^{x^2} = e^{3x} \cdot e^{-2}$$
$$e^{x^2} = e^{3x-2}$$
$$x^2 = 3x - 2$$
$$x^2 - 3x + 2 = 0$$
$$(x-2)(x-1) = 0$$
$$x - 2 = 0 \quad \text{or} \quad x - 1 = 0$$
$$x = 2 \qquad\qquad x = 1$$
The solution set is $\{1, 2\}$.

76.
$$\left(e^4\right)^x \cdot e^{x^2} = e^{12}$$
$$e^{4x} \cdot e^{x^2} = e^{12}$$
$$e^{4x+x^2} = e^{12}$$
$$x^2 + 4x = 12$$
$$x^2 + 4x - 12 = 0$$
$$(x+6)(x-2) = 0$$
$$x + 6 = 0 \quad \text{or} \quad x - 2 = 0$$
$$x = -6 \qquad\qquad x = 2$$
The solution set is $\{-6, 2\}$.

77. a. $f(4) = 2^4 = 16$

The point $(4, 16)$ is on the graph of f.

b. $f(x) = \dfrac{1}{16}$
$$2^x = \frac{1}{16}$$
$$2^x = \frac{1}{2^4}$$
$$2^x = 2^{-4}$$
$$x = -4$$
The point $\left(-4, \dfrac{1}{16}\right)$ is on the graph of f.

78. a. $f(4) = 3^4 = 81$

The point $(4, 81)$ is on the graph of f.

b. $f(x) = \dfrac{1}{9}$
$$3^x = \frac{1}{9}$$
$$3^x = \frac{1}{3^2}$$
$$3^x = 3^{-2}$$
$$x = -2$$
The point $\left(-2, \dfrac{1}{9}\right)$ is on the graph of f.

79. a. $g(-1) = 4^{-1} + 2 = \dfrac{1}{4} + 2 = \dfrac{9}{4}$

The point $\left(-1, \dfrac{9}{4}\right)$ is on the graph of g.

b. $g(x) = 66$
$$4^x + 2 = 66$$
$$4^x = 64$$
$$4^x = 4^3$$
$$x = 3$$
The point $(3, 66)$ is on the graph of g.

80. a. $g(-1) = 5^{-1} - 3 = \dfrac{1}{5} - 3 = -\dfrac{14}{5}$

The point $\left(-1, -\dfrac{14}{15}\right)$ is on the graph of g.

b. $g(x) = 122$
$$5^x - 3 = 122$$
$$5^x = 125$$
$$5^x = 5^3$$
$$x = 3$$
The point $(3, 122)$ is on the graph of g.

81. a. $H(-2) = 3\left(\dfrac{1}{2}\right)^{-2} - 2 = 3(2)^2 - 2 = 10$

The point $(-2, 10)$ is on the graph of H.

b. $H(x) = -\dfrac{13}{8}$

$3\left(\dfrac{1}{2}\right)^{x} - 2 = -\dfrac{13}{8}$

$3\left(\dfrac{1}{2}\right)^{x} = \dfrac{3}{8}$

$\left(\dfrac{1}{2}\right)^{x} = \dfrac{1}{8}$

$\left(\dfrac{1}{2}\right)^{x} = \dfrac{1}{2^3}$

$\left(\dfrac{1}{2}\right)^{x} = \left(\dfrac{1}{2}\right)^{3}$

$x = 3$

The point $\left(3, -\dfrac{13}{8}\right)$ is on the graph of H.

82. a. $F(-1) = -2\left(\dfrac{1}{3}\right)^{-1} + 1 = -2(3)^1 + 1 = -5$

The point $(-1, -5)$ is on the graph of F.

b. $F(x) = -53$

$-2\left(\dfrac{1}{3}\right)^{x} + 1 = -53$

$-2\left(\dfrac{1}{3}\right)^{x} = -54$

$\left(\dfrac{1}{3}\right)^{x} = 27$

$3^{-x} = 3^3$

$-x = 3$

$x = -3$

The point $(-3, -53)$ is on the graph of F.

83. If $4^x = 7$, then $\left(4^x\right)^{-2} = 7^{-2}$

$4^{-2x} = \dfrac{1}{7^2}$

$4^{-2x} = \dfrac{1}{49}$

84. If $2^x = 3$, then $\left(2^x\right)^{-2} = 3^{-2}$

$2^{-2x} = \dfrac{1}{3^2}$

$\left(2^2\right)^{-x} = \dfrac{1}{9}$

$4^{-x} = \dfrac{1}{9}$

85. If $3^{-x} = 2$, then $\left(3^{-x}\right)^{-2} = 2^{-2}$

$3^{2x} = \dfrac{1}{2^2}$

$3^{2x} = \dfrac{1}{4}$

86. If $5^{-x} = 3$, then $\left(5^{-x}\right)^{-3} = 3^{-3}$

$5^{3x} = \dfrac{1}{3^3}$

$5^{3x} = \dfrac{1}{27}$

87. We need a function of the form $f(x) = k \cdot a^{p \cdot x}$, with $a > 0$, $a \neq 1$. The graph contains the points $\left(-1, \dfrac{1}{3}\right)$, $(0, 1)$, $(1, 3)$, and $(2, 9)$. In other words, $f(-1) = \dfrac{1}{3}$, $f(0) = 1$, $f(1) = 3$, and $f(2) = 9$.

Therefore, $f(0) = k \cdot a^{p \cdot (0)}$

$1 = k \cdot a^0$

$1 = k \cdot 1$

$1 = k$

and $f(1) = a^{p \cdot (1)}$

$3 = a^p$

Let's use $a = 3$, $p = 1$. Then $f(x) = 3^x$. Now we need to verify that this function yields the other known points on the graph. $f(-1) = 3^{-1} = \dfrac{1}{3}$;

$f(2) = 3^2 = 9$

So we have the function $f(x) = 3^x$.

88. We need a function of the form $f(x) = k \cdot a^{p \cdot x}$, with $a > 0$, $a \neq 1$. The graph contains the points $\left(-1, \frac{1}{5}\right)$, $(0,1)$, and $(1,5)$. In other words,

$f(-1) = \frac{1}{5}$, $f(0) = 1$, and $f(1) = 5$. Therefore,

$f(0) = k \cdot a^{p \cdot (0)}$

$\quad 1 = k \cdot a^0$

$\quad 1 = k \cdot 1$

$\quad 1 = k$

and $f(1) = a^{p \cdot (1)}$

$\quad 5 = a^p$

Let's use $a = 5$, $p = 1$. Then $f(x) = 5^x$. Now we need to verify that this function yields the other known point on the graph.

$f(-1) = 5^{-1} = \frac{1}{5}$

So we have the function $f(x) = 5^x$.

89. We need a function of the form $f(x) = k \cdot a^{p \cdot x}$, with $a > 0$, $a \neq 1$. The graph contains the points $\left(-1, -\frac{1}{6}\right)$, $(0,-1)$, $(1,-6)$, and $(2,-36)$. In other words, $f(-1) = -\frac{1}{6}$, $f(0) = -1$, $f(1) = -6$, and

$f(2) = -36$.

Therefore, $f(0) = k \cdot a^{p \cdot (0)}$

$\quad -1 = k \cdot a^0$

$\quad -1 = k \cdot 1$

$\quad -1 = k$

and $f(1) = -a^{p \cdot (1)}$

$\quad -6 = -a^p$

$\quad 6 = a^p$

Let's use $a = 6$, $p = 1$. Then $f(x) = -6^x$.

Now we need to verify that this function yields the other known points on the graph.

$f(-1) = -6^{-1} = -\frac{1}{6}$

$f(2) = -6^2 = -36$

So we have the function $f(x) = -6^x$.

90. We need a function of the form $f(x) = k \cdot a^{p \cdot x}$, with $a > 0$, $a \neq 1$. The graph contains the points $\left(-1, -\frac{1}{e}\right)$, $(0,-1)$, $(1,-e)$, and $(2,-e^2)$. In other words, $f(-1) = -\frac{1}{e}$, $f(0) = -1$, $f(1) = -e$, and

$f(2) = -e^2$.

Therefore, $f(0) = k \cdot a^{p \cdot (0)}$

$\quad -1 = k \cdot a^0$

$\quad -1 = k \cdot 1$

$\quad -1 = k$

and $f(1) = -a^{p \cdot (1)}$

$\quad -e = -a^p$

$\quad e = a^p$

Let's use $a = e$, $p = 1$. Then $f(x) = -e^x$. Now we need to verify that this function yields the other known points on the graph.

$f(-1) = -e^{-1} = -\frac{1}{e}$

$f(2) = -e^2$

So we have the function $f(x) = -e^x$.

91. $f(x) = \begin{cases} e^{-x} & \text{if } x < 0 \\ e^x & \text{if } x \geq 0 \end{cases}$

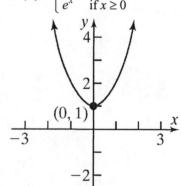

Domain: $(-\infty, \infty)$

Range: $\{y \mid y \geq 1\}$ or $[1, \infty)$

Intercept: $(0,1)$

92. $f(x) = \begin{cases} e^x & \text{if } x < 0 \\ e^{-x} & \text{if } x \geq 0 \end{cases}$

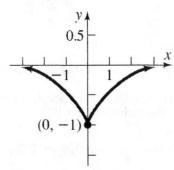

Domain: $(-\infty, \infty)$

Range: $\{y \mid 0 < y \leq 1\}$ or $(0,1]$

Intercept: $(0,1)$

93. $f(x) = \begin{cases} -e^x & \text{if } x < 0 \\ -e^{-x} & \text{if } x \geq 0 \end{cases}$

Domain: $(-\infty, \infty)$

Range: $\{y \mid -1 \leq y < 0\}$ or $[-1,0)$

Intercept: $(0,-1)$

94. $f(x) = \begin{cases} -e^{-x} & \text{if } x < 0 \\ -e^x & \text{if } x \geq 0 \end{cases}$

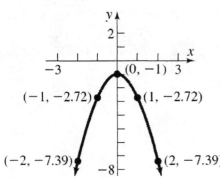

Domain: $(-\infty, \infty)$

Range: $\{y \mid y \leq -1\}$ or $(-\infty, -1]$

Intercept: $(0,-1)$

95. $p(n) = 100(0.97)^n$

  a. $p(10) = 100(0.97)^{10} \approx 74\%$ of light

  b. $p(25) = 100(0.97)^{25} \approx 47\%$ of light

96. $p(h) = 760e^{-0.145h}$

  a. $p(2) = 760e^{-0.145(2)}$
    $= 760e^{-0.290}$
    ≈ 568.68 mm of mercury

  b. $p(10) = 760e^{-0.145(10)}$
    $= 760e^{-1.45}$
    ≈ 178.27 mm of mercury

97. $p(x) = 16,630(0.90)^x$

  a. $p(3) = 16,630(0.90)^3 \approx \$12,123$

  b. $p(9) = 16,630(0.90)^9 \approx \$6,443$

98. $A(n) = A_0 e^{-0.35n}$

  a. $A(3) = 100e^{-0.35(3)}$
    $= 100e^{-1.05}$
    ≈ 34.99 square millimeters

  b. $A(10) = 100e^{-0.35(10)}$
    $= 100e^{-3.5}$
    ≈ 3.02 square millimeters

99. $D(h) = 5e^{-0.4h}$
  $D(1) = 5e^{-0.4(1)} = 5e^{-0.4} \approx 3.35$
  After 1 hours, 3.35 milligrams will be present.
  $D(6) = 5e^{-0.4(6)} = 5e^{-2.4} \approx 0.45$ milligrams
  After 6 hours, 0.45 milligrams will be present.

100. $N = P\left(1 - e^{-0.15d}\right)$
  $N(3) = 1000\left(1 - e^{-0.15(3)}\right)$
    $= 1000\left(1 - e^{-0.45}\right) \approx 362$
  After 3 days, 362 students will have heard the rumor.

615

101. $F(t) = 1 - e^{-0.1t}$

a. $F(10) = 1 - e^{-0.1(10)} = 1 - e^{-1} \approx 0.632$

The probability that a car will arrive within 10 minutes of 12:00 PM is 0.632.

b. $F(40) = 1 - e^{-0.1(40)} = 1 - e^{-4} \approx 0.982$

The probability that a car will arrive within 40 minutes of 12:00 PM is 0.982.

c. As $t \to \infty$, $F(t) = 1 - e^{-0.1t} \to 1 - 0 = 1$

d. Graphing the function:

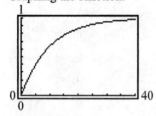

e. $F(7) \approx 0.50$, so about 7 minutes are needed for the probability to reach 50%.

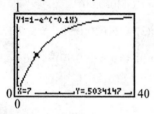

102. $F(t) = 1 - e^{-0.15t}$

a. $F(15) = 1 - e^{-0.15(15)} = 1 - e^{-2.25} \approx 0.895$

The probability that a car will arrive within 15 minutes of 5:00 PM is 0.895.

b. $F(30) = 1 - e^{-0.15(30)} = 1 - e^{-4.5} \approx 0.989$

The probability that a car will arrive within 30 minutes of 5:00 PM is 0.989.

c. As $t \to \infty$, $F(t) = 1 - e^{-0.15t} \to 1 - 0 = 1$

d. Graphing the function:

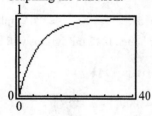

e. $F(6) \approx 0.60$, so 6 minutes are needed for the probability to reach 60%.

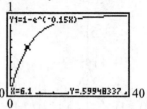

103. $P(x) = \dfrac{20^x e^{-20}}{x!}$

a. $P(15) = \dfrac{20^{15} e^{-20}}{15!} \approx 0.0516$ or 5.16%

The probability that 15 cars will arrive between 5:00 PM and 6:00 PM is 5.16%.

b. $P(20) = \dfrac{20^{20} e^{-20}}{20!} \approx 0.0888$ or 8.88%

The probability that 20 cars will arrive between 5:00 PM and 6:00 PM is 8.88%.

104. $P(x) = \dfrac{4^x e^{-4}}{x!}$

a. $P(5) = \dfrac{4^5 e^{-4}}{5!} \approx 0.1563$ or 15.63%

The probability that 5 people will arrive within the next minute is 15.63%.

b. $P(8) = \dfrac{4^8 e^{-4}}{8!} \approx 0.0298$ or 2.98%

The probability that 8 people will arrive within the next minute is 2.98%.

105. $R = 10^{\left(\frac{4221}{T+459.4} - \frac{4221}{D+459.4} + 2\right)}$

a. $R = 10^{\left(\frac{4221}{50+459.4} - \frac{4221}{41+459.4} + 2\right)} \approx 70.95\%$

b. $R = 10^{\left(\frac{4221}{68+459.4} - \frac{4221}{59+459.4} + 2\right)} \approx 72.62\%$

c. $R = 10^{\left(\frac{4221}{T+459.4} - \frac{4221}{T+459.4} + 2\right)} = 10^2 = 100\%$

106. $L(t) = 500\left(1 - e^{-0.0061\,t}\right)$

   a. $L(30) = 500\left(1 - e^{-0.0061(30)}\right)$

$$= 500\left(1 - e^{-0.183}\right)$$

$$\approx 84$$

   The student will learn about 84 words after 30 minutes.

   b. $L(60) = 500\left(1 - e^{-0.0061(60)}\right)$

$$= 500\left(1 - e^{-0.366}\right)$$

$$\approx 153$$

   The student will learn about 153 words after 60 minutes.

107. $I = \dfrac{E}{R}\left[1 - e^{-\left(\frac{R}{L}\right)t}\right]$

   a. $I_1 = \dfrac{120}{10}\left[1 - e^{-\left(\frac{10}{5}\right)0.3}\right] = 12\left[1 - e^{-0.6}\right] \approx 5.414$

   amperes after 0.3 second

$$I_1 = \dfrac{120}{10}\left[1 - e^{-\left(\frac{10}{5}\right)0.5}\right] = 12\left[1 - e^{-1}\right] \approx 7.585$$

   amperes after 0.5 second

$$I_1 = \dfrac{120}{10}\left[1 - e^{-\left(\frac{10}{5}\right)1}\right] = 12\left[1 - e^{-2}\right] \approx 10.376$$

   amperes after 1 second

   b. As $t \to \infty$, $e^{-\left(\frac{10}{5}\right)t} \to 0$. Therefore, as,

$$t \to \infty,\ I_1 = \dfrac{120}{10}\left[1 - e^{-\left(\frac{10}{5}\right)t}\right] \to 12[1 - 0] = 12,$$

   which means the maximum current is 12 amperes.

   c. See the graph at the bottom of the page.

   d. $I_2 = \dfrac{120}{5}\left[1 - e^{-\left(\frac{5}{10}\right)0.3}\right] = 24\left[1 - e^{-0.15}\right]$

$$\approx 3.343 \text{ amperes after 0.3 second}$$

$$I_2 = \dfrac{120}{5}\left[1 - e^{-\left(\frac{5}{10}\right)0.5}\right] = 24\left[1 - e^{-0.25}\right]$$

$$\approx 5.309 \text{ amperes after 0.5 second}$$

$$I_2 = \dfrac{120}{5}\left[1 - e^{-\left(\frac{5}{10}\right)1}\right] = 24\left[1 - e^{-0.5}\right]$$

$$\approx 9.443 \text{ amperes after 1 second}$$

   e. As $t \to \infty$, $e^{-\left(\frac{5}{10}\right)t} \to 0$. Therefore, as,

$$t \to \infty,\ I_1 = \dfrac{120}{5}\left[1 - e^{-\left(\frac{10}{5}\right)t}\right] \to 24[1 - 0] = 24,$$

   which means the maximum current is 24 amperes.

   f. See the graph at the bottom of the page.

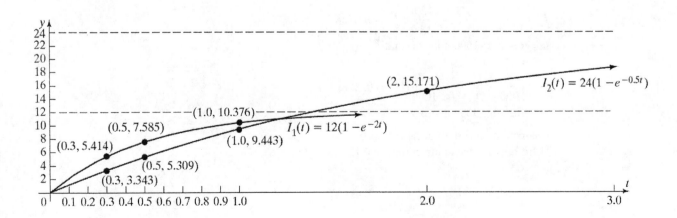

108. $I = \dfrac{E}{R} \cdot e^{\left(\frac{-t}{RC}\right)}$

a. $I_1 = \dfrac{120}{2000} \cdot e^{\left(\frac{-0}{2000 \cdot 1}\right)} = \dfrac{120}{2000} e^0 = 0.06$
amperes initially.

$I_1 = \dfrac{120}{2000} \cdot e^{\left(\frac{-1000}{2000 \cdot 1}\right)} = \dfrac{120}{2000} e^{-1/2} \approx 0.0364$
amperes after 1000 microseconds

$I_1 = \dfrac{120}{2000} \cdot e^{\left(\frac{-3000}{2000 \cdot 1}\right)} = \dfrac{120}{2000} e^{-1.5} \approx 0.0134$
amperes after 3000 microseconds

b. The maximum current occurs at $t = 0$.
Therefore, the maximum current is 0.06
amperes.

c. Graphing the function:

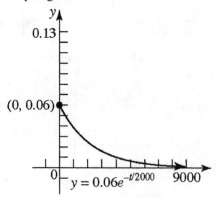

$y = 0.06e^{-t/2000}$

d. $I_2 = \dfrac{120}{1000} \cdot e^{\left(\frac{-0}{1000 \cdot 2}\right)} = \dfrac{120}{1000} e^0 = 0.12$
amperes initially.

$I_2 = \dfrac{120}{1000} \cdot e^{\left(\frac{-1000}{1000 \cdot 2}\right)} = \dfrac{120}{1000} e^{-1/2} \approx 0.0728$
amperes after 1000 microseconds

$I_2 = \dfrac{120}{1000} \cdot e^{\left(\frac{-3000}{1000 \cdot 2}\right)} = \dfrac{120}{1000} e^{-1.5} \approx 0.0268$
amperes after 3000 microseconds

e. The maximum current occurs at $t = 0$.
Therefore, the maximum current is 0.12
amperes.

f. Graphing the functions:

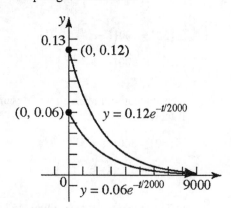

$y = 0.12e^{-t/2000}$

$y = 0.06e^{-t/2000}$

109. $2 + \dfrac{1}{2!} + \dfrac{1}{3!} + \dfrac{1}{4!} + \ldots + \dfrac{1}{n!}$

$n = 4; \quad 2 + \dfrac{1}{2!} + \dfrac{1}{3!} + \dfrac{1}{4!} \approx 2.7083$

$n = 6; \quad 2 + \dfrac{1}{2!} + \dfrac{1}{3!} + \dfrac{1}{4!} + \dfrac{1}{5!} + \dfrac{1}{6!} \approx 2.7181$

$n = 8; \quad 2 + \dfrac{1}{2!} + \dfrac{1}{3!} + \dfrac{1}{4!} + \dfrac{1}{5!} + \dfrac{1}{6!} + \dfrac{1}{7!} + \dfrac{1}{8!}$
≈ 2.7182788

$n = 10; \quad 2 + \dfrac{1}{2!} + \dfrac{1}{3!} + \dfrac{1}{4!} + \dfrac{1}{5!} + \dfrac{1}{6!} + \dfrac{1}{7!} + \dfrac{1}{8!} + \dfrac{1}{9!} + \dfrac{1}{10!}$
≈ 2.7182818

$e \approx 2.718281828$

110. $2 + 1 = 3$

$2 + \dfrac{1}{1+1} = 2.5$

$2 + \dfrac{1}{1 + \dfrac{1}{2+2}} = 2.8$

$2 + \dfrac{1}{1 + \dfrac{1}{2 + \dfrac{2}{3+3}}} = 2.7$

$2 + \dfrac{1}{1 + \dfrac{1}{2 + \dfrac{2}{3 + \dfrac{3}{4+4}}}} \approx 2.721649485$

618

$$\cfrac{2+1}{\cfrac{1+1}{\cfrac{2+2}{\cfrac{3+3}{\cfrac{4+4}{5+5}}}}} \approx 2.717770035$$

$$\cfrac{2+1}{\cfrac{1+1}{\cfrac{2+2}{\cfrac{3+3}{\cfrac{4+4}{\cfrac{5+5}{6+6}}}}}} \approx 2.718348855$$

$e \approx 2.718281828$

111. $f(x) = a^x$

$$\frac{f(x+h) - f(x)}{h} = \frac{a^{x+h} - a^x}{h}$$

$$= \frac{a^x a^h - a^x}{h}$$

$$= \frac{a^x \left(a^h - 1\right)}{h}$$

$$= a^x \left(\frac{a^h - 1}{h}\right)$$

112. $f(x) = a^x$

$$f(A+B) = a^{A+B} = a^A \cdot a^B = f(A) \cdot f(B)$$

113. $f(x) = a^x$

$$f(-x) = a^{-x} = \frac{1}{a^x} = \frac{1}{f(x)}$$

114. $f(x) = a^x$

$$f(\alpha x) = a^{\alpha x} = \left(a^x\right)^\alpha = [f(x)]^\alpha$$

115. $\sinh x = \dfrac{1}{2}\left(e^x - e^{-x}\right)$

   a. $f(-x) = \sinh(-x)$

$$= \frac{1}{2}\left(e^{-x} - e^x\right)$$

$$= -\frac{1}{2}\left(e^x - e^{-x}\right)$$

$$= -\sinh x$$

$$= -f(x)$$

Therefore, $f(x) = \sinh x$ is an odd function.

   b. Let $Y_1 = \dfrac{1}{2}\left(e^x - e^{-x}\right)$.

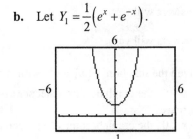

116. $\cosh x = \dfrac{1}{2}\left(e^x + e^{-x}\right)$

   a. $f(-x) = \cosh(-x)$

$$= \frac{1}{2}\left(e^{-x} + e^x\right)$$

$$= \frac{1}{2}\left(e^x + e^{-x}\right)$$

$$= \cosh x$$

$$= f(x)$$

Thus, $f(x) = \cosh x$ is an even function.

   b. Let $Y_1 = \dfrac{1}{2}\left(e^x + e^{-x}\right)$.

619

c. $(\cosh x)^2 - (\sinh x)^2$

$$= \left(\frac{e^x + e^{-x}}{2}\right)^2 - \left(\frac{e^x - e^{-x}}{2}\right)^2$$

$$= \frac{e^{2x} + 2 + e^{-2x}}{4} - \frac{e^{2x} - 2 + e^{-2x}}{4}$$

$$= \frac{e^{2x} + 2 + e^{-2x} - e^{2x} + 2 - e^{-2x}}{4}$$

$$= \frac{4}{4}$$

$$= 1$$

117. $f(x) = 2^{\left(2^x\right)} + 1$

$$f(1) = 2^{\left(2^1\right)} + 1 = 2^2 + 1 = 4 + 1 = 5$$

$$f(2) = 2^{\left(2^2\right)} + 1 = 2^4 + 1 = 16 + 1 = 17$$

$$f(3) = 2^{\left(2^3\right)} + 1 = 2^8 + 1 = 256 + 1 = 257$$

$$f(4) = 2^{\left(2^4\right)} + 1 = 2^{16} + 1 = 65,536 + 1 = 65,537$$

$$f(5) = 2^{\left(2^5\right)} + 1 = 2^{32} + 1 = 4,294,967,296 + 1$$
$$= 4,294,967,297$$
$$= 641 \times 6,700,417$$

118. Since the number of bacteria doubles every minute, half of the container is full one minute before it is full. Thus, it takes 59 minutes to fill the container.

119. Answers will vary.

120. Answers will vary.

121. Given the function $f(x) = a^x$, with $a > 1$,
If $x > 0$, the graph becomes steeper as a increases.
If $x < 0$, the graph becomes less steep as a increases.

122. Using the laws of exponents, we have:

$$a^{-x} = \frac{1}{a^x} = \left(\frac{1}{a}\right)^x. \text{ So } y = a^{-x} \text{ and }$$

$y = \left(\frac{1}{a}\right)^x$ will have the same graph.

Section 6.4

1. $3x - 7 \le 8 - 2x$
$5x \le 15$
$x \le 3$
The solution set is $\{x \mid x \le 3\}$.

2. $x^2 - x - 6 > 0$
We graph the function $f(x) = x^2 - x - 6$. The intercepts are
y-intercept: $f(0) = -6$
x-intercepts: $\quad x^2 - x - 6 = 0$
$$(x + 2)(x - 3) = 0$$
$$x = -2, x = 3$$
The vertex is at $x = \frac{-b}{2a} = \frac{-(-1)}{2(1)} = \frac{1}{2}$. Since
$f\left(\frac{1}{2}\right) = -\frac{25}{4}$, the vertex is $\left(\frac{1}{2}, -\frac{25}{4}\right)$.

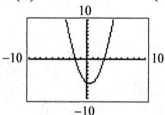

The graph is above the x-axis when $x < -2$ or $x > 3$. Since the inequality is strict, the solution set is $\{x \mid x < -2 \text{ or } x > 3\}$ or, using interval notation, $(-\infty, -2) \cup (3, \infty)$.

3. $\frac{x - 1}{x + 4} > 0$

$$f(x) = \frac{x - 1}{x + 4}$$

f is zero or undefined when $x = 1$ or $x = -4$.

Interval	$(-\infty, -4)$	$(-4, 1)$	$(1, \infty)$
Test Value	-5	0	2
Value of f	6	$-\dfrac{1}{4}$	$\dfrac{1}{6}$
Conclusion	positive	negative	positive

The solution set is $\{x \mid x < -4 \text{ or } x > 1\}$ or, using interval notation, $(-\infty, -4) \cup (1, \infty)$.

4. $\{x \mid x > 0\}$ or $(0, \infty)$

5. $\left(\dfrac{1}{a}, -1\right)$, $(1, 0)$, $(a, 1)$

6. 1

7. False. If $y = \log_a x$, then $x = a^y$.

8. True

9. $9 = 3^2$ is equivalent to $2 = \log_3 9$.

10. $16 = 4^2$ is equivalent to $2 = \log_4 16$.

11. $a^2 = 1.6$ is equivalent to $2 = \log_a 1.6$.

12. $a^3 = 2.1$ is equivalent to $3 = \log_a 2.1$.

13. $2^x = 7.2$ is equivalent to $x = \log_2 7.2$.

14. $3^x = 4.6$ is equivalent to $x = \log_3 4.6$.

15. $e^x = 8$ is equivalent to $x = \ln 8$.

16. $e^{2.2} = M$ is equivalent to $2.2 = \ln M$.

17. $\log_2 8 = 3$ is equivalent to $2^3 = 8$.

18. $\log_3\left(\dfrac{1}{9}\right) = -2$ is equivalent to $3^{-2} = \dfrac{1}{9}$.

19. $\log_a 3 = 6$ is equivalent to $a^6 = 3$.

20. $\log_b 4 = 2$ is equivalent to $b^2 = 4$.

21. $\log_3 2 = x$ is equivalent to $3^x = 2$.

22. $\log_2 6 = x$ is equivalent to $2^x = 6$.

23. $\ln 4 = x$ is equivalent to $e^x = 4$.

24. $\ln x = 4$ is equivalent to $e^4 = x$.

25. $\log_2 1 = 0$ since $2^0 = 1$.

26. $\log_8 8 = 1$ since $8^1 = 8$.

27. $\log_5 25 = 2$ since $5^2 = 25$.

28. $\log_3\left(\dfrac{1}{9}\right) = -2$ since $3^{-2} = \dfrac{1}{9}$.

29. $\log_{1/2} 16 = -4$ since $\left(\dfrac{1}{2}\right)^{-4} = 2^4 = 16$.

30. $\log_{1/3} 9 = -2$ since $\left(\dfrac{1}{3}\right)^{-2} = 3^2 = 9$.

31. $\log_{10} \sqrt{10} = \dfrac{1}{2}$ since $10^{1/2} = \sqrt{10}$.

32. $\log_5 \sqrt[3]{25} = \dfrac{2}{3}$ since $5^{2/3} = 25^{1/3} = \sqrt[3]{25}$.

33. $\log_{\sqrt{2}} 4 = 4$ since $\left(\sqrt{2}\right)^4 = 4$.

34. $\log_{\sqrt{3}} 9 = 4$ since $\left(\sqrt{3}\right)^4 = 9$.

35. $\ln \sqrt{e} = \dfrac{1}{2}$ since $e^{1/2} = \sqrt{e}$.

36. $\ln e^3 = 3$ since $e^3 = e^3$.

37. $f(x) = \ln(x - 3)$ requires $x - 3 > 0$.
$$x - 3 > 0$$
$$x > 3$$
The domain of f is $\{x \mid x > 3\}$ or $(3, \infty)$.

38. $g(x) = \ln(x - 1)$ requires $x - 1 > 0$.
$$x - 1 > 0$$
$$x > 1$$
The domain of g is $\{x \mid x > 1\}$ or $(1, \infty)$.

39. $F(x) = \log_2 x^2$ requires $x^2 > 0$.
$$x^2 > 0 \text{ for all } x \neq 0.$$
The domain of F is $\{x \mid x \neq 0\}$.

40. $H(x) = \log_5 x^3$ requires $x^3 > 0$.
$$x^3 > 0 \text{ for all } x > 0.$$
The domain of H is $\{x \mid x > 0\}$ or $(0, \infty)$.

41. $f(x) = 3 - 2\log_4\left[\frac{x}{2} - 5\right]$ requires $\frac{x}{2} - 5 > 0$.

$$\frac{x}{2} - 5 > 0$$
$$\frac{x}{2} > 5$$
$$x > 10$$

The domain of f is $\{x \mid x > 10\}$ or $(10, \infty)$.

42. $g(x) = 8 + 5\ln(2x + 3)$ requires $2x + 3 > 0$.

$$2x + 3 > 0$$
$$2x > -3$$
$$x > -\frac{3}{2}$$

The domain of g is $\left\{x \mid x > -\frac{3}{2}\right\}$ or $\left(-\frac{3}{2}, \infty\right)$.

43. $f(x) = \ln\left(\frac{1}{x+1}\right)$ requires $\frac{1}{x+1} > 0$.

$p(x) = \frac{1}{x+1}$ is undefined when $x = -1$.

Interval	$(-\infty, -1)$	$(-1, \infty)$
Test Value	-2	0
Value of p	-1	1
Conclusion	negative	positive

The domain of f is $\{x \mid x > -1\}$ or $(-1, \infty)$.

44. $g(x) = \ln\left(\frac{1}{x-5}\right)$ requires $\frac{1}{x-5} > 0$.

$p(x) = \frac{1}{x-5}$ is undefined when $x = 5$.

Interval	$(-\infty, 5)$	$(5, \infty)$
Test Value	4	6
Value of p	-1	1
Conclusion	negative	positive

The domain of g is $\{x \mid x > 5\}$ or $(5, \infty)$.

45. $g(x) = \log_5\left(\frac{x+1}{x}\right)$ requires $\frac{x+1}{x} > 0$.

$p(x) = \frac{x+1}{x}$ is zero or undefined when $x = -1$ or $x = 0$.

Interval	$(-\infty, -1)$	$(-1, 0)$	$(0, \infty)$
Test Value	-2	$-\frac{1}{2}$	1
Value of p	$\frac{1}{2}$	-1	2
Conclusion	positive	negative	positive

The domain of g is $\{x \mid x < -1 \text{ or } x > 0\}$; $(-\infty, -1) \cup (0, \infty)$.

46. $h(x) = \log_3\left(\frac{x}{x-1}\right)$ requires $\frac{x}{x-1} > 0$.

$p(x) = \frac{x}{x-1}$ is zero or undefined when $x = 0$ or $x = 1$.

Interval	$(-\infty, 0)$	$(0, 1)$	$(1, \infty)$
Test Value	-1	$-\frac{1}{2}$	2
Value of p	$\frac{1}{2}$	-1	2
Conclusion	positive	negative	positive

The domain of h is $\{x \mid x < 0 \text{ or } x > 1\}$; $(-\infty, 0) \cup (1, \infty)$.

47. $f(x) = \sqrt{\ln x}$ requires $\ln x \geq 0$ and $x > 0$

$$\ln x \geq 0$$
$$x \geq e^0$$
$$x \geq 1$$

The domain of h is $\{x \mid x \geq 1\}$ or $[1, \infty)$.

48. $g(x) = \frac{1}{\ln x}$ requires $\ln x \neq 0$ and $x > 0$

$$\ln x \neq 0$$
$$x \neq e^0$$
$$x \neq 1$$

The domain of h is $\{x \mid x > 0 \text{ and } x \neq 1\}$; $(0, 1)$ or $(1, \infty)$.

49. $\ln\left(\frac{5}{3}\right) \approx 0.511$

50. $\frac{\ln(5)}{3} \approx 0.536$

51. $\dfrac{\ln\dfrac{10}{3}}{0.04} \approx 30.099$

52. $\dfrac{\ln\dfrac{2}{3}}{-0.1} \approx 4.055$

53. $\dfrac{\ln 4 + \ln 2}{\log 4 + \log 2} \approx 2.303$

54. $\dfrac{\log 15 + \log 20}{\ln 15 + \ln 20} \approx 0.434$

55. $\dfrac{2\ln 5 + \log 50}{\log 4 - \ln 2} \approx -53.991$

56. $\dfrac{3\log 80 - \ln 5}{\log 5 + \ln 20} \approx 1.110$

57. If the graph of $f(x) = \log_a x$ contains the point $(2, 2)$, then $f(2) = \log_a 2 = 2$. Thus,
$$\log_a 2 = 2$$
$$a^2 = 2$$
$$a = \pm\sqrt{2}$$
Since the base a must be positive by definition, we have that $a = \sqrt{2}$.

58. If the graph of $f(x) = \log_a x$ contains the point $\left(\dfrac{1}{2}, -4\right)$, then $f\left(\dfrac{1}{2}\right) = \log_a\left(\dfrac{1}{2}\right) = -4$. Thus,
$$\log_a\left(\dfrac{1}{2}\right) = -4$$
$$a^{-4} = \dfrac{1}{2}$$
$$\dfrac{1}{a^4} = \dfrac{1}{2}$$
$$a^4 = 2$$
$$a = 2^{1/4} \approx 1.189$$

59.

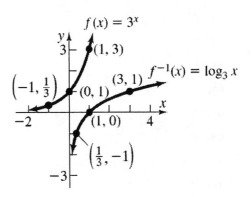

60.

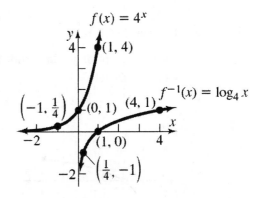

61.

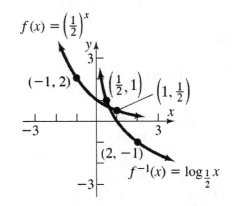

62.

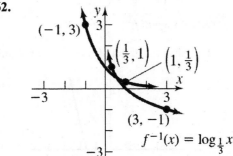

623

63. B

64. F

65. D

66. H

67. A

68. C

69. E

70. G

71. $f(x) = \ln(x+4)$

   a. Domain: $(-4, \infty)$

   b. Using the graph of $y = \ln x$, shift the graph 4 units to the left.

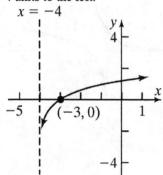

   c. Range: $(-\infty, \infty)$

      Vertical Asymptote: $x = -4$

   d. $\quad f(x) = \ln(x+4)$

$$y = \ln(x+4)$$
$$x = \ln(y+4) \quad \text{Inverse}$$
$$y + 4 = e^x$$
$$y = e^x - 4$$
$$f^{-1}(x) = e^x - 4$$

   e. Range of f: $(-\infty, \infty)$

   f. Shift the graph of $y = e^x$ down 4 units.

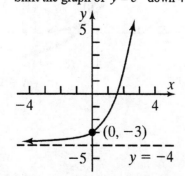

72. $f(x) = \ln(x-3)$

   a. Domain: $(3, \infty)$

   b. Using the graph of $y = \ln x$, shift the graph 3 units to the right.

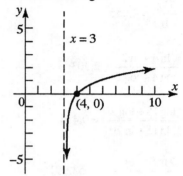

   c. Range: $(-\infty, \infty)$

      Vertical Asymptote: $x = 3$

   d. $\quad f(x) = \ln(x-3)$

$$y = \ln(x-3)$$
$$x = \ln(y-3) \quad \text{Inverse}$$
$$y - 3 = e^x$$
$$y = e^x + 3$$
$$f^{-1}(x) = e^x + 3$$

   e. Range of f: $(-\infty, \infty)$

   f. Using the graph of $y = e^x$, shift the graph 3 units up.

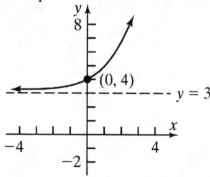

73. $f(x) = 2 + \ln x$

   a. Domain: $(0, \infty)$

   b. Using the graph of $y = \ln x$, shift up 2 units.

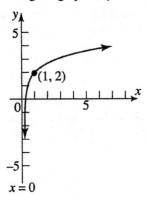

   c. Range: $(-\infty, \infty)$

      Vertical Asymptote: $x = 0$

   d.
$$f(x) = 2 + \ln x$$
$$y = 2 + \ln x$$
$$x = 2 + \ln y \quad \text{Inverse}$$
$$x - 2 = \ln y$$
$$y = e^{x-2}$$
$$f^{-1}(x) = e^{x-2}$$

   e. Range of f: $(-\infty, \infty)$

   f. Using the graph of $y = e^x$, shift the graph 2 units to the right.

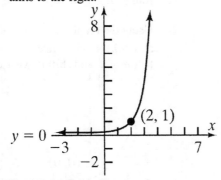

74. $f(x) = -\ln(-x)$

   a. Domain: $(-\infty, 0)$

   b. Using the graph of $y = \ln x$, reflect the graph about the y-axis, and reflect about the x-axis.

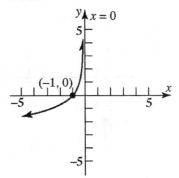

   c. Range: $(-\infty, \infty)$

      Vertical Asymptote: $x = 0$

   d.
$$f(x) = -\ln(-x)$$
$$y = -\ln(-x)$$
$$x = -\ln(-y) \quad \text{Inverse}$$
$$-x = \ln(-y)$$
$$-y = e^{-x}$$
$$y = -e^{-x}$$
$$f^{-1}(x) = -e^{-x}$$

   e. Range of f: $(-\infty, \infty)$

   f. Using the graph of $y = e^x$, reflect the graph about the y-axis, and reflect about the x-axis.

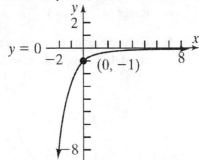

75. $f(x) = \ln(2x) - 3$

   a. Domain: $(0, \infty)$

   b. Using the graph of $y = \ln x$, compress the graph horizontally by a factor of $\frac{1}{2}$, and shift down 3 units.

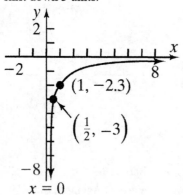

   c. Range: $(-\infty, \infty)$

      Vertical Asymptote: $x = 0$

   d. $\quad f(x) = \ln(2x) - 3$

$$y = \ln(2x) - 3$$
$$x = \ln(2y) - 3 \quad \text{Inverse}$$
$$x + 3 = \ln(2y)$$
$$2y = e^{x+3}$$
$$y = \frac{1}{2}e^{x+3}$$
$$f^{-1}(x) = \frac{1}{2}e^{x+3}$$

   e. Range of f: $(-\infty, \infty)$

   f. Using the graph of $y = e^x$, reflect the graph about the y-axis, and reflect about the x-axis.

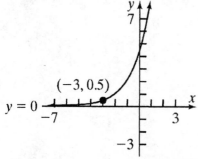

76. $f(x) = -2\ln(x + 1)$

   a. Domain: $(-1, \infty)$

   b. Using the graph of $y = \ln x$, shift the graph to the left 1 unit, reflect about the x-axis and stretch vertically by a factor of 2.

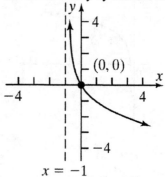

   c. Range: $(-\infty, \infty)$

      Vertical Asymptote: $x = -1$

   d. $\quad f(x) = -2\ln(x + 1)$

$$y = -2\ln(x + 1)$$
$$x = -2\ln(y + 1) \quad \text{Inverse}$$
$$-\frac{x}{2} = \ln(y + 1)$$
$$y + 1 = e^{-x/2}$$
$$y = e^{-x/2} - 1$$
$$f^{-1}(x) = e^{-x/2} - 1$$

   e. Range of f: $(-\infty, \infty)$

   f. Using the graph of $y = e^x$, reflect the graph about the y-axis, stretch horizontally by a factor of 2, and shift down 1 unit.

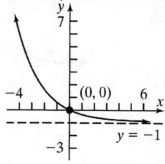

77. $f(x) = \log(x-4) + 2$

   a. Domain: $(4, \infty)$

   b. Using the graph of $y = \log x$, shift the graph 4 units to the right and 2 units up.

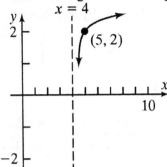

   c. Range: $(-\infty, \infty)$

      Vertical Asymptote: $x = 4$

   d.
$$f(x) = \log(x-4) + 2$$
$$y = \log(x-4) + 2$$
$$x = \log(y-4) + 2 \quad \text{Inverse}$$
$$x - 2 = \log(y-4)$$
$$y - 4 = 10^{x-2}$$
$$y = 10^{x-2} + 4$$
$$f^{-1}(x) = 10^{x-2} + 4$$

   e. Range of f: $(-\infty, \infty)$

   f. Using the graph of $y = 10^x$, shift the graph 2 units to the right and 4 units up.

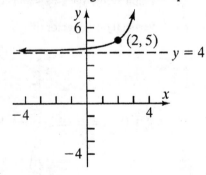

78. $f(x) = \dfrac{1}{2}\log x - 5$

   a. Domain: $(0, \infty)$

   b. Using the graph of $y = \log x$, compress the graph vertically by a factor of $\dfrac{1}{2}$, and shift it 5 units down.

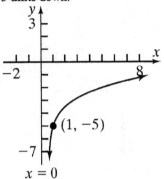

   c. Range: $(-\infty, \infty)$

      Vertical Asymptote: $x = 0$

   d.
$$f(x) = \frac{1}{2}\log x - 5$$
$$y = \frac{1}{2}\log x - 5$$
$$x = \frac{1}{2}\log y - 5 \quad \text{Inverse}$$
$$x + 5 = \frac{1}{2}\log y$$
$$2(x+5) = \log y$$
$$y = 10^{2(x+5)}$$
$$f^{-1}(x) = 10^{2(x+5)}$$

   e. Range of f: $(-\infty, \infty)$

   f. Using the graph of $y = 10^x$, shift the graph 5 units to the left, and compress horizontally by a factor of $\dfrac{1}{2}$.

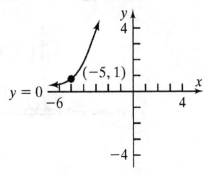

79. $f(x) = \frac{1}{2}\log(2x)$

   a. Domain: $(0, \infty)$

   b. Using the graph of $y = \log x$, compress the graph horizontally by a factor of $\frac{1}{2}$, and compress vertically by a factor of $\frac{1}{2}$.

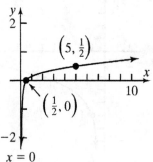

   c. Range: $(-\infty, \infty)$

      Vertical Asymptote: $x = 0$

   d. $f(x) = \frac{1}{2}\log(2x)$

$$y = \frac{1}{2}\log(2x)$$

$$x = \frac{1}{2}\log(2y) \quad \text{Inverse}$$

$$2x = \log(2y)$$

$$2y = 10^{2x}$$

$$y = \frac{1}{2} \cdot 10^{2x}$$

$$f^{-1}(x) = \frac{1}{2} \cdot 10^{2x}$$

   e. Range of f: $(-\infty, \infty)$

   f. Using the graph of $y = 10^x$, compress the graph horizontally by a factor of $\frac{1}{2}$, and compress vertically by a factor of $\frac{1}{2}$.

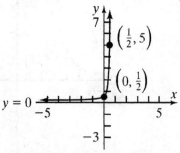

80. $f(x) = \log(-2x)$

   a. Domain: $(-\infty, 0)$

   b. Using the graph of $y = \log x$, reflect the graph across the y-axis and compress horizontally by a factor of $\frac{1}{2}$.

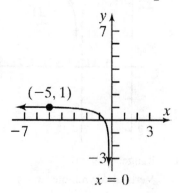

   c. Range: $(-\infty, \infty)$

      Vertical Asymptote: $x = 0$

   d. $f(x) = \log(-2x)$

$$y = \log(-2x)$$

$$x = \log(-2y) \quad \text{Inverse}$$

$$-2y = 10^x$$

$$f^{-1}(x) = -\frac{1}{2} \cdot 10^x$$

   e. Range of f: $(-\infty, \infty)$

   f. Using the graph of $y = 10^x$, reflect the graph across the x-axis and compress vertically by a factor of $\frac{1}{2}$.

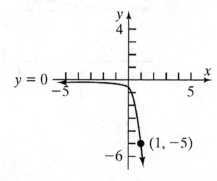

81. $f(x) = 3 + \log_3(x+2)$

   a. Domain: $(-2, \infty)$

   b. Using the graph of $y = \log_3 x$, shift 2 units to the left, and shift up 3 units.

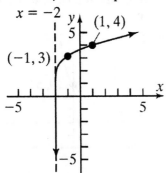

   c. Range: $(-\infty, \infty)$
       Vertical Asymptote: $x = -2$

   d.
$$f(x) = 3 + \log_3(x+2)$$
$$y = 3 + \log_3(x+2)$$
$$x = 3 + \log_3(y+2) \quad \text{Inverse}$$
$$x - 3 = \log_3(y+2)$$
$$y + 2 = 3^{x-3}$$
$$y = 3^{x-3} - 2$$
$$f^{-1}(x) = 3^{x-3} - 2$$

   e. Range of f: $(-\infty, \infty)$

   f. Using the graph of $y = 3^x$, shift 3 units to the right, and shift down 2 units.

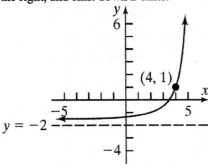

82. $f(x) = 2 - \log_3(x+1)$

   a. Domain: $(-1, \infty)$

   b. Using the graph of $y = \log_3 x$, shift 1 unit to the left, reflect the graph about the x-axis, and shift 2 units up.

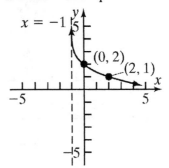

   c. Range: $(-\infty, \infty)$
       Vertical Asymptote: $x = -1$

   d.
$$f(x) = 2 - \log_3(x+1)$$
$$y = 2 - \log_3(x+1)$$
$$x = 2 - \log_3(y+1) \quad \text{Inverse}$$
$$x - 2 = -\log_3(y+1)$$
$$2 - x = \log_3(y+1)$$
$$y + 1 = 3^{2-x}$$
$$y = 3^{2-x} - 1$$
$$f^{-1}(x) = 3^{2-x} - 1$$

   e. Range of f: $(-\infty, \infty)$

   f. Using the graph of $y = 3^x$, reflect the graph about the y-axis, shift 2 units to the right, and shift down 1 unit.

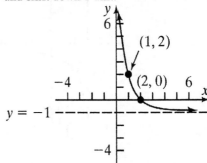

629

83. $f(x) = e^{x+2} - 3$

    a. Domain: $(-\infty, \infty)$

    b. Using the graph of $y = e^x$, shift the graph two units to the left, and shift 3 units down.

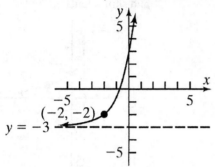

    c. Range: $(-3, \infty)$

    Horizontal Asymptote: $y = -3$

    d. $f(x) = e^{x+2} - 3$

         $y = e^{x+2} - 3$

         $x = e^{y+2} - 3$ Inverse

         $x + 3 = e^{y+2}$

         $y + 2 = \ln(x+3)$

         $y = \ln(x+3) - 2$

        $f^{-1}(x) = \ln(x+3) - 2$

    e. Range of f: $(-3, \infty)$

    f. Using the graph of $y = \ln x$, shift 3 units to the left, and shift down 2 units.

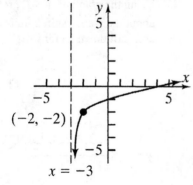

84. $f(x) = 3e^x + 2$

    a. Domain: $(-\infty, \infty)$

    b. Using the graph of $y = e^x$, stretch the graph vertically by a factor of 3, and shift 2 units up.

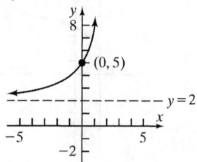

    c. Range: $(2, \infty)$

    Horizontal Asymptote: $y = 2$

    d. $f(x) = 3e^x + 2$

         $y = 3e^x + 2$

         $x = 3e^y + 2$ Inverse

         $x - 2 = 3e^y$

         $\dfrac{x-2}{3} = e^y$

         $y = \ln\left(\dfrac{x-2}{3}\right)$

       $f^{-1}(x) = \ln\left(\dfrac{x-2}{3}\right)$

    e. Range of f: $(2, \infty)$

    f. Using the graph of $y = \ln x$, shift 3 units to the left, and shift down 2 units.

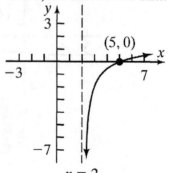

630

85. $f(x) = 2^{x/3} + 4$

   a. Domain: $(-\infty, \infty)$

   b. Using the graph of $y = 2^x$, stretch the graph horizontally by a factor of 3, and shift 4 units up.

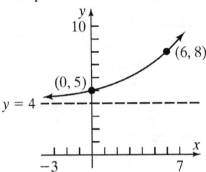

   c. Range: $(4, \infty)$

      Horizontal Asymptote: $y = 4$

   d.
$$f(x) = 2^{x/3} + 4$$
$$y = 2^{x/3} + 4$$
$$x = 2^{y/3} + 4 \quad \text{Inverse}$$
$$x - 4 = 2^{y/3}$$
$$\frac{y}{3} = \log_2(x - 4)$$
$$y = 3\log_2(x - 4)$$
$$f^{-1}(x) = 3\log_2(x - 4)$$

   e. Range of f: $(4, \infty)$

   f. Using the graph of $y = \log_2 x$, shift 4 units to the right, and stretch vertically by a factor of 3.

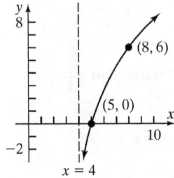

86. $f(x) = -3^{x+1}$

   a. Domain: $(-\infty, \infty)$

   b. Using the graph of $y = 3^x$, shift the graph to the left 1 unit, and reflect about the x-axis.

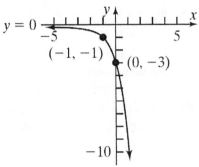

   c. Range: $(-\infty, 0)$

      Horizontal Asymptote: $y = 0$

   d.
$$f(x) = -3^{x+1}$$
$$y = -3^{x+1}$$
$$x = -3^{y+1} \quad \text{Inverse}$$
$$-x = 3^{y+1}$$
$$y + 1 = \log_3(-x)$$
$$y = \log_3(-x) - 1$$
$$f^{-1}(x) = \log_3(-x) - 1$$

   e. Range of f: $(-\infty, 0)$

   f. Using the graph of $y = \log_3 x$, reflect the graph across the y-axis, and shift down 1 unit.

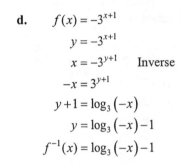

87. $\log_3 x = 2$

$x = 3^2$

$x = 9$

The solution set is $\{9\}$.

88. $\log_5 x = 3$

$x = 5^3$

$x = 125$

The solution set is $\{125\}$.

89. $\log_2(2x+1) = 3$

$2x+1 = 2^3$

$2x+1 = 8$

$2x = 7$

$x = \dfrac{7}{2}$

The solution set is $\left\{\dfrac{7}{2}\right\}$.

90. $\log_3(3x-2) = 2$

$3x-2 = 3^2$

$3x-2 = 9$

$3x = 11$

$x = \dfrac{11}{3}$

The solution set is $\left\{\dfrac{11}{3}\right\}$.

91. $\log_x 4 = 2$

$x^2 = 4$

$x = 2 \quad (x \neq -2,\ \text{base is positive})$

The solution set is $\{2\}$.

92. $\log_x\left(\dfrac{1}{8}\right) = 3$

$x^3 = \dfrac{1}{8}$

$x = \dfrac{1}{2}$

The solution set is $\left\{\dfrac{1}{2}\right\}$.

93. $\ln e^x = 5$

$e^x = e^5$

$x = 5$

The solution set is $\{5\}$.

94. $\ln e^{-2x} = 8$

$e^{-2x} = e^8$

$-2x = 8$

$x = -4$

The solution set is $\{-4\}$.

95. $\log_4 64 = x$

$4^x = 64$

$4^x = 4^3$

$x = 3$

The solution set is $\{3\}$.

96. $\log_5 625 = x$

$5^x = 625$

$5^x = 5^4$

$x = 4$

The solution set is $\{4\}$.

97. $\log_3 243 = 2x+1$

$3^{2x+1} = 243$

$3^{2x+1} = 3^5$

$2x+1 = 5$

$2x = 4$

$x = 2$

The solution set is $\{2\}$.

98. $\log_6 36 = 5x+3$

$6^{5x+3} = 36$

$6^{5x+3} = 6^2$

$5x+3 = 2$

$5x = -1$

$x = -\dfrac{1}{5}$

The solution set is $\left\{-\dfrac{1}{5}\right\}$.

99. $e^{3x} = 10$

$3x = \ln 10$

$x = \dfrac{\ln 10}{3}$

The solution set is $\left\{\dfrac{\ln 10}{3}\right\}$.

100. $e^{-2x} = \dfrac{1}{3}$

$-2x = \ln\left(\dfrac{1}{3}\right)$

$-2x = \ln\left(3^{-1}\right)$

$-2x = -\ln 3$

$2x = \ln 3$

$x = \dfrac{\ln 3}{2}$

The solution set is $\left\{\dfrac{\ln 3}{2}\right\}$.

101. $e^{2x+5} = 8$

$2x + 5 = \ln 8$

$2x = -5 + \ln 8$

$x = \dfrac{-5 + \ln 8}{2}$

The solution set is $\left\{\dfrac{-5 + \ln 8}{2}\right\}$.

102. $e^{-2x+1} = 13$

$-2x + 1 = \ln 13$

$-2x = -1 + \ln 13$

$x = \dfrac{-1 + \ln 13}{-2} = \dfrac{1 - \ln 13}{2}$

The solution set is $\left\{\dfrac{1 - \ln 13}{2}\right\}$.

103. $\log_3\left(x^2 + 1\right) = 2$

$x^2 + 1 = 3^2$

$x^2 + 1 = 9$

$x^2 = 8$

$x = \pm\sqrt{8} = \pm 2\sqrt{2}$

The solution set is $\left\{-2\sqrt{2},\ 2\sqrt{2}\right\}$.

104. $\log_5\left(x^2 + x + 4\right) = 2$

$x^2 + x + 4 = 5^2$

$x^2 + x + 4 = 25$

$x^2 + x - 21 = 0$

$x = \dfrac{-1 \pm \sqrt{1^2 - 4(1)(-21)}}{2(1)} = \dfrac{-1 \pm \sqrt{85}}{2}$

The solution set is $\left\{\dfrac{-1 - \sqrt{85}}{2},\ \dfrac{-1 + \sqrt{85}}{2}\right\}$.

105. $\log_2 8^x = -3$

$8^x = 2^{-3}$

$\left(2^3\right)^x = 2^{-3}$

$2^{3x} = 2^{-3}$

$3x = -3$

$x = -1$

The solution set is $\{-1\}$.

106. $\log_3 3^x = -1$

$3^x = 3^{-1}$

$x = -1$

The solution set is $\{-1\}$.

107. $5e^{0.2x} = 7$

$e^{0.2x} = \dfrac{7}{5}$

$0.2x = \ln\dfrac{7}{5}$

$5(0.2x) = 5\left(\ln\dfrac{7}{5}\right)$

$x = 5\ln\dfrac{7}{5}$

The solution set is $\left\{5\ln\dfrac{7}{5}\right\}$.

108. $8 \cdot 10^{2x-7} = 3$

$10^{2x-7} = \dfrac{3}{8}$

$2x - 7 = \log\dfrac{3}{8}$

$2x = 7 + \log\dfrac{3}{8}$

$x = \dfrac{1}{2}\left(7 + \log\dfrac{3}{8}\right)$

The solution set is $\left\{\dfrac{1}{2}\left(7 + \log\dfrac{3}{8}\right)\right\}$.

109. $2 \cdot 10^{2-x} = 5$

$$10^{2-x} = \frac{5}{2}$$

$$2 - x = \log \frac{5}{2}$$

$$-x = -2 + \log \frac{5}{2}$$

$$x = 2 - \log \frac{5}{2}$$

The solution set is $\left\{ 2 - \log \frac{5}{2} \right\}$.

110. $4e^{x+1} = 5$

$$e^{x+1} = \frac{5}{4}$$

$$x + 1 = \ln \frac{5}{4}$$

$$x = -1 + \ln \frac{5}{4}$$

The solution set is $\left\{ -1 + \ln \frac{5}{4} \right\}$.

111. a. $G(x) = \log_3 (2x+1)$

We require that $2x+1$ be positive.
$$2x + 1 > 0$$
$$2x > -1$$
$$x > -\frac{1}{2}$$

Domain: $\left\{ x \mid x > -\frac{1}{2} \right\}$ or $\left(-\frac{1}{2}, \infty \right)$

b. $G(40) = \log_3 (2 \cdot 40 + 1)$
$$= \log_3 81$$
$$= 4$$
The point $(40, 4)$ is on the graph of G.

c. $G(x) = 2$
$$\log_3 (2x+1) = 2$$
$$2x + 1 = 3^2$$
$$2x + 1 = 9$$
$$2x = 8$$
$$x = 4$$
The point $(4, 2)$ is on the graph of G.

112. a. $F(x) = \log_2 (x+1) - 3$

We require that $x+1$ be positive.
$$x + 1 > 0$$
$$x > -1$$
Domain: $\{ x \mid x > -1 \}$ or $(-1, \infty)$

b. $F(7) = \log_2 (7+1) - 3$
$$= \log_2 (8) - 3$$
$$= 3 - 3$$
$$= 0$$
The point $(7, 0)$ is on the graph of F.

c. $F(x) = -1$
$$\log_2 (x+1) - 3 = -1$$
$$\log_2 (x+1) = 2$$
$$x + 1 = 2^2$$
$$x + 1 = 4$$
$$x = 3$$
The point $(3, -1)$ is on the graph of F.

113. $f(x) = \begin{cases} \ln(-x) & \text{if } x < 0 \\ \ln x & \text{if } x > 0 \end{cases}$

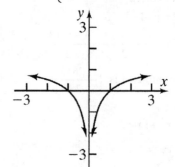

Domain: $\{ x \mid x \neq 0 \}$

Range: $(-\infty, \infty)$

Intercepts: $(-1, 0)$, $(1, 0)$

114. $f(x) = \begin{cases} \ln(-x) & \text{if } x \le -1 \\ -\ln(-x) & \text{if } -1 < x < 0 \end{cases}$

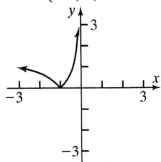

Domain: $\{x \mid x < 0\}$; $(-\infty, 0)$

Range: $\{y \mid y \ge 0\}$; $[-, \infty)$

Intercept: $(-1, 0)$

115. $f(x) = \begin{cases} -\ln x & \text{if } 0 < x < 1 \\ \ln x & \text{if } x \ge 1 \end{cases}$

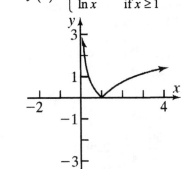

Domain: $\{x \mid x > 0\}$; $(0, \infty)$

Range: $\{y \mid y \ge 0\}$; $[0, \infty)$

Intercept: $(1, 0)$

116. $f(x) = \begin{cases} \ln x & \text{if } 0 < x < 1 \\ -\ln x & \text{if } x \ge 1 \end{cases}$

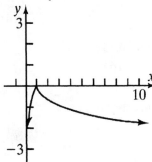

Domain: $\{x \mid x > 0\}$; $(0, \infty)$

Range: $\{y \mid y \le 0\}$; $(-\infty, 0]$

Intercept: $(1, 0)$

117. $\text{pH} = -\log_{10}\left[\text{H}^+\right]$

a. $\text{pH} = -\log_{10}\left[0.1\right] = -(-1) = 1$

b. $\text{pH} = -\log_{10}\left[0.01\right] = -(-2) = 2$

c. $\text{pH} = -\log_{10}\left[0.001\right] = -(-3) = 3$

d. As the H^+ decreases, the pH increases.

e. $3.5 = -\log_{10}\left[\text{H}^+\right]$

$-3.5 = \log_{10}\left[\text{H}^+\right]$

$\left[\text{H}^+\right] = 10^{-3.5}$

$\approx 3.16 \times 10^{-4}$

$= 0.000316$

f. $7.4 = -\log_{10}\left[\text{H}^+\right]$

$-7.4 = \log_{10}\left[\text{H}^+\right]$

$\left[\text{H}^+\right] = 10^{-7.4}$

$\approx 3.981 \times 10^{-8}$

$= 0.00000003981$

118. $H = -\left(p_1 \log p_1 + p_2 \log p_2 + \cdots + p_n \log p_n\right)$

$= -p_1 \log p_1 - p_2 \log p_2 - \cdots - p_n \log p_n$

a. $H = -0.014\log(0.014) - 0.041\log(0.041)$

$\qquad - 0.124\log(0.124) - 0.128\log(0.128)$

$\qquad - 0.003\log(0.003) - 0.690\log(0.690)$

≈ 0.4283

b. $H_{\max} = \log(6) \approx 0.7782$

c. $E = \dfrac{H}{H_{\max}} \approx 0.5504$

119. $p = 760e^{-0.145h}$

a. $320 = 760e^{-0.145h}$

$\dfrac{320}{760} = e^{-0.145h}$

$\ln\left(\dfrac{320}{760}\right) = -0.145h$

$h = \dfrac{\ln\left(\dfrac{320}{760}\right)}{-0.145} \approx 5.97$

Approximately 5.97 kilometers.

b. $667 = 760e^{-0.145h}$

$$\frac{667}{760} = e^{-0.145h}$$

$$\ln\left(\frac{667}{760}\right) = -0.145h$$

$$h = \frac{\ln\left(\frac{667}{760}\right)}{-0.145} \approx 0.90$$

Approximately 0.90 kilometers.

120. $A = A_0 e^{-0.35n}$

a. $50 = 100e^{-0.35n}$

$$0.5 = e^{-0.35n}$$

$$\ln(0.5) = -0.35n$$

$$t = \frac{\ln(0.5)}{-0.35} \approx 1.98$$

Approximately 2 days.

b. $10 = 100e^{-0.35n}$

$$0.1 = e^{-0.35n}$$

$$\ln(0.1) = -0.35n$$

$$t = \frac{\ln(0.1)}{-0.35} \approx 6.58$$

About 6.58 days, or 6 days and 14 hours.

121. $F(t) = 1 - e^{-0.1t}$

a. $0.5 = 1 - e^{-0.1t}$

$$-0.5 = -e^{-0.1t}$$

$$0.5 = e^{-0.1t}$$

$$\ln(0.5) = -0.1t$$

$$t = \frac{\ln(0.5)}{-0.1} \approx 6.93$$

Approximately 6.93 minutes.

b. $0.8 = 1 - e^{-0.1t}$

$$-0.2 = -e^{-0.1t}$$

$$0.2 = e^{-0.1t}$$

$$\ln(0.2) = -0.1t$$

$$t = \frac{\ln(0.2)}{-0.1} \approx 16.09$$

Approximately 16.09 minutes.

c. It is impossible for the probability to reach 100% because $e^{-0.1t}$ will never equal zero; thus, $F(t) = 1 - e^{-0.1t}$ will never equal 1.

122. $F(t) = 1 - e^{-0.15t}$

a. $0.50 = 1 - e^{-0.15t}$

$$-0.5 = e^{-(R/L)t}$$

$$0.5 = e^{-0.15t}$$

$$\ln(0.5) = -0.15t$$

$$t = \frac{\ln(0.5)}{-0.15} \approx 4.62$$

Approximately 4.62 minutes, or 4 minutes and 37 seconds.

b. $0.80 = 1 - e^{-0.15t}$

$$-0.2 = -e^{-0.15t}$$

$$0.2 = e^{-0.15t}$$

$$\ln(0.2) = -0.15t$$

$$t = \frac{\ln(0.2)}{-0.15} \approx 10.73$$

Approximately 10.73 minutes, or 10 minutes and 44 seconds.

123. $D = 5e^{-0.4h}$

$$2 = 5e^{-0.4h}$$

$$0.4 = e^{-0.4h}$$

$$\ln(0.4) = -0.4h$$

$$h = \frac{\ln(0.4)}{-0.4} \approx 2.29$$

Approximately 2.29 hours, or 2 hours and 17 minutes.

124. $N = P\left(1 - e^{-0.15d}\right)$

$$450 = 1000\left(1 - e^{-0.15d}\right)$$

$$0.45 = 1 - e^{-0.15d}$$

$$-0.55 = -e^{-0.15d}$$

$$0.55 = e^{-0.15d}$$

$$\ln(0.55) = -0.15d$$

$$d = \frac{\ln(0.55)}{-0.15} \approx 3.99$$

Approximately 4 days.

125. $I = \dfrac{E}{R}\left[1 - e^{-(R/L)t}\right]$

Substituting $E = 12$, $R = 10$, $L = 5$, and $I = 0.5$, we obtain:

$$0.5 = \dfrac{12}{10}\left[1 - e^{-(10/5)t}\right]$$

$$\dfrac{5}{12} = 1 - e^{-2t}$$

$$e^{-2t} = \dfrac{7}{12}$$

$$-2t = \ln(7/12)$$

$$t = \dfrac{\ln(7/12)}{-2} \approx 0.2695$$

It takes approximately 0.2695 second to obtain a current of 0.5 ampere.

Substituting $E = 12$, $R = 10$, $L = 5$, and $I = 1.0$, we obtain:

$$1.0 = \dfrac{12}{10}\left[1 - e^{-(10/5)t}\right]$$

$$\dfrac{10}{12} = 1 - e^{-2t}$$

$$e^{-2t} = \dfrac{1}{6}$$

$$-2t = \ln(1/6)$$

$$t = \dfrac{\ln(1/6)}{-2} \approx 0.8959$$

It takes approximately 0.8959 second to obtain a current of 0.5 ampere.

Graphing:

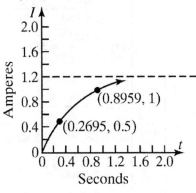

126. $L(t) = A\left(1 - e^{-kt}\right)$

a. $20 = 200\left(1 - e^{-k(5)}\right)$

$$0.1 = 1 - e^{-5k}$$

$$e^{-5k} = 0.9$$

$$-5k = \ln 0.9$$

$$k = -\dfrac{\ln 0.9}{5} \approx 0.0211$$

b. $L(10) = 200\left(1 - e^{-\left(-\frac{\ln 0.9}{5}\right)(10)}\right)$

$$= 200\left(1 - e^{2\ln 0.9}\right)$$

$$= 38 \text{ words}$$

c. $L(15) = 200\left(1 - e^{-\left(-\frac{\ln 0.9}{5}\right)(15)}\right)$

$$= 200\left(1 - e^{3\ln 0.9}\right)$$

$$\approx 54 \text{ words}$$

d. $180 = 200\left(1 - e^{-\left(-\frac{\ln 0.9}{5}\right)t}\right)$

$$0.9 = 1 - e^{\frac{\ln 0.9}{5}t}$$

$$e^{\frac{\ln 0.9}{5}t} = 0.1$$

$$\dfrac{\ln 0.9}{5}t = \ln 0.1$$

$$t = \dfrac{\ln 0.1}{\frac{\ln 0.9}{5}} \approx 109.27 \text{ minutes}$$

127. $L\left(10^{-7}\right) = 10 \log\left(\dfrac{10^{-7}}{10^{-12}}\right)$

$$= 10 \log\left(10^{5}\right)$$

$$= 10 \cdot 5$$

$$= 50 \text{ decibels}$$

128. $L\left(10^{-1}\right) = 10 \log\left(\dfrac{10^{-1}}{10^{-12}}\right)$

$$= 10 \log\left(10^{11}\right)$$

$$= 10 \cdot 11$$

$$= 110 \text{ decibels}$$

129. $L\left(10^{-3}\right) = 10 \log\left(\dfrac{10^{-3}}{10^{-12}}\right)$

$$= 10 \log\left(10^{9}\right)$$

$$= 10 \cdot 9$$

$$= 90 \text{ decibels}$$

637

130. Intensity of car:

$$70 = 10 \log\left(\frac{x}{10^{-12}}\right)$$

$$7 = \log\left(\frac{x}{10^{-12}}\right)$$

$$10^7 = \frac{x}{10^{-12}}$$

$$x = 10^{-5}$$

Intensity of truck is $10 \cdot 10^{-5} = 10^{-4}$.

$$L\left(10^{-4}\right) = 10 \log\left(\frac{10^{-4}}{10^{-12}}\right)$$

$$= 10 \log\left(10^8\right)$$

$$= 10 \cdot 8$$

$$= 80 \text{ decibels}$$

131. $M(125,892) = \log\left(\dfrac{125,892}{10^{-3}}\right) \approx 8.1$

132. $M(7943) = \log\left(\dfrac{7943}{10^{-3}}\right) \approx 6.9$

133. $R = e^{kx}$

a.
$$1.4 = e^{k(0.03)}$$
$$1.4 = e^{0.03k}$$
$$\ln(1.4) = 0.03k$$
$$k = \frac{\ln(1.4)}{0.03} \approx 11.216$$

b. $R = e^{11.216(0.17)} = e^{1.90672} \approx 6.73$

c.
$$100 = e^{11.216x}$$
$$100 = e^{11.216x}$$
$$\ln(100) = 11.216x$$
$$x = \frac{\ln(100)}{11.216} \approx 0.41$$

d.
$$5 = e^{11.216x}$$
$$\ln 5 = 11.216x$$
$$x = \frac{\ln 5}{11.216} \approx 0.143$$

At a percent concentration of 0.143 or higher, the driver should be charged with a DUI.

e. Answers will vary.

134. No. Explanations will vary.

135. If the base of a logarithmic function equals 1, we would have the following:

$$f(x) = \log_1(x)$$
$$f^{-1}(x) = 1^x = 1 \text{ for every real number } x.$$

In other words, f^{-1} would be a constant function and, therefore, f^{-1} would not be one-to-one.

136. $\text{New} = \text{Old}\left(e^{Rt}\right)$

Age	Depriciation rate
1	$38,000 = 36,600e^{R\,(1)}$ $\dfrac{38,000}{36,600} = e^{R}$ $R = \ln\left(\dfrac{38,000}{36,600}\right) \approx 0.03754 \approx 3.8\%$
2	$38,000 = 32,400e^{R\,(2)}$ $\dfrac{38,000}{32,400} = e^{2R}$ $\ln\left(\dfrac{38,000}{32,400}\right) = 2R$ $R = \dfrac{\ln\left(\dfrac{38,000}{32,400}\right)}{2} \approx 0.07971 \approx 8\%$
3	$38,000 = 28,750e^{R\,(3)}$ $\dfrac{38,000}{28,750} = e^{3R}$ $\ln\left(\dfrac{38,000}{28,750}\right) = 3R$ $R = \dfrac{\ln\left(\dfrac{38,000}{28,750}\right)}{3} \approx 0.0930 \approx 9.3\%$
4	$38,000 = 25,400e^{R\,(4)}$ $\dfrac{38,000}{25,400} = e^{4R}$ $\ln\left(\dfrac{38,000}{25,400}\right) = 4R$ $R = \dfrac{\ln\left(\dfrac{38,000}{24,500}\right)}{4} \approx 0.1007 \approx 10.1\%$

Age	Depriciation rate
5	$38,000 = 21,200e^{R\,(5)}$
	$\dfrac{38,000}{21,200} = e^{5R}$
	$\ln\left(\dfrac{38,000}{21,200}\right) = 5R$
	$R = \dfrac{\ln\left(\dfrac{38,000}{21,200}\right)}{5} \approx 0.1167 \approx 11.7\%$

Answers will vary.

Section 6.5

1. sum

2. 7

3. $r\log_a M$

4. False

5. False

6. True

7. $\log_3 3^{71} = 71$

8. $\log_2 2^{-13} = -13$

9. $\ln e^{-4} = -4$

10. $\ln e^{\sqrt{2}} = \sqrt{2}$

11. $2^{\log_2 7} = 7$

12. $e^{\ln 8} = 8$

13. $\log_8 2 + \log_8 4 = \log_8(4\cdot 2) = \log_8 8 = 1$

14. $\log_6 9 + \log_6 4 = \log_6(9\cdot 4)$
$= \log_6 36$
$= \log_6 6^2$
$= 2$

15. $\log_6 18 - \log_6 3 = \log_6 \dfrac{18}{3} = \log_6 6 = 1$

16. $\log_8 16 - \log_8 2 = \log_8 \dfrac{16}{2} = \log_8 8 = 1$

17. $\log_2 6 \cdot \log_6 4 = \log_6 4^{\log_2 6}$
$= \log_6\left(2^2\right)^{\log_2 6}$
$= \log_6 2^{2\log_2 6}$
$= \log_6 2^{\log_2 6^2}$
$= \log_6 6^2$
$= 2$

18. $\log_3 8 \cdot \log_8 9 = \log_8 9^{\log_3 8}$
$= \log_8\left(3^2\right)^{\log_3 8}$
$= \log_8 3^{2\log_3 8}$
$= \log_8 3^{\log_3 8^2}$
$= \log_8 8^2$
$= 2$

19. $3^{\log_3 5 - \log_3 4} = 3^{\log_3 \frac{5}{4}} = \dfrac{5}{4}$

20. $5^{\log_5 6 + \log_5 7} = 5^{\log_5(6\cdot 7)} = 5^{\log_5 42} = 42$

21. $e^{\log_{e^2} 16}$
Let $a = \log_{e^2} 16$, then $\left(e^2\right)^a = 16$.
$e^{2a} = 16$
$e^{2a} = 4^2$
$\left(e^{2a}\right)^{1/2} = \left(4^2\right)^{1/2}$
$e^a = 4$
$a = \ln 4$
Thus, $e^{\log_{e^2} 16} = e^{\ln 4} = 4$.

22. $e^{\log_{e^2} 9}$
Let $a = \log_{e^2} 9$, then $\left(e^2\right)^a = 9$.
$e^{2a} = 9$
$e^{2a} = 3^2$
$\left(e^{2a}\right)^{1/2} = \left(3^2\right)^{1/2}$
$e^a = 3$
$a = \ln 3$
Thus, $e^{\log_{e^2} 9} = e^{\ln 3} = 3$.

23. $\ln 6 = \ln(2 \cdot 3) = \ln 2 + \ln 3 = a + b$

24. $\ln \dfrac{2}{3} = \ln 2 - \ln 3 = a - b$

25. $\ln 1.5 = \ln \dfrac{3}{2} = \ln 3 - \ln 2 = b - a$

26. $\ln 0.5 = \ln \dfrac{1}{2} = \ln 1 - \ln 2 = 0 - a = -a$

27. $\ln 8 = \ln 2^3 = 3 \cdot \ln 2 = 3a$

28. $\ln 27 = \ln 3^3 = 3 \cdot \ln 3 = 3b$

29. $\ln \sqrt[5]{6} = \ln 6^{1/5}$

$\qquad = \dfrac{1}{5} \ln 6$

$\qquad = \dfrac{1}{5} \ln(2 \cdot 3)$

$\qquad = \dfrac{1}{5} (\ln 2 + \ln 3)$

$\qquad = \dfrac{1}{5} (a + b)$

30. $\ln \sqrt[4]{\dfrac{2}{3}} = \ln \left(\dfrac{2}{3} \right)^{1/4}$

$\qquad = \dfrac{1}{4} \ln \dfrac{2}{3}$

$\qquad = \dfrac{1}{4} (\ln 2 - \ln 3)$

$\qquad = \dfrac{1}{4} (a - b)$

31. $\log_5 (25x) = \log_5 25 + \log_5 x = 2 + \log_5 x$

32. $\log_3 \dfrac{x}{9} = \log_3 \dfrac{x}{3^2} = \log_3 x - \log_3 3^2 = \log_3 x - 2$

33. $\log_2 z^3 = 3 \log_2 z$

34. $\log_7 x^5 = 5 \log_7 x$

35. $\ln(ex) = \ln e + \ln x = 1 + \ln x$

36. $\ln \dfrac{e}{x} = \ln e - \ln x = 1 - \ln x$

37. $\ln(xe^x) = \ln x + \ln e^x = \ln x + x$

38. $\ln \left(\dfrac{x}{e^x} \right) = \ln x - \ln e^x = \ln x - x$

39. $\log_a \left(u^2 v^3 \right) = \log_a u^2 + \log_a v^3$

$\qquad\qquad\quad = 2 \log_a u + 3 \log_a v$

40. $\log_2 \left(\dfrac{a}{b^2} \right) = \log_2 a - \log_2 b^2 = \log_2 a - 2 \log_2 b$

41. $\ln \left(x^2 \sqrt{1-x} \right) = \ln x^2 + \ln \sqrt{1-x}$

$\qquad\qquad\quad = \ln x^2 + \ln(1-x)^{1/2}$

$\qquad\qquad\quad = 2 \ln x + \dfrac{1}{2} \ln(1-x)$

42. $\ln \left(x\sqrt{1+x^2} \right) = \ln x + \ln \sqrt{1+x^2}$

$\qquad\qquad\quad = \ln x + \ln \left(1+x^2 \right)^{1/2}$

$\qquad\qquad\quad = \ln x + \dfrac{1}{2} \ln \left(1+x^2 \right)$

43. $\log_2 \left(\dfrac{x^3}{x-3} \right) = \log_2 x^3 - \log_2 (x-3)$

$\qquad\qquad\quad = 3 \log_2 x - \log_2 (x-3)$

44. $\log_5 \left(\dfrac{\sqrt[3]{x^2+1}}{x^2-1} \right)$

$\qquad = \log_5 \left(x^2+1 \right)^{1/3} - \log_5 (x^2-1)$

$\qquad = \dfrac{1}{3} \log_5 \left(x^2+1 \right) - \log_5 \left(x^2-1 \right)$

$\qquad = \dfrac{1}{3} \log_5 \left(x^2+1 \right) - \log_5 \left((x+1)(x-1) \right)$

$\qquad = \dfrac{1}{3} \log_5 \left(x^2+1 \right) - \log_5 (x+1) - \log_5 (x-1)$

45. $\log \left[\dfrac{x(x+2)}{(x+3)^2} \right] = \log \left[x(x+2) \right] - \log(x+3)^2$

$\qquad\qquad\quad = \log x + \log(x+2) - 2\log(x+3)$

46. $\log \left[\dfrac{x^3 \sqrt{x+1}}{(x-2)^2} \right] = \log \left(x^3 \sqrt{x+1} \right) - \log(x-2)^2$

$\qquad\qquad\quad = \log x^3 + \log(x+1)^{1/2} - 2\log(x-2)$

$\qquad\qquad\quad = 3 \log x + \dfrac{1}{2} \log(x+1) - 2\log(x-2)$

640

47. $\ln\left[\dfrac{x^2-x-2}{(x+4)^2}\right]^{1/3}$

$=\dfrac{1}{3}\ln\left[\dfrac{(x-2)(x+1)}{(x+4)^2}\right]$

$=\dfrac{1}{3}\left[\ln(x-2)(x+1)-\ln(x+4)^2\right]$

$=\dfrac{1}{3}\left[\ln(x-2)+\ln(x+1)-2\ln(x+4)\right]$

$=\dfrac{1}{3}\ln(x-2)+\dfrac{1}{3}\ln(x+1)-\dfrac{2}{3}\ln(x+4)$

48. $\ln\left[\dfrac{(x-4)^2}{x^2-1}\right]^{2/3}$

$=\dfrac{2}{3}\ln\left[\dfrac{(x-4)^2}{x^2-1}\right]$

$=\dfrac{2}{3}\left[\ln(x-4)^2-\ln\left(x^2-1\right)\right]$

$=\dfrac{2}{3}\left[2\ln(x-4)-\ln((x+1)(x-1))\right]$

$=\dfrac{2}{3}\left[2\ln(x-4)-\ln(x+1)-\ln(x-1)\right]$

$=\dfrac{4}{3}\ln(x-4)-\dfrac{2}{3}\ln(x+1)-\dfrac{2}{3}\ln(x-1)$

49. $\ln\dfrac{5x\sqrt{1+3x}}{(x-4)^3}$

$=\ln\left(5x\sqrt{1+3x}\right)-\ln(x-4)^3$

$=\ln 5+\ln x+\ln\sqrt{1+3x}-3\ln(x-4)$

$=\ln 5+\ln x+\ln(1+3x)^{1/2}-3\ln(x-4)$

$=\ln 5+\ln x+\dfrac{1}{2}\ln(1+3x)-3\ln(x-4)$

50. $\ln\left[\dfrac{5x^2\sqrt[3]{1-x}}{4(x+1)^2}\right]$

$=\ln\left(5x^2\sqrt[3]{1-x}\right)-\ln\left(4(x+1)^2\right)$

$=\ln 5+\ln x^2+\ln(1-x)^{1/3}-\left[\ln 4+\ln(x+1)^2\right]$

$=\ln 5+2\ln x+\dfrac{1}{3}\ln(1-x)-\ln 4-2\ln(x+1)$

51. $3\log_5 u+4\log_5 v=\log_5 u^3+\log_5 v^4$

$=\log_5\left(u^3 v^4\right)$

52. $2\log_3 u-\log_3 v=\log_3 u^2-\log_3 v$

$=\log_3\left(\dfrac{u^2}{v}\right)$

53. $\log_3\sqrt{x}-\log_3 x^3=\log_3\left(\dfrac{\sqrt{x}}{x^3}\right)$

$=\log_3\left(\dfrac{x^{1/2}}{x^3}\right)$

$=\log_3 x^{-5/2}$

$=-\dfrac{5}{2}\log_3 x$

54. $\log_2\left(\dfrac{1}{x}\right)+\log_2\left(\dfrac{1}{x^2}\right)=\log_2\left(\dfrac{1}{x}\cdot\dfrac{1}{x^2}\right)$

$=\log_2\left(\dfrac{1}{x^3}\right)$

$=\log_2 x^{-3}$

$=-3\log_2 x$

55. $\log_4\left(x^2-1\right)-5\log_4(x+1)$

$=\log_4\left(x^2-1\right)-\log_4(x+1)^5$

$=\log_4\left[\dfrac{x^2-1}{(x+1)^5}\right]$

$=\log_4\left[\dfrac{(x+1)(x-1)}{(x+1)^5}\right]$

$=\log_4\left[\dfrac{x-1}{(x+1)^4}\right]$

56. $\log\left(x^2+3x+2\right)-2\log_2(x+1)$

$=\log\left(x^2+3x+2\right)-\log_2(x+1)^2$

$=\log\left(\dfrac{x^2+3x+2}{(x+1)^2}\right)$

$=\log\left(\dfrac{(x+2)(x+1)}{(x+1)^2}\right)$

$=\log\left(\dfrac{x+2}{x+1}\right)$

641

57. $\ln\left(\dfrac{x}{x-1}\right)+\ln\left(\dfrac{x+1}{x}\right)-\ln\left(x^2-1\right)$

$=\ln\left[\dfrac{x}{x-1}\cdot\dfrac{x+1}{x}\right]-\ln\left(x^2-1\right)$

$=\ln\left[\dfrac{x+1}{x-1}\div\left(x^2-1\right)\right]$

$=\ln\left[\dfrac{x+1}{(x-1)\left(x^2-1\right)}\right]$

$=\ln\left[\dfrac{x+1}{(x-1)(x-1)(x+1)}\right]$

$=\ln\left(\dfrac{1}{(x-1)^2}\right)$

$=\ln(x-1)^{-2}$

$=-2\ln(x-1)$

58. $\log\left(\dfrac{x^2+2x-3}{x^2-4}\right)-\log\left(\dfrac{x^2+7x+6}{x+2}\right)$

$=\log\left[\dfrac{\left(\dfrac{x^2+2x-3}{x^2-4}\right)}{\left(\dfrac{x^2+7x+6}{x+2}\right)}\right]$

$=\log\left[\dfrac{(x+3)(x-1)}{(x-2)(x+2)}\cdot\dfrac{x+2}{(x+6)(x+1)}\right]$

$=\log\left[\dfrac{(x+3)(x-1)}{(x-2)(x+6)(x+1)}\right]$

59. $8\log_2\sqrt{3x-2}-\log_2\left(\dfrac{4}{x}\right)+\log_2 4$

$=\log_2\left(\sqrt{3x-2}\right)^8-\left(\log_2 4-\log_2 x\right)+\log_2 4$

$=\log_2(3x-2)^4-\log_2 4+\log_2 x+\log_2 4$

$=\log_2(3x-2)^4+\log_2 x$

$=\log_2\left[x(3x-2)^4\right]$

60. $21\log_3\sqrt[3]{x}+\log_3\left(9x^2\right)-\log_3 9$

$=\log_3\left(x^{1/3}\right)^{21}+\log_3(9)+\log_3\left(x^2\right)-\log_3 9$

$=\log_3 x^7+\log_3 x^2$

$=\log_3\left(x^7\cdot x^2\right)$

$=\log_3\left(x^9\right)$

61. $2\log_a\left(5x^3\right)-\dfrac{1}{2}\log_a(2x+3)$

$=\log_a\left(5x^3\right)^2-\log_a(2x+3)^{1/2}$

$=\log_a\left(25x^6\right)-\log_a\sqrt{2x+3}$

$=\log_a\left[\dfrac{25x^6}{\sqrt{2x+3}}\right]$

62. $\dfrac{1}{3}\log\left(x^3+1\right)+\dfrac{1}{2}\log\left(x^2+1\right)$

$=\log\left(x^3+1\right)^{1/3}+\log\left(x^2+1\right)^{1/2}$

$=\log\left[\sqrt[3]{x^3+1}\cdot\sqrt{x^2+1}\right]$

63. $2\log_2\left(x+1\right)-\log_2\left(x+3\right)-\log_2\left(x-1\right)$

$=\log_2\left(x+1\right)^2-\log_2\left(x+3\right)-\log_2\left(x-1\right)$

$=\log_2\dfrac{\left(x+1\right)^2}{\left(x+3\right)}-\log_2\left(x-1\right)$

$=\log_2\left[\dfrac{\left(x+1\right)^2}{\left(x+3\right)(x-1)}\right]$

64. $3\log_5\left(3x+1\right)-2\log_5\left(2x-1\right)-\log_5 x$

$=\log_5\left(3x+1\right)^3-\log_5\left(2x-1\right)^2-\log_5 x$

$=\log_5\dfrac{\left(3x+1\right)^3}{\left(2x-1\right)^2}-\log_5 x$

$=\log_5\left[\dfrac{\left(3x+1\right)^3}{x\left(2x-1\right)^2}\right]$

65. $\log_3 21=\dfrac{\log 21}{\log 3}\approx 2.771$

66. $\log_5 18=\dfrac{\log 18}{\log 5}\approx 1.796$

67. $\log_{1/3} 71=\dfrac{\log 71}{\log\left(1/3\right)}=\dfrac{\log 71}{-\log 3}\approx -3.880$

68. $\log_{1/2} 15=\dfrac{\log 15}{\log\left(1/2\right)}=\dfrac{\log 15}{-\log 2}\approx -3.907$

69. $\log_{\sqrt{2}} 7=\dfrac{\log 7}{\log\sqrt{2}}\approx 5.615$

70. $\log_{\sqrt{5}} 8 = \dfrac{\log 8}{\log \sqrt{5}} \approx 2.584$

71. $\log_{\pi} e = \dfrac{\ln e}{\ln \pi} \approx 0.874$

72. $\log_{\pi} \sqrt{2} = \dfrac{\ln \sqrt{2}}{\ln \pi} \approx 0.303$

73. $y = \log_4 x = \dfrac{\ln x}{\ln 4}$ or $y = \dfrac{\log x}{\log 4}$

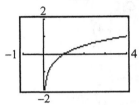

74. $y = \log_5 x = \dfrac{\ln x}{\ln 5}$ or $y = \dfrac{\log x}{\log 5}$

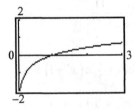

75. $y = \log_2 (x+2) = \dfrac{\ln(x+2)}{\ln 2}$ or $y = \dfrac{\log(x+2)}{\log 2}$

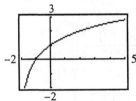

76. $y = \log_4 (x-3) = \dfrac{\ln(x-3)}{\ln 4}$ or $y = \dfrac{\log(x-3)}{\log 4}$

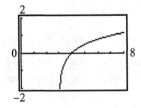

77. $y = \log_{x-1}(x+1) = \dfrac{\ln(x+1)}{\ln(x-1)}$ or $y = \dfrac{\log(x+1)}{\log(x-1)}$

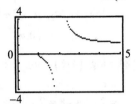

78. $y = \log_{x+2}(x-2) = \dfrac{\ln(x-2)}{\ln(x+2)}$ or $y = \dfrac{\log(x-2)}{\log(x+2)}$

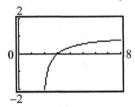

79. $f(x) = \ln x$; $g(x) = e^x$; $h(x) = x^2$

   a. $(f \circ g)(x) = f(g(x)) = \ln(e^x) = x$

      Domain: $\{x \mid x \text{ is any real number}\}$ or $(-\infty, \infty)$

   b. $(g \circ f)(x) = g(f(x)) = e^{\ln x} = x$

      Domain: $\{x \mid x > 0\}$ or $(0, \infty)$

      (Note: the restriction on the domain is due to the domain of $\ln x$)

   c. $(f \circ g)(5) = 5$ [from part (a)]

   d. $(f \circ h)(x) = f(h(x)) = \ln(x^2)$

      Domain: $\{x \mid x \neq 0\}$

   e. $(f \circ h)(e) = \ln(e^2) = 2\ln e = 2 \cdot 1 = 2$

80. $f(x) = \log_2 x$; $g(x) = 2^x$; $h(x) = 4x$

   a. $(f \circ g)(x) = f(g(x)) = \log_2(2^x) = x$

      Domain: $\{x \mid x \text{ is any real number}\}$ or $(-\infty, \infty)$

   b. $(g \circ f)(x) = g(f(x)) = 2^{\log_2 x} = x$

      Domain: $\{x \mid x > 0\}$ or $(0, \infty)$

      (Note: the restriction on the domain is due to the domain of $\log_2 x$)

   c. $(f \circ g)(3) = 3$ [from part (a)]

d. $(f \circ h)(x) = f(h(x)) = \log_2(4x)$

or

$$= \log_2 4 + \log_2 x = 2 + \log_2 x$$

Domain: $\{x \mid x > 0\}$ or $(0, \infty)$

e. $(f \circ h)(8) = \log_2(4 \cdot 8) = \log_2 32 = 5$

or

$$= 2 + \log_2 8 = 2 + 3 = 5$$

81. $\ln y = \ln x + \ln C$

$\ln y = \ln(xC)$

$y = Cx$

82. $\ln y = \ln(x + C)$

$y = x + C$

83. $\ln y = \ln x + \ln(x+1) + \ln C$

$\ln y = \ln(x(x+1)C)$

$y = Cx(x+1)$

84. $\ln y = 2\ln x - \ln(x+1) + \ln C$

$\ln y = \ln\left(\dfrac{x^2 C}{x+1}\right)$

$y = \dfrac{Cx^2}{x+1}$

85. $\ln y = 3x + \ln C$

$\ln y = \ln e^{3x} + \ln C$

$\ln y = \ln(Ce^{3x})$

$y = Ce^{3x}$

86. $\ln y = -2x + \ln C$

$\ln y = \ln e^{-2x} + \ln C$

$\ln y = \ln(Ce^{-2x})$

$y = Ce^{-2x}$

87. $\ln(y-3) = -4x + \ln C$

$\ln(y-3) = \ln e^{-4x} + \ln C$

$\ln(y-3) = \ln(Ce^{-4x})$

$y - 3 = Ce^{-4x}$

$y = Ce^{-4x} + 3$

88. $\ln(y+4) = 5x + \ln C$

$\ln(y+4) = \ln e^{5x} + \ln C$

$\ln(y+4) = \ln(Ce^{5x})$

$y + 4 = Ce^{5x}$

$y = Ce^{5x} - 4$

89. $3\ln y = \dfrac{1}{2}\ln(2x+1) - \dfrac{1}{3}\ln(x+4) + \ln C$

$\ln y^3 = \ln(2x+1)^{1/2} - \ln(x+4)^{1/3} + \ln C$

$\ln y^3 = \ln\left[\dfrac{C(2x+1)^{1/2}}{(x+4)^{1/3}}\right]$

$y^3 = \dfrac{C(2x+1)^{1/2}}{(x+4)^{1/3}}$

$y = \left[\dfrac{C(2x+1)^{1/2}}{(x+4)^{1/3}}\right]^{1/3}$

$y = \dfrac{\sqrt[3]{C}(2x+1)^{1/6}}{(x+4)^{1/9}}$

90. $2\ln y = -\dfrac{1}{2}\ln x + \dfrac{1}{3}\ln(x^2+1) + \ln C$

$\ln y^2 = -\ln x^{1/2} + \ln(x^2+1)^{1/3} + \ln C$

$\ln y^2 = \ln\left[\dfrac{C(x^2+1)^{1/3}}{x^{1/2}}\right]$

$y^2 = \dfrac{C(x^2+1)^{1/3}}{x^{1/2}}$

$y = \left[\dfrac{C(x^2+1)^{1/3}}{x^{1/2}}\right]^{1/2}$

$y = \dfrac{\sqrt{C}(x^2+1)^{1/6}}{x^{1/4}}$

91. $\log_2 3 \cdot \log_3 4 \cdot \log_4 5 \cdot \log_5 6 \cdot \log_6 7 \cdot \log_7 8$

$= \dfrac{\log 3}{\log 2} \cdot \dfrac{\log 4}{\log 3} \cdot \dfrac{\log 5}{\log 4} \cdot \dfrac{\log 6}{\log 5} \cdot \dfrac{\log 7}{\log 6} \cdot \dfrac{\log 8}{\log 7}$

$= \dfrac{\log 8}{\log 2} = \dfrac{\log 2^3}{\log 2}$

$= \dfrac{3\log 2}{\log 2}$

$= 3$

92. $\log_2 4 \cdot \log_4 6 \cdot \log_6 8 = \dfrac{\log 4}{\log 2} \cdot \dfrac{\log 6}{\log 4} \cdot \dfrac{\log 8}{\log 6}$

$\qquad\qquad\qquad\qquad = \dfrac{\log 8}{\log 2}$

$\qquad\qquad\qquad\qquad = \dfrac{\log 2^3}{\log 2}$

$\qquad\qquad\qquad\qquad = \dfrac{3\log 2}{\log 2}$

$\qquad\qquad\qquad\qquad = 3$

93. $\log_2 3 \cdot \log_3 4 \cdots \log_n (n+1) \cdot \log_{n+1} 2$

$\qquad = \dfrac{\log 3}{\log 2} \cdot \dfrac{\log 4}{\log 3} \cdots \dfrac{\log (n+1)}{\log n} \cdot \dfrac{\log 2}{\log (n+1)}$

$\qquad = \dfrac{\log 2}{\log 2}$

$\qquad = 1$

94. $\log_2 2 \cdot \log_2 4 \cdot \ldots \cdot \log_2 2^n$

$\qquad = \log_2 2 \cdot \log_2 2^2 \cdots \log_2 2^n$

$\qquad = 1 \cdot 2 \cdot 3 \cdots n$

$\qquad = n!$

95. $\log_a \left(x + \sqrt{x^2 - 1} \right) + \log_a \left(x - \sqrt{x^2 - 1} \right):$

$\qquad = \log_a \left[\left(x + \sqrt{x^2 - 1} \right)\left(x - \sqrt{x^2 - 1} \right) \right]$

$\qquad = \log_a \left[x^2 - \left(x^2 - 1 \right) \right]$

$\qquad = \log_a \left[x^2 - x^2 + 1 \right]$

$\qquad = \log_a 1$

$\qquad = 0$

96. $\log_a \left(\sqrt{x} + \sqrt{x-1} \right) + \log_a \left(\sqrt{x} - \sqrt{x-1} \right)$

$\qquad = \log_a \left[\left(\sqrt{x} + \sqrt{x-1} \right)\left(\sqrt{x} - \sqrt{x-1} \right) \right]$

$\qquad = \log_a \left[x - (x-1) \right]$

$\qquad = \log_a \left[x - x + 1 \right]$

$\qquad = \log_a 1$

$\qquad = 0$

97. $2x + \ln\left(1 + e^{-2x} \right) = \ln e^{2x} + \ln\left(1 + e^{-2x} \right)$

$\qquad\qquad\qquad\qquad = \ln\left(e^{2x} \left(1 + e^{-2x} \right) \right)$

$\qquad\qquad\qquad\qquad = \ln\left(e^{2x} + e^0 \right)$

$\qquad\qquad\qquad\qquad = \ln\left(e^{2x} + 1 \right)$

98. $\dfrac{f(x+h) - f(x)}{h} = \dfrac{\log_a (x+h) - \log_a x}{h}$

$\qquad\qquad\qquad = \dfrac{\log_a \left(\dfrac{x+h}{x} \right)}{h}$

$\qquad\qquad\qquad = \dfrac{1}{h} \cdot \log_a \left(1 + \dfrac{h}{x} \right)$

$\qquad\qquad\qquad = \log_a \left(1 + \dfrac{h}{x} \right)^{\frac{1}{h}}, \quad h \neq 0$

99. $f(x) = \log_a x$ means that $x = a^{f(x)}$.

Now, raising both sides to the -1 power, we

obtain $x^{-1} = \left(a^{f(x)} \right)^{-1} = \left(a^{-1} \right)^{f(x)} = \left(\dfrac{1}{a} \right)^{f(x)}$.

$x^{-1} = \left(\dfrac{1}{a} \right)^{f(x)}$ means that $\log_{1/a} x^{-1} = f(x)$.

Thus, $\log_{1/a} x^{-1} = f(x)$

$\qquad -\log_{1/a} x = f(x)$

$\qquad -f(x) = \log_{1/a} x$

100. $f(AB) = \log_a (AB)$

$\qquad\quad = \log_a A + \log_a B$

$\qquad\quad = f(A) + f(B)$

101. $f(x) = \log_a x$

$f\left(\dfrac{1}{x} \right) = \log_a \left(\dfrac{1}{x} \right)$

$\qquad\quad = \log_a 1 - \log_a x$

$\qquad\quad = -\log_a x$

$\qquad\quad = -f(x)$

102. $f(x) = \log_a x$

$f\left(x^\alpha \right) = \log_a x^\alpha = \alpha \log_a x = \alpha f(x)$

103. If $A = \log_a M$ and $B = \log_a N$, then $a^A = M$ and $a^B = N$.

$$\log_a\left(\frac{M}{N}\right) = \log_a\left(\frac{a^A}{a^B}\right)$$
$$= \log_a a^{A-B}$$
$$= A - B$$
$$= \log_a M - \log_a N$$

104. $\log_a\left(\dfrac{1}{N}\right) = \log_a N^{-1}$
$$= -1 \cdot \log_a N$$
$$= -\log_a N, \quad a \neq 1$$

105. $Y_1 = \log x^2$ $\qquad\qquad$ $Y_2 = 2\log x$

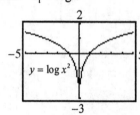 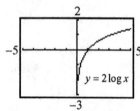

The domain of $Y_1 = \log_a x^2$ is $\left\{x \,\middle|\, x \neq 0\right\}$. The domain of $Y_2 = 2\log_a x$ is $\left\{x \,\middle|\, x > 0\right\}$. These two domains are different because the logarithm property $\log_a x^n = n \cdot \log_a x$ holds only when $\log_a x$ exists.

106. Answers may vary. One possibility follows: Let $a = 2$, $x = 8$, and $r = 3$. Then $\left(\log_a x\right)^r = \left(\log_2 8\right)^3 = 3^3 = 27$. But $r\log_a x = 3\log_2 8 = 3 \cdot 3 = 9$. Thus, $\left(\log_2 8\right)^3 \neq 3\log_2 8$ and, in general, $\left(\log_a x\right)^r \neq r\log_a x$.

107. Answers may vary. One possibility follows: Let $x = 4$ and $y = 4$. Then $\log_2(x+y) = \log_2(4+4) = \log_2 8 = 3$. But $\log_2 x + \log_2 y = \log_2 4 + \log_2 4 = 2 + 2 = 4$. Thus, $\log_2(4+4) \neq \log_2 4 + \log_2 4$ and, in general, $\log_2(x+y) \neq \log_2 x + \log_2 y$.

108. No. $\log_3(-5)$ does not exist.

Section 6.6

1. $x^2 - 7x - 30 = 0$
$$(x+3)(x-10) = 0$$
$$x + 3 = 0 \quad \text{or} \quad x - 10 = 0$$
$$x = -3 \quad \text{or} \qquad x = 10$$
The solution set is $\{-3,\ 10\}$.

2. Let $u = x + 3$. Then
$$(x+3)^2 - 4(x+3) + 3 = 0$$
$$u^2 - 4u + 3 = 0$$
$$(u-1)(u-3) = 0$$
$$u - 1 = 0 \quad \text{or} \quad u - 3 = 0$$
$$u = 1 \quad \text{or} \qquad u = 3$$
Back substituting $u = x + 3$, we obtain
$$x + 3 = 1 \quad \text{or} \quad x + 3 = 3$$
$$x = -2 \quad \text{or} \qquad x = 0$$
The solution set is $\{-2,\ 0\}$.

3. $x^3 = x^2 - 5$
Using INTERSECT to solve:
$y_1 = x^3$; $y_2 = x^2 - 5$

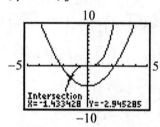

Thus, $x \approx -1.43$, so the solution set is $\{-1.43\}$.

4. $x^3 - 2x + 2 = 0$
Using ZERO to solve: $y_1 = x^3 - 2x + 2$

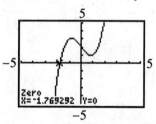

Thus, $x \approx -1.77$, so the solution set is $\{-1.77\}$.

646

5. $\log_4 x = 2$

$\quad x = 4^2$

$\quad x = 16$

The solution set is $\{16\}$.

6. $\log (x+6) = 1$

$\quad x + 6 = 10^1$

$\quad x + 6 = 10$

$\quad\quad x = 4$

The solution set is $\{4\}$.

7. $\log_2(5x) = 4$

$\quad 5x = 2^4$

$\quad 5x = 16$

$\quad x = \dfrac{16}{5}$

The solution set is $\left\{\dfrac{16}{5}\right\}$.

8. $\log_3(3x-1) = 2$

$\quad 3x - 1 = 3^2$

$\quad 3x - 1 = 9$

$\quad 3x = 10$

$\quad x = \dfrac{10}{3}$

The solution set is $\left\{\dfrac{10}{3}\right\}$.

9. $\log_4(x+2) = \log_4 8$

$\quad x + 2 = 8$

$\quad x = 6$

The solution set is $\{6\}$.

10. $\log_5(2x+3) = \log_5 3$

$\quad 2x + 3 = 3$

$\quad 2x = 0$

$\quad x = 0$

The solution set is $\{0\}$.

11. $\dfrac{1}{2}\log_3 x = 2\log_3 2$

$\quad \log_3 x^{1/2} = \log_3 2^2$

$\quad x^{1/2} = 4$

$\quad x = 16$

The solution set is $\{16\}$.

12. $-2\log_4 x = \log_4 9$

$\quad \log_4 x^{-2} = \log_4 9$

$\quad x^{-2} = 9$

$\quad \dfrac{1}{x^2} = 9$

$\quad x^2 = \dfrac{1}{9}$

$\quad x = \pm\dfrac{1}{3}$

Since $\log_4\left(-\dfrac{1}{3}\right)$ is undefined, the solution set is

$\left\{\dfrac{1}{3}\right\}$.

13. $3\log_2 x = -\log_2 27$

$\quad \log_2 x^3 = \log_2 27^{-1}$

$\quad x^3 = 27^{-1}$

$\quad x^3 = \dfrac{1}{27}$

$\quad x = \dfrac{1}{3}$

The solution set is $\left\{\dfrac{1}{3}\right\}$.

14. $2\log_5 x = 3\log_5 4$

$\quad \log_5 x^2 = \log_5 4^3$

$\quad x^2 = 64$

$\quad x = \pm 8$

Since $\log_5(-8)$ is undefined, the solution set is

$\{8\}$.

15. $3\log_2(x-1) + \log_2 4 = 5$

$\quad \log_2(x-1)^3 + \log_2 4 = 5$

$\quad \log_2\left(4(x-1)^3\right) = 5$

$\quad 4(x-1)^3 = 2^5$

$\quad (x-1)^3 = \dfrac{32}{4}$

$\quad (x-1)^3 = 8$

$\quad x - 1 = 2$

$\quad x = 3$

The solution set is $\{3\}$.

16. $2\log_3(x+4) - \log_3 9 = 2$

$$\log_3(x+4)^2 - \log_3 3^2 = 2$$
$$\log_3(x+4)^2 - 2 = 2$$
$$\log_3(x+4)^2 = 4$$
$$(x+4)^2 = 3^4$$
$$(x+4)^2 = 81$$
$$x+4 = \pm 9$$
$$x = -4 \pm 9$$
$$x = 5 \text{ or } x = -13$$

Since $\log_3(-13+4) = \log_3(-9)$ is undefined, the solution set is $\{5\}$.

17. $\log x + \log(x+15) = 2$

$$\log(x(x+15)) = 2$$
$$x(x+15) = 10^2$$
$$x^2 + 15x - 100 = 0$$
$$(x+20)(x-5) = 0$$
$$x = -20 \text{ or } x = 5$$

Since $\log(-20)$ is undefined, the solution set is $\{5\}$.

18. $\log x + \log(x-21) = 2$

$$\log(x(x-21)) = 2$$
$$x(x-21) = 10^2$$
$$x^2 - 21x - 100 = 0$$
$$(x+4)(x-25) = 0$$
$$x = -4 \text{ or } x = 25$$

Since $\log(-4)$ is undefined, the solution set is $\{25\}$.

19.
$$\log(2x+1) = 1 + \log(x-2)$$
$$\log(2x+1) - \log(x-2) = 1$$
$$\log\left(\frac{2x+1}{x-2}\right) = 1$$
$$\frac{2x+1}{x-2} = 10^1$$
$$2x+1 = 10(x-2)$$
$$2x+1 = 10x - 20$$
$$-8x = -21$$
$$x = \frac{-21}{-8} = \frac{21}{8}$$

The solution set is $\left\{\dfrac{21}{8}\right\}$.

20. $\log(2x) - \log(x-3) = 1$

$$\log\left(\frac{2x}{x-3}\right) = 1$$
$$\frac{2x}{x-3} = 10^1$$
$$2x = 10(x-3)$$
$$2x = 10x - 30$$
$$-8x = -30$$
$$x = \frac{-30}{-8} = \frac{15}{4}$$

The solution set is $\left\{\dfrac{15}{4}\right\}$.

21. $\log_2(x+7) + \log_2(x+8) = 1$

$$\log_2[(x+7)(x+8)] = 1$$
$$(x+7)(x+8) = 2^1$$
$$x^2 + 8x + 7x + 56 = 2$$
$$x^2 + 15x + 54 = 0$$
$$(x+9)(x+6) = 0$$
$$x = -9 \text{ or } x = -6$$

Since $\log_2(-9+7) = \log_2(-2)$ is undefined, the solution set is $\{-6\}$.

22. $\log_6(x+4) + \log_6(x+3) = 1$

$$\log_6[(x+4)(x+3)] = 1$$
$$(x+4)(x+3) = 6^1$$
$$x^2 + 3x + 4x + 12 = 6$$
$$x^2 + 7x + 6 = 0$$
$$(x+6)(x+1) = 0$$
$$x = -6 \text{ or } x = -1$$

Since $\log_6(-6+4) = \log_6(-2)$ is undefined, the solution set is $\{-1\}$.

23.
$$\log_8(x+6) = 1 - \log_8(x+4)$$
$$\log_8(x+6) + \log_8(x+4) = 1$$
$$\log_8[(x+6)(x+4)] = 1$$
$$(x+6)(x+4) = 8^1$$
$$x^2 + 4x + 6x + 24 = 8$$
$$x^2 + 10x + 16 = 0$$
$$(x+8)(x+2) = 0$$
$$x = -8 \text{ or } x = -2$$

Since $\log_8(-8+6) = \log_8(-2)$ is undefined, the solution set is $\{-2\}$.

24.
$$\log_5(x+3) = 1 - \log_5(x-1)$$
$$\log_5(x+3) + \log_5(x-1) = 1$$
$$\log_5\left[(x+3)(x-1)\right] = 1$$
$$(x+3)(x-1) = 5^1$$
$$x^2 - x + 3x - 3 = 5$$
$$x^2 + 2x - 8 = 0$$
$$(x+4)(x-2) = 0$$
$$x = -4 \text{ or } x = 2$$
Since $\log_5(-4+3) = \log_5(-1)$ is undefined, the solution set is $\{2\}$.

25.
$$\ln x + \ln(x+2) = 4$$
$$\ln\left(x(x+2)\right) = 4$$
$$x(x+2) = e^4$$
$$x^2 + 2x - e^4 = 0$$
$$x = \frac{-2 \pm \sqrt{2^2 - 4(1)(-e^4)}}{2(1)}$$
$$= \frac{-2 \pm \sqrt{4 + 4e^4}}{2}$$
$$= \frac{-2 \pm 2\sqrt{1 + e^4}}{2}$$
$$= -1 \pm \sqrt{1 + e^4}$$
$$x = -1 - \sqrt{1+e^4} \text{ or } x = -1 + \sqrt{1+e^4}$$
$$\approx -8.456 \qquad \approx 6.456$$
Since $\ln(-8.456)$ is undefined, the solution set is $\left\{-1+\sqrt{1+e^4}\right\} \approx \{6.456\}$.

26. $\ln(x+1) - \ln x = 2$
$$\ln\left(\frac{x+1}{x}\right) = 2$$
$$\frac{x+1}{x} = e^2$$
$$x + 1 = e^2 x$$
$$e^2 x - x = 1$$
$$x\left(e^2 - 1\right) = 1$$
$$x = \frac{1}{e^2 - 1} \approx 0.157$$
The solution set is $\left\{\dfrac{1}{e^2-1}\right\} \approx \{0.157\}$.

27. $\log_3(x+1) + \log_3(x+4) = 2$
$$\log_3\left[(x+1)(x+4)\right] = 2$$
$$(x+1)(x+4) = 3^2$$
$$x^2 + 4x + x + 4 = 9$$
$$x^2 + 5x - 5 = 0$$
$$x = \frac{-5 \pm \sqrt{5^2 - 4(1)(-5)}}{2(1)}$$
$$= \frac{-5 \pm \sqrt{45}}{2}$$
$$= \frac{-5 \pm 3\sqrt{5}}{2}$$
$$x = \frac{-5 - 3\sqrt{5}}{2} \text{ or } x = \frac{-5 + 3\sqrt{5}}{2}$$
$$\approx -5.854 \qquad \approx 0.854$$
Since $\log_3(-8.854+1) = \log_3(-7.854)$ is undefined, the solution set is
$$\left\{\frac{-5+3\sqrt{5}}{2}\right\} \approx \{0.854\}.$$

28. $\log_2(x+1) + \log_2(x+7) = 3$
$$\log_2\left[(x+1)(x+7)\right] = 3$$
$$(x+1)(x+7) = 2^3$$
$$x^2 + 7x + x + 7 = 8$$
$$x^2 + 8x - 1 = 0$$
$$x = \frac{-8 \pm \sqrt{8^2 - 4(1)(-1)}}{2(1)}$$
$$= \frac{-8 \pm \sqrt{68}}{2}$$
$$= \frac{-8 \pm 2\sqrt{17}}{2}$$
$$= -4 \pm \sqrt{17}$$
$$x = -4 - \sqrt{17} \text{ or } x = -4 + \sqrt{17}$$
$$\approx -8.123 \qquad \approx 0.123$$
Since $\log_2(-8.123+1) = \log_2(-7.123)$ is undefined, the solution set is
$$\left\{-4+\sqrt{17}\right\} \approx \{0.123\}.$$

29. $\log_{1/3}(x^2+x)-\log_{1/3}(x^2-x)=-1$

$$\log_{1/3}\left(\frac{x^2+x}{x^2-x}\right)=-1$$

$$\frac{x^2+x}{x^2-x}=\left(\frac{1}{3}\right)^{-1}$$

$$\frac{x^2+x}{x^2-x}=3$$

$$x^2+x=3\left(x^2-x\right)$$

$$x^2+x=3x^2-3x$$

$$-2x^2+4x=0$$

$$-2x\left(x-2\right)=0$$

$$-2x=0 \quad\text{or}\quad x-2=0$$

$$x=0 \quad\text{or}\quad\quad x=2$$

Since each of the original logarithms are not defined for $x=0$, but are defined for $x=2$, the solution set is $\{2\}$.

30. $\log_4(x^2-9)-\log_4(x+3)=3$

$$\log_4\left(\frac{x^2-9}{x+3}\right)=3$$

$$\frac{(x-3)(x+3)}{x+3}=4^3$$

$$x-3=64$$

$$x=67$$

Since each of the original logarithms is defined for $x=67$, the solution set is $\{67\}$.

31. $\log_a(x-1)-\log_a(x+6)=\log_a(x-2)-\log_a(x+3)$

$$\log_a\left(\frac{x-1}{x+6}\right)=\log_a\left(\frac{x-2}{x+3}\right)$$

$$\frac{x-1}{x+6}=\frac{x-2}{x+3}$$

$$(x-1)(x+3)=(x-2)(x+6)$$

$$x^2+2x-3=x^2+4x-12$$

$$2x-3=4x-12$$

$$9=2x$$

$$x=\frac{9}{2}$$

Since each of the original logarithms is defined for $x=\frac{9}{2}$, the solution set is $\left\{\frac{9}{2}\right\}$.

32. $\log_a x+\log_a(x-2)=\log_a(x+4)$

$$\log_a\left(x(x-2)\right)=\log_a(x+4)$$

$$x(x-2)=x+4$$

$$x^2-2x=x+4$$

$$x^2-3x-4=0$$

$$(x-4)(x+1)=0$$

$$x=4 \quad\text{or}\quad x=-1$$

Since $\log_a(-1)$ is undefined, the solution set is $\{4\}$.

33. $2^{x-5}=8$

$$2^{x-5}=2^3$$

$$x-5=3$$

$$x=8$$

The solution set is $\{8\}$.

34. $5^{-x}=25$

$$5^{-x}=5^2$$

$$-x=2$$

$$x=-2$$

The solution set is $\{-2\}$.

35. $2^x=10$

$$x=\log_2 10=\frac{\ln 10}{\ln 2}\approx 3.322$$

The solution set is

$$\{\log_2 10\}=\left\{\frac{\ln 10}{\ln 2}\right\}\approx\{3.322\}.$$

36. $3^x=14$

$$x=\log_3 14=\frac{\ln 14}{\ln 3}\approx 2.402$$

The solution set is

$$\{\log_3 14\}=\left\{\frac{\ln 14}{\ln 3}\right\}\approx\{2.402\}.$$

37. $8^{-x}=1.2$

$$-x=\log_8 1.2$$

$$x=-\log_8 1.2=-\frac{\log(1.2)}{\log 8}\approx -0.088$$

The solution set is

$$\{-\log_8 1.2\}=\left\{\frac{\log(1.2)}{-\log 8}\right\}\approx\{-0.088\}.$$

38. $2^{-x} = 1.5$

$-x = \log_2 1.5$

$x = -\log_2 1.5 = -\dfrac{\log 1.5}{\log 2} \approx -0.585$

The solution set is

$\left\{ -\log_2 1.5 \right\} = \left\{ -\dfrac{\log 1.5}{\log 2} \right\} \approx \left\{ -0.585 \right\}$.

39. $5\left(2^{3x}\right) = 8$

$2^{3x} = \dfrac{8}{5}$

$3x = \log_2\left(\dfrac{8}{5}\right)$

$x = \dfrac{1}{3}\log_2\left(\dfrac{8}{5}\right) = \dfrac{\ln(8/5)}{3\ln 2} \approx 0.226$

The solution set is

$\left\{ \dfrac{1}{3}\log_2\left(\dfrac{8}{5}\right) \right\} = \left\{ \dfrac{\ln(8/5)}{3\ln 2} \right\} \approx \left\{ 0.226 \right\}$.

40. $0.3\left(4^{0.2x}\right) = 0.2$

$4^{0.2x} = \dfrac{2}{3}$

$0.2x = \log_4\left(\dfrac{2}{3}\right)$

$x = \dfrac{\log_4(2/3)}{0.2} = \dfrac{\ln(2/3)}{0.2\ln 4} \approx -1.462$

The solution set

is $\left\{ \dfrac{\log_4(2/3)}{0.2} \right\} = \left\{ \dfrac{\ln(2/3)}{0.2\ln 4} \right\} \approx \left\{ -1.462 \right\}$.

41. $3^{1-2x} = 4^x$

$\ln\left(3^{1-2x}\right) = \ln\left(4^x\right)$

$(1-2x)\ln 3 = x\ln 4$

$\ln 3 - 2x\ln 3 = x\ln 4$

$\ln 3 = 2x\ln 3 + x\ln 4$

$\ln 3 = x(2\ln 3 + \ln 4)$

$x = \dfrac{\ln 3}{2\ln 3 + \ln 4} \approx 0.307$

The solution set is $\left\{ \dfrac{\ln 3}{2\ln 3 + \ln 4} \right\} \approx \left\{ 0.307 \right\}$.

42. $2^{x+1} = 5^{1-2x}$

$\ln\left(2^{x+1}\right) = \ln\left(5^{1-2x}\right)$

$(x+1)\ln 2 = (1-2x)\ln 5$

$x\ln 2 + \ln 2 = \ln 5 - 2x\ln 5$

$x\ln 2 + 2x\ln 5 = \ln 5 - \ln 2$

$x(\ln 2 + 2\ln 5) = \ln 5 - \ln 2$

$x = \dfrac{\ln 5 - \ln 2}{\ln 2 + 2\ln 5} \approx 0.234$

The solution set is $\left\{ \dfrac{\ln 5 - \ln 2}{\ln 2 + 2\ln 5} \right\} \approx \left\{ 0.234 \right\}$.

43. $\left(\dfrac{3}{5}\right)^x = 7^{1-x}$

$\ln\left(\dfrac{3}{5}\right)^x = \ln\left(7^{1-x}\right)$

$x\ln(3/5) = (1-x)\ln 7$

$x\ln(3/5) = \ln 7 - x\ln 7$

$x\ln(3/5) + x\ln 7 = \ln 7$

$x\left(\ln(3/5) + \ln 7\right) = \ln 7$

$x = \dfrac{\ln 7}{\ln(3/5) + \ln 7} \approx 1.356$

The solution set is $\left\{ \dfrac{\ln 7}{\ln(3/5) + \ln 7} \right\} \approx \left\{ 1.356 \right\}$.

44. $\left(\dfrac{4}{3}\right)^{1-x} = 5^x$

$\ln\left(\dfrac{4}{3}\right)^{1-x} = \ln\left(5^x\right)$

$(1-x)\ln(4/3) = x\ln 5$

$\ln(4/3) - x\ln(4/3) = x\ln 5$

$\ln(4/3) = x\ln 5 + x\ln(4/3)$

$\ln(4/3) = x\left(\ln 5 + \ln(4/3)\right)$

$x = \dfrac{\ln(4/3)}{\ln 5 + \ln(4/3)} \approx 0.152$

The solution set is $\left\{ \dfrac{\ln(4/3)}{\ln 5 + \ln(4/3)} \right\} \approx \left\{ 0.152 \right\}$.

651

45.
$$1.2^x = (0.5)^{-x}$$
$$\ln 1.2^x = \ln(0.5)^{-x}$$
$$x \ln(1.2) = -x \ln(0.5)$$
$$x \ln(1.2) + x \ln(0.5) = 0$$
$$x\big(\ln(1.2) + \ln(0.5)\big) = 0$$
$$x = 0$$
The solution set is $\{0\}$.

46.
$$0.3^{1+x} = 1.7^{2x-1}$$
$$\ln\big(0.3^{1+x}\big) = \ln\big(1.7^{2x-1}\big)$$
$$(1+x)\ln(0.3) = (2x-1)\ln(1.7)$$
$$\ln(0.3) + x\ln(0.3) = 2x\ln(1.7) - \ln(1.7)$$
$$x\ln(0.3) - 2x\ln(1.7) = -\ln(1.7) - \ln(0.3)$$
$$x\big(\ln(0.3) - 2\ln(1.7)\big) = -\ln(1.7) - \ln(0.3)$$
$$x = \frac{-\ln(1.7) - \ln(0.3)}{\ln(0.3) - 2\ln(1.7)} \approx -0.297$$
The solution set is
$$\left\{ \frac{-\ln(1.7) - \ln(0.3)}{\ln(0.3) - 2\ln(1.7)} \right\} \approx \{-0.297\}.$$

47.
$$\pi^{1-x} = e^x$$
$$\ln \pi^{1-x} = \ln e^x$$
$$(1-x)\ln \pi = x$$
$$\ln \pi - x\ln \pi = x$$
$$\ln \pi = x + x\ln \pi$$
$$\ln \pi = x(1 + \ln \pi)$$
$$x = \frac{\ln \pi}{1 + \ln \pi} \approx 0.534$$
The solution set is $\left\{ \dfrac{\ln \pi}{1 + \ln \pi} \right\} \approx \{0.534\}$.

48.
$$e^{x+3} = \pi^x$$
$$\ln e^{x+3} = \ln \pi^x$$
$$x + 3 = x\ln \pi$$
$$3 = x\ln \pi - x$$
$$3 = x(\ln \pi - 1)$$
$$x = \frac{3}{\ln \pi - 1} \approx 20.728$$
The solution set is $\left\{ \dfrac{3}{\ln \pi - 1} \right\} \approx \{20.728\}$.

49.
$$2^{2x} + 2^x - 12 = 0$$
$$\big(2^x\big)^2 + 2^x - 12 = 0$$
$$\big(2^x - 3\big)\big(2^x + 4\big) = 0$$
$$2^x - 3 = 0 \qquad \text{or} \qquad 2^x + 4 = 0$$
$$2^x = 3 \qquad \text{or} \qquad 2^x = -4$$
$$\ln\big(2^x\big) = \ln 3 \qquad\qquad \text{No solution}$$
$$x\ln 2 = \ln 3$$
$$x = \frac{\ln 3}{\ln 2} \approx 1.585$$
The solution set is $\left\{ \dfrac{\ln 3}{\ln 2} \approx 1.585 \right\}$.

50.
$$3^{2x} + 3^x - 2 = 0$$
$$\big(3^x\big)^2 + 3^x - 2 = 0$$
$$\big(3^x - 1\big)\big(3^x + 2\big) = 0$$
$$3^x - 1 = 0 \quad \text{or} \quad 3^x + 2 = 0$$
$$3^x = 1 \quad \text{or} \quad 3^x = -2$$
$$x = 0 \qquad\qquad \text{No solution}$$
The solution set is $\{0\}$.

51.
$$3^{2x} + 3^{x+1} - 4 = 0$$
$$\big(3^x\big)^2 + 3 \cdot 3^x - 4 = 0$$
$$\big(3^x - 1\big)\big(3^x + 4\big) = 0$$
$$3^x - 1 = 0 \quad \text{or} \quad 3^x + 4 = 0$$
$$3^x = 1 \quad \text{or} \quad 3^x = -4$$
$$x = 0 \qquad\qquad \text{No solution}$$
The solution set is $\{0\}$.

52.
$$2^{2x} + 2^{x+2} - 12 = 0$$
$$\big(2^x\big)^2 + 2^2 \cdot 2^x - 12 = 0$$
$$\big(2^x - 2\big)\big(2^x + 6\big) = 0$$
$$2^x - 2 = 0 \quad \text{or} \quad 2^x + 6 = 0$$
$$2^x = 2 \quad \text{or} \quad 2^x = -6$$
$$x = 1 \qquad\qquad \text{No solution}$$
The solution set is $\{1\}$.

53. $16^x + 4^{x+1} - 3 = 0$

$\left(4^2\right)^x + 4 \cdot 4^x - 3 = 0$

$\left(4^x\right)^2 + 4 \cdot 4^x - 3 = 0$

Let $u = 4^x$.

$u^2 + 4u - 3 = 0$

$a = 1, b = 4, c = -3$

$u = \dfrac{-4 \pm \sqrt{4^2 - 4(1)(-3)}}{2(1)} = \dfrac{-4 \pm \sqrt{28}}{2}$

$ = \dfrac{-4 \pm 2\sqrt{7}}{2} = -2 \pm \sqrt{7}$

Therefore, we get

$\cancel{4^x = -2 - \sqrt{7}}$ or $4^x = -2 + \sqrt{7}$

$\phantom{4^x = -2 + \sqrt{7}} x = \log_4\left(-2 + \sqrt{7}\right)$

(we ignore the first solution since 4^x is never negative)

The solution set is $\left\{\log_4\left(-2 + \sqrt{7}\right)\right\} \approx \{-0.315\}$.

54. $9^x - 3^{x+1} + 1 = 0$

$\left(3^2\right)^x - 3 \cdot 3^x + 1 = 0$

$\left(3^x\right)^2 - 3 \cdot 3^x + 1 = 0$

Let $u = 3^x$.

$u^2 - 3u + 1 = 0$

$a = 1, b = -3, c = 1$

$u = \dfrac{3 \pm \sqrt{(-3)^2 - 4(1)(1)}}{2(1)} = \dfrac{3 \pm \sqrt{5}}{2}$

Therefore, we get

$3^x = \dfrac{3 \pm \sqrt{5}}{2}$

$x = \log_3\left(\dfrac{3 \pm \sqrt{5}}{2}\right)$

The solution set is

$\left\{\log_3\left(\dfrac{3 - \sqrt{5}}{2}\right), \log_3\left(\dfrac{3 + \sqrt{5}}{2}\right)\right\}$

$\approx \{-0.876, 0.876\}$.

55. $25^x - 8 \cdot 5^x = -16$

$\left(5^2\right)^x - 8 \cdot 5^x = -16$

$\left(5^x\right)^2 - 8 \cdot 5^x = -16$

Let $u = 5^x$.

$u^2 - 8u = -16$

$u^2 - 8u + 16 = 0$

$\left(u - 4\right)^2 = 0$

$u = 4$

Therefore, we get

$5^x = 4$

$x = \log_5 4$

The solution set is $\left\{\log_5 4\right\} \approx \{0.861\}$.

56. $36^x - 6 \cdot 6^x = -9$

$\left(6^2\right)^x - 6 \cdot 6^x + 9 = 0$

$\left(6^x\right)^2 - 6 \cdot 6^x + 9 = 0$

$\left(6^x - 3\right)^2 = 0$

$6^x = 3$

$x = \log_6 3$

The solution set is $\left\{\log_6 3\right\} \approx \{0.613\}$.

57. $3 \cdot 4^x + 4 \cdot 2^x + 8 = 0$

$3 \cdot \left(2^2\right)^x + 4 \cdot 2^x + 8 = 0$

$3 \cdot \left(2^x\right)^2 + 4 \cdot 2^x + 8 = 0$

Let $u = 2^x$.

$3u^2 + 4u + 8 = 0$

$a = 3, b = 4, c = 8$

$u = \dfrac{-4 \pm \sqrt{4^2 - 4(3)(8)}}{2(3)}$

$ = \dfrac{-4 \pm \sqrt{-80}}{6} = \text{not real}$

The equation has no real solution.

58. $2 \cdot 49^x + 11 \cdot 7^x + 5 = 0$

$2 \cdot \left(7^2\right)^x + 11 \cdot 7^x + 5 = 0$

$2 \cdot \left(7^x\right)^2 + 11 \cdot 7^x + 5 = 0$

Let $u = 7^x$.

$2u^2 + 11u + 5 = 0$

$(2u + 1)(u + 5) = 0$

$2u + 1 = 0$ or $u + 5 = 0$

$2u = -1$ $u = -5$

$u = -\dfrac{1}{2}$

Therefore, we get

$7^x = -\dfrac{1}{2}$ or $7^x = -5$

Since $7^x > 0$ for all x, the equation has no real solution.

59. $4^x - 10 \cdot 4^{-x} = 3$

Multiply both sides of the equation by 4^x.

$\left(4^x\right)^2 - 10 \cdot 4^{-x} \cdot 4^x = 3 \cdot 4^x$

$\left(4^x\right)^2 - 10 = 3 \cdot 4^x$

$\left(4^x\right)^2 - 3 \cdot 4^x - 10 = 0$

$\left(4^x - 5\right)\left(4^x + 2\right) = 0$

$4^x - 5 = 0$ or $4^x + 2 = 0$

$4^x = 5$ ~~$4^x = -2$~~

$x = \log_4 5$

The solution set is $\left\{\log_4 5\right\} \approx \{1.161\}$.

60. $3^x - 14 \cdot 3^{-x} = 5$

Multiply both sides of the equation by 3^x.

$\left(3^x\right)^2 - 14 \cdot 3^{-x} \cdot 3^x = 5 \cdot 3^x$

$\left(3^x\right)^2 - 14 = 5 \cdot 3^x$

$\left(3^x\right)^2 - 5 \cdot 3^x - 14 = 0$

$\left(3^x - 7\right)\left(3^x + 2\right) = 0$

$3^x - 7 = 0$ or $3^x + 2 = 0$

$3^x = 7$ ~~$3^x = -2$~~

$x = \log_3 7$

The solution set is $\left\{\log_3 7\right\} \approx \{1.771\}$.

61. $\log_5(x + 1) - \log_4(x - 2) = 1$

Using INTERSECT to solve:

$y_1 = \ln(x + 1) / \ln(5) - \ln(x - 2) / \ln(4)$

$y_2 = 1$

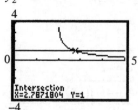

Thus, $x \approx 2.79$, so the solution set is $\{2.79\}$.

62. $\log_2(x - 1) - \log_6(x + 2) = 2$

Using INTERSECT to solve:

$y_1 = \ln(x - 1) / \ln(2) - \ln(x + 2) / \ln(6)$

$y_2 = 2$

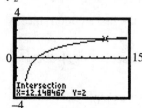

Thus, $x \approx 12.15$, so the solution set is $\{12.15\}$.

63. $e^x = -x$

Using INTERSECT to solve: $y_1 = e^x$; $y_2 = -x$

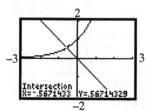

Thus, $x \approx -0.57$, so the solution set is $\{-0.57\}$.

64. $e^{2x} = x + 2$

Using INTERSECT to solve:

$y_1 = e^{2x}$; $y_2 = x + 2$

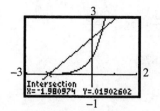 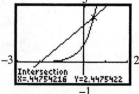

Thus, $x \approx -1.98$ or $x \approx 0.45$, so the solution set is $\{-1.98, \ 0.45\}$.

65. $e^x = x^2$

Using INTERSECT to solve:

$y_1 = e^x$; $y_2 = x^2$

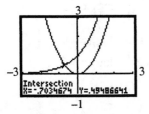

Thus, $x \approx -0.70$, so the solution set is $\{-0.70\}$.

66. $e^x = x^3$

Using INTERSECT to solve:

$y_1 = e^x$; $y_2 = x^3$

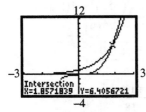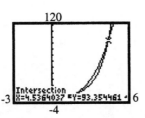

Thus, $x \approx 1.86$ or $x \approx 4.54$, so the solution set is $\{1.86, \ 4.54\}$.

67. $\ln x = -x$

Using INTERSECT to solve:

$y_1 = \ln x$; $y_2 = -x$

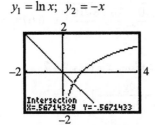

Thus, $x \approx 0.57$, so the solution set is $\{0.57\}$.

68. $\ln(2x) = -x + 2$

Using INTERSECT to solve:

$y_1 = \ln(2x)$; $y_2 = -x + 2$

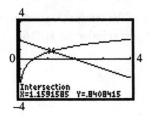

Thus, $x \approx 1.16$, so the solution set is $\{1.16\}$.

69. $\ln x = x^3 - 1$

Using INTERSECT to solve:

$y_1 = \ln x$; $y_2 = x^3 - 1$

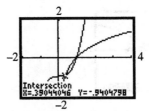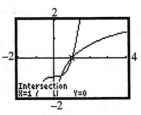

Thus, $x \approx 0.39$ or $x = 1$, so the solution set is $\{0.39, \ 1\}$.

70. $\ln x = -x^2$

Using INTERSECT to solve:

$y_1 = \ln x$; $y_2 = -x^2$

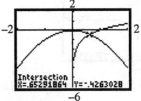

Thus, $x \approx 0.65$, so the solution set is $\{0.65\}$.

71. $e^x + \ln x = 4$

Using INTERSECT to solve:

$y_1 = e^x + \ln x$; $y_2 = 4$

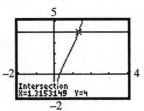

Thus, $x \approx 1.32$, so the solution set is $\{1.32\}$.

72. $e^x - \ln x = 4$

Using INTERSECT to solve:

$y_1 = e^x - \ln x$; $y_2 = 4$

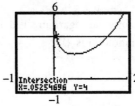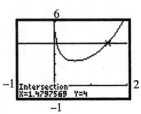

Thus, $x \approx 0.05$ or $x \approx 1.48$, so the solution set is $\{0.05, \ 1.48\}$.

73. $e^{-x} = \ln x$

Using INTERSECT to solve:

$y_1 = e^{-x}; \quad y_2 = \ln x$

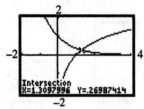

Thus, $x \approx 1.31$, so the solution set is $\{1.31\}$.

74. $e^{-x} = -\ln x$

Using INTERSECT to solve:

$y_1 = e^{-x}; \quad y_2 = -\ln x$

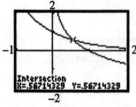

Thus, $x \approx 0.57$, so the solution set is $\{0.57\}$

75. $\log_2(x+1) - \log_4 x = 1$

$\log_2(x+1) - \dfrac{\log_2 x}{\log_2 4} = 1$

$\log_2(x+1) - \dfrac{\log_2 x}{2} = 1$

$2\log_2(x+1) - \log_2 x = 2$

$\log_2(x+1)^2 - \log_2 x = 2$

$\log_2\left(\dfrac{(x+1)^2}{x}\right) = 2$

$\dfrac{(x+1)^2}{x} = 2^2$

$x^2 + 2x + 1 = 4x$

$x^2 - 2x + 1 = 0$

$(x-1)^2 = 0$

$x - 1 = 0$

$x = 1$

Since each of the original logarithms is defined for $x = 1$, the solution set is $\{1\}$.

76. $\log_2(3x+2) - \log_4 x = 3$

$\log_2(3x+2) - \dfrac{\log_2 x}{\log_2 4} = 3$

$\log_2(3x+2) - \dfrac{\log_2 x}{2} = 3$

$2\log_2(3x+2) - \log_2 x = 6$

$\log_2(3x+2)^2 - \log_2 x = 6$

$\log_2\left(\dfrac{(3x+2)^2}{x}\right) = 6$

$\dfrac{(3x+2)^2}{x} = 2^6$

$9x^2 + 12x + 4 = 64x$

$9x^2 - 52x + 4 = 0$

$x = \dfrac{52 \pm \sqrt{(-52)^2 - 4(9)(4)}}{2(9)}$

$= \dfrac{52 \pm \sqrt{2560}}{18}$

$= \dfrac{52 \pm 16\sqrt{10}}{18}$

$= \dfrac{26 \pm 8\sqrt{10}}{9}$

$\approx 5.700 \text{ or } 0.078$

Since each of the original logarithms is defined for $x = 0.078$ and $x = 5.700$, the solution set is

$\left\{\dfrac{26 - 8\sqrt{10}}{9}, \dfrac{26 + 8\sqrt{10}}{9}\right\} \approx \{0.078, 5.700\}$.

77. $\log_{16} x + \log_4 x + \log_2 x = 7$

$\dfrac{\log_2 x}{\log_2 16} + \dfrac{\log_2 x}{\log_2 4} + \log_2 x = 7$

$\dfrac{\log_2 x}{4} + \dfrac{\log_2 x}{2} + \log_2 x = 7$

$\log_2 x + 2\log_2 x + 4\log_2 x = 28$

$7\log_2 x = 28$

$\log_2 x = 4$

$x = 2^4 = 16$

Since each of the original logarithms is defined for $x = 16$, the solution set is $\{16\}$.

78. $\log_9 x + 3\log_3 x = 14$

$\dfrac{\log_3 x}{\log_3 9} + 3\log_3 x = 14$

$\dfrac{\log_3 x}{2} + 3\log_3 x = 14$

$\dfrac{7}{2}\log_3 x = 14$

$\log_3 x = 4$

$x = 3^4 = 81$

Since each of the original logarithms is defined for $x = 81$, the solution set is $\{81\}$.

79. $\left(\sqrt[3]{2}\right)^{2-x} = 2^{x^2}$

$\left(2^{1/3}\right)^{2-x} = 2^{x^2}$

$2^{\frac{1}{3}(2-x)} = 2^{x^2}$

$\dfrac{1}{3}(2-x) = x^2$

$2 - x = 3x^2$

$3x^2 + x - 2 = 0$

$(3x-2)(x+1) = 0$

$x = \dfrac{2}{3}$ or $x = -1$

The solution set is $\left\{-1, \dfrac{2}{3}\right\}$.

80. $\log_2 x^{\log_2 x} = 4$

$\log_2 x \cdot \log_2 x = 4$

$\left(\log_2 x\right)^2 = 4$

$\log_2 x = -2$ or $\log_2 x = 2$

$x = 2^{-2}$ or $x = 2^2$

$x = \dfrac{1}{4}$ or $x = 4$

Since each of the original logarithms is defined for both $x = \dfrac{1}{4}$ and $x = 4$, the solution set is

$\left\{\dfrac{1}{4}, 4\right\}$.

81. $\dfrac{e^x + e^{-x}}{2} = 1$

$e^x + e^{-x} = 2$

$e^x(e^x + e^{-x}) = 2e^x$

$e^{2x} + 1 = 2e^x$

$(e^x)^2 - 2e^x + 1 = 0$

$(e^x - 1)^2 = 0$

$e^x - 1 = 0$

$e^x = 1$

$x = 0$

The solution set is $\{0\}$.

82. $\dfrac{e^x + e^{-x}}{2} = 3$

$e^x + e^{-x} = 6$

$e^x(e^x + e^{-x}) = 6e^x$

$e^{2x} + 1 = 6e^x$

$(e^x)^2 - 6e^x + 1 = 0$

$e^x = \dfrac{6 \pm \sqrt{(-6)^2 - 4(1)(1)}}{2(1)}$

$= \dfrac{6 \pm \sqrt{32}}{2} = \dfrac{6 \pm 4\sqrt{2}}{2} = 3 \pm 2\sqrt{2}$

$x = \ln\left(3 - 2\sqrt{2}\right)$ or $x = \ln\left(3 + 2\sqrt{2}\right)$

$x \approx -1.763$ or $x \approx 1.763$

The solution set is

$\left\{\ln\left(3 - 2\sqrt{2}\right),\ \ln\left(3 + 2\sqrt{2}\right)\right\} \approx \{-1.763, 1.763\}$.

83. $\dfrac{e^x - e^{-x}}{2} = 2$

$e^x - e^{-x} = 4$

$e^x(e^x - e^{-x}) = 4e^x$

$e^{2x} - 1 = 4e^x$

$(e^x)^2 - 4e^x - 1 = 0$

$e^x = \dfrac{-(-4) \pm \sqrt{(-4)^2 - 4(1)(-1)}}{2(1)}$

$= \dfrac{4 \pm \sqrt{20}}{2} = \dfrac{4 \pm 2\sqrt{5}}{2} = 2 \pm \sqrt{5}$

$x = \ln\left(2 - \sqrt{5}\right)$ or $x = \ln\left(2 + \sqrt{5}\right)$

$x \approx \ln(-0.236)$ or $x \approx 1.444$

Since $\ln(-0.236)$ is undefined, the solution set is

$\left\{\ln\left(2 + \sqrt{5}\right)\right\} \approx \{1.444\}$.

84.

$$\frac{e^x - e^{-x}}{2} = -2$$

$$e^x - e^{-x} = -4$$

$$e^x \left(e^x - e^{-x} \right) = -4e^x$$

$$e^{2x} - 1 = -4e^x$$

$$\left(e^x \right)^2 + 4e^x - 1 = 0$$

$$e^x = \frac{-4 \pm \sqrt{4^2 - 4(1)(-1)}}{2(1)}$$

$$= \frac{-4 \pm \sqrt{20}}{2}$$

$$= \frac{-4 \pm 2\sqrt{5}}{2} = -2 \pm \sqrt{5}$$

$$x = \ln\left(-2 - \sqrt{5}\right) \text{ or } x = \ln\left(-2 + \sqrt{5}\right)$$

$$x \approx \ln(-4.236) \text{ or } x \approx -1.444$$

Since $\ln(-4.236)$ is undefined, the solution set is $\left\{ \ln\left(-2 + \sqrt{5}\right) \right\} \approx \{-1.444\}$.

85.

$$\log_5 x + \log_3 x = 1$$

$$\frac{\ln x}{\ln 5} + \frac{\ln x}{\ln 3} = 1$$

$$\left(\ln x \right)\left(\frac{1}{\ln 5} + \frac{1}{\ln 3} \right) = 1$$

$$\ln x = \frac{1}{\dfrac{1}{\ln 5} + \dfrac{1}{\ln 3}}$$

$$\ln x = \frac{(\ln 5)(\ln 3)}{\ln 3 + \ln 5}$$

$$\ln x = \frac{(\ln 5)(\ln 3)}{\ln 15}$$

$$x = e^{\left(\frac{(\ln 5)(\ln 3)}{\ln 15} \right)} \approx 1.921$$

The solution set is $\left\{ e^{\left(\frac{(\ln 5)(\ln 3)}{\ln 15} \right)} \right\} \approx \{1.921\}$.

86.

$$\log_2 x + \log_6 x = 3$$

$$\frac{\ln x}{\ln 2} + \frac{\ln x}{\ln 6} = 3$$

$$\left(\ln x \right)\left(\frac{1}{\ln 2} + \frac{1}{\ln 6} \right) = 3$$

$$\ln x = \frac{3}{\dfrac{1}{\ln 2} + \dfrac{1}{\ln 6}}$$

$$\ln x = \frac{3(\ln 2)(\ln 6)}{\ln 6 + \ln 2}$$

$$\ln x = \frac{3(\ln 2)(\ln 6)}{\ln 12}$$

$$x = e^{\left(\frac{3(\ln 2)(\ln 6)}{\ln 12} \right)} \approx 4.479$$

The solution set is $\left\{ e^{\left(\frac{3(\ln 2)(\ln 6)}{\ln 12} \right)} \right\} \approx \{4.479\}$.

87. a.

$$f(x) = 3$$

$$\log_2 (x + 3) = 3$$

$$x + 3 = 2^3$$

$$x + 3 = 8$$

$$x = 5$$

The solution set is $\{5\}$. The point $(5, 3)$ is on the graph of f.

b.

$$g(x) = 4$$

$$\log_2 (3x + 1) = 4$$

$$3x + 1 = 2^4$$

$$3x + 1 = 16$$

$$3x = 15$$

$$x = 5$$

The solution set is $\{5\}$. The point $(5, 4)$ is on the graph of g.

c.

$$f(x) = g(x)$$

$$\log_2 (x + 3) = \log_2 (3x + 1)$$

$$x + 3 = 3x + 1$$

$$2 = 2x$$

$$1 = x$$

The solution set is $\{1\}$, so the graphs intersect when $x = 1$. That is, at the point $(1, 2)$.

d.
$$f(x) + g(x) = 7$$
$$\log_2(x+3) + \log_2(3x+1) = 7$$
$$\log_2\left[(x+3)(3x+1)\right] = 7$$
$$(x+3)(3x+1) = 2^7$$
$$3x^2 + 10x + 3 = 128$$
$$3x^2 + 10x - 125 = 0$$
$$(3x+25)(x-5) = 0$$
$$\cancel{3x+25=0} \quad \text{or} \quad x-5=0$$
$$\cancel{3x=-25} \qquad\qquad x=5$$
$$\cancel{x = -\frac{25}{3}}$$

The solution set is $\{5\}$.

e.
$$f(x) - g(x) = 2$$
$$\log_2(x+3) - \log_2(3x+1) = 2$$
$$\log_2\frac{x+3}{3x+1} = 2$$
$$\frac{x+3}{3x+1} = 2^2$$
$$x+3 = 4(3x+1)$$
$$x+3 = 12x + 4$$
$$-1 = 11x$$
$$-\frac{1}{11} = x$$

The solution set is $\left\{-\dfrac{1}{11}\right\}$.

88. a.
$$f(x) = 2$$
$$\log_3(x+5) = 2$$
$$x+5 = 3^2$$
$$x+5 = 9$$
$$x = 4$$

The solution set is $\{4\}$. The point $(4,2)$ is on the graph of f.

b.
$$g(x) = 3$$
$$\log_3(x-1) = 3$$
$$x-1 = 3^3$$
$$x-1 = 27$$
$$x = 28$$

The solution set is $\{28\}$. The point $(28,3)$ is on the graph of g.

c.
$$f(x) = g(x)$$
$$\log_3(x+5) = \log_3(x-1)$$
$$x+5 = x-1$$
$$5 = -1 \quad \text{False}$$

This is a contradiction, so the equation has no solution. The graphs do not intersect.

d.
$$f(x) + g(x) = 3$$
$$\log_3(x+5) + \log_3(x-1) = 3$$
$$\log_3\left[(x+5)(x-1)\right] = 3$$
$$(x+5)(x-1) = 3^3$$
$$x^2 + 4x - 5 = 27$$
$$x^2 + 4x - 32 = 0$$
$$(x+8)(x-4) = 0$$
$$\cancel{x+8=0} \quad \text{or} \quad x-4=0$$
$$\cancel{x=-8} \qquad\qquad x=4$$

The solution set is $\{4\}$.

e.
$$f(x) - g(x) = 2$$
$$\log_3(x+5) - \log_3(x-1) = 2$$
$$\log_3\frac{x+5}{x-1} = 2$$
$$\frac{x+5}{x-1} = 3^2$$
$$x+5 = 9(x-1)$$
$$x+5 = 9x - 9$$
$$14 = 8x$$
$$\frac{7}{4} = x$$

The solution set is $\left\{\dfrac{7}{4}\right\}$.

89. a.

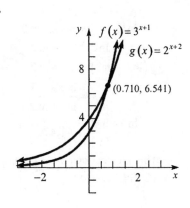

$$f(x) = 3^{x+1}$$
$$g(x) = 2^{x+2}$$
$$(0.710, 6.541)$$

b.
$$f(x) = g(x)$$
$$3^{x+1} = 2^{x+2}$$
$$\ln(3^{x+1}) = \ln(2^{x+2})$$
$$(x+1)\ln 3 = (x+2)\ln 2$$
$$x\ln 3 + \ln 3 = x\ln 2 + 2\ln 2$$
$$x\ln 3 - x\ln 2 = 2\ln 2 - \ln 3$$
$$x(\ln 3 - \ln 2) = 2\ln 2 - \ln 3$$
$$x = \frac{2\ln 2 - \ln 3}{\ln 3 - \ln 2} \approx 0.710$$
$$f\left(\frac{2\ln 2 - \ln 3}{\ln 3 - \ln 2}\right) \approx 6.541$$
The intersection point is roughly $(0.710, 6.541)$.

c. Based on the graph, $f(x) > g(x)$ for $x > 0.710$. The solution set is $\{x \mid x > 0.710\}$ or $(0.710, \infty)$.

90. a.

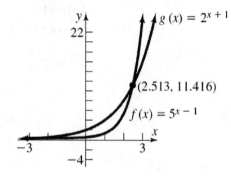

b.
$$f(x) = g(x)$$
$$5^{x-1} = 2^{x+1}$$
$$\ln(5^{x-1}) = \ln(2^{x+1})$$
$$(x-1)\ln 5 = (x+1)\ln 2$$
$$x\ln 5 - \ln 5 = x\ln 2 + \ln 2$$
$$x\ln 5 - x\ln 2 = \ln 5 + \ln 2$$
$$x(\ln 5 - \ln 2) = \ln 5 + \ln 2$$
$$x = \frac{\ln 5 + \ln 2}{\ln 5 - \ln 2} \approx 2.513$$
$$f\left(\frac{\ln 5 + \ln 2}{\ln 5 - \ln 2}\right) \approx 11.416$$
The intersection point is roughly $(2.513, 11.416)$.

c. Based on the graph, $f(x) > g(x)$ for $x > 2.513$. The solution set is $\{x \mid x > 2.513\}$ or $(2.513, \infty)$.

91. a., b.

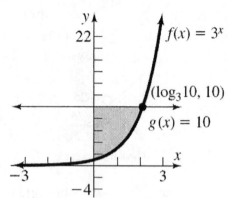

c.
$$f(x) = g(x)$$
$$3^x = 10$$
$$x = \log_3 10$$
The intersection point is $(\log_3 10, 10)$.

92. a., b.

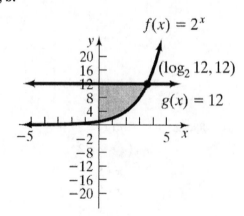

c.
$$f(x) = g(x)$$
$$2^x = 12$$
$$x = \log_2 12$$
The intersection point is $(\log_2 12, 12)$.

93. a., b.

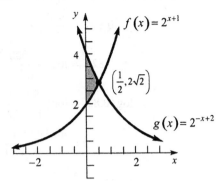

c. $f(x) = g(x)$

$2^{x+1} = 2^{-x+2}$

$x + 1 = -x + 2$

$2x = 1$

$x = \dfrac{1}{2}$

$f\left(\dfrac{1}{2}\right) = 2^{1/2+1} = 2^{3/2} = 2\sqrt{2}$

The intersection point is $\left(\dfrac{1}{2}, 2\sqrt{2}\right)$.

94. a., b.

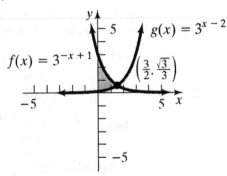

c. $f(x) = g(x)$

$3^{-x+1} = 3^{x-2}$

$-x + 1 = x - 2$

$-2x = -3$

$x = \dfrac{3}{2}$

$f\left(\dfrac{3}{2}\right) = 3^{-3/2+1} = 3^{-1/2} = \dfrac{1}{\sqrt{3}} = \dfrac{\sqrt{3}}{3}$

The intersection point is $\left(\dfrac{3}{2}, \dfrac{\sqrt{3}}{3}\right)$.

95. a. $f(x) = 2^x - 4$

Using the graph of $y = 2^x$, shift the graph down 4 units.

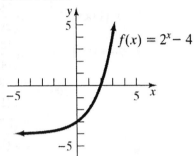

b. Based on the graph, $f(x) < 0$ when $x < 2$.

The solution set is $\{x \mid x < 2\}$ or $(-\infty, 2)$.

96. a. $g(x) = 3^x - 9$

Using the graph of $y = 3^x$, shift the graph down nine units.

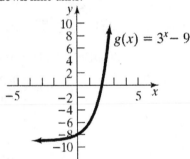

b. Based on the graph, $g(x) > 0$ when $x > 2$.

The solution set is $\{x \mid x > 2\}$ or $(2, \infty)$.

97. a.
$$298(1.009)^{t-2006} = 310$$
$$(1.009)^{t-2006} = \frac{310}{298}$$
$$\ln(1.009)^{t-2006} = \ln\left(\frac{310}{298}\right)$$
$$(t-2006)\ln(1.009) = \ln\left(\frac{155}{149}\right)$$
$$t - 2006 = \frac{\ln(155/149)}{\ln(1.009)}$$
$$t = \frac{\ln(155/149)}{\ln(1.009)} + 2006$$
$$\approx 2010.41$$

According to the model, the population of the U.S. will reach 310 million people around the middle of the year 2010.

661

b.
$$298(1.009)^{t-2006} = 360$$
$$(1.009)^{t-2006} = \frac{360}{298}$$
$$\ln(1.009)^{t-2006} = \ln\left(\frac{360}{298}\right)$$
$$(t-2006)\ln(1.009) = \ln\left(\frac{180}{149}\right)$$
$$t-2006 = \frac{\ln(180/149)}{\ln(1.009)}$$
$$t = \frac{\ln(180/149)}{\ln(1.009)} + 2006$$
$$\approx 2027.10$$

According to the model, the population of the U.S. will reach 360 million people in the beginning of the year 2027.

98. a.
$$6.53(1.0114)^{t-2006} = 9.25$$
$$(1.0114)^{t-2006} = \frac{9.25}{6.53}$$
$$\ln(1.0114)^{t-2006} = \ln\left(\frac{9.25}{6.53}\right)$$
$$(t-2006)\ln(1.0114) = \ln(9.25/6.53)$$
$$t-2006 = \frac{\ln(9.25/6.53)}{\ln(1.0114)}$$
$$t = \frac{\ln(9.25/6.53)}{\ln(1.0114)} + 2006$$
$$\approx 2036.72$$

According to the model, the population of the world will reach 9.25 billion people late in the year 2036.

b.
$$6.53(1.0114)^{t-2006} = 11.75$$
$$(1.0114)^{t-2006} = \frac{11.75}{6.53}$$
$$\ln(1.0114)^{t-2006} = \ln\left(\frac{11.75}{6.53}\right)$$
$$(t-2006)\ln(1.0114) = \ln(11.75/6.53)$$
$$t-2006 = \frac{\ln(11.75/6.53)}{\ln(1.0114)}$$
$$t = \frac{\ln(11.75/6.53)}{\ln(1.0114)} + 2006$$
$$\approx 2057.82$$

According to the model, the population of the world will reach 11.75 billion people late in the year 2057.

99. a.
$$14,512(0.82)^t = 9,000$$
$$(0.82)^t = \frac{9,000}{14,512}$$
$$\log(0.82)^t = \log\left(\frac{9,000}{14,512}\right)$$
$$t\log(0.82) = \log\left(\frac{9,000}{14,512}\right)$$
$$t = \frac{\log(9,000/14,512)}{\log(0.82)}$$
$$\approx 2.4$$

According to the model, the car will be worth $9,000 after about 2.4 years.

b.
$$14,512(0.82)^t = 4,000$$
$$(0.82)^t = \frac{4,000}{14,512}$$
$$\log(0.82)^t = \log\left(\frac{4,000}{14,512}\right)$$
$$t\log(0.82) = \log\left(\frac{4,000}{14,512}\right)$$
$$t = \frac{\log(4,000/14,512)}{\log(0.82)}$$
$$\approx 6.5$$

According to the model, the car will be worth $4,000 after about 6.5 years.

c.
$$14,512(0.82)^t = 2,000$$
$$(0.82)^t = \frac{2,000}{14,512}$$
$$\log(0.82)^t = \log\left(\frac{2,000}{14,512}\right)$$
$$t\log(0.82) = \log\left(\frac{2,000}{14,512}\right)$$
$$t = \frac{\log(2,000/14,512)}{\log(0.82)}$$
$$\approx 10.0$$

According to the model, the car will be worth $2,000 after about 10 years.

100. a. $19,282(0.84)^t = 15,000$

$$(0.84)^t = \frac{15,000}{19,282}$$

$$\log(0.84)^t = \log\left(\frac{15,000}{19,282}\right)$$

$$t\log(0.84) = \log\left(\frac{15,000}{19,282}\right)$$

$$t = \frac{\log(15,000/19,282)}{\log(0.84)} \approx 1.4$$

According to the model, the car will be worth $15,000 after about 1.4 years.

b. $19,282(0.84)^t = 8,000$

$$(0.84)^t = \frac{8,000}{19,282}$$

$$\log(0.84)^t = \log\left(\frac{8,000}{19,282}\right)$$

$$t\log(0.84) = \log\left(\frac{8,000}{19,282}\right)$$

$$t = \frac{\log(8,000/19,282)}{\log(0.84)} \approx 5.0$$

According to the model, the car will be worth $8,000 after about 5 years.

c. $19,282(0.84)^t = 2,000$

$$(0.84)^t = \frac{2,000}{19,282}$$

$$\log(0.84)^t = \log\left(\frac{2,000}{19,282}\right)$$

$$t\log(0.84) = \log\left(\frac{2,000}{19,282}\right)$$

$$t = \frac{\log(2,000/19,282)}{\log(0.84)} \approx 13.0$$

According to the model, the car will be worth $2,000 after about 13 years.

101. Solution A: change to exponential expression; square root method; meaning of $\pm$; solve.

Solution B: $\log_a M^r = r\log_a M$; divide by 2; change to exponential expression; solve.

The power rule $\log_a M^r = r\log_a M$ only applies when $M > 0$. In this equation, $M = x-1$. Now, $x = -2$ causes $M = -2-1 = -3$. Thus, if we use the power rule, we lose the valid solution $x = -2$.

Section 6.7

1. $P = \$500$, $r = 0.06$, $t = 6$ months $= 0.5$ year
$I = Prt = (500)(0.06)(0.5) = \$15.00$

2. $P = \$5000$, $t = 9$ months $= 0.75$ year, $I = \$500$
$500 = 5000r(0.75)$
$$r = \frac{500}{(5000)(0.75)}$$
$$= \frac{2}{15} = \frac{2}{15} \cdot 100\% = \frac{40}{3}\% = 13\frac{1}{3}\%$$

The per annum interest rate was $13\frac{1}{3}\%$.

3. $P = \$100$, $r = 0.04$, $n = 4$, $t = 2$
$$A = P\left(1+\frac{r}{n}\right)^{nt} = 100\left(1+\frac{0.04}{4}\right)^{(4)(2)} \approx \$108.29$$

4. $P = \$50$, $r = 0.06$, $n = 12$, $t = 3$
$$A = P\left(1+\frac{r}{n}\right)^{nt} = 50\left(1+\frac{0.06}{12}\right)^{(12)(3)} \approx \$59.83$$

5. $P = \$500$, $r = 0.08$, $n = 4$, $t = 2.5$
$$A = P\left(1+\frac{r}{n}\right)^{nt} = 500\left(1+\frac{0.08}{4}\right)^{(4)(2.5)} \approx \$609.50$$

6. $P = \$300$, $r = 0.12$, $n = 12$, $t = 1.5$
$$A = P\left(1+\frac{r}{n}\right)^{nt} = 300\left(1+\frac{0.12}{12}\right)^{(12)(1.5)} \approx \$358.84$$

7. $P = \$600$, $r = 0.05$, $n = 365$, $t = 3$
$$A = P\left(1+\frac{r}{n}\right)^{nt} = 600\left(1+\frac{0.05}{365}\right)^{(365)(3)} \approx \$697.09$$

8. $P = \$700$, $r = 0.06$, $n = 365$, $t = 2$
$$A = P\left(1+\frac{r}{n}\right)^{nt} = 700\left(1+\frac{0.06}{365}\right)^{(365)(2)} \approx \$789.24$$

9. $P = \$10$, $r = 0.11$, $t = 2$
$A = Pe^{rt} = 10e^{(0.11)(2)} \approx \$12.46$

10. $P = \$40$, $r = 0.07$, $t = 3$
$A = Pe^{rt} = 40e^{(0.07)(3)} \approx \$49.35$

11. $P = \$100$, $r = 0.10$, $t = 2.25$
$A = Pe^{rt} = 100e^{(0.10)(2.25)} \approx \$125.23$

663

12. $P = \$100$, $r = 0.12$, $t = 3.75$

$A = Pe^{rt} = 100e^{(0.12)(3.75)} \approx \$156.83$

13. $A = \$100$, $r = 0.06$, $n = 12$, $t = 2$

$P = A\left(1 + \dfrac{r}{n}\right)^{-nt} = 100\left(1 + \dfrac{0.06}{12}\right)^{(-12)(2)} \approx \$88.72$

14. $A = \$75$, $r = 0.08$, $n = 4$, $t = 3$

$P = A\left(1 + \dfrac{r}{n}\right)^{-nt} = 75\left(1 + \dfrac{0.08}{4}\right)^{(-4)(3)} \approx \$59.14$

15. $A = \$1000$, $r = 0.06$, $n = 365$, $t = 2.5$

$P = A\left(1 + \dfrac{r}{n}\right)^{-nt}$

$= 1000\left(1 + \dfrac{0.06}{365}\right)^{(-365)(2.5)} \approx \$860.72$

16. $A = \$800$, $r = 0.07$, $n = 12$, $t = 3.5$

$P = A\left(1 + \dfrac{r}{n}\right)^{-nt}$

$= 800\left(1 + \dfrac{0.07}{12}\right)^{(-12)(3.5)} \approx \$626.61$

17. $A = \$600$, $r = 0.04$, $n = 4$, $t = 2$

$P = A\left(1 + \dfrac{r}{n}\right)^{-nt} = 600\left(1 + \dfrac{0.04}{4}\right)^{(-4)(2)} \approx \$554.09$

18. $A = \$300$, $r = 0.03$, $n = 365$, $t = 4$

$P = A\left(1 + \dfrac{r}{n}\right)^{-nt}$

$= 300\left(1 + \dfrac{0.03}{365}\right)^{(-365)(4)} \approx \$266.08$

19. $A = \$80$, $r = 0.09$, $t = 3.25$

$P = Ae^{-rt} = 80e^{(-0.09)(3.25)} \approx \$59.71$

20. $A = \$800$, $r = 0.08$, $t = 2.5$

$P = Ae^{-rt} = 800e^{(-0.08)(2.5)} \approx \$654.98$

21. $A = \$400$, $r = 0.10$, $t = 1$

$P = Ae^{-rt} = 400e^{(-0.10)(1)} \approx \$361.93$

22. $A = \$1000$, $r = 0.12$, $t = 1$

$P = Ae^{-rt} = 1000e^{(-0.12)(1)} \approx \$886.92$

23. 6% compounded quarterly:

$A = 10{,}000\left(1 + \dfrac{0.06}{4}\right)^{(4)(1)} = \$10{,}613.64$

$6\frac{1}{4}\%$ compounded annually:

$A = 10{,}000(1 + 0.0625)^{1} = \$10{,}625$

$6\frac{1}{4}\%$ compounded annually yields the larger amount.

24. 9% compounded quarterly:

$A = 10{,}000\left(1 + \dfrac{0.09}{4}\right)^{(4)(1)} \approx \$10{,}930.83$

$9\frac{1}{4}\%$ compounded annually:

$A = 10{,}000(1 + 0.0925)^{1} = \$10{,}925$

9% compounded quarterly yields the larger amount.

25. 9% compounded monthly:

$A = 10{,}000\left(1 + \dfrac{0.09}{12}\right)^{(12)(1)} = \$10{,}938.07$

8.8% compounded daily:

$A = 10{,}000\left(1 + \dfrac{0.088}{365}\right)^{365} = \$10{,}919.77$

9% compounded monthly yields the larger amount.

26. 8% compounded semiannually:

$A = 10{,}000\left(1 + \dfrac{0.08}{2}\right)^{(2)(1)} = \$10{,}816$

7.9% compounded daily:

$A = 10{,}000\left(1 + \dfrac{0.079}{365}\right)^{365} = \$10{,}821.95$

7.9% compounded daily yields the larger amount.

27. Suppose P dollars are invested for 1 year at 5%. Compounded quarterly yields:

$A = P\left(1 + \dfrac{0.05}{4}\right)^{(4)(1)} \approx 1.05095P$.

The interest earned is
$I = 1.05095P - P = 0.05095P$
Thus, $I = Prt$
           $0.05095P = P \cdot r \cdot 1$
           $0.05095 = r$
The effective interest rate is 5.095%.

664

28. Suppose P dollars are invested for 1 year at 6%.

Compounded monthly yields:

$A = P\left(1+\dfrac{0.06}{12}\right)^{(12)(1)} \approx 1.06168P$.

The interest earned is
$I = 1.06168P - P = 0.06168P$
Thus, $\qquad I = Prt$
$\qquad 0.06168P = P \cdot r \cdot 1$
$\qquad 0.06168 = r$
The effective interest rate is 6.168%.

29. Suppose P dollars are invested for 1 year at 5%.

Compounded continuously yields:
$A = Pe^{(0.05)(1)} \approx 1.05127P$
The interest earned is
$I = 1.05127P - P = 0.05127P$
Thus, $\qquad I = Prt$
$\qquad 0.05127P = P \cdot r \cdot 1$
$\qquad .05127 = r$
The effective interest rate is 5.127%.

30. Suppose P dollars are invested for 1 year at 6%.

Compounded continuously yields:
$A = Pe^{(0.06)(1)} \approx 1.06184P$
The interest earned is
$I = 1.06184P - P = 0.06184P$
Thus, $\qquad I = Prt$
$\qquad 0.06184P = P \cdot r \cdot 1$
$\qquad 0.06184 = r$
The effective interest rate is 6.184%.

31. $2P = P\left(1+\dfrac{r}{1}\right)^{3(1)}$
$2P = P(1+r)^3$
$2 = (1+r)^3$
$\sqrt[3]{2} = 1+r$
$r = \sqrt[3]{2} - 1 \approx 0.25992$
The required rate is 25.992%.

32. $2P = P\left(1+\dfrac{r}{1}\right)^{6(1)}$
$2P = P(1+r)^6$
$2 = (1+r)^6$
$\sqrt[6]{2} = 1+r$
$r = \sqrt[6]{2} - 1 \approx 0.12246$
The required rate is 12.246%.

33. $3P = P\left(1+\dfrac{r}{1}\right)^{5(1)}$
$3P = P(1+r)^5$
$3 = (1+r)^5$
$\sqrt[5]{3} = 1+r$
$r = \sqrt[5]{3} - 1 \approx 0.24573$
The required rate is 24.573%.

34. $3P = P\left(1+\dfrac{r}{1}\right)^{10(1)}$
$3P = P(1+r)^{10}$
$3 = (1+r)^{10}$
$\sqrt[10]{3} = 1+r$
$r = \sqrt[10]{3} - 1 \approx 0.11612$
The required rate is 11.612%.

35. a. $2P = P\left(1+\dfrac{0.08}{12}\right)^{12t}$
$2 = \left(1+\dfrac{0.08}{12}\right)^{12t}$
$\ln 2 = \ln\left(1+\dfrac{0.08}{12}\right)^{12t}$
$\ln 2 = 12t \ln\left(1+\dfrac{0.08}{12}\right)$
$t = \dfrac{\ln 2}{12\ln\left(1+\dfrac{0.08}{12}\right)} \approx 8.69$
It will take about 8.69 years to double.

b. $2P = Pe^{0.08t}$
$2 = e^{0.08t}$
$\ln 2 = 0.08t$
$t = \dfrac{\ln 2}{0.08} \approx 8.66$
It will take about 8.66 years to double.

36. a. $3P = P\left(1+\dfrac{0.06}{12}\right)^{12t}$
$3 = (1.005)^{12t}$
$\ln 3 = \ln(1.005)^{12t}$
$\ln 3 = 12t \ln(1.005)$
$t = \dfrac{\ln 3}{12\ln(1.005)} \approx 18.36$
It will take about 18.36 years to triple.

b. $3P = Pe^{0.06t}$

$3 = e^{0.06t}$

$\ln 3 = 0.06t$

$t = \dfrac{\ln 3}{0.06} \approx 18.31$

It will take about 18.31 years to triple.

37. Since the effective interest rate is 7%, we have:

$I = Prt$

$I = P \cdot 0.07 \cdot 1$

$I = 0.07P$

Thus, the amount in the account is

$A = P + 0.07P = 1.07P$

Let x be the required interest rate. Then,

$1.07P = P\left(1 + \dfrac{r}{4}\right)^{(4)(1)}$

$1.07 = \left(1 + \dfrac{r}{4}\right)^{4}$

$\sqrt[4]{1.07} = 1 + \dfrac{r}{4}$

$\sqrt[4]{1.07} - 1 = \dfrac{r}{4}$

$r = 4\left(\sqrt[4]{1.07} - 1\right) \approx 0.06823$

Thus, an interest rate of 6.823% compounded quarterly has an effective interest rate of 7%.

38. Since the effective interest rate is 6%, we have:

$I = Prt$

$I = P \cdot 0.06 \cdot 1$

$I = 0.06P$

Thus, the amount in the account is

$A = P + 0.06P = 1.06P$

Let x be the required interest rate. Then,

$1.06P = Pe^{(r)(1)}$

$1.06 = e^{r}$

$r = \ln(1.06) \approx 0.05827$

Thus, an interest rate of 5.827% compounded continuously has an effective interest rate of 6%.

39. $150 = 100\left(1 + \dfrac{0.08}{12}\right)^{12t}$

$1.5 \approx (1.006667)^{12t}$

$\ln 1.5 \approx 12t \ln(1.006667)$

$t \approx \dfrac{\ln 1.5}{12 \ln(1.006667)} \approx 5.09$

Compounded monthly, it will take about 5.09 years (or 61.02 months).

$150 = 100e^{0.08t}$

$1.5 = e^{0.08t}$

$\ln 1.5 = 0.08t$

$t = \dfrac{\ln 1.5}{0.08} \approx 5.07$

Compounded continuously, it will take about 5.07 years (or 60.82 months).

40. $175 = 100\left(1 + \dfrac{0.10}{12}\right)^{12t}$

$1.75 \approx (1.008333)^{12t}$

$\ln 1.75 \approx 12t \ln(1.008333)$

$t \approx \dfrac{\ln 1.75}{12 \ln(1.008333)} \approx 5.62$

Compounded monthly, it will take about 5.62 years (or 67.43 months).

$175 = 100e^{0.10t}$

$1.75 = e^{0.10t}$

$\ln 1.75 = 0.10t$

$t = \dfrac{\ln 1.75}{0.10} \approx 5.60$

Compounded continuously, it will take about 5.60 years (or 67.15 months).

41. $25,000 = 10,000e^{0.06t}$

$2.5 = e^{0.06t}$

$\ln 2.5 = 0.06t$

$t = \dfrac{\ln 2.5}{0.06} \approx 15.27$

It will take about 15.27 years (or 15 years, 3 months).

42. $80,000 = 25,000e^{0.07t}$

$3.2 = e^{0.07t}$

$\ln 3.2 = 0.07t$

$t = \dfrac{\ln 3.2}{0.07} \approx 16.62$

It will take about 16.62 years (or 16 years, 7 months).

43. $A = 90,000(1 + 0.03)^5 = \$104,335$

The house will cost \$104,335 in three years.

44. $A = 200(1 + 0.0125)^6 \approx \$215.48$

Her bill will be \$215.48 after 6 months.

45. $P = 15,000e^{(-0.05)(3)} \approx \$12,910.62$

Jerome should ask for $12,910.62.

46. $P = 3,000\left(1 + \dfrac{0.03}{12}\right)^{(-12)(0.5)} \approx \$2955.39$

John should save $2955.39.

47. $A = 15(1 + 0.15)^5 = 15(1.15)^5 \approx \$30.17$ per share

for a total of about $3017.

48. $850,000 = 650,000(1 + r)^3$

$$\dfrac{85}{65} = (1 + r)^3$$

$$\sqrt[3]{\dfrac{85}{65}} = 1 + r$$

$$r \approx \sqrt[3]{1.3077} - 1 \approx 0.0935$$

The annual return is approximately 9.35%.

49. 5.6% compounded continuously:

$A = 1000e^{(0.056)(1)} = \$1057.60$

Jim will not have enough money to buy the computer.

5.9% compounded monthly:

$$A = 1000\left(1 + \dfrac{0.059}{12}\right)^{12} = \$1060.62$$

The second bank offers the better deal.

50. 6.8% compounded continuously for 3 months:

Amount on April 1:

$A = 1000e^{(0.068)(0.25)} = \$1017.15$

5.25% compounded monthly for 1 month:

Amount on May 1

$$A = 1017.15\left(1 + \dfrac{0.0525}{12}\right)^{(12)(1/12)} = \$1021.60$$

51. Will: 9% compounded semiannually:

$$A = 2000\left(1 + \dfrac{0.09}{2}\right)^{(2)(20)} = \$11,632.73$$

Henry: 8.5% compounded continuously:

$A = 2000e^{(0.085)(20)} = \$10,947.89$

Will has more money after 20 years.

52. Value of $1000 compounded continuously at 10% for 3 years:

$A = 1000e^{(0.10)(3)} = \$1349.86$

April will have more money if she takes the $1000 now and invests it.

53. a. Let $x =$ the year, then the average cost C of a 4-year private college is by the function

$C(x) = 29,026(1.055)^{x-2005}$.

$$C(2015) = 29,026(1.055)^{2015-2005}$$

$$= 29,026(1.055)^{10}$$

$$\approx 49,581$$

In 2015, the average cost of college at a 4-year private college will be about $49,581.

b. $A = Pe^{rt}$

$49,581 = Pe^{0.04(10)}$

$$P = \dfrac{49,581}{e^{0.04(10)}} \approx 33,235$$

An investment of $33,235 in 2005 would pay for the cost of college at a 4-year private college in 2015.

54. $P = 100,000;\ t = 5$

a. Simple interest at 12% per annum:

$A = 100,000 + 100,000(0.12)(5) = \$160,000$

$I = \$160,000 - \$100,000 = \$60,000$

b. 11.5% compounded monthly:

$$A = 100,000\left(1 + \dfrac{0.115}{12}\right)^{(12)(5)} \approx \$177,227$$

$I = \$177,227 - \$100,000 = \$77,227$

c. 11.25% compounded continuously:

$A = 100,000e^{(0.1125)(5)} \approx \$175,505$

$I = \$175,505 - \$100,000 = \$75,505$

Thus, simple interest at 12% is the best option since it results in the least interest.

55. $A = P\left(1 + \dfrac{r}{n}\right)^{nt}$

$$A = 319\left(1 + \dfrac{0.032}{2}\right)^{2(20)} = 319(1.016)^{40} \approx 602$$

The government would have to pay back approximately $602 billion in 2025.

56. From 2006 to 2007, the deficit decreased at a rate of $r = \dfrac{423 - 354}{423} \approx 0.16312$ or 16.312%.

The deficit t years after 2007 is given by

$D = 354(1 - 0.16312)^t = 354(0.83688)^t$.

Now, if $D = 100$ million, then

$354(0.83688)^t = 100$

$(0.83688)^t = \dfrac{100}{354}$

$\ln(0.83688)^t = \ln\left(\dfrac{100}{354}\right)$

$t \ln(0.83688) = \ln\left(\dfrac{100}{354}\right)$

$t = \dfrac{\ln\left(\dfrac{100}{354}\right)}{\ln(0.83688)} \approx 7.1$

The deficit will be \$100 billion approximately 7.1 years after 2007, or in the fiscal year 2014.

57. $P = 1000,\ r = 0.03,\ n = 2$

$A = 1000(1 - 0.03)^2 = \$940.90$

58. $P = 1000,\ r = 0.02,\ n = 3$

$A = 1000(1 - 0.02)^3 \approx \$941.19$

59. $P = 1000,\ A = 950,\ n = 2$

$950 = 1000(1 - r)^2$

$0.95 = (1 - r)^2$

$\pm\sqrt{0.95} = 1 - r$

$r = 1 \pm \sqrt{0.95}$

$r \approx 0.0253$ or $r \approx 1.9747$

Disregard $r \approx 1.9747$. The inflation rate was 2.53%.

60. $P = 1000,\ A = 930,\ n = 2$

$930 = 1000(1 - r)^2$

$0.93 = (1 - r)^2$

$\pm\sqrt{0.93} = 1 - r$

$r = 1 \pm \sqrt{0.93}$

$r \approx 0.0356$ or $r \approx 1.9644$

Disregard $r \approx 1.9644$. The inflation rate was 3.56%.

61. $r = 0.02$

$\dfrac{1}{2}P = P(1 - 0.02)^t$

$0.5P = P(0.98)^t$

$0.5 = (0.98)^t$

$t = \log_{0.98}(0.5)$

$= \dfrac{\ln 0.5}{\ln 0.98} \approx 34.31$

The purchasing power will be half in 34.31 years.

62. $r = 0.04$

$\dfrac{1}{2}P = P(1 - 0.04)^t$

$0.5P = P(0.96)^t$

$0.5 = (0.96)^t$

$t = \log_{0.96}(0.5)$

$= \dfrac{\ln 0.5}{\ln 0.96} \approx 16.98$

The purchasing power will be half in 16.98 years.

63. a. $A = \$10{,}000,\ r = 0.10,\ n = 12,\ t = 20$

$P = 10{,}000\left(1 + \dfrac{0.10}{12}\right)^{(-12)(20)} \approx \$1364.62$

b. $A = \$10{,}000,\ r = 0.10,\ t = 20$

$P = 10{,}000 e^{(-0.10)(20)} \approx \$1353.35$

64. $A = \$40{,}000,\ r = 0.08,\ n = 1,\ t = 17$

$P = 40{,}000\left(1 + \dfrac{0.08}{1}\right)^{-17} \approx \$10{,}810.76$

65. $A = \$10{,}000,\ r = 0.08,\ n = 1,\ t = 10$

$P = 10{,}000\left(1 + \dfrac{0.08}{1}\right)^{(-1)(10)} \approx \$4631.93$

66. $A = \$25{,}000,\ P = 12{,}485.52,\ n = 1,\ t = 8$

$25{,}000 = 12{,}485.52\left(1 + r^8\right)$

$\dfrac{25{,}000}{12{,}485.52} = (1 + r)^8$

$\sqrt[8]{\dfrac{25{,}000}{12{,}485.52}} = 1 + r$

$r = \sqrt[8]{\dfrac{25{,}000}{12{,}485.52}} - 1$

$r \approx 0.090665741$

The annual rate of return is about 9.07%.

67. a. $t = \dfrac{\ln 2}{1 \cdot \ln\left(1 + \dfrac{0.12}{1}\right)}$

$= \dfrac{\ln 2}{\ln(1.12)} \approx 6.12$ years

b. $t = \dfrac{\ln 3}{4 \cdot \ln\left(1 + \dfrac{0.06}{4}\right)}$

$= \dfrac{\ln 3}{4\ln(1.015)} \approx 18.45$ years

c. $mP = P\left(1 + \dfrac{r}{n}\right)^{nt}$

$m = \left(1 + \dfrac{r}{n}\right)^{nt}$

$\ln m = nt \cdot \ln\left(1 + \dfrac{r}{n}\right)$

$t = \dfrac{\ln m}{n \cdot \ln\left(1 + \dfrac{r}{n}\right)}$

68. a. $t = \dfrac{\ln 8000 - \ln 1000}{0.10} \approx 20.79$ years

b. $35 = \dfrac{\ln 30{,}000 - \ln 2000}{r}$

$r = \dfrac{\ln 30{,}000 - \ln 2000}{35}$

≈ 0.0774

$r \approx 7.74\%$

c. $A = Pe^{rt}$

$\dfrac{A}{P} = e^{rt}$

$\ln\left(\dfrac{A}{P}\right) = rt$

$\ln A - \ln P = rt$

$t = \dfrac{\ln A - \ln P}{r}$

69. a. $CPI_0 = 152.4,\ CPI = 195.3,$
$n = 2005 - 1995 = 10$

$195.3 = 152.4\left(1 + \dfrac{r}{100}\right)^{10}$

$\dfrac{195.3}{152.4} = \left(1 + \dfrac{r}{100}\right)^{10}$

$1 + \dfrac{r}{100} = \sqrt[10]{\dfrac{195.3}{152.4}}$

$\dfrac{r}{100} = \sqrt[10]{\dfrac{195.3}{152.4}} - 1$

$r = 100\left(\sqrt[10]{\dfrac{195.3}{152.4}} - 1\right) \approx 2.51\%$

b. $CPI_0 = 152.4,\ CPI = 300,\ r = 2.51$

$300 = 152.4\left(1 + \dfrac{2.51}{100}\right)^{n}$

$\dfrac{300}{152.4} = \left(1 + \dfrac{2.51}{100}\right)^{n}$

$\ln\left(\dfrac{300}{152.4}\right) = \ln\left(1 + \dfrac{2.51}{100}\right)^{n}$

$\ln\left(\dfrac{300}{152.4}\right) = n\ln\left(1 + \dfrac{2.51}{100}\right)$

$n = \dfrac{\ln\left(\dfrac{300}{152.4}\right)}{\ln\left(1 + \dfrac{2.51}{100}\right)} \approx 27.3$ years

The CPI will reach 300 about 27 years after 1995, or in the year 2022.

70. $CPI_0 = 234.2,\ r = 2.8\%,\ n = 5$

$CPI = 234.2\left(1 + \dfrac{2.8}{100}\right)^{5} \approx 268.9$

In 5 years, the CPI index will be about 268.9.

71. $r = 3.1\%$

$2 \cdot CPI_0 = CPI_0\left(1 + \dfrac{3.1}{100}\right)^{n}$

$2 = (1.031)^{n}$

$n = \log_{1.031} 2 = \dfrac{\ln 2}{\ln 1.031} \approx 22.7$

It will take about 22.7 years for the CPI index to double.

72. $CPI_0 = 100,\ CPI = 456.5,\ r = 5.57$

$$456.5 = 100\left(1 + \frac{5.57}{100}\right)^n$$

$$456.5 = 100(1.0557)^n$$

$$4.565 = (1.0557)^n$$

$$n = \log_{1.0558}(4.565)$$

$$= \frac{\ln 4.565}{\ln 1.0558} \approx 28.0 \text{ years}$$

The yeas that was used as the base period for the CPI was about 28 years before 1995, or the year 1967.

73. Answers will vary.

74. Answers will vary.

75. Answers will vary.

Section 6.8

1. $P(t) = 500e^{0.02t}$

  a. $P(0) = 500e^{(0.02)\cdot(0)} = 500$ insects

  b. growth rate: $k = 0.02 = 2\%$

  c. $P(10) = 500e^{(0.02)\cdot(10)} \approx 611$ insects

  d. Find t when $P = 800$:

  $$800 = 500e^{0.02t}$$

  $$1.6 = e^{0.02t}$$

  $$\ln 1.6 = 0.02t$$

  $$t = \frac{\ln 1.6}{0.02} \approx 23.5 \text{ days}$$

  e. Find t when $P = 1000$:

  $$1000 = 500e^{0.02t}$$

  $$2 = e^{0.02t}$$

  $$\ln 2 = 0.02t$$

  $$t = \frac{\ln 2}{0.02} \approx 34.7 \text{ days}$$

2. $N(t) = 1000e^{0.01t}$

  a. $N(0) = 1000e^{(0.01)\cdot(0)} = 1000$ bacteria

  b. growth rate: $k = 0.01 = 1\%$

  c. $N(4) = 1000e^{(0.01)\cdot(4)} \approx 1041$ bacteria

  d. Find t when $N = 1700$:

  $$1700 = 1000e^{0.01t}$$

  $$1.7 = e^{0.01t}$$

  $$\ln 1.7 = 0.01t$$

  $$t = \frac{\ln 1.7}{0.01} \approx 53.1 \text{ hours}$$

  e. Find t when $N = 2000$:

  $$2000 = 1000e^{0.01t}$$

  $$2 = e^{0.01t}$$

  $$\ln 2 = 0.01t$$

  $$t = \frac{\ln 2}{0.01} \approx 69.3 \text{ hours}$$

3. $A(t) = A_0 e^{-0.0244t} = 500e^{-0.0244t}$

  a. decay rate: $k = -0.0244 = -2.44\%$

  b. $A(10) = 500e^{(-0.0244)(10)} \approx 391.7$ grams

  c. Find t when $A = 400$:

  $$400 = 500e^{-0.0244t}$$

  $$0.8 = e^{-0.0244t}$$

  $$\ln 0.8 = -0.0244t$$

  $$t = \frac{\ln 0.8}{-0.0244} \approx 9.1 \text{ years}$$

  d. Find t when $A = 250$:

  $$250 = 500e^{-0.0244t}$$

  $$0.5 = e^{-0.0244t}$$

  $$\ln 0.5 = -0.0244t$$

  $$t = \frac{\ln 0.5}{-0.0244} \approx 28.4 \text{ years}$$

4. $A(t) = A_0 e^{-0.087t} = 100e^{-0.087t}$

  a. decay rate: $k = -0.087 = -8.7\%$

  b. $A(9) = 100e^{(-0.087)(9)} \approx 45.7$ grams

  c. Find t when $A = 70$:

  $$70 = 100e^{-0.087t}$$

  $$0.7 = e^{-0.087t}$$

  $$\ln 0.7 = -0.087t$$

  $$t = \frac{\ln 0.7}{-0.087} \approx 4.1 \text{ days}$$

d. Find t when $A = 50$:

$$50 = 100e^{-0.087t}$$
$$0.5 = e^{-0.087t}$$
$$\ln 0.5 = -0.087t$$
$$t = \frac{\ln 0.5}{-0.087} \approx 7.97 \text{ days}$$

5. a. $N(t) = N_0 e^{kt}$

b. If $N(t) = 1800$, $N_0 = 1000$, and $t = 1$, then

$$1800 = 1000e^{k(1)}$$
$$1.8 = e^k$$
$$k = \ln 1.8$$

If $t = 3$, then $N(3) = 1000e^{(\ln 1.8)(3)} = 5832$ mosquitoes.

c. Find t when $N(t) = 10,000$:

$$10,000 = 1000e^{(\ln 1.8)t}$$
$$10 = e^{(\ln 1.8)t}$$
$$\ln 10 = (\ln 1.8)t$$
$$t = \frac{\ln 10}{\ln 1.8} \approx 3.9 \text{ days}$$

6. a. $N(t) = N_0 e^{kt}$

b. If $N(t) = 800$, $N_0 = 500$, and $t = 1$, then

$$800 = 500e^{k(1)}$$
$$1.6 = e^k$$
$$k = \ln 1.6$$

If $t = 5$, then $N(5) = 500e^{(\ln 1.6)(5)} \approx 5243$ bacteria

c. Find t when $N(t) = 20,000$:

$$20,000 = 500e^{(\ln 1.6)t}$$
$$40 = e^{(\ln 1.6)t}$$
$$\ln 40 = (\ln 1.6)t$$
$$t = \frac{\ln 40}{\ln 1.6} \approx 7.85 \text{ hours}$$

7. a. $N(t) = N_0 e^{kt}$

b. Note that 18 months = 1.5 years, so $t = 1.5$.

$$2N_0 = N_0 e^{k(1.5)}$$
$$2 = e^{1.5k}$$
$$\ln 2 = 1.5k$$
$$k = \frac{\ln 2}{1.5}$$

If $N_0 = 10,000$ and $t = 2$, then

$$P(2) = 10,000e^{\left(\frac{\ln 2}{1.5}\right)(2)} \approx 25,198$$

The population 2 years from now will be 25,198.

8. a. $N(t) = N_0 e^{kt}$, $k < 0$

b. If $N(t) = 800,000$, $N_0 = 900,000$, and $t = 2005 - 2003 = 2$, then

$$800,000 = 900,000e^{k(2)}$$
$$\frac{8}{9} = e^{2k}$$
$$\ln\left(\frac{8}{9}\right) = 2k$$
$$k = \frac{\ln(8/9)}{2}$$

If $t = 2007 - 2003 = 4$, then

$$P(4) = 900,000e^{\left(\frac{\ln(8/9)}{2}\right)(4)} \approx 711,111$$

The population in 2007 will be 711,111.

9. Use $A = A_0 e^{kt}$ and solve for k:

$$0.5A_0 = A_0 e^{k(1690)}$$
$$0.5 = e^{1690k}$$
$$\ln 0.5 = 1690k$$
$$k = \frac{\ln 0.5}{1690}$$

When $A_0 = 10$ and $t = 50$:

$$A = 10e^{\left(\frac{\ln 0.5}{1690}\right)(50)} \approx 9.797 \text{ grams}$$

10. Use $A = A_0 e^{kt}$ and solve for k:

$$0.5A_0 = A_0 e^{k\left(1.3\times10^9\right)}$$
$$0.5 = e^{\left(1.3\times10^9\right)k}$$
$$\ln 0.5 = 1.3\times10^9 k$$
$$k = \frac{\ln 0.5}{1.3\times10^9}$$

When $A_0 = 10$ and $t = 100$:

$$A = 10e^{\left(\frac{\ln 0.5}{1.3\times10^9}\right)(100)} \approx 9.999999467 \text{ grams}$$

When $A_0 = 10$ and $t = 1000$:

$$A = 10e^{\left(\frac{\ln 0.5}{1.3\times10^9}\right)(1000)} \approx 9.999994668 \text{ grams}$$

11. Use $A = A_0 e^{kt}$ and solve for k:

half-life = 5600 years

$$0.5A_0 = A_0 e^{k(5600)}$$

$$0.5 = e^{5600k}$$

$$\ln 0.5 = 5600k$$

$$k = \frac{\ln 0.5}{5600}$$

Solve for t when $A = 0.3A_0$:

$$0.3A_0 = A_0 e^{\left(\frac{\ln 0.5}{5600}\right)t}$$

$$0.3 = e^{\left(\frac{\ln 0.5}{5600}\right)t}$$

$$\ln 0.3 = \left(\frac{\ln 0.5}{5600}\right)t$$

$$t = \frac{5600}{\ln 0.5}(\ln 0.3) \approx 9727$$

The tree died approximately 9727 years ago.

12. Use $A = A_0 e^{kt}$ and solve for k:

half-life = 5600 years

$$0.5A_0 = A_0 e^{k(5600)}$$

$$0.5A_0 = A_0 e^{k(5600)}$$

$$0.5 = e^{5600k}$$

$$\ln 0.5 = 5600k$$

$$k = \frac{\ln 0.5}{5600}$$

Solve for t when $A = 0.7A_0$:

$$0.7A_0 = A_0 e^{\left(\frac{\ln 0.5}{5600}\right)t}$$

$$0.7 = e^{\left(\frac{\ln 0.5}{5600}\right)t}$$

$$\ln 0.7 = \left(\frac{\ln 0.5}{5600}\right)t$$

$$t = \frac{5600}{\ln 0.5}(\ln 0.7) \approx 2882$$

The fossil is about 2882 years old.

13. a. Using $u = T + (u_0 - T)e^{kt}$ with $t = 5$,

$T = 70$, $u_0 = 450$, and $u = 300$:

$$300 = 70 + (450 - 70)e^{k(5)}$$

$$230 = 380e^{5k}$$

$$\frac{230}{380} = e^{5k}$$

$$\ln\left(\frac{23}{38}\right) = 5k$$

$$k = \frac{1}{5}\ln\left(\frac{23}{38}\right) \approx -0.1004$$

$T = 70$, $u_0 = 450$, $u = 135$:

$$135 = 70 + (450 - 70)e^{\frac{\ln(23/38)}{5}t}$$

$$65 = 380e^{\frac{\ln(23/38)}{5}t}$$

$$\frac{65}{380} = e^{\frac{\ln(23/38)}{5}t}$$

$$\ln\left(\frac{65}{380}\right) = \frac{\ln(23/38)}{5}t$$

$$t = \frac{5}{\ln(23/38)}\cdot\ln\left(\frac{65}{380}\right) \approx 18 \text{ minutes}$$

The temperature of the pan will be 135°F at about 5:18 PM.

b. $T = 70$, $u_0 = 450$, $u = 160$:

$$160 = 70 + (450 - 70)e^{\left(\frac{\ln(23/38)}{5}\right)t}$$

$$90 = 380e^{\left(\frac{\ln(23/38)}{5}\right)t}$$

$$\frac{90}{380} = e^{\left(\frac{\ln(23/38)}{5}\right)t}$$

$$\ln\left(\frac{90}{380}\right) = \frac{\ln(23/38)}{5}t$$

$$t = \frac{5}{\ln(23/38)}\cdot\ln\left(\frac{90}{380}\right) \approx 14.3 \text{ minutes}$$

The pan will be 160°F after about 14.3 minutes.

c. As time passes, the temperature of the pan approaches 70°F.

14. a. Using $u = T + (u_0 - T)e^{kt}$ with $t = 2$,
$T = 38$, $u_0 = 72$, and $u = 60$:

$$60 = 38 + (72 - 38)e^{k(2)}$$
$$22 = 34e^{2k}$$
$$\frac{22}{34} = e^{2k}$$
$$\ln\left(\frac{22}{34}\right) = 2k$$
$$k = \frac{\ln(22/34)}{2}$$

$T = 38$, $u_0 = 72$, $t = 7$

$$u = 38 + (72 - 38)e^{\left(\frac{\ln(22/34)}{2}\right)(7)}$$
$$u = 38 + 34e^{\left(\frac{\ln(22/34)}{2}\right)(7)} \approx 45.41°\,F$$

After 7 minutes the thermometer will read about 45.41°F.

b. Find t when $u = 39°\,F$

$$39 = 38 + (72 - 38)e^{\left(\frac{\ln(22/34)}{2}\right)t}$$
$$1 = 34e^{\left(\frac{\ln(22/34)}{2}\right)t}$$
$$\frac{1}{34} = e^{\left(\frac{\ln(22/34)}{2}\right)t}$$
$$\ln\left(\frac{1}{34}\right) = \left(\frac{\ln(22/34)}{2}\right)t$$
$$t = \frac{2}{\ln(22/34)} \cdot \ln\left(\frac{1}{34}\right) \approx 16.2$$

The thermometer will read 39 degrees after about 16.2 minutes.

c. $T = 38$, $u_0 = 72$, $u = 45$:

$$45 = 38 + (72 - 38)e^{\frac{\ln(22/34)}{2}t}$$
$$7 = 34e^{\frac{\ln(22/34)}{2}t}$$
$$\frac{7}{34} = e^{\frac{\ln(22/34)}{2}t}$$
$$\ln\left(\frac{7}{34}\right) = \frac{\ln(22/34)}{2}t$$
$$t = \frac{2}{\ln(22/34)} \cdot \ln\left(\frac{7}{34}\right) \approx 7.26 \text{ minutes}$$

The thermometer will read $45°F$ after about 7.26 minutes.

d. As time passes, the temperature gets closer to 38°F.

15. Using $u = T + (u_0 - T)e^{kt}$ with $t = 3$, $T = 35$, $u_0 = 8$, and $u = 15$:

$$15 = 35 + (8 - 35)e^{k(3)}$$
$$-20 = -27e^{3k}$$
$$\frac{20}{27} = e^{3k}$$
$$\ln\left(\frac{20}{27}\right) = 3k$$
$$k = \frac{\ln(20/27)}{3}$$

At $t = 5$:

$$u = 35 + (8 - 35)e^{\left(\frac{\ln(20/27)}{3}\right)(5)} \approx 18.63°C$$

After 5 minutes, the thermometer will read approximately 18.63°C.

At $t = 10$:

$$u = 35 + (8 - 35)e^{\left(\frac{\ln(20/27)}{3}\right)(10)} \approx 25.1°C$$

After 10 minutes, the thermometer will read approximately 25.1°C

16. Using $u = T + (u_0 - T)e^{kt}$ with $t = 10$, $T = 70$, $u_0 = 28$, and $u = 35$:

$$35 = 70 + (28 - 70)e^{k(10)}$$
$$-35 = -42e^{10k}$$
$$\frac{35}{42} = e^{10k}$$
$$\ln\left(\frac{35}{42}\right) = 10k$$
$$k = \frac{\ln(35/42)}{10}$$

At $t = 30$:

$$u = 70 + (28 - 70)e^{\left(\frac{\ln(35/42)}{10}\right)(30)} \approx 45.69°F$$

After 30 minutes, the temperature of the stein will be approximately $45.69°F$.

Find the value of t so that the $u = 45°F$:

$$45 = 70 + (28 - 70)e^{\left(\frac{\ln(35/42)}{10}\right)t}$$

$$-25 = -42e^{\left(\frac{\ln(35/42)}{10}\right)t}$$

$$\frac{25}{42} = e^{\left(\frac{\ln(35/42)}{10}\right)t}$$

$$\ln\left(\frac{25}{42}\right) = \left(\frac{\ln(35/42)}{10}\right)t$$

$$t = \frac{10}{\ln(35/42)} \cdot \ln\left(\frac{25}{42}\right) \approx 28.46$$

The temperature of the stein will be $45°F$ after about 28.46 minutes.

17. Use $A = A_0 e^{kt}$ and solve for k:

$$2.2 = 2.5e^{k(24)}$$

$$0.88 = e^{24k}$$

$$\ln 0.88 = 24k$$

$$k = \frac{\ln 0.88}{24}$$

When $A_0 = 2.5$ and $t = 72$:

$$A = 2.5e^{\left(\frac{\ln 0.88}{24}\right)(72)} \approx 1.70$$

After 3 days (72 hours), the amount of free chlorine will be 1.70 parts per million.

Find t when $A = 1$:

$$1 = 2.5e^{\left(\frac{\ln 0.88}{24}\right)t}$$

$$0.4 = e^{\left(\frac{\ln 0.88}{24}\right)t}$$

$$\ln 0.4 = \left(\frac{\ln 0.88}{24}\right)t$$

$$t = \frac{24}{\ln 0.88} \cdot \ln 0.4 \approx 172$$

Ben will have to shock his pool again after 172 hours (or 7.17 days) when the level of free chlorine reaches 1.0 parts per million.

18. Use $A = A_0 e^{kt}$ and solve for k:

$$0.15 = 0.25e^{k(17)}$$

$$0.6 = e^{17k}$$

$$\ln 0.6 = 17k$$

$$k = \frac{\ln 0.6}{17}$$

When $A_0 = 0.25$ and $t = 30$:

$$A = 0.25e^{\left(\frac{\ln 0.6}{17}\right)(30)} \approx 0.10$$

After 30 minutes, approximately 0.10 M of dinitrogen pentoxide will remain.

Find t when $A = 0.01$:

$$0.01 = 0.25e^{\left(\frac{\ln 0.6}{17}\right)t}$$

$$0.04 = e^{\left(\frac{\ln 0.6}{17}\right)t}$$

$$\ln 0.04 = \left(\frac{\ln 0.6}{17}\right)t$$

$$t = \frac{17}{\ln 0.6} \cdot \ln 0.04 \approx 107$$

It will take approximately 107 minutes until 0.01 M of dinitrogen pentoxide remains.

19. Use $A = A_0 e^{kt}$ and solve for k:

$$0.36 = 0.40e^{k(30)}$$

$$0.9 = e^{30k}$$

$$\ln 0.9 = 30k$$

$$k = \frac{\ln 0.9}{30}$$

Note that 2 hours = 120 minutes.
When $A_0 = 0.40$ and $t = 120$:

$$A = 0.40e^{\left(\frac{\ln 0.9}{30}\right)(120)} \approx 0.26$$

After 2 hours, approximately 0.26 M of sucrose will remain.

Find t when $A = 0.10$:

$$0.10 = 0.40e^{\left(\frac{\ln 0.9}{30}\right)t}$$

$$0.25 = e^{\left(\frac{\ln 0.9}{30}\right)t}$$

$$\ln 0.25 = \left(\frac{\ln 0.9}{30}\right)t$$

$$t = \frac{30}{\ln 0.9} \cdot \ln 0.25 \approx 395$$

It will take approximately 395 minutes (or 6.58 hours) until 0.10 M of sucrose remains.

20. Use $A = A_0 e^{kt}$ and solve for k:

$$15 = 25e^{k(10)}$$
$$0.6 = e^{10k}$$
$$\ln 0.6 = 10k$$
$$k = \frac{\ln 0.6}{10}$$

When $A_0 = 25$ and $t = 24$:

$$A = 25e^{\left(\frac{\ln 0.6}{10}\right)(24)} \approx 7.34$$

There will be about 7.34 kilograms of salt left after 1 day.

Find t when $A = 0.5A_0$:

$$0.5 = 25e^{\left(\frac{\ln 0.6}{10}\right)t}$$
$$0.02 = e^{\left(\frac{\ln 0.6}{10}\right)t}$$
$$\ln 0.02 = \left(\frac{\ln 0.6}{10}\right)t$$
$$t = \frac{10}{\ln 0.6} \cdot \ln 0.02 \approx 76.6$$

It will take about 76.6 hours until ½ kilogram of salt is left.

21. Use $A = A_0 e^{kt}$ and solve for k:

$$0.5A_0 = A_0 e^{k(8)}$$
$$0.5 = e^{8k}$$
$$\ln 0.5 = 8k$$
$$k = \frac{\ln 0.5}{8}$$

Find t when $A = 0.1A_0$:

$$0.1A_0 = A_0 e^{\left(\frac{\ln 0.5}{8}\right)t}$$
$$0.1 = e^{\left(\frac{\ln 0.5}{8}\right)t}$$
$$\ln 0.1 = \left(\frac{\ln 0.5}{8}\right)t$$
$$t = \frac{8}{\ln 0.5} \cdot \ln 0.1 \approx 26.6$$

The farmers need to wait about 26.6 days before using the hay.

22. Using $u = T + (u_0 - T)e^{kt}$ with $t = 2$, $T = 325$, $u_0 = 75$, and $u = 100$:

$$100 = 325 + (75 - 325)e^{k(2)}$$
$$-225 = -250e^{2k}$$
$$0.9 = e^{2k}$$
$$2k = \ln 0.9$$
$$k = \frac{\ln 0.9}{2}$$

Find the value of t so that $u = 175°F$:

$$175 = 325 + (75 - 325)e^{\left(\frac{\ln 0.9}{2}\right)t}$$
$$-150 = -250e^{\left(\frac{\ln 0.9}{2}\right)t}$$
$$0.6 = e^{\left(\frac{\ln 0.9}{2}\right)t}$$
$$\ln 0.6 = \left(\frac{\ln 0.9}{2}\right)t$$
$$t = \frac{2}{\ln 0.9} \cdot \ln 0.6 \approx 9.7$$

The hotel may serve their guests about 9.7 hours after noon or at about 9:42 PM.

23. a. The maximum proportion is the carrying capacity, $c = 0.9 = 90\%$.

b. $P(0) = \dfrac{0.9}{1 + 6e^{-0.32(0)}} = \dfrac{0.9}{1 + 6 \cdot 1} = \dfrac{0.9}{7} = 0.1286$

In 2000, about 12.86% of U.S. households owned a DVD player.

c. $t = 2005 - 2000 = 5$

$$P(5) = \frac{0.9}{1 + 6e^{-0.32(5)}} = \frac{0.9}{1 + 6e^{-1.6}} \approx 0.4070$$

In 2005, about 40.7% of U.S. households owned a DVD player.

d. We need to find t such that $P = 0.8$.

$$0.8 = \frac{0.9}{1 + 6e^{-0.32t}}$$
$$1 + 6e^{-0.32t} = \frac{9}{8}$$
$$6e^{-0.32t} = \frac{1}{8}$$
$$e^{-0.32t} = \frac{1}{48}$$
$$-0.32t = \ln(1/48)$$
$$t = \frac{\ln(1/48)}{-0.32} \approx 12.1$$

Since $2000 + 12.1 = 2012.1$, 80% of households will own a DVD player in 2012.

24. a. The maximum proportion is the carrying capacity, $c = 0.90 = 90\%$.

b. $P(0) = \dfrac{0.90}{1+3.5e^{-0.339(0)}} = \dfrac{0.90}{1+3.5\cdot1}$

$= \dfrac{0.90}{4.5} = 0.2$

When it is first introduced, Intel's latest coprocessor will be in 20% of computers sold at Best Buy.

c. $P(4) = \dfrac{0.90}{1+3.5e^{-0.339(4)}}$

$= \dfrac{0.90}{1+3.5e^{-1.356}} \approx 0.473$

After 4 months, Intel's latest coprocessor will be in about 47.3% of PCs sold at Best Buy.

d. We need to find t such that $P = 0.75$.

$0.75 = \dfrac{0.90}{1+3.5e^{-0.339t}}$

$1+3.5e^{-0.339t} = 1.2$

$3.5e^{-0.339t} = 0.2$

$e^{-0.339t} = \dfrac{2}{35}$

$-0.339t = \ln(2/35)$

$t = \dfrac{\ln(2/35)}{-0.339} \approx 8.44$

75% of PCs sold at Best Buy have Intel's latest coprocessor about 8.44 months after it has been introduced.

e. We need to find t such that $P = 0.45$.

$0.45 = \dfrac{0.90}{1+3.5e^{-0.339t}}$

$1+3.5e^{-0.339t} = 2$

$3.5e^{-0.339t} = 1$

$e^{-0.339t} = \dfrac{2}{7}$

$-0.339t = \ln(2/7)$

$t = \dfrac{\ln(2/7)}{-0.339} \approx 3.70$

45% of PCs sold at Best Buy have Intel's latest coprocessor about 3.7 months after it has been introduced.

25. a. As $t \to \infty$, $e^{-0.439t} \to 0$. Thus, $P(t) \to 1000$. The carrying capacity is 1000 grams of bacteria.

b. Growth rate $= 0.439 = 43.9\%$.

c. $P(0) = \dfrac{1000}{1+32.33e^{-0.439(0)}} = \dfrac{1000}{33.33} = 30$

The initial population was 30 grams of bacteria.

d. $P(9) = \dfrac{1000}{1+32.33e^{-0.439(9)}} \approx 616.6$

After 9 hours, the population of bacteria will be about 616.6 grams.

e. We need to find t such that $P = 700$:

$700 = \dfrac{1000}{1+32.33e^{-0.439t}}$

$1+32.33e^{-0.439t} = \dfrac{10}{7}$

$32.33e^{-0.439t} = \dfrac{3}{7}$

$e^{-0.439t} = \dfrac{3}{226.31}$

$-0.439t = \ln(3/226.31)$

$t = \dfrac{\ln(3/226.31)}{-0.439} \approx 9.85$

The population of bacteria will be 700 grams after about 9.85 hours.

f. We need to find t such that

$P = \dfrac{1}{2}(1000) = 500$:

$500 = \dfrac{1000}{1+32.33e^{-0.439t}}$

$1+32.33e^{-0.439t} = 2$

$32.33e^{-0.439t} = 1$

$e^{-0.439t} = \dfrac{1}{32.33}$

$-0.439t = \ln(1/32.33)$

$t = \dfrac{\ln(1/32.33)}{-0.439} \approx 7.9$

The population of bacteria will reach one-half of is carrying capacity after about 7.9 hours.

26. a. As $t \to \infty$, $e^{-0.162t} \to 0$. Thus, $P(t) \to 500$.
The carrying capacity is 500 bald eagles.

b. Growth rate $= 0.162 = 16.2\%$.

c. $P(3) = \dfrac{500}{1+83.33e^{-0.162(3)}} \approx 9.56$
After 3 years, the population is almost 10 bald eagles.

d. We need to find t such that $P = 300$:
$$300 = \frac{500}{1+83.33e^{-0.162t}}$$
$$1+83.33e^{-0.162t} = \frac{5}{3}$$
$$83.33e^{-0.162t} = \frac{2}{3}$$
$$e^{-0.162t} \approx 0.008$$
$$-0.162t = \ln(0.008)$$
$$t = \frac{\ln(0.008)}{-0.162} \approx 29.8$$
The bald eagle population will be 300 in approximately 29.8 years.

e. We need to find t such that
$$P = \frac{1}{2}(500) = 250:$$
$$250 = \frac{500}{1+83.33e^{-0.162t}}$$
$$1+83.33e^{-0.162t} = 2$$
$$83.33e^{-0.162t} = 1$$
$$e^{-0.162t} \approx 0.012$$
$$-0.162t = \ln(0.012)$$
$$t = \frac{\ln(0.012)}{-0.162} \approx 27.3$$

The bald eagle population will reach one-half of its carrying capacity after about 27.3 years.

27. a. $y = \dfrac{6}{1+e^{-(5.085-0.1156(100))}} \approx 0.00923$
At $100°\text{F}$, the predicted number of eroded or leaky primary O-rings will be about 0.

b. $y = \dfrac{6}{1+e^{-(5.085-0.1156(60))}} \approx 0.81$
At $60°\text{F}$, the predicted number of eroded or leaky primary O-rings will be about 1.

c. $y = \dfrac{6}{1+e^{-(5.085-0.1156(30))}} \approx 5.01$
At $30°\text{F}$, the predicted number of eroded or leaky primary O-rings will be about 5.

d. $Y_1 = \dfrac{6}{1+e^{-(5.085-0.1156x)}}$

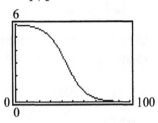

Use INTERSECT with $Y_2 = 1$, 3, and 5:

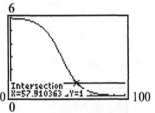

The predicted number of eroded or leaky O-rings is 1 when the temperature is about $57.91°\text{F}$.

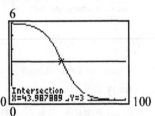

The predicted number of eroded or leaky O-rings is 3 when the temperature is about $43.99°\text{F}$.

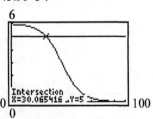

The predicted number of eroded or leaky O-rings is 5 when the temperature is about $30.07°\text{F}$.

Section 6.9

1. a.

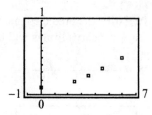

b. Using EXPonential REGression on the data
yields: $y = 0.0903(1.3384)^x$

c. $y = 0.0903(1.3384)^x$

$$= 0.0903\left(e^{\ln(1.3384)}\right)^x$$

$$= 0.0903 e^{\ln(1.3384)x}$$

$$N(t) = 0.0903 e^{0.2915t}$$

d. $Y_1 = 0.0903 e^{0.2915x}$

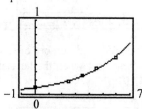

e. $N(7) = 0.0903 e^{(0.2915) \cdot 7} \approx 0.69$ bacteria

f. We need to find t when $N = 0.75$:

$$0.0903 e^{(0.2915)t} = 0.75$$

$$e^{(0.2915)t} = \frac{0.75}{0.0903}$$

$$0.2915t = \ln\left(\frac{0.75}{0.0903}\right)$$

$$t \approx \frac{\ln\left(\dfrac{0.75}{0.0903}\right)}{0.2915} \approx 7.26 \text{ hours}$$

2. a.

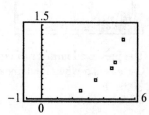

b. Using EXPonential REGression on the data
yields: $y = 0.0339(1.9474)^x$

c. $y = 0.0339(1.9474)^x$

$$= 0.0339\left(e^{\ln(1.9474)}\right)^x$$

$$= 0.0339 e^{\ln(1.9474)x}$$

$$N(t) = 0.0339 e^{(0.6665)t}$$

d. $Y_1 = 0.0339 e^{(0.6665)x}$

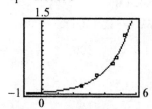

e. $N(6) = 0.0339 e^{(0.6665) \cdot 6} \approx 1.85$ bacteria

f. We need to find t when $N = 2.1$:

$$0.0339 e^{(0.6665)t} = 2.1$$

$$e^{(0.6665)t} = \frac{2.1}{0.0339}$$

$$0.6665t = \ln\left(\frac{2.1}{0.0339}\right)$$

$$t \approx \frac{\ln\left(\dfrac{2.1}{0.0339}\right)}{0.6665} \approx 6.19 \text{ hours}$$

3. a.

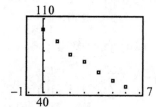

b. Using EXPonential REGression on the data
yields: $y = 100.3263(0.8769)^x$

c. $y = 100.3263(0.8769)^x$

$$= 100.3263\left(e^{\ln(0.8769)}\right)^x$$

$$= 100.3263 e^{\ln(0.8769)x}$$

$$A(t) = 100.3263 e^{(-0.1314)t}$$

d. $Y_1 = 100.3263 e^{(-0.1314)x}$

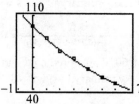

e. We need to find t when $A(t) = 0.5 \cdot A_0$

$$100.3263e^{(-0.1314)t} = (0.5)(100.3263)$$

$$e^{(-0.1314)t} = 0.5$$

$$-0.1314t = \ln 0.5$$

$$t = \frac{\ln 0.5}{-0.1314} \approx 5.3 \text{ weeks}$$

f. $A(50) = 100.3263e^{(-0.1314) \cdot 50} \approx 0.14$ grams

g. We need to find t when $A(t) = 20$.

$$100.3263e^{(-0.1314)t} = 20$$

$$e^{(-0.1314)t} = \frac{20}{100.3263}$$

$$-0.1314t = \ln\left(\frac{20}{100.3263}\right)$$

$$t = \frac{\ln\left(\dfrac{20}{100.3263}\right)}{-0.1314} \approx 12.3 \text{ weeks}$$

4. a.

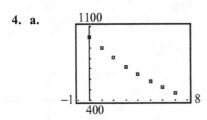

b. Using EXPonential REGression on the data yields: $y = 998.907(0.8976)^x$

c. $y = 998.907(0.8976)^x$

$$= 998.907\left(e^{\ln(0.8976)}\right)^x$$

$$= 998.907e^{\ln(0.8976)x}$$

$$A(t) = 998.907e^{(-0.1080)t}$$

d. $Y_1 = 998.907e^{(-0.1080)x}$

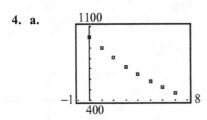

e. We need to find t when $A(t) = 0.5 \cdot A_0$

$$998.907e^{(-0.1080)t} = (0.5)(998.907)$$

$$e^{(-0.1080)t} = 0.5$$

$$-0.1080t = \ln 0.5$$

$$t = \frac{\ln 0.5}{-0.1080} \approx 6.42 \text{ days}$$

f. $A(20) = 998.907e^{(-0.1080) \cdot 20} \approx 115$ grams

g. We need to find t when $A = 200$:

$$998.907e^{(-0.1080)t} = 200$$

$$e^{(-0.1080)t} = \frac{200}{998.907}$$

$$-0.1080t = \ln\left(\frac{200}{998.907}\right)$$

$$t = \frac{\ln\left(\dfrac{200}{998.907}\right)}{-0.1080} \approx 14.9 \text{ days}$$

5. a. Let $x = 0$ correspond to 1995, $x = 3$ correspond to 1998, etc.

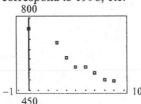

b. Using EXPonential REGression on the data yields: $y = 751.4698(0.95188)^x$

c. $y = 751.4698(0.95188)^x$

$$= 751.4698\left(e^{\ln(0.95188)}\right)^x$$

$$= 751.4698e^{\ln(0.95188)x}$$

$$A(t) = 751.470e^{(-0.04932)t}$$

d. $Y_1 = 751.470e^{(-0.04932)x}$

e. Note that 2010 is represented by $t = 15$.
$A(15) = 751.470e^{(-0.04932) \cdot 15} \approx 359$ billion cigarettes.

f. We need to find t when $A(t) = 230$.

$751.470e^{(-0.04932)t} = 230$

$e^{(-0.04932)t} = \dfrac{230}{751.470}$

$-0.04932t = \ln\left(\dfrac{230}{751.470}\right)$

$t = \dfrac{\ln\left(\dfrac{230}{751.470}\right)}{-0.04932} \approx 24$ years

Now $1995 + 24 = 2019$. The number of cigarettes produced in the U.S. will decrease to 230 billion in the year 2019.

6. a. Let $x = 0$ correspond to 1995, $x = 3$ correspond to 1998, etc.

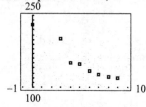

b. Using EXPonential REGression on the data yields: $y = 228.4370(0.92301)^x$

c. $y = 228.4370\left(e^{\ln(0.92301)}\right)^x$
$= 228.4370e^{\ln(0.92301)x}$
$A(t) = 228.437e^{(-0.08012)t}$

d. $Y_1 = 228.437e^{(-0.08012)t}$

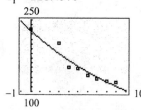

e. Note that 2010 is represented by $t = 15$.
$A(15) = 228.437e^{(-0.08012) \cdot 15} \approx 68.7$ billion cigarettes.

f. We need to find t when $A(t) = 230$.

$228.437e^{(-0.08012)t} = 50$

$e^{(-0.08012)t} = \dfrac{50}{228.437}$

$-0.08012t = \ln\left(\dfrac{50}{228.437}\right)$

$t = \dfrac{\ln\left(\dfrac{50}{228.437}\right)}{-0.08012} \approx 19$ years

Now $1995 + 19 = 2014$. The number of cigarettes exported from the U.S. will decrease to 50 billion in the year 2014.

7. a.

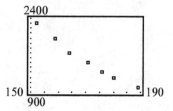

b. Using LnREGression on the data yields:
$y = 32,741.02 - 6070.96 \ln x$

c. $Y_1 = 32,741.02 - 6070.96 \ln x$

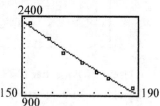

d. We need to find x when $y = 1650$:
$1650 = 32,741.02 - 6070.96 \ln x$

$-31,091.02 = -6070.96 \ln x$

$\dfrac{-31,091.02}{-6070.96} = \ln x$

$5.1213 \approx \ln x$

$e^{5.1213} \approx x$

$x \approx 168$

If the price were \$1650, then approximately 168 computers would be demanded.

8. a.

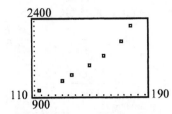

b. Using LnREGression on the data
yields: $y = -11,850.72 + 2688.50 \ln x$

c. $Y_1 = -11,850.72 + 2688.50 \ln x$

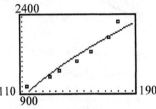

d. Find x when $y = 1650$:
$$1650 = -11,850.72 + 2688.50 \ln x$$
$$13,500.72 = 2688.50 \ln x$$
$$\frac{13,500.72}{2688.50} = \ln x$$
$$5.0216 \approx \ln x$$
$$e^{5.0216} \approx x$$
$$x \approx 152$$
If the price were \$1650, then approximately 152 computers would be demanded.

9. a. Let $x = 0$ correspond to 1900, $x = 10$ correspond to 1910, $x = 20$ correspond to 1920, etc.

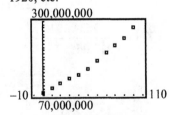

b. Using LOGISTIC REGression on the data
yields: $y = \dfrac{799,475,916.5}{1 + 9.1968e^{-0.01603x}}$

c. $Y_1 = \dfrac{799,475,916.5}{1 + 9.1968e^{-0.01603x}}$

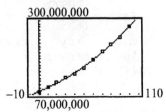

d. As $x \to \infty$, $9.1968e^{-0.01603x} \to 0$, which means $1 + 9.1968e^{-0.01603x} \to 1$, so
$$y = \frac{799,475,916.5}{1 + 9.1968e^{-0.01603x}} \to 799,475,916.5$$
Therefore, the carrying capacity of the United States is approximately 799,475,917 people.

e. The year 2004 corresponds to $x = 104$, so
$$y = \frac{799,475,916.5}{1 + 9.1968e^{-0.01603(104)}}$$
$$\approx 292,177,932 \text{ people}$$

f. Find x when $y = 300,000,000$
$$\frac{799,475,916.5}{1 + 9.1968e^{-0.01603x}} = 300,000,000$$
$$799,475,916.5 = 300,000,000\left(1 + 9.1968e^{-0.01603x}\right)$$
$$\frac{799,475,916.5}{300,000,000} = 1 + 9.1968e^{-0.01603x}$$
$$\frac{799,475,916.5}{300,000,000} - 1 = 9.1968e^{-0.01603x}$$
$$1.6649 \approx 9.1968e^{-0.01603x}$$
$$\frac{1.6649}{9.1968} \approx e^{-0.01603x}$$
$$\ln\left(\frac{1.6649}{9.1968}\right) \approx -0.01603x$$
$$\frac{\ln\left(\frac{1.6649}{9.1968}\right)}{-0.01603} \approx x$$
$$x \approx 107$$
Therefore, the United States population will be 300,000,000 around the year 2007.

10. a. Let $x = 1$ correspond to 1993, $x = 2$ correspond to 1994, etc.

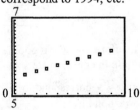

(b) Using LOGISTIC REGression on the data
yields: $y = \dfrac{10.05267}{1 + 0.8439e^{-0.0320x}}$

c. $Y_1 = \dfrac{10.05267}{1+0.8439e^{-0.0320x}}$:

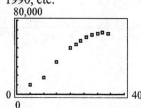

(graph from 5 to 10, with vertical axis labeled 7 and 0)

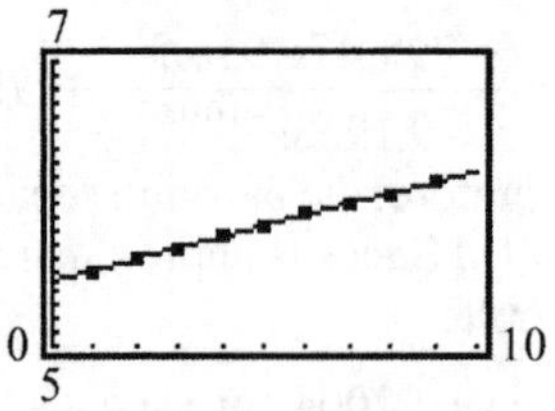

d. As $x \to \infty$, $0.8439e^{-0.0320x} \to 0$, which means $1+0.8439e^{-0.0320x} \to 1$, so

$$y = \frac{10.05267}{1+0.8439e^{-0.0320x}} \to 10.05267$$

Therefore, the carrying capacity of the world is approximately 10.053 billion people.

e. The year 2004 corresponds to $x = 12$, so

$$y = \frac{10.05267}{1+0.8439e^{-0.0320(12)}} \approx 6.38.$$

In 2004, the population of the world was approximately 6.38 billion people.

f. We need to find x when $y = 7$:

$$\frac{10.05267}{1+0.8439e^{-0.0320x}} = 7$$

$$10.05267 = 7\left(1+0.8439e^{-0.0320x}\right)$$

$$\frac{10.05267}{7} = 1+0.8439e^{-0.0320x}$$

$$\frac{10.05267}{7}-1 = 0.8439e^{-0.0320x}$$

$$0.4361 \approx 0.8439e^{-0.0320x}$$

$$\frac{0.4361}{0.8439} \approx e^{-0.0320x}$$

$$\ln\left(\frac{0.4361}{0.8439}\right) \approx -0.0320x$$

$$x \approx \frac{\ln\left(\dfrac{0.4361}{0.8439}\right)}{-0.0320} \approx 21$$

Therefore, the world population will be 7 billion in approximately the year 2013.

11. a. Let $x = 5$ correspond to 1975, $x = 10$ correspond to 1980, $x = 20$ correspond to 1990, etc.

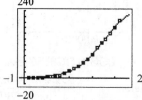

(graph from 0 to 40, vertical axis labeled 80,000 and 0)

b. Using LOGISTIC REGression on the data yields: $y = \dfrac{68,684.7826}{1+18.9416e^{-0.19743x}}$

c. $Y_1 = \dfrac{68,684.7826}{1+18.9416e^{-0.19743x}}$

(graph from 0 to 40, vertical axis labeled 80,000 and 0)

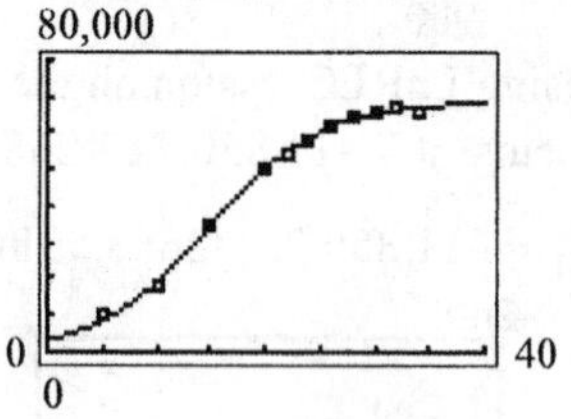

d. As $x \to \infty$, $18.9416e^{-0.19743x} \to 0$, which means $1+18.9416e^{-0.19743x} \to 1$, so

$$y = \frac{68,684.7826}{1+18.9416e^{-0.19743x}} \to 68,684.7826$$

Therefore, the carrying capacity of the cable TV market in the U.S. is about 68,685,000 subscribers.

e. The year 2015 corresponds to $x = 45$, so

$$y = \frac{68,684.7826}{1+18.9416e^{-0.19743(45)}} \approx 68,505.$$

In 2015, cable TV will have approximately 68,505,000 subscribers in the U.S.

12. a. Let $x = 1$ correspond to 1985, $x = 2$ correspond to 1986, $x = 3$ correspond to 1980, etc. Using LOGISTIC REGression on the data yields: $y = \dfrac{268.9893}{1+219.0605e^{-0.3086x}}$

b. $Y_1 = \dfrac{268.9893}{1+219.0605e^{-0.3086x}}$

(graph from -1 to 23, vertical axis labeled 240 and -20)

c. As $x \to \infty$, $219.0605e^{-0.3086x} \to 0$, which means $1+219.0605e^{-0.3086x} \to 1$, so

$$y = \frac{268.9893}{1+219.0605e^{-0.3086x}} \to 268.9893$$

Therefore, the carrying capacity of the cellular phone market in the U.S. is about 268,989,300 subscribers.

d. The year 2009 corresponds to $x = 25$, so

$$y = \frac{268.9893}{1 + 219.0605e^{-0.3086(25)}} \approx 245.04 \,.$$

For 2009, the function predicts that the number of cell phone subscribers will be approximately 245,040,000 subscribers.

e. The answer in part (e) of Example 1 predicts 1,512,010,000 cell phone subscribers in the U.S. in 2009. This prediction is more than 6 times our prediction in part (d). The function in Example 1 assumes exponential growth which is unlimited growth. Our logistic function in part (d) assumes that the growth is limited.

Chapter 6 Review Exercises

1. $f(x) = 3x - 5 \qquad g(x) = 1 - 2x^2$

   a. $(f \circ g)(2) = f(g(2))$
$$= f\left(1 - 2(2)^2\right)$$
$$= f(-7)$$
$$= 3(-7) - 5$$
$$= -26$$

   b. $(g \circ f)(-2) = g(f(-2))$
$$= g\left(3(-2) - 5\right)$$
$$= g(-11)$$
$$= 1 - 2(-11)^2$$
$$= -241$$

   c. $(f \circ f)(4) = f(f(4))$
$$= f\left(3(4) - 5\right)$$
$$= f(7)$$
$$= 3(7) - 5$$
$$= 16$$

   d. $(g \circ g)(-1) = g(g(-1))$
$$= g\left(1 - 2(-1)^2\right)$$
$$= g(-1)$$
$$= 1 - 2(-1)^2$$
$$= -1$$

2. $f(x) = 4 - x \qquad g(x) = 1 + x^2$

   a. $(f \circ g)(2) = f(g(2))$
$$= f\left(1 + 2^2\right)$$
$$= f(5)$$
$$= 4 - 5$$
$$= -1$$

   b. $(g \circ f)(-2) = g(f(-2))$
$$= g\left(4 - (-2)\right)$$
$$= g(6)$$
$$= 1 + 6^2$$
$$= 37$$

   c. $(f \circ f)(4) = f(f(4))$
$$= f\left(4 - 4\right)$$
$$= f(0)$$
$$= 4 - 0$$
$$= 4$$

   d. $(g \circ g)(-1) = g(g(-1))$
$$= g\left(1 + (-1)^2\right)$$
$$= g(2)$$
$$= 1 + 2^2$$
$$= 5$$

3. $f(x) = \sqrt{x + 2} \qquad g(x) = 2x^2 + 1$

   a. $(f \circ g)(2) = f(g(2))$
$$= f\left(2(2)^2 + 1\right)$$
$$= f(9)$$
$$= \sqrt{9 + 2}$$
$$= \sqrt{11}$$

   b. $(g \circ f)(-2) = g(f(-2))$
$$= g\left(\sqrt{-2 + 2}\right)$$
$$= g(0)$$
$$= 2(0)^2 + 1$$
$$= 1$$

   c. $(f \circ f)(4) = f(f(4))$
$$= f\left(\sqrt{4 + 2}\right)$$
$$= f\left(\sqrt{6}\right)$$
$$= \sqrt{\sqrt{6} + 2}$$

   d. $(g \circ g)(-1) = g(g(-1))$
$$= g\left(2(-1)^2 + 1\right)$$
$$= g(3)$$
$$= 2(3)^2 + 1$$
$$= 19$$

4. $f(x) = 1 - 3x^2 \qquad g(x) = \sqrt{4-x}$

   a. $(f \circ g)(2) = f(g(2))$
$$= f\left(\sqrt{4-2}\right)$$
$$= f\left(\sqrt{2}\right)$$
$$= 1 - 3\left(\sqrt{2}\right)^2$$
$$= 1 - 3 \cdot 2$$
$$= -5$$

   b. $(g \circ f)(-2) = g(f(-2))$
$$= g\left(1 - 3(-2)^2\right)$$
$$= g(-11)$$
$$= \sqrt{4-(-11)}$$
$$= \sqrt{15}$$

   c. $(f \circ f)(4) = f(f(4))$
$$= f\left(1 - 3(4)^2\right)$$
$$= f(-47)$$
$$= 1 - 3(-47)^2$$
$$= -6626$$

   d. $(g \circ g)(-1) = g(g(-1))$
$$= g\left(\sqrt{4-(-1)}\right)$$
$$= g\left(\sqrt{5}\right)$$
$$= \sqrt{4-\sqrt{5}}$$

5. $f(x) = e^x \qquad g(x) = 3x - 2$

   a. $(f \circ g)(2) = f(g(2))$
$$= f(3(2)-2)$$
$$= f(4)$$
$$= e^4$$

   b. $(g \circ f)(-2) = g(f(-2))$
$$= g\left(e^{-2}\right)$$
$$= 3e^{-2} - 2$$
$$= \frac{3}{e^2} - 2$$

   c. $(f \circ f)(4) = f(f(4))$
$$= f\left(e^4\right)$$
$$= e^{e^4}$$

   d. $(g \circ g)(-1) = g(g(-1))$
$$= g(3(-1)-2)$$
$$= g(-5)$$
$$= 3(-5) - 2$$
$$= -17$$

6. $f(x) = \dfrac{2}{1+2x^2} \qquad g(x) = 3x$

   a. $(f \circ g)(2) = f(g(2))$
$$= f(3(2))$$
$$= f(6)$$
$$= \frac{2}{1+2(6)^2}$$
$$= \frac{2}{73}$$

   b. $(g \circ f)(-2) = g(f(-2))$
$$= g\left(\frac{2}{1+2(-2)^2}\right)$$
$$= g\left(\frac{2}{9}\right)$$
$$= 3\left(\frac{2}{9}\right)$$
$$= \frac{2}{3}$$

   c. $(f \circ f)(4) = f(f(4))$
$$= f\left(\frac{2}{1+2(4)^2}\right)$$
$$= f\left(\frac{2}{33}\right)$$
$$= \frac{2}{1+2\left(\frac{2}{33}\right)^2}$$
$$= \frac{2}{\left(\frac{1097}{1089}\right)}$$
$$= \frac{2178}{1097}$$

   d. $(g \circ g)(-1) = g(g(-1))$
$$= g(3(-1))$$
$$= g(-3)$$
$$= 3(-3)$$
$$= -9$$

7. $f(x) = 2 - x \qquad g(x) = 3x + 1$

The domain of f is $\{x \mid x \text{ is any real number}\}$.

The domain of g is $\{x \mid x \text{ is any real number}\}$.

$$(f \circ g)(x) = f(g(x))$$
$$= f(3x + 1)$$
$$= 2 - (3x + 1)$$
$$= 2 - 3x - 1$$
$$= 1 - 3x$$

Domain: $\{x \mid x \text{ is any real number}\}$.

$$(g \circ f)(x) = g(f(x))$$
$$= g(2 - x)$$
$$= 3(2 - x) + 1$$
$$= 6 - 3x + 1$$
$$= 7 - 3x$$

Domain: $\{x \mid x \text{ is any real number}\}$.

$$(f \circ f)(x) = f(f(x))$$
$$= f(2 - x)$$
$$= 2 - (2 - x)$$
$$= 2 - 2 + x$$
$$= x$$

Domain: $\{x \mid x \text{ is any real number}\}$.

$$(g \circ g)(x) = g(g(x))$$
$$= g(3x + 1)$$
$$= 3(3x + 1) + 1$$
$$= 9x + 3 + 1$$
$$= 9x + 4$$

Domain: $\{x \mid x \text{ is any real number}\}$.

8. $f(x) = 2x - 1 \qquad g(x) = 2x + 1$

The domain of f is $\{x \mid x \text{ is any real number}\}$.

The domain of g is $\{x \mid x \text{ is any real number}\}$.

$$(f \circ g)(x) = f(g(x))$$
$$= f(2x + 1)$$
$$= 2(2x + 1) - 1$$
$$= 4x + 2 - 1$$
$$= 4x + 1$$

Domain: $\{x \mid x \text{ is any real number}\}$.

$$(g \circ f)(x) = g(f(x))$$
$$= g(2x - 1)$$
$$= 2(2x - 1) + 1$$
$$= 4x - 2 + 1$$
$$= 4x - 1$$

Domain: $\{x \mid x \text{ is any real number}\}$.

$$(f \circ f)(x) = f(f(x))$$
$$= f(2x - 1)$$
$$= 2(2x - 1) - 1$$
$$= 4x - 2 - 1$$
$$= 4x - 3$$

Domain: $\{x \mid x \text{ is any real number}\}$.

$$(g \circ g)(x) = g(g(x))$$
$$= g(2x + 1)$$
$$= 2(2x + 1) + 1$$
$$= 4x + 2 + 1$$
$$= 4x + 3$$

Domain: $\{x \mid x \text{ is any real number}\}$.

9. $f(x) = 3x^2 + x + 1 \qquad g(x) = |3x|$

The domain of f is $\{x \mid x \text{ is any real number}\}$.

The domain of g is $\{x \mid x \text{ is any real number}\}$.

$$(f \circ g)(x) = f(g(x))$$
$$= f(|3x|)$$
$$= 3(|3x|)^2 + (|3x|) + 1$$
$$= 27x^2 + 3|x| + 1$$

Domain: $\{x \mid x \text{ is any real number}\}$.

$$(g \circ f)(x) = g(f(x))$$
$$= g(3x^2 + x + 1)$$
$$= |3(3x^2 + x + 1)|$$
$$= 3|3x^2 + x + 1|$$

Domain: $\{x \mid x \text{ is any real number}\}$.

$(f \circ f)(x) = f(f(x))$

$= f\left(3x^2 + x + 1\right)$

$= 3\left(3x^2 + x + 1\right)^2 + \left(3x^2 + x + 1\right) + 1$

$= 3\left(9x^4 + 6x^3 + 7x^2 + 2x + 1\right) + 3x^2 + x + 1 + 1$

$= 27x^4 + 18x^3 + 24x^2 + 7x + 5$

Domain: $\left\{x \mid x \text{ is any real number}\right\}$.

$(g \circ g)(x) = g(g(x))$

$= g\left(\left|3x\right|\right)$

$= \left|3\left|3x\right|\right|$

$= 9\left|x\right|$

Domain: $\left\{x \mid x \text{ is any real number}\right\}$.

10. $f(x) = \sqrt{3x}$ $\qquad g(x) = 1 + x + x^2$

The domain of f is $\left\{x \mid x \geq 0\right\}$.

The domain of g is $\left\{x \mid x \text{ is any real number}\right\}$.

$(f \circ g)(x) = f(g(x))$

$= f\left(1 + x + x^2\right)$

$= \sqrt{3\left(1 + x + x^2\right)}$

$= \sqrt{3 + 3x + 3x^2}$

Domain: $\left\{x \mid x \text{ is any real number}\right\}$.

$(g \circ f)(x) = g(f(x))$

$= g\left(\sqrt{3x}\right)$

$= 1 + \sqrt{3x} + \left(\sqrt{3x}\right)^2$

$= 1 + \sqrt{3x} + 3x$

Domain: $\left\{x \mid x \geq 0\right\}$.

$(f \circ f)(x) = f(f(x)) = f\left(\sqrt{3x}\right) = \sqrt{3\sqrt{3x}}$

Domain: $\left\{x \mid x \geq 0\right\}$.

$(g \circ g)(x) = g(g(x))$

$= g\left(1 + x + x^2\right)$

$= 1 + \left(1 + x + x^2\right) + \left(1 + x + x^2\right)^2$

$= 1 + 1 + x + x^2 + 1 + 2x + 3x^2 + 2x^3 + x^4$

$= 3 + 3x + 4x^2 + 2x^3 + x^4$

Domain: $\left\{x \mid x \text{ is any real number}\right\}$.

11. $f(x) = \dfrac{x+1}{x-1}$ $\qquad g(x) = \dfrac{1}{x}$

The domain of f is $\left\{x \mid x \neq 1\right\}$.

The domain of g is $\left\{x \mid x \neq 0\right\}$.

$(f \circ g)(x) = f\left(g(x)\right)$

$= f\left(\dfrac{1}{x}\right) = \dfrac{\dfrac{1}{x} + 1}{\dfrac{1}{x} - 1}$

$= \dfrac{\left(\dfrac{1}{x} + 1\right)x}{\left(\dfrac{1}{x} - 1\right)x} = \dfrac{1 + x}{1 - x}$

Domain $\left\{x \mid x \neq 0, \, x \neq 1\right\}$.

$(g \circ f)(x) = g\left(f(x)\right)$

$= g\left(\dfrac{x+1}{x-1}\right) = \dfrac{1}{\left(\dfrac{x+1}{x-1}\right)} = \dfrac{x-1}{x+1}$

Domain $\left\{x \mid x \neq -1, \, x \neq 1\right\}$

$(f \circ f)(x) = f\left(f(x)\right)$

$= f\left(\dfrac{x+1}{x-1}\right) = \dfrac{\dfrac{x+1}{x-1} + 1}{\dfrac{x+1}{x-1} - 1}$

$= \dfrac{\left(\dfrac{x+1}{x-1} + 1\right)(x-1)}{\left(\dfrac{x+1}{x-1} - 1\right)(x-1)}$

$= \dfrac{x+1+x-1}{x+1-(x-1)} = \dfrac{2x}{2} = x$

Domain $\left\{x \mid x \neq 1\right\}$.

$(g \circ g)(x) = g\left(g(x)\right) = g\left(\dfrac{1}{x}\right) = \dfrac{1}{\left(\dfrac{1}{x}\right)} = x$

Domain $\left\{x \mid x \neq 0\right\}$.

12. $f(x) = \sqrt{x-3}$ $\qquad g(x) = \dfrac{3}{x}$

The domain of f is $\{x \mid x \geq 3\}$.

The domain of g is $\{x \mid x \neq 0\}$.

$$(f \circ g)(x) = f(g(x))$$
$$= f\left(\dfrac{3}{x}\right)$$
$$= \sqrt{\dfrac{3}{x} - 3}$$
$$= \sqrt{\dfrac{3-3x}{x}}$$

To find the domain, we must find where

$p(x) = \dfrac{3-3x}{x} > 0$. $\;p$ is zero or undefined

when $x = 1$ and $x = 0$

Interval	$(-\infty, 0)$	$(0,1)$	$(1,\infty)$
Test Value	-1	$\dfrac{1}{2}$	2
Value of p	-6	3	$-\dfrac{3}{2}$
Conclusion	negative	positive	negative

Domain $\{x \mid 0 < x \leq 1\}$.

$$(g \circ f)(x) = g(f(x)) = g\left(\sqrt{x-3}\right) = \dfrac{3}{\sqrt{x-3}}$$

To find the domain, solve $x - 3 > 0$

$$x > 3$$

Domain $\{x \mid x > 3\}$

$$(f \circ f)(x) = f(f(x)) = f\left(\sqrt{x-3}\right) = \sqrt{\sqrt{x-3}-3}$$

To find the domain, solve $\sqrt{x-3} - 3 \geq 0$

$$\sqrt{x-3} \geq 3$$
$$x - 3 \geq 9$$
$$x \geq 12$$

Domain $\{x \mid x \geq 12\}$.

$$(g \circ g)(x) = g(g(x)) = g\left(\dfrac{3}{x}\right) = \dfrac{3}{\left(\dfrac{3}{x}\right)} = 3\left(\dfrac{x}{3}\right) = x$$

Domain $\{x \mid x \neq 0\}$.

13. a. The function is one-to-one because there are no two distinct inputs that correspond to the same output.

 b. The inverse is $\{(2,1),(5,3),(8,5),(10,6)\}$.

14. a. The function is one-to-one because there are no two distinct inputs that correspond to the same output.

 b. The inverse is $\{(4,-1),(2,0),(5,1),(7,3)\}$.

15. The function f is one-to-one because every horizontal line intersects the graph at exactly one point.

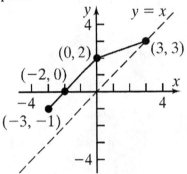

16. The function f is one-to-one because every horizontal line intersects the graph at exactly one point.

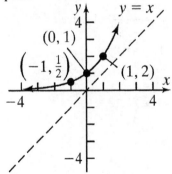

17. $f(x) = \dfrac{2x+3}{5x-2}$

$y = \dfrac{2x+3}{5x-2}$

$x = \dfrac{2y+3}{5y-2}$ Inverse

$x(5y-2) = 2y+3$

$5xy - 2x = 2y + 3$

$5xy - 2y = 2x + 3$

$y(5x-2) = 2x+3$

$y = \dfrac{2x+3}{5x-2}$

$f^{-1}(x) = \dfrac{2x+3}{5x-2}$

Domain of f = Range of f^{-1}

     = All real numbers except $\dfrac{2}{5}$.

Range of f = Domain of f^{-1}

     = All real numbers except $\dfrac{2}{5}$.

18. $f(x) = \dfrac{2-x}{3+x}$

$y = \dfrac{2-x}{3+x}$

$x = \dfrac{2-y}{3+y}$ Inverse

$x(3+y) = 2-y$

$3x + xy = 2 - y$

$xy + y = 2 - 3x$

$y(x+1) = 2 - 3x$

$y = \dfrac{2-3x}{x+1}$

$f^{-1}(x) = \dfrac{2-3x}{x+1}$

Domain of f = Range of f^{-1}
     = All real numbers except -3

Range of f = Domain of f^{-1}
     = All real numbers except -1

19. $f(x) = \dfrac{1}{x-1}$

$y = \dfrac{1}{x-1}$

$x = \dfrac{1}{y-1}$ Inverse

$x(y-1) = 1$

$xy - x = 1$

$xy = x + 1$

$y = \dfrac{x+1}{x}$

$f^{-1}(x) = \dfrac{x+1}{x}$

Domain of f = Range of f^{-1}

     = All real numbers except 1

Range of f = Domain of f^{-1}

     = All real numbers except 0

20. $f(x) = \sqrt{x-2}$

$y = \sqrt{x-2}$

$x = \sqrt{y-2}$ Inverse

$x^2 = y - 2 \quad x \ge 0$

$y = x^2 + 2 \quad x \ge 0$

$f^{-1}(x) = x^2 + 2 \quad x \ge 0$

Domain of f = Range of $f^{-1} = \{x \mid x \ge 2\}$

Range of f = Domain of $f^{-1} = \{x \mid x \ge 0\}$

21. $f(x) = \dfrac{3}{x^{1/3}}$

$y = \dfrac{3}{x^{1/3}}$

$x = \dfrac{3}{y^{1/3}}$ Inverse

$xy^{1/3} = 3$

$y^{1/3} = \dfrac{3}{x}$

$y = \left(\dfrac{3}{x}\right)^3 = \dfrac{27}{x^3}$

$f^{-1}(x) = \dfrac{27}{x^3}$

Domain of f = Range of f^{-1}

     = All real numbers except 0

Range of f = Domain of f^{-1}

     = All real numbers except 0

22. $f(x) = x^{1/3} + 1$

$y = x^{1/3} + 1$

$x = y^{1/3} + 1$ Inverse

$y^{1/3} = x - 1$

$y = (x-1)^3$

$f^{-1}(x) = (x-1)^3$

Domain of f = Range of f^{-1}

   = All real numbers

Range of f = Domain of f^{-1}

   = All real numbers

23. a. $f(4) = 3^4 = 81$

b. $g(9) = \log_3(9) = \log_3\left(3^2\right) = 2$

c. $f(-2) = 3^{-2} = \dfrac{1}{9}$

d. $g\left(\dfrac{1}{27}\right) = \log_3\left(\dfrac{1}{27}\right) = \log_3\left(3^{-3}\right) = -3$

24. a. $f(1) = 3^1 = 3$

b. $g(81) = \log_3(81) = \log_3\left(3^4\right) = 4$

c. $f(-4) = 3^{-4} = \dfrac{1}{81}$

d. $g\left(\dfrac{1}{243}\right) = \log_3\left(\dfrac{1}{243}\right) = \log_3\left(3^{-5}\right) = -5$

25. $5^2 = z$ is equivalent to $2 = \log_5 z$

26. $a^5 = m$ is equivalent to $5 = \log_a m$

27. $\log_5 u = 13$ is equivalent to $5^{13} = u$

28. $\log_a 4 = 3$ is equivalent to $a^3 = 4$

29. $f(x) = \log(3x - 2)$ requires:

$3x - 2 > 0$

$x > \dfrac{2}{3}$

Domain: $\left\{x \mid x > \dfrac{2}{3}\right\}$ or $\left(\dfrac{2}{3}, \infty\right)$

30. $F(x) = \log_5(2x + 1)$ requires:

$2x + 1 > 0$

$x > -\dfrac{1}{2}$

Domain: $\left\{x \mid x > -\dfrac{1}{2}\right\}$ or $\left(-\dfrac{1}{2}, \infty\right)$

31. $H(x) = \log_2\left(x^2 - 3x + 2\right)$ requires

$p(x) = x^2 - 3x + 2 > 0$

$(x-2)(x-1) > 0$

$x = 2$ and $x = 1$ are the zeros of p.

Interval	$(-\infty, 1)$	$(1, 2)$	$(2, \infty)$
Test Value	0	$\dfrac{3}{2}$	3
Value of p	2	$-\dfrac{1}{4}$	2
Conclusion	positive	negative	positive

Thus, the domain of $H(x) = \log_2\left(x^2 - 3x + 2\right)$

is $\{x \mid x < 1 \text{ or } x > 2\}$ or $(-\infty, 1) \cup (2, \infty)$.

32. $F(x) = \ln\left(x^2 - 9\right)$ requires

$p(x) = x^2 - 9 > 0$

$(x+3)(x-3) > 0$

$x = -3$ and $x = 3$ are the zeros of p.

Interval	$(-\infty, -3)$	$(-3, 3)$	$(3, \infty)$
Test Value	-4	0	4
Value of p	7	-9	7
Conclusion	positive	negative	positive

Thus, the domain of $F(x) = \ln\left(x^2 - 9\right)$ is

$\{x \mid x < -3 \text{ or } x > 3\}$ or $(-\infty, 3) \cup (3, \infty)$.

33. $\log_2\left(\dfrac{1}{8}\right) = \log_2 2^{-3} = -3\log_2 2 = -3$

34. $\log_3 81 = \log_3 3^4 = 4\log_3 3 = 4$

35. $\ln e^{\sqrt{2}} = \sqrt{2}$

36. $e^{\ln 0.1} = 0.1$

37. $2^{\log_2 0.4} = 0.4$

38. $\log_2 2^{\sqrt{3}} = \sqrt{3}\log_2 2 = \sqrt{3}$

39. $\log_3\left(\dfrac{uv^2}{w}\right) = \log_3 uv^2 - \log_3 w$

$$= \log_3 u + \log_3 v^2 - \log_3 w$$
$$= \log_3 u + 2\log_3 v - \log_3 w$$

40. $\log_2\left(a^2\sqrt{b}\right)^4 = 4\log_2\left(a^2\sqrt{b}\right)$

$$= 4\left(\log_2 a^2 + \log_2 b^{1/2}\right)$$
$$= 4\left(2\log_2 a + \frac{1}{2}\log_2 b\right)$$
$$= 8\log_2 a + 2\log_2 b$$

41. $\log\left(x^2\sqrt{x^3+1}\right) = \log x^2 + \log\left(x^3+1\right)^{1/2}$

$$= 2\log x + \frac{1}{2}\log\left(x^3+1\right)$$

42. $\log_5\left(\dfrac{x^2+2x+1}{x^2}\right) = \log_5(x+1)^2 - \log_5\left(x^2\right)$

$$= 2\log_5(x+1) - 2\log_5 x$$

43. $\ln\left(\dfrac{x\sqrt[3]{x^2+1}}{x-3}\right) = \ln\left(x\sqrt[3]{x^2+1}\right) - \ln(x-3)$

$$= \ln x + \ln\left(x^2+1\right)^{1/3} - \ln(x-3)$$
$$= \ln x + \frac{1}{3}\ln\left(x^2+1\right) - \ln(x-3)$$

44. $\ln\left(\dfrac{2x+3}{x^2-3x+2}\right)^2$

$$= 2\ln\left(\dfrac{2x+3}{x^2-3x+2}\right)$$
$$= 2\left(\ln(2x+3) - \ln\left[(x-1)(x-2)\right]\right)$$
$$= 2\left(\ln(2x+3) - \ln(x-1) - \ln(x-2)\right)$$
$$= 2\ln(2x+3) - 2\ln(x-1) - 2\ln(x-2)$$

45. $3\log_4 x^2 + \dfrac{1}{2}\log_4\sqrt{x} = \log_4\left(x^2\right)^3 + \log_4\left(x^{1/2}\right)^{1/2}$

$$= \log_4 x^6 + \log_4 x^{1/4}$$
$$= \log_4\left(x^6\cdot x^{1/4}\right)$$
$$= \log_4 x^{25/4}$$
$$= \frac{25}{4}\log_4 x$$

46. $-2\log_3\left(\dfrac{1}{x}\right) + \dfrac{1}{3}\log_3\sqrt{x}$

$$= \log_3\left(x^{-1}\right)^{-2} + \log_3\left(x^{1/2}\right)^{1/3}$$
$$= \log_3 x^2 + \log_3 x^{1/6}$$
$$= \log_3\left(x^2\cdot x^{1/6}\right)$$
$$= \log_3 x^{13/6}$$
$$= \frac{13}{6}\log_3 x$$

47. $\ln\left(\dfrac{x-1}{x}\right) + \ln\left(\dfrac{x}{x+1}\right) - \ln\left(x^2-1\right)$

$$= \ln\left(\dfrac{x-1}{x}\cdot\dfrac{x}{x+1}\right) - \ln\left(x^2-1\right)$$
$$= \ln\left[\dfrac{\dfrac{x-1}{x+1}}{x^2-1}\right]$$
$$= \ln\left(\dfrac{x-1}{x+1}\cdot\dfrac{1}{(x-1)(x+1)}\right)$$
$$= \ln\dfrac{1}{(x+1)^2}$$
$$= \ln(x+1)^{-2}$$
$$= -2\ln(x+1)$$

48. $\log\left(x^2-9\right) - \log\left(x^2+7x+12\right)$

$$= \log\left(\dfrac{(x-3)(x+3)}{(x+3)(x+4)}\right)$$
$$= \log\left(\dfrac{x-3}{x+4}\right)$$

49. $2\log 2 + 3\log x - \dfrac{1}{2}\left[\log(x+3) + \log(x-2)\right]$

$= \log 2^2 + \log x^3 - \dfrac{1}{2}\log\left[(x+3)(x-2)\right]$

$= \log\left(4x^3\right) - \log\left((x+3)(x-2)\right)^{1/2}$

$= \log\left(\dfrac{4x^3}{\left[(x+3)(x-2)\right]^{1/2}}\right)$

50. $\dfrac{1}{2}\ln\left(x^2+1\right) - 4\ln\dfrac{1}{2} - \dfrac{1}{2}\left[\ln(x-4) + \ln x\right]$

$= \ln\left(x^2+1\right)^{1/2} - \ln\left(\dfrac{1}{2}\right)^4 - \ln\left(x(x-4)\right)^{1/2}$

$= \ln\left(\dfrac{\left(x^2+1\right)^{1/2}}{\dfrac{1}{16}\left[x(x-4)\right]^{1/2}}\right)$

$= \ln\left(\dfrac{16\sqrt{x^2+1}}{\sqrt{x(x-4)}}\right)$

51. $\log_4 19 = \dfrac{\ln 19}{\ln 4} \approx 2.124$

52. $\log_2 21 = \dfrac{\ln 21}{\ln 2} \approx 4.392$

53. $Y_1 = \log_3 x = \dfrac{\ln x}{\ln 3}$

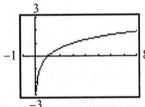

54. $Y_1 = \log_7 x = \dfrac{\ln x}{\ln 7}$

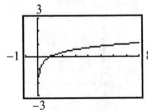

55. $f(x) = 2^{x-3}$

  a. Domain: $(-\infty, \infty)$

  b. Using the graph of $y = 2^x$, shift the graph horizontally 3 units to the right.

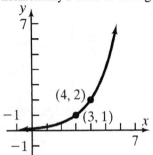

  c. Range: $(0, \infty)$

     Horizontal Asymptote: $y = 0$

  d. $\quad f(x) = 2^{x-3}$

$y = 2^{x-3}$

$x = 2^{y-3} \quad$ Inverse

$y - 3 = \log_2 x$

$y = 3 + \log_2 x$

$f^{-1}(x) = 3 + \log_2 x$

  e. Range of f: $(0, \infty)$

  f. Using the graph of $y = \log_2 x$, shift the graph vertically 3 units up.

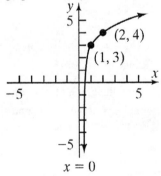

56. $f(x) = -2^x + 3$

a. Domain: $(-\infty, \infty)$

b. Using the graph of $y = 2^x$, reflect the graph about the x-axis, and shift vertically 3 units up.

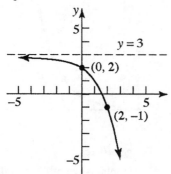

c. Range: $(-\infty, 3)$
Horizontal Asymptote: $y = 3$

d.
$$f(x) = -2^x + 3$$
$$y = -2^x + 3$$
$$x = -2^y + 3 \quad \text{Inverse}$$
$$x - 3 = -2^y$$
$$3 - x = 2^y$$
$$y = \log_2(3 - x)$$
$$f^{-1}(x) = \log_2(3 - x)$$

e.
$$3 - x > 0$$
$$-x > -3$$
$$x < 3$$
Range of f: $(-\infty, 3)$

f. Using the graph of $y = \log_2 x$, reflect the graph about the y-axis, and shift horizontally to the right 3 units.

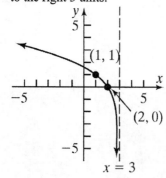

57. $f(x) = \frac{1}{2}\left(3^{-x}\right)$

a. Domain: $(-\infty, \infty)$

b. Using the graph of $y = 3^x$, reflect the graph about the y-axis, and compress vertically by a factor of $\frac{1}{2}$.

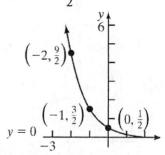

c. Range: $(0, \infty)$
Horizontal Asymptote: $y = 0$

d.
$$f(x) = \frac{1}{2}\left(3^{-x}\right)$$
$$y = \frac{1}{2}\left(3^{-x}\right)$$
$$x = \frac{1}{2}\left(3^{-y}\right) \quad \text{Inverse}$$
$$2x = 3^{-y}$$
$$-y = \log_3(2x)$$
$$y = -\log_3(2x)$$
$$f^{-1}(x) = -\log_3(2x)$$

e.
$$2x > 0$$
$$x > 0$$
Range of f: $(0, \infty)$

f. Using the graph of $y = \log_3 x$, compress the graph horizontally by a factor of $\frac{1}{2}$, and reflect about the x-axis.

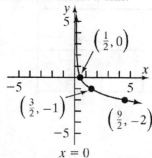

58. $f(x) = 1 + 3^{-x}$

    a. Domain: $(-\infty, \infty)$

    b. Using the graph of $y = 3^x$, reflect the graph about the y-axis, and shift vertically 1 unit up.

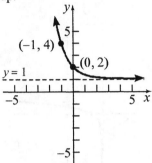

    c. Range: $(1, \infty)$

       Horizontal Asymptote: $y = 1$

    d. $f(x) = 1 + 3^{-x}$

$$y = 1 + 3^{-x}$$
$$x = 1 + 3^{-y} \quad \text{Inverse}$$
$$x - 1 = 3^{-y}$$
$$-y = \log_3(x - 1)$$
$$y = -\log_3(x - 1)$$
$$f^{-1}(x) = -\log_3(x - 1)$$

    e. $x - 1 > 0$

$$x > 1$$

       Range of f: $(1, \infty)$

    f. Using the graph of $y = \log_3 x$, shift the graph horizontally to the right 1 unit, and reflect vertically about the x-axis.

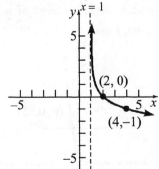

59. $f(x) = 1 - e^{-x}$

    a. Domain: $(-\infty, \infty)$

    b. Using the graph of $y = e^x$, reflect about the y-axis, reflect about the x-axis, and shift up 1 unit.

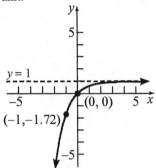

    c. Range: $(-\infty, 1)$

       Horizontal Asymptote: $y = 1$

    d. $f(x) = 1 - e^{-x}$

$$y = 1 - e^{-x}$$
$$x = 1 - e^{-y} \quad \text{Inverse}$$
$$x - 1 = -e^{-y}$$
$$1 - x = e^{-y}$$
$$-y = \ln(1 - x)$$
$$y = -\ln(1 - x)$$
$$f^{-1}(x) = -\ln(1 - x)$$

    e. $1 - x > 0$

$$-x > -1$$
$$x < 1$$

       Range of f: $(-\infty, 1)$

    f. Using the graph of $y = \ln x$, reflect the graph about the y-axis, shift to the right 1 unit, and reflect about the x-axis.

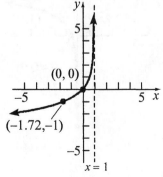

60. $f(x) = 3e^{x-2}$

   a. Domain: $(-\infty, \infty)$

   b. Using the graph of $y = e^x$, shift the graph two units horizontally to the right, and stretch vertically by a factor of 3.

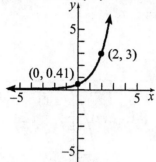

   c. Range: $(0, \infty)$
       Horizontal Asymptote: $y = 0$

   d. $f(x) = 3e^{x-2}$

$$y = 3e^{x-2}$$
$$x = 3e^{y-2} \quad \text{Inverse}$$
$$\frac{x}{3} = e^{y-2}$$
$$y - 2 = \ln\left(\tfrac{x}{3}\right)$$
$$y = 2 + \ln\left(\tfrac{x}{3}\right)$$
$$f^{-1}(x) = 2 + \ln\left(\tfrac{x}{3}\right)$$

   e. Range of f: $(0, \infty)$

   f. Using the graph of $y = \ln x$, stretch horizontally by a factor of 3, and shift vertically up 2 units.

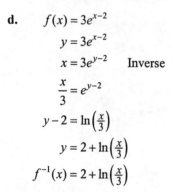

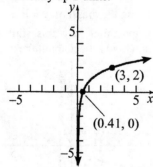

61. $f(x) = \frac{1}{2}\ln(x+3)$

   a. Domain: $(-3, \infty)$

   b. Using the graph of $y = \ln x$, shift the graph to the left 3 units and compress vertically by a factor of $\frac{1}{2}$.

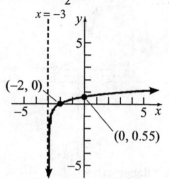

   c. Range: $(-\infty, \infty)$
       Vertical Asymptote: $x = -3$

   d. $f(x) = \frac{1}{2}\ln(x+3)$

$$y = \frac{1}{2}\ln(x+3)$$
$$x = \frac{1}{2}\ln(y+3) \quad \text{Inverse}$$
$$2x = \ln(y+3)$$
$$y + 3 = e^{2x}$$
$$y = e^{2x} - 3$$
$$f^{-1}(x) = e^{2x} - 3$$

   e. Range of f: $(-\infty, \infty)$

   f. Using the graph of $y = e^x$, compress horizontally by a factor of $\frac{1}{2}$, and shift down 3 units.

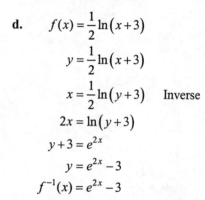

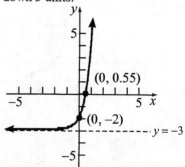

62. $f(x) = 3 + \ln(2x)$

  a. Domain: $(0, \infty)$

  b. Using the graph of $y = \ln x$, compress the graph horizontally by a factor of $\frac{1}{2}$, and shift up 3 units.

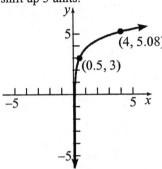

      (4, 5.08)

      (0.5, 3)

  c. Range: $(-\infty, \infty)$

     Vertical Asymptote: $x = 0$

  d.
$$f(x) = 3 + \ln(2x)$$
$$y = 3 + \ln(2x)$$
$$x = 3 + \ln(2y) \qquad \text{Inverse}$$
$$x - 3 = \ln(2y)$$
$$2y = e^{x-3}$$
$$y = \frac{1}{2}e^{x-3}$$
$$f^{-1}(x) = \frac{1}{2}e^{x-3}$$

  e. Range of f: $(-\infty, \infty)$

  f. Using the graph of $y = e^x$, shift to horizontally to the right 3 units, and compress vertically by a factor of $\frac{1}{2}$.

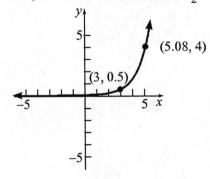

      (5.08, 4)

      (3, 0.5)

63.
$$4^{1-2x} = 2$$
$$\left(2^2\right)^{1-2x} = 2$$
$$2^{2-4x} = 2^1$$
$$2 - 4x = 1$$
$$-4x = -1$$
$$x = \frac{1}{4}$$

The solution set is $\left\{\frac{1}{4}\right\}$.

64.
$$8^{6+3x} = 4$$
$$\left(2^3\right)^{6+3x} = 2^2$$
$$2^{18+9x} = 2^2$$
$$18 + 9x = 2$$
$$9x = -16$$
$$x = -\frac{16}{9}$$

The solution set is $\left\{-\frac{16}{9}\right\}$.

65.
$$3^{x^2+x} = \sqrt{3}$$
$$3^{x^2+x} = 3^{1/2}$$
$$x^2 + x = \frac{1}{2}$$
$$2x^2 + 2x - 1 = 0$$
$$x = \frac{-2 \pm \sqrt{2^2 - 4(2)(-1)}}{2(2)}$$
$$= \frac{-2 \pm \sqrt{12}}{4} = \frac{-2 \pm 2\sqrt{3}}{4} = \frac{-1 \pm \sqrt{3}}{2}$$

The solution is $\left\{\frac{-1-\sqrt{3}}{2}, \frac{-1+\sqrt{3}}{2}\right\} \approx \{-1.366, 0.366\}$.

66.
$$4^{x-x^2} = \frac{1}{2}$$
$$2^{2\left(x-x^2\right)} = 2^{-1}$$
$$2x - 2x^2 = -1$$
$$2x^2 - 2x - 1 = 0$$
$$x = \frac{-(-2) \pm \sqrt{(-2)^2 - 4(2)(-1)}}{2(2)}$$
$$= \frac{2 \pm \sqrt{12}}{4} = \frac{2 \pm 2\sqrt{3}}{4} = \frac{1 \pm \sqrt{3}}{2}$$

The solution is $\left\{\frac{1-\sqrt{3}}{2}, \frac{1+\sqrt{3}}{2}\right\} \approx \{-0.366, 1.366\}$.

Chapter 6: Exponential and Logarithmic Functions

67. $\log_x 64 = -3$

$x^{-3} = 64$

$\left(x^{-3}\right)^{-1/3} = 64^{-1/3}$

$x = \dfrac{1}{\sqrt[3]{64}} = \dfrac{1}{4}$

The solution set is $\left\{\dfrac{1}{4}\right\}$.

68. $\log_{\sqrt{2}} x = -6$

$x = \left(\sqrt{2}\right)^{-6}$

$= \left(2^{1/2}\right)^{-6}$

$= 2^{-3} = \dfrac{1}{8}$

The solution set is $\left\{\dfrac{1}{8}\right\}$.

69. $5^x = 3^{x+2}$

$\ln\left(5^x\right) = \ln\left(3^{x+2}\right)$

$x\ln 5 = (x+2)\ln 3$

$x\ln 5 = x\ln 3 + 2\ln 3$

$x\ln 5 - x\ln 3 = 2\ln 3$

$x(\ln 5 - \ln 3) = 2\ln 3$

$x = \dfrac{2\ln 3}{\ln 5 - \ln 3} \approx 4.301$

The solution set is $\left\{\dfrac{2\ln 3}{\ln 5 - \ln 3}\right\} \approx \{4.301\}$.

70. $5^{x+2} = 7^{x-2}$

$\ln\left(5^{x+2}\right) = \ln\left(7^{x-2}\right)$

$(x+2)\ln 5 = (x-2)\ln 7$

$x\ln 5 + 2\ln 5 = x\ln 7 - 2\ln 7$

$x\ln 5 - x\ln 7 = -2\ln 7 - 2\ln 5$

$x(\ln g\, 5 - \ln 7) = -2\ln 7 - 2\ln 5$

$x = \dfrac{-2\ln 7 - 2\ln 5}{\ln 5 - \ln 7}$

$= \dfrac{-2\left(\ln 7 + \ln 5\right)}{\ln 5 - \ln 7}$

$= \dfrac{2\left(\ln 7 + \ln 5\right)}{\ln 7 - \ln 5} \approx 21.133$

The solution set is $\left\{\dfrac{2\left(\ln 7 + \ln 5\right)}{\ln 7 - \ln 5}\right\} \approx \{21.133\}$.

71. $9^{2x} = 27^{3x-4}$

$\left(3^2\right)^{2x} = \left(3^3\right)^{3x-4}$

$3^{4x} = 3^{9x-12}$

$4x = 9x - 12$

$-5x = -12$

$x = \dfrac{12}{5}$

The solution set is $\left\{\dfrac{12}{5}\right\}$.

72. $25^{2x} = 5^{x^2-12}$

$\left(5^2\right)^{2x} = 5^{x^2-12}$

$5^{4x} = 5^{x^2-12}$

$4x = x^2 - 12$

$x^2 - 4x - 12 = 0$

$(x-6)(x+2) = 0$

$x = 6 \text{ or } x = -2$

The solution set is $\{-2, 6\}$.

73. $\log_3 \sqrt{x-2} = 2$

$\sqrt{x-2} = 3^2$

$\sqrt{x-2} = 9$

$x - 2 = 9^2$

$x - 2 = 81$

$x = 83$

Check: $\log_3 \sqrt{83-2} = \log_3 \sqrt{81}$

$= \log_3 9$

$= 2$

The solution set is $\{83\}$.

74. $2^{x+1} \cdot 8^{-x} = 4$

$2^{x+1} \cdot \left(2^3\right)^{-x} = 2^2$

$2^{x+1} \cdot 2^{-3x} = 2^2$

$2^{-2x+1} = 2^2$

$-2x + 1 = 2$

$-2x = 1$

$x = -\dfrac{1}{2}$

The solution set is $\left\{-\dfrac{1}{2}\right\}$.

696

75. $8 = 4^{x^2} \cdot 2^{5x}$

$2^3 = \left(2^2\right)^{x^2} \cdot 2^{5x}$

$2^3 = 2^{2x^2 + 5x}$

$3 = 2x^2 + 5x$

$0 = 2x^2 + 5x - 3$

$0 = (2x - 1)(x + 3)$

$x = \dfrac{1}{2}$ or $x = -3$

The solution set is $\left\{-3, \dfrac{1}{2}\right\}$.

76. $2^x \cdot 5 = 10^x$

$\ln\left(2^x \cdot 5\right) = \ln 10^x$

$\ln 2^x + \ln 5 = \ln 10^x$

$x \ln 2 + \ln 5 = x \ln 10$

$\ln 5 = x \ln 10 - x \ln 2$

$\ln 5 = x(\ln 10 - \ln 2)$

$\dfrac{\ln 5}{\ln 10 - \ln 2} = x$

$x = \dfrac{\ln 5}{\ln \dfrac{10}{2}} = \dfrac{\ln 5}{\ln 5} = 1$

The solution set is $\{1\}$.

77. $\log_6(x + 3) + \log_6(x + 4) = 1$

$\log_6\left((x + 3)(x + 4)\right) = 1$

$(x + 3)(x + 4) = 6^1$

$x^2 + 7x + 12 = 6$

$x^2 + 7x + 6 = 0$

$(x + 6)(x + 1) = 0$

$x = -6$ or $x = -1$

Since $\log_6(-6 + 3) = \log_6(-3)$ is undefined, the solution set is $\{-1\}$.

78. $\log(7x - 12) = 2 \log x$

$\log(7x - 12) = \log x^2$

$7x - 12 = x^2$

$x^2 - 7x + 12 = 0$

$(x - 4)(x - 3) = 0$

$x = 4$ or $x = 3$

Since each original logarithm is defined, for $x = 3$ and $x = 4$, the solution set is $\{3, 4\}$.

79. $e^{1-x} = 5$

$1 - x = \ln 5$

$-x = -1 + \ln 5$

$x = 1 - \ln 5 \approx -0.609$

The solution set is $\{1 - \ln 5\} \approx \{-0.609\}$.

80. $e^{1-2x} = 4$

$1 - 2x = \ln 4$

$-2x = -1 + \ln 4$

$x = \dfrac{1 - \ln 4}{2} \approx -0.193$

The solution set is $\left\{\dfrac{1 - \ln 4}{2}\right\} \approx \{-0.193\}$.

81. $9^x + 4 \cdot 3^x - 3 = 0$

$\left(3^2\right)^x + 4 \cdot 3^x - 3 = 0$

$\left(3^x\right)^2 + 4 \cdot 3^x - 3 = 0$

Let $u = 3^x$.

$u^2 + 4u - 3 = 0$

$a = 1, b = 4, c = -3$

$u = \dfrac{-(4) \pm \sqrt{(4)^2 - 4(1)(-3)}}{2(1)}$

$= \dfrac{-4 \pm \sqrt{28}}{2} = \dfrac{-4 \pm 2\sqrt{7}}{2} = -2 \pm \sqrt{7}$

$\cancel{3^x = -2 - \sqrt{7}}$ or $3^x = -2 + \sqrt{7}$

3^x can't be negative $x = \log_3\left(-2 + \sqrt{7}\right)$

The solution set is $\left\{\log_3\left(-2 + \sqrt{7}\right)\right\} \approx \{-0.398\}$.

82. $4^x - 14 \cdot 4^{-x} = 5$

Multiply both sides of the equation by 4^x.

$\left(4^x\right)^2 - 14 \cdot 4^{-x} \cdot 4^x = 5 \cdot 4^x$

$\left(4^x\right)^2 - 14 = 5 \cdot 4^x$

$\left(4^x\right)^2 - 5 \cdot 4^x - 14 = 0$

$\left(4^x - 7\right)\left(4^x + 2\right) = 0$

$4^x - 7 = 0$ or $4^x + 2 = 0$

$4^x = 7$ $\cancel{4^x = -2}$

$x = \log_4 7$ 4^x can't be negative

The solution set is $\left\{\log_4 7\right\} \approx \{1.404\}$.

697

83. a. $f(x) = \log_2(x-2) + 1$

Using the graph of $y = \log_2 x$, shift the graph right 2 units and up 1 unit.

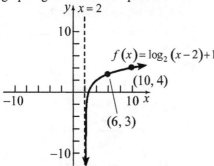

b. $f(6) = \log_2(6-2) + 1$
$= \log_2(4) + 1 = 2 + 1 = 3$

The solution set is $\{3\}$. The point $(6,3)$ is on the graph of f.

c. $f(x) = 4$
$\log_2(x-2) + 1 = 4$
$\log_2(x-2) = 3$
$x - 2 = 2^3$
$x - 2 = 8$
$x = 10$

The solution set is $\{10\}$. The point $(10,4)$ is on the graph of f.

d. $f(x) = 0$
$\log_2(x-2) + 1 = 0$
$\log_2(x-2) = -1$
$x - 2 = 2^{-1}$
$x - 2 = \dfrac{1}{2}$
$x = \dfrac{5}{2}$

Based on the graph drawn in part (a),
$f(x) > 0$ when $x > \dfrac{5}{2}$. The solution set is
$\left\{ x \mid x > \dfrac{5}{2} \right\}$ or $\left(\dfrac{5}{2}, \infty \right)$.

e. $f(x) = \log_2(x-2) + 1$
$y = \log_2(x-2) + 1$
$x = \log_2(y-2) + 1$ Inverse
$x - 1 = \log_2(y-2)$
$y - 2 = 2^{x-1}$
$y = 2^{x-1} + 2$
$f^{-1}(x) = 2^{x-1} + 2$

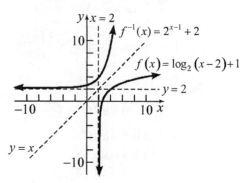

84. a. $f(x) = \log_3(x+1) - 4$

Using the graph of $\log_3 x$, shift the graph left 1 unit and down 4 units.

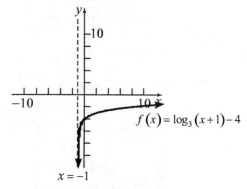

b. $f(8) = \log_3(8+1) - 4$
$= \log_3(9) - 4 = 2 - 4 = -2$

The solution set is $\{-2\}$. The point $(8,-2)$ is on the graph of f.

c. $f(x) = -3$
$\log_3(x+1) - 4 = -3$
$\log_3(x+1) = 1$
$x + 1 = 3^1$
$x + 1 = 3$
$x = 2$

The solution set is $\{2\}$. The point $(2,-3)$ is on the graph of f.

d.
$$f(x) = 0$$
$$\log_3(x+1) - 4 = 0$$
$$\log_3(x+1) = 4$$
$$x+1 = 3^4$$
$$x+1 = 81$$
$$x = 80$$

Based on the graph in part (a), $f(x) < 0$ for $-1 < x < 80$. The solution set is $\{x \mid -1 < x < 80\}$ or $(-1, 80)$.

e.
$$f(x) = \log_3(x+1) - 4$$
$$y = \log_3(x+1) - 4$$
$$x = \log_3(y+1) - 4 \qquad \text{Inverse}$$
$$x+4 = \log_3(y+1)$$
$$y+1 = 3^{x+4}$$
$$y = 3^{x+4} - 1$$
$$f^{-1}(x) = 3^{x+4} - 1$$

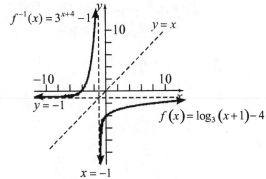

85.
$$h(300) = (30(0) + 8000)\log\left(\frac{760}{300}\right)$$
$$\approx 3229.5 \text{ meters}$$

86.
$$h(500) = (30(5) + 8000)\log\left(\frac{760}{500}\right)$$
$$\approx 1482 \text{ meters}$$

87. $P = 25e^{0.1d}$

a. $P = 25e^{0.1(4)} = 25e^{0.4} \approx 37.3$ watts

b.
$$50 = 25e^{0.1d}$$
$$2 = e^{0.1d}$$
$$\ln 2 = 0.1d$$
$$d = \frac{\ln 2}{0.1} \approx 6.9 \text{ decibels}$$

88. $L = 9 + (5.1)\log d$

a. $L = 9 + (5.1)\log 3.5 \approx 11.77$

b.
$$14 = 9 + (5.1)\log d$$
$$5 = (5.1)\log d$$
$$\log d = \frac{5}{5.1} \approx 0.9804$$
$$d \approx 10^{0.9804} \approx 9.56 \text{ inches}$$

89. a. $n = \dfrac{\log 10{,}000 - \log 90{,}000}{\log(1 - 0.20)} \approx 9.85$ years

b. $n = \dfrac{\log(0.5i) - \log(i)}{\log(1 - 0.15)}$
$$= \frac{\log\left(\dfrac{0.5i}{i}\right)}{\log 0.85} = \frac{\log 0.5}{\log 0.85} \approx 4.27 \text{ years}$$

90. In 18 years, $A = 10{,}000\left(1 + \dfrac{0.04}{2}\right)^{(2)(18)}$
$$= 10{,}000(1.02)^{36}$$
$$\approx \$20{,}398.87$$

The effective interest rate is computed as follows:

When $t = 1$, $A = 10{,}000\left(1 + \dfrac{0.04}{2}\right)^{(2)(1)}$
$$= 10{,}000(1.02)^2$$
$$= \$10{,}404$$

Note, $\dfrac{10{,}404 - 10{,}000}{10{,}000} = \dfrac{404}{10{,}000} = 0.0404$, so the effective interest rate is 4.04%.

In order for the bond to double in value, we have the equation: $A = 2P$.
$$10{,}000\left(1 + \frac{0.04}{2}\right)^{2t} = 20{,}000$$
$$(1.02)^{2t} = 2$$
$$2t\ln 1.02 = \ln 2$$
$$t = \frac{\ln 2}{2\ln 1.02} \approx 17.5 \text{ years}$$

91. $P = A\left(1 + \dfrac{r}{n}\right)^{-nt} = 85{,}000\left(1 + \dfrac{0.04}{2}\right)^{-2(18)}$
$$\approx \$41{,}668.97$$

92. a.
$$5000 = 620.17e^{r(20)}$$
$$\frac{5000}{620.17} \approx e^{20r}$$
$$\ln\left(\frac{5000}{620.17}\right) \approx 20r$$
$$r \approx \frac{\ln\left(\dfrac{5000}{620.17}\right)}{20} \approx 0.10436$$
$$r \approx 10.436\%$$

b. $A = 4000e^{0.10436(20)} \approx \$32,249.24$
The bank's claim is correct.

93.
$$A = A_0 e^{kt}$$
$$0.5A_0 = A_0 e^{k(5600)}$$
$$0.5 = e^{5600k}$$
$$\ln 0.5 = 5600k$$
$$k = \frac{\ln 0.5}{5600}$$
$$0.05A_0 = A_0 e^{\left(\frac{\ln 0.5}{5600}\right)t}$$
$$0.05 = e^{\left(\frac{\ln 0.5}{5600}\right)t}$$
$$\ln 0.05 = \left(\frac{\ln 0.5}{5600}\right)t$$
$$t = \frac{\ln 0.05}{\left(\dfrac{\ln 0.5}{5600}\right)} \approx 24,203$$

The man died approximately 24,203 years ago.

94. Using $u = T + (u_0 - T)e^{kt}$, with $t = 5$, $T = 70$, $u_0 = 450$, and $u = 400$.
$$400 = 70 + (450 - 70)e^{k(5)}$$
$$330 = 380e^{5k}$$
$$\frac{330}{380} = e^{5k}$$
$$\ln\left(\frac{330}{380}\right) = 5k$$
$$k = \frac{\ln(330/380)}{5}$$

Find time for temperature of 150°F:
$$150 = 70 + (450 - 70)e^{\left(\frac{\ln(330/380)}{5}\right)t}$$
$$80 = 380e^{\left(\frac{\ln(330/380)}{5}\right)t}$$
$$\frac{80}{380} = e^{\left(\frac{\ln(330/380)}{5}\right)t}$$
$$\ln\left(\frac{80}{380}\right) = \left(\frac{\ln(330/380)}{5}\right)t$$
$$t = \frac{\ln\left(\dfrac{80}{380}\right)}{\dfrac{\ln(330/380)}{5}} \approx 55.22$$

The temperature of the skillet will be 150°F after approximately 55.22 minutes (or 55 minutes, 13 seconds).

95. $P_0 = 6,451,058,790$, $k = 0.0115$, and
$$t = 2015 - 2005 = 10$$
$$P = P_0 e^{kt} = 6,451,058,790e^{0.0115(10)}$$
$$\approx 7,237,271,501 \text{ people}$$

96.
$$A = A_0 e^{kt}$$
$$0.5A_0 = A_0 e^{k(5.27)}$$
$$0.5 = e^{5.27k}$$
$$\ln 0.5 = 5.27k$$
$$k = \frac{\ln 0.5}{5.27}$$

In 20 years: $A = 100e^{\left(\frac{\ln 0.5}{5.27}\right)(20)} \approx 7.204$ grams

In 40 years: $A = 100e^{\left(\frac{\ln 0.5}{5.27}\right)(40)} \approx 0.519$ grams

97. $A = P\left(1 + \dfrac{r}{n}\right)^{nt}$
$$A = 319\left(1 + \frac{0.0425}{1}\right)^{1(10)}$$
$$= 319(1.0425)^{10} \approx 483.67$$

The government would have to pay back approximately \$483.67 billion in 2015.

700

98. a. $P(0) = \dfrac{0.8}{1+1.67e^{-0.16(0)}} = \dfrac{0.8}{1+1.67} \approx 0.3$

In 2006, about 30% of cars had a GPS.

b. The maximum proportion is the carrying capacity, $c = 0.8 = 80\%$.

c. $Y_1 = \dfrac{0.8}{1+1.67e^{-0.16x}}$

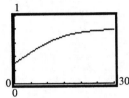

d. Find t such that $P(t) = 0.75$.

$$\dfrac{0.8}{1+1.67e^{-0.16t}} = 0.75$$

$$0.8 = 0.75\left(1+1.67e^{-0.16t}\right)$$

$$\dfrac{0.8}{0.75} = 1+1.67e^{-0.16t}$$

$$\dfrac{0.8}{0.75} - 1 = 1.67e^{-0.16t}$$

$$\dfrac{\frac{0.8}{0.75}-1}{1.67} = e^{-0.16t}$$

$$\ln\left(\dfrac{\frac{0.8}{0.75}-1}{1.67}\right) = -0.16t$$

$$t = \dfrac{\ln\left(\dfrac{\frac{0.8}{0.75}-1}{1.67}\right)}{-0.16} \approx 20.13$$

Note that $2006 + 20.13 = 2026.13$, so 75% of new cars will have GPS in 2026.

99. a.

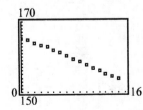

b. Using EXPonential REGression on the data yields: $y = (165.73)(0.9951)^x$

c. $Y_1 = (165.73)(0.9951)^x$

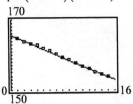

d. Find x when $y = 110$.

$$(165.73)(0.9951)^x = 110$$

$$(0.9951)^x = \dfrac{110}{165.73}$$

$$x\ln 0.9951 = \ln\left(\dfrac{110}{165.73}\right)$$

$$x = \dfrac{\ln\left(\dfrac{110}{165.73}\right)}{\ln 0.9951} \approx 83$$

Therefore, it will take approximately 83 seconds for the probe to reach a temperature of 110°F.

100. a.

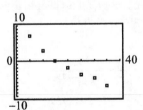

b. Using LnREGression on the data yields: $y = 18.9028 - 7.0963\ln x$ where $y =$ wind chill and $x =$ wind speed.

c. $Y_1 = 18.9028 - 7.0963\ln x$

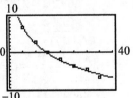

d. If $x = 23$, then
$y = 18.9028 - 7.0963\ln 23 \approx -3°\text{F}$.

101. a.

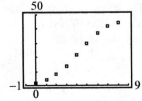

The data appear to have a logistic relation

701

b. Using LOGISTIC REGression on the data yields:

$$C = \frac{46.93}{1 + 21.273e^{-0.7306t}}$$

c. $Y_1 = \dfrac{46.93}{1 + 21.273e^{-0.7306t}}$

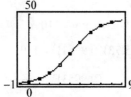

d. As $t \to \infty$, $21.2733e^{-0.7306t} \to 0$, which means $1 + 21.2733e^{-0.7306t} \to 1$, so

$$C = \frac{46.9292}{1 + 21.2733e^{-0.7306t}} \to 46.9292$$

Therefore, according to the function, a maximum of about 47 people can catch the cold.

In reality, all 50 people living in the town might catch the cold.

e. Find t when $C = 10$.

$$\frac{46.9292}{1 + 21.2733e^{-0.7306t}} = 10$$

$$46.9292 = 10\left(1 + 21.2733e^{-0.7306t}\right)$$

$$\frac{46.9292}{10} = 1 + 21.2733e^{-0.7306t}$$

$$\frac{46.9292}{10} - 1 = 21.2733e^{-0.7306t}$$

$$3.69292 = 21.2733e^{-0.7306t}$$

$$\frac{3.69292}{21.2733} = e^{-0.7306t}$$

$$\ln\left(\frac{3.69292}{21.2733}\right) = -0.7306t$$

$$\frac{\ln\left(\dfrac{3.69292}{21.2733}\right)}{-0.7306} = t$$

$$t \approx 2.4$$

Therefore, after approximately 2.4 days (during the 10th hour on the 3rd day), 10 people had caught the cold.

f. Find t when $C = 46$.

$$\frac{46.9292}{1 + 21.2733e^{-0.7306t}} = 46$$

$$46.9292 = 46\left(1 + 21.2733e^{-0.7306t}\right)$$

$$\frac{46.9292}{46} = 1 + 21.2733e^{-0.7306t}$$

$$\frac{46.9292}{46} - 1 = 21.2733e^{-0.7306t}$$

$$0.0202 = 21.2733e^{-0.7306t}$$

$$\frac{0.0202}{21.2733} = e^{-0.7306t}$$

$$\frac{0.0202}{21.2733} = e^{-0.7306t}$$

$$\ln\left(\frac{0.0202}{21.2733}\right) = -0.7306t$$

$$\frac{\ln\left(\dfrac{0.0202}{21.2733}\right)}{-0.7306} = t$$

$$t \approx 9.5$$

Therefore, after approximately 9.5 days (during the 12th hour on the 10th day), 46 people had caught the cold.

Chapter 6 Test

1. $f(x) = \dfrac{x+2}{x-2}$ $g(x) = 2x + 5$

The domain of f is $\{x \mid x \neq 2\}$.

The domain of g is all real numbers.

a. $(f \circ g)(x) = f(g(x))$

$$= f(2x+5)$$

$$= \frac{(2x+5)+2}{(2x+5)-2}$$

$$= \frac{2x+7}{2x+3}$$

Domain $\left\{x \mid x \neq -\dfrac{3}{2}\right\}$.

b. $(g \circ f)(x) = g(f(-2))$

$$= g\left(\frac{-2+2}{-2-2}\right)$$

$$= g(0)$$

$$= 2(0)+5$$

$$= 5$$

c. $(f \circ g)(x) = f(g(-2)) = f(2(-2)+5)$

$$= f(1) = \frac{1+2}{1-2} = \frac{3}{-1} = -3$$

2. a. Graph $y = 4x^2 + 3$:

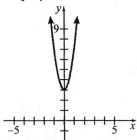

The function is not one-to-one because it fails the horizontal line test. A horizontal line (for example, $y = 4$) intersects the graph twice.

b. Graph $y = \sqrt{x+3} - 5$:

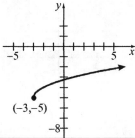

$(-3,-5)$

The function is one-to-one because it passes the horizontal line test. Every horizontal line intersects the graph at most once.

3. $f(x) = \dfrac{2}{3x-5}$

$y = \dfrac{2}{3x-5}$

$x = \dfrac{2}{3y-5}$ Inverse

$x(3y-5) = 2$

$3xy - 5x = 2$

$3xy = 5x + 2$

$y = \dfrac{5x+2}{3x}$

$f^{-1}(x) = \dfrac{5x+2}{3x}$

Domain of f = Range of f^{-1}

$= $ All real numbers except $\dfrac{5}{3}$.

Range of f = Domain of f^{-1}

$= $ All real numbers except 0.

4. If the point $(3, -5)$ is on the graph of f, then the point $(-5, 3)$ must be on the graph of f^{-1}.

5. $3^x = 243$

$3^x = 3^5$

$x = 5$

6. $\log_b 16 = 2$

$b^2 = 16$

$b = \pm\sqrt{16} = \pm 4$

Since the base of a logarithm must be positive, the only viable solution is $b = 4$.

7. $\log_5 x = 4$

$x = 5^4$

$x = 625$

8. $e^3 + 2 \approx 22.086$

9. $\log 20 \approx 1.301$

10. $\log_3 21 = \dfrac{\ln 21}{\ln 3} \approx 2.771$

11. $\ln 133 \approx 4.890$

12. $f(x) = 4^{x+1} - 2$

a. Domain: $(-\infty, \infty)$

b. Using the graph of $y = 4^x$, shift the graph 1 unit to the left, and shift 2 units down.

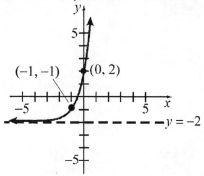

$(-1,-1)$ $(0, 2)$

$y = -2$

c. Range: $(-2, \infty)$
Horizontal Asymptote: $y = -2$

d. $f(x) = 4^{x+1} - 2$

$\qquad y = 4^{x+1} - 2$

$\qquad x = 4^{y+1} - 2 \qquad$ Inverse

$\qquad x + 2 = 4^{y+1}$

$\qquad y + 1 = \log_4(x+2)$

$\qquad y = \log_4(x+2) - 1$

$\qquad f^{-1}(x) = \log_4(x+2) - 1$

e. Range of f: $(-2, \infty)$

f. Using the graph of $y = \log_4 x$, shift the graph 2 units to the left, and shift down 1 unit.

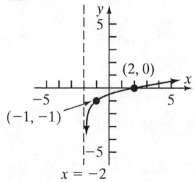

13. $f(x) = 1 - \log_5(x-2)$

a. Domain: $(2, \infty)$

b. Using the graph of $y = \log_5 x$, shift the graph to the right 2 units, reflect vertically about the *y*-axis, and shift up 1 unit.

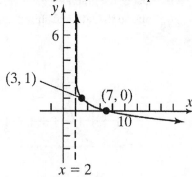

c. Range: $(-\infty, \infty)$

Vertical Asymptote: $x = 2$

d. $f(x) = 1 - \log_5(x-2)$

$\qquad y = 1 - \log_5(x-2)$

$\qquad x = 1 - \log_5(y-2) \qquad$ Inverse

$\qquad x - 1 = -\log_5(y-2)$

$\qquad 1 - x = \log_5(y-2)$

$\qquad y - 2 = 5^{1-x}$

$\qquad y = 5^{1-x} + 2$

$\qquad f^{-1}(x) = 5^{1-x} + 2$

e. Range of f: $(-\infty, \infty)$

f. Using the graph of $y = 5^x$, reflect the graph horizontally about the *y*-axis, shift to the right 1 unit, and shift up 2 units.

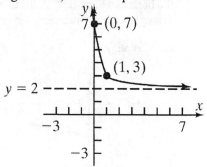

14. $5^{x+2} = 125$

$\qquad 5^{x+2} = 5^3$

$\qquad x + 2 = 3$

$\qquad x = 1$

The solution set is $\{1\}$.

15. $\log(x+9) = 2$

$\qquad x + 9 = 10^2$

$\qquad x + 9 = 100$

$\qquad x = 91$

The solution set is $\{91\}$.

16. $8 - 2e^{-x} = 4$

$\qquad -2e^{-x} = -4$

$\qquad e^{-x} = 2$

$\qquad -x = \ln 2$

$\qquad x = -\ln 2 \approx -0.693$

The solution set is $\{-\ln 2\} \approx \{-0.693\}$.

17. $\log\left(x^2+3\right)=\log\left(x+6\right)$

$$x^2+3=x+6$$

$$x^2-x-3=0$$

$$x=\frac{-(-1)\pm\sqrt{(-1)^2-4(1)(-3)}}{2(1)}=\frac{1\pm\sqrt{13}}{2}$$

The solution set is $\left\{\dfrac{1-\sqrt{13}}{2},\ \dfrac{1+\sqrt{13}}{2}\right\}$

$\approx\left\{-1.303,\ 2.303\right\}$.

18.
$$7^{x+3}=e^x$$

$$\ln 7^{x+3}=\ln e^x$$

$$(x+3)\ln 7=x$$

$$x\ln 7+3\ln 7=x$$

$$x\ln 7-x=-3\ln 7$$

$$x(\ln 7-1)=-3\ln 7$$

$$x=\frac{-3\ln 7}{\ln 7-1}=\frac{3\ln 7}{1-\ln 7}\approx-6.172$$

The solution set is $\left\{\dfrac{3\ln 7}{1-\ln 7}\right\}\approx\left\{-6.172\right\}$.

19. $\log_2\left(x-4\right)+\log_2\left(x+4\right)=3$

$$\log_2\left[(x-4)(x+4)\right]=3$$

$$\log_2\left(x^2-16\right)=3$$

$$x^2-16=2^3$$

$$x^2-16=8$$

$$x^2=24$$

$$x=\pm\sqrt{24}=\pm2\sqrt{6}$$

Because $x=-2\sqrt{6}$ results in a negative arguments for the original logarithms, the only viable solution is $x=2\sqrt{6}$. That is, the solution set is $\left\{2\sqrt{6}\right\}\approx\left\{4.899\right\}$.

20. $\log_2\left(\dfrac{4x^3}{x^2-3x-18}\right)$

$=\log_2\left(\dfrac{2^2 x^3}{(x+3)(x-6)}\right)$

$=\log_2\left(2^2 x^3\right)-\log_2\left[(x-6)(x+3)\right]$

$=\log_2 2^2+\log_2 x^3-\left[\log_2(x-6)+\log_2(x+3)\right]$

$=2+3\log_2 x-\log_2(x-6)-\log_2(x+3)$

21.
$$A=A_0 e^{kt}$$

$$34=50e^{k(30)}$$

$$0.68=e^{30k}$$

$$\ln 0.68=30k$$

$$k=\frac{\ln 0.68}{30}$$

Thus, the decay model is $A=50e^{\left(\frac{\ln 0.68}{30}\right)t}$.
We need to find t when $A=2$:

$$2=50e^{\left(\frac{\ln 0.68}{30}\right)t}$$

$$0.04=e^{\left(\frac{\ln 0.68}{30}\right)t}$$

$$\ln 0.04=\left(\frac{\ln 0.68}{30}\right)t$$

$$t=\frac{\ln 0.04}{\left(\dfrac{\ln 0.68}{30}\right)}\approx 250.39$$

There will be 2 mg of the substance remaining after about 250.39 days.

22. a. Note that 8 months $=\dfrac{2}{3}$ year. Thus,

$$P=1000,\ r=0.05,\ n=12,\text{ and }t=\frac{2}{3}.$$

So, $A=1000\left(1+\dfrac{0.05}{12}\right)^{(12)(2/3)}$

$=1000\left(1+\dfrac{0.05}{12}\right)^{8}$

$\approx\$1033.82$

b. Note that 9 months $=\dfrac{3}{4}$ year. Thus,

$$A=1000,\ r=0.05,\ n=4,\text{ and }t=\frac{3}{4}.\text{ So,}$$

$$1000=A_0\left(1+\frac{0.05}{4}\right)^{(4)(3/4)}$$

$$1000=A_0\left(1.0125\right)^3$$

$$A_0=\frac{1000}{\left(1.0125\right)^3}\approx\$963.42$$

c. $r = 0.06$ and $n = 1$. So,

$$2A_0 = A_0 \left(1 + \frac{0.06}{1}\right)^{(1)t}$$

$$2A_0 = A_0 (1.06)^t$$

$$2 = (1.06)^t$$

$$t = \log_{1.06} 2 = \frac{\ln 2}{\ln 1.06} \approx 11.9$$

It will take about 11.9 years to double your money under these conditions.

23. a. $80 = 10 \log\left(\dfrac{I}{10^{-12}}\right)$

$$8 = \log\left(\frac{I}{10^{-12}}\right)$$

$$8 = \log I - \log 10^{-12}$$

$$8 = \log I - (-12)$$

$$8 = \log I + 12$$

$$-4 = \log I$$

$$I = 10^{-4} = 0.0001$$

If one person shouts, the intensity is 10^{-4} watts per square meter. Thus, if two people shout at the same time, the intensity will be 2×10^{-4} watts per square meter. Thus, the loudness will be

$$D = 10 \log\left(\frac{2 \times 10^{-4}}{10^{-12}}\right) = 10 \log\left(2 \times 10^8\right) \approx 83$$

decibels

b. Let n represent the number of people who must shout. Then the intensity will be $n \times 10^{-4}$. If $D = 125$, then

$$125 = 10 \log\left(\frac{n \times 10^{-4}}{10^{-12}}\right)$$

$$125 = 10 \log\left(n \times 10^8\right)$$

$$12.5 = \log\left(n \times 10^8\right)$$

$$n \times 10^8 = 10^{12.5}$$

$$n = 10^{4.5} \approx 31,623$$

About 31,623 people would have to shout at the same time in order for the resulting sound level to meet the pain threshold.

Chapter 6 Cumulative Review

1. The graph represents a function since it passes the Vertical Line Test.

The function is not a one-to-one function since the graph fails the Horizontal Line Test.

2. $f(x) = 2x^2 - 3x + 1$

a. $f(3) = 2(3)^2 - 3(3) + 1 = 18 - 9 + 1 = 10$

b. $f(-x) = 2(-x)^2 - 3(-x) + 1 = 2x^2 + 3x + 1$

c. $f(x+h) = 2(x+h)^2 - 3(x+h) + 1$

$$= 2\left(x^2 + 2xh + h^2\right) - 3x - 3h + 1$$

$$= 2x^2 + 4xh + 2h^2 - 3x - 3h + 1$$

3. $x^2 + y^2 = 1$

a. $\left(\dfrac{1}{2}\right)^2 + \left(\dfrac{1}{2}\right)^2 = \dfrac{1}{4} + \dfrac{1}{4} = \dfrac{1}{2} \neq 1$; $\left(\dfrac{1}{2}, \dfrac{1}{2}\right)$ is not on the graph.

b. $\left(\dfrac{1}{2}\right)^2 + \left(\dfrac{\sqrt{3}}{2}\right)^2 = \dfrac{1}{4} + \dfrac{3}{4} = 1$; $\left(\dfrac{1}{2}, \dfrac{\sqrt{3}}{2}\right)$ is on the graph.

4. $3(x-2) = 4(x+5)$

$$3x - 6 = 4x + 20$$

$$-26 = x$$

The solution set is $\{-26\}$.

5. $2x - 4y = 16$

x-intercept: y-intercept:

$2x - 4(0) = 16$ $2(0) - 4y = 16$

$2x = 16$ $-4y = 16$

$x = 8$ $y = -4$

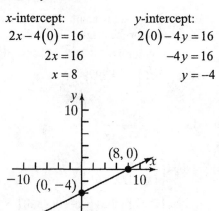

6. a. $f(x) = -x^2 + 2x - 3$; $a = -1, b = 2, c = -3$.

Since $a = -1 < 0$, the graph opens down.

The x-coordinate of the vertex is

$$x = -\frac{b}{2a} = -\frac{2}{2(-1)} = -\frac{2}{-2} = 1.$$

The y-coordinate of the vertex is

$$f\left(-\frac{b}{2a}\right) = f(1)$$
$$= -1^2 + 2(1) - 3$$
$$= -1 + 2 - 3$$
$$= -2$$

Thus, the vertex is $(1, -2)$.

The axis of symmetry is the line $x = 1$.

The discriminant is:
$$b^2 - 4ac = 2^2 - 4(-1)(-3) = 4 - 12 = -8 < 0.$$

The graph has no x-intercepts.

The y-intercept is $f(0) = -0^2 + 2(0) - 3 = -3$.

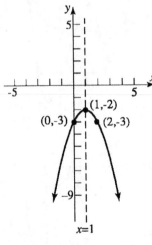

b. The graph of $f(x) = -x^2 + 2x - 3$ indicates that $f(x) \le 0$ for all values of x. Thus, the solution to $f(x) \le 0$ is $(-\infty, \infty)$.

7. Given that the graph of $f(x) = ax^2 + bx + c$ has vertex $(4, -8)$ and passes through the point $(0, 24)$, we can conclude $-\frac{b}{2a} = 4$, $f(4) = -8$, and $f(0) = 24$. Notice that
$$f(0) = 24$$
$$a(0)^2 + b(0) + c = 24$$
$$c = 24$$

Therefore, $f(x) = ax^2 + bx + c = ax^2 + bx + 24$.

Furthermore, $-\frac{b}{2a} = 4$, so that $b = -8a$, and
$$f(4) = -8$$
$$a(4)^2 + b(4) + 24 = -8$$
$$16a + 4b + 24 = -8$$
$$16a + 4b = -32$$
$$4a + b = -8$$
Replacing b with $-8a$ in this equation yields
$$4a - 8a = -8$$
$$-4a = -8$$
$$a = 2$$
So $b = -8a = -8(2) = -16$.

Therefore, we have the function
$$f(x) = 2x^2 - 16x + 24.$$

8. $f(x) = 3(x+1)^3 - 2$

Using the graph of $y = x^3$, shift the graph 1 unit to the left, stretch vertically by a factor of 3, and shift 2 units down.

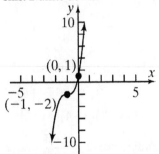

9. $f(x) = x^2 + 2$ $\quad g(x) = \frac{2}{x-3}$

$$f(g(x)) = f\left(\frac{2}{x-3}\right)$$
$$= \left(\frac{2}{x-3}\right)^2 + 2$$
$$= \frac{4}{(x-3)^2} + 2$$

The domain of f is $\{x \mid x \text{ is any real number}\}$.

The domain of g is $\{x \mid x \ne 3\}$.

So, the domain of $f(g(x))$ is $\{x \mid x \ne 3\}$.

$$f(g(5)) = \frac{4}{(5-3)^2} + 2 = \frac{4}{2^2} + 2 = \frac{4}{4} + 2 = 3$$

10. $f(x) = 4x^3 + 9x^2 - 30x - 8$

   a. The graph of $Y_1 = 4x^3 + 9x^2 - 30x - 8$ appears to indicate zeros at $x = -4$ and $x = 2$.

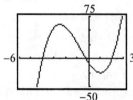

$$f(-4) = 4(-4)^3 + 9(-4)^2 - 30(-4) - 8$$
$$= -256 + 144 + 120 - 8$$
$$= 0$$

$$f(2) = 4(2)^3 + 9(2)^2 - 30(2) - 8$$
$$= 32 + 36 - 60 - 8$$
$$= 0$$

Therefore, $x = -4$ and $x = 2$ are real zeros for f.

Using synthetic division:

$$\begin{array}{r|rrrr} 2 & 4 & 9 & -30 & -8 \\ & & 8 & 34 & 8 \\ \hline & 4 & 17 & 4 & 0 \end{array}$$

$$f(x) = 4x^3 + 9x^2 - 30x - 8$$
$$= (x-2)(4x^2 + 17x + 4)$$
$$= (x-2)(x+4)(4x+1)$$

Therefore, $x = 2$, $x = -\dfrac{1}{4}$ and $x = -4$ are real zeros of f.

   b. f has x-intercepts at $x = 2$, $x = -\dfrac{1}{4}$ and $x = -4$.

f has y-intercept at
$$f(0) = 4 \cdot 0^3 + 9 \cdot 0^2 - 30 \cdot 0 - 8 = -8$$

   c. Use MAXIMUM to determine that f has a local maximum at the point $(-2.5, 60.75)$.

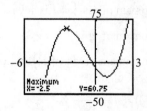

Use MINIMUM to determine that f has a local minimum at the point $(1, -25)$.

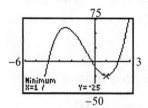

Thus, f has a local maximum of 60.75 that occurs at $x = -2.5$, and f has a local minimum of -25 that occurs at $x = 1$.

   d. Graphing by hand:
The graph of f is above the x-axis for
$$\left(-4, -\frac{1}{4}\right) \text{ and } (2, \infty).$$
The graph of f is below the x-axis for
$$(-\infty, -4).$$

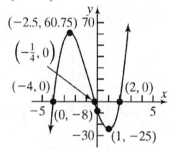

11. a. $g(x) = 3^x + 2$

Using the graph of $y = 3^x$, shift up 2 units.

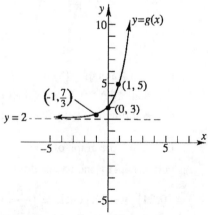

Domain of g: $(-\infty, \infty)$

Range of g: $(2, \infty)$

Horizontal Asymptote for g: $y = 2$

708

b.
$$g(x) = 3^x + 2$$
$$y = 3^x + 2$$
$$x = 3^y + 2 \qquad \text{Inverse}$$
$$x - 2 = 3^y$$
$$y = \log_3(x-2)$$
$$g^{-1}(x) = \log_3(x-2)$$

Domain of g^{-1}: $(2, \infty)$

Range of g^{-1}: $(-\infty, \infty)$

Vertical Asymptote for g^{-1}: $x = 2$

c.

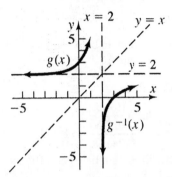

12.
$$4^{x-3} = 8^{2x}$$
$$\left(2^2\right)^{x-3} = \left(2^3\right)^{2x}$$
$$2^{2x-6} = 2^{6x}$$
$$2x - 6 = 6x$$
$$-6 = 4x$$
$$x = -\frac{6}{4} = -\frac{3}{2}$$

The solution set is $\left\{-\dfrac{3}{2}\right\}$.

13. $\log_3(x+1) + \log_3(2x-3) = \log_9 9$
$$\log_3\big((x+1)(2x-3)\big) = 1$$
$$(x+1)(2x-3) = 3^1$$
$$2x^2 - x - 3 = 3$$
$$2x^2 - x - 6 = 0$$
$$(2x+3)(x-2) = 0$$
$$x = -\frac{3}{2} \quad \text{or} \quad x = 2$$

Since $\log_3\left(-\dfrac{3}{2}+1\right) = \log_3\left(-\dfrac{1}{2}\right)$ is undefined

the solution set is $\{2\}$.

14. a. $\log_3(x+2) = 0$
$$x + 2 = 3^0$$
$$x + 2 = 1$$
$$x = -1$$
The solution set is $\{-1\}$.

b. $\log_3(x+2) > 0$
$$x + 2 > 3^0$$
$$x + 2 > 1$$
$$x > -1$$
The solution set is $\{x \mid x > -1\}$.

c. $\log_3(x+2) = 3$
$$x + 2 = 3^3$$
$$x + 2 = 27$$
$$x = 25$$
The solution set is $\{25\}$.

15. a.

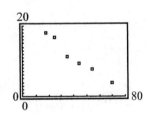

b. Answers will vary.

c. Answers will vary.

Chapter 6 Projects

Project I

a. Newton's Law of Cooling:
$$u(t) = T + (u_0 - T)e^{kt}, \; k < 0$$
Container 1: $u_0 = 200°F$, $T = 70°F$, $u(30)=100°F$, $t = 30$ mins.
$$100 = 70 + (200 - 70)e^{30k}$$
$$30 = 130e^{30k}$$
$$\frac{30}{130} = e^{30k}$$
$$30k = \ln\left(\frac{30}{130}\right)$$
$$k = \frac{1}{30}\ln\left(\frac{30}{130}\right) \approx -0.04888$$
$$u_1(t) = 70 + 130e^{-0.04888t}$$

Container 2: $u_0 = 200°F$, $T = 60°F$, $u(25)=110°F$, $t = 25$ mins.

$$100 = 60 + (200 - 60)e^{25k}$$

$$50 = 140e^{25k}$$

$$\frac{50}{140} = e^{25k}$$

$$25k = \ln\left(\frac{50}{140}\right)$$

$$k = \frac{\ln\left(\frac{50}{140}\right)}{25} \approx -0.04118$$

$$u_2(t) = 60 + 140e^{-0.04118t}$$

Container 3: $u_0 = 200°F$, $T = 65°F$, $u(20)=120°F$, $t = 20$ mins.

$$100 = 65 + (200 - 65)e^{20k}$$

$$55 = 135e^{20k}$$

$$\frac{55}{135} = e^{20k}$$

$$20k = \ln\left(\frac{55}{135}\right)$$

$$k = \frac{\ln\left(\frac{55}{135}\right)}{20} \approx -0.04490$$

$$u_3(t) = 65 + 135e^{-0.04490t}$$

b. We need time for each of the problems, so solve for t first then substitute the specific values for each container:

$$u = T + (u_0 - T)e^{kt}$$

$$u - T = (u_0 - T)e^{kt}$$

$$\frac{u - T}{u_0 - T} = e^{kt}$$

$$kt = \ln\left(\frac{u - T}{u_0 - T}\right)$$

$$t = \frac{\ln\left(\frac{u - T}{u_0 - T}\right)}{k}$$

Container 1:

$$t = \frac{\ln\left(\frac{130 - 70}{200 - 70}\right)}{-0.04888} \approx 15.82 \text{ minutes}$$

Container 2:

$$t = \frac{\ln\left(\frac{130 - 60}{200 - 60}\right)}{-0.04118} \approx 16.83 \text{ minutes}$$

Container 3:

$$t = \frac{\ln\left(\frac{130 - 65}{200 - 65}\right)}{-0.04490} \approx 16.28 \text{ minutes}$$

c. Container 1:

$$t = \frac{\ln\left(\frac{110 - 70}{130 - 70}\right)}{-0.04888} \approx 8.295$$

It will remain between 110° and 130° for about 8.3 minutes.

Container 2:

$$t = \frac{\ln\left(\frac{110 - 60}{130 - 60}\right)}{-0.04118} \approx 8.171$$

It will remain between 110° and 130° for about 8.17 minutes

Container 3:

$$t = \frac{\ln\left(\frac{110 - 65}{130 - 65}\right)}{-0.04490} \approx 8.190$$

It will remain between 110° and 130° for about 8.19 minutes.

d. All three graphs basically lie on top of each other.

e. Container 1 would be the best. It cools off the quickest but it stays in a warm beverage range the longest.

f. Since all three containers are within seconds of each other in cooling and staying warm, the cost would have an effect. The cheaper one would be the best recommendation.

Project II

Solder Joint Strain, εp	X=ln(εp)	Fatigue Cycles, Nf	Y=ln(Nf)
0.01	−4.605	10,000	9.210
0.035	−3.352	1000	6.908
0.1	−2.303	100	4.605
0.4	−0.916	10	2.303
1.5	0.405	1	0

1.

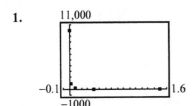

2.

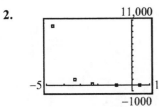

The shape becomes exponential.

3.

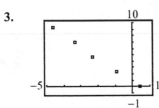

The shape became linear.

4.

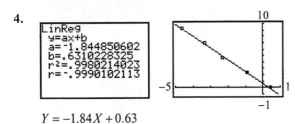

$$Y = -1.84X + 0.63$$

5. $Y = -1.84X + 0.63$

$\ln(Nf) = -1.84\ln(\varepsilon p) + 0.63$

$\ln(Nf) = \ln\left((\varepsilon p)^{-1.84}\right) + \ln(e^{0.63})$

$\ln(Nf) = \ln\left(\left((\varepsilon p)^{-1.84}\right)(e^{0.63})\right)$

$Nf = \left((\varepsilon p)^{-1.84}\right)(e^{0.63})$

$Nf = e^{0.63}(\varepsilon p)^{-1.84}$

6. $Nf = e^{0.63}(0.02)^{-1.84}$

$Nf = 2510.21\ cycles$

$Nf = e^{0.63}(\varepsilon p)^{-1.84}$

$3000 = e^{0.63}(\varepsilon p)^{-1.84}$

$\dfrac{3000}{e^{0.63}} = (\varepsilon p)^{-1.84}$

$\varepsilon p = \left(\dfrac{3000}{e^{0.63}}\right)^{-\frac{1}{1.84}}$

$\varepsilon p = 0.018$

7. $Nf = e^{0.63}(\varepsilon p)^{-1.84}$ $\varepsilon p = 1.41(Nf)^{-.543}$

$Nf = 1.88(\varepsilon p)^{-1.84}$ $\varepsilon p = 1.41(3000)^{-.543}$

$\dfrac{Nf}{1.88} = (\varepsilon p)^{-1.84}$ $\varepsilon p = 0.018$

$\varepsilon p = (0.53Nf)^{-\frac{1}{1.84}}$

$\varepsilon p = (0.53Nf)^{-.543}$

$\varepsilon p = 1.41(Nf)^{-.543}$

Project III

Chart: Answers will vary depending upon the values for the car chosen.

a. Answers will vary.

b. Answers will vary, but in general, they will be in the form $y = ab^x$

c. $A = A_0 b^t$

$A = A_0 e^{rt}$

$\therefore e^r = b$

$r = \ln b$

$A = A_0 e^{(\ln b)t}$

d. A_0 is the purchase price of the vehicle, or a close approximation to it.

e. Answers will vary.

f. Answers will vary.

g. Answers will vary. However, one might consider how well a car will "hold its value" over time. In other words, one would prefer to purchase a vehicle with a low depreciation rate.